ELECTRICAL ENGINEERING

FE Review Manual

KAPLAN

ENGINEERING EDUCATION

Executive Director of Engineering Education: Brian S. Reitzel, PE

ELECTRICAL ENGINEERING FE REVIEW MANUAL

Published by Kaplan Engineering Education

1-877-884-0828

www.kaplanengineering.com

Printed in the United States of America.

14 15 16 10 9 8 7 6 5 4 3 2 1

ISBN: 978-1-4277-4530-9 / 1-4277-4530-7
PPN: 3200-3315

CONTENTS

PERMISSIONS

"Rules of Professional Conduct," Chapter 5, reprinted by permission of NCEES. Source: Model Rules, National Council of Examiners for Engineering and Surveying, 2007. www.ncees.org

Chapter 7 Exhibit 2 and Figures 7.4a-b, 7.5a-b, 7.6a, 7.9, 7.10, 7.18, 7.21, 7.22, and 7.23 reprinted with permission of John Wiley & Sons, Inc.
Source: Callister, William D., Jr. *Materials Science and Engineering: An Introduction*, 6e. J. Wiley & Sons. 2003.

Figures 7.4c, 7.5c, and 7.6b reprinted by permission of the estate of William G. Moffatt.
Source: Moffatt, William G. *The Structure and Property of Materials, Volume 1*. J. Wiley & Sons. 1964.

Tables 7.4 and 7.5 reprinted by permission of McGraw-Hill Companies.
Source: Fontana, M., *Corrosion Engineering*. McGraw-Hill Companies.

Figure 7.13 used by permission of ASM International.
Source: Mason, Clyde W., *Introductory Physical Metallurgy*: p. 33. 1947.

Figure 7.26 used by permission of ASM International.
Source: Rinebolt, J.A., and W. J. Harris, Jr., "Effect of Alloying Elements on Notch Toughness of Pearlitic Steels." Transactions of ASM, Volume 43: pp. 1175–1201. 1951.

CHAPTER 1

Introduction

Ernest M. Kim, PhD, PE

OUTLINE

HOW TO USE THIS BOOK

Fundamentals of Engineering FE/EIT Exam Preparation is designed to help you prepare for the Fundamentals of Engineering/Engineer-in-Training exam. The book covers the full breadth and depth of topics covered by the new Fundamentals of Engineering exams.

Each chapter of this book covers a major topic on the exam, reviewing important terms, equations, concepts, analysis methods, and typical problems. Solved examples are provided throughout each chapter to help you apply the concepts and to model problems you may see on the exam. After reviewing the topic, you can work the end-of-chapter problems to test your understanding. The problems are typical of what you will see on the exam, and complete solutions are provided so that you can check your work and further refine your solution methodology.

The following sections provide you with additional details on the process of becoming a licensed professional engineer and on what to expect at the exam.

BECOMING A PROFESSIONAL ENGINEER

To achieve registration as a Professional Engineer, there are four distinct steps: (1) education, (2) the Fundamentals of Engineering/Engineer-in-Training (FE/EIT) exam, (3) professional experience, and (4) the professional engineer (PE) exam. These steps are described in the following sections.

Education

Generally, no college degree is required to be eligible to take the FE/EIT exam. The exact rules vary, but all states allow engineering students to take the FE/EIT exam before they graduate, usually in their senior year. Some states, in fact, have no education requirement at all. One merely need apply and pay the application fee. Perhaps the best time to take the exam is immediately following completion of related coursework. For most engineering students, this will be the end of the senior year.

Fundamentals of Engineering/ Engineer-in-Training Examination

This six-hour, multiple-choice examination is known by a variety of names—Fundamentals of Engineering, Engineer-in-Training (EIT), and Intern Engineer—but no matter what it is called, the exam is the same in all states. It is prepared and graded by the National Council of Examiners for Engineering and Surveying (NCEES).

Experience

States that allow engineering seniors to take the FE/EIT exam have no experience requirement. These same states, however, generally will allow other applicants to substitute acceptable experience for coursework. Still other states may allow a candidate to take the FE/EIT exam without any education or experience requirements.

Typically, several years of acceptable experience is required before you can take the Professional Engineer exam—the duration varies by state, and you should check with your state licensing board for details.

Professional Engineer Examination

The second national exam is called Principles and Practice of Engineering by NCEES, but many refer to it as the Professional Engineer exam or PE exam. All states, plus Guam, the District of Columbia, and Puerto Rico, use the same NCEES exam. Review materials for this exam are found in other engineering license review books.

FUNDAMENTALS OF ENGINEERING/ENGINEER-IN-TRAINING EXAMINATION

Laws have been passed that regulate the practice of engineering in order to protect the public from incompetent practitioners. Beginning in 1907 the individual states began passing *title* acts regulating who could call themselves engineers and offer services to the public. As the laws were strengthened, the practice of engineering was limited to those who were registered engineers, or to those working under the supervision of a registered engineer. Originally the laws were limited to civil engineering, but over time they have evolved so that the titles, and sometimes the practice, of most branches of engineering are included.

There is no national licensure law; licensure is based on individual state laws and is administered by boards of registration in each state. You can find a list of contact information for and links to the various state boards of registration at the Kaplan Engineering Web site: *www.kaplanengineering.com.* This list also shows the exam registration deadline for each state.

Examination Development

Initially, the states wrote their own examinations, but beginning in 1966 NCEES took over the task for some of the states. Now the NCEES exams are used by all states. Thus it is easy for engineers who move from one state to another to achieve licensure in the new state. About 50,000 engineers take the FE/EIT exam annually. This represents about 65% of the engineers graduated in the United States each year.

The development of the FE/EIT exam is the responsibility of the NCEES Committee on Examination for Professional Engineers. The committee is composed of people from industry, consulting, and education, all of whom are subject-matter experts. The test is intended to evaluate an individual's understanding of mathematics, basic sciences, and engineering sciences obtained in an accredited bachelor degree of engineering. Every five years or so, NCEES conducts an engineering task analysis survey. People in education are surveyed periodically to ensure the FE/EIT exam specifications reflect what is being taught.

The exam questions are prepared by the NCEES committee members, subject matter experts, and other volunteers. All people participating must hold professional licensure. When the questions have been written, they are circulated for review in workshop meetings and by mail. You will see mostly metric units (SI) on the exam. Some problems are posed in U.S. customary units (USCS) because the topics typically are taught that way. All problems are four-way multiple choice.

Examination Structure

The FE/EIT exam will be six hours in length, which includes a tutorial, a break, the exam, and a brief survey at the conclusion of the exam. There are 110 total questions on the exam.

The exam will be divided into two sections with a 25-minute break in the middle. Examinees will be given 5 hours and 20 minutes to complete approximately 55 questions prior to the scheduled break and the remaining questions afterward.

Seven different exams are in the afternoon test booklet, including one for each of the following six branches: civil, mechanical, electrical, chemical, industrial, environmental. An Other Disciplines exam is included for those examinees not covered by the six engineering branches. If you are taking the FE/EIT as a graduation requirement, your school may compel you to take the exam that matches the engineering discipline in which you are obtaining your degree. Otherwise, you can choose the exam you wish to take.

Examination Dates

Beginning in January 2014, the FE exam will be administered during four testing windows throughout the year: January–February, April–May, July–August, and October–November. Registration will be open year-round. Those wishing to take the exam must apply to their state board several months before the exam date.

Examination Procedure

Registration for the computer-based FE exam is scheduled to open on November 4, 2013, and will be open year-round. You will register and schedule your appointment through your My NCEES account on the NCEES Web site. You will first select your exam location, and then you will be presented with a list of available exam

dates for your appointment. If you are not happy with the choices, you can browse through the available dates at another NCEES-approved testing center.

The examination is closed book. You may not bring any reference materials with you to the exam. To replace your own materials, NCEES has prepared a *Fundamentals of Engineering (FE) Supplied-Reference Handbook*. The handbook contains engineering, scientific, and mathematical formulas and tables for use in the examination. Examinees will receive the handbook from their state registration board prior to the examination. The *Fundamentals of Engineering Supplied-Reference Handbook* is also included in the exam materials distributed at the beginning of each exam period.

Examination-Taking Suggestions

Those familiar with the psychology of examinations have several suggestions for examinees:

1. There are really two skills that examinees can develop and sharpen. One is the skill of illustrating one's knowledge. The other is the skill of familiarization with examination structure and procedure. The first can be enhanced by a systematic review of the subject matter. The second, exam-taking skills, can be improved by practice with sample problems—that is, problems that are presented in the exam format with similar content and level of difficulty.
2. Examinees should answer every problem, even if it is necessary to guess. There is no penalty for guessing. The best approach to guessing is to try to eliminate one or two of the four alternatives. If this can be done, the chance of selecting a correct answer obviously improves from 1 in 4 to 1 in 2 or 3.
3. Plan ahead with a strategy and a time allocation. There are 120 morning problems in 12 subject areas. Compute how much time you will allow for each of the 12 subject areas. You might allocate a little less time per problem for the areas in which you are most proficient, leaving a little more time in subjects that are more difficult for you. Your time plan should include a reserve block for especially difficult problems, for checking your scoring sheet, and finally for making last-minute guesses on problems you did not work. Your strategy might also include time allotments for two passes through the exam—the first to work all problems for which answers are obvious to you, the second to return to the more complex, time-consuming problems and the ones at which you might need to guess.
4. Read all four multiple-choice answer options before making a selection. All distractors (wrong answers) are designed to be plausible. Only one option will be the best answer.
5. Do not change an answer unless you are absolutely certain you have made a mistake. Your first reaction is likely to be correct.
6. If time permits, check your work.
7. Do not sit next to a friend, a window, or other potential distraction.

License Review Books

To prepare for the FE/EIT exam you need one or two review books.

1. This book, to provide a review of the discipline-specific examination.
2. *Fundamentals of Engineering (FE) Supplied-Reference Handbook.* At some point this NCEES-prepared book will be provided to applicants by their state registration board. You may want to obtain a copy sooner so you will have ample time to study it before the exam. Pay close attention to the *Fundamentals of Engineering Supplied-Reference Handbook* and the notation used in it, because it is the only book you will have at the exam.

Textbooks

If you still have your university textbooks, they can be useful in preparing for the exam, unless they are out of date. To a great extent the books will be like old friends with familiar notation. You probably need both textbooks and license review books for efficient study and review.

Examination Day Preparations

The exam day will be a stressful and tiring one. You should take steps to eliminate the possibility of unpleasant surprises. If at all possible, visit the examination site ahead of time to determine the following:

1. How much time should you allow for travel to the exam on that day? Plan to arrive about 15 minutes early. That way you will have ample time, but not too much time. Arriving too early, and mingling with others who are also anxious, can increase your anxiety and nervousness.
2. Where will you park?
3. How does the exam site look? Will you have ample workspace? Will it be overly bright (sunglasses), or cold (sweater), or noisy (earplugs)? Would a cushion make the chair more comfortable?
4. Where are the drinking fountain and lavatory facilities?
5. What about food? Most states do not allow food in the test room (exceptions for ADA). Should you take something along for energy in the exam? A light bag lunch during the break makes sense.

Items to Take to the Examination

Although you may not bring books to the exam, you should bring the following:

- *Calculator*—NCEES has implemented a more stringent policy regarding permitted calculators. For a list of permitted models, see the NCEES Web site *(www.ncees.org)*. You also need to determine whether your state permits pre-programmed calculators. Bring extra batteries for your calculator just in case, and many people feel that bringing a second calculator is also a very good idea.
- *Clock*—You must have a time plan and a clock or wristwatch.
- *Exam Assignment Paperwork*—Take along the letter assigning you to the exam at the specified location to prove that you are the registered person. Also bring something with your name and picture (driver's license or identification card).
- *Items Suggested by Your Advance Visit*—If you visit the exam site, it will probably suggest an item or two that you need to add to your list.
- *Clothes*—Plan to wear comfortable clothes. You probably will do better if you are slightly cool, so it is wise to wear layered clothing.

Special Medical Condition

If you have a medical situation that may require special accommodation, notify the licensing board well in advance of exam day.

Examination Scoring and Results

Examinees will be notified via e-mail when their results are available for viewing in My NCEES. The process is still being finalized, but most examinees should receive their results within 7–10 business days.

Errata

The authors and publisher of this book have been careful to avoid errors, employing technical reviewers, copyeditors, and proofreaders to ensure the material is as flawless as possible. Any known errata and corrections are posted on the product page at our Web site, *www.kaplanengineering.com*. If you believe you have discovered an inaccuracy, please notify Customer Service at *Kaplanaeinfo@kaplan.com*.

CHAPTER 2

Mathematics: Precalculus and Analytic Geometry

OUTLINE

ALGEBRA

Factorials

Definition. The factorial of a non-negative integer, n, is defined as $n!$ $n! = n(n-1)(n-2)(n-3)\ldots$ and so forth.

For example, $6! = 6(5)(4)(3)(2)(1) = 720$.

Also, $1! = 1$ and $0! = 1$.

Factorials can be written as multiples of other factorials:

$$6! = 6(5!) = 6(5)(4!) = 6(5)(4)(3!) = 6(5)(4)(3)(2!) = 6(5)(4)(3)(2)(1!) = 720$$

Factorials can be multiplied and divided.

$$\frac{n!}{(n-1)!} = \frac{n(n-1)!}{(n-1)!} = n$$

Exponents

Definition. Any number defined as base, b, can be multiplied by itself x number of times, which is denoted as b^x.

For example, $b^4 = b(b)(b)(b)$.

Properties of Exponents

$$b^0 = 1; \quad b^1 = b; \quad b^{-1} = \frac{1}{b}; \quad b^{-x} = \frac{1}{b^x}$$

$$b^{x+y} = \left(b^x\right)\left(b^y\right); \quad b^{x-y} = \frac{b^x}{b^y}; \quad b^{x \times y} = \left(b^x\right)^y$$

$$b^{\frac{1}{2}} = \sqrt{b}; \quad b^{\frac{1}{x}} \sqrt[x]{b}; \quad b^{\frac{x}{y}} = \left(\sqrt[y]{b}\right)^x$$

Logarithms

Definition. If b is a finite positive number, other than 1, and $b^x = N$, then x is the logarithm of N to the base b, or $\log_b N = x$. If $\log_b N = x$, then $b^x = N$.

Properties of Logarithms

$$\log_b b = 1;\ \log_b 1 = 0;\ \log_b 0 = \begin{cases} +\infty, \text{ when } b \text{ lies between 0 and 1} \\ +\infty, \text{ when } b \text{ lies between 1 and } \infty \end{cases}$$

$$\log_b (M \circ N) = \log_b M + \log_b N \quad \log_b M/N = \log_b M - \log_b N$$

$$\log_b N^P = p \log_b N \quad \log_b \sqrt[r]{N^P} = \frac{p}{r} \log_b N$$

$$\log_b N = \log_a N / \log_a b;\quad \log_b b^N = N;\quad b^{\log_b N} = N$$

Systems of Logarithms

Common (Briggsian)—base 10.

Natural (Napierian or hyperbolic)—base 2.7183 (designated by e or ε).

The abbreviation of *common logarithm* is log, and the abbreviation of *natural logarithm* is ln.

Example 2.1

(i) Solve for a if $\log_a 10 = 0.25$ and (ii) find $\log(\frac{1}{x})$, if $\log x = 0.3332$.

Solution

(i) If $\log_a N = x$, then $N = a^x$ or $a = N^{(1/x)}$

Here, $N = 10$ and $x = 0.25$; then $a = 10^{\frac{1}{0.25}} = 10{,}000$

(ii) Since $\log \frac{M}{N} = \log M - \log N$, $\log(\frac{1}{x}) = \log 1 - \log x = -0.3332$

Example 2.2

Solve the equation $\log x + \log(x - 3) - \log 4 = 0$.

Solution

Since $(\log M + \log N - \log P) = \log(\frac{MN}{P})$, $\log x + \log(x - 3) - \log 4$

$= \log\left[\frac{x(x-3)}{4}\right] = 0$

$\left[\frac{x(x-3)}{4}\right] = 10^0 = 1$; simplifying, $x^2 - 3x - 4 = 0$. Finding the roots,

$x = 4$ and -1; then $x = 4$ (-1 is not an answer because the log of a negative number is undefined).

The Solution of Algebraic Equations

Definition. A root, x, is any value such that $f(x) = 0$.

The Quadratic Equation

If $ax^2 + bx + c = 0$, then

$$x = \frac{-b \pm \sqrt{b^2 - 4ac}}{2a}$$

If $b^2 - 4ac > 0$, the two roots are real and unequal; if $b^2 - 4ac = 0$, the two roots are real and equal; if $b^2 - 4ac < 0$, the two roots are imaginary.

Example 2.3

Find the root(s) of the following equations (i) $x + 4 = 0$, (ii) $x^2 + 4x + 3 = 0$, (iii) $x^2 - 4x + 4 = 0$, (iv) $x^2 + 4 = 0$, and (v) $3x^3 + 3x^2 - 18x = 0$.

Solution

For the quadratic equations in (ii), (iii), and (iv), use either the equation or simply a scientific calculator to find the roots. The results yield:

(i) –4, (ii) –1 and –3 (real and distinct roots), (iii) 2 and 2 (real and equal roots),

(iv) $+i2$ and $-i2$ (complex roots; always occur in pairs called *conjugates*)

For (v), factoring, $3x(x^2 + x - 6) = 0$. Roots are 0, –3, and 2.

Example 2.4

Find the equation whose roots are 3 and –2.

Solution

If the roots are x_1, x_2, x_3, etc., the equation is $(x - x_1)(x - x_2)(x - x_3)\ldots = 0$; here, $(x - 3)(x - (-2)) = 0$; $(x - 3)(x + 2) = 0$; $x^2 - x - 6 = 0$.

Progressions

Arithmetic Progression

An arithmetic progression is $a, a + d, a + 2d, a + 3d, \ldots$, where d = common difference.

The nth term is $t_n = a + (n - 1)d$

The sum of n terms is $S_n = \frac{n}{2}[2a + (n-1)d] = \frac{n}{2}(a + t_n)$

Geometric Progression

A geometric progression is $a, ar, ar^2, ar^3, \ldots$, where r = common ratio.

The nth term is $t_n = ar^{n-1}$

The sum of n terms is $S_n = a\left(\frac{1-r^n}{1-r}\right)$

If $r^2 < 1$, S_n approaches a definite limit as n increases indefinitely, and

$$S_\infty = \frac{a}{1-r}$$

Example 2.5

Consider the arithmetic progression 1, 3, 5, 7, 9, 11, 13, . . . (i) Find the sum of the first seven terms and (ii) the 18th term of the progression.

Solution

(i) First term $a = 1$, number of terms $n = 7$, and the common difference $d = 2$

sum $S_n = \frac{n}{2}\left[2a + (n-1)d\right] = \frac{7}{2}\left[2 + 6(2)\right] = 49$

(ii) Number of terms $n = 18$, first term $a = 1$, and the common difference $d = 2$

The last term or the 18th term is $= a + (n - 1)\,d = 1 + (18 - 1)2 = 35$.

Example 2.6

Find the sum of the series 1, 0.5, 0.25, 0.125, 0.0625, . . .

Solution

This geometric series is convergent. First term $a = 1$ and the common ratio $r = 0.5$.

As the number of terms tend to infinity, sum $S = \frac{a}{1-r} = \frac{1}{1-0.5} = 2$

Example 2.7

Consider the geometric progression 2, 4, 8, 16, 32, 64, 128, . . . (i) Find the sum of the first seven terms and (ii) the 20th term of the series.

Solution

(i) First term $a = 2$, common ratio $r = 2$, and the number of terms $n = 7$

sum $S = a\frac{(1-r^n)}{(1-r)} = \frac{2(1-2^7)}{(1-2)} = 256$

(ii) The 20th term of the series is $= ar^{(n-1)} = 2(2)^{(20-1)} = 1{,}048{,}576$.

COMPLEX QUANTITIES

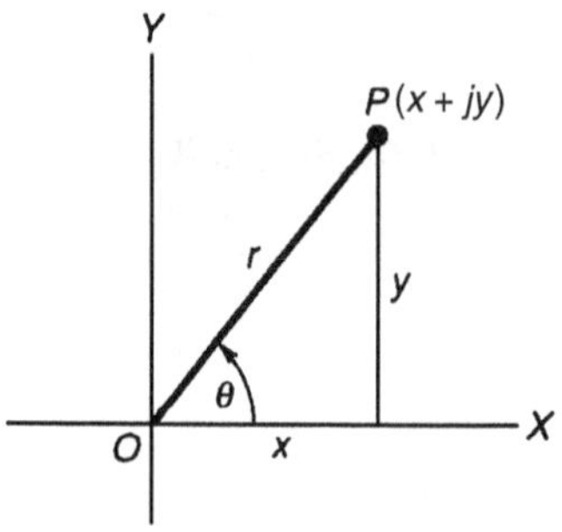

Figure 2.1

Definition and Representation of a Complex Quantity

If $z = x + jy$, where $j = \sqrt{-1}$ and x and y are real, z is called a complex quantity and is completely determined by x and y. In the mathematics portion of the exam, the imaginary number may be denoted at $i = j = \sqrt{-1}$.

If $P(x, y)$ is a point in the plane (Figure 2.1), then the segment OP in magnitude and direction is said to represent the complex quantity $z = x + jy$.

If θ is the angle from OX to OP and r is the length of OP, then $z = x + jy = r(\cos\theta + j\sin\theta) = re^{j\theta}$, where $\theta = \tan^{-1} y/x$, $r = +\sqrt{x^2+y^2}$ and e is the base of natural logarithms. The pair $x + jy$ and $x - jy$ are called complex conjugate quantities.

Properties of Complex Quantities

Let z, z_1, and z_2 represent complex quantities; then

Sum or difference: $z_1 \pm z_2 = (x_1 \pm x_2) + j(y_1 \pm y_2)$

Equation: If $z_1 = z_2$, then $x_1 = x_2$ and $y_1 = y_2$

Periodicity: $z = r(\cos\theta + j\sin\theta) = r[\cos(\theta + 2k\pi) + j\sin(\theta + 2k\pi)]$, or $z = re^{j\theta} = re^{j(\theta+2k\pi)}$ and $e^{j2k\pi} = 1$, where k is any integer.

Exponential-trigonometric relations: $e^{jz} = \cos z + j\sin z$, $e^{-jz} = \cos z - j\sin z$,

$$\cos z = \frac{1}{2}\left(e^{jz} + e^{-jz}\right), \quad \sin z = \frac{1}{2j}\left(e^{jz} - e^{-jz}\right)$$

TRIGONOMETRY

Definition of an Angle

An angle is the amount of rotation (in a fixed plane) by which a straight line may be changed from one direction to any other direction. If the rotation is counter-clockwise, the angle is said to be positive; if clockwise, negative.

Measure of an Angle

A degree is $\frac{1}{360}$ of the plane angle about a point, and a radian is the angle subtended at the center of a circle by an arc equal in length to the radius. One complete circle contains 180 degrees or 2π radians; 1 radian = $\pi/180$ degrees.

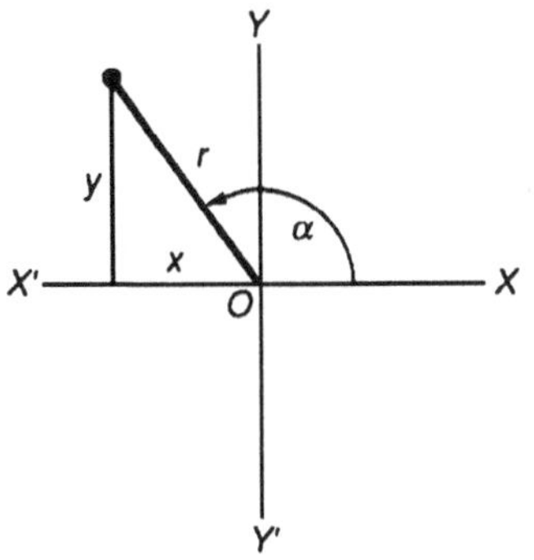

Figure 2.2

Trigonometric Functions of an Angle

sine (sin) $\alpha = y/r$ cosecant (csc) $\alpha = r/y$

cosine (cos) $\alpha = x/r$ secant (sec) $\alpha = r/x$

tangent (tan) $\alpha = y/x$ cotangent (cot) $\alpha = x/y$

The variable x is positive when measured along OX and negative along OX'. Similarly, y is positive when measured parallel to OY, and negative parallel to OY'.

$$\sin 0° = 0;\ \sin 90° = 1;\ \sin 180° = 0;\ \sin 270° = -1$$

$$\cos 0° = 1;\ \cos 90° = 0;\ \cos 180° = -1;\ \cos 270° = 0$$

Fundamental Relations Among the Functions

$$\sin\alpha = \frac{1}{\csc\alpha};\quad \cos\alpha = \frac{1}{\sec\alpha};\quad \tan\alpha = \frac{1}{\cot\alpha} = \frac{\sin\alpha}{\cos\alpha}$$

$$\csc\alpha = \frac{1}{\sin\alpha};\quad \sec\alpha = \frac{1}{\cos\alpha};\quad \cot\alpha = \frac{1}{\tan\alpha} = \frac{\cos\alpha}{\sin\alpha}$$

$$\sin^2\alpha + \cos^2\alpha = 1;\quad \sec^2\alpha - \tan^2\alpha = 1;\quad \csc^2\alpha - \cot^2\alpha = 1$$

Functions of Multiple Angles

$$\sin 2\alpha = 2\sin\alpha\cos\alpha$$

$$\cos 2\alpha = 2\cos^2\alpha - 1 = 1 - 2\sin^2\alpha = \cos^2\alpha - \sin^2\alpha$$

$$\tan 2\alpha = (2\tan\alpha)/(1 - \tan^2\alpha)$$

$$\cot 2\alpha = (\cot^2\alpha - 1)/(2\cot\alpha)$$

Functions of Half Angles

$$\sin\frac{1}{2}\alpha = \sqrt{\frac{1-\cos\alpha}{2}};\quad \cos\frac{1}{2}\alpha = \sqrt{\frac{1+\cos\alpha}{2}}$$

$$\tan\frac{1}{2}\alpha = \frac{1-\cos\alpha}{\sin\alpha} = \frac{\sin\alpha}{1+\cos\alpha} = \sqrt{\frac{1-\cos\alpha}{1+\cos\alpha}}$$

Functions of Sum or Difference of Two Angles

$$\sin(\alpha \pm \beta) = \sin\alpha\cos\beta \pm \cos\alpha\sin\beta$$

$$\cos(\alpha \pm \beta) = \cos\alpha\cos\beta \mp \sin\alpha\sin\beta$$

$$\tan(\alpha \pm \beta) = \frac{\tan\alpha \pm \tan\beta}{1 \mp \tan\alpha\tan\beta}$$

SUMS, DIFFERENCES, AND PRODUCTS OF TWO FUNCTIONS

$$\sin\alpha + \sin\beta = 2\sin\frac{1}{2}(\alpha+\beta)\cos\frac{1}{2}(\alpha-\beta)$$

$$\sin\alpha - \sin\beta = 2\cos\frac{1}{2}(\alpha+\beta)\sin\frac{1}{2}(\alpha-\beta)$$

$$\cos\alpha + \cos\beta = 2\cos\frac{1}{2}(\alpha+\beta)\cos\frac{1}{2}(\alpha-\beta)$$

$$\cos\alpha - \cos\beta = 2\sin\frac{1}{2}(\alpha+\beta)\sin\frac{1}{2}(\alpha-\beta)$$

$$\tan\alpha \pm \tan\beta = \frac{\sin(\alpha+\beta)}{\cos\alpha\cos\beta}$$

$$\sin^2\alpha - \sin^2\beta = \sin(\alpha+\beta)\sin(\alpha-\beta)$$

$$\cos^2\alpha - \cos^2\beta = \sin(\alpha+\beta)\sin(\alpha-\beta)$$

$$\cos^2\alpha - \sin^2\beta = \cos(\alpha+\beta)\cos(\alpha-\beta)$$

$$\sin\alpha\sin\beta = \frac{1}{2}\cos(\alpha-\beta) - \frac{1}{2}\cos(\alpha+\beta)$$

$$\cos\alpha\cos\beta = \frac{1}{2}\cos(\alpha-\beta) + \frac{1}{2}\cos(\alpha+\beta)$$

$$\sin\alpha\cos\beta = \frac{1}{2}\sin(\alpha+\beta) + \frac{1}{2}\sin(\alpha-\beta)$$

Example 2.8

Simplify the following expressions to trigonometric functions of angles less than 90 degrees. Note: There is more than one correct answer for each.

i) cos 370°
ii) sin 120°

Solution

Typical strategies for simplifying the functions are shown below:

i) cos 370° = cos (360° + 10°) = (cos 360°)(cos 10°) – (sin 360°)(sin 10°) = (1)(cos 10°) – (0)(sin 10°) = cos 10°

ii) sin 120° = sin (90° + 30°) = (sin 90°)(cos 30°) + (cos 90°)(sin 30°) = (1)(cos 30°) + (0)(sin 30°) = cos 30°

or

sin 120° = sin (180° – 60°) = (sin 180°)(cos 60°) – (cos 180°)(sin 60°) = (0)(cos 60°) – (–1)(sin 60°) = sin 60°

Properties of Plane Triangles

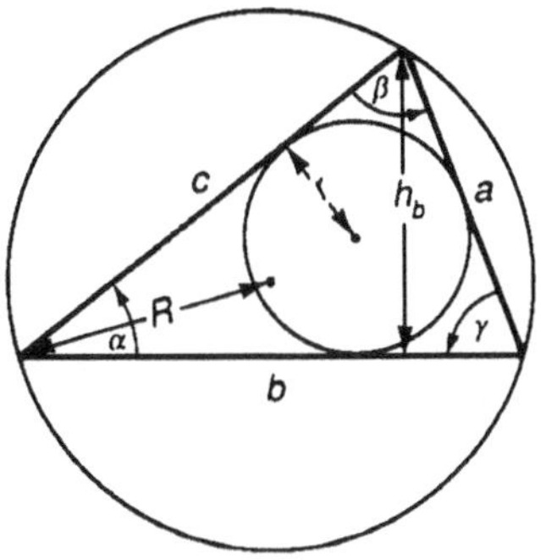

Figure 2.3

Notation. α, β, γ = angles; a, b, c = sides; A = area; h_b = altitude on b; $s = \frac{1}{2}(a+b+c)$; r = radius of inscribed circle; R = radius of circumscribed circle

$$\alpha + \beta + \gamma = 180° = \pi \text{ radians}$$

$$\frac{a}{\sin\alpha} = \frac{b}{\sin\beta} = \frac{c}{\sin\gamma}$$

$$\frac{a+b}{a-b} = \frac{\tan\frac{1}{2}(\alpha+\beta)}{\tan\frac{1}{2}(\alpha-\beta)}$$

$$a^2 = b^2 + c^2 - 2bc\cos\alpha \qquad a = b\cos\gamma + c\cos\beta$$

$$\cos\alpha = \frac{b^2+c^2-a^2}{2bc} \qquad \sin\alpha = \frac{2}{bc}\sqrt{s(s-a)(s-b)(s-c)}$$

$$\sin\frac{\alpha}{2}\sqrt{\frac{(s-b)(s-c)}{bc}} \qquad \cos\frac{\alpha}{2} = \sqrt{\frac{s(s-a)}{bc}}$$

$$\tan\frac{\alpha}{2} = \sqrt{\frac{(s-b)(s-c)}{s(s-a)}} = \frac{r}{s-a}$$

$$h_b = c\sin\alpha = a\sin\gamma = \frac{2}{b}\sqrt{s(s-a)(s-b)(s-c)}$$

$$r = \sqrt{\frac{(s-a)(s-b)(s-c)}{s}} = (s-a)\tan\frac{\alpha}{2}$$

$$R = \frac{a}{2\sin\alpha} = \frac{abc}{4A}$$

$$A = \frac{1}{2}bh_b = \frac{1}{2}ab\sin\gamma = \frac{a^2\sin\beta\sin\gamma}{2\sin\alpha} = \sqrt{s(s-a)(s-b)(s-c)} = rs$$

Example 2.9

Find the side b and the angles A and C for the triangle in Figure 2.4.

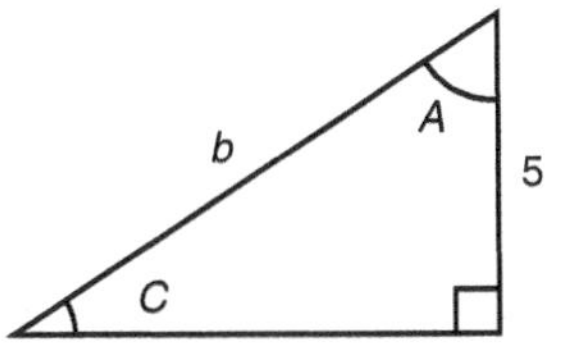

Figure 2.4

Solution

$\tan(A) = 12/5$; then, Angle $A = \tan^{-1}(12/5) = 67.38°$

Since the sum $(A + C + 90°) = 180°$; $C = 90° - A = 22.62°$

Now, $\cos(A) = \frac{5}{b}$; then, $b = \frac{5}{\cos(A)} = 13$

Example 2.10

Find the side c and the angles A and B for the triangle in Figure 2.5.

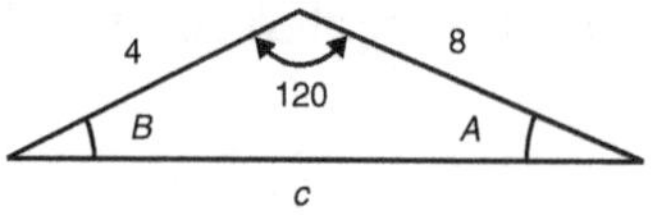

Figure 2.5

Solution

Since two sides and an included angle are given, use the law of cosines.

$c^2 = 4^2 + 8^2 - 2(4)(8)\cos 120$; solving $c = 10.583$

Now use law of sines to find the remaining angles.

$\frac{10.583}{\sin 120} = \frac{4}{\sin A} = \frac{8}{\sin B}$; solving, $A = 19.1°$ and $B = 40.89°$

(Check: sum of the angles = 180°)

Example 2.11

Simplify: (i) $(\sec^2\theta)(\sin^2\theta)$ (ii) $\sin(A+B) + \sin(A-B)$
(iii) $2\sin^2\theta + 1 + \cos^2\theta$

Solution

(i) $(1/\cos^2\theta)\sin^2\theta = \tan^2\theta$ (ii) $2\sin A \cos B$

(iii) $2\sin^2\theta + 1 + (2\cos^2\theta - 1) = 2(\sin^2\theta + \cos^2\theta) = 2$

GEOMETRY AND GEOMETRIC PROPERTIES (MENSURATION)

Notation. a, b, c, d, and s denote lengths, A denotes area, V denotes volume

Right Triangle

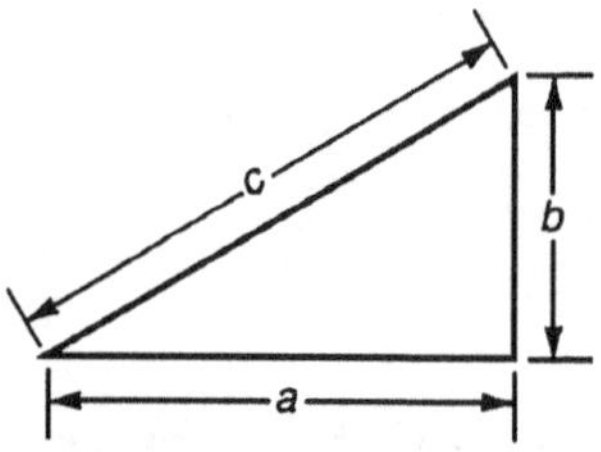

Figure 2.6

$$A = \frac{1}{2}ab$$

$$c = \sqrt{a^2 + b^2},\ a = \sqrt{c^2 - b^2},\ b = \sqrt{c^2 - a^2}$$

Oblique Triangle

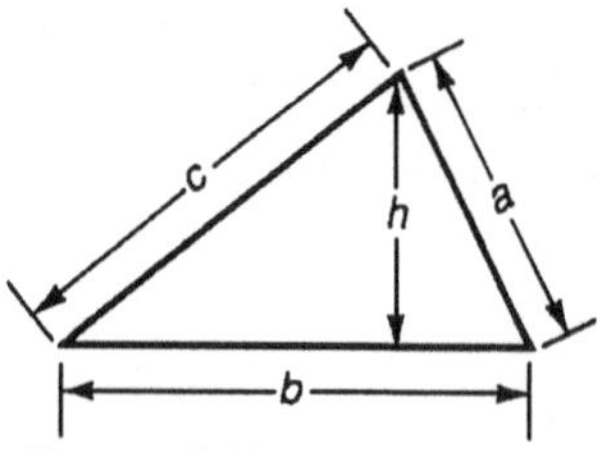

Figure 2.7

$$A = \frac{1}{2}bh$$

Equilateral Triangle

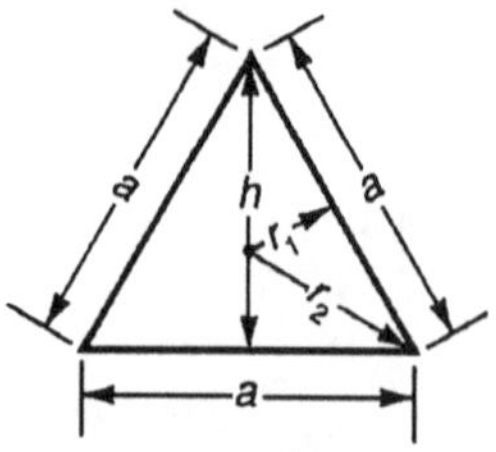

Figure 2.8

All sides are equal and all angles are 60°.

$$A = \frac{1}{2}ah = \frac{1}{4}a^2\sqrt{3}, \quad h = \frac{1}{2}a\sqrt{3}, \quad r_1 = \frac{a}{2\sqrt{3}}, \quad r_2 = \frac{a}{\sqrt{3}}$$

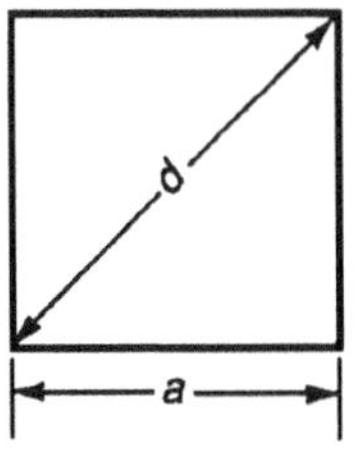

Figure 2.9

Square

All sides are equal, and all angles are 90°.

$$A = a^2, \qquad d = a\sqrt{2}$$

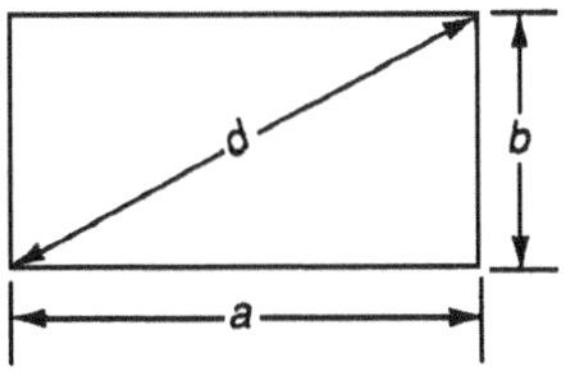

Figure 2.10

Rectangle

Opposite sides are equal and parallel, and all angles are 90°.

$$A = ab, \qquad d = \sqrt{a^2 + b^2}$$

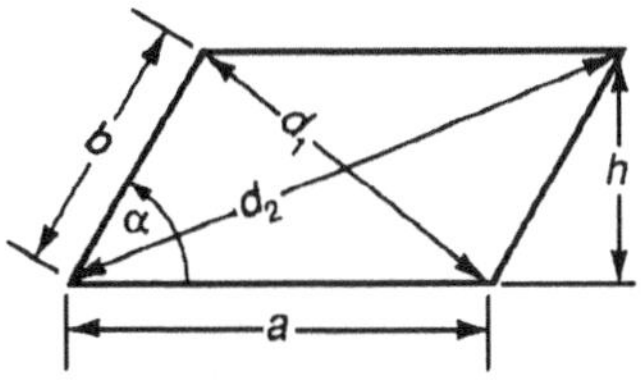

Figure 2.11

Parallelogram

Opposite sides are equal and parallel, and opposite angles are equal.

$$A = ah = ab \sin\alpha, \ d_1 = \sqrt{a^2 + b^2 - 2ab\cos\alpha}, \ d_2 = \sqrt{a^2 + b^2 + 2ab\cos\alpha}$$

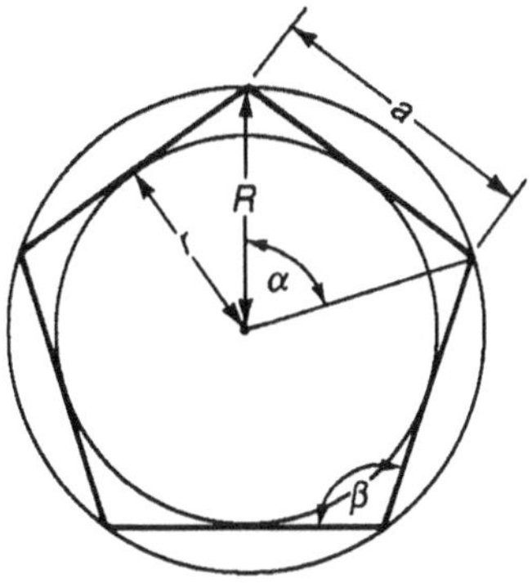

Figure 2.12

Regular Polygon of *n* Sides

All sides and all angles are equal.

$$\beta = \frac{n-2}{n}180° = \frac{n-2}{n}\pi \text{ radians}, \qquad \alpha\frac{360°}{n} = \frac{2\pi}{n} \text{ radians}, \qquad A = \frac{nar}{2}$$

Circle

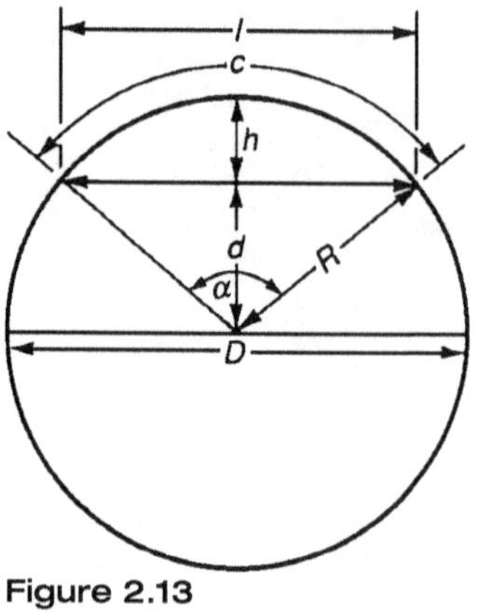

Figure 2.13

Notation. C = circumference, α = central angle in radians

$$C = \pi D = 2\pi R$$

$$c = R\alpha = \frac{1}{2}D\alpha = D\cos^{-1}\frac{d}{R} = D\tan^{-1}\frac{1}{2d}$$

$$l = 2\sqrt{R^2 - d^2} = 2R\sin\frac{\alpha}{2} = 2d\tan\frac{\alpha}{2} = 2d\tan\frac{c}{D}$$

$$d = \frac{1}{2}\sqrt{4R^2 - l^2} = \frac{1}{2}\sqrt{D^2 - l^2} = R\cos\frac{\alpha}{2}$$

$$h = R - d$$

$$\alpha = \frac{c}{R} = \frac{2c}{D} = 2\cos^{-1}\frac{d}{R}$$

$$A_{(circle)} = \pi R^2 = \frac{1}{4}\pi D^2 = \frac{1}{2}RC = \frac{1}{4}DC$$

$$A_{(sector)} = \frac{1}{2}Rc = \frac{1}{2}R^2\alpha = \frac{1}{8}D^2\alpha$$

Ellipse

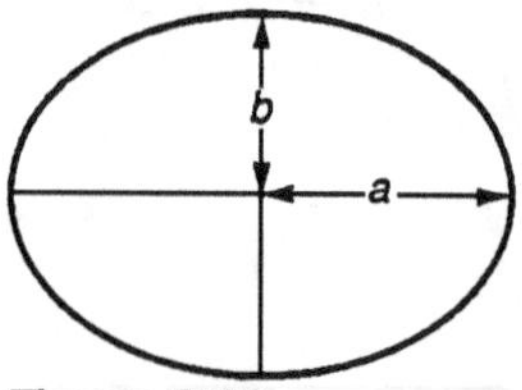

Figure 2.14

$$A = \pi ab$$

$$\text{Perimeter } (s) = \pi(a+b)\left[1 + \frac{1}{4}\left(\frac{a-b}{a+b}\right)^2 + \frac{1}{64}\left(\frac{a-b}{a+b}\right)^4 + \frac{1}{256}\left(\frac{a-b}{a+b}\right)^6 + \cdots\right]$$

$$\text{Perimeter } (s) \approx \pi\frac{a+b}{4}\left[3(1+\lambda) + \frac{1}{1-\lambda}\right], \quad \text{where } \lambda = \left[\frac{a-b}{2(a+b)}\right]^2$$

Parabola

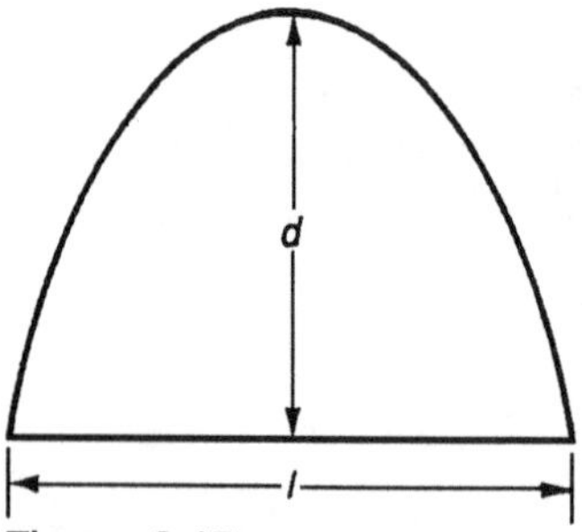

Figure 2.15

$$A = \frac{2}{3}ld$$

Cube

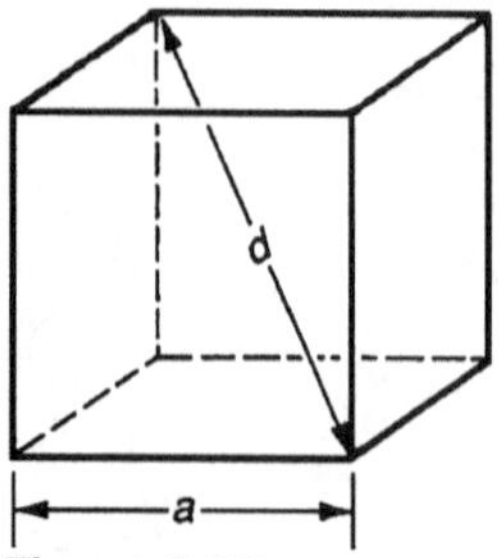

Figure 2.16

$$V = a^3 \qquad d = a\sqrt{3}$$

Total surface area $= 6a^2$

Prism or Cylinder

$V =$ (area of base) (altitude, h)

Lateral area = (perimeter of right section)(lateral edge, e)

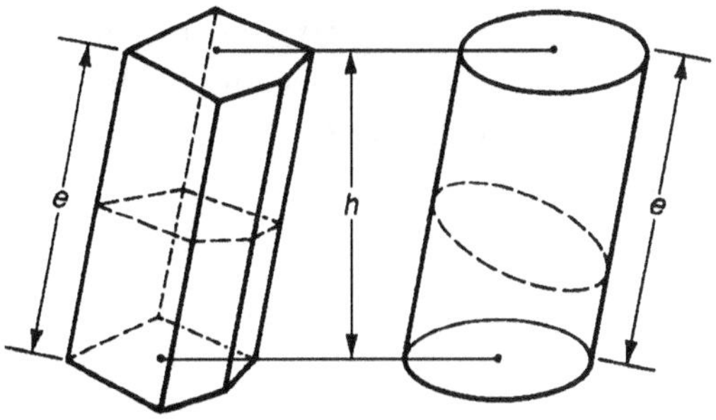

Figure 2.17

Pyramid or Cone

$V = \frac{1}{3}$ (area of base) (altitude, h)

Lateral area of regular figure = $\frac{1}{2}$ (perimeter of base)(slant height, s)

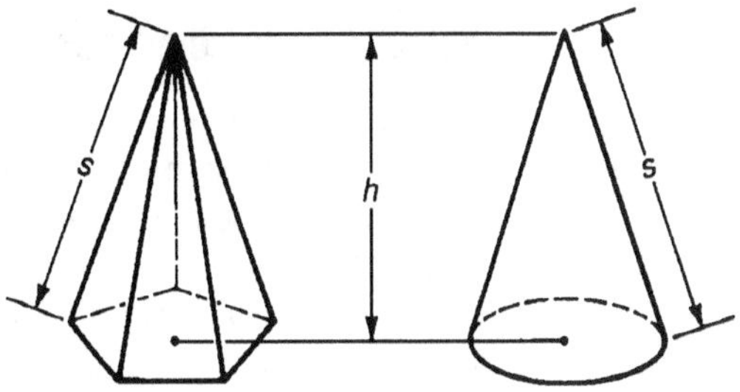

Figure 2.18

Sphere

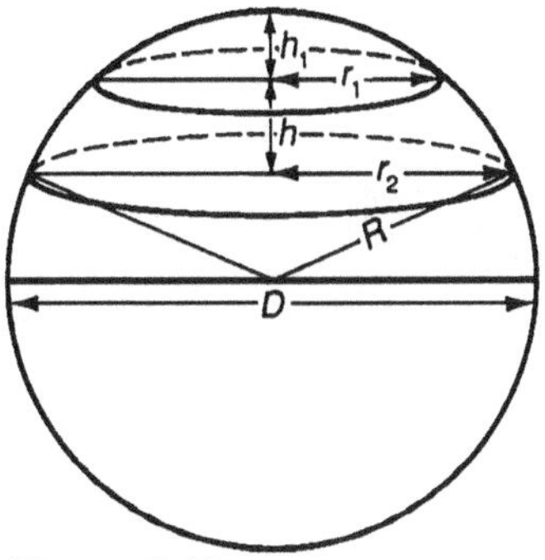

Figure 2.19

$$A_{(sphere)} = 4\pi R^2 = \pi D^2$$

$$A_{(zone)} = 2\pi Rh = \pi Dh$$

$$V_{(sphere)} = \frac{4}{3}\pi R^3 = \frac{1}{6}\pi D^3$$

$$V_{(spherical\ sector)} = \frac{2}{3}\pi R^2 h = \frac{1}{6}\pi D^2 h$$

PLANE ANALYTIC GEOMETRY

Rectangular Coordinates

Let two perpendicular lines, $X'X$ (x-axis) and $Y'Y$ (y-axis) meet at a point O (origin). The position of any point $P(x, y)$ is fixed by the distances x (abscissa) and y (ordinate) from $Y'Y$ and $X'X$, respectively, to P. Values of x are positive to the right and negative to the left of $Y'Y$; values of y are positive above and negative below $X'X$.

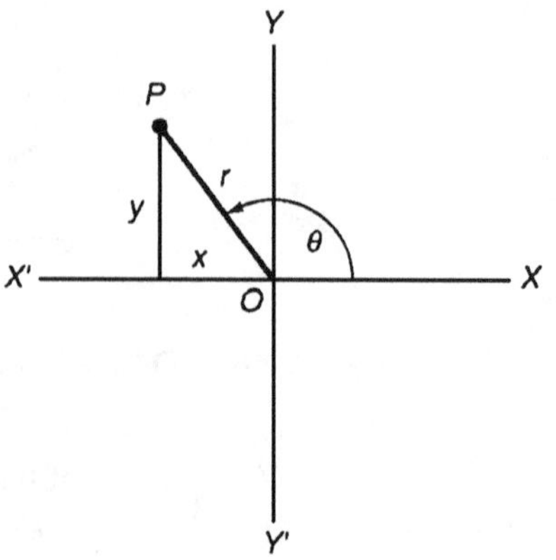

Figure 2.20

Polar Coordinates

Let O (origin or pole) be a point in the plane and OX (initial line) be any line through O. The position of any point $P\ (r, \theta)$ is fixed by the distance r (radius vector) from O to the point and the angle θ (vectorial angle) measured from OX to OP (Figure 2.20).

A value for r is positive and is measured along the terminal side of θ; a value for θ is positive when measured counterclockwise and negative when measured clockwise.

Relations Connecting Rectangular and Polar Coordinates

$$x = r\cos\theta, \quad y = r\sin\theta$$

$$r = \sqrt{x^2 + y^2}, \quad \theta = \tan^{-1}\frac{y}{x}, \quad \sin\theta = \frac{y}{\sqrt{x^2 + y^2}},$$

$$\cos\theta = \frac{x}{\sqrt{x^2 + y^2}}, \quad \tan\theta = \frac{y}{x}$$

Points and Slopes

Let $P_1(x_1, y_1)$ and $P_2(x_2, y_2)$ be any two points, and let α_1 be the angle from the x axis to P_1P_2, measured counterclockwise.

The length P_1P_2 is $d = \sqrt{(x_2 - x_1)^2 + (y_2 - y_1)^2}$.

The midpoint of P_1P_2 is $\left(\frac{x_1+x_2}{2}, \frac{y_1+y_2}{2}\right)$.

The point that divides P_1P_2 in the ratio $n_1{:}n_2$ is $\left(\frac{n_1x_2+n_2x_1}{n_1+n_2}, \frac{n_1y_2+n_2y_1}{n_1+n_2}\right)$.

The slope of P_1P_2 is $\tan\alpha = m = \frac{y_2-y_1}{x_2-x_1}$.

The angle between two lines of slopes m_1 and m_2 is $\beta = \tan^{-1}\frac{m_2-m_1}{1+m_1m_2}$.

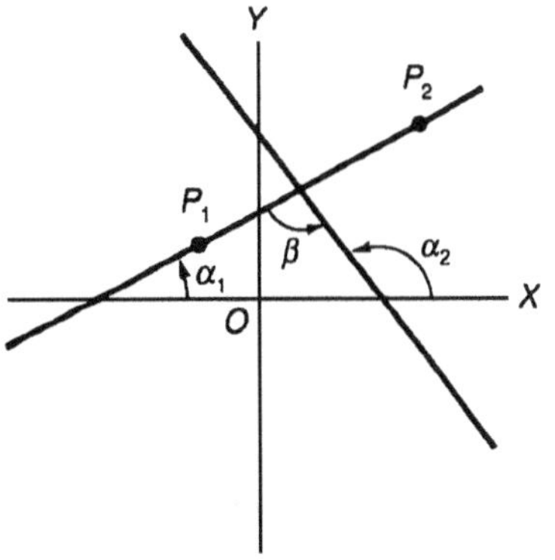

Figure 2.21

Two lines of slopes m_1 and m_2 are perpendicular if $m_2 = -\frac{1}{m_1}$.

Example **2.12**

Find the distance between the points (1, –2) and (–4, 2).

Solution

The distance is $d = \sqrt{(x_2-x_1)^2+(y_2-y_1)^2} = \sqrt{[1-(-4)]^2+[-2-2]^2}$
$= \sqrt{5^2+4^2} = 6.4$

Locus and Equation

The collection of all points that satisfy a given condition is called the **locus** of that condition; the condition expressed by means of the variable coordinates of any point on the locus is called the **equation of the locus**.

The locus may be represented by equations of three kinds: (1) a rectangular equation involves the rectangular coordinates (x, y); (2) a polar equation involves the polar coordinates (r, θ); and (3) parametric equations express x and y or r and θ in terms of a third independent variable called a parameter.

The following equations are generally given in the system in which they are most simply expressed; sometimes several forms of the equation in one or more systems are given.

Straight Line

$Ax + By + C = 0$ [$-A/B$ = slope]

$y = mx + b$ [m = slope, b = intercept on OY]

$y - y_1 = m(x - x_1)$ [m = slope, $P_1(x_1, y_1)$ is a known point on the line]

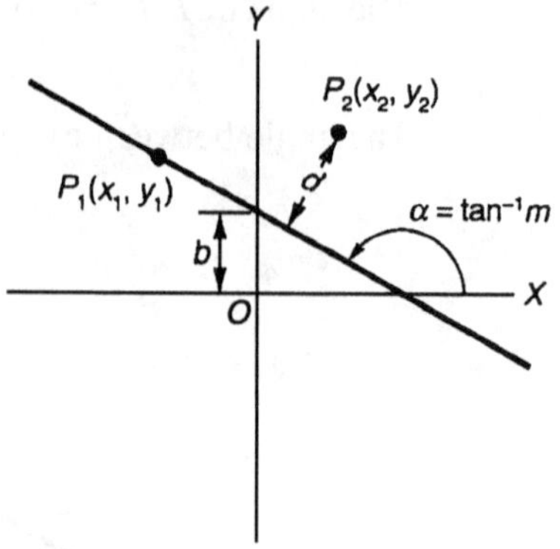

Figure 2.22

Example 2.13

Find the equation of the line passing through the points (2, 1) and (3, –3).

Solution

Slope can be found as $m = \dfrac{y_2 - y_1}{x_2 - x_1} = \dfrac{1-(-3)}{2-3} = -4.$

The point-slope form is $(y - 1) = -4(x - 2)$ or $(y + 3) = -4(x - 3)$.

Simplifying, either equation yields $y = -4x + 9$ or equivalently $4x + y - 9 = 0$.

Example 2.14

Find the equation of the straight line passing through the point (3, 1) and perpendicular to the line passing through the points (3, –2) and (–3, 7).

Solution

Slope of the line passing through (3, –2) and (–3, 7) is

$$m_1 = \frac{y_2 - y_1}{x_2 - x_1} = \frac{7-(-2)}{-3-3} = -\frac{3}{2}$$

Slope of the line passing through (3, 1) is $m_2 = -\dfrac{1}{m_1} = \dfrac{2}{3}$, since the two lines are perpendicular to each other.

Equation is $(y-1) = \dfrac{2}{3}(x - 3)$ or $2x - 3y - 3 = 0$.

Circle

The locus of a point at a constant distance (radius) from a fixed point C (center) is a circle.

$(x-h)^2+(y-k)^2=a^2$	$C(h, k)$, radius $= a$	
$r^2+b^2\pm 2\,br\cos(\theta-\beta)=a^2$	$C(b, \beta)$, radius $= a$	[Figure 2.23(a)]
$x^2+y^2=2ax$	$C(a, 0)$, radius $= a$	
$r=2a\cos\theta$	$C(a, 0)$, radius $= a$	[Figure 2.23(b)]
$x^2+y^2=2ay$	$C(0, a)$, *radius* $= a$	
$r=2a\sin\theta$	$C(0, a)$, *radius* $= a$	[Figure 2.23(c)]
$x^2+y^2=a^2$	$C(0, 0)$, radius $= a$	
$r=a$	$C(0, 0)$, radius $= a$	[Figure 2.23(d)]
$x=a\cos\phi,\ y=a\sin\phi$	ϕ = angle from OX to radius	

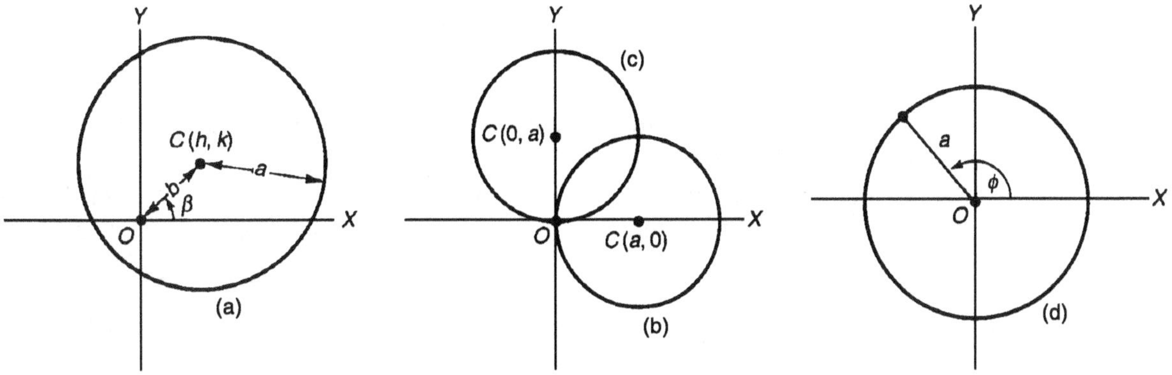

Figure 2.23

Example 2.15

Find the equation of the circle (i) with center at (0, 0) and radius 3, and (ii) with center at (1, 2) and radius 4.

Solution

Equation of a circle with center at (h, k) and radius r is $(x-h)^2+(y-k)^2=r^2$.

i) Here, $h = 0$, $k = 0$, and $r = 3$; equation of the circle is $x^2+y^2=3^2$ or $x^2+y^2-9=0$

ii) Here, $h = 1$, $k = 2$, and $r = 4$; equation of the circle is $(x-1)^2+(y-2)^2=4^2$
Simplifying, $x^2-2x+y^2-4y-11=0$

Example 2.16

Given an equation of a circle, x2 + 6x + y2 – 10y = 2, the radius of this circle is:

a). 12

b). 51

c). 6

d). 36

The first method is to find the radius by completing the square of the given equation knowing that the equation of a circuit as given by the NCEES Handbook is $(x-h)^2 + (y-k)^2 = r^2$.

$$\left(x^2+6x\right)+\left(\frac{6}{2}\right)^2+\left(y^2-10y\right)+\left(\frac{-10}{2}\right)^2=2+\left(\frac{6}{2}\right)^2+\left(\frac{-10}{2}\right)^2$$

$$\left(x^2+6x+9\right)+\left(y^2-10y+25\right)=2+9+25$$

$$(x+3)^2+(y-5)^2=36=(6)^2$$

This is in the form of the equation of a circle with $r = 6$.
Therefore, the answer is c). 6.
The second method is to use an alternate normal form of the conic section equation definition given in the NCEES handbook on page 22 on the bottom left:

$$x^2 + y^2 + 2ax + 2by + c = 0$$

where $h=-a, k=-b,$ and $r=\sqrt{a^2+b^2-c}$.

Using this last equation to solve for $r = \sqrt{3^2+-5^2-(-2)}=\sqrt{36}=6,$

where $a = 6/2 = 3$, $b = -10/2 = -5$, and $c = -2$.

Conic

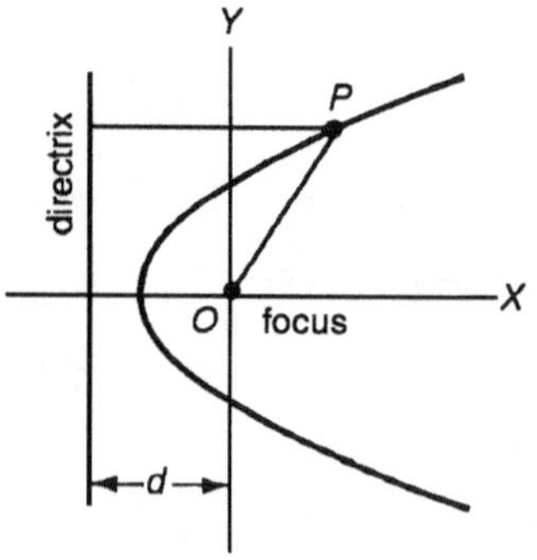

Figure 2.24

A **conic** is the locus of a point whose distance from a fixed point (focus) is in a constant ratio e, called the eccentricity, to its distance from a fixed straight line (directrix).

$$x^2+y^2=e^2(d+x)^2 \qquad d = \text{distance from focus to directrix}$$

$$r=\frac{de}{1-e\cos\theta}$$

The conic is called a parabola when $e = 1$, an ellipse when $e < 1$, and a hyperbola when $e > 1$.

Conic Section Equation

The general form of the conic section equation is

$$Ax^2 + Bxy + Cy^2 + Dx + Ey + F = 0$$

where not both A and C are zero.

If $B^2 - 4AC < 0$, an *ellipse* is defined.
If $B^2 - 4AC > 0$, an *hyperbola* is defined.
If $B^2 - 4AC = 0$, the conic is a *parabola*.
If $A = C$ and $B = 0$, a *circle* is defined.
If $A = B = C = 0$, a *straight line* is defined.

$$x^2 + y^2 + 2ax + 2by + c = 0$$

is the normal form of the conic section equation, if that conic section has a principal axis parallel to a coordinate axis.

$$h = -a; k = -b$$

$$r = \sqrt{a^2 + b^2 - c}$$

Example 2.17

Which conic section is represented by each of the following equations: (i) $x^2 + 4xy + 4y^2 + 2x = 10$ and (ii) $x^2 + y^2 - 2x - 4y - 11 = 0$.

Solution

The general equation of a conic section is $Ax^2 + 2Bxy + Cy^2 + 2Dx + 2Ey + F = 0$, where both A and C are not zeros. If $B^2 - AC > 0$, a *hyperbola* is defined; if $B^2 - AC = 0$, a *parabola* is defined; if $B^2 - AC < 0$, an *ellipse* is defined. (Note: If B is zero and A = C, a *circle* is defined.)

If A = B = C = 0, a *straight line* is defined.

If B = 0, A = C, a *circle* is defined with equation $x^2 + y^2 + 2ax + 2by + c = 0$.

Center is at (–a, –b) and radius = $\sqrt{a^2 + b^2 - c}$ provided $a^2 + b^2 - c > 0$.

(i) Here, A = 1, B = 2, and C = 4. Then, $B^2 - AC = (2)^2 - (1)(4) = 0$. The equation represents a parabola.

(ii) Here, A = 1, B = 0, C = 1. Because A = C and B = 0, the equation represents a circle.

[Note that the center is at (1, 2), and the radius is $\sqrt{(-1)^2 + (-2)^2 - (-11)} = 4$.]

Parabola

A parabola is a special case of a conic where $e = 1$.

$(y-k)^2 = a(x-h)$ Vertex (h, k), axis $\parallel OX$
$y^2 = ax$ Vertex (0, 0), axis along OX [Figure 2.25(a)]

$(x-h)^2 = a(y-k)$ Vertex (h, k), axis $\parallel OY$

$x^2 = ay$ Vertex $(0, 0)$, axis along OY [Figure 2.25(b)]

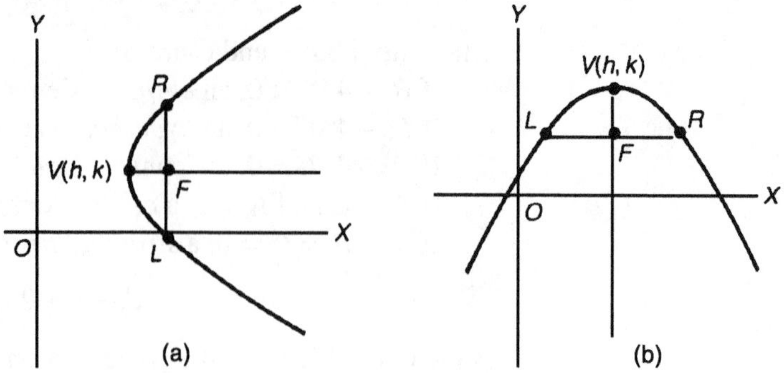

Figure 2.25

Distance from vertex to focus $= VF = \frac{1}{4}a$. Latus rectum $= LR = a$.

Example 2.18

Find the equation of a parabola (i) with center at (0, 0) and focus at (4, 0) and (ii) with center at (4, 2) and focus at (8, 2).

Solution

The equation of a parabola with center at (h, k) and focus at $(h + p/2, k)$ is given as

$(y-k)^2 = 2p(x-h)$

(i) $h = 0$; $k = 0$; $h + p/2 = 4$; then, $p = 8$ and the equation is $y^2 = 16x$.

(ii) $h = 4$; $k = 2$; $h + p/2 = 8$; then, $p = 8$ and the equation is $(y-2)^2 = 16(x-4)$.

Ellipse

This is a special case of a conic where $e < 1$.

$$\frac{(x-h)^2}{a^2} + \frac{(y-k)^2}{b^2} = 1 \quad \text{Center } (h, k), \text{ axes } \parallel OX, OY$$

$$\frac{x^2}{a^2} + \frac{y^2}{b^2} = 1 \quad \text{Center } (0, 0), \text{ axes along } OX, OY$$

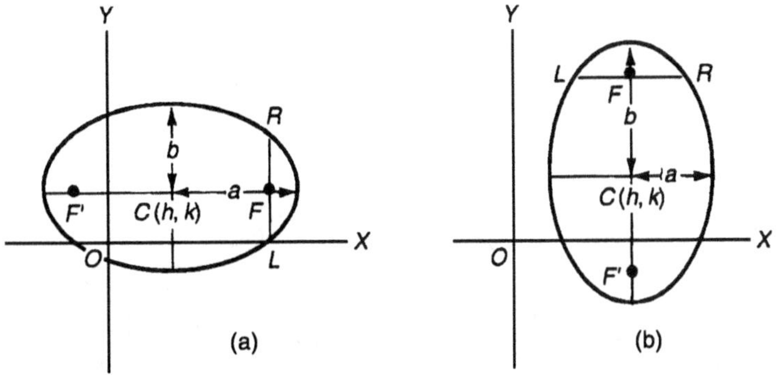

Figure 2.26

	$a > b$, Figure 2.26(a)	$b > a$, Figure 2.26(b)
Major axis	$2a$	$2b$
Minor axis	$2b$	$2a$
Distance from center to either focus	$\sqrt{a^2 - b^2}$	$\sqrt{b^2 - a^2}$
Latus rectum	$\frac{2b^2}{a}$	$\frac{2a^2}{b}$
Eccentricity, e	$\sqrt{\frac{a^2 - b^2}{a}}$	$\sqrt{\frac{b^2 - a^2}{b}}$
Sum of distances of any point P from the foci, $PF' + PF$	$2a$	$2b$

Example 2.19

Find the equation of an ellipse with center at origin, x-axis intercept (4, 0), and y-axis intercept (0, 2).

Solution

Equation of an ellipse with center at origin and x-axis intercept of $(a, 0)$ and y-axis intercept of $(0, b)$ is $\frac{x^2}{a^2} + \frac{y^2}{b^2} = 1$. Here, $a = 4$ and $b = 2$; then, the equation is $\frac{x^2}{4^2} + \frac{y^2}{2^2} = 1$.

Hyperbola

This is a special case of a conic where $e > 1$.

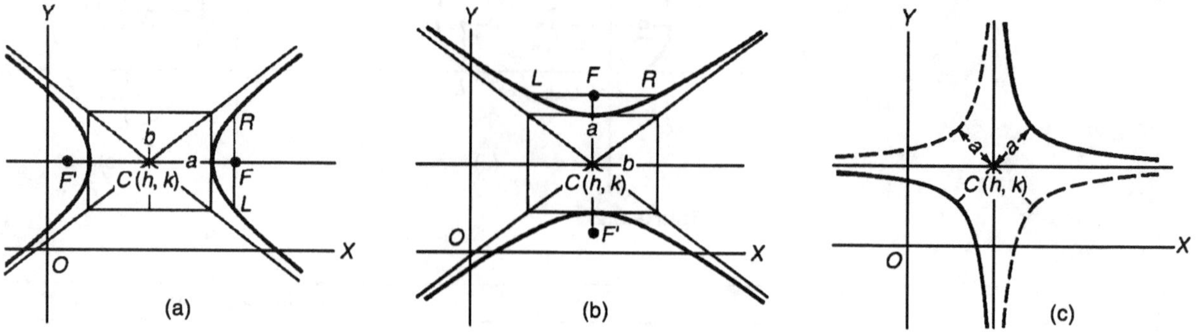

Figure 2.27

$$\frac{(x-h)^2}{a^2} - \frac{(y-k)^2}{b^2} = 1 \qquad C(h, k), \text{ transverse axis } \parallel OX$$

$$\frac{x^2}{a^2} - \frac{y^2}{b^2} = 1 \qquad C(0, 0), \text{ transverse axis along } OX$$

$$\frac{(y-k)^2}{a^2} - \frac{(x-h)^2}{b^2} = 1 \qquad C(h, k), \text{ transverse axis } \parallel OY$$

$$\frac{y^2}{a^2} - \frac{x^2}{b^2} = 1 \qquad C(0, 0), \text{ transverse along } OY$$

Transverse axis $= 2a$; conjugate axis $= 2b$

Distance from center to either focus $= \sqrt{a^2 + b^2}$

Latus rectum $= \dfrac{2b^2}{a}$

Eccentricity, $e = \dfrac{\sqrt{a^2 + b^2}}{a}$

Difference of distances of any point from the foci $= 2a$.

The asymptotes are two lines through the center to which the branches of the hyperbola approach arbitrarily closely; their slopes are $\pm b/a$ [Figure 2.27(a)] or $\pm a/b$ [Figure 2.27(b)].

The rectangular (equilateral) hyperbola has $b = a$. The asymptotes are perpendicular to each other.

$$(x-h)(y-k) = \pm e = \sqrt{2} \qquad \text{Center } (h, k), \text{ asymptotes } \parallel OX, OY$$

$$xy = \pm e = \sqrt{2} \qquad \text{Center } (0, 0), \text{ asymptotes along } OX, OY$$

The + sign gives the solid curves in Figure 2.27(c); the – sign gives the dotted curves in Figure 2.27(c).

Example 2.20

What is the equation of the hyperbola with center at origin, passing through (±2, 0), and an eccentricity of $\sqrt{10}$?

Solution

Equation of a hyperbola with center at origin, x-axis intercepts of (± a, 0), and eccentricity e is $\frac{x^2}{a^2} - \frac{y^2}{b^2} = 1$, where $b = a\sqrt{e^2 - 1}$. Here, $a = 2$; $e = \sqrt{10}$; then, $b = a\sqrt{e^2 - 1} = 2\sqrt{10 - 1} = 6$; equation is $\frac{x^2}{2^2} - \frac{y^2}{6^2} = 1$.

VECTORS

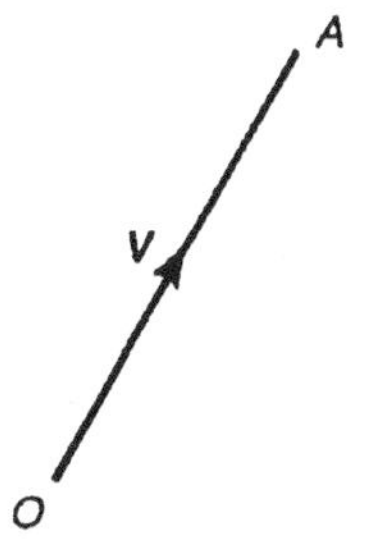

Figure 2.28

Definition and Graphical Representation of a Vector

A vector (**V**) is a quantity that is completely specified by magnitude *and* a direction. A scalar (s) is a quantity that is completely specified by a magnitude *only*.

The vector (**V**) may be represented geometrically by the segment $\overrightarrow{OA}$, the length of OA signifying the magnitude of **V** and the arrow carried by OA signifying the direction of **V**. The segment $\overrightarrow{AO}$ represents the vector –**V**.

Graphical Summation of Vectors

If $\mathbf{V}_1$ and $\mathbf{V}_2$ are two vectors, their graphical sum $\mathbf{V} = \mathbf{V}_1 + \mathbf{V}_2$ is formed by drawing the vector $\mathbf{V}_1 = \overrightarrow{OA}$, from any point O, and the vector $\mathbf{V}_2 = \overrightarrow{AB}$ from the end of $\mathbf{V}_1$ and joining O and B; then $\mathbf{V} = \overrightarrow{OB}$. Also, $\mathbf{V}_1 + \mathbf{V}_2 = \mathbf{V}_2 + \mathbf{V}_1$ and $\mathbf{V}_1 + \mathbf{V}_2 - \mathbf{V} = 0$ (Figure 2.29(a)).

Similarly, if $\mathbf{V}_1, \mathbf{V}_2, \mathbf{V}_3, \ldots, \mathbf{V}_n$ are any number of vectors drawn so that the initial point of one is the end point of the preceding one, then their graphical sum $\mathbf{V} = \mathbf{V}_1 + \mathbf{V}_2 + \ldots + \mathbf{V}_n$ is the vector joining the initial point of $\mathbf{V}_1$ with the end point of $\mathbf{V}_n$ (Figure 2.29(b)).

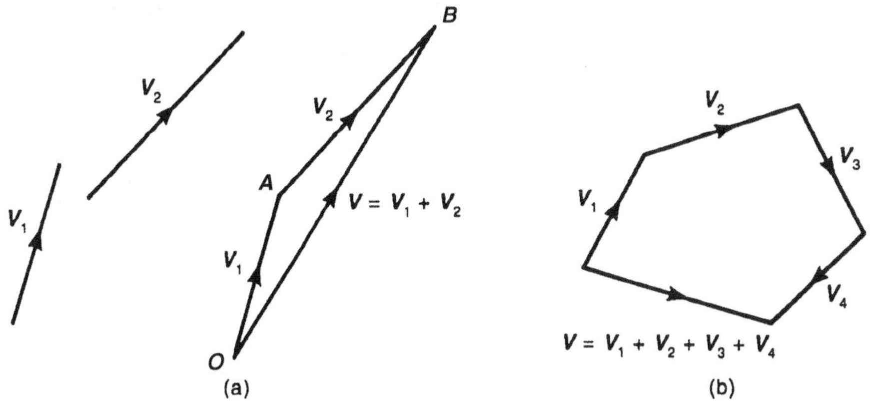

Figure 2.29

Analytic Representation of Vector Components

A vector **V** that is considered as lying in the *x*-*y* coordinate plane (Figure 2.30(a)) is completely determined by its horizontal and vertical components *x* and *y*. If **i** and **j** represent vectors of unit magnitude along *OX* and *OY*, respectively, and *a* and *b* are the magnitude of *x* and *y*, then **V** may be represented by $\mathbf{V} = a\mathbf{i} + b\mathbf{j}$, its magnitude by $|\mathbf{V}| = +\sqrt{a^2 + b^2}$, and its direction by $\alpha = \tan^{-1} b/a$.

A vector **V** in three-dimensional in space is completely determined by its components *x*, *y*, and *z* along three mutually perpendicular lines *OX*, *OY*, and *OZ*, directed as shown in Figure 2.30(b). If **i**, **j**, and **k** represent vectors of unit magnitude along *OX*, *OY*, *OZ*, respectively, and *a*, *b*, and *c* are the magnitudes of the components *x*, *y*, and *z*, respectively, then **V** may be represented by $\mathbf{V} = a\mathbf{i} + b\mathbf{j} + c\mathbf{k}$, its magnitude by, $|\mathbf{V}| = +\sqrt{a^2 + b^2 + c^2}$, and its direction by $\cos\alpha : \cos\beta : \cos\gamma = a : b : c$.

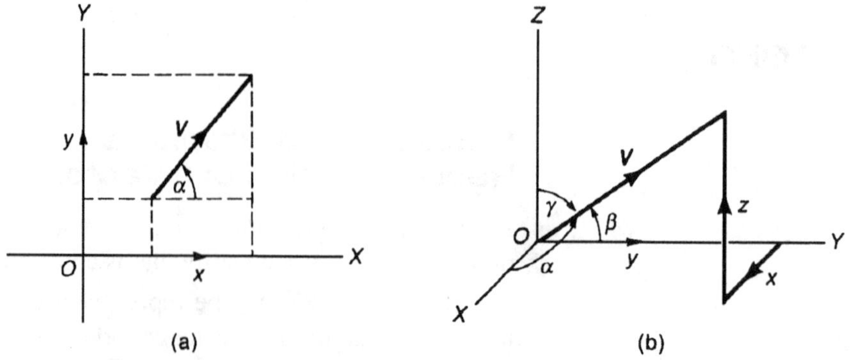

Figure 2.30

Properties of Vectors

$\mathbf{V} = a\mathbf{i} + b\mathbf{j}$ or $\mathbf{V} = a\mathbf{i} + b\mathbf{j} + c\mathbf{k}$

Vector Sum V of any Number of Vectors, $\mathbf{V}_1, \mathbf{V}_2, \mathbf{V}_3, \ldots$

$$\mathbf{V} = \mathbf{V}_1 + \mathbf{V}_2 + \mathbf{V}_3 + \ldots = (a_1 + a_2 + a_3 + \ldots)\,\mathbf{i} + (b_1 + b_2 + b_3 + \ldots)\,\mathbf{j} + (c_1 + c_2 + c_3 + \ldots)\,\mathbf{k}$$

Product of a Vector V and a Scalar *s*

The product $s\mathbf{V}$ has the same direction as **V**, and its magnitude is *s* times the magnitude of **V**.

$$s\mathbf{V} = (sa)\,\mathbf{i} + (sb)\,\mathbf{j} + (sc)\,\mathbf{k}$$

$$(s_1 + s_2)\,\mathbf{V} = s_1\mathbf{V} + s_2\mathbf{V} \qquad (\mathbf{V}_1 + \mathbf{V}_2)s = \mathbf{V}_1 s + \mathbf{V}_2 s$$

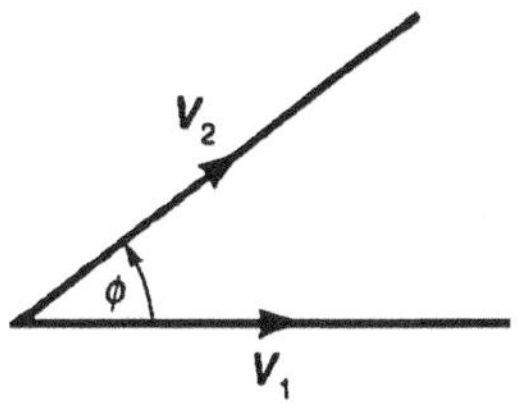

Figure 2.31

Scalar Product or Dot Product of Two Vectors: $V_1 \bullet V_2$

$$\mathbf{V}_1 \bullet \mathbf{V}_2 = |\mathbf{V}_1||\mathbf{V}_2|\cos\phi, \text{ where } \phi \text{ is the angle between } \mathbf{V}_1 \text{ and } \mathbf{V}_2$$

$$\mathbf{V}_1 \bullet \mathbf{V}_2 = \mathbf{V}_2 \bullet \mathbf{V}_1; \quad \mathbf{V}_1 \bullet \mathbf{V}_1 = |\mathbf{V}_1|^2; \quad (\mathbf{V}_1 + \mathbf{V}_2) \bullet \mathbf{V}_3 = \mathbf{V}_1 \bullet \mathbf{V}_3 + \mathbf{V}_2 \bullet \mathbf{V}_3$$

$$(\mathbf{V}_1 + \mathbf{V}_2) \bullet (\mathbf{V}_3 + \mathbf{V}_4) = \mathbf{V}_1 \bullet \mathbf{V}_3 + \mathbf{V}_1 \bullet \mathbf{V}_4 + \mathbf{V}_2 \bullet \mathbf{V}_3 + \mathbf{V}_2 \bullet \mathbf{V}_4$$

$$\mathbf{i} \bullet \mathbf{i} = \mathbf{j} \bullet \mathbf{j} = \mathbf{k} \bullet \mathbf{k} = 1; \quad \mathbf{i} \bullet \mathbf{j} = \mathbf{j} \bullet \mathbf{k} = \mathbf{k} \bullet \mathbf{i} = 0$$

In a plane, $\mathbf{V}_1 \bullet \mathbf{V}_2 = a_1a_2 + b_1b_2$; in space, $\mathbf{V}_1 \bullet \mathbf{V}_2 = a_1a_2 + b_1 b_2 + c_1c_2$.

The scalar product of two vectors $\mathbf{V}_1 \bullet \mathbf{V}_2$ is a scalar quantity and may physically represent the work done by a constant force of magnitude $|\mathbf{V}_1|$ on a particle moving through a distance $|\mathbf{V}_2|$, where ϕ is the angle between the direction of the force and the direction of motion.

Vector Product or Cross Product of Two Vectors: $V_1 \times V_2$

The vector product is $\mathbf{V}_1 \times \mathbf{V}_2 = \mathbf{l}\,|\mathbf{V}_1|\mathbf{V}_2|\sin\phi$, where ϕ is the angle from $\mathbf{V}_1$ to $\mathbf{V}_2$ and $\mathbf{l}$ is a unit vector perpendicular to the plane of the vectors $\mathbf{V}_1$ to $\mathbf{V}_2$ and so directed that a right-handed screw driven in the direction of $\mathbf{l}$ would carry $\mathbf{V}_1$ into $\mathbf{V}_2$.

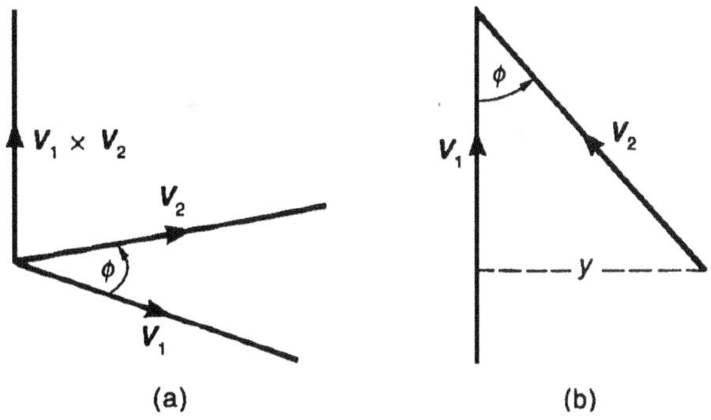

Figure 2.32

$$\mathbf{V}_1 \times \mathbf{V}_2 = -\mathbf{V}_2 \times \mathbf{V}_1; \quad \mathbf{V}_1 \times \mathbf{V}_1 = 0$$

$$(\mathbf{V}_1 + \mathbf{V}_2) \times \mathbf{V}_3 = \mathbf{V}_1 \times \mathbf{V}_3 + \mathbf{V}_2 \times \mathbf{V}_3$$

$$\mathbf{V}_1 \bullet (\mathbf{V}_2 \times \mathbf{V}_3) = \mathbf{V}_2 \bullet (\mathbf{V}_3 \times \mathbf{V}_1) = \mathbf{V}_3 \bullet (\mathbf{V}_1 \times \mathbf{V}_2)$$

$$\mathbf{i} \times \mathbf{i} = \mathbf{j} \times \mathbf{j} = \mathbf{k} \times \mathbf{k} = 0; \quad \mathbf{i} \times \mathbf{j} = \mathbf{k}; \quad \mathbf{j} \times \mathbf{k} = \mathbf{i}; \quad \mathbf{k} \times \mathbf{i} = \mathbf{j}$$

In the x-y plane, $\mathbf{V}_1 \times \mathbf{V}_2 = (a_1b_2 - a_2b_1)\mathbf{k}$.

In space, $\mathbf{V}_1 \times \mathbf{V}_2 = (b_2c_3 - b_3c_2)\,\mathbf{i} + (c_3a_1 - c_1a_3)\,\mathbf{j} + (a_1b_2 - a_2b_1)\,\mathbf{k}$.

The vector product of two vectors is a vector quantity and may physically represent the moment of a force $\mathbf{V}_1$ about a point O placed so that the moment arm is $y = |\mathbf{V}_2| \sin\phi$ (see Figure 2.32(b)).

Example 2.21

Vectors **A** and **B** are defined as: $\mathbf{A} = i - 2j + 3k$, $\mathbf{B} = 2i + j - 2k$

Find (i) **A** + **B**, (ii) **A** – **B**, (iii) 2**A**, (iv) |**A**|, (v) dot product **A**• **B**, and (vi) the cross product **A** × **B**.

Solution

(i) $\mathbf{A} + \mathbf{B} = 3i - j + k$ (ii) $\mathbf{A} - \mathbf{B} = -i - 3j + 5k$ (iii) $2\mathbf{A} = 2i - 4j + 6k$

(iv) $|\mathbf{A}| = \sqrt{1^2 + (-2)^2 + 3^2} = \sqrt{14}$

(v) Dot product $\mathbf{A} \bullet \mathbf{B} = (2) + (-2) + (-6) = -6$

(vi) Cross product $\mathbf{A} \times \mathbf{B} = \begin{vmatrix} i & j & k \\ 1 & -2 & 3 \\ 2 & 1 & -2 \end{vmatrix} = i + 8j + 5k$

Example 2.22

What is the angle between the vectors A_1 and A_2?

$$A_1 = 4_i + 5_j + 6_k$$
$$A_2 = 7_i + 8_j + 9_k$$

$$\cos\theta = \frac{A_1 \bullet A_2}{|A_1||A_2|}$$

$$= \frac{28 + 40 + 54}{\left(\sqrt{16 + 25 + 36}\right)\left(\sqrt{49 + 64 + 81}\right)} = 0.998$$

$$\theta = \cos^{-1}(0.998) = 3.62°$$

LINEAR ALGEBRA

Matrix Operations

Matrices are rectangular arrays of real or complex numbers. Their great importance arises from the variety of operations that may be performed on them. Using the standard convention, the across-the-page lines are called **rows** and the up-and-down-the-page lines are **columns**. Entries in a matrix are **addressed** with double subscripts (always row first, then column). Thus the matrix

$$\mathbf{A} = \begin{bmatrix} 1 & 2 & 3 \\ 0 & 9 & -3 \end{bmatrix}$$

is 2 × 3, and the "9" is a_{22}. The "2" is a_{12} and the "0" is a_{21}. One also can refer to entries with square brackets, the "9" being $[A]_{22}$ and the "3" $[A]_{13}$.

If two matrices are the same size, they may be added: $[A + B]_{ij} = [A]_{ij} + [B]_{ij}$. Thus,

$$\begin{bmatrix} 1 & 2 & 3 \\ 0 & 9 & -3 \end{bmatrix} + \begin{bmatrix} 1 & 3 \\ 2 & 4 \end{bmatrix}$$

is not defined, but

$$\begin{bmatrix} 1 & 2 & 3 \\ 0 & 9 & -3 \end{bmatrix} + \begin{bmatrix} 1 & 3 & 5 \\ 2 & 4 & 6 \end{bmatrix} = \begin{bmatrix} 2 & 5 & 8 \\ 2 & 13 & 3 \end{bmatrix}$$

is proper.

Any matrix may be multiplied by a **scalar** (a number): $[c\mathbf{A}]_{ij} = c[\mathrm{A}]_{ij}$, so that

$$5\begin{bmatrix} 1 & 5 \\ 0 & 6 \end{bmatrix} = \begin{bmatrix} 5 & 25 \\ 0 & 30 \end{bmatrix}$$

The most peculiar matrix operation (and the most useful) is matrix multiplication. If **A** is $m \times n$ and **B** is $n \times p$, then $\mathbf{A} \bullet \mathbf{B}$ (or **AB**) is of size $m \times p$, and

$$[AB]_{ij} = \sum_{k=1}^{n} a_{jk} \bullet b_{kj}$$

The **dot product** (scalar product) of the *i*th row of **A** with the *j*th column of **B**, as in

$$\begin{bmatrix} 1 & 2 & 3 \\ 0 & 9 & -3 \end{bmatrix} \bullet \begin{bmatrix} 1 & 5 \\ 0 & 6 \end{bmatrix}$$

is not defined (owing to the mismatch of row and column lengths), but

$$\begin{bmatrix} 1 & 2 & 3 \\ 0 & 9 & -3 \end{bmatrix} \bullet \begin{bmatrix} 1 & 5 \\ 0 & 6 \\ 7 & 8 \end{bmatrix} = \begin{bmatrix} 1\,(1) + 2\,(0) + 3\,(7) & 1\,(5) + 2\,(6) + 3\,(8) \\ 0\,(1) + 9\,(0) - 3\,(7) & 0\,(5) + 9\,(6) - 3\,(8) \end{bmatrix} = \begin{bmatrix} 22 & 41 \\ -21 & 30 \end{bmatrix}$$

is correct.

A matrix with only one row or one column is called a vector, so a matrix times a vector is a vector (if defined). Thus $\mathbf{A}\,(m \times n) \bullet \mathbf{X}\,(n \times 1) = \mathbf{Y}(m \times 1)$, so a matrix can be thought of as an **operator** that takes vectors to vectors.

Another useful way of working with matrices is transposition: If **A** is $m \times n$, $\mathbf{A}^t$ is $n \times m$ and is the result of interchanging rows and columns. Hence

$$\begin{bmatrix} 1 & 2 & 3 \\ 0 & 9 & -3 \end{bmatrix}^t = \begin{bmatrix} 1 & 0 \\ 2 & 9 \\ 3 & -3 \end{bmatrix}$$

These various operations interact in the usual pleasant ways (and one decidedly unpleasant way); the standard convention is that all of the following combinations are defined:

$$\begin{gathered}
\mathbf{A}+\mathbf{B}=\mathbf{B}+\mathbf{A}\\
\mathbf{A}+(\mathbf{B}+\mathbf{C}) = (\mathbf{A}+\mathbf{B})+\mathbf{C}\\
c(\mathbf{A}+\mathbf{B})=c\mathbf{A}+c\mathbf{B}\\
(c+d)\,\mathbf{A}=c\mathbf{A}+d\mathbf{A}\\
(-1)\mathbf{A}+\mathbf{A}=(0\mathbf{A})\\
\mathbf{A}\bullet\mathbf{B}\neq\mathbf{B}\bullet\mathbf{A}\text{ (in general)}\\
\mathbf{A}\bullet(\mathbf{B}\bullet\mathbf{C})=(\mathbf{A}\bullet\mathbf{B})\bullet\mathbf{C}\\
\mathbf{A}\bullet(\mathbf{B}+\mathbf{C})=\mathbf{A}\bullet\mathbf{B}+\mathbf{A}\bullet\mathbf{C}\\
(\mathbf{A}+\mathbf{B})\bullet\mathbf{C}=\mathbf{A}\bullet\mathbf{C}+\mathbf{B}\bullet\mathbf{C}\\
(\mathbf{A}+\mathbf{B})' = \mathbf{A}'+\mathbf{B}'\\
(\mathbf{A}\bullet\mathbf{B})' = \mathbf{B}'\bullet\mathbf{A}'
\end{gathered}$$

In addition, matrices **I**, which are $n \times n$ and whose entries are 1 on the diagonal $i = j$ and 0 elsewhere, are multiplicative identities: $\mathbf{A} \bullet \mathbf{I} = \mathbf{A}$ and $\mathbf{I} \bullet \mathbf{A} = \mathbf{A}$. Here the two **I** matrices may be different sizes; for example,

$$\begin{bmatrix}1 & 2 & 3\\ 0 & 9 & -3\end{bmatrix}\bullet\begin{bmatrix}1 & 0 & 0\\ 0 & 1 & 0\\ 0 & 0 & 1\end{bmatrix}=\begin{bmatrix}1 & 2 & 3\\ 0 & 9 & -3\end{bmatrix}$$

but

$$\begin{bmatrix}1 & 0\\ 0 & 1\end{bmatrix}\bullet\begin{bmatrix}1 & 2 & 3\\ 0 & 9 & -3\end{bmatrix}=\begin{bmatrix}1 & 2 & 3\\ 0 & 9 & -3\end{bmatrix}$$

I is called the identity matrix, and the size is understood from context.

Example 2.23

Verify that the transpose of $\mathbf{A} + \mathbf{BC}$ is $\mathbf{C}'\mathbf{B}' + \mathbf{A}'$ if

$$\mathbf{A}=\begin{bmatrix}1 & 1\\ 2 & 3\end{bmatrix}\quad \mathbf{B}=\begin{bmatrix}1 & 2 & 3\\ 0 & 9 & -3\end{bmatrix}\quad \mathbf{C}=\begin{bmatrix}1 & 5\\ 0 & 6\\ 7 & 8\end{bmatrix}$$

Solution

$$\mathbf{BC}\begin{bmatrix}22 & 41\\ -21 & 30\end{bmatrix}\text{, so }\mathbf{A}+\mathbf{BC}=\begin{bmatrix}23 & 42\\ -19 & 33\end{bmatrix}\text{ and }[\mathbf{A}+\mathbf{BC}]'=\begin{bmatrix}23 & -19\\ 42 & 33\end{bmatrix}$$

On the other hand, $\mathbf{C}^t\mathbf{B}^t = \begin{bmatrix} 1 & 0 & 7 \\ 5 & 6 & 8 \end{bmatrix} \bullet \begin{bmatrix} 1 & 0 \\ 2 & 9 \\ 3 & -3 \end{bmatrix} = \begin{bmatrix} 22 & -21 \\ 41 & 30 \end{bmatrix}$ and

$$\mathbf{A}^t = \begin{bmatrix} 1 & 2 \\ 1 & 3 \end{bmatrix}, \text{ so } \mathbf{A}^t + \mathbf{C}^t\mathbf{B}^t = \mathbf{C}^t\mathbf{B}^t + \mathbf{A}^t = \begin{bmatrix} 23 & -19 \\ 42 & 33 \end{bmatrix}$$

Types of Matrices

Matrices are classified according to their appearance or the way they act. If **A** is square and $\mathbf{A}^t = \mathbf{A}$, then **A** is called symmetric. If $\mathbf{A}' = -\mathbf{A}$, then it is skew-symmetric.

If **A** has complex entries, **A*** then is called the Hermitian adjoint of **A**. If $\mathbf{A}^* = \mathbf{A}^t$ (complex conjugate), then

$$\begin{bmatrix} 1+i & i \\ 3 & 4-i \end{bmatrix}^* = \begin{bmatrix} 1-i & -i \\ 3 & 4+i \end{bmatrix}^t = \begin{bmatrix} 1-i & 3 \\ -i & 4+i \end{bmatrix}$$

If $\mathbf{A} = \mathbf{A}^*$, then A is called Hermitian. If $\mathbf{A}^* = -\mathbf{A}$, the name is skew-Hermitian.

If **A** is square and $a_{ij} = 0$ unless $i = j$, **A** is called diagonal. If **A** is square and zero below the diagonal ($[\mathbf{A}]_{ij} = 0$ if $i > j$), **A** is called upper triangular. The transpose of such a matrix is called lower triangular.

If A is square and there is a matrix $\mathbf{A}^{-1}$ such that $\mathbf{A}^{-1} \bullet \mathbf{A} = \mathbf{A} \bullet \mathbf{A}^{-1} = \mathbf{I}$, **A** is nonsingular. Otherwise, it is singular. If **A** and **B** are both nonsingular $n \times n$ matrices, then **AB** is nonsingular and $(\mathbf{AB})^{-1} = \mathbf{B}^{-1}\mathbf{A}^{-1}$, because $(\mathbf{AB})(\mathbf{B}^{-1}\mathbf{A}^{-1}) = \mathbf{A}(\mathbf{B}\mathbf{B}^{-1})\mathbf{A}^{-1} = \mathbf{AIA}^{-1} = \mathbf{AA}^{-1} = \mathbf{I}$, as does $(\mathbf{B}^{-1}\mathbf{A}^{-1}) \bullet (\mathbf{AB})$.

If $\mathbf{A}^t\mathbf{A} = \mathbf{AA}^t = \mathbf{I}$ and **A** is real, it is called orthogonal (the reason will appear below). If $\mathbf{A}^*\mathbf{A} = \mathbf{AA}^* = \mathbf{I}$ (**A** complex), **A** is called unitary. If **A** commutes with **A***, so that $\mathbf{AA}^* = \mathbf{A}^*\mathbf{A}$, then **A** is called normal.

Elementary Row and Column Operations

The most important tools used in dealing with matrices are the elementary operations: *R* for row, *C* for column. If **A** is given matrix, performing $R(i \leftrightarrow j)$ on **A** means interchanging Row *i* and Row *j*. $R_i(c)$ means multiplying Row *i* by the number *c* (except $c = 0$). $R_j + cR_i$ means multiply Row *i* by *c* and add this result into Row *j* ($i \neq j$). Thus, if

$$\mathbf{A} = \begin{bmatrix} 1 & 2 & 3 \\ 4 & 5 & 6 \\ 7 & 8 & 0 \end{bmatrix}$$

then

$$R(2 \leftrightarrow 3)(\mathbf{A}) = \begin{bmatrix} 1 & 2 & 3 \\ 7 & 8 & 0 \\ 4 & 5 & 6 \end{bmatrix} \qquad C_1(2)(\mathbf{A}) = \begin{bmatrix} 2 & 2 & 3 \\ 8 & 5 & 6 \\ 14 & 8 & 0 \end{bmatrix}$$

$$R_1 - R_2(\mathbf{A}) = \begin{bmatrix} -3 & -3 & -3 \\ 4 & 5 & 6 \\ 7 & 8 & 0 \end{bmatrix}$$

These operations are used in reducing matrix problems to simpler ones.

Example 2.24

Solve $\mathbf{AX} = \mathbf{B}$ where

$$\mathbf{A} = \begin{bmatrix} 1 & 2 & 3 \\ 4 & 5 & 6 \\ 7 & 8 & 9 \end{bmatrix}, \quad \mathbf{X} = \begin{bmatrix} x \\ y \\ z \end{bmatrix}, \quad \mathbf{B} = \begin{bmatrix} 1 \\ 1 \\ 1 \end{bmatrix}$$

Solution

Form the "augmented" matrix

$$[\mathbf{A}|\mathbf{B}] = \begin{bmatrix} 1 & 2 & 3 & 1 \\ 4 & 5 & 6 & 1 \\ 7 & 8 & 9 & 1 \end{bmatrix}$$

and perform elementary row operations on this matrix until the solution is apparent:

$$\begin{bmatrix} 1 & 2 & 3 & 1 \\ 4 & 5 & 6 & 1 \\ 7 & 8 & 9 & 1 \end{bmatrix} \begin{matrix} R_2 - 4R_1 \\ R_3 - 7R_1 \end{matrix} \begin{bmatrix} 1 & 2 & 3 & 1 \\ 0 & -3 & -6 & -3 \\ 7 & -6 & -12 & -6 \end{bmatrix} \begin{matrix} R_2\left(-\frac{1}{3}\right) \\ \\ R_3\left(-\frac{1}{6}\right) \end{matrix} \begin{bmatrix} 1 & 2 & 3 & 1 \\ 0 & 1 & 2 & 1 \\ 0 & 1 & 2 & 1 \end{bmatrix}$$

$$R_3 - R_2 \begin{bmatrix} 1 & 2 & 3 & 1 \\ 0 & 1 & 2 & 1 \\ 0 & 0 & 0 & 0 \end{bmatrix}$$

The answer is now apparent: $y + 2z = 1$ and $x + 2y + 3z = 1$, or, z arbitrary, $y = 1 - 2z$, $x = 1 - 2(1 - 2z) - 3z = -1 + z$. This system of equations has an infinite number of solutions.

Example 2.25

Solve the system of equations

$$x + y - z = a$$
$$2x - y + 3z = 2$$
$$3x + 2y + z = 1$$

for x, y, and z in terms of a.

Solution

Strip off the variables x, y, and z:

$$\begin{bmatrix} 1 & 1 & -1 & a \\ 2 & -1 & 3 & 2 \\ 3 & 2 & 1 & 1 \end{bmatrix} \begin{matrix} R_2 - 2R_1 \\ R_3 - 3R_1 \end{matrix} \begin{bmatrix} 1 & 1 & -1 & a \\ 0 & -3 & 5 & 2-2a \\ 0 & -1 & 4 & 1-3a \end{bmatrix}$$

$$\begin{matrix} R_2(2 \leftrightarrow 3) \\ R_2(-1) \end{matrix} \begin{bmatrix} 1 & 1 & -1 & a \\ 0 & 1 & -4 & 3a-1 \\ 0 & -3 & 5 & 2-2a \end{bmatrix} \begin{matrix} R_1 - R_2 \\ R_3 + 3R_2 \end{matrix} \begin{bmatrix} 1 & 0 & 3 & 1-2a \\ 0 & 1 & -4 & 3a-1 \\ 0 & 0 & -7 & 7a-1 \end{bmatrix}$$

The solution is now clear:

$$z = \frac{7a-1}{-7} = -a + \frac{1}{7}$$
$$y = 3a - 1 + 4z = 3a - 1 - 4a + \frac{4}{7} = -a - \frac{3}{7}$$
$$x = 1 - 2a - 3z = 1 - 2a + 3a - \frac{3}{7} = a + \frac{4}{7}$$

Example 2.26

Find $\mathbf{A}^{-1}$ if

$$\mathbf{A} = \begin{bmatrix} 1 & 1 & -1 \\ 1 & 2 & 3 \\ 3 & 2 & 1 \end{bmatrix}$$

Solution

Since this amounts to solving $\mathbf{AX} = \mathbf{B}$ three times, with

$$\mathbf{B} = \begin{bmatrix} 1 \\ 0 \\ 0 \end{bmatrix} \quad \mathbf{B} = \begin{bmatrix} 0 \\ 1 \\ 0 \end{bmatrix} \quad \mathbf{B} = \begin{bmatrix} 0 \\ 0 \\ 1 \end{bmatrix}$$

form

$$[\mathbf{A}|\mathbf{I}] = \begin{bmatrix} 1 & 1 & -1 & 1 & 0 & 0 \\ 1 & 2 & 3 & 0 & 1 & 0 \\ 3 & 2 & 1 & 0 & 0 & 1 \end{bmatrix}$$

and perform row operations until a solution emerges.

$$[\mathbf{A}|\mathbf{I}] = \frac{R_2 - R_1}{R_3 - 3R_1}\begin{bmatrix} 1 & 1 & -1 & 1 & 0 & 0 \\ 0 & 1 & 4 & -1 & 1 & 0 \\ 0 & -1 & 4 & -3 & 0 & 1 \end{bmatrix}$$

$$\frac{R_1 - R_2}{R_3 + R_2} z \begin{bmatrix} 1 & 0 & -5 & 2 & -1 & 0 \\ 0 & 1 & 4 & -1 & 1 & 0 \\ 0 & 0 & 8 & -4 & 1 & 1 \end{bmatrix}$$

$$R_3\left(\frac{1}{8}\right) \frac{R_2 - 4R_3}{R_1 + 5R_3} \begin{bmatrix} 1 & 0 & 0 & -\frac{1}{2} & -\frac{3}{8} & \frac{5}{8} \\ 0 & 1 & 0 & 1 & \frac{1}{2} & -\frac{1}{2} \\ 0 & 0 & 1 & -\frac{1}{2} & \frac{1}{8} & \frac{1}{8} \end{bmatrix}$$

Thus,

$$\mathrm{A}^{-1} = \begin{bmatrix} -\frac{1}{2} & -\frac{3}{8} & \frac{5}{8} \\ 1 & \frac{1}{2} & -\frac{1}{2} \\ -\frac{1}{2} & \frac{1}{8} & \frac{1}{8} \end{bmatrix}$$

Example 2.27

Verify that $\mathbf{A}^{-1}\mathbf{A} = \mathbf{I}$ in Example 2.26.

Solution

$$8A^{-1}A = \begin{bmatrix} -4 & -3 & 5 \\ 8 & 4 & -4 \\ -4 & 1 & 1 \end{bmatrix}\begin{bmatrix} 1 & 1 & -1 \\ 1 & 2 & 3 \\ 3 & 2 & 1 \end{bmatrix}$$

$$= \begin{bmatrix} -4-3+15 & -4-6+10 & 4-9+5 \\ 8+4-12 & 8+8-8 & -8+12-4 \\ -4+1+3 & -4+2+2 & 4+3+1 \end{bmatrix} = 8\begin{bmatrix} 1 & 0 & 0 \\ 0 & 1 & 0 \\ 0 & 0 & 1 \end{bmatrix} = 8\mathbf{I}$$

Example 2.28

Describe the set of solutions of **AX = B**.

Solution

If $\mathbf{AX}_0 = \mathbf{B}$ is one solution, and $\mathbf{AY} = 0$, then $\mathbf{A}(\mathbf{X}_0 + \mathbf{Y})$ is a solution, so all solutions are of the form $\mathbf{X} = \mathbf{X}_0 + \mathbf{Y}$ where $\mathbf{AY} = 0$. Thus, if $\mathbf{N} = \{\mathbf{Y} : \mathbf{AY} = 0\}$ is the null space of **A**, the set of solutions to $\mathbf{AX} = \mathbf{B}$ is $\mathbf{X}_0 + \mathbf{N} = \{\mathbf{X}_0 + \mathbf{Y} : \mathbf{Y} \in \mathbf{N}\}$.

Determinants

The determinant of a square matrix is a scalar representing the *volume* of the matrix in some sense. Matrices that are not square do not have determinants.

The determinant is frequently indicated by vertical lines, viz. $|A|$. It is a complicated formula, and one way to find it is by induction. The determinant of a 1×1 matrix is $|a| = a$. The determinant of a 2×2 matrix is

$$\begin{vmatrix} a & b \\ c & d \end{vmatrix} = ad - bc$$

For a third-order determinant:

$$\begin{vmatrix} a_1 & a_2 & a_3 \\ b_1 & b_2 & b_3 \\ c_1 & c_2 & c_3 \end{vmatrix} = a_1b_2c_3 + a_2b_3c_1 + a_3b_1c_2 - a_3b_2c_1 - a_2b_1c_3 - a_1b_3c_2$$

The determinant of an $n \times n$ matrix is given in terms of n determinants, each of size $(n-1) \times (n-1)$. If **A** is $n \times n$ and $\mathbf{M}_{ij}$ is the matrix obtained by removing the ith row and the jth column from **A**, then

$$|A| = \sum_{j=1}^{n} (-1)^{1+j} a_{1j} \, |M_{1j}|$$

Example 2.29

Find the determinant

$$\begin{vmatrix} 1 & 2 & 3 \\ 4 & 0 & 6 \\ 7 & 8 & 9 \end{vmatrix}$$

Solution

$$\begin{aligned} |A| &= (-1)^{1+1} a_{11} |M_{11}| + (-1)^{1+2} a_{12} |M_{12}| + (-1)^{1+3} a_{13} |M_{13}| \\ &= 1\begin{vmatrix} 0 & 6 \\ 8 & 9 \end{vmatrix} - 2\begin{vmatrix} 4 & 6 \\ 7 & 9 \end{vmatrix} + 3\begin{vmatrix} 4 & 0 \\ 7 & 8 \end{vmatrix} \\ &= -48 - 2(36 - 42) + 3(32) = 60 \end{aligned}$$

Example 2.30

Find the determinant

$$\begin{vmatrix} 0 & 0 & 2 & 0 \\ 1 & 2 & 7 & 3 \\ 4 & 0 & 3 & 6 \\ 7 & 8 & -6 & 9 \end{vmatrix}$$

Solution

$$\begin{aligned} |A| &= a_{11}|M_{11}| - a_{12}|M_{12}| + a_{13}|M_{13}| - a_{14}|M_{14}| \\ &= 0|M_{11}| - 0|M_{12}| + 2|M_{13}| - 0|M_{14}| = 2\,(60) = 120 \end{aligned}$$

The last example provides a clue to the evaluation of large determinants, but the use of the first row of **A** in the definition of a determinant was arbitrary. For any row or column (fix i or j),

$$|A| = \sum_{j=1}^{n} (-1)^{1+j} a_{i1j} |M_{ij}|$$

The interaction of the determinant with elementary row or column operations is simple: Interchanging two rows changes the sign of the determinant; multiplying a row by a constant multiplies the determinant by that constant.

Example 2.31

Evaluate the determinant

$$\begin{vmatrix} 1 & 2 & 3 & 4 \\ 1 & 1 & 1 & 0 \\ 4 & 0 & 3 & 2 \\ 0 & 3 & 0 & 1 \end{vmatrix}$$

Solution

Choose a row or column with many zeroes and introduce still more:

$$|A| = C_2 - 3C_4\,|A| = \begin{vmatrix} 1 & -10 & 3 & 4 \\ 1 & 1 & 1 & 0 \\ 4 & -6 & 3 & 2 \\ 0 & 0 & 0 & 1 \end{vmatrix} = (-1)^{4+4} a_{44} \begin{vmatrix} 1 & -10 & 3 \\ 1 & 1 & 1 \\ 4 & -6 & 3 \end{vmatrix}$$

$$\underset{R_3 - 4R_1}{\overset{R_2 - R_1}{=}} \begin{vmatrix} 1 & -10 & 3 \\ 0 & 11 & -2 \\ 0 & 34 & -9 \end{vmatrix} = (-1)^{1+1} a_{11} \begin{vmatrix} 11 & -2 \\ 34 & -9 \end{vmatrix} = -99 + 68 = -31$$

Example 2.32

Find which values, if any, of the number c make $\mathbf{A}$ singular if

$$\mathbf{A} = \begin{vmatrix} 1 & 2 & c \\ 4 & 5 & 6 \\ 1 & 1 & 1 \end{vmatrix}$$

Solution

$|\mathbf{A}| = (-1)^2(5-6) + (-1)^3(2)(4-6) + (-1)^4 c(4-5) = -1 + 4 - c = 0.$ Hence $\mathbf{A}$ is singular for only one value of c, $c = 3$.

Cramer's Rule is a consequence of adj(A): If $\mathbf{A}$ is nonsingular, the ith component of the solution of $\mathbf{AX} = \mathbf{B}$ is $x_i = \dfrac{|A_i|}{|A|}$, where A_i is the result of replacing the ith column of $\mathbf{A}$ by $\mathbf{B}$.

Example 2.33

Find x_2 in $\mathbf{AX} = \mathbf{B}$ by Cramer's Rule if

$$\mathbf{A} = \begin{bmatrix} 1 & 2 & 1 & 1 \\ 3 & 4 & 5 & -2 \\ 6 & 7 & 1 & 5 \\ -1 & 0 & 2 & 0 \end{bmatrix} \quad \text{and} \quad \mathbf{B} = \begin{bmatrix} 1 \\ 2 \\ 3 \\ 4 \end{bmatrix}$$

Solution

First,

$$|A| = \begin{vmatrix} 1 & 2 & 3 & 1 \\ 3 & 4 & 11 & -2 \\ 6 & 7 & 13 & 5 \\ -1 & 0 & 0 & 0 \end{vmatrix} = (-1)^{4+1}(-1)\begin{vmatrix} 2 & 3 & 1 \\ 4 & 11 & -2 \\ 7 & 13 & 5 \end{vmatrix}$$

$$= \begin{vmatrix} 0 & 0 & 1 \\ 8 & 17 & -2 \\ -3 & -2 & 5 \end{vmatrix} = (-1)^{1+3}(1)\begin{vmatrix} 8 & 17 \\ -3 & -2 \end{vmatrix} = -16 + 51 = 35$$

Next, the numerator of x_2 is

$$\begin{vmatrix} 1 & 1 & 1 & 1 \\ 3 & 2 & 5 & -2 \\ 6 & 3 & 1 & 5 \\ -1 & 4 & 2 & 0 \end{vmatrix} = \begin{vmatrix} 1 & 0 & 0 & 0 \\ 3 & -1 & 2 & -5 \\ 6 & -3 & -5 & -1 \\ -1 & 5 & 3 & 1 \end{vmatrix} = \begin{vmatrix} -1 & 2 & -5 \\ -3 & -5 & -1 \\ 5 & 3 & 1 \end{vmatrix} = \begin{vmatrix} -1 & 2 & -5 \\ 0 & -11 & 14 \\ 0 & 13 & -24 \end{vmatrix}$$

$$= -\begin{vmatrix} -11 & 14 \\ 13 & -24 \end{vmatrix} = -\begin{vmatrix} -11 & 14 \\ 2 & -10 \end{vmatrix} = -(110 - 28) = -82, x_2 = -\frac{82}{35}$$

$$A^{-1} = \frac{adj(A)}{|A|}$$

The **classical adjoint** of matrix A is the transpose of the cofactor of matrix A, and $|A|$ is the determinant of matrix A.

The cofactor operation is best described through example.

The cofactor matrix of

$$A = \begin{bmatrix} 4 & 2 & 3 \\ 3 & 2 & 2 \\ 2 & 1 & 4 \end{bmatrix}$$

is generated by first establishing the sign conventions of the cofactor operation.

The sign convention used for the cofactor matrix is alternating positive and negative signs. For a two by two matrix, the cofactor sign convention is:

$$\begin{bmatrix} + & - \\ - & + \end{bmatrix}$$

For a three by three matrix, the cofactor sign convention is:

$$\begin{bmatrix} + & - & + \\ - & + & - \\ + & - & + \end{bmatrix}$$

The cofactor matrix of A is then

$$cofactor\begin{bmatrix} 4 & 2 & 3 \\ 3 & 2 & 2 \\ 2 & 1 & 4 \end{bmatrix} = \begin{bmatrix} +\begin{vmatrix} 2 & 2 \\ 1 & 4 \end{vmatrix} & -\begin{vmatrix} 3 & 2 \\ 2 & 4 \end{vmatrix} & +\begin{vmatrix} 3 & 2 \\ 2 & 1 \end{vmatrix} \\ -\begin{vmatrix} 2 & 3 \\ 1 & 4 \end{vmatrix} & +\begin{vmatrix} 4 & 3 \\ 2 & 4 \end{vmatrix} & -\begin{vmatrix} 4 & 2 \\ 2 & 1 \end{vmatrix} \\ +\begin{vmatrix} 2 & 3 \\ 2 & 2 \end{vmatrix} & -\begin{vmatrix} 4 & 3 \\ 3 & 2 \end{vmatrix} & +\begin{vmatrix} 4 & 2 \\ 3 & 2 \end{vmatrix} \end{bmatrix}$$

$$= \begin{bmatrix} (8-2) & -(12-4) & (3-4) \\ -(8-3) & (16-6) & -(4-4) \\ (4-6) & -(8-9) & (8-6) \end{bmatrix} = \begin{bmatrix} 6 & -8 & -1 \\ -5 & 10 & 0 \\ -2 & 1 & 2 \end{bmatrix}$$

The Adjoint [A] = Transpose {Cofactor [A]}

$$\text{Adjoint}\begin{bmatrix}4 & 2 & 3\\3 & 2 & 2\\2 & 1 & 4\end{bmatrix} = \text{Transpose}\left\{\text{Cofactor}\begin{bmatrix}4 & 2 & 3\\3 & 2 & 2\\2 & 1 & 4\end{bmatrix}\right\}$$

$$= \text{Transpose}\begin{bmatrix}6 & -8 & -1\\-5 & 10 & 0\\-2 & 1 & 2\end{bmatrix}$$

$$= \begin{bmatrix}6 & -5 & -2\\-8 & 10 & 1\\-1 & 0 & 2\end{bmatrix}$$

So the inverse of matrix $A = A^{-1}$ is by definition,

$$\begin{bmatrix}4 & 2 & 3\\3 & 2 & 2\\2 & 1 & 4\end{bmatrix}^{-1} = \frac{\text{Adjoint}\begin{bmatrix}4 & 2 & 3\\3 & 2 & 2\\2 & 1 & 4\end{bmatrix}}{\begin{vmatrix}4 & 2 & 3\\3 & 2 & 2\\2 & 1 & 4\end{vmatrix}}$$

$$= \frac{\begin{bmatrix}6 & -5 & -2\\-8 & 10 & 1\\-1 & 0 & 2\end{bmatrix}}{\begin{vmatrix}4 & 2 & 3\\3 & 2 & 2\\2 & 1 & 4\end{vmatrix}}$$

NUMERICAL METHODS

This portion of numerical methods includes techniques of finding roots of polynomials by the Routh-Hurwitz criterion and Newton methods, Euler's techniques of numerical integration and the trapezoidal methods, and techniques of numerical solutions of differential equations.

Newton's Method

The use of Newton's method of solving a polynomial and the use of iterative methods can greatly simplify a problem. This method utilizes synthetic division and is based upon the remainder theorem. This synthetic division requires estimating a root at the start, and, of course, the best estimate is the actual root. The root is the correct one when the remainder is zero. (There are several ways of estimating this root, including a slight modification of the Routh-Hurwitz criterion.)

If a $P_n(x)$ polynomial (see Equation (2.1)) is divided by an estimated factor $(x - x_1)$, the result is a reduced polynomial of degree $n - 1$, $Q_{n-1}(x)$, plus a constant remainder of b_{n-1}. Thus, another way of describing Equation (2.1) is

$$P_n(x)/(x - x_1) = Q_{n-1}(x) + b_{n-1}/(x - x_1) \quad \text{or} \quad P_n(x) = (x - x_1)Q_{n-1}(x) + b_{n-1} \tag{2.2}$$

If one lets $x = x_1$, Equation (2.2) becomes

$$P_n(x = x_1) = (0)Q_{n-1}(x) + b_{n-1} = b_{n-1} \tag{2.3}$$

Equation 2.3 leads directly to the remainder theorem: "The remainder on division by $(x - x_1)$ is the value of the polynomial at $x = x_1$, $P_n(x_1)$."[1]

Newton's method (actually, the Newton-Raphson method) for finding the roots for an nth-order polynomial is an iterative process involving obtaining an estimated value of a root (leading to a simple computer program). The key to the process is getting the first estimate of a possible root. Without getting too involved, recall that the coefficient of x^{n-1} represents the sum of all of the roots and the last term represents the product of all n roots; then the first estimate can be "guessed" within a reasonable magnitude. After a first root is chosen, find the rate of change of the polynomial at the chosen value of the root to get the next, closer value of the root x_{n+1}. Thus the new root estimate is based on the last value chosen:

$$x_{n+1} = x_n - P_n(x_n)/P_n'(x_n), \quad \text{where } P_n'(x_n) = dP_n(x)/dx \text{ evaluated at } x = x_n \tag{2.4}$$

Example **2.34**

Using Newton's Method

Find the square root of 612 using Newton's Method. This is equivalent to finding the solution to

$$x^2 = 612$$

The function to use in Newton's method is then,

$$f(x) = x^2 - 612$$

with derivative,

$$f'(x) = 2x.$$

With an initial guess of 10, the sequence given by Newton's method is

$$x_1 = x_0 - \frac{f(x_0)}{f'(x_0)} = 10 - \frac{10^2 - 612}{2 \cdot 10} = 35.6$$

$$x_2 = x_1 - \frac{f(x_1)}{f'(x_1)} = 35.6 - \frac{35.6^2 - 612}{2 \cdot 35.6} = \underline{2}6.3955056$$

$$x_3 = \quad \vdots \quad = \quad \vdots \quad = \underline{24.7}906355$$

$$x_4 = \quad \vdots \quad = \quad \vdots \quad = \underline{24.7386}883$$

$$x_5 = \quad \vdots \quad = \quad \vdots \quad = \underline{24.7386338}$$

[1] Gerald & Wheatley, *Applied Numerical Analysis*, 3rd ed., Addison-Wesley, 1985.

where the correct digits are underlined. With only a few iterations, one can obtain a solution accurate to many decimal places.

Newton's Method of Root Extraction

Consider the problem of finding the positive number x with $\cos(x) = x^3$. We can rephrase that as finding the zero of $f(x) = \cos(x) - x^3$. We have $f'(x) = -\sin(x) - 3x^2$. Since $\cos(x) \le 1$ for all x and $x^3 > 1$ for $x > 1$, we know that our zero lies between 0 and 1. We try a starting value of $x_0 = 0.5$. (Note that a starting value of 0 will lead to an undefined result, showing the importance of using a starting point that is close to the zero.)

$$
\begin{aligned}
x_1 &= x_0 - \frac{f(x_0)}{f'(x_0)} = 0.5 - \frac{\cos(0.5) - (0.5)^3}{-\sin(0.5) - 3(0.5)^2} &&= 1.112141637097 \\
x_2 &= x_1 - \frac{f(x_1)}{f'(x_1)} = \quad \vdots &&= \underline{0.9}09672693736 \\
x_3 &= \quad \vdots \quad = \quad \vdots &&= \underline{0.86}7263818209 \\
x_4 &= \quad \vdots \quad = \quad \vdots &&= \underline{0.86547}7135298 \\
x_5 &= \quad \vdots \quad = \quad \vdots &&= \underline{0.8654740331}1 \\
x_6 &= \quad \vdots \quad = \quad \vdots &&= \underline{0.865474033102}
\end{aligned}
$$

NUMERICAL INTEGRATION

Numerical integration routines are extremely useful in almost all simulation-type programs, design of digital filters, theory of z-transforms, and almost any problem solution involving differential equations. And because digital computers have essentially replaced analog computers (which were almost true integration devices), the techniques of approximating integration are well developed. Several of the techniques are briefly reviewed below.

Euler's Method

For a simple first-order differential equation, say $dx/dt + ax = af$, one could write the solution as a continuous integral or as an interval type one:

$$x(t) = \int^{t} [-ax(\tau) + af(\tau)]d\tau \quad \textbf{(2.5a)}$$

$$x(kT) = \int^{kT-T} [-ax + af]d\tau + \int_{kT-T}^{kT} [-ax + af]d\tau = x(kT - T) + A_{rect} \quad \textbf{(2.5b)}$$

Here, A_{rect} is the area of $(-ax + af)$ over the interval $(kT - T) < \tau < kT$. One now has a choice looking back over the rectangular area or looking forward. The

rectangular width is, of course, T. For the forward-looking case, a first approximation for x_1 is[2]

$$\begin{aligned} x_1(kT) &= x_1(kT-T) + T[ax_1(kT-T) + af(kT-T)] \\ &= (1-aT)x_1(kT-T) + aTf(kT-T) \end{aligned} \tag{2.5c}$$

Or, in general, for Euler's forward rectangle method, the integral may be approximated in its simplest form (using the notation $t_{k+1} - t_k$ for the width, instead of T, which is $kT–T$) as

$$\int_{t_k}^{t_{k+1}} x(\tau)\,d\tau \approx (t_{k+1} - t_k)x(t_k) \tag{2.6}$$

Trapezoidal Rule

This trapezoidal rule is based upon a straight-line approximation between the values of a function, $f(t)$, at t_0 and t_1. To find the area under the function, say a curve, is to evaluate the integral of the function between points a and b. The interval between these points is subdivided into subintervals; the area of each subinterval is approximated by a trapezoid between the end points. It will be necessary only to sum these individual trapezoids to get the whole area; by making the intervals all the same size, the solution will be simpler. For each interval of delta t (i.e., $t_{k+1} - t_k$), the area is then given by

$$\int_{t_k}^{t_{k+1}} x(\tau)\,d\tau \approx (1/2)(t_{k+1} - t_k)[x(t_{k+1}) + x(t_k)] \tag{2.7}$$

This equation gives good results if the delta t's are small, but it is for only one interval and is called the "local error." This error may be shown to be – (1/12) (delta t)$^3 f''(t = \xi_1)$, where ξ_1 is between t_0 and t_1. For a larger "global error" it may be shown that

$$\text{Global error} = -(1/12)(\text{delta } t)^3\,[f''(\xi_1) + f''(\xi_2) + \cdots + f''(\xi_n)] \tag{2.8}$$

Following through on Equation 2.8 allows one to predict the error for the trapezoidal integration. This technique is beyond the scope of this review or probably the examination; however, for those interested, please refer to pages 249–250 of the previously mentioned reference to Gerald & Wheatley.

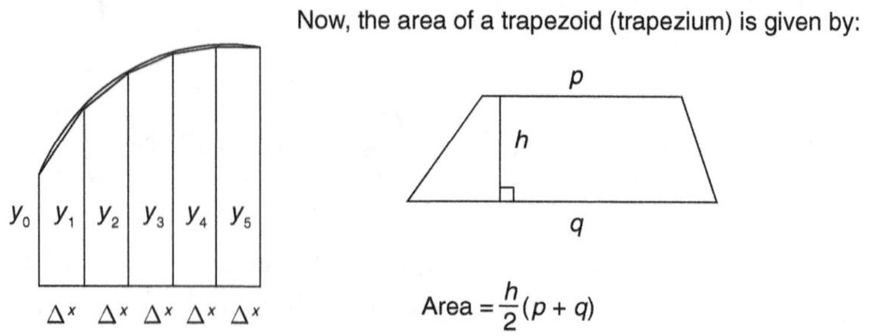

Figure 2.33 Trapezoidal Rule

---

2 This method is as presented in Franklin & Powell, *Digital Control of Dynamic Systems*, Addison-Wesley, 1980, page 55.

Example 2.35

Exercise: Using $n = 5$, approximate

$$\int_0^1 \sqrt{x^2+1}dx$$

Here, $a = 0$ and $b = 1$.

$$\Delta x = \frac{b-a}{n} = \frac{1-0}{5} = 0.2$$

$$y_0 = f(a) = f(0) = \sqrt{0^2+1} = 1$$

$$y_1 = f(a+\Delta x) = f(0.2) = \sqrt{0.2^2+1} = 1.0198039$$

$$y_2 = f(a+2\Delta x) = f(0.4) = \sqrt{0.4^2+1} = 1.0770330$$

$$y_3 = f(a+3\Delta x) = f(0.6) = \sqrt{0.6^2+1} = 1.1661904$$

$$y_4 = f(a+4\Delta x) = f(0.8) = \sqrt{0.8^2+1} = 1.2806248$$

$$y_5 = f(b) = f(1) = \sqrt{1^2+1} = 1.4142136$$

So the area =

$$0.2(\frac{1}{2}\times 1 + 1.0198039 + 1.0770330 + 1.1661904$$

$$+1.2806248\ldots + \frac{1}{2}\times 1.4142136)$$

$$= 1.150$$

$$\text{So} \int_0^1 \sqrt{x^2+1}dx \approx 1.150$$

In reality, any definite integral may be found using an NCEES-approved calculator.

Numerical Integration: Simpson's Rule

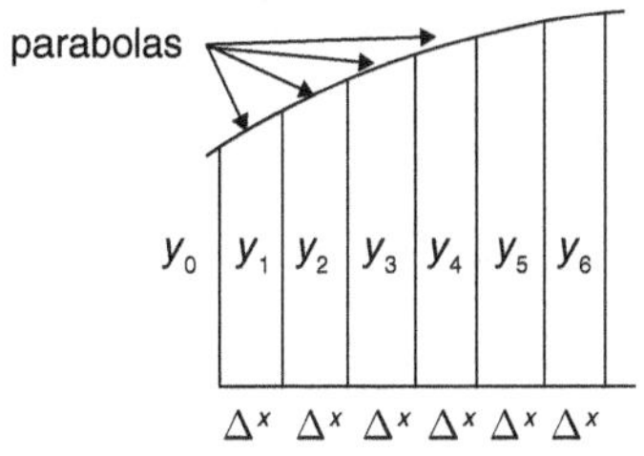

Figure 2.34 Simpson's Rule

We can show (by integrating the area under each parabola and adding these areas) that the approximate area is given by **Simpson's Rule**:

$$\text{Area} = \int_a^b f(x)dx \approx \frac{\Delta x}{3}\left(y_0 + 4y_1 + 2y_2 + 4y_3 + 2y_4 + \ldots + 4y_{n-1} + y_n\right)$$

Note: In Simpon's Rule, n must be even.

Example 2.36

Approximate $\int_2^3 \frac{dx}{x+1}$ using Simpson's Rule with n= 4.

Solution

$$\Delta x = (3-2)/4 = 0.25$$

$$y_0 = f(a) = f(2) = 1/(2+1) = 0.3333333$$

$$y_1 = f(a+\Delta x) = f(2.25) = 1/(2.25+1) = 0.3076923$$

$$y_2 = f(a+2\Delta x) = f(2.5) = 1/(2.5+1) = 0.2857142$$

$$y_3 = f(a+3\Delta x) = f(2.75) = 1/(2.75+1) = 0.2666667$$

$$y_4 = f(b) = f(3) = 1/(3+1) = 0.25$$

$$\text{Area} = \int_a^b f(x)dx \approx \frac{0.25}{3}(0.333333 + 4(0.3076923) + 2(0.2857142) + 4(0.2666667) + 0.25) = 0.2876831$$

(The actual answer to this problem is 0.287682, so our Simpson's Rule approximation has an error of only 3.6×10^{-4}%.)

NUMERICAL SOLUTIONS OF DIFFERENTIAL EQUATIONS

This solution will be based upon first-order ordinary differential equations. However, the method may be extended to higher-ordered equations by converting them to a matrix of first-ordered ones.

Integration routines produce values of system variables at specific points in time and update this information at each interval of delta time as T (delta $t = T = t_{k+1} - t_k$). Instead of a continuous function of time, $x(t)$, the variable x will be represented with discrete values such that $x(t)$ is represented by $x_0, x_1, x_2, \ldots, x_n$. Consider a simple differential equation as before as based upon Euler's method,

$$dx/dt + ax = f(t)$$

Now assume the delta time periods, T, are fixed (not all routines use fixed step sizes); then one writes the continuous equations as a difference equation where $dx/dt \approx (x_{k+1} - x_k)/T = -ax_k + f_k$ or, solving for the updated value, x_{k+1},

$$x_{k+1} = x_k - Tax_k + Tf_k \qquad \textbf{(2.9a)}$$

For fixed increments by knowing the first value of $x_{k=0}$ (or the initial condition), one may calculate the solution for as many "next values" of x_{k+1} as desired for some value of T. The difference equation may be programmed in almost any high-level language on a digital computer; however, T must be small as compared to the shortest time constant of the equation (here, $1/a$).

The following equation—with the "f" term meaning "a function of" rather than as a "forcing function" term as used in Equation (2.5a)—is a more general form of Equation (2.9a). This equation is obtained by letting the notation x_{k+1} become $y\,[k+1\ \Delta t]$ and is written (perhaps somewhat more confusingly) as

$$y[(k+1)\Delta t] = y(k\Delta t) + \Delta t f[y(k\Delta t), k\Delta t)] \qquad \textbf{(2.9b)}$$

Reduction of Differential Equation Order

To reduce the order of a linear time-dependent differential equation, the following technique is used. For example, assume a second-order equation: $x'' + ax' + bx = f(t)$. If we define $x = x_1$ and $x' = x_1{}' = x_2$, then

$$x_2' + ax_2 + bx_1 = f(t)$$
$$x_1' = x_2 \text{ (by definition)}$$
$$x_2' = -b_{x1} - ax_2 + f(t)$$

This technique can be extended to higher-order systems and, of course, be put into a matrix form (called the state variable form). And it can easily be set up as a matrix of first-order difference equations for solving digitally.

PROBLEMS

2.1 The simplest value of $\dfrac{[(n+1)!]^2}{n!(n-1)!}$ is:

a. n^2
b. $n(n+1)$
c. $n+1$
d. $n(n+1)^2$

2.2 If $x^{3/4} = 8$, x equals:

a. 6
b. 9
c. –9
d. 16

2.3 If $\log_a 10 = 0.250$, $\log_{10} a$ equals:

a. 4
b. 0.50
c. 2
d. 0.25

2.4 If $\log_5 x = -1.8$, $\log_x 5$ is:

a. 0.35
b. 0.79
c. –0.56
d. undefined

2.5 If $\log x + \log(x - 10) - \log 2 = 1$, x is:

a. –1.708
b. 5.213
c. 7.824
d. 11.708

2.6 A right circular cone, cut parallel with the axis of symmetry, reveals a(n):

a. circle
b. hyperbola
c. eclipse
d. parabola

2.7 The expression $\frac{6!}{3!0!}$ is equal to:

a. ∞
b. 120
c. 2!
d. 0

2.8 To find the angles of a triangle, given only the lengths of the sides, one would use:

a. the law of cosines
b. the law of tangents
c. the law of sines
d. the inverse-square law

2.9 If $\sin\alpha = \dfrac{a}{\sqrt{a^2+b^2}}$, which of the following equations is true?

a. $\tan^{-1}\dfrac{b}{a} = \dfrac{\pi}{2} - \alpha$

b. $\tan^{-1}\dfrac{b}{a} = -\alpha$

c. $\cos^{-1}\dfrac{b}{\sqrt{a^2+b^2}} = \dfrac{\pi}{2} - \alpha$

d. $\cos^{-1}\dfrac{a}{\sqrt{a^2+b^2}} = \alpha$

2.10 The sine of 840° equals:
a. –cos 30°
b. –cos 60°
c. sin 30°
d. sin 60°

2.11 One root of $x^3 - 8x - 3 = 0$ is:
a. 2
b. 3
c. 4
d. 5

2.12 Roots of the equation $3x^3 - 3x^2 - 18x = 0$ are:
a. –2, 3
b. 0, – 2, 3
c. $2 + 1i$, $2 - 1i$
d. 0, 2, –3

2.13 The equation whose roots are $-1 + i1$ and $-1 - i1$ is given as:
a. $x^2 + 2x + 2 = 0$
b. $x^2 - 2x - 2 = 0$
c. $x^2 + 2 = 0$
d. $x^2 - 2 = 0$

2.14 Natural logarithms have a base of:
a. 3.1416
b. 2.171828
c. 10
d. 2.71828

2.15 $(5.743)^{1/30}$ equals:
a. 1.03
b. 1.04
c. 1.05
d. 1.06

2.16 The value of tan($A + B$), where tan $A = 1/3$ and tan $B = 1/4$ (A and B are acute angles) is:
a. 7/12
b. 1/11
c. 7/11
d. 7/13

2.17 To cut a right circular cone in such a way as to reveal a parabola, it must be cut:
a. perpendicular to the axis of symmetry
b. at any acute angle to the axis of symmetry
c. at any obtuse angle to the axis of symmetry
d. none of these

2.18 The equation of the line perpendicular to $3y + 2x = 5$ and passing through $(-2, 5)$ is:
a. $2x = 3y$ c. $2y = 3x + 16$
b. $2y = 3x$ d. $3x = 2y + 8$

2.19 Equation of a line that has a slope of -2 and passes through $(2, 0)$ is:
a. $y = -2x$ c. $y = -2x + 4$
b. $y = 2x + 4$ d. $y = 2x - 4$

2.20 Equation of a line that intercepts the x-axis at $x = 4$ and the y-axis at $y = -6$ is:
a. $3x - 2y = 12$ c. $x + y = 6$
b. $2x - 3y = 12$ d. $x - y = 4$

2.21 The x-axis intercept and the y-axis intercept of the line $x + 3y + 9 = 0$ are:
a. 0 and 3 c. -3 and -9
b. -9 and -3 d. 9 and 0

2.22 The distance between the points $(1, 0, -2)$ and $(0, 2, 3)$ is:
a. 3.45 c. 6.71
b. 5.39 d. 7.48

2.23 The equation of a parabola with center at $(0, 0)$ and directrix at $x = -2$ is:
a. $y^2 = 4x$ c. $y^2 = 8x$
b. $y = 2x^2$ d. $y^2 = 2x$

2.24 The equation of the directrix of the parabola $y^2 = -4x$ is:
a. $y = 2$ c. $x + y = 0$
b. $x = 1$ d. $x = -2$

2.25 The equation of an ellipse with foci at $(\pm 2, 0)$ and directrix at $x = 6$ is:

a. $\dfrac{x^2}{12}+\dfrac{y^2}{8}=1$

b. $\dfrac{x^2}{8}+\dfrac{y^2}{8}=1$

c. $\dfrac{x^2}{12}+\dfrac{y^2}{12}=1$

d. $\dfrac{x^2}{4}+\dfrac{y^2}{4}=1$

2.26 The foci of the ellipse $\left(\dfrac{x}{3}\right)^2+\left(\dfrac{y}{2}\right)^2=1$ are at:

a. $(\pm\sqrt{5}, 0)$ c. $(0, \pm\sqrt{2})$
b. $(\pm\sqrt{2}, 0)$ d. $(0, \pm\sqrt{5})$

2.27 The equation of a hyperbola with center at (0, 0), foci at $(\pm 4, 0)$, and eccentricity of 3 is:

a. $\dfrac{x^2}{16}-\dfrac{y^2}{16}=1$

b. $\dfrac{x^2}{16}-\dfrac{y^2}{128}=1$

c. $\dfrac{x^2}{64}-\dfrac{y^2}{48}=1$

d. $\dfrac{x^2}{128}-\dfrac{y^2}{128}=1$

2.28 The equation of a circle with center at (1, 2) and passing through the point (4, 6) is:

a. $x^2 + y^2 = 25$

b. $(x + 1)^2 + (y - 2)^2 = 25$

c. $x^2 + (y - 2)^2 = 25$

d. $(x - 1)^2 + (y - 2)^2 = 25$

2.29 The length of the tangent from (4, 8) to the circle $x^2 + (y - 1)^2 = 3^2$ is:

a. 3.81 c. 5.66
b. 4.14 d. 7.48

2.30 The conic section described by the equation $x^2 - 10xy + y^2 + x + y + 1 = 0$ is:

a. circle c. hyperbola
b. parabola d. ellipse

2.31 A triangle has sides of length 2, 3, and 4. The angle subtended by the sides of length 2 and 4 is:

a. 21.2° c. 46.6°
b. 35.0° d. 61.2°

2.32 Length a of one side of the triangle below is:

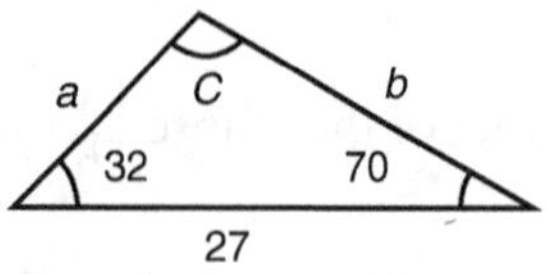

a. 25.9 c. 12.7
b. 19.1 d. 4.8

2.33 The relation $\sec\theta - (\sec\theta)(\sin^2\theta)$ can be simplified as:

a. $\sin\theta$ c. $\cot\theta$
b. $\tan\theta$ d. $\cos\theta$

2.34 If $\sin\theta = m$, $\cot\theta$ is:

a. $\dfrac{\sqrt{1-m^2}}{m}$

b. $\dfrac{m}{\sqrt{1-m^2}}$

c. $\sqrt{1-m^2}$

d. m

2.35 If vectors $\mathbf{A} = 3i - 6j + 2k$ and $\mathbf{B} = 10i + 4j - 6k$, their cross product $\mathbf{A} \times \mathbf{B}$ is:

a. $-12\mathbf{i} + 38\mathbf{j}$ c. $-12\mathbf{i} + 18\mathbf{j} + 24\mathbf{k}$
b. $12\mathbf{i} + 24\mathbf{j} + 36\mathbf{k}$ d. $28\mathbf{i} + 38\mathbf{j} + 72\mathbf{k}$

2.36 The sum of all integers from 10 to 50 (both inclusive) is:

a. 990 c. 1230
b. 1110 d. 1420

2.37 The 50th term of the series 10, 16, 22, 28, 34, 40. . . is:

a. 272 c. 428
b. 304 d. 584

2.38 Sum of the infinite series 4, 2, 1, 0.5, 0.25. . . is:

a. 8 c. 10,400
b. 128 d. ∞

2.39 If $\mathbf{A}=\begin{bmatrix}1 & 2 & 3\\ 1 & 2 & 9\end{bmatrix}$ and $\mathbf{B}=\begin{bmatrix}5 & 1\\ 6 & 0\\ 4 & 7\end{bmatrix}$, the (2,1) entry of AB is:

a. 29 c. 33
b. 53 d. 64

2.40 The inverse of the matrix $\begin{bmatrix}1 & 1\\ 3 & 2\end{bmatrix}$ is:

a. $\begin{bmatrix}2 & -1\\ -3 & 1\end{bmatrix}$ b. $\begin{bmatrix}2 & 3\\ 1 & 1\end{bmatrix}$ c. $\begin{bmatrix}1 & 3\\ 1 & 2\end{bmatrix}$ d. $\begin{bmatrix}-2 & 1\\ 3 & -1\end{bmatrix}$

2.41 The determinant of the matrix $\begin{bmatrix}1 & 2 & -1\\ 3 & 0 & 2\\ 2 & -2 & -1\end{bmatrix}$ is:

a. 4 c. 24
b. 16 d. –16

2.42 In the system of equations

$$\begin{aligned}3x_1+2x_2-x_3&=5\\ x_2-x_3&=2\\ x_1+2x_2-3x_3&=-1\end{aligned}$$

the value of $x_2 =$ is:
a. 2 c. 4
b. –1 d. 6

2.43 What is the determinant of M?

$$\boldsymbol{M}=\begin{bmatrix}0 & 1 & 1 & 1\\ 1 & 1 & 1 & 1\\ 1 & 1 & 3 & 1\\ 2 & 1 & 3 & 4\end{bmatrix}$$

a. –6 c. 0
b. 6 d. 7

SOLUTIONS

2.1 d. The value $(n + 1)!$ may be written as $(n + 1)(n)\,[(n - 1)!]$. It may be written also as $n!(n + 1)$. Hence the given expression may be written as follows:

$$\frac{\{(n+1)(n)\,[(n-1)!]\}\ \{n\,!(n+1)\}}{n\,!(n-1)!} = (n+1)^2 n$$

2.2 d. Raise both sides of the equation to the 4/3 power:

$$[x^{3/4}]^{4/3} = 8^{4/3}$$

$$x = \sqrt[3]{8^4} = \sqrt[3]{(2^3)^4} = 2^{\frac{3\bullet 4}{3}} = 2^4 = 16$$

2.3 a. $\log_a 10 = 0.250$ can be written as $10 = a^{0.250}$. Taking $\log_{10}$,

$$\log_{10} 10 = \log_{10} a^{0.250}$$

$$1 = 0.250 \log_{10} a$$

and

$$\log_{10} a = \frac{1}{0.250} = 4$$

2.4 c. Since $(\log_5 x)(\log_x 5) = 1$, $\log_x 5 = \dfrac{1}{-1.8} = -0.556$

2.5 d. Since $\log(a) + \log(b) - \log(c) = \log \dfrac{ab}{c}$, the given equation simplifies to $\log \dfrac{x(x-10)}{2} = 1$. Equivalently, $\dfrac{x(x-10)}{2} = 10$ or

$x^2 - 10x - 20 = 0$. The roots are 11.708 and −1.708. Since log is not defined for negative values, $x = 11.708$.

2.6 b.

2.7 b.

$$\frac{6!}{3!0!} = \frac{6(5)(4)(3)!}{3!(1)} = 120$$

2.8 a. The law of cosines is $a^2 = b^2 + c^2 - 2bc \cos A$ for any plane triangle with angles A, B, C and sides a, b, c, respectively.

This law can be applied to solve for the angles, given three sides in a plane triangle (Exhibit 2.8).

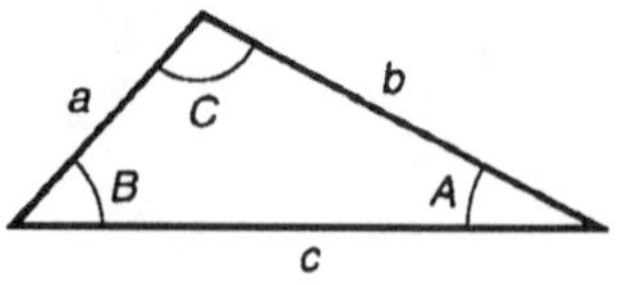

Exhibit 2.8

2.9 a. The triangle appears in Exhibit 2.9.

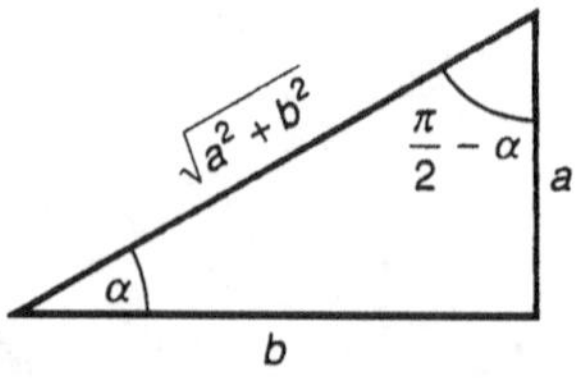

Exhibit 2.9

$$\tan\left(\frac{\pi}{2} - \alpha\right) = \frac{b}{a}$$

$$\tan^{-1}\frac{b}{a} = \frac{\pi}{2} - \alpha$$

2.10 d.

$$840° = 2(360) + 120 = 2(2\pi)\text{ rad} + 120°$$
$$\sin\,[2(2\pi)\text{ rad} + 120°] = \sin 120° = \sin 60°$$

2.11 b. The solution is obtained by seeing which of the five answers satisfies the equation.

x	$x^3 - 8x - 3$
2	–11
3	0
4	29
5	82
6	165

2.12 b. Any scientific calculator can be used to find the roots as 0, 3, and –2.

2.13 a. If x_1 and x_2 are the roots, the equation is $(x - x_1)(x - x_2) = 0$. Since the roots are $-1 + i$ and $-1 - i$, the equation is $(x - (-1 + i))(x - (-1 - i)) = 0$ or $(x + 1 - i)(x + 1 + i) = 0$ or $x^2 + 2x + 2 = 0$.

2.14 d. Common logarithms have base 10. Natural, or napierian, logarithms have base $e = 2.71828$.

2.15 d.

$$\log\,(5.743)^{1/30} = \frac{1}{30}\log 5.743 = \frac{1}{30}(0.7592) = 0.0253$$

The antilogarithm of 0.0253 is 1.06.

2.16 c.

$$\sin\,(A + B) = (\sin A \cos B) + (\cos A \sin B)$$

$$\cos\,(A + B) = (\cos A \cos B) - (\sin A \sin B)$$

$$\tan\,(A + B) = \frac{\sin(A + B)}{\cos(A + B)} = \frac{(\sin A \cos B) + (\cos A \sin B)}{(\cos A \cos B) - (\sin A \sin B)}$$

Dividing by $\cos A \cos B$,

$$\tan(A + B) = \frac{\dfrac{(\sin A \cos B)}{(\cos A \cos B)} + \dfrac{(\cos A \sin B)}{(\cos A \cos B)}}{\dfrac{(\cos A \cos B)}{(\cos A \cos B)} - \dfrac{(\sin A \sin B)}{(\cos A \cos B)}} = \frac{\tan A + \tan B}{1 - \tan A \tan B}$$

$$= \frac{\dfrac{1}{3} + \dfrac{1}{4}}{1 - \dfrac{1}{3} \times \dfrac{1}{4}} = \frac{\dfrac{4}{12} + \dfrac{3}{12}}{1 - \dfrac{1}{12}} = \frac{\dfrac{7}{12}}{\dfrac{11}{12}} = \frac{7}{11}$$

The problem could also be solved by determining angle A (whose tangent is 1/3) and angle B (whose tangent is 1/4). Then we could find the tangent of $(A + B)$.

$$\tan^{-1}\frac{1}{3} = 18.435° \quad \tan^{-1}\frac{1}{4} = 14.036°$$

$$\tan(18.435 + 14.036)° = \tan(32.471°) = 0.6364 = \frac{7}{11}$$

2.17 d. To reveal a parabola, a right circular cone must be cut parallel to an element of the cone and intersecting the axis of symmetry.

2.18 c. Rewriting the given line, $y = \frac{5}{3} - \frac{2}{3}x$. This line has slope $-\frac{2}{3}$, so a perpendicular line must have slope $\frac{3}{2}$. Using the point-slope form, $\frac{y-5}{x+3} = \frac{3}{2}$. Simplifying, $y = \frac{3}{2}x + 8$.

2.19 d. The equation of a straight line is $y = mx + b$ where the slope is m, (x, y) is any point on the line, and b is the y-axis intercept. Here, $m = -2$ and $(2, 0)$ is a point. Substituting these values, $0 = -2(2) + b$ or $b = 4$. Then, the equation is $y = -2x + 4$ or $y + 2x = 4$.

2.20 a. (4,0) and (0, –6) are two points on the straight line. Then, the slope $m = \frac{y_2 - y_1}{x_2 - x_1} = \frac{0-(-6)}{4-0} = \frac{3}{2}$. Substituting one of the points, say, (0, –6) in the general equation $y = mx + b$; $-6 = 0 + b$. Then, $b = -6$ and the equation is $y = \left(\frac{3}{2}\right)x - 6$ or $3x - 2y = 12$.

2.21 b. For y-axis intercept, $x = 0$. Substituting this in the equation, $0 + 3y + 9 = 0$ or $y = -3$ is the y-axis intercept. For x-axis intercept, $y = 0$. Substituting this in the equation, $x + 0 + 9 = 0$ or $x = -9$ is the x-axis intercept.

2.22 b. Distance d between any two points (x_1, y_1, z_1) and (x_2, y_2, z_2) can be determined as $d^2 = (x_1 - x_2)^2 + (y_1 - y_2)^2 + (z_1 - z_2)^2$. Here, $d^2 = (1 - 0)^2 + (0 - 2)^2 + (-2 - 3)^2 = 30$; $d = 5.385$.

2.23 c. Directrix, $x = -p/2 = -2$ or $p = 4$. Equation of a parabola with center at origin is $y^2 = 2px$; as $p = 4$, $y^2 = 8x$.

2.24 b. Equation of a parabola with center at origin is $y^2 = 2px$. Since $y^2 = -4x$, $2p = -4$ or $p = -2$. Equation of a directrix is $x = (-p/2)$; since $p = 2$, the equation is $x = 1$.

2.25 a. Focus $ae = 2$ and directrix $\frac{a}{e} = 6$. Solving, $a^2 = 12$ and $e = 1/\sqrt{3}$.

But $e = \sqrt{1 - \frac{b^2}{a^2}}$; solving, $b^2 = 8$. The equation of an ellipse is

$$\frac{x^2}{a^2} + \frac{y^2}{b^2} = 1 \text{ or } \frac{x^2}{12} + \frac{y^2}{8} = 1.$$

2.26 a. The equation of an ellipse is $\frac{x^2}{a^2} + \frac{y^2}{b^2} = 1$. Here, $a = 3$ and $b = 2$.

The eccentricity $e = \sqrt{1 - \frac{b^2}{a^2}} = \sqrt{\frac{5}{9}}$, and the foci = $(\pm\, ae, 0) = (\pm\, \sqrt{5}, 0)$.

2.27 b. Focus $ae = 4$ and eccentricity $e = 3$. Solving, $a = 4/3$.

Also, $b = a\sqrt{e^2 - 1} = \frac{4\sqrt{8}}{3}$. Equation for a hyperbola is

$$\frac{x^2}{a^2} - \frac{y^2}{b^2} = 1 \Rightarrow \frac{x^2}{16} - \frac{y^2}{128} = 1.$$

2.28 d. Radius of a circle with center at (h, k) and passing through a point (x, y) is $r^2 = (x - h)^2 + (y - k)^2$. Here, $r^2 = (4 - 1)^2 + (6 - 2)^2 = 25$. Equation of a circle with center at (h, k) is $(x - h)^2 + (y - k)^2 = r^2$; here, $(x - 1)^2 + (y - 2)^2 = 25$.

2.29 d. Length of the tangent from any point (x', y') outside a circle with center at (h, k) and radius r is given as $t^2 = (x' - h)^2 + (y' - k)^2 - r^2$. Here, $(x', y') = (4, 8)$, center $(h, k) = (0, 1)$, and $r^2 = 3^2$. Then, $t^2 = (4 - 0)^2 + (8 - 1)^2 - 3^2 = 56$ or $t = 7.483$.

2.30 c. General equation of a conic section is $Ax^2 + 2Bxy + Cy^2 + 2Dx + 2Ey + F = 0$, where both A and C are not zeros. Here, $A = 1$; $B = -5$; $C = 1$; then, $(B^2 - AC) > 0 \Rightarrow$ hyperbola.

2.31 c. Since three sides of a triangle are given, use the law of cosines; $3^2 = 2^2 + 4^2 - 2(2)(4)\cos(\theta)$ where θ is the angle opposite to side 3. Solving, $\theta = 46.6°$.

2.32 a. Angle $C = 180 - (70 + 32) = 78°$. Using the law of sines,

$$\frac{a}{\sin 70} = \frac{b}{\sin 32} = \frac{27}{\sin 78}.$$ Solving, $a = 25.94$.

2.33 d. $(\sec\theta)(1 - \sin^2\theta) = \sec\theta\cos^2\theta = \frac{1}{\cos\theta}\cos^2\theta = \cos\theta$

2.34 **a.** $\sin\theta = \frac{m}{1} = \frac{\text{opposite side}}{\text{hypotenuse}}$; then, adjacent side $= \sqrt{1-m^2}$

and $\cos\theta = \frac{\text{adjacent side}}{\text{hypotenuse}} = \frac{\sqrt{1-m^2}}{1}$; then, $\cot\theta = \frac{\cos\theta}{\sin\theta} = \frac{\sqrt{1-m^2}}{m}$

2.35 **d.** Cross product, $\mathbf{A} \times \mathbf{B} = \begin{vmatrix} i & j & k \\ 3 & -6 & 2 \\ 10 & 4 & -6 \end{vmatrix}$

Expanding, $i[(-6)(-6) - (2)(4)] - j[(3)(-6) - (2)(10)] + k[(3)(4) - (-6)(10)] = 28\mathbf{i} + 38\mathbf{j} + 72\mathbf{k}$

2.36 **c.** This is an arithmetic series; first term $a = 10$, last term $l = 50$, and common difference $d = 1$. The number of terms, n, can be calculated as, $l = a + (n - 1)d$; $50 = 10 + (n - 1)1$; solving, $n = 41$.

sum $S = \frac{n(a+1)}{2} = \frac{41}{2}(10+50) = 1230$

2.37 **b.** This is an arithmetic series; first term $a = 10$ and the common difference $d = 6$. Taking the number of terms n as 50, the nth term (last term) can be calculated as, $l = a + (n - 1)d$. In this case, $l = 10 + (50 - 1)6 = 304$.

2.38 **a.** This is a geometric series; first term $a = 4$ and common ratio $r = 0.5$. Since $r < 1$, the series is convergent and the sum as the number of terms n tend to infinity is $S = \frac{a}{1-r} = \frac{4}{1-0.5} = 8$.

2.39 **b.** To compute the (2,1) entry, take [1 2 9] • [5 6 4] = 5 + 12 + 36 = 53.

2.40 **d.** To invert a 2×2 matrix,

$$\begin{bmatrix} a & b \\ c & d \end{bmatrix}^{-1} = \frac{1}{ad-bc}\begin{bmatrix} d & -b \\ -c & a \end{bmatrix} = \frac{1}{2-3}\begin{bmatrix} 2 & -1 \\ -3 & 1 \end{bmatrix}$$

2.41 **c.** This 3×3 determinant can be computed quickly be expanding it in minors, especially around the second column:

$$\begin{vmatrix} 1 & 2 & -1 \\ 3 & 0 & 2 \\ 2 & -2 & 1 \end{vmatrix} = (-1)^{1+2}(2)\begin{vmatrix} 3 & 2 \\ 2 & -1 \end{vmatrix} + (-1)^{2+2}(0)\begin{vmatrix} 1 & -1 \\ 2 & -1 \end{vmatrix} + (-1)^{3+2}(-2)\begin{vmatrix} 1 & -1 \\ 3 & 2 \end{vmatrix}$$

$$= -2(-3-4) + 0 + 2(2+3) = 24$$

2.42 d. By Cramer's Rule,

$$x_2 = \frac{\text{Det}\begin{bmatrix} 3 & 5 & -1 \\ 0 & 2 & -1 \\ 1 & -1 & -3 \end{bmatrix}}{\text{Det}\begin{bmatrix} 3 & 2 & -1 \\ 0 & 1 & -1 \\ 1 & 2 & -3 \end{bmatrix}} = \frac{3\begin{vmatrix} 2 & -1 \\ -1 & -3 \end{vmatrix} + 1\begin{vmatrix} 5 & -1 \\ 2 & -1 \end{vmatrix}}{3\begin{vmatrix} 1 & -1 \\ 2 & -3 \end{vmatrix} + 1\begin{vmatrix} 2 & -1 \\ 1 & -1 \end{vmatrix}} = \frac{3(-7) + (-3) = -24}{3(-1) + (-1) = -4} = 6$$

2.43 a. To evaluate a 4 × 4 matrix, one must do some row or column operations and expand by minors:

$$\begin{bmatrix} 0 & 1 & 1 & 1 \\ 1 & 1 & 1 & 1 \\ 1 & 1 & 3 & 1 \\ 2 & 1 & 3 & 4 \end{bmatrix} \sim \begin{bmatrix} 0 & 1 & 1 & 1 \\ 1 & 1 & 1 & 1 \\ 0 & 0 & 2 & 0 \\ 0 & -1 & 1 & 2 \end{bmatrix}$$

Taking minors of column 1,

$$\text{Det}(M) = (1)(-1)^{2+1}\,\text{Det}\begin{bmatrix} 1 & 1 & 1 \\ 0 & 2 & 0 \\ -1 & 1 & 2 \end{bmatrix} = -(4+2) = -6$$

CHAPTER 3

Mathematics: Calculus and Differential Equations

OUTLINE

DIFFERENTIAL CALCULUS

Definition of a Function

Notation. A variable y is said to be a function of another variable x if, when x is given, y is determined. The symbols $f(x)$, $F(x)$, etc., represent various functions of x. The symbol $f(a)$ represents the value of $f(x)$ when $x = a$.

Definition of a Derivative

Let $y = f(x)$. If Δx is any increment (increase or decrease) given to x, and Δy is the corresponding increment in y, then the derivative of y with respect to x is the limit of the ratio of Δy to Δx as Δx approaches zero; that is,

$$\frac{dy}{dx} = \lim_{\Delta x \to 0} \frac{\Delta y}{\Delta x} = \lim_{\Delta x \to 0} \frac{f(x+\Delta x) - f(x)}{\Delta x} = f'(x)$$

Some Relations Among Derivatives

$$\text{If } x = f(y), \text{ then } \frac{dy}{dx} = 1 \div \frac{dx}{dy}$$

$$\text{If } x = f(t) \text{ and } y = F(t), \text{ then } \frac{dy}{dx} = \frac{dy}{dt} \div \frac{dx}{dt}$$

$$\text{If } y = f(u) \text{ and } u = F(x), \text{ then } \frac{dy}{dx} = \frac{dy}{du} \times \frac{du}{dx}$$

$$\text{If } x = f(t), \text{ then } f''(t) = \frac{d^2x}{dt^2} = \frac{d}{dt}\left(\frac{dx}{dt}\right)$$

Table of Derivatives

Functions of x are represented by u and v, and constants are represented by a, n, and e.

$$\frac{d}{dx}(x) = 1 \qquad \frac{d}{dx}(a) = 0$$

$$\frac{d}{dx}(u \pm v \pm \ldots) = \frac{du}{dx} \pm \frac{dv}{dx} \pm \ldots \qquad \frac{d}{dx}(au) = a\frac{du}{dx}$$

$$\frac{d}{dx}(uv) = u\frac{dv}{dx} + v\frac{du}{dx} \qquad \frac{d}{dx}\left(\frac{u}{v}\right) = \frac{v\frac{du}{dx} - u\frac{dv}{dx}}{v^2}$$

$$\frac{d}{dx}(u^n) = nu^{n-1}\frac{du}{dx} \qquad \frac{d}{dx}\log_a u = \frac{\log_a e}{u}\frac{du}{dx}$$

$$\frac{d}{dx}a^u = a^u \ln a \frac{du}{dx}$$

$$\frac{d}{dx}e^u = e^u\frac{du}{dx} \qquad \frac{d}{dx}u^v = vu^{v-1}\frac{du}{dx} + u^v \ln u \frac{dv}{dx}$$

$$\frac{d}{dx}\sin u = \cos u \frac{du}{dx} \qquad \frac{d}{dx}\cot u = -\csc^2 u \frac{du}{dx}$$

$$\frac{d}{dx}\cos u = -\sin u \frac{du}{dx} \qquad \frac{d}{dx}\sec u = \sec u \tan u \frac{du}{dx}$$

$$\frac{d}{dx}\tan u = \sec^2 u \frac{du}{dx} \qquad \frac{d}{dx}\csc u = -\csc u \cot u \frac{du}{dx}$$

$$\frac{d}{dx}\sin^{-1}u = \frac{1}{\sqrt{1-u^2}}\frac{du}{dx} \quad \text{where} \quad -\pi/2 \le \sin^{-1}u \ge \pi/2$$

$$\frac{d}{dx}\cos^{-1}u = -\frac{1}{\sqrt{1-u^2}}\frac{du}{dx} \quad \text{where} \quad 0 \le \cos^{-1}u \ge \pi$$

$$\frac{d}{dx}\tan^{-1}u = \frac{1}{1+u^2}\frac{du}{dx}$$

$$\frac{d}{dx}\cot^{-1}u = -\frac{1}{1+u^2}\frac{du}{dx}$$

$$\frac{d}{dx}\sec^{-1}u = \frac{1}{u\sqrt{u^2-1}}\frac{du}{dx} \quad \text{where} \quad 0 \le \sec^{-1}u \le \pi/2 \text{ and } -\pi \le \sec^{-1}u \le -\pi/2$$

$$\frac{d}{dx}\csc^{-1}u = -\frac{1}{u\sqrt{u^2-1}}\frac{du}{dx} \quad \text{where} \quad -\pi < \csc^{-1}u \le -\pi/2 \text{ and } 0 < \csc^{-1}u \le \pi/2$$

Example 3.1

Find the derivatives of the following functions with respect to x.

(i) $x^3 + 4e^{-2x}$, (ii) $x^2 \sin x$, (iii) $2\sin^2 x$, (iv) $(\frac{e^{-x}}{x})$

Solution

(i) $\frac{d}{dx}(x^3 + 4e^{-2x}) = \frac{d}{dx}(x^3) + \frac{d}{dx}(4e^{-2x}) = 3x^2 + 4(-2)e^{-2x} = 3x^2 - 8e^{-2x}$

(ii) $\frac{d}{dx}(x^2 \sin x) = x^2\frac{d}{dx}(\sin x) + (\sin x)\frac{d}{dx}(x^2) = x^2\cos x + 2x\sin x$

(iii) $\frac{d}{dx}(2\sin^2 x) = 2(2)(\sin^{2-1}x)\frac{d}{dx}(\sin x) = (4\sin x)\cos x$

(iv) $\frac{d}{dx}(\frac{e^{-x}}{x}) = \dfrac{x\frac{d}{dx}(e^{-x}) - e^{-x}\frac{d}{dx}(x)}{x^2} = \dfrac{x(-e^{-x}) - (e^{-x})1}{x^2} = \dfrac{-e^{-x}(x+1)}{x^2}$

Slope of a Curve: Tangent and Normal

The slope of the curve (slope of the tangent line to the curve) whose equation is $y = f(x)$ is

$$\text{Slope} = m = \tan\phi = \frac{dy}{dx} = f'(x)$$

$$\text{Slope at } x_1 \text{ is } m_1 = f'(x_1)$$

The equation of a tangent line at $P_1(x_1, y_1)$ is $y - y_1 = m_1(x - x_1)$. The equation of a normal at $P_1(x_1, y_1)$ is

$$y - y_1 = -\frac{1}{m_1}(x - x_1)$$

The angle β of the intersection of two curves whose slopes at a common point are m_1 and m_2 is

$$\beta = \tan^{-1} \frac{m_2 - m_1}{1 + m_1 m_2}$$

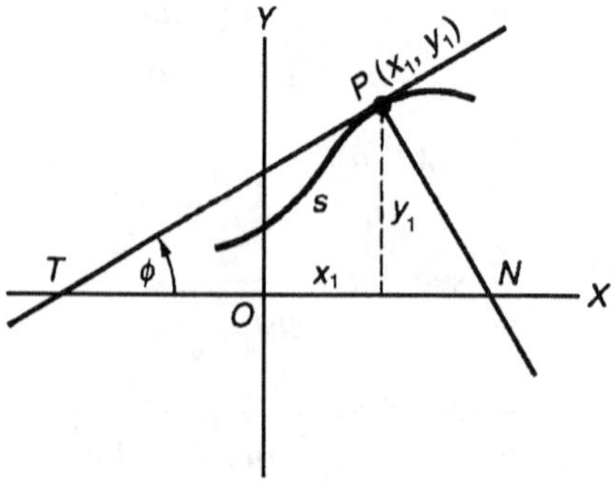

Figure 3.1

Example 3.2

Find the slope of the curve $y = (4x^2 - 8)$ at $x = 1$.

Solution

Slope $\frac{dy}{dx} = \frac{d}{dx}(4x^2 - 8) = \frac{d}{dx}(4x^2) - \frac{d}{dx}(8) = 4\frac{d}{dx}(x^2) - 0 = 8x$;
at $x = 1$, slope = 8

Example 3.3

Find the equation of the tangent to the curve $y = (x^2 - x - 4)$ at $(1, -4)$.

Solution

Slope of the curve $\frac{dy}{dx} = \frac{d}{dx}(x^2 - x - 4) = \frac{d}{dx}(x^2) - \frac{d}{dx}(x) - \frac{d}{dx}(4) = 2x - 1$;
at $(1, -4)$, slope $= 2(1) - 1 = 1$

Equation of the tangent is $(y + 4) = 1(x - 1)$ or $y = x - 5$.

Maximum and Minimum Values of a Function

The maximum or minimum value of a function $f(x)$ in an interval from $x = a$ to $x = b$ is the value of the function that is larger or smaller, respectively, than the values of the function in its immediate vicinity. Thus, the values of the function at M_1 and M_2 in Figure 3.2 are maxima, and its values at m_1 and m_2 are minima.

Test for a maximum at $x = x_1$: $f'(x_1) = 0$ or ∞, and $f''(x_1) < 0$

Test for minimum at $x = x_1$: $f'(x_1) = 0$ or ∞, and $f''(x_1) > 0$

If $f''(x_1) = 0$ or ∞, then for a maximum, $f'''(x_1) = 0$ or ∞ and $f^{IV}(x_1) < 0$; for a minimum, $f'''(x_1) = 0$ or ∞ and $f^{IV}(x_1) > 0$, and similarly if $f^{IV}(x_1) = 0$ or ∞, and so on, where f^{IV} represents the fourth derivative.

In a practical problem that suggests that the function $f(x)$ has a maximum or has a minimum in an interval from $x = a$ to $x = b$, simply equate $f'(x)$ to 0 and solve for the required value of x. To find the largest or smallest values of a function $f(x)$ in an interval from $x = a$ to $x = b$, find also the values $f(a)$ and $f(b)$. L and S may be the largest and smallest values, although they are not maximum or minimum values (see Figure 3.2).

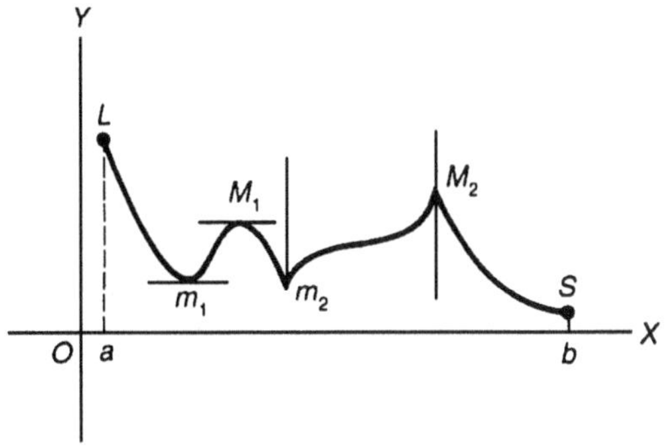

Figure 3.2

Points of Inflection of a Curve

Wherever $f''(x) < 0$, the curve is concave down.

Wherever $f''(x) > 0$, the curve is concave up.

The curve is said to have a point of inflection at $x = x_1$ if $f''(x_1) = 0$ or ∞, and the curve is concave up on one side of $x = x_1$ and concave down on the other (see points I_1 and I_2 in Figure 3.3).

Example 3.4

For the function $y = f(x) = (x^3 - 3x)$, find the maximum, minimum, and the point of inflection.

Solution

The derivative of $f(x)$, $f'(x) = 3x^2 - 3$.

Equating $f'(x)$ to 0, $3x^2 - 3 = 0$, which has roots at $x = 1$ and -1.

The derivative of $f'(x)$, $f''(x) = 6x$. At $x = 1, f''(1) = 6$ and at $x = -1, f''(-1) = -6$.

Minimum occurs at $x = 1$, since $f''(1) > 0$ and $f''(1) = 0$. Value of minimum $= f(1) = -2$.

Maximum occurs at $x = -1$, since $f'(-1) < 0$ and $f'(-1) = 0$. Value of maximum $= f(-1) = 2$.

$f''(x) = 0$ at $x = 0$; $f''(x)$ changes sign as x passes through 0; then $x = 0$ is the inflection point (it is between 1 and -1).

Taylor and Maclaurin Series

In general, any $f(x)$ may be expanded into a **Taylor series**:

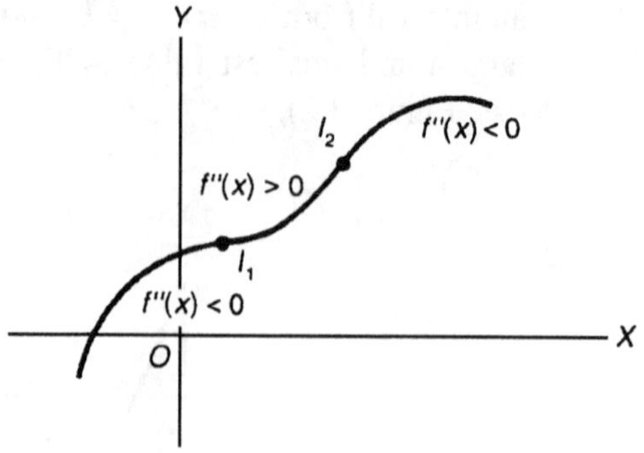

Figure 3.3

$$f(x)=f(a)+f'(a)\frac{x-a}{1}+f''(a)\frac{(x-a)^2}{2!}+f'''(a)\frac{(x-a)^3}{3!}+\dots$$

$$+f^{(n-1)}(a)\frac{(x-a)^{n-1}}{(n-1)!}+R_n$$

where a is any quantity whatever, so chosen that none of the expressions $f(a)$, $f'(a), f''(a),\dots$ become infinite. If the series is to be used for the purpose of computing the approximate value of $f(x)$ for a given value of x, a should be chosen such that $(x - a)$ is numerically very small, and thus only a few terms of the series need be used. If $a = 0$, this series is called a Maclaurin series.

Example 3.5

Find the power series expansion of sin x about the point 0.

Solution

In the Taylor's series expansion, $f(x) = \sin(x)$ and $a = 0$. Derivatives of $f(x)$ are: $f'(x) = \cos(x), f''(x) = -\sin(x), f'''(x) = -\cos(x)$, and so on.

Substituting $f(x)$ and its derivatives at a in the expansion,

$$\sin(x)=\sin(0)+x\cos(0)+\frac{x^2(-\sin(0))}{2!}+\frac{x^3(-\cos(0))}{3!}+\dots=x-\frac{x^3}{3!}+\frac{x^5}{5!}-\dots$$

Evaluation of Indeterminate Forms

Let $f(x)$ and $F(x)$ be two functions of x, and let a be a value of x.

1. If $\frac{f(a)}{F(a)}=\frac{0}{0}$ or $\frac{\infty}{\infty}$, use $\frac{f'(a)}{F'(a)}$ for the value of this fraction.

   If $\frac{f'(a)}{F'(a)}=\frac{0}{0}$ or $\frac{\infty}{\infty}$, use $\frac{f''(a)}{F''(a)}$ for the value of this fraction, and so on.

2. If $f(a) \bullet F(a) = 0 \bullet \infty$ or if $f(a) - F(a) = \infty - \infty$, evaluate the expression by changing the product or difference to the form $\frac{0}{0}$ or $\frac{\infty}{\infty}$ and use the previous rule.

3. If $f(a)^{F(a)} = 0^0$ or ∞^0 or 1^∞, then form $e^{F(a) \bullet \ln f(a)}$, and the exponent, being of the form $0 \bullet \infty$, may be evaluated by rule 2.

Example 3.6

Find the following limits: (i) $\lim_{x \to 0} \frac{\sin x}{x}$ (ii) $\lim_{x \to 0} \frac{1 - \cos x}{x^2}$

Solution

(i) Since $\frac{\sin(0)}{0} = \frac{0}{0}$, we apply the limiting theorem:

$$\lim_{x \to 0} \frac{\sin x}{x} = \lim_{x \to 0} \frac{d(\sin x)}{d(x)} = \lim_{x \to 0} \frac{\cos x}{1} = 1$$

(ii) Since $\frac{1 - \cos(0)}{0^2} = \frac{0}{0}$, we apply the limiting theorem:

$$\lim_{x \to 0} \frac{1 - \cos x}{x^2} = \lim_{x \to 0} \frac{\sin x}{2x} = \lim_{x \to 0} \frac{\cos x}{2} = \frac{1}{2}$$

Example 3.7

The cubic $y = x^3 + x^2 - 3$ has one point of inflection. Where does it occur?

Solution

The answer requires knowing where y' changes sign. Now $y' = 3x^2 + 2x$ and $y'' = 6x + 2$, which is 0 where $x = -\frac{1}{3}$. Thus the only inflection point is at $x = -\frac{1}{3}$.

Example 3.8

The function of Example 3.7 has one local maximum and one local minimum. Where are they?

Solution

Setting $y' = 0$ ($3x^2 + 2x = 0$) yields $x = 0$ or $x = -\frac{2}{3}$. Since the second derivative is 2 at $x = 0$, this is the local minimum. At $x = -\frac{2}{3}$, $y'' = -2$, so $x = -\frac{2}{3}$ is the local maximum.

Differential of a Function

If $y = f(x)$ and Δx is an increment in x, then the differential of x equals the increment of x, or $dx = \Delta x$; and the differential of y is the derivative of y multiplied by the differential of x; thus

$$dy = \frac{dy}{dx}dx = \frac{df(x)}{dx}dx = f'(x)\,dx \quad \text{and} \quad \frac{dy}{dx} = dy \div dx$$

If $x = f_1(t)$ and $y = f_2(t)$, then $dx = f_1'(t)\,dt$, and $dy = f_2'(t)\,dt$.

Every derivative formula has a corresponding differential formula; thus, from the Table of Derivatives subsection, we have, for example,

$$d(uv) = u\,dv + v\,du; \quad d(\sin u) = \cos\,u\,du; \quad d(\tan^{-1} u) = \frac{du}{1+u^2}$$

Functions of Several Variables, Partial Derivatives, and Differentials

Let z be a function of two variables, $z = f(x, y)$; then its partial derivatives are

$$\frac{\partial z}{\partial x} = \frac{dz}{dx} \text{ when } y \text{ is kept constant} \qquad \frac{\partial z}{\partial y} = \frac{dz}{dy} \text{ when } x \text{ is kept constant}$$

Example 3.9

Find the partial derivatives of $f(x, y) = 4x^2y - 2y$ (i) with respect to x, and (ii) with respect to y.

Solution

(i) $$\frac{\partial f}{\partial x} = \frac{\partial}{\partial x}(4x^2y - 2y) = 4y\frac{\partial(x^2)}{\partial x} - 0 = (4y)(2x) = 8xy$$

(ii) $$\frac{\partial f}{\partial y} = \frac{\partial}{\partial y}(4x^2y - 2y) = 4x^2\frac{\partial(y)}{\partial y} - \frac{\partial(2y)}{\partial y} = 4x^2 - 2$$

Example 3.10

Two automobiles are approaching the origin. The first one is traveling from the left on the x-axis at 30 mph. The second is traveling from the top on the y-axis at 45 mph. How fast is the distance between them changing when the first is at (–5, 0) and the second is at (0, 10)? (Both coordinates are in miles.)

Solution

If $x(t)$ is taken as the position of the first auto at time t and $y(t)$ as the position of the second auto at time t, then the distance between them at time t is $s(t)=\sqrt{[x(t)]^2+[y(t)]^2}$. Using the chain rule,

$$s'(t)=\frac{ds}{dt}=\frac{1}{d_2 s(t)}\frac{d}{dt}\{[x(t)]^2+[y(t)]^2\}=\frac{1}{2s(t)}[2x(t)x'(t)+2y(t)y'(t)]$$

Now $x'(t) = 30$ and $y'(t) = -45$ for all t; and when $t = t_0$, $x(t_0) = -5$ and $y(t_0) = 10$.

Therefore,

$$s'(t_0)=\frac{-2(5)(30)-2(10)(45)}{2\sqrt{(-5)^2+(10)^2}}=\frac{-1200}{2\sqrt{125}}=\frac{-120}{\sqrt{5}}=24\sqrt{5}\approx 54$$

Thus, the two automobiles are “closing” at about 54 mph.

Example 3.11

How close do the two automobiles in Example 3.10 get?

Solution

One wants to minimize $s(t)$ in Example 3.10, so set $s'(t) = 0$. Thus,

$$\frac{xx'+yy'}{s}=0 \quad \text{or} \quad xx'+yy'=0$$

Since $x' = 30$ and $y' = -45$, $30x = 45y$. However, since $x'(t) = 30$, $x(t) = 30t + x_0$, and similarly $y(t) = -45t + y_0$. If one takes $t_0 = 0$ when the problem starts, $x_0 = -5$ and $y_0 = 10$, so $30(30t-5) = 45(-45t + 10)$ gives time of minimum distance. Solving for t, factor out 75 from both sides to get $2(6t-1) = 3(-9t + 2)$, or $39t = 8$.

Thus the minimum distance occurs at 8/39 of an hour after the initial conditions of Example 3.10. At this time $x = -5 + 240/39$ and $y = 10 - 360/39$, so $x = 45/39$ and $y = 30/39$. The minimum distance is

$$s\left(\frac{8}{39}\right)=\frac{\sqrt{(45)^2+(30)^2}}{39}=\frac{15}{39}\sqrt{9+4}=\frac{15\sqrt{13}}{39}\approx 1.4 \text{ miles}$$

Example 3.12

In Example 3.10, which reaches the origin car first, Car 1 or 2?

Solution

This is obvious if, in Example 3.11, one notices that x is positive and y is (still) positive. Alternatively, notice that Car 1 takes 5/30 of an hour to reach the origin and Car 2 takes 10/45 of an hour. The time 5/30 < 10/45, so Car 1 gets there first.

INTEGRAL CALCULUS

Definition of an Integral

The function $F(x)$ is said to be the integral of $f(x)$ if the derivative of $F(x)$ is $f(x)$, or if the differential of $F(x)$ is $f(x)\,dx$. In symbols,

$$F(x) = \int f(x)\,dx \quad \text{if} \quad \frac{dF(x)}{dx} = f(x), \qquad \text{or} \quad dF(x) = f(x)dx$$

In general, $\int f(x)\,dx = F(x) + C$, where C is an arbitrary constant.

Fundamental Theorems on Integrals

$$\int df(x) = f(x) + C$$

$$\int df(x)\,dx = f(x)\,dx$$

$$\int [f_1(x) \pm f_2(x) \pm \cdots]\,dx = \int f_1(x)\,dx \pm \int f_2(x)\,dx \pm \cdots$$

$$\int af(x)\,dx = a\int f(x)\,dx, \text{ where } a \text{ is any constant}$$

$$\int u^n\,du = \frac{u^{n+1}}{n+1} + C \quad (n \neq -1), \text{ where } u \text{ is any function of } x$$

$$\int \frac{du}{u} = \ln u + C, \text{ where } u \text{ is any function of } x$$

$$\int u\,dv = uv - \int v\,du, \text{ where } u \text{ and } v \text{ are any functions of } x$$

$$\int [u(x) \pm v(x)]\,dx = \int u(x)\,dx \pm \int v(x)\,dx$$

$$\int \frac{dx}{ax+b} = \frac{1}{a}\ln|ax+b|$$

$$\int \frac{dx}{\sqrt{x}} = 2\sqrt{x}$$

$$\int a^x\,dx = \frac{a^x}{\ln a}$$

$$\int \sin x \, dx = -\cos x$$

$$\int \sin^2 x \, dx = \frac{x}{2} - \frac{\sin 2x}{4}$$

$$\int x \sin x \, dx = \sin x - x \cos x$$

$$\int \cos x \, dx = \sin x$$

$$\int \cos^2 x \, dx = \frac{x}{2} + \frac{\sin 2x}{4}$$

$$\int x \cos x \, dx = \cos x + \sin x$$

$$\int \sin x \cos x \, dx = (\sin^2 x)/2$$

$$\int \tan x \, dx = -\ln|\cos x| = \ln|\sec x|$$

$$\int \tan^2 x \, dx = \tan x - x$$

$$\int \cot x \, dx = -\ln|\csc x| = \ln|\sin x|$$

$$\int \cot^2 x \, dx = -\cot x - x$$

$$\int e^{ax} dx = (1/a)e^{ax}$$

$$\int \ln x \, dx = x[\ln(x) - 1] \qquad (x > 0)$$

Example 3.13

Evaluate the following integrals:

(i) $\int (x^3 + 4)dx$ (ii) $\int \sin 3x dx$ (iii) $\int \sqrt{(1-x)}dx$

Solution

(i) $$\int (x^3 + 4)dx = \left(\frac{x^4}{4} + 4x\right) + \text{constant}$$

(ii) $\int \sin 3x dx$; let $t = 3x$; then $dt = 3dx$ and

$$\int \frac{1}{3} \sin t dt = -\frac{\cos t}{3} = \frac{-\cos 3x}{3} + \text{constant}$$

(iii) $\int \sqrt{(1-x)}dx$; let $t = 1 - x$; then $dt = -dx$;

$$\int -\sqrt{t} dt = -\frac{2}{3} t^{\frac{3}{2}} = -\frac{2}{3}(1-x)^{\frac{3}{2}} + \text{constant}$$

Moment of Inertia

Moment of inertia J of a mass m:

$$\text{About } OX: I_x = \int y^2 dm = \int r^2 \sin^2\theta \, dm$$

$$\text{About } OY: I_y = \int x^2 dm = \int r^2 \cos^2\theta \, dm$$

$$\text{About } O: J_0 = \int (x^2 + y^2)\, dm = \int r^2 \, dm$$

Center of Gravity

Coordinates $(\bar{x}, \bar{y})$ of the center of gravity of a mass m:

$$\bar{x} = \frac{\int x \, dm}{\int dm}, \qquad \bar{y} = \frac{\int y \, dm}{\int dm}$$

The center of gravity of the differential element of area may be taken at its midpoint. In the above equations, x and y are the coordinates of the center of gravity of the element.

Work

The work W done in moving a particle from $s = a$ to $s = b$ against a force whose component in the direction of motion is F_s is

$$dW = F_s \, ds, \qquad W = \int_a^b F_s \, ds$$

where F_s must be expressed as a function of s.

Example 3.14

Consider the function $y = x^2 + 1$ between $x = 0$ and $x = 2$. What is the area between the curve and the x-axis?

Solution

$$A = \int_0^2 (x^2 + 1)\, dx = \left(\frac{x^3}{3} + x\right)\Bigg|_0^2 = \frac{8}{3} + 2 = \frac{14}{3}$$

Example 3.15

Consider the area bounded by $x = y^2$, the x-axis, and the line $x = 4$. Find (1) the area; (2) the first moment of area with respect to the x-axis; (3) the first moment of area with respect to the y-axis; (4) the centroid; (5) the second moment of area with respect to the x-axis; (6) the second moment of area with respect to the y-axis; (7) the moment of inertia about the line $x = -2$; and (8) the moment of inertia about the line $y = 4$.

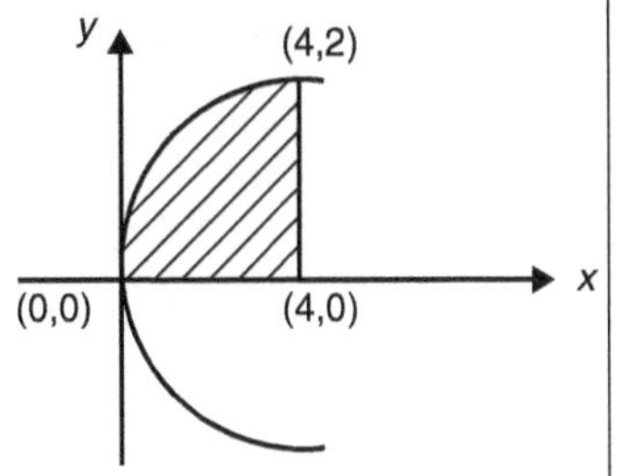

Exhibit 1

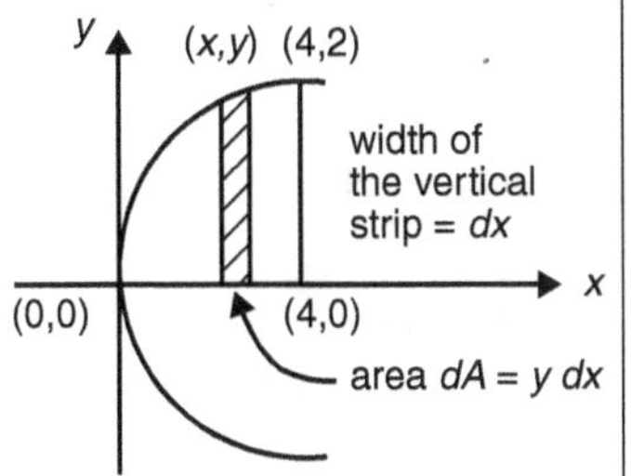

Exhibit 2

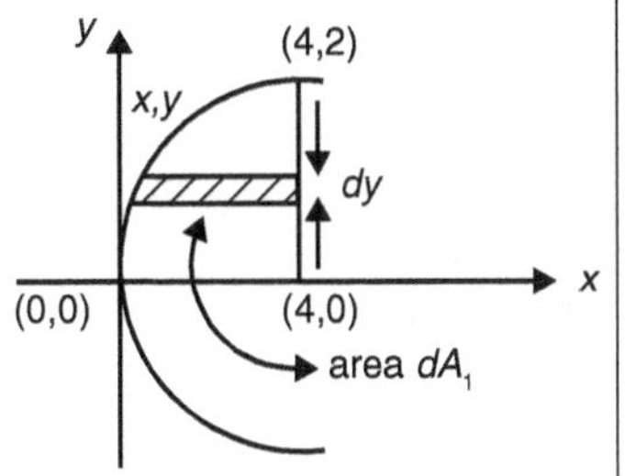

Exhibit 3

Solution

The area is shown shaded in Exhibit 1.

For the vertical strip shown in Exhibit 2, $dA = y\,dx = \sqrt{x}dx$.

$$\text{(1) area } A = \int dA = \int y dx = \int_0^4 \sqrt{x} dx = \frac{16}{3}\text{cm}^2$$

$$\text{(3) first moment with respect to } y\text{-axis } M_y = \int x dA = \int_0^4 x\sqrt{x} dx = 12.8 \text{ cm}^3$$

(6) second moment with respect to y-axis

$$I_y = \int x^2 dA = \int_0^4 x^2 \sqrt{x} dx = 36.57 \text{ cm}^4$$

For the horizontal strip shown in Exhibit 3, $dA_1 = (4 - x)\,dy = (4 - y^2)\,dy$

$$\text{Note: area } A = \int_0^2 (4 - y^2) dy$$

$$\text{(2) first moment with respect to } x\text{-axis } M_x = \int y dA_1 = \int_0^2 y(4 - y^2) dy = 4 \text{ cm}^3$$

$$\text{(4) } x \text{ coordinate of centroid } x_c = \frac{M_y}{A} = \frac{12.8}{5.33} = 2.4 \text{ cm}$$

$$y \text{ coordinate of the centroid } y_c = \frac{M_x}{A} = \frac{4}{5.33} = 0.75 \text{ cm}$$

(5) second moment with respect to the x-axis

$$I_x = \int y^2 dA_1 = \int_0^2 y^2 (4 - y^2) dy = 4.27 \text{ cm}^4$$

Now, using parallel-axis theorem,

(7) moment of inertia about the line $x = -2$ is $I_y + Ad^2 = 36.57 + (5.333)(2 + 2.4)^2 = 139.8\ \text{cm}^4$

(8) moment of inertia about the line $y = 4$ is $I_x + Ad^2 = 4.27 + (5.333)(4 - 0.75)^2 = 60.6\ \text{cm}^4$

DIFFERENTIAL EQUATIONS

Definitions

A **differential equation** is an equation involving differentials or derivatives.

The **order** of a differential equation is the order of the derivative of highest order that it contains.

The **degree** of a differential equation is the power to which the derivative of highest order in the equation is raised, that derivative entering the equation free from radicals.

The **solution** of a differential equation is the relation involving only the variables (but not their derivatives) and arbitrary constants, consistent with the given differential equation.

The most **general solution** of a differential equation of the *n*th order contains *n* arbitrary constants. If particular values are assigned to these arbitrary constants, the solution is called a particular solution.

Notation

Symbol or Abbreviation	Definition
M, N	Functions of x and y
X	Function of x alone or a constant
Y	Function of y alone or a constant
C, c	Arbitrary constants of integration
$a, b, k, 1, m, n$	Given constants

Equations of First Order and First Degree: M dx 1 N dy 5 0

Variables Separable: $X_1 Y_1\, dx + X_2 Y_2\, dy = 0$

Solution

$$\int \frac{X_1}{X_2} dx + \int \frac{Y_2}{Y_1} dy = 0$$

Linear Equation: $dy + (X_1 Y - X_2)\, dx = 0$

Solution

$$y = e^{-\int X_1 dx}\left(\int X_2 e^{\int X_1 dx} dx + C\right)$$

Second-Order Differential Equations

A second-order differential expression, $L(x, y, y', y'')$, is linear if

$$L(x, ay_1 + by_2, ay_1' + by_2', ay_1'' + by_2'') = aL(x, y_1, y_1', y_1'') + bL(x, y_2, y_2', y_2'')$$

or, if it has the form

$$L(x, y_1, y_1', y_1'') = f(x)y + g(x)y' + h(x)y''$$

A second-order linear differential equation is

$$L(x, y, y', y'') = F(x)$$

If $F(x) \equiv 0$, it is homogeneous; if $F(x)$ is nonzero, it is inhomogeneous.

Constant Coefficients

If $L = ay'' + by' + cy$ where a, b, and c are constants with $a \neq 0$, the first step is to solve the associated homogeneous equation $ay'' + by' + cy = 0$. By replacing y by $1, y'$ by r, and y'' by r^2, one obtains the characteristic equation $ar^2 + bc + c = 0$ with roots r_1 and r_2 obtained from factoring or from the quadratic formula. There are three cases to consider:

Case 1: $r_1 \neq r_2$, both real; $y = c_1 e^{r_1 x} + c_2 e^{r_2 x}$, where c_1 and c_2 are arbitrary constants.

Case 2: $r_1 = r_2$; $y = c_1 e^{r_1 x} + c_2 x e^{r_2 x}$.

Case 3: $r_1 = \alpha + j\beta$, $r_2 = \alpha - j\beta$, where α and β are real and $j^2 = -1$; $y = d_1 e^{r_1 x} + d_2 e^{r_2 x} = e^{\alpha x}\left(c_1 \sin \beta x + c_2 \cos \beta x\right)$. In particular, if $\alpha = 0$, $y = c_1 \sin \beta x + c_2 \cos \beta x$.

After finding the two solutions to the associated homogeneous equation (y_1 is the result of setting $c_1 = 1$ and $c_2 = 0$, whereas y_2 has $c_1 = 0$ and $c_2 = 1$), one proceeds in either of the following two ways.

Variation of Parameters

If $L(y) = F(x)$ in which the coefficient of y'' is 1, and $W(x) = y_1(x)y_2'(x) - y_1'(x)y_2(x)$ in which y_1 and y_2 are those solutions found above, and if

$$u_1' = \frac{-F(x)y_2(x)}{W(x)} \quad \text{and} \quad u_2' = \frac{F(x)y_1(x)}{W(x)}$$

one solution to the inhomogeneous equation is $y_p = u_1(x)y_1(x) + u_2(x)y_2(x)$.

Undetermined Coefficients

In this technique, one guesses y_p by using the following patterns.

One guesses that the solution may be of the same form as the $F(x)$ function but with coefficients to be determined. This method requires modification if $F(x)$ and $c_1 y_1 + c_2 y_2$ from the associated homogeneous equation interfere, but it is frequently

easier than the integration required in the Variation of Parameters technique to construct u_1 and u_2 from their derivatives.

To guess, classify $F(x)$. If it is a polynomial of degree k, the guess will be a polynomial of degree k. However, if $r = 0$ occurs in the homogeneous equation, increase the degree of the polynomial by one. If $F(x)$ is a polynomial times e^{Ax}, so will be the guess. Once again, the degree may have to be increased by one. If $F(x)$ contains sines and cosines, so should the guess.

After making the guess, differentiate it twice and put it into the equation. The coefficients may be determined at this time.

When mixed forms of functions are present in $F(x)$—for example, $x^2 + 2 + 3 \sin 2x$—treat the terms $x^2 + 2$ and $3 \sin 2x$ independently. The principle of *superposition* then permits you to add the results.

Now, after finding the solution $c_1y_1 + c_2y_2$ to the associated homogeneous equation, and the particular solution y_p to the inhomogeneous equation, form the general solution $y = c_1y_1 + c_2y_2 + y_p$. If initial values are required, such as $y(1) = 2$ and $y'(1) = 3$, the final step is to determine the values of c_1 and c_2 that fit the initial conditions.

Example 3.16

Specify the order of each of the following differential equations and also identify each as linear/nonlinear and homogeneous/nonhomogeneous.

Note: $y' = \dfrac{dy}{dt}$; $y'' = \dfrac{d^2y}{dt^2}$

(i) $y'' + 4y' + 4y = 0$ (ii) $3y' + 2y = 0$ (iii) $y'' + 2y' + 2y = e^{-t}$

(iv) $2y' + y + 2 = 0$ (v) $y' + y^2 + 4 = 0$

Solution

(i) second order, linear, homogeneous

(ii) first order, linear, homogeneous

(iii) second order, linear, nonhomogeneous

(iv) first order, linear, nonhomogeneous

(v) first order, nonlinear, nonhomogeneous

Example 3.17

Find the homogeneous solutions for each of the following differential equations and specify whether it belongs to either overdamped, underdamped, or critically damped case.

(i) $y'' + 3y' + 2y = 0$ (ii) $y'' + 2y' + y = 4$ (iii) $y'' + 2y' + 2y = 0$

Solution

(i) Characteristic equation is $s^2 + 3s + 2 = 0$, and the characteristic roots are -1 and -2. Homogeneous solution is $y_h(t) = C_1e^{-1t} + C_2e^{-2t}$. The roots are real and distinct, so the function is overdamped.

(ii) Characteristic equation is $s^2 + 2s + 1 = 0$, and the characteristic roots are -1 and -1. Homogeneous solution is $y_h(t) = (C_1 + C_2t)e^{-1t}$. The roots are real and equal, so the function is critically damped.

(iii) Characteristic root is $s^2 + 2s + 2 = 0$ and the characteristic roots are $-1 + i1$ and $-1 - i1$. Homogeneous solution is $y_h(t) = e^{-1t}(C_1 \cos t + C_2 \sin t)$. As the roots are complex, the function is underdamped.

Example 3.18

Solve the differential equation $y' + 2y = 0$ with initial condition $y(0) = 3$.

Solution

This is a first-order, linear, homogeneous differential equation with constant coefficient.

Characteristic equation is $s + 2 = 0$, and the root is -2; solution is $y(t) = Ce^{-2t}$.

To find C, $y(0) = C = 3$; then, $y(t) = 3e^{-2t}$.

Example 3.19

Solve the differential equation $y'' + 2y' + y = 4$ with initial conditions $y(0) = 0$, $y'(0) = 1$.

Solution

Characteristic equation is $s^2 + 2s + 1 = 0$.

Characteristic roots are: –1 and –1 (roots are real and equal; the solution is critically damped).

Natural or homogeneous solution $y_h(t) = (C_1 + C_2 t)e^{-t}$

Particular solution $y_p(t) = B$ due to forcing function $f(t) = 4$, a constant

Substituting $y_p(t)$ in the differential equation, $y_p'' + 2y_p' + y_p = 4$; $0 + 0 + B = 4$; or $B = 4$

Complete solution $y(t) = y_h(t) + y_p(t) = C_1 e^{-t} + C_2 t e^{-t} + 4$

To find C_1 and C_2, use the initial conditions in $y(t)$ and $y'(t)$; $y'(t) = -C_1 e^{-t} - C_2 t e^{-t} + C_2 e^{-t}$

$y(0) = C_1 + B = 0$ and $y'(0) = -C_1 + C_2 = 1$; solving $C_1 = -4$; $C_2 = -3$

Complete solution is $y(t) = -4e^{-t} - 3te^{-t} + 4$.

Example 3.20

Find the solution of $y'' + 2y' = x^2 + 2 + 3\sin 2x$ subject to $y(0) = 1$, $y'(0) = 0$.

Solution

Begin with $y'' + 2y' = 0$. The characteristic equation is $r^2 + 2r = 0$, which has roots 0 and –2. Thus, the two solutions to the associated homogeneous equation are $y_1 = 1$ and $y_2 = e^{-2x}$. To use the method of Undetermined Coefficients, guess $(ax^2 + bx + c) \bullet x$ for the $x^2 + 2$ term (the x is needed because $y_1 = 1$). Differentiate twice and insert in the equation: $(6ax + 2b) + 2(3ax^2 + 2bx + c)$ should be the same as $x^2 + 2$. Thus, $6a = 1, 4b + 6a = 0$, and $2b + 2c = 2$. Consequently, $a = \frac{1}{6}$, $b = -\frac{1}{4}$, and $c = \frac{5}{4}$. Next, guess $c \sin 2x + d \cos 2x$ for the other term. Then $y'' + 2y' = -4c \sin 2x - 4d \cos 2x + 2(2c \cos 2x - 2d \sin 2x)$ should match $3 \sin 2x$, so $-4c - 4d = 3$ and $-4d + 4c = 0$. Thus $c = d = -\frac{3}{8}$.

Putting all this together, one has the general solution

$$y = A + Be^{-2x} + \frac{1}{6}x^3 - \frac{1}{4}x^2 + \frac{5}{4}x - \frac{3}{8}\sin 2x - \frac{3}{8}\cos 2x$$

Now to fit the initial conditions,

$$y(0) = 1 = A + B - \frac{3}{8} \text{ and } y'(0) = 0 = -2B + \frac{5}{4} - \frac{3}{4}$$

Hence, $B = \frac{1}{4}$ and $A = \frac{9}{8}$, so

$$y = \frac{9}{8} + \frac{1}{4}e^{-2x} + \frac{1}{6}x^3 - \frac{1}{4}x^2 + \frac{5}{4}x - \frac{3}{8}\sin 2x - \frac{3}{8}\cos 2x$$

Euler Equations

An equation of the form $x^2 y'' + axy' + by = F(x)$, with a and b constants, may be solved as readily as the constant coefficient case. These are called **Euler equations**. Upon substituting $y = x^m$, one obtains the *indicial equation* $m(m-1) + am + b = 0$. This quadratic equation has two roots, m_1 and m_2.

If $m_1 \neq m_2$, both real, then $y = c_1 |x|^{m_1} + c_2 |x|^{m_2}$.

If $m_1 = m_2$, then $y = |x|^{m_1} (c_1 + c_2 \ln|x|)$.

If $m_1 = p + jq$ and $m_2 = p - jq$, then $y = |x|^p [c_1 \cos(q \ln|x|) + c_2 \sin(q \ln|x|)]$.

Once y is determined, y_p for the inhomogeneous equation may be found by Variation of Parameters. The method of Undetermined Coefficients is not recommended for Euler equations.

Higher-order linear equations with constant coefficients or of Euler form may be solved analogously.

Laplace Transform

The Laplace transform is an operation that converts functions of x on the half-line $[0, \infty]$ into functions of p on some half-line (a, ∞). The damping power of e^{-xp} is the basis for this useful technique. If $f(x)$ is a piecewise continuous function on $[0, \infty]$ that does not grow too fast, $L(f)$ is the function of p defined by

$$L[f(p)] = \int_0^\infty e^{-xp} f(x)\, dx$$

for the values of p for which the integral converges. For example, if $f(x) \equiv 1$,

$$L(f) = L(1) = \int_0^\infty e^{-xp}\, dx = \frac{1}{p} \quad (\text{for } p > 0)$$

As a further example,

$$L(f) = L(e^{ax}) = \int_0^\infty e^{-xp} e^{ax}\, dx = \int_0^\infty e^{-x(p-a)}\, dx = \frac{1}{p-a} \quad (\text{for } p > a)$$

The basic connection between the Laplace transform and differential equations is the following result achieved by integration by parts:

$$L[y'(p)] = \int_0^\infty e^{-xp} y'(x)\, dx = y(x) e^{-xp} \Big|_0^\infty + p\int_0^\infty e^{-xp} y(x)\, dx = -y(0) + pL[y(p)]$$

Consequently, the solution to $ay'' + by' + cy = F(x)$ may be obtained by transforming $L[ay''+ by' + cy] = L(F)$, so $a[p^2L(y) - py(0) - y'(0)] + b[pL(y) - y(0)] + cL(y) = L(F)$. Solving for $L(y)$,

$$L(y) = \frac{L(F) + apy(0) + ay'(0) + by(0)}{ap^2 + bp + c}$$

If one were able to "invert" this result,

$$y = L^{-1}\left[\frac{L(F) + apy(0) + ay'(0) + by(0)}{ap^2 + bp + c}\right]$$

the solution would appear, complete with initial values. The Laplace transform is invertible, and the process of finding $L^{-1}[f(p)]$ as a function of x is much like the process of integration.

Table 3.1 presents a tabulation of selected transforms, where the transform of $f(x)$ is called $F(p)$. Line 3 in Table 3.1 reveals that the operation of multiplying by x corresponds to the negative of the operation of differentiating with respect to p. Lines 2 and 8 have been previously discussed. The δ in Line 1 is a *pseudo-function* with great utility defined by $\delta(x) = 0$ for all x except $x = 0$, and $\int_0^\infty \delta(x)\,dx = 1$, so $\delta(0) = +\infty$. The u in Line 7 is called the *Heaviside function*, and it is *zero* until $x - c > 0$. Thus $u(x-c)f(x-c)$ is $f(x)$ shifted right to the point $x = c$. For example, if $f(x) = x$ and $c = 1$, $u(x - 1)f(x - 1)$ has the graph shown in Figure 3.4, whereas f has the graph shown in Figure 3.5. The operation in the left column of Line 9 is a new way to multiply functions, called **convolution**.

Table 3.1 Selected transforms

$f(x)$	$F(p)$
1. δ	1
2. 1	p^{-1}
3. $xf(x)$	$\frac{-dF}{dp}$
4. $e^{ax}f(x)$	$F(p-a)$
5. $\sin ax$	$\frac{a}{p^2+a^2}$
6. $\cos ax$	$\frac{p}{p^2+a^2}$
7. $u(x-c)f(x-c)$	$e^{-cp}F(p)$
8. $f'(x)$	$pF(p) - f(0)$
9. $\int_0^x f(u)g(x-u)du$	$F(p) \bullet G(p)$
10. $f(x)$, if f is periodic, of period L	$\frac{\int_0^L e^{-px}f(x)dx}{1-e^{-pL}}$

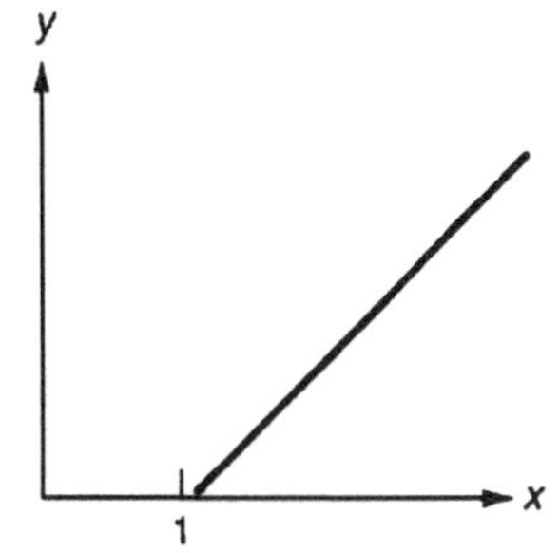

Figure 3.4

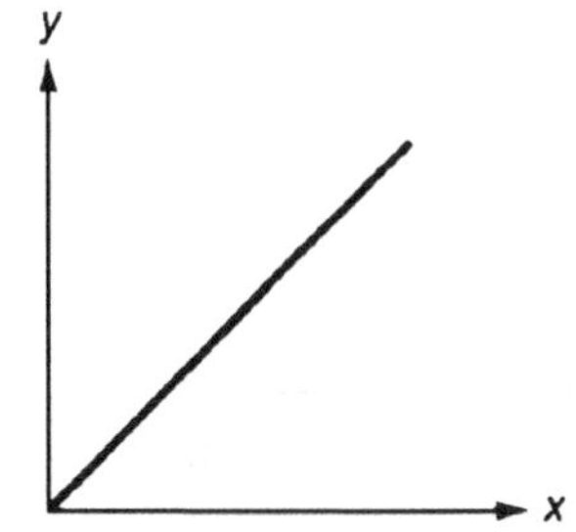

Figure 3.5

For an example of inversion of a transform, consider

$$F(p)=\frac{2p+3}{(p^2+1)(p-2)}$$

Begin by using partial fractions to write

$$F(p)=\frac{A}{p-2}+\frac{Bp+C}{p^2+1}$$

from which

$$F(p)=\frac{7/5}{p-2}+\frac{(-7/5)p-4/5}{p^2+1}$$

Table 3.1 shows that $p/(p^2+1)$ is $L(\cos x)$, so

$$L^{-1}\left[\frac{(-7/5)p}{p^2+1}\right]$$

is $-(7/5)\cos x$, and similarly

$$L^{-1}\left(-\frac{4}{5}\bullet\frac{1}{p^2+1}\right)$$

is $-(4/5)\sin x$. Since $L(1) = 1/p$, $L(e^{2x})$ is $1/(p-2)$ by Line 4, and combining these three terms yields

$$f(x)=\frac{7}{5}e^{2x}-\frac{7}{5}\cos x-\frac{4}{5}\sin x$$

The *Heaviside* operation in Line 7 leads to an easy solution of differential equations whose right-hand side is not continuous. For example, consider the response of $y''+y$ to a driving function $f(x)$ that is 1 for x between 0 and 2 and then becomes 0. Suppose $y(0) = 1$ and $y'(0) = 3$. By applying Line 8 in Table 3.1 twice,

$$L(y)=\frac{L(f)+p+3}{p^2+1}$$

and since $f(x) = 1 - u(x-2)$,

$$L(f)=\frac{1}{p}-\frac{e^{-2p}}{p}$$

so

$$L(y)=\frac{p+3+\left(1-e^{-2p}\right)/p}{p^2+1}$$

The e^{-2p} portion represents delay, so write

$$L(y)=\frac{p^2+3p+1}{p(p^2+1)}-\frac{e^{-2p}}{p(p^2+1)}=\frac{1}{p}+\frac{3}{p^2+1}-e^{-2p}\left(\frac{1}{p}-\frac{p}{p^2+1}\right)$$

from which $y=1+3\sin x-u(x-2)+u(x-2)\cos(x-2)$.

Example 3.21

Find the Laplace transform of each of the following functions:

(i) $2\,u(t) + e^{-3t}$ (ii) $2te^{-t}$ (iii) $e^{-t}\sin 4t$ (iv) $\sin 4t$ (v) $\cos 2t$

Solution

(i) $\dfrac{2}{s}+\dfrac{1}{s+3}=\dfrac{2s+7}{s(s+3)}$ (ii) $\dfrac{2}{(s+1)^2}$ (iii) $\dfrac{4}{(s+1)^2+4^2}$

(iv) $\dfrac{4}{s^2+4^2}$ (v) $\dfrac{s}{s^2+2^2}$

Example 3.22

Find an expression for $Y(s)$ = £ $y(t)$ for each of the following differential equations.

(i) $\dfrac{dy}{dt}+6\,y(t)=4\,u(t);\; y(0)=0$

(ii) $\dfrac{dy}{dt}+2\,y(t)=0;\; y(0)=-2$

(iii) $\dfrac{d^2y}{dt^2}+2\dfrac{dy}{dt}+3\,y(t)=\sin 2t$ with zero initial conditions

(iv) $\dfrac{d^2y}{dt^2}+2\dfrac{dy}{dt}+y(t)=e^{-2t}$ with initial conditions $y(0)=-1$ and $\dfrac{dy(0)}{dt}=1$

Solution

(i) $[sY(s)-0]+6Y(s)=\dfrac{4}{s};\; Y(s)=\dfrac{4}{s(s+6)}$

(ii) $[sY(s)-(-2)]+2Y(s)=0;\; Y(s)=-\dfrac{2}{s+2}$

(iii) $[s^2Y(s)-0-0]+2[sY(s)-0]+3Y(s)=\dfrac{2}{s^2+4};$

$Y(s)=\dfrac{2}{(s^2+4)(s^2+2s+3)}$

(iv) $[s^2Y(s)-(-s)-1]+2[sY(s)-(-1)]+Y(s)=\dfrac{1}{s+2}$

simplifying $Y(s)=\dfrac{(-s^2-3s-1)}{(s+2)(s^2+2s+1)}$

Example 3.23

Find the initial and final values of the functions whose Laplace transforms are given:

(i) $F(s) = \dfrac{2(s+1)}{s(s+4)(s+6)}$ (ii) $F(s) = \dfrac{4s}{s^2+2s+2}$

Solution

(i) Initial value is: $\lim_{t\to 0} f(t) = \lim_{s\to\infty} sF(s) = \lim_{s\to\infty} s\dfrac{2(s+1)}{s(s+4)(s+6)} = 0$

Final value is: $\lim_{t\to\infty} f(t) = \lim_{s\to 0} sF(s) = \lim_{s\to 0} s\dfrac{2(s+1)}{s(s+4)(s+6)} = \dfrac{1}{12}$

(ii) Initial value is: $\lim_{t\to 0} f(t) = \lim_{s\to\infty} sF(s) = \lim_{s\to\infty} s\dfrac{4s}{s^2+2s+2} = 4$

Final value is: $\lim_{t\to\infty} f(t) = \lim_{s\to 0} sF(s) = \lim_{s\to 0} s\dfrac{4s}{s^2+2s+2} = 0$

FOURIER SERIES AND FOURIER TRANSFORM

Fourier Series

A periodic function $F(t)$ with period T can be expanded into Fourier series as

$$F(t) = a_0 + \sum_{n=1}^{\infty}(a_n \cos n\omega_0 t + b_n \sin n\omega_0 t) \qquad \textbf{(3.1)}$$

where $\omega_0 = \dfrac{2\pi}{T}$ and the Fourier coefficients are defined as

$$a_0 = \left(\frac{1}{T}\right)\int_0^T F(t)dt \qquad \textbf{(3.1a)}$$

$$a_n = \left(\frac{2}{T}\right)\int_0^T F(t)\cos(n\omega_0 t)dt \qquad \textbf{(3.1b)}$$

$$b_n = \left(\frac{2}{T}\right)\int_0^T F(t)\sin(nw_0 t)dt \qquad \textbf{(3.1c)}$$

For a truncated series, the root mean square (RMS) value F_N is defined as

$$F_N^{\ 2} = a_0^{\ 2} + \left(\frac{1}{2}\right)\sum_{n=1}^{N}(a_n^{\ 2} + b_n^{\ 2}) \qquad \textbf{(3.2)}$$

Example 3.24

Find the Fourier coefficients of the periodic waveform shown in Exhibit 4 and the RMS value of the truncated Fourier series including five harmonics.

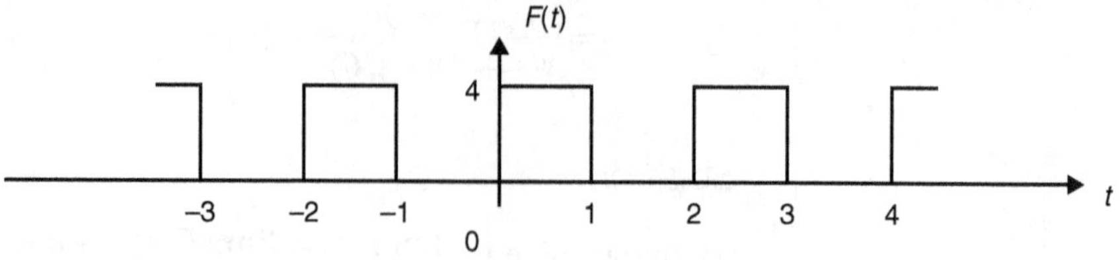

Exhibit 4

Solution

Period $T = 2\ s$; $w_0 = \frac{2\pi}{T} = \pi\ rad/s$

From Equation (3.1a) $a_0 = \frac{1}{2}\left[\int_0^1 4dt + \int_1^2 0dt\right] = 2$

From Equation (3.1b) $a_n = \frac{2}{2}\left[\int_0^1 4\cos n\omega_0 t dt + \int_1^2 0dt\right] = 0, \text{when } n \neq 0$

From Equation (3.1c) $b_n = \frac{2}{2}\int_0^1 4\sin n\omega_0 t dt + \int_1^2 0dt = \frac{4}{n\pi}(1 - \cos n\pi)$

$b_n = 0$ for all even n; $b_n = \frac{8}{n\pi}$ for all odd n

Fourier series is $F(t) = 2 + \frac{8}{\pi}\sin\ \omega_0 t + \frac{8}{3\pi}\sin\ 3\omega_0 t + \frac{8}{5\pi}\sin\ 5\omega_0 t + \ldots$

From Equation (3.2), for $N = 5$, $F_N^2 = 2^2 + \frac{1}{2}\left[(\frac{8}{\pi})^2 + (\frac{8}{3\pi})^2 + (\frac{8}{5\pi})^2\right] = 7.732;$

$$F_N = 2.7807$$

Fourier Transform

The Fourier transform of a function $x(t)$ and its inverse relation are:

$$X(f) = \int_{-\infty}^{+\infty} x(t)\exp(-j2\pi ft)\,dt \qquad \textbf{(3.3a)}$$

$$X(t) = \int_{-\infty}^{+\infty} x(f)\exp(j2\pi ft)\,dt \qquad \textbf{(3.3b)}$$

Table 3.2 lists the Fourier transforms for a few commonly used functions in communication systems. The NCEES *Fundamentals of Engineering Supplied-Reference Handbook* includes a more complete table of Fourier transform pairs.

Table 3.2 Fourier Transform Pairs

<table>
<tr><th>$x(t)$</th><th></th><th>$X(f)$</th></tr>
<tr><td>Impulse at $t = 0$, $\delta(t)$</td><td>
</td><td>1</td></tr>
<tr><td>Unit step function, $u(t)$</td><td>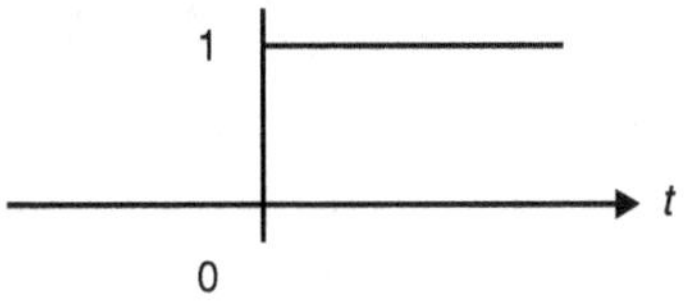
</td><td>$\frac{1}{2}\delta(f)+\frac{1}{j2\pi f}$</td></tr>
<tr><td>Rectangular pulse, $\Pi(t/\tau)$</td><td>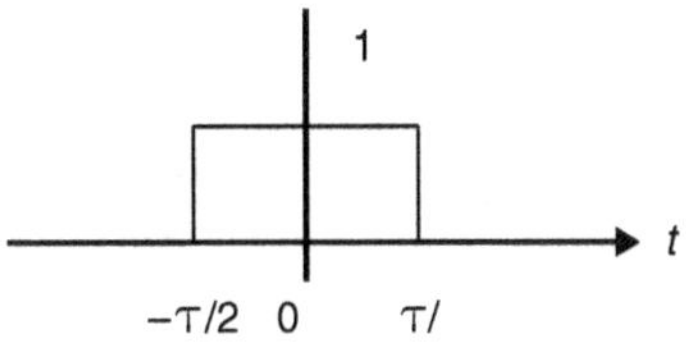
</td><td>$\tau f \sin c(\tau f)$</td></tr>
<tr><td>Sinc function, sinc(at)</td><td>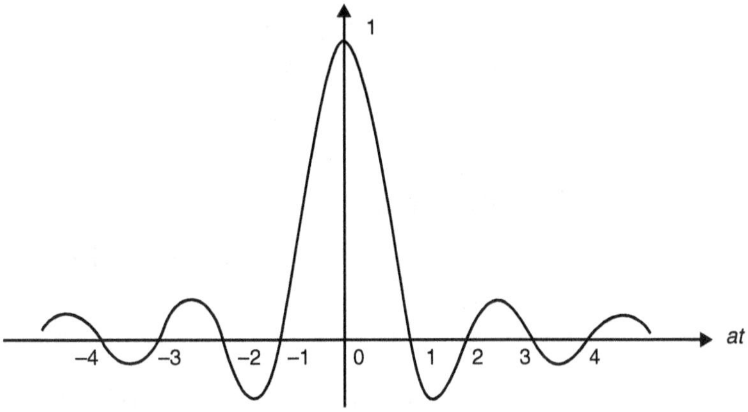
</td><td>$\frac{1}{a}\Pi\left(\frac{f}{a}\right)$</td></tr>
<tr><td>Triangular pulse, $\Lambda(t/\tau)$</td><td>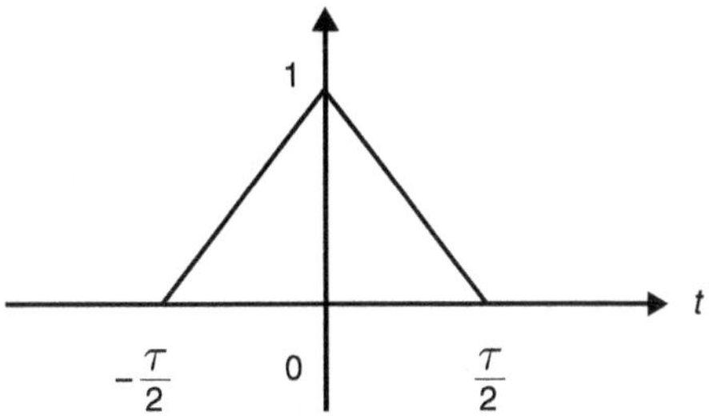
</td><td>$\tau f \sin c^2(\tau f)$</td></tr>
</table>

Example 3.25

Find the Fourier transform of (i) 4 $\delta(t)$, (ii) 2 $u(t)$, (iii) $\Pi(t/2)$, and (iv) 6 $\cos(100\pi t)$.

Solution

(i) 4 (ii) $\delta(f) + 1/j\pi f$ (iii) $2f\,\text{sinc}(2f)$ (iv) $3[\delta(f-50) + \delta(f+50)]$

DIFFERENCE EQUATIONS AND Z-TRANSFORMS

Difference equations are used to model discrete systems; they are analogous to differential equations that describe continuous systems. The equations $y(k) - y(k-1) = 10$ and $y(k+1) - y(k) = 5$ are some examples of first order linear difference equations; $y(k) = y(k-1) + y(k-2)$ is an example of second order difference equation.

Example 3.26

Find the values of $y(1)$, $y(2)$, and $y(3)$ of the equation $y(k) - 1.01y(k-1) = -50$ with the initial condition $y(0) = 1000$.

Solution

y(1) – 1.01 $y(0) = -50$; $y(1) =$ \$960

$y(2) - 1.01\,y(1) = -50$; $y(2) =$ \$919.60

$y(3) - 1.01\,y(2) = -50$; $y(3) =$ \$878.80 and so on

Z-Transforms

Z-transform of a discrete sequence is defined as

$$F(z) = \sum_{k=0}^{\infty} f[k]z^{-k} \tag{3.4}$$

For example, if the discrete sequence is $f[k] = 0, 1, 4$, then its z-transform is $(F_z) = 0 + z^{-1} + 4z^{-2}$.

Example 3.27

Find the z-transform of the function $f(k) = 3\,u(k) + 2^k$ for $k \geq 0$.

Solution

Using the Z-transform table from the *Fundamentals of Engineering Supplied-Reference Handbook*, $F(z) =$

$$\frac{3}{1-z^{-1}} + \frac{1}{1-2z^{-1}}$$

Simplifying, $F(z) = \dfrac{3(1-2z^{-1}) + (1-z^{-1})}{(1-z^{-1})(1-2z^{-1})} = \dfrac{4-7z^{-1}}{(1-z^{-1})(1-2_z^{-1})}$

Multiplying by z^2, $F(z) = \dfrac{4z^2 - 7z}{z^2 - 3z + 2}$

PROBLEMS

3.1 $\int_{\pi/2}^{\pi} \sin 2x\, dx =$

a. 2
b. 1
c. 0
d. –1

3.2 $\int_0^2 x^2\sqrt{1+x^3}\, dx =$

a. 52/9
b. 0
c. 52/3
d. 26/3

3.3 $\int_1^e x(\ln x)dx =$

a. $\frac{1}{2}e^2+1$
b. $\frac{1}{2}e^2-e+\frac{1}{2}$
c. $\frac{1}{4}e^2+\frac{1}{4}$
d. $\frac{1}{4}e^2-\frac{1}{2}e+\frac{1}{4}$

3.4 If the first derivative of the equation of a curve is constant, the curve is a:
a. circle
b. hyperbola
c. parabola
d. straight line

3.5 Which of the following is a characteristic of all trigonometric functions?
a. The values of all functions repeat themselves every 45 degrees.
b. All functions have units of length or angular measure.
c. The graphs of all functions are continuous.
d. All functions have dimensionless units.

3.6 For a given curve $y=f(x)$ that is continuous between $x=a$ and $x=b$, the average value of the curve between the ordinates at $x=a$ and $x=b$ is represented by:

a. $\dfrac{\int_a^b x^2\, dy}{b-a}$
b. $\dfrac{\int_a^b y^2 dx}{b-a}$
c. $\dfrac{\int_a^b x\, dy}{a-b}$
d. $\dfrac{\int_a^b y\, dx}{b-a}$

3.7 If $y=\cos x$, $\dfrac{dy}{dx}$ is:

a. $\sin x$
b. $-\tan x \cos x$
c. $\dfrac{1}{\sec x}$
d. $\sec x \sin x$

3.8 The derivative of $\cos^3 5x$ is:

a. $3\sin^2 5x$
b. $15\sin^2 5x$
c. $\cos^2 5x \sin x$
d. $-15\cos^2 5x \sin 5x$

3.9 The slope of the curve $y = 2x^3 - 3x$ at $x = 1$ is:

a. -1
b. 0
c. 3
d. 5

3.10 A stone is dropped from the top of a building at $t = 0$. The position of the stone is given by the equation $s(t) = 16\,t^2$ m. Acceleration of the stone (in m/s^2) 2 seconds after it is dropped is:

a. 64
b. 32
c. 24
d. 16

3.11 Maximum value of the function $f(x) = x^3 - 5x - 4$ occurs at:

a. 0
b. 1.29
c. -0.30
d. -1.29

3.12 The partial derivative with respect to x of the function $xy^2 - 5y + 6$ is:

a. xy
b. $2y$
c. y^2
d. $-5y$

3.13 The power series expansion of $\cos(x)$ about the point $x = 0$ is:

a. $1-\dfrac{x^2}{2!}+\dfrac{x^4}{4!}-\dfrac{x^6}{6!}+\ldots$
b. $1+\dfrac{x^2}{2!}+\dfrac{x^4}{4!}+\dfrac{x^6}{6!}+\ldots$
c. $1-\dfrac{x}{2!}+\dfrac{x}{4!}-\dfrac{x}{6!}+\ldots$
d. $1+\dfrac{x}{2!}+\dfrac{x}{4!}+\dfrac{x}{6!}+\ldots$

3.14 The value of $\lim\limits_{x\to 2}\dfrac{x^2-4}{x-2}$ is:

a. 0
b. ∞
c. 1
d. 4

3.15 If $A = \displaystyle\int_0^{\frac{\pi}{4}} \sin^2\theta\, d\theta$, the value of A is:

a. 0.29
b. 0.58
c. 1.75
d. 3.14

3.16 If $x^3 + 3x^2y + y^3 = 4$ defines y implicitly, $dy/dx =$

a. $-\dfrac{x^2+2xy}{x^2+y^2}$ c. $-\dfrac{x^2+y^2}{x^2+2xy}$

b. $3x^2+3y^2$ d. $-\dfrac{x^2+2xy}{x^2+y^2}$

3.17 Estimate $\sqrt{34}$ using differentials. The answer is closest to:

a. $6+\dfrac{1}{6}$ c. 6

b. $6-\dfrac{1}{6}$ d. $6-\dfrac{1}{3}$

3.18 The only relative maximum of $f(x)=x^4-\dfrac{4}{3}x^3-12x^2+1$ is:

a. −1 c. 0

b. 1 d. −1

3.19 The area between $y = x^2$ and $y = 2x + 3$ is:

a. 9 c. $6\dfrac{1}{3}$

b. 20 d. $10\dfrac{2}{3}$

3.20 The area enclosed by the curve $r = 2(\sin\theta + \cos\theta)$ is:

a. π c. 2π

b. $\dfrac{\pi}{2}$ d. $\pi\sqrt{2}$

3.21 The curve in Exhibit 3.21 has the equation $y = f(x)$. At point A, what are the values of $\dfrac{dy}{dx}$ and $\dfrac{d^2y}{dx^2}$?

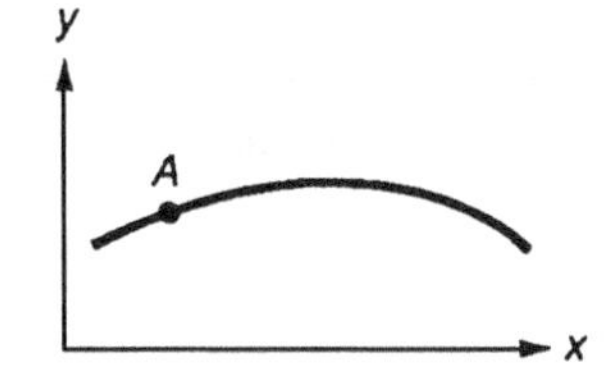

Exhibit 3.21

a. $\dfrac{dy}{dx}<0,\ \dfrac{d^2y}{dx^2}<0$ c. $\dfrac{dy}{dx}=0,\ \dfrac{d^2y}{dx^2}=0$

b. $\dfrac{dy}{dx}<0,\ \dfrac{d^2y}{dx^2}>0$ d. $\dfrac{dy}{dx}>0,\ \dfrac{d^2y}{dx^2}<0$

3.22 The area of the shaded region in Exhibit 3.22 is:

a. 1.37 c. 5.33

b. 3.82 d. 6.80

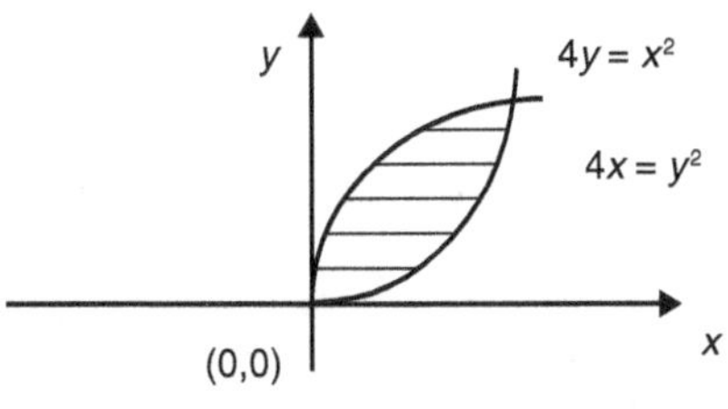

Exhibit 3.22

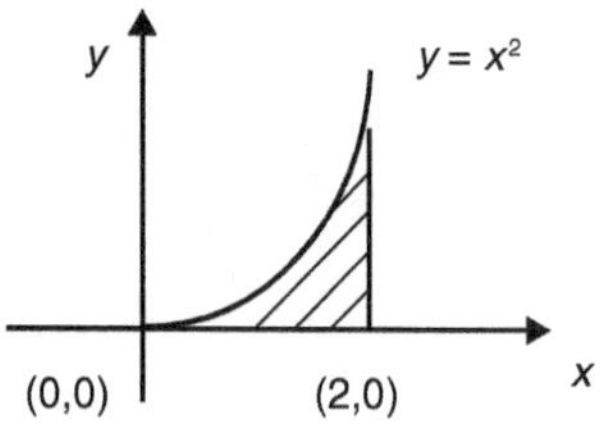

Exhibit 3.23

Refer to Exhibit 3.23 for problems 3.23 through 3.28.

3.23 Area of the shaded region is:

a. 1.10 c. 4.02
b. 2.67 d. 6.80

3.24 The first moment of the shaded area with respect to the x-axis is:

a. 1.20 c. 3.20
b. 2.30 d. 4.60

3.25 The first moment of the shaded area with respect to the y-axis is:

a. 0.85 c. 3.07
b. 1.90 d. 4.00

3.26 The centroid of the shaded area is:

a. (1.5, 1.2) c. (0, 1.2)
b. (1.5, 0) d. (1.0, 1.0)

3.27 The second moment of the shaded area with respect to the x-axis is:

a. 6.10 c. 12.11
b. 9.05 d. 18.32

3.28 The second moment of the shaded area with respect to the y-axis is:

a. 1.98 c. 4.63
b. 3.12 d. 6.40

3.29 If the characteristic roots of a differential equation are $-4 - i4$ and $-4 + i4$, the homogeneous solution is:

a. $C_1 \cos 4x + C_2 \sin 4x$ c. $C_1 e^{-i4x} + C_2 e^{i4x}$
b. $e^{-4x}(C_1 \cos 4x + C_2 \sin 4x)$ d. $C_1 \cos(4x + \theta)$

3.30 Characteristic roots of a differential equation are -2 and -2. If the forcing function is e^{-2x}, the particular solution, $y_p(x)$ is:

a. Ax^2 c. Axe^{-2x}
b. Ae^{-2x} d. Ax^2e^{-2x}

3.31 The solution of the differential equation $y'' + 5y' + 6y = 2e^{-2x}$ with zero initial conditions is:

a. $y = -2e^{-2x} + 2e^{-3x} + 2xe^{-2x}$ c. $y = 2e^{-3x} + 2xe^{-2x}$
b. $y = x - 2e^{-2x} + 2e^{-3x}$ d. $y = -2e^{-2x} + 2xe^{-2x}$

3.32 $\lim_{x\to 1}\dfrac{x^2-1}{x-1}=$

a. 2
b. ∞
c. 0
d. 1

3.33 The solution to $xy' + 2y = e^{3x}$ is:

a. $y = e^{3x} - \dfrac{e^{3x}}{x} + \dfrac{c}{x}$

b. $y = \dfrac{xe^{3x} - 3e^{3x} + 3c}{3x^2}$

c. $y = xe^{3x} - 3e^{3x} + c$

d. $y + x = e^{3x} + c$

3.34 Solve $xy'' - 2(x+1)y' + (x+2)y = 0$.

a. $y = Ae^x + Bx^3e^x$
b. $y = Ae^x + Be^{2x}$
c. $y = A\sin(x+1) + B\cos(x+2)$
d. $y = Ae^x + Be^{-x}$

3.35 Solve $y'' + 4y = 8\sin x$.

a. $y = Ae^{2x} + Be^{-2x}$
b. $y = A\sin 2x + B\cos 2x$
c. $y = A\sin 2x + B\cos 2x + \sin x$
d. $y = A\sin 2x + B\cos 2x + \dfrac{8}{3}\sin x$

3.36 The family of trajectories orthogonal to the family $x^2 + y^2 = 2cy$ is:

a. $x - y = c$
b. $x^2 - y^2 = cx$
c. $x^2 + y^2 = c$
d. $x^2 + y^2 = 2cx$

3.37 The Laplace transform of the function $e^{-t}\cos(t)$ is:

a. $\dfrac{s}{s^2+1^2}$

b. $\dfrac{(s+1)}{(s+1)^2+1^2}$

c. $\dfrac{(s+1)}{s^2+1^2}$

d. $\dfrac{(s-1)}{(s-1)^2+1^2}$

3.38 For the differential equation $\dfrac{d^2y}{dt^2} + 2\dfrac{dy}{dt} + y(t) = \cos 2t$ with zero initial conditions, the Laplace transform $Y(s)$ of $y(t)$ is:

a. $\dfrac{s}{(s^2+2s+1)}$

b. $\dfrac{2}{(s^2+2)(s^2+2s+1)}$

c. $\dfrac{s}{(s^2+4)(s^2+2s+1)}$

d. $\dfrac{s}{(s^2+4)(s^2+1)}$

3.39 The initial value of the function whose Laplace transform $F(s) = \frac{s+5}{s(s+1)(s+10)}$ is:

a. 2.0 c. 0.5
b. 1.0 d. 0

3.40 For the difference equation $y(k) = 2y(k-1) + 3y(k-2)$ with initial conditions $y(-1) = 1$; $y(-2) = 1$, the value of $y(1)$ is:

a. 1 c. 13
b. 5 d. 41

3.41 For the difference equation $y(k+1) + y(k) = u(k)$ with $y(0) = 0$, find $Y(z)$, the z-transform of the function $y(k)$ is:

a. $\frac{1}{(z-1)(z+2)}$ c. $\frac{z}{(z+1)(z-2)}$

b. $\frac{z}{(z-1)(z+2)}$ d. $\frac{2}{(z+1)(z+2)}$

3.42 The initial value of the function whose Z-transform $F(z) = \frac{z+2}{z-4}$ is:

a. 0 c. 0.5
b. –0.5 d. 1.0

3.43 Find the Fourier coefficient b_3 of the waveform shown in Exhibit 3.43.

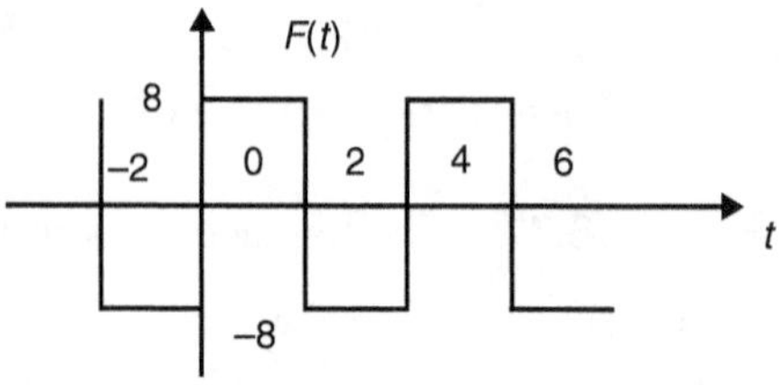

Exhibit 3.43

a. 1.17 c. 3.40
b. 2.23 d. 4.78

3.44 Find the Fourier transform, $F(f)$, of a triangular pulse of width 2.

a. $\text{sinc}(f)$ c. $\text{sinc}(2f)$
b. $\text{sinc}^2(f)$ d. $f\,\text{sinc}^2(f)$

3.45 Find the Fourier transform of $f(t) = \delta(t-1) + \delta(t+1)$.

a. $\exp(-j2\pi f)$ c. $2\cos(2\pi f)$
b. $\exp(j2\pi f)$ d. $j2\sin(2\pi f)$

3.46 Find $y(1)$ if $y(k) = 2y(k-1) + 3y(k-2)$ with $y(-1) = 1$; $y(-2) = 1$.

a. 1 c. 13
b. 5 d. 41

3.47 Find the final value of the function $f(k)$ whose Z-transform is $F(z) = \dfrac{2(z+1)}{(z-1)}$.

a. 1 c. 4
b. 2 d. ∞

SOLUTIONS

3.1 d.

$$\int_{\pi/2}^{\pi} \sin 2x \, dx = -\frac{1}{2} \cos 2x = -\frac{1}{2}\cos 2\pi + \frac{1}{2} \cos \pi = -\frac{1}{2} - \frac{1}{2} = -1$$

3.2 a. Let $u = 1 + x^3$, so $du = 3x^2 dx$. The integral becomes $\dfrac{1}{3}\displaystyle\int_1^9 \sqrt{u}\, du$
$= \dfrac{2}{9} u^{3/2} = \dfrac{2}{9}(27 - 1)$.

3.3 c. Prepare to solve using $\displaystyle\int u \, dv = uv - \int v \, du.$

Let $u = \ln x$ and $dv = x \, dx$.

Therefore, $du = \dfrac{1}{x} dx$ and $v = \dfrac{1}{2} x^2$

$$\int_1^e x(\ln x)dx = \ln x\left(\frac{1}{2}x^2\right)\Bigg|_1^e - \int_1^e \frac{1}{2}x^2\left(\frac{1}{x}\right)dx$$

$$= \ln x\left(\frac{1}{2}x^2\right)\Bigg|_1^e - \frac{1}{4}x^2\Bigg|_1^e = \ln e\left(\frac{1}{2}e^2\right) - \ln 1\left(\frac{1}{2}1^2\right) - \left[\frac{1}{4}e^2 - \frac{1}{4}1^2\right]$$

$$= \frac{1}{4}e^2 + \frac{1}{4}$$

3.4 d. If $\dfrac{dy}{dx} = m$, $y = \int m \, dx = m \int dx = mx + b$, so $y = mx + b$ is a straight line.

3.5 d. All trigonometric functions are ratios of lengths, with the result that they are dimensionless.

3.6 d.

$$\text{Area} = \int_a^b y\,dx$$

$$\text{Average value} = \frac{\text{Area}}{\text{Base width}} = \frac{\int_a^b y\,dx}{b-a}$$

3.7 b. Since $\frac{dy}{dx} = -\sin x$ and $\tan x = \frac{\sin x}{\cos x}$, then $\sin x = \tan x \cos x$. Thus, the derivative is

$$\frac{dy}{dx} = -\tan x \cos x$$

3.8 d. Apply the chain rule. The "outside" function is u^3, so $y' = 3\cos^2 5x\,(\cos 5x)' = 3\cos^2 5x\,(-\sin 5x)\,(5)$.

3.9 c. Derivative of y, $y' = 6x^2 - 3$. Since the slope is the derivative, at $x = 1$ the slope is $y'|_{x=1} = 3$.

3.10 b. Position $s(t) = 16t^2$; then, velocity $v(t) = s'(t) = 32t$ m/s and acceleration $a(t) = s''(t) = 32$ m/s^2; at any time the acceleration is 32 m/s^2.

3.11 d. Derivative of y is $y' = 3x^2 - 5$. Equating y' to 0, $3x^2 - 5 = 0$ has roots at $x = -1.29, +1.29$.

Second derivative of y is $y'' = 6x$.

$y''|_{x=-1.29} < 0$; then, the maximum of y occurs at $x = -1.29$.

(Note: value of $y_{max} = (-1.29)^3 - 5(-1.29) - 4 = 0.30$

$y''|_{x=1.29} > 0$; then, the minimum of y occurs at $x = 1.29$; $y_{min} = (1.29)^3 - 5(1.29) - 4 = -8.30$.

At the inflection point $y'' = 0$: $y'' = 6x = 0$; then, $x = 0$. Also, y'' changes sign at $x = 0$.)

3.12 c. y^2

3.13 a. $f(x) = \cos x$; $f'(x) = -\sin x$; $f''(x) = -\cos x$; $f'''(x) = \sin x$; $f^{iv}(x) = \cos x$
Substituting these values in the Taylor's series expansion,

$$f(x) = \cos(0) + \frac{-\sin 0}{1!}x + \frac{-\cos 0}{2!}x^2 + \frac{\sin 0}{3!}x^3 + \frac{\cos 0}{4!}x^4$$

$$= 1 - \frac{x^2}{2!} + \frac{x^4}{4!} - \frac{x^6}{6!} + \ldots$$

3.14 d. Using L'Hopital's rule, $\lim_{x\to 2}\frac{x^2-4}{x-2} = \lim_{x\to 2}\frac{2x}{1} = 4$.

3.15 **a.** Using the integral table, the integral =

$$2\left[\frac{\theta}{2}-\frac{\sin 2\theta}{4}\right]_0^{\pi/4}=\left[\left(\frac{\pi}{4}-\frac{1}{2}\right)-0\right]=0.285$$

3.16 **a.** Taking the derivative with respect to x,

$$3x^2+6xy+3x^2y'+3y^2y'=0, \text{ so } y'=-\frac{3x^2+6xy}{3x^2+3y^2}$$

3.17 **b.** Since $\sqrt{36}=6$, take $x_0=36$ and $f(x)=\sqrt{x}$. In general,

$$\Delta y=f(x)-f(x_0)=f'(x_0)(x-x_0)$$
$$\sqrt{34}-\sqrt{36}=\frac{1}{2}\frac{1}{\sqrt{36}}(-2)=-\frac{1}{6}$$

3.18 **b.** Here,

$f'(x)=4x^3-4x^2-24x=x(4x^2-4x-24)=4x(x-3)(x+2)=0$, so possible extrema are at 0, 3, and –2. Since $f''(0)=-24$, it is the maximum (3 and –2 are minima). Since $f(0)=1$, the relative maximum is 1.

3.19 **d.** The line and the parabola intersect when $x^2=2x+3$, or $x^2-2x+1=4$, or $(x-1)^2=2^2$. The line is above the parabola, so

$$A=\int_{-1}^{3}\left(2x+3-x^2\right)dx=\left(x^2+3x-\frac{1}{3}x^3\right)\Bigg|_{-1}^{3}=9-\left(-\frac{5}{3}\right)$$

3.20 **c.** Multiply by r to obtain $x^2+y^2=2y+2x$, or $x^2-2x+y^2-2y=0$, or $(x-1)^2+(y-1)^2=2$ a circle centered at (1, 1) of radius $\sqrt{2}$. The area is $\pi(\sqrt{2})^2=2\pi$.

3.21 **d.** The first derivative $\frac{dy}{dx}$ is the slope of the curve. At point A the slope is positive. The second derivative $\frac{d^2y}{dx^2}$ gives the direction of bending. A negative value indicates the curve is concave downward.

3.22 **c.** Point of intersection of the curves is determined as $y^2=4x=4\sqrt{4y}$, $y=4$; $x=4$.

Area of the strip in Exhibit 3.22a, $dA=(y_1-y_2)dx=\left(\sqrt{4x}-\frac{x^2}{4}\right)dx$

$$\text{Area}=A=\int_{x=0}^{4}\left(\sqrt{4x}-\frac{x^2}{4}\right)dx=\frac{16}{3}$$

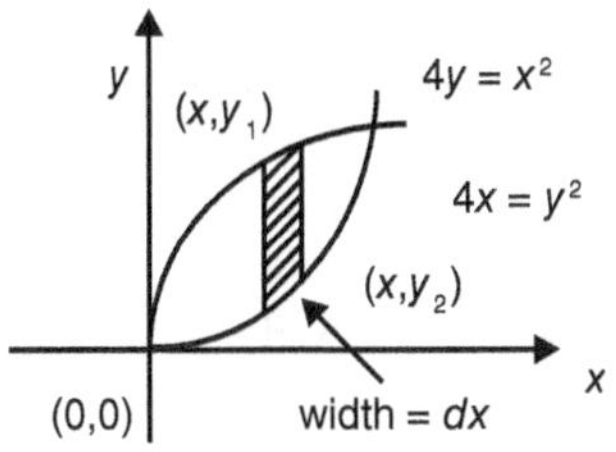

Exhibit 3.22a

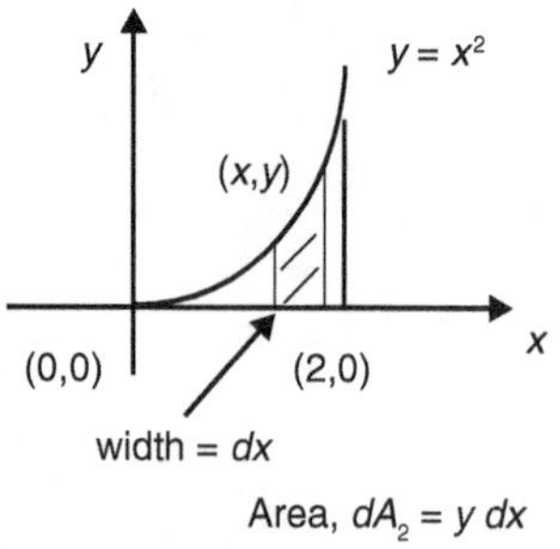

Exhibit 3.23a

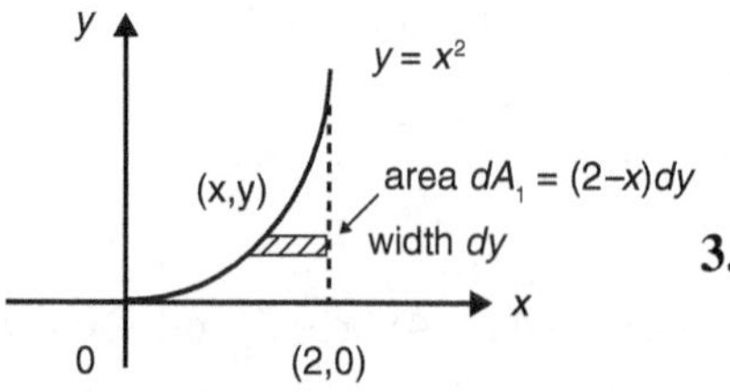

Exhibit 3.24

3.23 b. In Exhibit 3.23a, area $dA_2 = ydx$.

$$\text{Shaded area} = \int dA_2 = \int_{x=0}^{2} y.dx = \int_{x=0}^{2} x^2 dx = \frac{8}{3}$$

3.24 c. In Exhibit 3.24, area $dA_1 = (2 - x)dy$.

First moment with respect to x-axis of this area $dM_x = y\, dA_1$

First moment with respect to x-axis of shaded area is

$$M_x = \int dM_x = \int_{y=0}^{4} y(2-x)dy = \int_{0}^{4} y(2-\sqrt{y})dy = 3.2$$

3.25 d. From Exhibit 3.23a, first moment with respect to y-axis of the shaded area dA_2 is $dM_y = x\, dA_2 = xy\, dx$; first moment with respect to y-axis of shaded area is

$$M_y = \int dM_y = \int_{x=0}^{2} x.y.dx = \int_{0}^{2} x.x^2 dx = 4$$

3.26 a. x-coordinate $x_c = \dfrac{M_y}{area} = \dfrac{4}{2.67} = 1.5$; y-coordinate y_c

$$= \frac{M_x}{area} = \frac{3.2}{2.67} = 1.2$$

3.27 a. From Exhibit 3.24, moment of inertia with respect to x-axis of area dA_1 is $dMI_x = y^2 dA_1$. Moment of inertia with respect to x-axis of shaded area:

$$MI_x = \int dMI_x = \int y^2 dA_1 = \int_{y=0}^{4} y^2(2-x)dy = \int_{0}^{4} y^2(2-\sqrt{y})dy$$

Integrating, $MI_x = 6.095$.

3.28 d. From Exhibit 3.23a, moment of inertia with respect to y-axis of area dA_2 is $dMI_y = x^2 dA_2$. Moment of inertia with respect to y-axis of shaded area:

$$MI_y = \int dMI_y = \int x^2 dA_2 = \int_{x=0}^{2} x^2.ydx = \int_{x=0}^{2} x^4 dx = 6.4$$

3.29 b. Homogeneous solution, $y_h(x) = e^{-4x}(C_1 \cos 4x + C_2 \sin 4x)$ or $e^{-4x}\, C_3 \cos(4x + \theta)$

3.30 d. Since the characteristic roots are –2 and –2, the particular solution is $y_p(x) = A\, x^2 e^{-2x}$.

3.31 **a.** The characteristic equation is $r^2 + 5r + 6 = 0$ and the characteristic roots are –2, –3. Then, the homogeneous solution is $y_h(x) = c_1e^{-2x} + c_2e^{-3x}$.

The particular solution due to e^{-2x} is $y_p(x) = Bxe^{-2x}$.

[As –2 is a characteristic root, e^{-2x} cannot be a particular solution.]

$y_p' = -2Be^{-2x}.x + Be^{-2x}$ and $y_p'' = 4Be^{-2x}.x - 2Be^{-2x} - 2Be^{-2x}$

$y_p'' + 5y_p' + 6y = 2e^{-2x}$ yields $B = 2$

$y(x) = 2e^{-2x}x + c_1e^{-2x} + c_2e^{-3x}$ $\quad y(0) = c_1 + c_2 = 0 \quad c_1 = -2$

$y'(x) = 2e^{-2x} - 4xe^{-2x} - 2c_1e^{-2x} - 3c_22e^{-3x}$ $\quad y'(0) = 2 - 2c_1 - 3c_2 = 0 \quad c_2 = 2$

The solution is $y = -2e^{-2x} + 2e^{-3x} + 2xe^{-2x}$.

3.32 **a.**

$$\lim_{x\to1}\frac{x^2-1}{x-1} = \lim_{x\to1}\frac{(x-1)(x+1)}{x-1} = \lim_{x\to1}(x+1) = 2$$

3.33 **b.** This is linear equation, $y' + \frac{2}{x}y = \frac{1}{x}e^{3x}$. The integrating factor is $e\int\frac{2}{x}dx = x^2$ so the equation becomes $d(x^2y) = xe^{3x}\,dx$. Integrating,

$x^2y = \frac{1}{3}xe^{3x} - \frac{1}{9}e^{3x} + c$, or $y = \frac{1}{3x}e^{3x} - \frac{1}{9x^2}e^{3x} + \frac{c}{x^2}$.

3.34 **a.** By inspection, $y_1 = e^x$ is one solution. Use reduction of order to obtain

$$\left(\frac{y_2}{y_1}\right)' = \frac{e^{\int\frac{-2(x+1)}{x}dx}}{y_1^2} = \frac{e^{2x+2\ln x}}{e^{2x}} = x^2$$

Hence $\frac{y_2}{y_1} = \frac{x^3}{3}$, so $y_2 = \frac{x^3}{3}y_1$. Suppressing the $\frac{1}{3}$, $y_2 = x^3e^x$.

3.35 **d.** The associated homogeneous equation, $y'' + 4y = 0$, has the solution $y_h = A\sin 2x + B\cos 2x$. Using the method of undetermined coefficients,

$$\begin{aligned}
y_p &= a\sin x + b\cos x\\
y_p'' &= -a\sin x - b\cos x\\
y_p'' + 4y_p &= (-a+4a)\sin x + (-b+4b)\cos x = 8\sin x\\
3a\sin x &= 8\sin x\\
3b\cos x &= 0\cos x
\end{aligned}$$

Thus, $b = 0$ and $a = \frac{8}{3}$.

3.36 d. Begin by eliminating c by solving for it from the derivative of the given equation: $2x + 2yy' = 2cy'$, $c = \dfrac{x + yy'}{y'}$,

$$x^2 + y^2 = 2\frac{x + yy'}{y'}y',\ x^2y' + y^2y' = 2xy + 2y^2y', \text{ and}$$

$$y' = \frac{2xy}{x^2 - y^2}.$$

Now, the orthogonal family will have $y'_{\text{new}} = -\dfrac{1}{y'_{\text{old}}}$, so $y'_{\text{old}} = \dfrac{y^2 - x^2}{2xy}$.

Letting $u = \dfrac{y}{x}$, $xu' + u = \dfrac{u^2 - 1}{2u}$, $xu' = \dfrac{u^2 - 1 - 2u^2}{2u} = -\dfrac{1 + u^2}{2u}$,

and $\dfrac{2u\,du}{1 + u^2} = -\dfrac{dx}{x}$. Integrating, $\ln(1 + u^2) = -\ln|x| + c$, and

$$\ln\left\{\left[1 + \left(\frac{y}{x}\right)^2\right]|x|\right\} = c$$

$$\left|x + \frac{y^2}{x}\right| = e^c = c_1 > 0, \quad \text{or} \quad x + \frac{y^2}{x} = c_2\ (= \pm c_1)$$

Thus $x^2 + y^2 = c_2x$, or $x^2 + y^2 = 2cx$.

3.37 b. Using Laplace transform table, the transform is $\dfrac{(s + 1)}{(s + 1)^2 + 1^2}$.

3.38 c. Taking the Laplace transform of the differential equation and simplifying,

$$s^2Y(s) + 2sY(s) + Y(s) = \frac{s}{s^2 + 2^2} \Rightarrow Y(s) = \frac{s}{(s^2 + 4)(s^2 + 2s + 1)}$$

3.39 d. Initial value, $\lim\limits_{t \to 0} f(t) = \lim\limits_{s \to \infty} s\dfrac{(s + 5)}{s(s + 1)(s + 10)} = 0$

3.40 c. $y(k) = 2y(k - 1) + 3y(k - 2)$ with $y(-1) = 1$ and $y(-2) = 1$
For $k = 0$, $y(0) = 2y(-1) + 3y(-2) = 2(1) + 3(1) = 5$
For $k = 1$, $y(1) = 2y(0) + 3y(-1) = 2(5) + 3(1) = 13$

3.41 a. $y(k+1) + y(k) = u(k)$; taking Z-transform, $[z\,y(z) - 0] + y(z)$

$= \dfrac{1}{1 - z^{-1}}$. Simplifying, $y(z) = \dfrac{z}{(z - 1)(z + 2)}$.

3.42 d. Using the initial value theorem, the initial value,

$$\lim_{k \to 0} f(k) = \lim_{z \to \infty} \frac{z + 2}{z - 4} = 1$$

3.43 **c.** Period T = 4 s; $\omega_0 = \frac{2\pi}{T} = \frac{\pi}{2}$ rad/s;

$$b_3 = \frac{2}{4}\left[\int_0^2 8\sin\left(\frac{3\pi t}{2}\right)dt + \int_2^4 -8\sin\left(\frac{3\pi t}{2}\right)dt\right] = \frac{16}{3\pi}(1-\cos 3\pi) = 3.40$$

3.44 **d.** Since the pulse width is 2, $\tau = 1$ and from the Table, $X(f) = f\,\text{sinc}^2(f)$.

3.45 **c.** Using time shift theorem for Fourier transforms,

$X(f) = 1\exp(-j2\pi f) + 1\exp(+j2\pi f) = 2\cos(2\pi f)$

3.46 **c.** Substituting $k = 0$, $y(0) = 2y(-1) + 3y(-2) = 2 + 3 = 5$

Substituting $k = 1$, $y(1) = 2y(0) + 3y(-1) = 10 + 3 = 13$

3.47 **c.** Final value $= \lim_{k\to\infty} f(k) = \lim_{z\to 1}(1-z^{-1})F(z) = \lim_{z\to 1}(1-z^{-1})\frac{2(z+1)}{(z-1)} = 4$

CHAPTER 4

Engineering Probability and Statistics

OUTLINE

SETS AND SET OPERATIONS

A set is any well-defined list, collection, or class of objects. The objects in a set can be anything: numbers, letters, cards, people, and so on. They are called the **elements**, or **members**, of a set.

The name of a set is usually denoted by a capital letter, such as A, B, Y, Z. The elements of a set are usually denoted by small letters, such as a, b, y, z.

To specify that an element a is a member of a set B, we say "a is in B," which is written

$$a \in B$$

A set is called the **null**, or **empty**, set, denoted by ø, if it has no elements. We say the set A is a subset of the set B, written $A \subset B$, if all the members of A are also in B. The universal set, denoted by U, is the set that contains all the members of the subsets. The **complement** of a set A, denoted as A', consists of all the elements in U that are not in A.

Sets are defined in either of two ways: (1) by listing the members in a tabular form (for example, if A consists of the numbers 1, 3, 5, and 7, we write $A = \{1, 3, 5, 7\}$), or (2) by stating the properties that the members must satisfy in a set-builder form. For example, a set B containing all the odd numbers is written $B = \{x|x \text{ is odd}\}$, where x is an element of the set and the vertical line "|" is read "such that." The full notation is read "B is the set of numbers x such that x is odd."

Example 4.1

Define the set R of all outcomes of the roll of a six-sided die.

Solution

$R = \{1, 2, 3, 4, 5, 6\}$

Example 4.2

Let U be the set of integers. Define the complement of $B = \{x|x \text{ is odd}\}$.

Solution

$B' = \{x|x \text{ is even}\}$

Set Operations

The **union** of two sets A and B is defined as the set of all elements in either A or B and is traditionally written as $A \cup B$ or, alternatively, as A or B.

The **intersection** of two sets A and B is defined as the set of all elements in both A and B and is traditionally written $A \cap B$.

Set operations are well-behaved mathematically and follow these laws:

identity $\quad A \cup 0 = A \quad A \cup U = U$
$\quad A \cap 0 = 0 \quad A \cap A = A$

complement $\quad A \cup A' = U \quad (A')' = A \quad A \cap A' = 0 \quad U' = 0$

commutative $\quad A \cup B = B \cup A \quad A \cap B = B \cap A$

associative $\quad (A \cup B) \cup C = A \cup (B \cup C)$
$\quad (A \cap B) \cap C = A \cap (B \cap C)$

distributive $\quad A \cup (B \cap C) = (A \cup B) \cap (A \cup C)$
$\quad A \cap (B \cup C) = (A \cap B) \cup (A \cap C)$

de Morgan's Law $\quad (A \cup B)' = A' \cap B'$
$\quad (A \cap B)' = A' \cup B'$

For example, define the following sets:

$U = \{x \mid x \text{ is a person}\}$

$A = \{a \mid a \text{ is American}\}$

$F = \{f \mid f \text{ is French}\}$

$B = \{b \mid b \text{ is a person with dual French and American citizenship}\}$

Then the union of the sets A and F is the set of all people who are either American or French and is written $A \cup F$. The set of people who are not American is A'. The set of people who are not French is F'.

The set of people who are not French and not American is $A' \cap F'$. This is the same as $(A \cup F)'$, according to de Morgan's Law. In this example, de Morgan's Law means that all the people who are neither American nor French is the same as the set of all the people who are not French and not American.

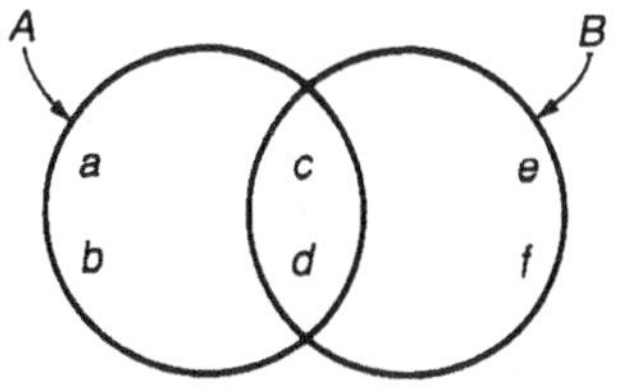

Figure 4.1

Venn Diagrams

A simple and intuitive way to represent these set relationships is known as the **Venn diagram**. Here we represent a set by a closed area and an element in the set by a point in the area. For example, let $A = \{a, b, c, d\}$ and $B = \{c, d, e, f\}$; the sets are represented in a **Venn diagram** as shown in Figure 4.1.

Relational properties such as the intersection of A and $B = \{c, d\}$ are intuitively understood as the overlap of two regions.

Example 4.3

Draw a Venn diagram of the relationship between the sets $U, A, F,$ and B as defined in the previous section.

Solution

1. $A \subset U$. Americans are a subset of people (Exhibit 1).
2. $A \cup F$ is the set of Americans and French (Exhibit 2).
3. $B = A \cap F$ is the intersection of two sets; it represents Americans who are also French (Exhibit 3).

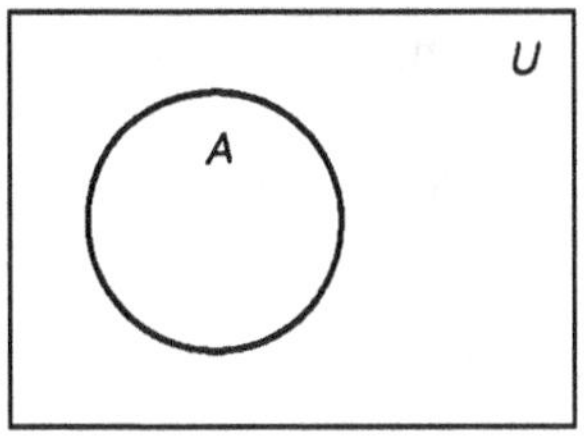

Exhibit 1

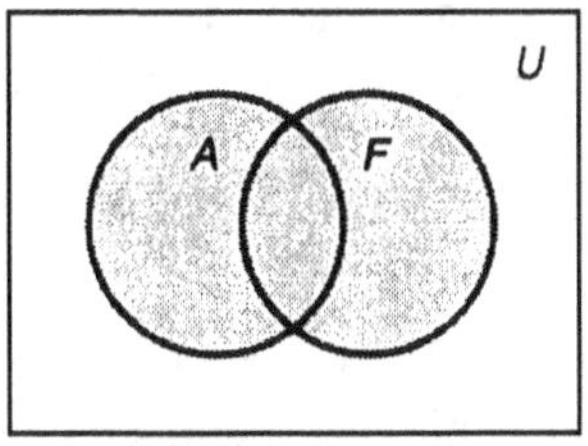

Exhibit 2

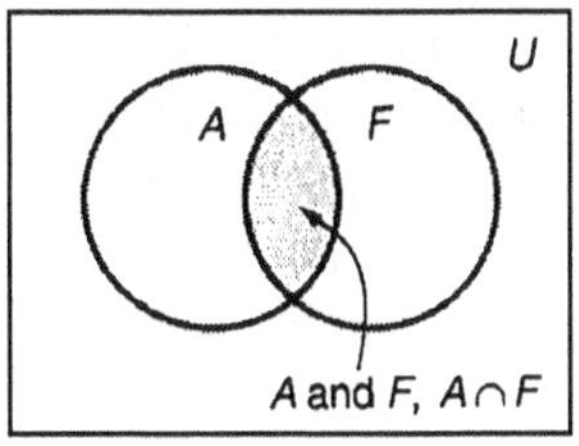

Exhibit 3

Product Sets

An ordered pair of elements a and b is denoted by (a, b). Two ordered pairs (a, b) and (c, d) are equal only if $a = c$ and $b = d$. For example, the ordered pairs (3, 4) and (4, 3) are different.

The product x of two sets A and B is denoted by $A \times B$ and consists of all ordered pairs of elements in A and B.

The two subsets of a product set can be treated like the intersection of two Cartesian coordinate axes. The subsets each act like a dimension, and the product set can be represented as a matrix where the elements of one subset are written along the row of the matrix and those of the other along the column.

For example, the set of results of a single coin toss is either heads (H) or tails (T) and is defined $R = \{H, T\}$. The result of two coin tosses is the product $R \times R$ and is defined as

$$R \times R = \{(H, H), (H, T), (T, H), (T, T)\}$$

COUNTING SETS

For discrete probability calculations it is important to count the number of elements in sets of possible outcomes. The primary method is simply to write down all the elements in a set and count them. For example, count the number of elements in the set S of all possible outcomes of a six-sided die throw. The set definition is $S = \{1, 2, 3, 4, 5, 6\}$. Simple counting gives six elements.

Most useful sets are large, and simple counting is too time-consuming. There are several methods for simplifying this task. One can use the product set concept introduced in the last section. If A is a set with n elements and B is a set with m elements, then the product set $A \times B$ has the arithmetic $n \times m$ number of elements. To simplify counting then, first count the sets making up the product set (usually containing a much smaller number of elements) and simply multiply these counts.

Example 4.4

Count the number of possible outcomes for tossing five coins.

Solution

The number of outcomes for a single toss defined by the set $R = \{H, T\}$ is 2. The result of five coin tosses is the product set $R \times R \times R \times R \times R$. The total number of possible outcomes is then the arithmetic product of the number of outcomes in each of the individual five tosses. This is $2 \times 2 \times 2 \times 2 \times 2 = 2^5 = 32$.

Permutations

If A is a set with n elements, a **permutation** of A is an ordered arrangement of A. Given the set $A = \{a, b, c\}$, the order a, b, c of the elements is one permutation. Any other order—for example, b, c, a—is another permutation.

The set B of all permutations of the set A is defined as the set of all arrangements of the three elements. These are

$$B = \{\{a, b, c\}, \{a, c, b\}, \{c, b, a\}, \{b, a, c\}, \{b, c, a\}, \{c, a, b\}\}$$

There are six permutations. This number also can be derived as follows. The number of ways an element can be chosen for the first space is three. Then there are two elements left. One of these can go in the second space. Then there is one element left. This must go in the third space. This gives the formula $3 \times 2 \times 1 = 6$. In general, the number of ways n distinct elements can be arranged is given by

$$n! = n \times (n-1) \times (n-2) \times \cdots 1$$

and is called the **factorial** of the number n. The factorial of 0 is 1 ($0! = 1$).

For example, count the number of ways a standard playing deck can be arranged. Since there are 52 distinct cards in a deck, there are 52! different arrangements, or permutations.

Now suppose we have the set of letters L in the word *obtuse* so that $L = \{o, b, t, u, s, e\}$. How many two-letter symbols could be made from this set? Notice that the letters are all distinct. We again count the number of ways the letters can be selected. For the first choice it is six; for the second choice it is five. The two selections are now complete. There are therefore $6 \times 5 = 30$ possibilities.

The general formula for the number of permutations, taking r items from a set of n, is given by

$$P(n, r) = n!/(n-r)!$$

Using this equation, one can express the previous example as $P(6, 2) = 6!/(6-2)! = 30$.

Example 4.5

A jeweler has nine different beads and a bracelet design that requires four beads. To find out which looks the best, he decides to try all the permutations. How many different bracelets will he have to try?

Solution

There are $n = 9$ beads. He selects $r = 4$ at a time. The order is important, because each arrangement of r beads on the bracelet makes a different bracelet. So the number of different bracelets is

$$P(9, 4) = 9!/(9-4)! = 9\times 8\times 7\times 6 = 3024$$

If the bracelet is a closed circle, there is no discernible difference when it is rotated. Then one observes four identical states for each unique bracelet. This is called ring permutation and is given by the formula

$$P_{\text{ring}}(n, r) = P(n, r)/r$$

There are only $3024/4 = 756$ distinct ring bracelets the jeweler can make.

Example 4.6

(i) In how many ways can four people be asked to form a line of three people?
(ii) In how many ways can the letters of the word BEAUTY be arranged?
(iii) In how many ways can the letters of the word GOOD be arranged?

Solution

(i) $P(4,3) = \dfrac{4!}{(4-3)!} = 24$

(ii) $P(6,6) = \dfrac{6!}{(6-6)!} = 720$

(iii) $P(4;1,1,2) = \dfrac{4!}{1!1!2!} = 12$

Combinations

When the order of the set of r things that are selected from the set of n things does not matter, we talk about combinations.

Again consider the standard playing deck of 52 cards. How many hands of 5 cards can we get from a deck of 52 cards? Count the number of ways the hands can be drawn. The first draw can be any of the 52 cards. The second draw can only be one of the remaining 51 cards. The third draw can only be one of the remaining 50, the next is one of 49, the last one of 48. So the result is

$$52 \times 51 \times 50 \times 49 \times 48 = 52!/(52-5)!$$

This is the formula for permutations discussed in the last section. But the order in which we receive the cards is not important, so many of the hands are the same. In fact there are 5! similar arrangements of cards that make the same hand. The number of distinct hands is

$$(52 \times 51 \times 50 \times 49 \times 48)/(5 \times 4 \times 3 \times 2 \times 1) = 52!/[5! \times (52 - 5)!]$$

The general form r items taken from a set of n items when order is not important is written as the binomial coefficient $C(n, r)$, also written $\binom{n}{r}$, and is given by the formula

$$C(n,r) = \frac{n!}{r!(n-r)!}$$

Example 4.7

There are six skiers staying in a cabin with four bunks. How many combinations of people will be able to sleep in beds?

Solution

$C(6, 4) = 6!/[4! \times (6 - 4)!] = (6 \times 5 \times 4 \times 3 \times 2 \times 1)/[(4 \times 3 \times 2 \times 1) \times (2 \times 1)] = 15$

PROBABILITY

Definitions

An **experiment**, or **trial**, is an action that can lead to a measurement.

Sampling is the act of taking a measurement. The **sample space** S is the set of all possible outcomes of an experiment (trial). An event e is one of the possible outcomes of the trial.

If an experiment can occur in n mutually exclusive and equally likely ways, and if m of these ways correspond to an event e, then the probability of the event is given by

$$P\{e\} = m/n$$

Example 4.8

A die is a cube of six faces designated as 1 through 6. The set of outcomes R of one die roll is defined as $R = \{1, 2, 3, 4, 5, 6\}$. If two dice are rolled, define trial, sample space, n, m, and the probability of rolling a seven when adding both dice together.

Solution

The trial is the rolling of two dice. The sample space is all possible outcomes of a two-dice roll, and the event is the outcome that the sum is 7.

The number of all possible outcomes, n, is the number of elements in the product set of the outcome of two dice when each is rolled independently. The product set is $R \times R$ and contains 36 elements.

The number of all possible ways, m, that the (7) event can occur is (1,6), (2,5), (3,4), (4,3), (5,2), and (6,1) for a total of six ways. The probability of rolling a 7 is $P\{7\} = \frac{6}{36} = \frac{1}{6}$.

Example 4.9

What is the probability of (i) a tail showing up when a fair coin is tossed, (ii) number 3 showing up when a fair die is tossed, and (iii) a red king is drawn from a deck of 52 cards.

Solution

(i) 1/2 (ii) 1/6 (iii) 2/52

General Character of Probability

The probability $P\{E\}$ of an event E is a real number in the range 0 through 1. Two theorems identify the range between which all probabilities are defined:

1. If ø is the null set, $P\{ø\} = 0$.
2. If S is the sample space, $P\{S\} = 1$.

The first states that the probability of an impossible event is zero, and the second states that, if an event is certain to occur, the probability is 1.

Complementary Probabilities

If E and E' are complementary events, $P\{E\} = 1 - P\{E'\}$. Complementary events are defined with respect to the sample space. The probability that an event E will happen is complementary to the probability that any of the other possible outcomes will happen.

Example 4.10

If the probability of throwing a 3 on a die is 1/6, what is the probability of not throwing a 3?

Solution

E is the probability of not throwing a 3, so $P\{E\} = 1 - P\{E'\} = 1 - \frac{1}{6} = \frac{5}{6}$.

Sometimes the complementary property of probabilities can be used to simplify calculations. This will happen when seeking the probability of an event that represents a larger fraction of the sample space than its complement.

Example 4.11

What is the probability $P\{E\}$ of getting at least one head in four coin tosses?

Solution

The complementary event $P\{E'\}$ to getting at least one head is getting no heads (or all tails) in four tosses. So the probability of getting at least one head is

$$P\{E\} = 1 - (0.5)^4 = 1 - 0.0625 = 0.9375$$

Joint Probability

The probability that a combination of events will occur is covered by joint probability rules. If E and F are two events, the joint probability is given by the rule

$$P\{E \cup F\} = P\{E\} + P\{F\} - P\{E \cap F\} \qquad \text{(Rule 1)}$$

A special case of the joint probability rule can be derived by considering two events, E and F, to be mutually exclusive. In this case the last term in Rule 1 is zero since $P\{E \cap F\} = P\{0\} = 0$. Thus, if E and F are mutually exclusive events,

$$P\{E \cup F\} = P\{E\} + P\{F\} \qquad \text{(Rule 2)}$$

Example 4.12

What is the probability of throwing a 7 or a 10 with two dice?

Solution

We will call the event of throwing a 7 A, and of throwing a 10 B. We know from previous examples that $P\{A\} = \frac{1}{6}$, and we can count outcomes to get $P\{B\} = \frac{1}{12}$. Applying the formula,

$$P\{A \cup B\} = P\{A\} + P\{B\} = \frac{1}{6} + \frac{1}{12} = \frac{1}{4}$$

If two events E and F are independent—that is, if they come from different sample spaces—then the probability that both will happen is given by the rule

$$P\{E \cap F\} = P\{E\} \times P\{F\} \qquad \text{(Rule 3)}$$

Example 4.13

What is the probability of throwing two heads in two coin tosses?

Solution

Call the throwing of one head E, the other F. The probability of throwing a single head is $P\{E\} = \frac{1}{2}$, and $P\{F\} = \frac{1}{2}$. The probability of throwing both heads is

$$P\{E \cap F\} = P\{E\} \times P\{F\} = \frac{1}{2} \times \frac{1}{2} = \frac{1}{4}$$

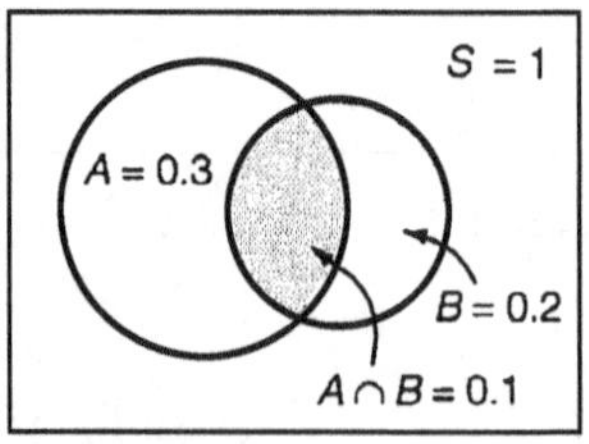

Figure 4.2
Venn diagram of joint probabilities

To visualize joint probabilities, we can use a Venn diagram showing two intersecting events, A and B, as shown in Figure 4.2. Let the normalized areas of each event represent the probability that the event will occur. For example, think of a random dart thrown at the Venn diagram: What are the chances of hitting one of the areas? Assume the areas correspond to probabilities and are given by $P\{S\} = 1$, $P\{A\} = 0.3$, $P\{B\} = 0.2$, and $P\{A \cap B\}$ is 0.6. The probability of hitting either area A or area B is calculated as the sum of the areas A and B minus the overlap area so it is not counted twice:

$$P\{A \cup B\} = 0.3 + 0.2 - .06 = .44$$

The result is also equal to the normalized area covered by A and B. The probability of hitting both A and B on one throw is simply the overlap area $P\{A \cap B\} = 0.1$.

If we throw two darts, the area S is used twice and represents two independent sample spaces. Hence Rule 3 applies.

Example 4.14

A die is tossed. Event A = {an odd number shows up}; event B = {a number > 4 shows up}.

(i) Find the probabilities, P(A) and P(B). (ii) What is the probability that either A or B or both occur?

Solution

(i) P(A) = P(1 or 3 or 5 showing up) = 3 (1/6) = 0.5
P(B) = P(5 or 6 showing up) = 2 (1/6) = 0.333

(ii) Event (A, B) = {5} and P(A, B) = 1/6;
then P(A + B) = P(A) + P(B) – P(AB) = 1/2 + 2/6 – 1/6 = 4/6
Check: Event (A + B) = {1,3,5,6}; then P(A + B) = 4/6

Conditional Probability

The conditional probability of an event E given an event F is denoted by $P\{E \mid F\}$ and is defined as

$$P\{E \mid F\} = P\{E \cap F\}/P\{F\} \qquad \text{for } P\{F\} \text{ not zero}$$

Example 4.15

Two six-sided dice, one red and one green, are tossed. What is the probability that the green die shows a 1, given that the sum of numbers on both dice is less than 4?

Solution

Let E be the event "green die shows 1" and let F be the event "sum of numbers shows less than four." Then

$$E = \{(1,1), (1,2), (1,3), (1,4), (1,5), (1,6)\}$$
$$F = \{(1,1), (1,2), (2,1)\}$$
$$E \cap F = \{(1,1), (1,2)\}$$
$$P\{E \mid F\} = P\{E \cap F\}/P\{F\} = (2/36)/(3/36) = 2/3$$

The generalized form of conditional probability is known as Bayes' theorem and is stated as follows: If $E_1, E_2, \ldots, E_n$ are n mutually exclusive events whose union is the sample space S, and E is any arbitrary event such that $P\{E\}$ is not zero, then

$$P\{E_k \mid E\} = \frac{P\{E_k\} \times P\{E \mid E_k\}}{\sum_{j=1}^{n} [P\{E_j\} \times P\{E \mid E_j\}]}$$

PROBABILITY SUMMARY

We can use different rules to find the probability of an event.

Rule 1:

$$P(A) + P(A') = 1$$

where A is the event, A' is the complement.

Rule 2:

For mutually exclusive events (disjoint events):

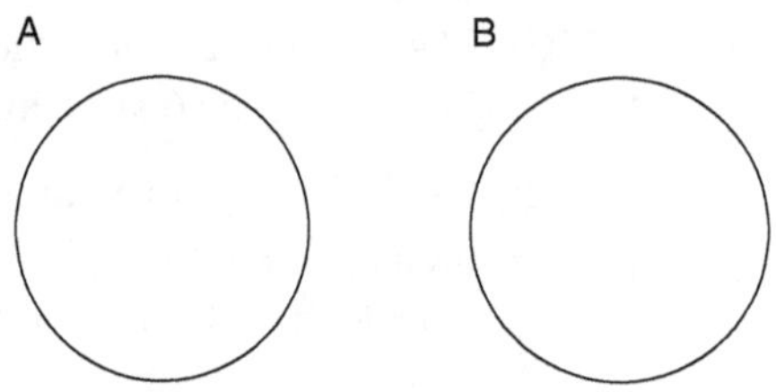

Figure 4.3 Property 2. Law of Total Probability

$$P(A + B) = P(A) + P(B) - P(A, B)$$

where

$P(A + B)$ = the probability that either A or B occur alone or that both occur together
$P(A)$ = the probability that A occurs
$P(B)$ = the probability that B occurs
$P(A, B)$ = the probability that both A and B occur simultaneously

In our case $P(A + B) = 0$ so $P(A + B) = P(A) + P(B)$

Rule 3:

For nonexclusive events (joint events):

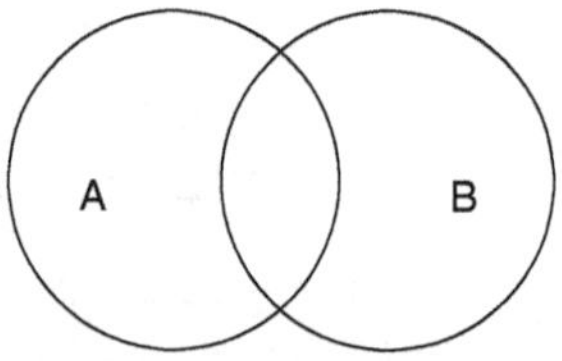

Figure 4.4 Venn diagram of joint events

$$P(A + B) = P(A) + P(B) - P(A, B)$$

In our case, $P(A, B)$ is the intersection of A and B.

Rule 4:

For independent events:

$$P(A, B) = P(A)P(B)$$

the intersection of A and B in the Venn Diagram.

If the events are not independent, then
Property 3. Law of Compound or Joint Probability

If neither $P(A)$ nor $P(B)$ is zero,

$$P(A, B) = P(A)P(B \mid A) = P(B)P(A \mid B)$$

where

$P(B \mid A)$ = the probability that B occurs given the fact that A has occured
$P(A \mid B)$ = the probability that A occurs given the fact that B has occured

If either $P(A)$ or $P(B)$ is zero, then $P(A, B) = 0$

Example 4.16

A fruit bowl contains five bananas, four apples, one orange, and two peaches. If a fruit is chosen from the bowl, find:

a). P (choosing a banana)

b). P (choosing a peach or an apple)

c). P (not choosing an apple)

Solution

B for bananas, number of bananas $n(B) = 5$

A for apples, number of apples $n(A) = 4$

O for orange, number of oranges $n(O) = 1$

P for peaches, number of peaches $n(P) = 2$

The total number of fruits in the fruit bowl is 12.

$$n(S) = 12$$

So, the P(choosing a banana) $= P(B)$

$$P(B) = \frac{n(B)}{n(S)} = \frac{5}{12}$$

$$P(A) = \frac{n(A)}{n(S)} = \frac{4}{12} = \frac{1}{3}$$

$$P(O) = \frac{n(O)}{n(S)} = \frac{1}{12}$$

$$P(P) = \frac{n(P)}{n(S)} = \frac{2}{12} = \frac{1}{6}$$

a). $P(\text{choosing a banana}) = P(B) = \dfrac{n(B)}{n(S)} = \dfrac{5}{12}$

b). $P(\text{choosing a peach or apple}) = P(P + A) = P(P) + P(A) - P(P, A)$,

but there is no intersection of peach and apple so $P(P, A) = 0$, so

$$P(P+A) = P(P) + P(A) + 0 = \frac{1}{6} + \frac{1}{3} = \frac{1}{2}$$

c). $P(\text{not choosing an apple}) = 1 - P(A) = 1 - \frac{1}{3} = \frac{2}{3}$

Example 4.17

A bag contains 12 red marbles and 8 black marbles. Two marbles are taken out in succession. Their colors are recorded and neither is replaced. What is the probability that:

a). both marbles will be red?

b). both marbles will be either red or black?

Solution

In this problem, once the marble is taken out, it is not placed back in the bag. This process is called **sampling without replacement**.

At the beginning, there are 20 marbles in the bag.

Let's take $R = \{\text{red marbles}\}$, $n(R) = 12$ and $B = \{\text{black marbles}\}$, $n(B) = 8$.

Total number of marbles $n(S) = 20$.

This problem can be shown in a probability tree diagram.

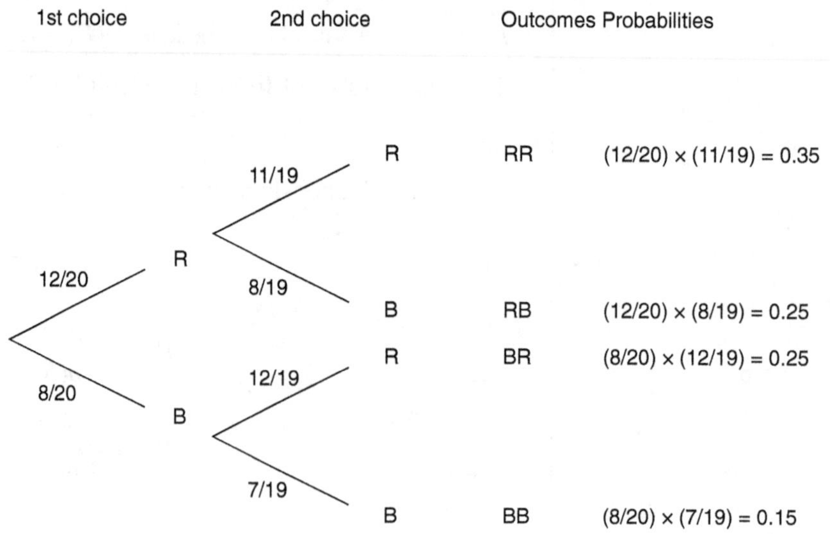

Exhibit 4 Probability outcomes

Example 4.18

A bag contains 12 red marbles and 8 black marbles. Two marbles are taken out in succession. Their colors are recorded and the marbles are replaced into the bag. What is the probability that:

a). both marbles will be red?

b). both marbles will be either red or black?

Solution:

In this problem, once the marble is taken out and its color recorded, it is placed back in the bag. This process is called **sampling with replacement**.

This problem can be shown in a probability tree diagram.

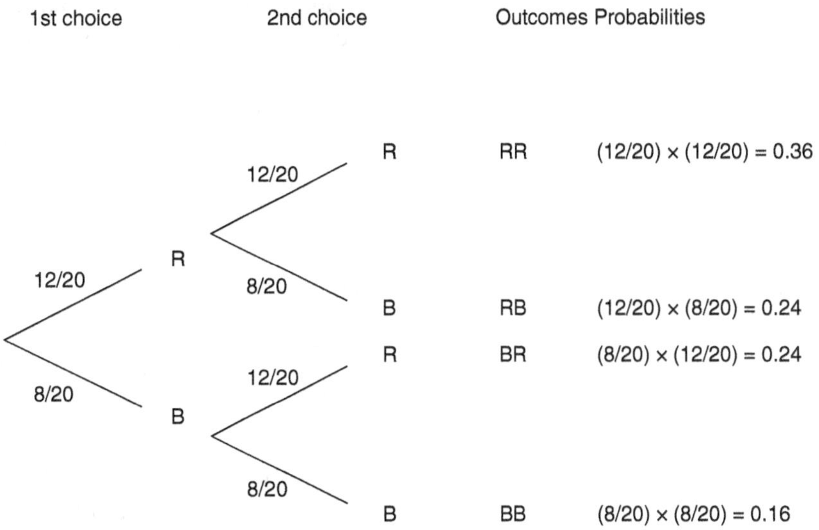

Exhibit 5 Probability outcomes with sample replacement

RANDOM VARIABLES

The method of random variables is a powerful concept. It casts the set-theory-based probability calculations of previous sections into a functional form and allows the application of standard mathematical tools to probability theory. It is often easy to solve fairly complex probability problems using random variables, although an approach different from the usual one is required.

A random variable, usually denoted by X, is a mapping of the sample space to some set of real numbers. The mapping transforms points of a sample space into points, or more accurately intervals, on the x-axis. The mapping, or random, variable X is called a discrete random variable if it assumes only a denumerable number of values on the x-axis. A random variable is called a continuous random variable if it assumes a continuum of values on the x-axis. The mapping is usually quite easy and intuitive for numerical events but provides no major advantage for nonnumerical discrete sample spaces, where counting remains the major tool.

Example 4.19

Cast the sample space of the outcomes of a roll of a die into random variable form.

Solution

The sample space is the set R defined by $R = \{1, 2, 3, 4, 5, 6\}$. These can easily by written along the x-axis as

$$R = \{1, 2, 3, 4, 5, 6\} \rightarrow 1 \mid 2 \mid 3 \mid 4 \mid 5 \mid 6 \mid x\text{-axis}$$

Probability Density Functions

A probability density function $f(x)$ is a mathematical rule that assigns a probability to the occurrence of the random variable x. Since the random variable is a mapping from trial outcomes, or events, to the numerical intervals on the x-axis, the probability that an event will occur is the area under the probability density function curve over the x interval defining the event.

For a continuous random variable the probability that an event E, mapped into an interval between x_1 and x_2, will occur is defined as

$$\int_{x_1}^{x_2} f(x)\,dx = P\{E\} \qquad \text{for } E \text{ mapped into } (x_1, x_2)$$

For a discrete case the formula is

$$\sum_{i=1}^{n} f(x_i) = P\{E\} \qquad \text{for } E \text{ containing } x_1, x_2, \ldots, x_n$$

It is assumed here that a step interval is associated with each value of x_i; therefore, the equivalent dx in the integral is 1 and is not required in the sum.

Example 4.20

The probability density function of a single six-sided die throw is shown graphically in Exhibit 6. The probability of throwing a 3 is given by the area under the curve over the interval assigned to the numeral 3, which is the step interval from 2.5 to 3.5.

Hence $P\{3\} = f(x) \times 1 = \frac{1}{6} \times 1 = \frac{1}{6}$.

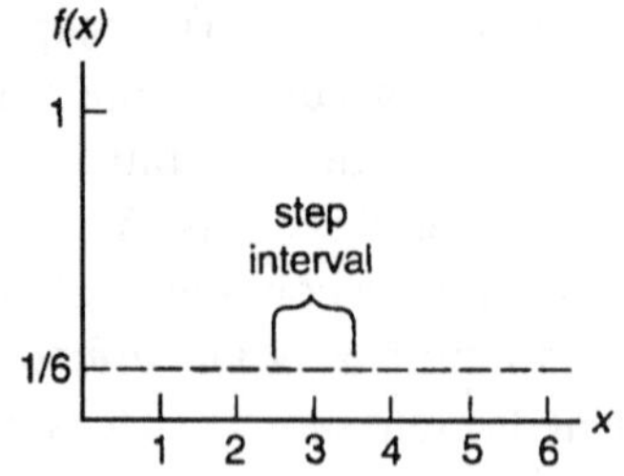

Exhibit 6

Example 4.21

A probability density function is defined as f(x) = Ax2 for –1 < x < 2 and zero elsewhere. Find the value of A so that it is a valid density function.

Solution

For a valid density function, $\int_{-\infty}^{\infty} f(x)\,dx = 1$

Then, $\int_{-1}^{2} Ax^2\,dx = A\frac{9}{3} = 3A = 1$; then $A = \frac{1}{3}$

Properties of Probability Density Functions

The expected value $E\{X\}$ of a probability density function is also called the mean, and for a discrete case it is given by

$$E\{X\} = \sum x_i \times f(x_i) = u$$

The expected value of a continuous random variable is

$$E\{X\} = \int_{-\inf}^{+\inf} x \times f(x) \times dx = u$$

The expected value for a discrete random variable of a function $g(X)$ is given by

$$E\{g(X)\} = \sum g(x_i) \times f(x_i)$$

The expected value of a continuous random variable is

$$E\{g(X)\} = \int_{-\inf}^{+\inf} g(x) \times f(x) \times dx$$

Of special interest are the functions of the form

$$g(x) = (x - u)^r$$

These are the powers of the random variables around the mean. The expected values of these power functions are called the rth moments about the mean of the distribution, where r is the power. The second moment about the mean is also known as the variance and is calculated as follows:

$$V\{X\} = E\{(x-u)^2\} = E\{(x^2 - 2xu + u^2)\} = E\{x^2\} - E\{2xu\} + E\{u^2\}$$

Since u is a constant, the second term is $2u^2$ and the third term evaluates to u^2; therefore, the second moment about the mean becomes

$$V\{X\} = E\{x^2\} - u^2 = \sigma^2$$

The square root of the variance is signified by the Greek letter sigma and is called the **standard deviation**.

Example 4.22

Calculate the mean and standard deviation of a single die throw.

Solution

This is a discrete function and can be calculated numerically by the discrete formulas given above. The mean, where $f(x_i) = \frac{1}{6}$ (all outcomes are equally likely), is given by

$$u = E\{X\} = \sum_{i=1}^{i=6} x_i \times f(x_i) = (1+2+3+4+5+6)/6 = \frac{21}{6} = 3.5$$

The standard deviation is given by

$$\sigma = \sqrt{V\{x\}} = \sqrt{E\{x^2\} - u^2} = \sqrt{[(1^2 + 2^2 + 3^2 + 4^2 + 5^2 + 6^2)/6] - 3.5^2} = 1.7$$

STATISTICAL TREATMENT OF DATA

Whether from the outcome of an experiment or trial, or simply the output of a number generator, we are constantly presented with numerical data. A statistical treatment of such data involves ordering, presentation, and analysis. The tools available for such treatment are generally applicable to a set of numbers and can be applied without much knowledge about the source of the data, although such knowledge is often necessary to make sensible use of the statistical results.

In its raw form, numerical data is simply a list of n numbers denoted by x_i, where $i = 1, 2, 3, \ldots, n$. There is no specific significance associated with the order implicit in the i numbers. They are names for the individuals in the list, although they are often associated with the order in which the raw data was recorded. For example, consider a box of 50 resistors. They are to be used in a sensitive circuit, and their resistances must be measured. The results of the 50 measurements are presented in Table 4.1.

Table 4.1 Table of Raw Measurements (Ω)

101	105	110	115	82
86	91	96	117	112
109	103	89	97	98
101	104	99	95	97
85	90	94	112	107
103	94	98	106	98
114	112	108	101	99
93	96	99	104	90
109	106	101	93	92
104	99	109	100	107

Each number is named by the variable x_i, and there are n = 50 of them. The numbers range from 82 to 117.

Frequency Distribution

A systematic tool used in ordering data is the frequency distribution. The method requires counting the number of occurrences of raw numbers whose values fall within step intervals. The step intervals (or bins) are usually chosen to (1) be of constant size, (2) cover the range of numbers in the raw data, (3) be small enough in quantity to limit the amount of writing yet not have many empty steps, and (4) be sufficient in quantity so that significant information is not lost.

For example, the aforementioned raw data of measured resistances may be ordered in a frequency distribution table such as Table 4.2. Here the step interval is the event E of a random variable that can be mapped onto the x-axis. The set of eight events is the sample space. If we take a number randomly from the raw measurement set, the probability that it will be in bin 5 is

$$f(E_5) = P\{E_5\} = 10/50 = 0.2$$

Table 4.2 Frequency and cumulative frequency table

Event, E_i	Range, Ω	Frequency	Cumulative Frequency	Probability Density Function, $f(E_i)$
1	80–84	1	1	0.02
2	85–89	3	4	0.06
3	90–94	8	12	0.16
4	95–99	12	24	0.24
5	100–104	10	34	0.20
6	105–109	9	43	0.18
7	110–114	5	48	0.10
8	115–119	2	50	0.04

The last column in Table 4.2 is the probability density function of the distribution. The probability table can be plotted along the x-axis in several ways, as shown in Figures 4.5 through 4.7.

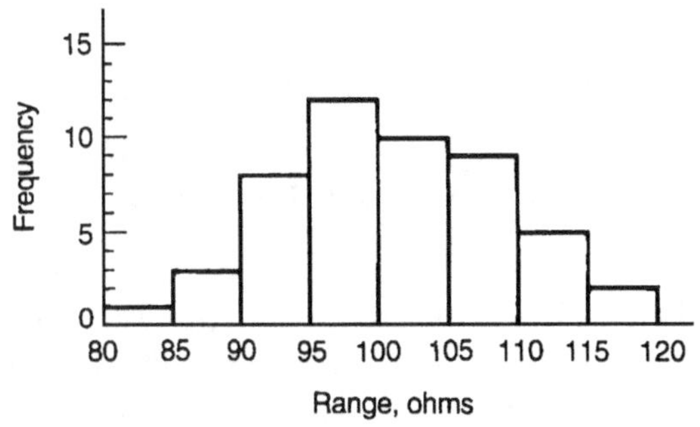

Figure 4.5 Histogram of resistance measurements

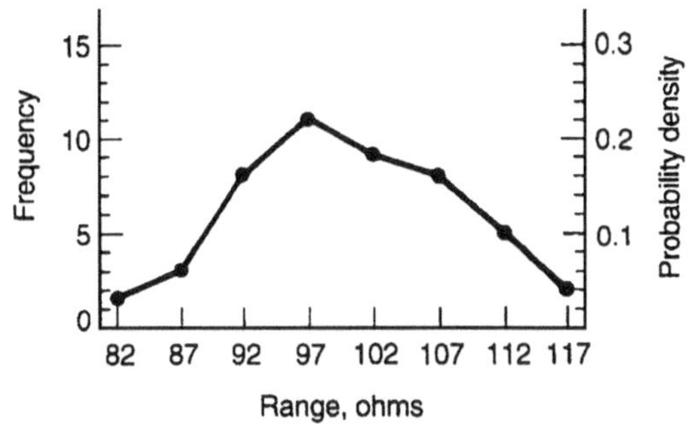

Figure 4.6 Frequency distribution and probability density plot

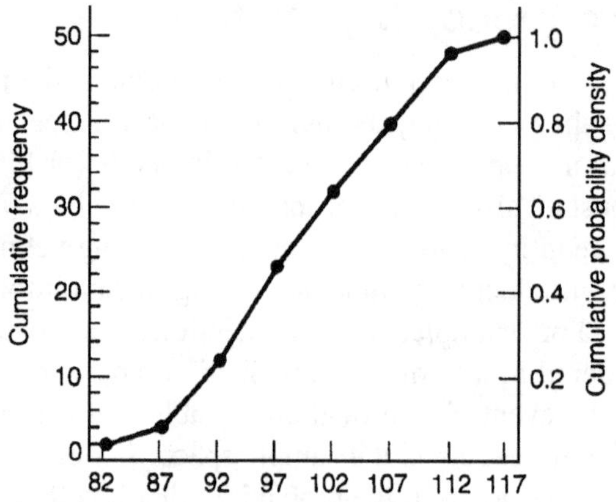

Figure 4.7 Cumulative frequency distribution and cumulative probability density

Standard Statistical Measures

There are several statistical quantities that can be calculated from a set of raw data and its distribution function. Some of the more important ones are listed here, together with the method of their calculation.

Mode The observed value that occurs most frequently; here the mode is bin 4 with a range of 95–99 Ω.

Median The point in the distribution that divides the number of observations such that half of the observations are above and half are below. The median is often the mean of the two middle values; here the median is 4.5 bins, 100 Ω.

Mean The arithmetic mean, or average, is calculated from raw data as

$$\mu = \frac{1}{n}\sum_{i=1}^{n} x_i = 100.6$$

It is calculated from the distribution function as

$$\mu = \sum_{i=1}^{m} b_i \times f(E_i) = 100.4$$

where b_i is the ith event value (for $i = 1$, $b_i = 82$) and m is the number of bins; $f(E_i)$ is the probability density function. (The two averages are not quite the same because of the information lost in assigning the step intervals.)

Standard deviation (a) Computational form for the raw data:

$$\sigma = \sqrt{\frac{1}{n}\left[\left(\sum_{i=1}^{n} x_i^2\right) - n \times \mu^2\right]} = 8.08$$

(b) Computational form for the distribution function:

$$\sigma = \sqrt{\left\{\left[\sum_{i=1}^{m} b_i^2 \times f(E_i)\right] - \mu^2\right\}} = 8.02$$

Sample standard deviation

If the data set is a sample of a larger population, then the sample standard deviation is the best estimate of the standard deviation of the larger population.

The computational form for the raw data set is

$$\sigma = \sqrt{\frac{1}{n-1}\left[\left(\sum_{i=1}^{n} x_i^2\right) - n \times \mu^2\right]} = 8.166$$

Sample standard deviations and the use of $(n - 1)$ in the denominator are discussed in the section on sampling.

Skewness

This is a measure of the frequency distribution asymmetry and is approximately

skewness ≅ 3(mean – median)/(standard deviation)

Example 4.23

Two professors give the following scores to their students. What is the mode and arithmetic mean?

Frequency	1	3	6	11	13	10	2
Score	35	45	55	65	75	85	95

Solution

mode = 75; N = 1 + 3 + 6 + 11 + 13 + 10 + 2 = 46

weighted arithmetic mean = $\overline{X_w} = [35(1) + 45(3) + \ldots 95(2)] / 46 = 70$

STANDARD DISTRIBUTION FUNCTIONS

In the previous section, we calculated several general properties of probability distribution functions.

To know the appropriate probability density function for an actual situation, two general methods are available:

1. The probability density function is actually calculated, as was done in the last section, by analyzing the physical mechanism by which experimental events and outcomes are generated and counting the number of ways an individual event occurs.
2. Recognition of an overall similarity between the present experiment and another for which the probability density function is already known permits the known behavior of the function to be applied to the new experiment. This work-saving method is by far the more popular one. Of course, to apply this method, it is necessary to have a repertoire of known probability functions and to understand the problem characteristics to which they apply.

This section lists several popular probability density functions and their characteristics.

Binomial Distribution

The binomial distribution applies when there is a set of discrete binary alternative outcomes. Deriving this distribution function helps one understand the class of problems to which it applies. For example, given a set of n events, each with a probability p of occurring, what is the probability that r of the events will occur and $(n - r)$ not occur?

The probability of one event occurring is p.

The probability of r events occurring is p^r.

The probability of $(n - r)$ events not occurring is $(1 - p)^{n-r}$.

The probability of exactly r events occurring and $(n - r)$ not occurring in a trial is given by the joint probability Rule 3:

$$P[r \cap (n-r)] = p^r \times (1-p)^{n-r}$$

However, there are many ways of choosing r occurrences out of n events. In fact, the number of different ways of choosing r items from a set of n items when order is not important is given by the binomial coefficient $C(n, r)$. The total probability of r occurrences from n trials, given an individual probability of occurrence as p, is thus given by

$$C(n,r) \times p^r \times (1-p)^{n-r} = f(r)$$

This is the **binomial probability density function.**

The mean of this density function is the first moment of the density function, or expected value, and is calculated as

$$E\{x\} = \sum_{r=0}^{n} r \times f(r) = \sum_{r=0}^{n} r \times \frac{n!}{(r)!(n-r)!} \times p^r \times (1-p)^{n-r}$$

This can be rewritten as

$$\sum_{r=1}^{n} \frac{n!}{(r-1)!(n-r)!} \times p^r \times (1-p)^{n-r}$$

We can now factor out the quantity $n \times p$ and let $r - 1 = y$. This can be rewritten as

$$n \times p \times \sum_{y=0}^{n-1} \frac{(n-1)!}{(y)!(n-1-y)!} \times p^y \times (1-p)^{n-1-y} = n \times p \times [p + (1-p)]^{n-1}$$

Since the sum is merely the expansion of a binomial raised to a power, and the number 1 raised to any power is 1, the mean is

$$\mu = n \times p$$

A similar calculation shows the variance is

$$\text{var} = n \times p \times (1 - p)$$

The standard deviation is

$$\sigma = \sqrt{\text{var}} = \sqrt{n \times p \times (1 - p)}$$

Example 4.24

A truck carrying dairy products and eggs damages its suspension and 5% of the eggs break.

(i) What is the probability that a carton of 12 eggs will have exactly one broken egg?

(ii) What is the probability that one or more eggs in a carton will be broken?

Solution

(i) Since an egg is either broken or not broken, the binomial distribution applies. The probability p that an egg is broken is 0.05 and that one is not broken is $(1 - p) = 0.95$. From the equation for the binomial distribution, with $n = 12$ and $r = 1$,

$$p\{1\} = f(1) = C(12, 1) \times 0.05^1 \times 0.95^{11} = 12 \times 0.05 \times 0.57 = 0.34$$

(ii) The probability that one or more eggs will be broken can be calculated as the sum of each individual probability:

$$p\{x > 0\} = p\{1\} + p\{2\} + \cdots + p\{12\}$$

However, this requires 12 calculations. The problem can also be solved using the complementary rule:

$$p\{x > 0\} = 1 - p\{0\} = C(12, 0) \times 0.05^0 \times 0.95^{12} = 0.95^{12} = 0.54$$

Example 4.25

A biased coin is tossed. Find the probability that a head appears once in three trials.

P(Head) = p = 0.6

Solution

Here q = P(Head not occurring) or P(Tail) = 1 – 0.6 = 0.4.

Then P(1 Head) = C(3,1) 0.6^1 0.4^2 = 0.2880.

Example 4.26

Binomial Distribution

On average, 30% of a certain business's customers are women. Ten customers are chosen at random to be surveyed. The probability that exactly three of them are women is most nearly:

a). 0.16

b). 0.27

c). 0.33

d). 0.42

Solution

$$p = 0.3$$

$$q = 1 - p = 1 - 0.3 = 0.7$$

$$p\{3\} = \left(\frac{n!}{x!(n-x)!}\right) p^x q^{n-x}$$

$$= \left(\frac{10!}{(3!)(10-3)!}\right)(0.3)^3 (0.7)^{10-3}$$

$$= 0.2668$$

The answer is b). 0.27.

Example 4.27

Flights for a certain airline are late 15% of the time. If 10 flights are randomly selected, find the probability that at most one flight will be late.

a). 7.34%

b). 54.4%

c). 19.68%

d). 34.74%

e). 57.54%

$$P(\text{at most } 1) = P(0) + P(1)$$

$$= {}_{10}C_0 (.15)^0 (.85)^{10} + {}_{10}C_1 (.15)^1 (.85)^9$$

$$= 0.197 + 0.347$$

$$= 0.544$$

The answer is b). 54.4.%.

Normal Distribution Function

The normal distribution, or Gaussian distribution, is widely used to represent the distribution of outcomes of experiments and measurements. It is popular because it can be derived from a few empirical assumptions about the errors presumed to cause the distribution of results about the mean. One assumption is that the error is the result of a combination of N elementary errors, each of magnitude e and equally likely to be positive or negative. The derivation then assumes $N \to \infty$ and $e \to 0$ in such a way as to leave the standard deviation constant. This error model is universal, since most experiments are analyzed to eliminate systematic errors. What remains is attributable to errors that are too small to explain systematically, so the normal probability distribution is evoked.

The form of the probability density and distribution functions for the **normal distribution** with a mean μ and variance σ^2 is given by

$$f(x) = \frac{e^{-(x-\mu)^2/2\sigma^2}}{\sigma\sqrt{2\pi}} \qquad -\infty < x < \infty$$

$$F(x) = \int_{-\infty}^{x} \frac{e^{-(x-\mu)^2/2\sigma^2}}{\sigma\sqrt{2\pi}}\, dt$$

The normal distribution is the typical bell-shaped curve shown in Figure 4.8. Here we see that the curve is symmetric about the mean μ. Its width and height are determined by the standard deviation σ. As σ increases, the curve becomes wider and lower.

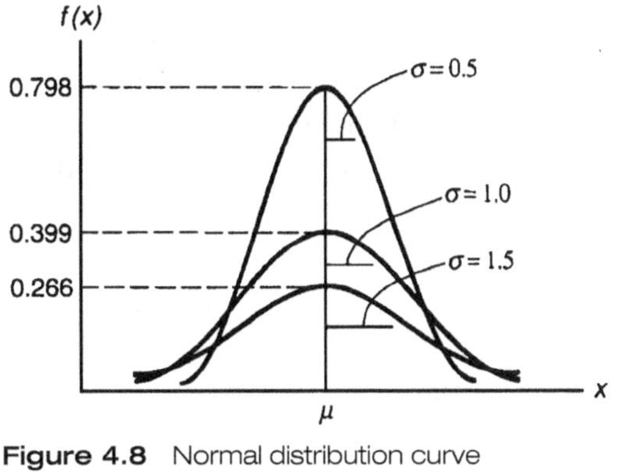

Figure 4.8 Normal distribution curve

Since this function is difficult to integrate, reference tables are used to calculate probabilities in a standard format; then the standard probabilities are converted to the actual variable required by the problem. The relation between the standard variable, z, and a typical problem variable, x, is

$$z = (x - \mu)/\sigma$$

Since μ and σ are constants, the standard probability at a value z is the same as the problem probability for the value at x.

The standard probability density function is

$$f(z) = \frac{1}{\sqrt{2\pi}} \times e^{-z^2/2}$$

Table 4.3 Standard probability table

z	$F(z)$	$f(z)$	z	$F(z)$	$f(z)$
0.0	0.5000	0.3989	2.0	0.9773	0.0540
0.1	0.5398	0.3970	2.1	0.9821	0.0440
0.2	0.5793	0.3910	2.2	0.9861	0.0355
0.3	0.6179	0.3814	2.3	0.9893	0.0283
0.4	0.6554	0.3683	2.4	0.9918	0.0224
0.5	0.6915	0.3521	2.5	0.9938	0.0175
0.6	0.7257	0.3332	2.6	0.9953	0.0136
0.7	0.7580	0.3123	2.7	0.9965	0.0104
0.8	0.7881	0.2897	2.8	0.9974	0.0079
0.9	0.8159	0.2661	2.9	0.9981	0.0060
1.0	0.8413	0.2420	3.0	0.9987	0.0044
1.1	0.8643	0.2179	3.1	0.9990	0.0033
1.2	0.8849	0.1942	3.2	0.9993	0.0024
1.3	0.9032	0.1714	3.3	0.9995	0.0017
1.4	0.9192	0.1497	3.4	0.9997	0.0012
1.5	0.9332	0.1295	3.5	0.9998	0.0009
1.6	0.9452	0.1109	3.6	0.9998	0.0006
1.7	0.9554	0.0940	3.7	0.9999	0.0004
1.8	0.9641	0.0790	3.8	0.9999	0.0003
1.9	0.9713	0.0656	3.9	1.0000	0.0002
			4.0	1.0000	0.0001

Example 4.28

The final scores of students in a graduate course are distributed normally with a mean of 72 and a standard deviation of 10. What is the probability that a student's score will be between 65 and 78?

Solution

Calculate standard normal values for the points of interest, 65 and 78.

$$Z = \frac{x-\mu}{\sigma}$$

$$Z_{65} = \frac{65-72}{10} = -0.70 \qquad Z_{78} = \frac{78-72}{10} = 0.60$$

The probability of a score falling between 65 and 78 is equal to the area under the unit normal curve between these two standard normal values. Determine this area by subtracting $F(Z_{65})$ from $F(Z_{78})$. Although the $F(Z)$ statistic is not tabulated for negative x values, the curve's symmetry allows the $R(x)$ statistic to be used instead.

$$F(x) = R(-x)$$

$$\begin{aligned} P(65 < x < 78) &= F(Z_{78}) - F(Z_{65}) \\ &= F(Z_{78}) - R(-Z_{65}) \end{aligned}$$

$= F(0.60) - R(0.70)$
$= 0.7257 - 0.2420 = 0.4837$

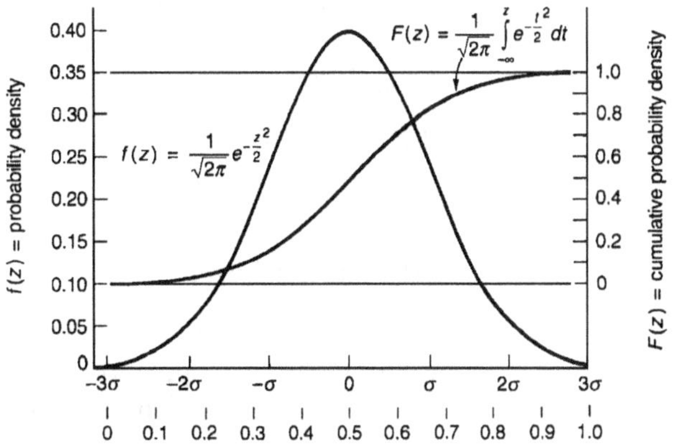

Figure 4.9 Normal error curve

The standard cumulative distribution function is

$$F(z) = \int_{-\infty}^{z} \frac{1}{\sqrt{2\pi}} \times e^{-t^2/2} \times dt$$

The standard probability function is shown graphically in Figure 4.9, and Table 4.3 shows the corresponding numerical values. The standard probability curve is symmetric about the origin and is given in terms of unit *sigma*. To use the table, remember that the function $F(z)$ is the area under the probability curve from minus infinity to the value z. The area under the curve up to $x = 0$ is therefore 0.5. Also, from symmetry,

$$F(-z) = 1 - F(z)$$

Example 4.29

Find the probability that the standard variable z lies within (i) 1σ, (ii) 2σ, and (iii) 3σ of the mean.

Solution

(i) The probability is $P_1 = F(1.0) - F(-1.0)$. From the symmetry of F, $F(-1.0) = 1 - F(1.0)$, so

$$P_1 = 2F(1.0) - 1 = 2(0.8413) - 1$$
$$= 0.6826$$

(ii) In this case, the probability is

$$P_2 = F(2.0) - F(-2.0)$$
$$= F(2.0) - [1 - F(2.0)]$$
$$= 2F(2.0) - 1 = 2(0.9773) - 1$$
$$= 0.9546$$

(iii) In the same way,

$$P_3 = 2F(3.0) - 1$$
$$= 2(0.9987) - 1$$
$$= 0.9974$$

Example 4.30

A Gaussian random variable has a mean of 1830 and standard deviation of 460. Find the probability that the variable will be more than 2750.

Solution

$P(X > 2750) = 1 - P(X \leq 2750) = 1 - F[(2750 - 1830)/460] = 1 - F(2.0) = 1 - 0.9772 = 0.0228$

t-Distribution

The *t*-distribution is often used to test an assumption about a population mean when the parent population is known to be normally distributed but its standard deviation is unknown. In this case, the inferences made about the parent mean will depend upon the size of the samples being taken.

It is customary to describe the *t*-distribution in terms of the standard variable t and the number of degrees of freedom ν. The number of degrees of freedom is a measure of the number of independent observations in a sample that can be used to estimate the standard deviation of the parent population; the number of degrees of freedom ν is one less than the sample size ($\nu = n - 1$).

The density function of the *t*-distribution is given by

$$f(t) = \frac{\Gamma\left(\frac{\nu+1}{2}\right)}{\sqrt{\nu\pi}\,\Gamma\left(\frac{\nu}{2}\right)\left(1 + t^2/\nu\right)^{(\nu+1)/2}}$$

and is provided in Table 4.4. The mean is $m = 0$, and the standard deviation is

$$\sigma = \sqrt{\frac{\nu}{\nu - 2}}$$

Table 4.4 *t*-Distribution; values of $t_{\alpha,\nu}$

Degrees of Freedom, ν	Area of the Tail				
	$\alpha = 0.10$	$\alpha = 0.05$	$\alpha = 0.025$	$\alpha = 0.01$	$\alpha = 0.005$
1	3.078	6.314	12.706	31.821	63.657
2	1.886	2.920	4.303	6.965	9.925
3	1.638	2.353	3.182	4.541	5.841
4	1.533	2.132	2.776	3.747	4.604
5	1.476	2.015	2.571	3.365	4.032
6	1.440	1.943	2.447	3.143	3.707
7	1.415	1.895	2.365	2.998	3.499
8	1.397	1.860	2.306	2.896	3.355
9	1.383	1.833	2.262	2.821	3.250
10	1.372	1.812	2.228	2.764	3.169
11	1.363	1.796	2.201	2.718	3.106
12	1.356	1.782	2.179	2.681	3.055
13	1.350	1.771	2.160	2.650	3.012
14	1.345	1.761	2.145	2.624	2.977
15	1.341	1.753	2.131	2.602	2.947
16	1.337	1.746	2.120	2.583	2.921
17	1.333	1.740	2.110	2.567	2.898
18	1.330	1.734	2.101	2.552	2.878
19	1.328	1.729	2.093	2.539	2.861
20	1.325	1.725	2.086	2.528	2.845
21	1.323	1.721	2.080	2.518	2.831
22	1.321	1.717	2.074	2.508	2.819
23	1.319	1.714	2.069	2.500	2.807
24	1.318	1.711	2.064	2.492	2.797
25	1.316	1.708	2.060	2.485	2.787
26	1.315	1.706	2.056	2.479	2.779
27	1.314	1.703	2.052	2.473	2.771
28	1.313	1.701	2.048	2.467	2.763
29	1.311	1.699	2.045	2.462	2.756
inf.	1.282	1.645	1.960	2.326	2.576

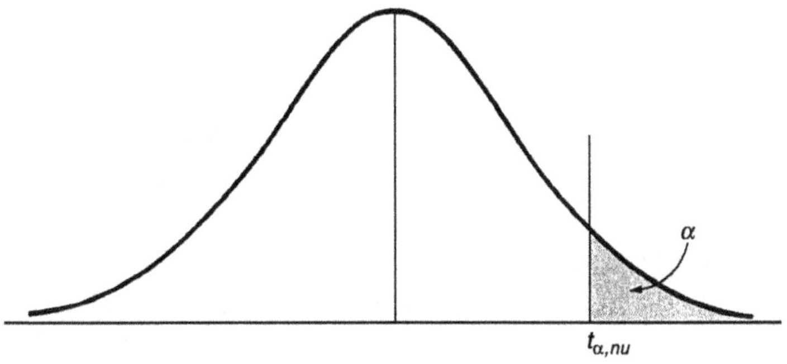

Figure 4.10

Probability questions involving the t-distribution can be answered by using the distribution function $t_{\alpha,\nu}$ shown in Figure 4.10. Table 4.4 gives the value of t as a function of the degrees of freedom v down the column and the area (α) of the tail across the top. The t-distribution is symmetric. As an example, the probability of t falling within ±3.0 when a sample size of 8 ($\nu = 7$) is selected is one minus twice the tail ($\alpha = 0.01$):

$$P\{-3.0 < t < 3.0\} = 1 - (2 \times 0.01) = 0.98$$

The t-distribution is a family of distributions that approaches the Gaussian distribution for large n.

Example 4.31

t-distribution

A t-distribution with 6 degrees of freedom has a mean of 2 and a standard deviation of 3. If 5% of the population is greater than a value, what is that value?

From t-Distribution Table:

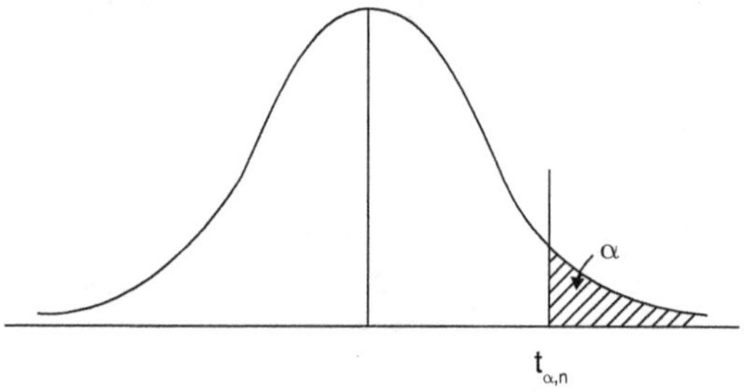

Exhibit 7

n	0.25	0.20	0.15	0.10	0.05	0.025	0.01	0.005	n
1	1.000	1.376	1.963	3.078	6.314	12.706	31.821	63.657	1
2	0.816	1.061	1.386	1.886	2.920	4.303	6.965	9.925	2
3	0.765	0.978	1.350	1.638	2.353	3.182	4.541	5.841	3
4	0.741	0.941	1.190	1.533	2.132	2.776	3.747	4.604	4
5	**0.727**	**0.920**	**1.156**	**1.476**	**2.015**	**2.571**	**3.365**	**4.032**	**5**
6	0.718	0.906	1.134	1.440	1.943	2.447	3.143	3.707	6

$$\alpha = 0.05 \text{ and } n = 6,$$

$$t_{n,\alpha} = 1.943$$

$$x = t_{n,\alpha}\sigma + \mu = (1.943)(3) + 2 = 7.829$$

X^2 DISTRIBUTION

In probability theory and statistics, the chi-square distribution (also chi-squared or x^2-distribution) is one of the most widely used theoretical probability distributions in inferential statistics (e.g., in statistical significance tests). It is useful because, under reasonable assumptions, easily calculated quantities can be proven to have

distributions that approximate to the chi-square distribution if the null hypothesis is true.

The best known situations in which the chi-square distribution is used are the common chi-square tests for goodness of fit of an observed distribution to a theoretical one, and of the independence of two criteria of classification of qualitative data. Many other statistical tests also lead to a use of this distribution.

If $Z_1, Z_2, \ldots, Z_n$ are independent unit normal random variables, then

$$\chi^2 = Z_1^2 + Z_2^2 + \ldots + Z_n^2$$

is said to have a chi-square distribution with n degrees of freedom.

$$Z^2 = \sum \left(\frac{(\text{observed frequency} - \text{expected frequency})^2}{\text{expected frequency}} \right)$$

If $Z_1, Z_2, \ldots, Z_n$ are independent unit normal random variables, then

$$X^2 = Z_1^2 + Z_2^2 + Z_3^2 + \cdots + Z_n^2$$

is said to have a Chi-square distribution with n degrees of freedom.

The table on page 45 of the NCEES FE Handbook gives values of $X_{\alpha,n}$ for selected values of α and n.

CRITICAL VALUES OF X^2 DISTRIBUTION

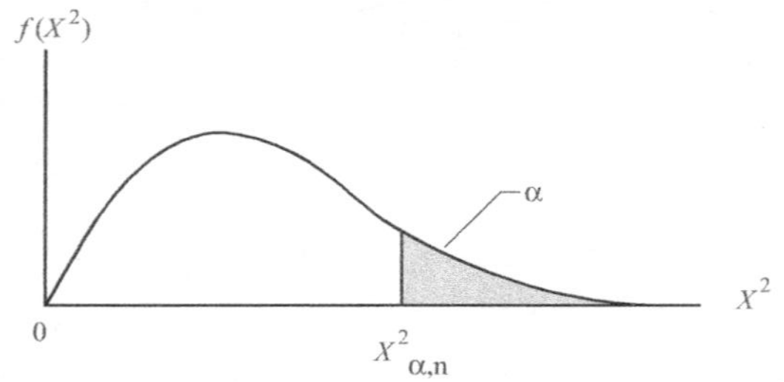

Degrees of Freedom	$X^2_{.995}$	$X^2_{.990}$	$X^2_{.975}$	$X^2_{.950}$	$X^2_{.900}$	$X^2_{.100}$	$X^2_{.050}$	$X^2_{.025}$	$X^2_{.010}$	$X^2_{.005}$
1	0.0000393	0.0001571	0.0009821	0.0039321	0.0157908	2.70554	3.84146	5.02389	6.63490	7.87944
2	0.0100251	0.0201007	0.0506356	0.102587	0.210720	4.60517	5.99147	7.37776	9.21034	10.5966
3	0.0717212	0.114832	0.215795	0.351846	0.584375	6.25139	7.81473	9.34840	11.3449	12.8381
4	0.206990	0.297110	0.484419	0.710721	1.063623	7.77944	9.48773	11.1433	13.2767	14.8602
5	0.411740	0.554300	0.831211	1.145476	1.61031	9.23635	11.0705	12.8325	15.0863	16.7496
6	0.675727	0.872085	1.237347	1.63539	2.20413	10.6446	12.5916	14.4494	16.8119	18.5476
7	0.989265	1.239043	1.68987	2.16735	2.83311	12.0170	14.0671	16.0128	18.4753	20.2777
8	1.344419	1.646482	2.17973	2.73264	3.48954	13.3616	15.5073	17.5346	20.0902	21.9550
9	1.734926	2.087912	2.70039	3.32511	4.16816	14.6837	16.9190	19.0228	21.6660	23.5893
10	2.15585	2.55821	3.24697	3.94030	4.86518	15.9871	18.3070	20.4831	23.2093	25.1882
11	2.60321	3.05347	3.81575	4.57481	5.57779	17.2750	19.6751	21.9200	24.7250	26.7569
12	3.07382	3.57056	4.40379	5.22603	6.30380	18.5494	21.0261	23.3367	26.2170	28.2995
13	3.56503	4.10691	5.00874	5.89186	7.04150	19.8119	22.3621	24.7356	27.6883	29.8194
14	4.07468	4.66043	5.62872	6.57063	7.78953	21.0642	23.6848	26.1190	29.1413	31.3193
15	4.60094	5.22935	6.26214	7.26094	8.54675	22.3072	24.9958	27.4884	30.5779	32.8013
16	5.14224	5.81221	6.90766	7.96164	9.31223	23.5418	26.2962	28.8454	31.9999	34.2672
17	5.69724	6.40776	7.56418	8.67176	10.0852	24.7690	27.5871	30.1910	33.4087	35.7185
18	6.26481	7.01491	8.23075	9.39046	10.8649	25.9894	28.8693	31.5264	34.8053	37.1564
19	6.84398	7.63273	8.90655	10.1170	11.6509	27.2036	30.1435	32.8523	36.1908	38.5822
20	7.43386	8.26040	9.59083	10.8508	12.4426	28.4120	31.4104	34.1696	37.5662	39.9968
21	8.03366	8.89720	10.28293	11.5913	13.2396	29.6151	32.6705	35.4789	38.9321	41.4010
22	8.64272	9.54249	10.9823	12.3380	14.0415	30.8133	33.9244	36.7807	40.2894	42.7956
23	9.26042	10.19567	11.6885	13.0905	14.8479	32.0069	35.1725	38.0757	41.6384	44.1813
24	9.88623	10.8564	12.4011	13.8484	15.6587	33.1963	36.4151	39.3641	42.9798	45.5585
25	10.5197	11.5240	13.1197	14.6114	16.4734	34.3816	37.6525	40.6465	44.3141	46.9278
26	11.1603	12.1981	13.8439	15.3791	17.2919	35.5631	38.8852	41.9232	45.6417	48.2899
27	11.8076	12.8786	14.5733	16.1513	18.1138	36.7412	40.1133	43.1944	46.9630	49.6449
28	12.4613	13.5648	15.3079	16.9279	18.9392	37.9159	41.3372	44.4607	48.2782	50.9933
29	13.1211	14.2565	16.0471	17.7083	19.7677	39.0875	42.5569	45.7222	49.5879	52.3356
30	13.7867	14.9535	16.7908	18.4926	20.5992	40.2560	43.7729	46.9792	50.8922	53.6720
40	20.7065	22.1643	24.4331	26.5093	29.0505	51.8050	55.7585	59.3417	63.6907	66.7659
50	27.9907	29.7067	32.3574	34.7642	37.6886	63.1671	67.5048	71.4202	76.1539	79.4900
60	35.5346	37.4848	40.4817	43.1879	46.4589	74.3970	79.0819	83.2976	88.3794	91.9517
70	43.2752	45.4418	48.7576	51.7393	55.3290	85.5271	90.5312	95.0231	100.425	104.215
80	51.1720	53.5400	57.1532	60.3915	64.2778	96.5782	101.879	106.629	112.329	116.321
90	59.1963	61.7541	65.6466	69.1260	73.2912	107.565	113.145	118.136	124.116	128.299
100	67.3276	70.0648	74.2219	77.9295	82.3581	118.498	124.342	129.561	135.807	140.169

Source: Thompson, C. M., "Tables of the Percentage Points of the X^2–Distribution," *Biometrika*, ©1941, 32, 188-189. Reproduced by permission of the *Biometrika* Trustees.

Source: NCEES, *FE Reference Handbook: 9.1 Version for Computer-Based Testing*, (Clemson, SC, 2013) 45.

Figure 4.11

The P-value is the probability of observing a test statistic at least as extreme in a chi-square distribution. Accordingly, since the cumulative distribution function (CDF) for the appropriate degrees of freedom (*df*) gives the probability of having obtained a value less extreme than this point, subtracting the CDF value from 1 gives the P-value.

A P-value of 0.05 or less is usually regarded as statistically significant.

The number of "categories" will determine the degrees of freedom, *df*.

Example 4.32

To determine if lions are selective predators, a sample of lion kills were taken in a region of the Serengeti Plain. The results showed the following prey percentages: zebras – 20%, wildebeests – 30%, and impalas – 50%. Of the total kills, 18 were zebras, 38 were wildebeests, and 31 were impalas.

Solution

State the null and alternative hypotheses and use the goodness of fit test to test the null hypothesis.

	Observed	Expected
Zebras	18	17.4
Wildebeest	38	26.1
Impalas	31	43.5

Next, plug in the numbers to the *Z* formula:

$$Z = \sum\left(\frac{(\text{observed frequency} - \text{expected frequency})^2}{\text{expected frequency}}\right)$$

There are three categories, so we will calculate three different values:

$$Z_1^2: \quad \frac{(18-17.4)^2}{17.4} = \frac{(6)^2}{17.4} = \frac{.36}{17.4} = .021$$

$$Z_3^2: \quad \frac{(38-26.1)^2}{26.1} = \frac{(11.9)^2}{26.1} = \frac{141.61}{26.1} = 5.426$$

$$Z_3^2: \quad \frac{(31-43.5)^2}{43.5} = \frac{(-12.5)^2}{43.5} = \frac{156.25}{43.5} = 3.592$$

Now we add these three values together to get our chi-square number:

$$\chi^2 = Z_1^2 + Z_2^2 + Z_3^2 = .021 + 5.426 + 3.592 = 9.039$$

Then, we find our critical value for 2 degrees of freedom

$$(df = \#\text{categories} - 1 = 3 - 1 = 2)$$

From the χ^2 Table, *CV* = 5.99.

Finally, we compare our critical value and chi-square value:

$$9.039 > 5.99$$

Chi-square is larger than critical value, so we reject the null hypothesis. (i.e., lions are selective predators).

Hypothesis Testing and Confidence Interval

A hypothesis test is a procedure that answers the question "Did these data come from a particular type of distribution?" The most simple hypothesis test determines whether an average value obtained from n repetitions of an experiment could have come from a population with known mean μ and standard deviation σ. Use the following equation:

$$z = \frac{\bar{x} - \mu}{\frac{\sigma}{\sqrt{n}}}$$

If $z \geq x$, the average can be assumed (with confidence level C) to have come from a different distribution.

Using

$$z = \frac{\bar{x} - \mu}{\sigma / \sqrt{n}}$$

and

$$n = \left[\frac{z_{\alpha/2}\sigma}{\bar{x} - \mu} \right]^2$$

The $Z_{\alpha/2}$ values are associated with the confidence intervals as shown in Table 4.5:

Table 4.5 Values of $Z_{\alpha/2}$

Confidence Interval	$Z_{\alpha/2}$
80%	1.2816
90%	1.6449
95%	1.9600
96%	2.0537
98%	2.3263
99%	2.5758

Example 4.33

When operating properly, a plant has a daily production rate that is normally distributed with a mean of 144 kg/d and a standard deviation of 25 kg/d. During an analysis period, the output is measured on 30 consecutive days, and the mean

output is found to be 135 kg/d. The probability that the plant is *NOT* operating properly is most nearly:

a). 1%

b). 5%

c). 95%

d). 99%

Solution

Because a specific direction in the variation is not given, a two-tail hypothesis test is used. The z-value corresponding to the confidence level is:

$$z = \left| \frac{\bar{x} - \mu}{\frac{\sigma}{\sqrt{n}}} \right| = \left| \frac{135\frac{\text{kg}}{\text{d}} - 144\frac{\text{kg}}{\text{d}}}{\frac{25\frac{\text{kg}}{\text{d}}}{\sqrt{30}}} \right|$$

$$= 1.97$$

Comparing the calculated value of

$$z = 1.97$$

with a table of z-values for various confidence levels in the table for the values of $Z_{\alpha/2}$ shows that the confidence interval is most nearly 95%.

Example 4.34

Find the 95% confidence interval for the true population mean of salaries of professors. A sample size of 60 professors was taken. The average of this sample is \$85,678, and the sample standard deviation is \$12,345.

a). $\$80{,}554 < \mu < \$89{,}802$

b). $\$81{,}555 < \mu < \$90{,}802$

c). $\$73{,}333 < \mu < \$98{,}023$

d). $\$84{,}678 < \mu < \$86{,}678$

e). $\$82{,}554 < \mu < \$88{,}802$

Solution

$$\bar{X} - Z_{\alpha/2}\frac{\sigma}{\sqrt{n}} \le \mu \le X + Z_{\alpha/2}\frac{\sigma}{\sqrt{n}}$$

$$85{,}678 - 1.96\left(\frac{12{,}345}{\sqrt{60}}\right) < \mu \le 85{,}678 + 1.96\left(\frac{12{,}345}{\sqrt{60}}\right)$$

The correct answer is e). $\$82{,}554 < \mu < \$88{,}802$.

Example 4.35

A 95% confidence interval for the population mean is $430 < \mu < 470$. The sample size of 100 items is used. What is the value of the sample standard deviation?

a). 107

b). 150

c). 450

d). 1.96

e). 102

Solution

Using the confidence interval $430 < \mu < 470$, we know:

$$450 - 20 \leq \mu \leq 450 - 20, \text{ so } \overline{X} = 450 \text{ and } E = 20$$

$$20 = Z_{\alpha/2} \frac{\sigma}{\sqrt{n}}$$

$$20 = 1.96 \frac{\sigma}{\sqrt{100}}$$

$$\sigma = \frac{20 \times 10}{1.96}$$

$$\sigma = 102$$

The correct answer is e). 102.

PROBLEMS

4.1 Define the set of all outcomes for the roll of two dice.

4.2 Draw a Venn diagram showing the following:

The universal set of all people in the United States as U

All the males as M

All the females as F

All the students of both sexes as S

All the students with grades above "B" as A

4.3 What is the probability of drawing a pair of aces in two cards when an ace has been drawn on the first card?

a. 1/13
b. 1/26
c. 3/51
d. 4/51

4.4 An auto manufacturer has three plants (A, B, C). Four out of 500 cars from Plant A must be recalled, 10 out of 800 from Plant B, and 10 out of 1000 from Plant C. Now a customer purchases a car from a dealer who gets 30% of his stock from Plant A, 40% from Plant B, and 30% from Plant C, and the car is recalled. What is the probability it was manufactured in Plant A?

a. 0.0008
b. 0.01
c. 0.0125
d. 0.2308

4.5 There are ten defectives per 1000 times of a product. What is the probability that there is one and only one defective in a random lot of 100?

a. 99×0.01^{99}
b. 0.01
c. 0.5
d. 0.99^{99}

4.6 The probability that both stages of a two-stage missile will function correctly is 0.95. The probability that the first stage will function correctly is 0.98. What is the probability that the second stage will function correctly given that the first one does?

a. 0.99
b. 0.98
c. 0.97
d. 0.95

4.7 A standard deck of 52 playing cards is thoroughly shuffled. The probability that the first four cards dealt from the deck will be the four aces is closest to:

a. 2.0×10^{-1}
b. 8.0×10^{-2}
c. 4.0×10^{-4}
d. 4.0×10^{-6}

4.8 In statistics, the standard deviation measures:

a. a standard distance
b. a normal distance
c. central tendency
d. dispersion

4.9 There are three bins containing integrated circuits (ICs). One bin has two premium ICs, one has two regular ICs, and one has one premium IC and one regular IC. An IC is picked at random. It is found to be a premium IC. What is the probability that the remaining IC in that bin is also a premium IC?

a. $\frac{1}{5}$ c. $\frac{1}{3}$

b. $\frac{1}{4}$ d. $\frac{2}{3}$

4.10 How many teams of four can be formed from 35 people?

a. About 25,000 c. About 50,000

b. About 2,000,000 d. About 200,000

4.11 A bin contains 50 bolts, 10 of which are defective. If a worker grabs 5 bolts from the bin in one grab, what is the probability that no more than 2 of the 5 are bad?

a. About 0.5 c. About 0.90

b. About 0.75 d. About 0.95

4.12 How many three-letter codes may be formed from the English alphabet if no repetitions are allowed?

a. 26^3 c. $26 \times 25 \times 24$

b. 26/3 d. $26^3/3$

4.13 A widget has three parts, A, B, and C, with probabilities of 0.1, 0.2, and 0.25, respectively, of being defective. What is the probability that exactly one of these parts is defective?

a. 0.375 c. 0.95

b. 0.55 d. 0.005

4.14 If three students work on a certain math problem, student A has a probability of success of 0.5; student B, 0.4; and student C, 0.3. If they work independently, what is the probability that no one works the problem successfully?

a. 0.12 c. 0.32

b. 0.25 d. 0.21

4.15 A sample of 50 light bulbs is drawn from a large collection in which each bulb is good with a probability of 0.9. What is the approximate probability of having less than 3 bad bulbs in the 50?

a. 0.1 c. 0.3

b. 0.2 d. 0.4

4.16 The number of different 3-digit numbers that can be formed from the digits 1, 2, 3, 7, 8, 9 without reusing the digits is:

a. 10 c. 30

b. 20 d. 40

4.17 The number of different ways that a party of seven councilmen can be seated in a row is:

a. 1 c. 2080
b. 560 d. 5040

4.18 A student must answer six out of eight questions on an exam. The number of different ways in which he can do the exam is:

a. 8 c. 28
b. 18 d. 48

4.19 Repeat Problem 5.18 if the first two questions are mandatory.

a. 4 c. 12
b. 8 d. 15

4.20 A group of five women wishes to form a subcommittee consisting of two of them. The number of possible ways to do so is:

a. 5 c. 15
b. 10 d. 20

4.21 An integer has to be chosen from numbers between 1 and 100 (both inclusive). The probability of choosing a number divisible by 9 (with a remainder of 0) is:

a. 0 c. 0.11
b. 0.01 d. 0.91

4.22 Four fair coins are tossed. The probability of either one head or two heads showing up is:

a. 1/8 c. 4/8
b. 2/8 d. 5/8

4.23 Two identical bags contain ten apples and five oranges each. The probability of selecting an apple from the first bag and an orange from the second bag is:

a. 1/9 c. 3/9
b. 2/9 d. 4/9

4.24 A bag contains 5 red, 10 orange, 15 green, 20 violet, and 25 black cards. The probability that you will get a black card or a red card if you remove a card from the bag is:

a. 5/85 c. 25/85
b. 15/85 d. 35/85

4.25 Two bags each contain two orange balls, five white balls, and three red balls. The probability of selecting an orange ball from the first bag or a white ball from the other bag is:

a. 0 c. 0.6
b. 0.2 d. 1.0

4.26 A bag contains 100 balls numbered 1 to 100. One ball is drawn from the bag. What is the probability that the number on the ball will be even or greater than 72?

a. 0.64 c. 0.28
b. 0.50 d. 0.14

4.27 A circuit has two switches connected in series. For a signal to pass through, both switches must be closed. The probability that the first switch is closed is 0.95, and the probability that a signal passes through is 0.90. The probability that the second switch is closed is:

a. 0.8545 c. 0.9474
b. 0.9000 d. 0.9871

4.28 Four probability density distributions are shown in Exhibit 4.28. The only valid distribution is:

a. $f_1(x)$ c. $f_3(x)$
b. $f_2(x)$ d. $f_4(x)$

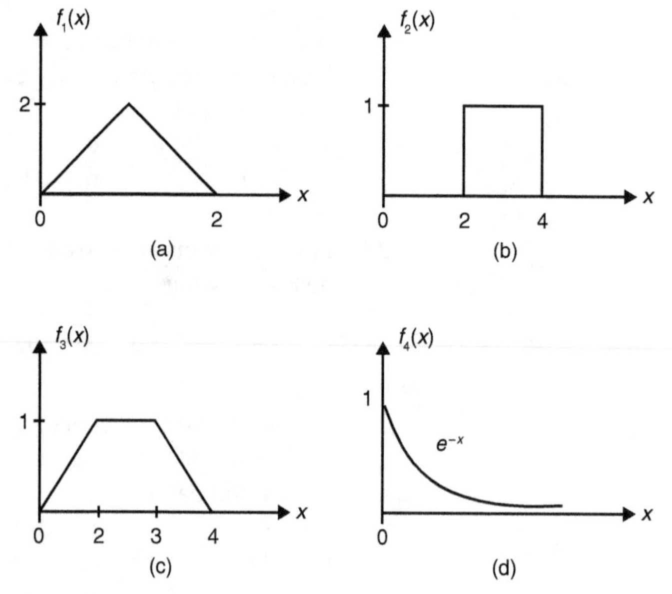

Exhibit 4.28

4.29 Four probability density distributions are shown in Exhibit 4.29. The only valid distribution is:

a. $f_1(x)$ c. $f_3(x)$
b. $f_2(x)$ d. $f_4(x)$

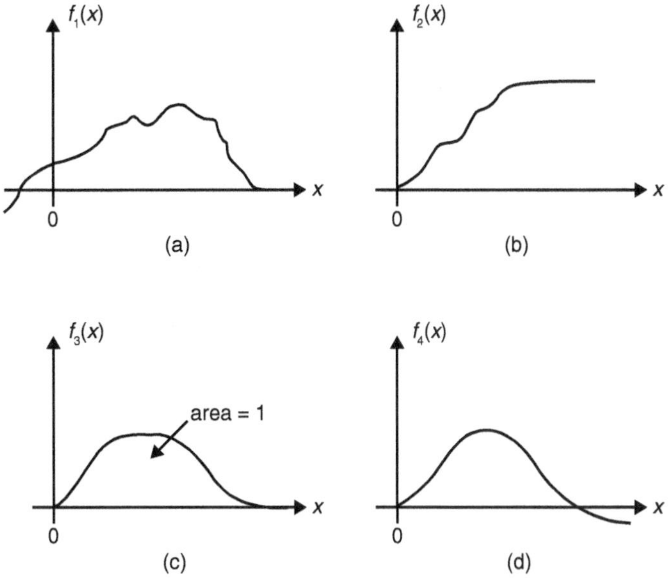

Exhibit 4.29

4.30 Four probability density distributions are shown in Exhibit 4.30. The only valid distribution is:

a. $f_1(x)$ c. $f_3(x)$
b. $f_2(x)$ d. $f_4(x)$

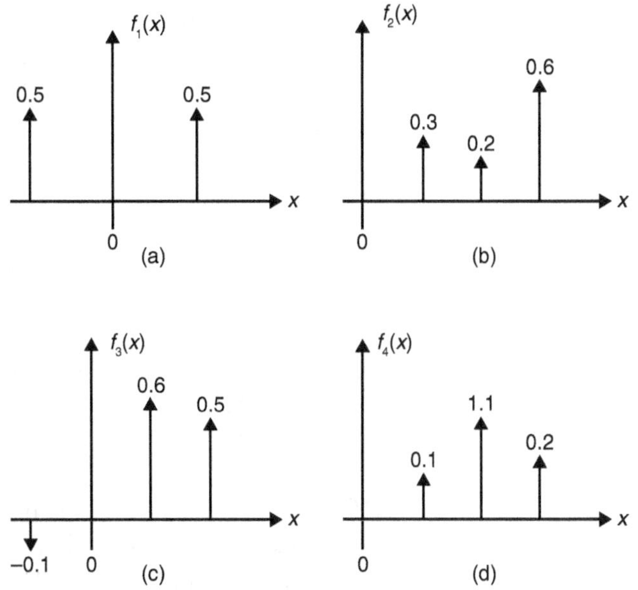

Exhibit 4.30

4.31 Four cumulative probability distribution functions are shown in Exhibit 4.31. The only valid distribution is:

a. $F_1(x)$ c. $F_3(x)$
b. $F_2(x)$ d. $F_4(x)$

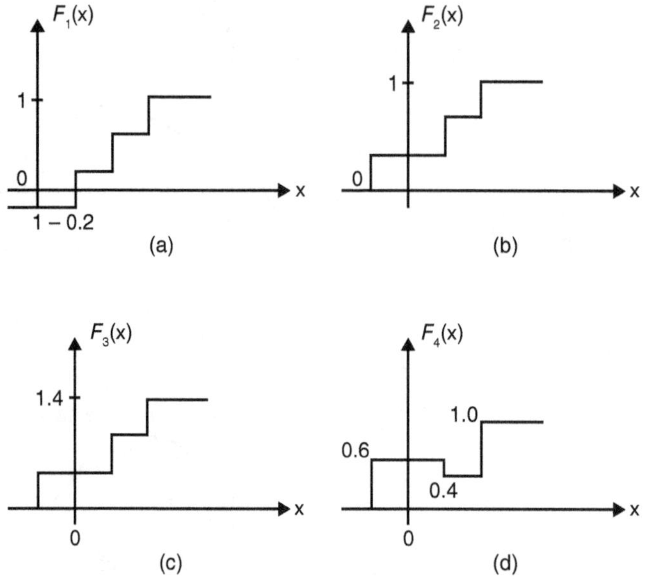

Exhibit 4.31

4.32 A coin is weighted so that heads is twice as likely to appear as tails. The probability that two heads occur in four tosses is:

a. 0.15 c. 0.45
b. 0.35 d. 0.75

4.33 It is given that 20% of all employees leave their jobs after one year. A company hired seven new employees. The probability that nobody will leave the company after one year is:

a. 0.1335 c. 0.3815
b. 0.2315 d. 0.6510

4.34 If four fair coins are tossed simultaneously, the probability that at least one head appears is:

a. 0.1335 c. 0.7815
b. 0.5635 d. 0.9375

4.35 For unit normal distribution, the probability that $(x > 3)$ is:

a. 0.0013 c. 0.1807
b. 0.0178 d. 0.5402

4.36 Scores in a particular game have a normal distribution with a mean of 30 and a standard deviation of 5. Contestants must score more than 26 to qualify for the finals. The probability of being disqualified in the qualifying round is:

a. 0.121 c. 0.304
b. 0.212 d. 0.540

4.37 The radial distance to the impact points for shells fired by a cannon is approximated by a normal Gaussian random variable with a mean of 2000 m and standard deviation of 40 m. When a target is located at 1980 m distance, the probability that shells will fall within ± 68 m of the target is:

a. 0.2341 c. 0.5847
b. 0.3248 d. 0.8710

4.38 The chance of a car being stolen from a residential area is 1 in 120. In one area there are five cars parked in front of the houses. The probability that none will be stolen is:

a. 0.0131 c. 0.5847
b. 0.3248 d. 0.9590

4.39 The standard deviation of the sequence 3, 4, 4, 5, 8, 8, 8, 10, 11, 15, 18, 20 is:

a. 5.36 c. 15.62
b. 9.35 d. 28.75

4.40 Weighted arithmetic mean of the following 50 data points is:

Frequency	3	8	18	12	9
Score	1.5	2.5	3.5	4.5	5.5

a. 1.56 c. 5.62
b. 3.82 d. 8.75

4.41 A green die and a red die are tossed. Let's define the events, $X = \{2$ with the green die$\}$ and $Y = \{5$ with the red die$\}$.

a. Find the $P(X)$.
b. Find the $P(Y)$.
c. Find the $P(X$ and $Y)$.
d. Are X and Y independent events?

4.42 A card is drawn from a normal pack of 52 playing cards. Find the probability that the card is:

a. a black card.
b. not a club.
c. an even-numbered card or a diamond.

4.43 A bag contains three marbles, one of each colored green, red, and blue. A marble is taken out, the color recorded, and then replaced in the bag before a second selection is made.

a. Find the P(two green marbles).
b. Find the P(selecting different colored marbles).

SOLUTIONS

4.1 We will write this in ordered pairs:

$$
\begin{aligned}
R = \{&(1,1),\\
&(1,2), (2,1),\\
&(1,3), (3,1), (2,2),\\
&(1,4), (4,1), (2,3), (3,2)\\
&(1,5), (5,1), (2,3), (3,2), (3,3),\\
&(1,6), (6,1), (5,2), (2,5), (3,4), (4,3),\\
&(2,6), (6,2), (5,3), (3,5), (4,4),\\
&(3,6), (6,3), (5,4), (4,5),\\
&(4,6), (6,4), (5,5),\\
&(5,6), (6,5),\\
&(6,6)\}
\end{aligned}
$$

4.2 See Exhibit 4.2.

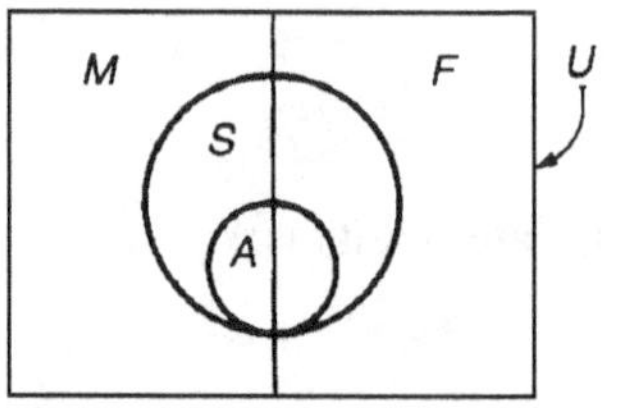

Exhibit 4.2

4.3 **c.** This is a conditional probability problem. Let B be "draw an ace," and let A be "draw a second ace": $P\{B\} = 4/52$ (1/13) and $P\{A\} = 3/51$. Then $P\{A|B\} = P\{A\} \times P\{B\}/P\{B\} = 3/51$.

4.4 **d.** This is a Bayes' theorem problem application because partitions are involved. The event E is a recall, with E_1 = Plant A, E_2 = Plant B, and E_3 = Plant C. The conditional probabilities of a recall from Plants E_1, E_2, and E_3 are

$$
\begin{aligned}
P(E \mid E_1) &= 4/500 = 0.008\\
P(E \mid E_2) &= 10/800 = 0.0125\\
P(E \mid E_3) &= 10/1000 = 0.01
\end{aligned}
$$

The probabilities that the dealer had a car from E_1, E_2, or E_3 are $P(E_1) = 0.3$, $P(E_2) = 0.4$, and $P(E_3) = 0.3$. Now applying Bayes' formula gives the probability that the recall was built in Plant A (E_1) as

$$
P\{E_1|\text{recall}\} = \frac{P\{E_1\} \times P\{E|E_1\}}{P\{E_1\} \times P\{E \mid E_1\} + P\{E_2\} \times P\{E|E_2\} + P\{E_3\} \times P\{E \mid E_3\}}
$$

$$
= \frac{0.3 \times 0.008}{0.3 \times 0.008 + 0.4 \times 0.0125 + 0.3 \times 0.01} = 0.2308
$$

4.5 **d.** The problem involves binomial probability. The probability that one item, selected at random, is defective is

$$
p_{\text{defective}} = \frac{10}{1000} = 0.01
$$

and the probability that one item is good (not defective) is

$$
p_{\text{good}} = 1 - p_{\text{defective}} = 0.99
$$

The probability that exactly one defective item will be found in a random sample of 100 items is given by the binomial $b(1, 100, 0.01)$, in which

No. defective; size sample; No. good

$$b(1, 100, 0.01) = C(100, 1)(0.01)^1(0.99)^{99}$$

$p_{defective}$; p_{good}

$C(n,r) = \binom{n}{r} = \frac{n!}{(n-r}$ is the number of combinations of n objects taken r at a time without concern for the order of arrangement.

$C(100, 1) = \frac{100!}{99!1!} = 100$, so $b(1, 100, 0.01) = 100(0.01)(0.99)^{99}$ $= 0.99^{99} = 0.3697$.

4.6 **c.** Here, $P(S_1) = 0.98$ and $P(S_2 \cap S_1) = 0.95$ are given. Hence the conditional probability $P(S_2 | S_1)$ is

$$P(S_2 | S_1) = \frac{P(S_2 \cap S_1)}{P(S_1)} = \frac{0.95}{0.98} = 0.97$$

4.7 **d.** The probability of drawing an ace on the first card is 4/52. The probability that the second card is an ace is 3/51. The probability that the third card is an ace is 2/50, and probability for the fourth ace is 1/49. The probability that the first four cards will all be aces is

$$P = \frac{4}{52} \bullet \frac{3}{51} \bullet \frac{2}{50} \bullet \frac{1}{49} = 0.00\,0037 = 3.7 \times 10^{-6}$$

4.8 **d.**

4.9 **d.** Since the first IC that is picked is a premium IC, it was drawn from either bin 1 or bin 3. From the distribution of premium ICs, the probability that the premium IC came from bin 1 is $\frac{2}{3}$, and from bin 3 is $\frac{1}{3}$.

In bin 1, the probability that the remaining IC is a premium IC is 1; in bin 3, the probability is 0. Thus, the probability that the remaining IC is a premium IC is

$$\frac{2}{3}(1) + \frac{1}{3}(0) = \frac{2}{3}$$

An alternative solution using Bayes' theorem for conditional probability is

$$P(\text{bin 1} \mid \text{drew premium}) = \frac{P(\text{bin 1 and premium})}{P(\text{premium})}$$

$$= \frac{P(\text{premium} \mid \text{bin 1}) \bullet P(\text{bin 1})}{\sum_{i=1}^{3} P(\text{premium} \mid \text{bin 1}) P(\text{bin 1})}$$

$$= \frac{1\left(\frac{1}{3}\right)}{1\left(\frac{1}{3}\right) + 0\left(\frac{1}{3}\right) + \frac{1}{2}\left(\frac{1}{3}\right)} = \frac{2}{3}$$

4.10 **c.** The answer is the binomial coefficient

$$\binom{35}{4} = \frac{35 \bullet 34 \bullet 33 \bullet 32}{4 \bullet 3 \bullet 2 \bullet 1} = 35 \bullet 34 \bullet 11 \bullet 4 = 52,360$$

4.11 **d.** The total number of choices of 5 is $\binom{50}{5}$. Of these, $\binom{40}{5}$ have no bad bolts, $\binom{40}{4} \times \binom{10}{1}$ have one bad bolt, and $\binom{40}{3}\binom{10}{2}$ have two bad bolts. Thus,

$$\frac{\binom{40}{5} + \binom{40}{4}\binom{10}{1} + \binom{40}{3}\binom{10}{2}}{\binom{50}{5}}$$

$$= \frac{\frac{40 \bullet 39 \bullet 38 \bullet 37 \bullet 36}{5 \bullet 4 \bullet 3 \bullet 2} + \frac{40 \bullet 39 \bullet 38 \bullet 37}{4 \bullet 3 \bullet 2} \bullet 10 + \frac{40 \bullet 39 \bullet 38}{3 \bullet 2} \bullet \frac{10 \bullet 9}{2}}{\frac{50 \bullet 49 \bullet 48 \bullet 47 \bullet 46}{5 \bullet 4 \bullet 3 \bullet 2}}$$

$$= \frac{658,008 + 913,900 + 444,600}{2,118,760} = 0.9517$$

4.12 **c.** There are 26 choices for the first letter; 25 remain for the second, and 24 for the third.

4.13 **a.** The probability that only A is defective is

$$0.1 \times (1 - 0.2) \times (1 - 0.25) = 0.06$$

The probability that only B is defective is

$$(1 - 0.1) \times (0.2) \times (1 - 0.25) = 0.135$$

The probability that only C is defective is

$$(1 - 0.1) \times (1 - 0.2) \times (0.25) = 0.18$$

Now add to find the final probability, which is

$$0.06 + 0.135 + 0.18 = 0.375$$

4.14 d. Simply multiply the complementary probabilities $(1 - 0.5) \times (1 - 0.4) \times (1 - 0.3) = 0.21$.

4.15 a. Apply the binomial distribution. The probability of 0 bad is $(0.9)^{50}$; of 1 bad, $\binom{50}{1}(0.1)(0.9)^{49}$; and of 2 bad, $\binom{50}{1}(0.1)^2(0.9)^{48}$. Adding these, $(0.9)^{48}[(0.9)^2 + 5.0(0.9) + 1225(0.1)^2] = 0.112$.

4.16 b. This is the permutation of arranging 3 objects out of 6:

$$P(6,3) = \frac{6!}{(6-3)!} = 20$$

4.17 d. This is the permutation of arranging 7 persons out of 7:

$$P(7,7) = \frac{7!}{(7-7)!} = 5040$$

4.18 c. This is the selection (or combination) of 6 out of 8:

$$C(8,6) = \frac{8!}{(8-6)6!} = 28$$

4.19 d. Since two questions are mandatory, only four questions have to be selected out of six.

Then, $C(6,4) = \frac{6!}{(6-4)!4!} = 15$.

4.20 b. This is the selection (or combination) of 2 out of 5:

$$C(5,2) = \frac{5!}{3!2!} = 10$$

4.21 c. Since there are 11 integers that are exactly divisible by 9, probability $= 11/100 = 0.11$.

4.22 d. $P(1 \text{ head}) = \frac{C(4,1)}{2^4} = \frac{4}{16}$; $P(2 \text{ heads}) = \frac{C(4,2)}{2^4} = \frac{6}{16}$

Since P(1 head AND 2 heads) is 0, P(1 head or 2 heads) = (4/16) + (6/16) = 5/8.

4.23 **b.** Let event A = (Apple from a bag) and event B = (Orange from the other bag).

Then, P(A) = 10/15 and P(B) = 5/15.

Since the events are independent, P(A AND B) = P(A) P(B) = (10/15) (5/15) = 2/9.

4.24 **d.** P(Black OR Red) = P(Black) + P(Red) – P(Black AND Red) = (5/85) + (30/85) – 0 = 35/85.

4.25 **c.** Let event A = (Orange from a bag) and event B = (White from the other bag).

P(A) = 2/10 = 0.2 and P(B) = 5/10 = 0.5

P(A OR B) = P(A) + P(B) – P(A AND B) = 0.2 + 0.5 – (0.2)(0.5) = 0.6

Note: P(A AND B) = P(A) P(B) as events A and B are independent.

4.26 **a.** Let event A = (number is even) and event B = (number > 72).

P(A) = 50/100 = 0.5 and P(B) = 28/100 = 0.28

Event (A and B) = (number is odd and > 72); P(A AND B) = 14/100 = 0.14

P(A OR B) = P(A) + P(B) – P(A AND B) = 0.50 + 0.28 – 0.14 = 0.64

4.27 **c.** P(both closed) = P(1 is closed) P(2 is closed)

0.90 = (0.95) P(2 is closed); then, P(2 is closed) = 0.90/0.95 = 0.9474

4.28 **d.** For a valid probability density function, $\int_{-\infty}^{\infty} f(x)\,dx = 1,$ or the total area under the curve should be 1. For $f_1(x)$, the area is (1/2)(2)(2) = 2; for $f_2(x)$, it is 1(4 – 2) = 2; for $f_3(x)$, it is (1/2)(4 + 1) = 2.5. For $f_4(x)$, $\int_0^{\infty} e^{-x}\,dx = 1.$ So, $f_4(x)$ is the only valid distribution.

4.29 **c.** For a valid probability distribution function, both $f(\infty)$ and $f(-\infty)$ should be zero and $f(x) \geq 0$ for all x. Also, $\int_{-\infty}^{\infty} f(x)\,dx = 1.$ Then, $f_1(x)$ and $f_4(x)$ are not valid since $f(x) < 0$ for certain values of x. $f_2(x)$ is not valid because $f(\infty)$ is not 0. $f_3(x)$ is the valid function as it satisfies all the conditions.

4.30 **a.** The distribution is discrete, but the rules are similar to those of Problem 5.29. $f_1(x)$ is the only valid distribution. $f_2(x)$ is not valid since the sum of the densities (equivalent to integrating) is more than 1. $f_3(x)$ has a negative value. $f_4(x)$ has a value more than 1.

4.31 b. For a valid cumulative probability distribution function $F(x)$, the following rules apply: $F(-\infty) = 0$, $F(\infty) = 1$, $0 \le F(x) \le 1$, and $F(x_1) \le F(x_2)$ if $x_1 < x_2$. For $F_1(x)$, $F(x)$ has a negative value; for $F_3(x)$, $F(\infty)$ is more than 1; for $F_4(x)$, the rule $F(x_1) \le F(x_2)$ if $x_1 < x_2$ fails. Only $F_2(x)$ obeys all the rules.

4.32 a. Let p = P(head on the first toss); then, P(tail on the first toss) = $1 - p$

But, $p = 2(1 - p)$; solving, $p = 0.667$.

P(two heads in four tosses) = $C(4,2)(0.667)^2(1 - 0.667)^2 = 0.1481$

4.33 a. P(leaving the job) = 0.25; P(none will leave the job) = $C(7,0)(0.25)^0 (1 - 0.25)^7 = 0.1335$

4.34 d. P(head) = $p = 0.5$; P(at least one head) = 1 – P(no head) = $1 - C(4,0)(0.5)^0(1 - 0.5)^4 = 0.9375$

4.35 a. Using the normal distribution table, P(X > 3) = 1 – F(3) = 0.0013.

4.36 b. $P\{X \le 26\} = F(26) = F\left(\frac{26 - 30}{5}\right) = F(-0.8) = 1 - F(0.8) = 1 - 0.7881 = 0.2119$

4.37 d. $P\{1980 - 68 < x \le 1980 + 68\} = F(2048) - F(1912)$

$$= F\left(\frac{2048 - 2000}{40}\right) - F\left(\frac{1912 - 2000}{40}\right) = F(1.20) - F(-2.2)$$

$$= 0.8849 - (1 - 0.9861) = 0.8710$$

4.38 d. $C(5,0)(1/120)^0(119/120)^5 = 0.9590$

4.39 a. $\text{mean} = \overline{X} = \frac{\sum x}{n} = \frac{114}{12} = 9.5$

$$\text{variance, } \sigma^2 = (1/12)\left[(3 - 9.5)^2 + (4 - 9.5)^2 + \ldots\right] = 28.75$$

standard deviation $\sigma = 5.36$

4.40 b. $\frac{3(1.5) + 8(2.5) + \ldots + 9(5.5)}{3 + 8 + 18 + \ldots + 9} = 3.82$

4.41 a. $P(X) = \frac{6}{36} = \frac{1}{6}$

b. $P(Y) = \frac{6}{36} = \frac{1}{6}$

c. $P(X,Y) = P(X) \cdot P(Y) = \frac{1}{6} \cdot \frac{1}{6} = \frac{1}{36}$

d. Yes, $P(X, Y) = P(X) \cdot P(Y)$; Intersection of A and B.

4.42 a. $P(\text{black card}) = \frac{26}{52} = \frac{1}{2}$

b. $P(\text{not a club}) = 1 - \frac{13}{52} = \frac{3}{4}$

c. $P(\text{an even number OR a diamond}) = \frac{28}{52} = \frac{7}{13}$

4.43 a. $P(\text{two green marbles}) = P(\text{green}) \cdot P(\text{green}) = \frac{1}{3} \cdot \frac{1}{3} = \frac{1}{9}$

b. $P(\text{different colored marbles}) = \frac{6}{9}$

CHAPTER 5

Ethics and Professional Practices

OUTLINE

The topic of ethics and business practices represents about 4% of the total FE/EIT exam. Questions in the section on ethics and business practices of the exam may cover the following topics:

- Code of ethics (professional and technical societies)
- Agreements and contracts
- Ethical versus legal behavior
- Professional liability
- Public protection issues (for example, licensing boards)

MORALS, PERSONAL ETHICS, AND PROFESSIONAL ETHICS

To put professional ethics for engineers in perspective, it is helpful to distinguish it from morals and personal ethics. *Morals* are beliefs about right and wrong behaviors that are widely held by significant portions of a given culture. Obviously, morals will vary from culture to culture, and though some are common across different cultures, there seems to be no universal moral code.

Personal ethics are the beliefs that individuals hold that often are more restrictive than and sometimes contradictory to the morals of the culture. An example of personal ethics that might be more restrictive than morals might be the belief of an individual that alcohol should not be consumed in a culture that accepts the use of alcohol.

Professional ethics, on the other hand, is the formally adopted code of behavior by a group of professionals held out to society as that profession's pledge about how the profession will interact with society. Such rules or codes represent the agreed-on basis for a successful relationship between the profession and the society it serves.

The engineering profession has adopted several such codes of ethics, and different practitioners may adhere to or be bound by codes that vary by professional discipline but are similar in their basics. Codes adopted by the state boards of registration are typically codified into law and are legally binding for licensed engineers in the respective state. Codes adopted by professional societies are not legally binding but are voluntarily adhered to by members of those societies. The successful understanding of professional ethics for engineers requires an understanding of various codes; for purposes of examining registration applicants, the NCEES has adopted a "model code" that includes many canons common to most codes adopted nationwide.

CODES OF ETHICS

Codes of ethics are published by professional and technical societies and by licensing boards. Why are codes published and why are they important? These fundamental questions are at the heart of the definition of a "profession." Some important aspects of the definition of a profession might include skills and knowledge vital to society; extensive and intellectual education and training important for proper practice in the profession; an importance of autonomous action by practitioners; a recognition by society of these aspects, leading to a governmentally endorsed monopoly on the practice of the profession; and a reliance on published standards of ethical conduct, usually in the form of a code of ethics (Harris, et al., 2005). Such codes are published and followed to maintain a high standard of confidence in the profession by the public served by the practicing professionals, because without high standards of confidence, the ability of a profession to serve the public need may be seriously impaired.

The FE exam questions on ethics and business practices are based on the NCEES code of ethics, a concise body of model rules designed to guide state boards and practitioners as a model of good practice in the regulation of engineering. These rules do not bind any engineer, but the codes of ethics published by individual state boards and of professional societies will be very similar to these in principle.

NCEES Model Rules of Professional Conduct

A. Licensee's Obligation to Society

1. Licensees, in the performance of their services for clients, employers, and customers, shall be cognizant that their first and foremost responsibility is to the public welfare.
2. Licensees shall approve and seal only those design documents and surveys that conform to accepted engineering and surveying standards and safeguard the life, health, property, and welfare of the public.
3. Licensees shall notify their employer or client and such other authority as may be appropriate when their professional judgment is overruled under circumstances where the life, health, property, or welfare of the public is endangered.
4. Licensees shall be objective and truthful in professional reports, statements, or testimony. They shall include all relevant and pertinent information in such reports, statements, or testimony.
5. Licensees shall express a professional opinion publicly only when it is founded upon an adequate knowledge of the facts and a competent evaluation of the subject matter.
6. Licensees shall issue no statements, criticisms, or arguments on technical matters which are inspired or paid for by interested parties, unless they explicitly identify the interested parties on whose behalf they are speaking and reveal any interest they have in the matters.
7. Licensees shall not permit the use of their name or firm name by, nor associate in the business ventures with, any person or firm which is engaging in fraudulent or dishonest business or professional practices.
8. Licensees having knowledge of possible violations of any of these Rules of Professional Conduct shall provide the board with the information and assistance necessary to make the final determination of such violation. (Section 150, Disciplinary Action, NCEES Model Law)

B. Licensee's Obligation to Employer and Clients

1. Licensees shall undertake assignments only when qualified by education or experience in the specific technical fields of engineering or surveying involved.
2. Licensees shall not affix their signatures or seals to any plans or documents dealing with subject matter in which they lack competence, nor to any such plan or document not prepared under their direct control and personal supervision.
3. Licensees may accept assignments for coordination of an entire project, provided that each design segment is signed and sealed by the licensee responsible for preparation of that design segment.
4. Licensees shall not reveal facts, data, or information obtained in a professional capacity without the prior consent of the client or employer except as authorized or required by law. Licensees shall not solicit or accept gratuities, directly or indirectly, from contractors, their agents, or other parties in connection with work for employers or clients.

5. Licensees shall make full prior disclosures to their employers or clients of potential conflicts of interest or other circumstances which could influence or appear to influence their judgment or the quality of their service.
6. Licensees shall not accept compensation, financial or otherwise, from more than one party for services pertaining to the same project, unless the circumstances are fully disclosed and agreed to by all interested parties.
7. Licensees shall not solicit or accept a professional contract from a governmental body on which a principal or officer of their organization serves as a member. Conversely, licensees serving as members, advisors, or employees of a government body or department, who are the principals or employees of a private concern, shall not participate in decisions with respect to professional services offered or provided by said concern to the governmental body which they serve. (Section 150, Disciplinary Action, NCEES Model Law)

C. Licensee's Obligation to Other Licensees

1. Licensees shall not falsify or permit misrepresentation of their, or their associates', academic or professional qualifications. They shall not misrepresent or exaggerate their degree of responsibility in prior assignments nor the complexity of said assignments. Presentations incident to the solicitation of employment or business shall not misrepresent pertinent facts concerning employers, employees, associates, joint ventures, or past accomplishments.
2. Licensees shall not offer, give, solicit, or receive, either directly or indirectly, any commission, or gift, or other valuable consideration in order to secure work, and shall not make any political contribution with the intent to influence the award of a contract by public authority.
3. Licensees shall not attempt to injure, maliciously or falsely, directly or indirectly, the professional reputation, prospects, practice, or employment of other licensees, nor indiscriminately criticize other licensees' work. (Section 150, Disciplinary Action, NCEES Model Law)

Many ethical questions arise in the formulation of business practices. Professionals should appreciate that expressions like "all is fair in business" and "let the buyer beware" can conflict with fundamental ideas about how a professional engineer should practice. The reputation of the profession, not only the individual professional, is critically important to the ability of all engineers to discharge their duty to protect the public health, safety, and welfare.

The *NCEES Model Rules* addressing a licensee's obligation to other licensees prohibit misrepresentation or exaggeration of academic or professional qualifications, experience, level of responsibility, prior projects, or any other pertinent facts that might be used by a potential client or employer to choose an engineer.

The *Model Rules* also prohibit gifts, commissions, or other valuable consideration to secure work. Political contributions intended to influence public authorities responsible for awarding contracts are also prohibited.

Often, these rules are misunderstood in the arena of foreign practice. Increasingly, engineering is practiced globally, and engineers must deal with foreign clients and foreign governmental officials, many times on foreign soil where laws and especially cultural practices vary greatly. In the United States, the federal Foreign Corrupt Practices Act (FCPA) is a relatively recent recognition and regulation of this problem. Among other purposes, it provides clearer legal boundaries for U.S. engineers involved with international projects.

According to the FCPA, it is not illegal for a U.S. engineer to make petty extortion payments ("grease payments," "expediting payments," and "facilitating payments" are common expressions) to governmental officials when progress of otherwise legitimate projects is delayed by demands for such payments consistent with prevailing practice in that country. It is illegal, however, for U.S. engineers to give valuable gifts or payments to develop contracts for *new business*. In some cultures, reciprocal, expensive gift giving is an important part of business relationships, and the reciprocal nature of this practice can make it acceptable under the FCPA. Most commonly, when the engineer's responsibilities include interactions with foreign clients or partners, the engineer's corporate employer will publish detailed and conservative guidelines intended to guide the engineer in these ethical questions.

The practicing engineer should always be watchful of established and, especially, new business practices to be sure the practices are consistent with the codes of ethics he or she is following.

Example 5.1

The *NCEES Model Rules of Professional Conduct* allow an engineer to do which one of the following?

(i) Accept money from contractors in connection with work for an employer or client

(ii) Compete with other engineers in seeking to provide professional services

(iii) Accept a professional contract from a governmental body even though a principal or officer of the engineer's firm serves as a member of the governmental body

(iv) Sign or seal all design segments of the project as the coordinator of an entire project

Solution

Although the other items are not allowed by the *Model Rules*, nowhere does it say that an engineer cannot compete with other engineers in seeking to provide professional services. But, of course, he or she should conduct business in an ethical manner. The correct answer is (ii).

AGREEMENTS AND CONTRACTS

One aspect of business practice is understanding the concepts and terminology of agreements and contracts.

Elements of a Contract

Contracts may be formed by two or more parties; that is, there must be a party to make an offer and a party to accept.

To be enforceable in a court of law, a contract must contain the following five essential elements:

1. There must be a mutual agreement.
2. The subject matter must be lawful.

3. There must be a valid consideration.
4. The parties must be legally competent.
5. To be a formal contract, the contract must comply with the provisions of the law with regard to form.

A *formal contract* depends on a particular form or mode of expression for legal efficacy. All other contracts are called *informal contracts* since they do not depend on mere formality for their legal existence.

Contract and Related Legal Terminology

Case law—the body of law created by courts interpreting statute law. Judges use precedents, the outcome of similar cases, to construct logically their decision in a given issue.

Changed or concealed conditions—in construction contracting, it is important to specify how changed or concealed conditions will be handled, usually by changes in the contract terms. For example, if an excavation project is slowed by a difficult soil pocket between soil corings, the excavation contractor may be able to support a claim for increased costs due to these unforeseen conditions. When the concealed conditions are such that they should have been foreseen, such claims are more difficult to support.

Common law—the body of rules of action and principles that derive their authority solely from usage and customs.

Damages for delays—in many contracts, completion time is an important concern, and contractual clauses addressing penalties for delays (or rewards for early completion) are often incorporated.

Equal or approved equivalent—terms used in specifications for materials to permit use of alternative but equal material when an original material is not available or an equivalent material can be obtained at lower cost. The engineer is responsible for approving the alternative material.

Equity—system of doctrines supplementing common and statute law, such as the Maxims of Equity.

Errors and omissions—term used to describe the kind of mistakes that can be made by engineers and architects leading to damage to the client. Often, this risk is protected by liability insurance policies.

Force account—a method of work by which the owner elects to do work with his or her own forces instead of employing a construction contractor. Under this method, the owner maintains direct supervision over the work, furnishes all materials and equipment, and employs workers on his or her own payroll.

Hold harmless—clauses are often included requiring one party to agree not to make a claim against the other and sometimes to cooperate in the defense of the other party if a claim is made by a third party.

Incorporate by reference—the act of making a document legally binding by referencing it within a contract, although it is not attached to or reproduced in the contract. This is done to eliminate unnecessary repetition.

Indemnify—to protect another person against loss or damage, as with an insurance policy.

Liquidated damages—a specific sum of money expressly stipulated as the amount of damages to be recovered by either party for a breach of the agreement by the other.

Mechanics' liens—legal mechanism by which unpaid contractors, suppliers, mechanics, or laborers are allowed to claim or repossess construction materials that have been delivered to the worksite in lieu of payment.

Plans—the drawings that show the physical characteristics of the work to be done. The plans and specifications form the guide and standards of performance that will be required.

Punitive damages—a sum of money used to punish the defendant in certain situations involving willful, wanton, malicious, or negligent torts.

Specifications—written instructions that accompany and supplement the plans. The specifications cover the quality of the materials, workmanship, and other technical requirements. The plans and specifications form the guide and standards of performance that will be required.

Statute law—acts or rules established by legislative action.

Statute of limitations—a time limit on claims resulting from design or construction errors, usually beginning with the date the work was performed, but in some cases beginning on the date the deficiency could first have been discovered.

Surety bond—bonds issued by a third party to guarantee the faithful performance of the contractor. Surety bonds are normally used in connection with competitive-bid contracts, namely, bid bonds, performance bonds, and payment bonds.

Workers' compensation—insurance protecting laborers and subcontractors in case of an on-the-job injury; it is often required of contractors.

ETHICAL VERSUS LEGAL BEHAVIOR

Engineers have a clear obligation to adhere to all laws and regulations in their work—what they do must be done legally. But the obligation goes beyond this. Unlike the world of business where cutthroat but legal practices are commonly condoned and frequently rewarded, engineers assume important obligations to the public and to the profession that restrict how they must practice and that often are much more stringent than law or regulation.

When you realize that restricting the practice of engineering to certain licensed professionals by the state is essentially a state-provided monopoly, you may begin to see why there is a difference. Competitive businesses compete in many ways to gain the kind of advantage in their field that engineers and other licensed professionals are given by the state.

Aggressive advertising is one example of a business practice that engineers avoid, even though it is not illegal or prohibited. Before 1978, it was common for professional societies to prohibit or narrowly restrict advertising by their practitioners; however, in 1978 the U.S. Supreme Court ruled such broad restrictions unconstitutional, allowing only reasonable restraints on advertising by professional societies. Since that time, engineering societies have adopted guidelines on advertising. Other professions have been less successful in regulating advertising. For example, the profusion of television advertising by lawyers, and the language of those advertisements, contrasts with the practice of engineering professionals where advertising is more commonly seen in technical journals or trade literature. Many believe the legal profession has suffered a loss of respect as a result, while the profession of engineering still is held in high regard by the public. It is in the interest of the engineering profession to avoid this kind of advertising, even though it is legal, because it can damage the reputation of the profession.

Another example of the importance of self-regulation is the engineer's responsibility to the environment. Although many laws and regulations restrict engineer-

ing practices that might damage the environment, there are still many legal ways to accomplish engineering projects that can have adverse environmental effects. Increasingly, codes of ethics are adding requirements for the engineer to consider the environment or the "sustainability" of proposed engineering projects. The engineer's ethical responsibility to work toward sustainable development may go beyond any legal requirements intended to prevent environmental damage.

Conflicts of Interest

A conflict of interest is any situation where the decision of an engineer can have some significant effect on his or her financial situation. It would be a clear conflict of interest for a designing engineer to specify exclusively some component that is only available from a supplier in which that engineer has a significant financial interest, when other components from other suppliers would serve equally well. Engineers must avoid even the *appearance* of a conflict of interest. This is critically important for the reputation of the profession, which the engineer is charged with protecting, in order for engineers to effectively serve the public interest.

An apparent conflict of interest is any situation that might appear to an outside observer to be an actual conflict of interest. For example, if the engineer in the case mentioned above had subsequently divested himself of all interest in the supplier, there is no longer an actual conflict of interest. However, to an outside observer with imperfect information, there might be the appearance of a conflict, resulting in the perception of unethical behavior in the public eye.

The usual remedy for conflicts of interest and apparent conflicts of interest is disclosure and, often, recusal. The engineer's interest must be disclosed in advance, generally to a supervisor, and recusal must at least be discussed. In many cases, recusal may not be necessary, but disclosure is vitally important. In every case, the public perception of the conflict must be considered, with the goal of protecting the reputation of the individuals and the profession.

PROFESSIONAL LIABILITY

Good engineering practice includes numerous checks and conservative principles of design to protect against blunders, but occasional errors and omissions can result in damage or injury. The engineer is responsible for such damage or injury, and it is good practice to carry errors and omissions insurance to provide appropriate compensation to any injured party, whether a client or a member of the public. Such insurance can be a significant cost in some fields of engineering, but it represents a cost of doing business that should be reflected in the fees charged. The most important factor in preventing errors and blunders is to provide adequate time for careful review of all steps in the project by knowledgeable senior licensed engineers. Frantic schedules and unrealistic deadlines can significantly increase the risk.

PUBLIC PROTECTION ISSUES

State boards in all 50 states and the District of Columbia are charged by their states with the responsibility for the licensing of engineers and the regulation of the practice of engineering to protect the health, safety, and welfare of the public. Licensed engineers in each state are legally bound by laws and regulations published by the respective state board. The boards are generally made up of engineers

appointed by the state governor; sometimes nonengineering members also are appointed to make sure the public is adequately represented.

State boards commonly issue cease and desist letters to nonengineers who have firms or businesses with names that imply engineering services are being offered to the public or who may actually be offering engineering services without the required state license. These boards also regulate the practice of engineering by their registrants, often sanctioning registrants for inappropriate business practices or engineering design decisions. Many boards require continuing education by registrants for maintenance of proficiency. A weakness of many boards is in the area of discipline for incompetent practices, but this weakness is often offset by tort law whereby incompetent practitioners who cause damage or injury are commonly subject to significant legal damages.

REFERENCES

Harris, Charles E., Jr., Michael S. Pritchard, and Michael J. Rabins. *Engineering Ethics: Concepts and Cases.* Thompson Wadsworth, 2005.

National Council of Examiners for Engineering and Surveying. *Model Rules*, September 2006.

PROBLEMS

5.1 Jim is a PE working for an HVAC designer who often must specify compressors and other equipment for his many clients. He reports to Joan, the VP of engineering. Jim specifies compressors from several different manufacturers and suppliers based on the technical specifications and on his experience with those products in past projects. Joan's long-time friend Charlie, who has been working in technical sales of construction materials, takes a new job with one of the compressor suppliers that Jim deals with from time to time. Charlie calls on Joan, inviting her and any of her HVAC designers to lunch to discuss a new line of high-efficiency compressors; Joan invites Jim to come along. Jim should:

a. decline to attend the lunch, citing concerns about conflict of interest
b. agree to attend the lunch but insist on paying for his own meal
c. agree to attend the lunch and learn about the new line of compressors
d. report Joan to the state board and never specify compressors from that supplier again

5.2 Harry C. is an experienced geotechnical engineer who has many years' experience as a PE designing geotechnical projects and who is very familiar with the rules regarding the requirement for trench shoring and trench boxes to protect construction workers during excavations. During a vacation visit to a neighboring state, he observes a city sewer construction project with several workers in an unprotected deep trench, which, to Harry's experienced eye, is probably not safe without a trench box or shoring. Harry should:

a. remember that he is not licensed in the neighboring state and has no authority to interfere
b. approach the contractor's construction foreman and insist that work be halted until the safety of the trench is investigated
c. advise all the workers in the trench that they are in danger and encourage them to go on strike for safer conditions
d. contact the city engineer to report his concerns

5.3 Engineering student Travis is eagerly anticipating his graduation in three months and has interviewed with several firms for entry-level employment as an electrical engineer. He has received two offers to work for firms A and B in a nearby city, and after comparing the jobs, salaries, and benefits and discussing the choice with his faculty advisor, he telephones firm A whose offer is more appealing and advises them he will accept their job offer. Two weeks later he is contacted by firm C in a different city with a job offer that includes a salary more than 15% higher than the offer he has accepted plus a generous relocation allowance. Travis should:

a. decline the offer from firm C, explaining that he has already accepted a position
b. contact firm A and ask if he can reconsider his decision
c. contact firm A to give them a fair chance to match the offer from firm C
d. advise firm C that he can accept their offer if they will contact firm A to inform them of this change

5.4 EIT Jerry works for a small civil engineering firm that provides general civil engineering design services for several municipalities in the region. He has become concerned that his PE supervisor Eddie is not giving careful reviews to Jerry's work before sealing the drawings and approving them for construction. Jerry asks Eddie to review with him the design assumptions from Jerry's latest design, a steel fire exit staircase to be added to an elementary school building, because he has concerns about the appropriate design loadings. But before the design assumptions are reviewed, Jerry notices the drawings have been approved and released to the fabricator. Jerry should:

a. quit his job and find another employer
b. take a review course in live loadings for steel structures
c. in the future mark each drawing he prepares "Not Approved for Construction"
d. None of the above

5.5 Dr. Willis Hemmings, PE, is an engineering professor whose research in fire protection engineering is nationally recognized. He is retained as an expert witness for the defendant, a structural engineering design firm, in a lawsuit filed by a firefighter who was injured while fighting a fire in a steel structure that collapsed during the fire. The plaintiff's lawyer alleges that the original design of certain components of the fire protection system protecting the steel structural members was inadequate. Hemmings reviews the original design documents, which call for a protective coating that is slightly thinner than is required by the local building code. Hemmings testifies that even though the specified coating is thinner than required, he believes that the design was sound because the product used is applied by a new process that is probably more efficient and the thinner coating probably gave the same level of protection. He bases his testimony on his national reputation as an expert in this field. Such expert testimony is:

a. a commonly accepted method of certifying good engineering design in tort law
b. legal only when given by a licensed professional engineer like Hemmings
c. unethical because it contradicts accepted practice without supporting tests or other data
d. effective only because Hemmings is involved in cutting-edge research

5.6 Jackie is a young PE who works for a garden tool manufacturer that has produced about 100,000 shovels, rakes, and other garden implements annually for more than 20 years. The company recently won a contract to manufacture and supply 5000 folding entrenching tools of an existing design to a Central American military client. The vice president of marketing has been working to develop contracts with other military clients and asks Jackie to prepare a statement of qualifications (SOQ). Jackie is asked to describe the design group (consisting of two engineers, one EIT, one student intern, three CAD technicians, and one IT technician) as a "team of eight tool design engineers," and to describe the company as "experienced in the design, testing, and manufacturing of

military equipment, with a recent production history of over two million entrenching tools and related hardware." Jackie should:

a. check the production records to be sure the figures cited are accurate
b. ask the vice president to sign off on the draft of the SOQ
c. object to describing the qualifications and experiences of her group in an exaggerated way
d. be sure to mention that she is a PE and list the states in which she is licensed

5.7 The Ford Motor Company paid millions of dollars to individuals injured and killed in crashes of the Ford Pinto, which had a fuel tank and filler system that sometimes ruptured in rear-end collisions, spilling gasoline and causing fires. While many considered the filler system design deficient because of this tendency, one important factor played a role in the lawsuits. An internal Ford memo was discovered that included the cost-benefit calculations Ford managers used in making the decision not to improve the tank/filler system design. This memo was significant because:

a. it is unethical to use the cost-benefit method for safety-related decisions
b. it is illegal to estimate the value of human life in cost-benefit calculations
c. state law requires estimates of the value of human life be at least $500,000 in such calculations
d. None of the above

5.8 Charles is tasked to write specifications for electric motors and pumps for a new sanitary sewage treatment plant his employer is designing for a municipal client. Charles is concerned that he doesn't have a very good knowledge about current pump design standards but is willing to learn. Charles's fiancée is an accountant employed by a pump distributor and offers to provide Charles with a binder of specifications for all the pumps her firm distributes. Charles should:

a. decline to accept the binder, citing concerns about conflict of interest
b. accept the binder but turn it over to his employer's technical librarian without reviewing it
c. accept the binder and study the materials to gain a better understanding of pump design and specifications
d. ask his fiancée if she knows an applications engineer at her firm who would draft specifications for him

5.9 Professor Martinez is a PE who teaches chemical engineering classes at a small engineering school. His student, Erica, recently graduated and took a job with WECHO, a small firm that provides chemicals and support to oil well drilling operations. WECHO has never employed an engineer and has hired Erica, partly on Prof. Martinez's strong recommendation, in hopes that she will one day become their chief engineer. After she has worked at WECHO for about two years, her supervisor Harry calls Prof. Martinez to explain that WECHO has been required to complete an environmental assessment before deploying a new surfactant, and the assessment must be sealed by a PE. Harry explains that Erica has done

all the research to collect data and answer questions on the assessment, and everyone at WECHO agrees that she has done a superb job in completing the assessment, but it still requires the seal of a PE before submission. Harry asks Prof. Martinez if he can review Erica's work and seal the report, reminding him that he had given a glowing recommendation of Erica at the time WECHO hired her. Prof. Martinez should:

a. negotiate a consulting contract to allow him sufficient time and funding to review the report before sealing it
b. require Erica to first sign the report as an EIT and graduate engineer before reviewing it
c. require WECHO to purchase a bond against environmental damage before sealing the report
d. decline to review or seal the report, citing responsible charge issues

5.10 Jack Krompten, PE, is an experienced civil engineer working for a land development firm that has completed several successful residential subdivision developments in WoodAcres, a suburban bedroom community of a large, sprawling, and rapidly growing city. The WoodAcres city engineer, who also served half-time as the mayor, has retired, and the city council realizes that with rapid growth ahead it will be important to hire a new city engineer. They approach Krompton with an offer of half-time city engineer, suggesting that he can keep his current job while discharging the responsibilities of the city engineer—primarily reviewing plans for future residential subdivision developments in WoodAcres. Krompton should:

a. recognize that by holding two jobs he is being paid by two parties for the same work
b. insist that he can only accept the offer if his present employer agrees to reduce his responsibilities to half-time
c. recognize that a 60-hour workweek schedule will take time away from his family
d. recognize that this arrangement will probably create a conflict of interest and refuse the offer

5.11 Willis is an aerospace engineering lab test engineer who works for a space systems contractor certifying components for spacecraft service. He is in charge of a team of technicians testing a new circuit breaker design made of lighter weight materials intended for service in unpressurized compartments in rockets and spacecraft. The new design has passed all tests except for some minor overheating during certain rare electrical load conditions. The lead technician notices that this overheating does not occur when a fan is used to cool the test apparatus and proposes to run the test with the fan to complete the certification process. He points out that the load conditions will only occur during thruster operation in space, which is a much colder environment. Willis should:

a. agree to the lead technician's suggestion, since he has many years of experience in testing and certification
b. agree to run the test as suggested but include a footnote explaining the use of the fan
c. insist on running the test as specified without the use of the fan
d. report the technician to the state board for falsifying test reports

5.12 Shamar is a registered PE mechanical engineer assigned as a project manager on a new transmission line project. He is tasked to build a project team to include several engineers and EITs that will be responsible for design and construction of 7.6 miles of high tension transmission lines consisting of steel towers and aluminum conductors in an existing right of way. He realizes that foundation design and soil mechanics will be an important technical area to his project, and he has never studied these subjects. He wonders if he is qualified to supervise such a project. He should:

a. meet with his supervisor to decline the assignment
b. decline the assignment and contact the state board to report that he is being asked to take responsibility for tasks he is not knowledgeable about
c. accept the assignment and check out an introductory soil mechanics textbook from the firm's technical library
d. accept the assignment and be sure his team includes licensed engineers with expertise in these areas

5.13 Julio is a design engineer working for a sheet metal fabricating firm. He is tasked with the design of a portable steel tank for compressed air to be mass produced and sold to consumers for pressurizing automobile tires. He designs a cylindrical tank to be manufactured by rolling sheet metal into a cylinder, closing with a longitudinal weld along the top, and welding on two elliptical heads. His design drawings are approved by his supervisor, Sonja, a licensed engineer, and by the vice president of manufacturing, but when the client reviews the designs, he asks the VP to change the design so that the longitudinal weld along the top is moved to the bottom where it will not be visible to improve the esthetics and marketability of the product. The VP agrees with this change. Julio learns of this change and objects, citing concerns about corrosion at the weld if it is on the bottom. Sonja forwards Julio's objection with a recommendation against the change to the VP, with a copy to the client, but the VP insists, saying esthetics is very important in this product. Julio should:

a. accept the fact that esthetics governs this aspect of the design
b. write a letter to the client stating his objections
c. put a clear disclaimer on the drawing indicating his objections
d. contact the state board to report that his recommendation has been overruled by the VP

5.14 William is a PE who designs industrial incineration systems. He is working on a system to incinerate toxic wastes, and his employer has developed advanced technology using higher temperatures and chemical-specific catalyst systems that minimize the risk to the environment, workers, and the public. A public hearing is scheduled to address questions of safety and environmental risk posed by the project, and William is briefed by the corporate VP for public affairs about how to handle questions from the public. He is told to buy a new suit, project an air of technical competence, point out that his firm is the industry leader with many successful projects around the world, and describe the proposed system as one with "zero risk" to the public. William should:

a. follow his instructions to the letter
b. insist that his old suit is adequate, because he refuses to appear more successful than he really is, but follow the other instructions
c. follow all instructions, except use the term "minimal risk" rather than "zero risk"
d. resign from his position and look for a different employer who won't ask him to face the public

5.15 Darlene is a metallurgical engineering EIT who works for a firm that manufactures automotive body panels. She has been tasked with improvements to the design of inner fender and trunk floor panels to reduce corrosion damage. After several weeks of study and comparison of alternatives, she submits a new trunk floor panel design utilizing a weldable stainless steel that will significantly reduce corrosion compared to the galvanized carbon steel alternatives she has been considering. The new panels will cost more, however, and after much study and debate, the VP of manufacturing rejects her design and approves an alternative made of a cheaper material. Darlene should:

a. accept the decision and work to finalize a workable design
b. resign from her position, since her employer has lost confidence in her
c. contact the state board to advise that her design decision has been overturned by a nonengineering manager
d. None of the above

5.16 Matt is a young PE who has just started his own consulting practice after six years of work with a small consulting firm providing structural engineering design services to architects. He has worked on steel and timber framed churches, prestressed and reinforced concrete parking structures, and many tilt-up strip center buildings. His expertise has been in the area of design of tilt-up concrete construction, where he has developed some innovative details regarding reinforcement at lifting points. His building designs, when constructed by experienced contractors, have reduced construction times and costs. Because of his expertise, he is approached by lawyer Marlene, who tells Matt that she represents a construction worker who is suing a project owner, contractor, and designer over a construction accident in which a tilt-up wall was dropped during construction, seriously injuring several workers. Marlene asks Matt to serve as an expert witness to assess the design and construction practices in the project and testify as to the causes of the accident. Marlene has taken the case on a contingency fee basis, in which she will earn 40% of any settlement, and she asks Matt if he would rather be paid by the hour for his study and testimony or instead accept 5% of any settlement, which she believes could be as high as $25 million. Matt should:

a. compare the 5% contingency fee with an expected fee based on his hourly rates, realizing that there is some chance he will earn nothing
b. be sure to have Marlene put the contingency fee arrangement in the form of a legal contract
c. decline the contingency fee arrangement and bill on an hourly basis
d. accept the contingency fee arrangement but donate the difference over his hourly rate to charity

5.17 Victor is a consulting engineer who is also in charge of a crew providing land surveying and subdivision design services to developers. He has been contracted to provide a survey of a 14-acre tract where a local developer is contemplating a subdivision, and he realizes that his crew had surveyed this same tract last month for another developer who has abandoned the project. He reprints the survey drawings, changing the title block for the new client. With respect to billing for the drawings, Victor should:

a. bill the new client the same as he billed the original client to be fair to both
b. bill the new client for half of the amount billed to the original client
c. bill the new client only for any work he did to change the drawings and reprint them
d. provide the new client with the drawings without any charge

5.18 Frank is a PE who works for ELEC, an electrical engineering design and construction firm. Frank's job is estimating construction costs, bidding construction projects, and supervision of design of electrical systems for buildings. Frank's bright EIT of five years, Linda, has just received her PE license and has resigned her position to open her own consulting business in a nearby community. Until she is replaced, Frank will have to also do all detail design of electrical systems for their projects. Frank receives a request for proposal (RFP) from a general contractor regarding design of electrical systems for a local independent school district. He realizes that his firm may be in competition with Linda for the engineering design, and knowing that Linda's salary was about half of his, he expects she may have a competitive advantage. Frank should:

a. ask Linda not to bid on this project
b. remind his contact with the general contractor that Linda has just left his firm, that she is inexperienced, and hint that she was sometimes slow to complete her design assignments
c. emphasize his 18 years of experience and subsequent design efficiency in his proposal
d. promote a CAD technician to a designer position so he can show a lower billing rate for engineering design hours

5.19 It is important to avoid the appearance of a conflict of interest because:

a. the engineer's judgment might be adversely affected
b. the engineer's client might suffer financial damages
c. the appearance of a conflict of interest is a misdemeanor
d. the appearance of a conflict of interest damages the reputation of the profession

5.20 The code of ethics published by the American Society of Civil Engineers is:

a. legally binding on all licensed engineers practicing civil engineering
b. adhered to voluntarily by members of the ASCE as a condition of membership
c. legally binding on all engineers with a degree in civil engineering
d. published only as a training guideline for young civil engineers

5.21 Which statement *MOST* accurately describes an engineer's responsibility to the environment?

a. The engineer has a legal obligation to make sure all development is sustainable.
b. The engineer has no obligation to the environment beyond protecting public health and safety.
c. The engineer has a moral obligation to consider the impact of his or her work on the environment.
d. The engineer's environmental responsibility is primarily governed by specific state laws.

SOLUTIONS

5.1 **c.** Jim can accept this invitation. We can assume there is no corporate policy prohibiting or restricting lunch invitations since VP Joan has accepted the invitation; therefore, there is no reason for Jim to decline the invitation. The opportunity to learn more about the new product is useful to him, his employer, and his clients; the cost of the lunch presumably would not be considered a "valuable" gift; and the lunch would not create either a conflict of interest or the appearance of a conflict to a reasonable person. If instead of lunch the offer involved a 10-day elk hunting trip or a vacation in the south of France, the solution would be very different because of the obvious "value" of the gift.

5.2 **d.** Doing nothing (a) is not an option if Harry really believes the trench represents a serious hazard to the workers. His code of ethics requires him to remember that his first and foremost responsibility is the public welfare, which includes the safety of the construction workers. Answers (b) and (c) are not the best way to proceed; his concerns should be reported to an engineer with some authority over the project. Since this is a city-contracted sewer improvement project, the city engineer will have project responsibility and will be the appropriate individual for Harry to take his concerns to.

5.3 **a.** Travis should decline the offer from firm C, explaining that he has already accepted an offer to work for firm A. While the *NCEES Model Rules* don't specifically address issues of personal integrity, it is clear that the engineer's obligation to employer and clients will not be satisfied by any decision that ignores Travis's verbal agreement to employment with firm A. Furthermore, such actions will tarnish his integrity in the eyes of firm A and by implication will harm the reputation and credibility of other students and the profession.

5.4 **d.** None of the first three solutions will address the concerns Jerry has raised about the safety of the particular project in question, so (d) is the correct solution. He should instead meet with Eddie to discuss the details of his design and make a determination if the design is completed safely. If it isn't, he will need to take further action to stop fabrication and construction while the design is reviewed and possibly modified to address any deficiencies. After this is done, he might want to consider all three of the other choices for his future. If he is thwarted in these responsibilities by Eddie, he should contact the state board with his concerns.

5.5 **c.** Hemmings cannot offer expert opinion that is contrary to accepted engineering practice without supporting that opinion with computer modeling, lab test results, or study of the literature. He can offer expert opinion that the design is not in line with accepted engineering practice without any supporting calculations, but he can't maintain that a substandard practice is acceptable without rational supporting evidence. Hemmings's credentials and experience may qualify him as

an expert, but they do not relieve him of the requirement to base his professional opinion on facts.

5.6 c. Jackie should object to the request to exaggerate the size, qualifications, and experience level of her design group. The *Model Rules* require engineers to "be objective and truthful" in all professional matters, and the suggested exaggerations are clearly in conflict with this requirement.

5.7 d. It is not unethical or illegal to use the cost-benefit method, nor are certain values for human life prescribed by law; the answer is none of the above. The assumed values and calculations in the memo may have appeared callous or inflammatory to the juries in the resulting lawsuits, but they were not unethical or illegal. They may have been imprudent—an important lesson is that the public (jury) apparently objected to a design decision that increased the risk of a post-crash fire for such a small net benefit. Even though risk of death had been considered by the designers, the mode of death (burning to death in otherwise survivable crashes) was a factor in the strong reactions by the juries.

5.8 c. Studying products from a distributor is perfectly acceptable and can be a good way to gain a better understanding of pump equipment on the market. Accepting the binder does not represent a conflict of interest as implied by choices (a) and (b). Option (d) would be clearly setting himself up for an apparent conflict of interest.

5.9 d. Since Prof. Martinez has not been in responsible charge of the development of the assessment, he can't seal it, regardless of the level of review or the capabilities of the EIT who has done the work. Engineering students should be cautious in accepting a position as the sole engineering employee in a small firm; they are first encouraged to gain experience as an EIT under the guidance of an experienced PE and qualify for licensure as a PE before taking a position where licensure might be needed.

5.10 d. Krompton should recognize that the proposed arrangement will create a conflict of interest by placing him in charge of reviewing and approving plans from developers and potential developers that are in direct competition with his own employer. Any decision by him that might tend to make development less profitable for other developers could be advantageous to his employer by making their services more cost effective. Even if he were able to make all decisions rationally and without bias, the appearance of a conflict of interest would be very real and would cause a loss of credibility in the city engineer's actions and damage the reputation of the engineering profession.

5.11 c. Willis should insist on running the test as specified. The technician's suggestion to use a fan to "fudge" the test is technically indefensible, as well as unethical, in any case—the fan simulates convection cooling, which does not occur in the vacuum of space. Even if the techni-

cian had suggested a way to simulate an increased radiative heat flux, changes to a specified test procedure are not made casually. Much more study, documentation, and higher level approvals are involved.

5.12 **d.** Shamar should accept the assignment and select team members so that all areas of needed expertise are represented by licensed individuals who can seal appropriate portions of the plans. Option (a) is not recommended for an engineer's career advancement—he is expected to accept assignments of increasing responsibility; (b) is detrimental to his career—he will cause unnecessary concern with the board and with his supervisors; and (c) studying an introductory soil mechanics textbook may give him a better understanding of the problem but probably won't qualify him to seal foundation plans for the project described.

5.13 **d.** Julio is objecting because he knows water accumulates in compressed air storage tanks and causes corrosion, particularly at the bottom where the water will collect. Because of the metallurgy at the weld, corrosion is more aggressive at the weld site, and Julio considers this fundamentally a bad design if the weld is at the bottom. Since his recommendation (based on technical reasons and an increased risk to the public) is overruled under circumstances where the safety of the public is endangered, he is obligated (by the NCEES rules) to "notify his employer or client and other such authority." Having already notified his employer (through Sonja and the VP of manufacturing) and the client, all of whom except Sonja are part of the problem, his next logical step is to contact the state board with his concerns. This is rarely necessary; in most cases, the client and VP will be very interested in Julio's objection as it is based on public safety and will serve to reduce the company's own liability. However, if the employer and VP of manufacturing persist as described here, Julio must take additional action. It is not unreasonable to expect that Julio may face some sort of sanction from a management team that has put him in this position. He may even need a lawyer as this unpleasant situation deteriorates. Whistle-blowing should be considered the solution of last resort, as in this case.

5.14 **c.** William should avoid the use of the term "zero risk"; he knows that no project has zero risk. He should instead look for ways to quantify the risk that will be informative and meaningful to the public and try to convey the attitude of concern for minimizing the risk consistent with the potential public benefits of the project (increased employment and tax base). He should not do (a), and (b) does not address the problem of misinforming the public about the risk. There is no need to resign; to do so will not help his career or the project.

5.15 **a.** Darlene should accept the decision and work to make the chosen design successful and profitable for her employer. She does not need to resign—the business decision probably does not reflect a lack of confidence. It was made based on costs and profitability, not public safety, so she should not contact authorities to complain

that a manager has overruled her. This kind of decision should be considered a "management decision" because it affects business and profits. Decisions that adversely affect public health, safety, or welfare should be considered "engineering decisions," and when these are overturned by nontechnical managers for other reasons, the engineer may be justified or even obligated to report this to authorities.

5.16 **c.** Matt should decline the contingency fee arrangement. While lawyers commonly work on contingency fee arrangements, engineers can't do this. Any contingency fee arrangement would put the engineer in a conflict of interest situation, where his engineering judgment can influence his income. In such a situation, his engineering judgment may not be sound or will at least appear to be conflicted to an outside observer.

5.17 **c.** Victor should be cautious in making sure that no additional surveying or resurveying is needed because of any changes to the tract. If additional fieldwork is not needed, he should bill the new client only for the work required to edit and reprint the drawings. He should not bill the new client the same as the original client, because that would be billing two clients for the same work, which is specifically prohibited by the *Model Rules*. Billing for half of the original amount is the same, just for an arbitrary amount. When two clients require the same survey simultaneously, it may make sense for Victor to facilitate a partnership in the project, but this is not always feasible when one client has already been billed for work done.

5.18 **c.** Option (c) is the only ethical and practical solution listed. Option (a) asking a competitor not to bid is not practical. Option (b) starting rumors about Linda's capabilities is clearly unethical. And option (d) is troublesome—experienced CAD technicians can do some aspects of design if closely supervised by a PE, but it isn't really necessary to make such a promotion just to show a lower billing rate. The billing rate for engineering design could be maintained at the same (competitive) level as when Linda was employed, even if the actual design work is done by Frank at twice the salary until a replacement for Linda can be hired. This in itself is not unethical, but if Frank does not budget sufficient time to do the design work in addition to his other work, it becomes a question of ethics. An engineer must allow sufficient time to do a professional job. The most practical and desirable solution is not listed—Frank should expedite hiring a qualified replacement for Linda, and he might have to consider declining the opportunity to bid on some projects until she is replaced.

5.19 **d.** Even the appearance of a conflict of interest can damage the reputation of the individuals involved and the profession as a whole, and such situations should be avoided. If there is no actual conflict of interest, the engineer's judgment will not be affected and the client will not suffer damages; nor is it criminal.

5.20 **b.** Codes of ethics published by professional societies are voluntarily adhered to by membership. They don't carry the weight of law but are much more than training guidelines—members who do not adhere to the society's code can be sanctioned by the society or forfeit their membership.

5.21 **c.** Many professional societies require the engineer to "consider" the impact on the environment. Some say he or she should consider whether the development is "sustainable." Most legal restrictions only require the engineer to prevent certain kinds of environmental damage and do not require sustainable development. There are, of course, specific state laws that must be followed, but many federal laws and regulations also apply. The engineer's responsibility is broader than laws and regulations in any event, making choice (c) the best answer.

CHAPTER 6

Engineering Economics

OUTLINE

This is a review of the field known as **engineering economics**, **engineering economy**, or **engineering economic analysis**. Since engineering economics is straightforward and logical, even people who have not had a formal course should be able to gain sufficient knowledge from this chapter to successfully solve most engineering economics problems.

There are 30 example problems throughout this review. These examples are an integral part of the review and should be examined as you come to them.

The field of engineering economics uses mathematical and economic techniques to systematically analyze situations that pose alternative courses of action. The initial step in engineering economics problems is to resolve a situation, or each possible alternative in a given situation, into its favorable and unfavorable consequences or factors. These are then measured in some common unit, usually money. Factors that cannot readily be equated to money are called **intangible** or **irreducible** factors. Such factors are considered in conjunction with the monetary analysis when making the final decision on proposed courses of action.

CASH FLOW

A cash flow table shows the *money consequences* of a situation and its timing. For example, a simple problem might be to list the year-by-year consequences of purchasing and owning a used car:

Year	Cash Flow	
Beginning of first year 0	−$4500	Car purchased now for $4500 cash. (The minus sign indicates a disbursement.)
End of year 1	−350	Maintenance costs are $350 per year.
End of year 2	−350	
End of year 3	−350	
End of year 4	−350 +2000	This car is sold at the end of the fourth year for $2000. (The plus sign represents the receipt of money.)

This same cash flow may be represented graphically, as shown in Figure 6.1. The upward arrow represents a receipt of money, and the downward arrows represent disbursements. The horizontal axis represents the passage of time.

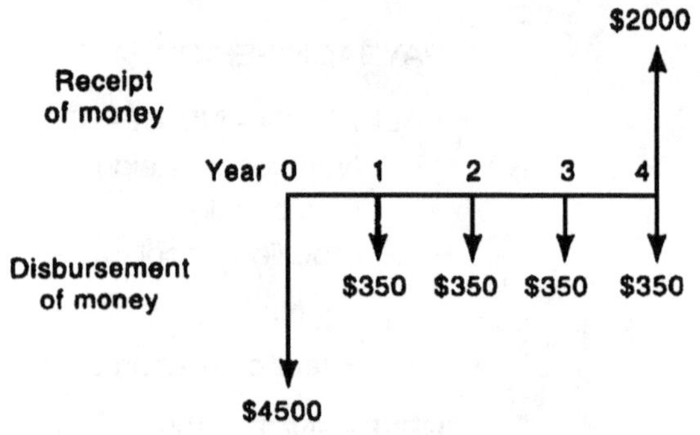

Figure 6.1 Cash flow diagram

Example **6.1**

In January 2003, a firm purchased a used copier for $500. Repairs cost nothing in 2003 or 2004. Repairs were $85 in 2005, $130 in 2006, and $140 in 2007. The machine was sold in 2007 for $300. Complete the cash flow table.

Solution

Unless otherwise stated, the customary assumption is a beginning-of-year purchase, followed by end-of-year receipts or disbursements, and an end-of-year resale or salvage value. Thus the copier repairs and the copier sale are assumed to occur at the end of the year. Letting a minus sign represent a disbursement of money and a plus sign a receipt of money, we are able to set up the cash flow table:

Year	Cash Flow
Beginning of 2003	–$500
End of 2003	0
End of 2004	0
End of 2005	–85
End of 2006	–130
End of 2007	+160

Notice that at the end of 2007, the cash flow table shows +160, which is the net sum of –140 and +300. If we define year 0 as the beginning of 2003, the cash flow table becomes:

Year	Cash Flow
0	–$500
1	0
2	0
3	–85
4	–130
5	+160

From this cash flow table, the definitions of year 0 and year 1 become clear. Year 0 is defined as the *beginning* of year 1. Year 1 is the *end* of year 1, and so forth.

TIME VALUE OF MONEY

When the money consequences of an alternative occur in a short period of time—say, less than one year—we might simply add up the various sums of money and obtain the net result. But we cannot treat money this way over longer periods of time. This is because money today does not have the same value as money at some future time.

Consider this question: Which would you prefer, $100 today or the assurance of receiving $100 a year from now? Clearly, you would prefer the $100 today. If you had the money today, rather than a year from now, you could use it for the year. And if you had no use for it, you could lend it to someone who would pay interest for the privilege of using your money for the year.

EQUIVALENCE

In the preceding section we saw that money at different points in time (for example, \$100 today or \$100 one year hence) may be equal in the sense that it is \$100, but \$100 a year hence is *not* an acceptable substitute for \$100 today. When we have acceptable substitutes, we say they are *equivalent* to each other. Thus at 8% interest, \$108 a year hence is equivalent to \$100 today.

Example 6.2

At a 10% per year (compound) interest rate, \$500 now is *equivalent* to how much three years hence?

Solution

A value of \$500 now will increase by 10% in each of the three years.

$$\begin{aligned} \text{Now} &= \$500.00 \\ \text{End of 1st year} &= 500 + 10\%(500) = \$550.00 \\ \text{End of 2nd year} &= 550 + 10\%(550) = \$605.00 \\ \text{End of 3rd year} &= 605 + 10\%(605) = \$665.50 \end{aligned}$$

Thus \$500 now is *equivalent* to \$665.50 at the end of three years. Note that interest is charged each year on the original \$500 plus the unpaid interest.

Equivalence is an essential factor in engineering economics. Suppose we wish to select the better of two alternatives. First, we must compute their cash flows. For example:

	Alternative	
Year	***A***	***B***
0	–\$2000	–\$2800
1	+800	+1100
2	+800	+1100
3	+800	+1100

The larger investment in alternative *B* results in larger subsequent benefits, but we have no direct way of knowing whether it is better than alternative *A*. So we do not know which to select. To make a decision, we must resolve the alternatives into *equivalent* sums so that they may be compared accurately.

COMPOUND INTEREST

To facilitate equivalence computations, a series of compound interest factors will be derived here, and their use will be illustrated in examples.

Symbols and Functional Notation

i = effective interest rate per interest period. In equations, the interest rate is stated as a decimal (i.e., 8% interest is 0.08).

n = number of interest periods. Usually, the interest period is one year, in which case n would be number of years.

P = a present sum of money.

F = a future sum of money. The future sum F is an amount n interest periods from the present that is equivalent to P at interest rate i.

A = an end-of-period cash receipt or disbursement (annuity) in a uniform series continuing for n periods. The entire series is equivalent to P or F at interest rate i.

G = uniform period-by-period increase in cash flows; the uniform gradient.

r = nominal annual interest rate.

From Table 6.1 we can see that the functional notation scheme is based on writing (to find/given, i, n). Thus, if we wished to find the future sum F, given a uniform series of receipts A, the proper compound interest factor to use would be $(F/A, i, n)$.

Table 6.1 Periodic compounding: Functional notation and formulas

Factor	Given	To Find	Functional Notation	Formula
Single payment				
Compound amount factor	P	F	$(F/P, i\%, n)$	$F = P(1+i)^n$
Present worth factor	F	P	$(P/F, i\%, n)$	$P = F(1+i)^{-n}$
Uniform payment series				
Sinking fund factor	F	A	$(A/F, i\%, n)$	$A = F\left[\frac{i}{(1+i)^n - 1}\right]$
Capital recovery factor	P	A	$(A/P, i\%, n)$	$A = P\left[\frac{i(1+i)^n}{(1+i)^n - 1}\right]$
Compound amount factor	A	F	$(F/A, i\%, n)$	$F = A\left[\frac{(1+i)^n - 1}{i}\right]$
Present worth factor	A	P	$(P/A, i\%, n)$	$P = A\left[\frac{(1+i)^n - 1}{i(1+i)^n}\right]$
Uniform gradient				
Gradient present worth	G	P	$(P/G, i\%, n)$	$P = G\left[\frac{(1+i)^n - 1}{i^2(1+i)^n} - \frac{n}{i(1+i)^n}\right]$
Gradient future worth	G	F	$(F/G, i\%, n)$	$F = G\left[\frac{(1+i)^n - 1}{i^2} - \frac{n}{1}\right]$
Gradient uniform series	G	A	$(A/G, i\%, n)$	$A = G\left[\frac{1}{i} - \frac{n}{(1+i)^n - 1}\right]$

Single-Payment Formulas

Suppose a present sum of money P is invested for one year at interest rate i. At the end of the year, the initial investment P is received together with interest equal to Pi, or a total amount $P + Pi$. Factoring P, the sum at the end of one year is $P(1 + i)$. If the investment is allowed to remain for subsequent years, the progression is as follows:

Amount at Beginning of the Period	+	Interest for the Period	=	Amount at End of the Period
1st year, P	+	Pi	=	$P(1 + i)$
2nd year, $P(1 + i)$	+	$Pi(1 + i)$	=	$P(1 + i)^2$
3rd year, $P(1 + i)^2$	+	$Pi(1 + i)^2$	=	$P(1 + i)^3$
nth year, $P(1 + i)^{n-1}$	+	$Pi(1 + i)^{n-1}$	=	$P(1 + i)^n$

The present sum P increases in n periods to $P(1 + i)^n$. This gives a relation between a present sum P and its equivalent future sum F:

$$\text{Future sum} = (\text{present sum})(1 + i)^n$$
$$F = P(1 + i)^n$$

This is the **single-payment compound amount formula**. In functional notation it is written

$$F = P(F/P, i, n)$$

The relationship may be rewritten as

$$\text{Present sum} = (\text{Future sum})\ (1 + i)^{-n}$$
$$P = F(1 + i)^{-n}$$

This is the **single-payment present worth formula**. It is written

$$P = F(P/F, i, n)$$

Example 6.3

At a 10% per year interest rate, \$500 now is *equivalent* to how much three years hence?

Solution

This problem was solved in Example 6.2. Now it can be solved using a single-payment formula. $P = \$500$, $n = 3$ years, $i = 10\%$, and F = unknown:

$$F = P(1 + i)^n = 500(1 + 0.10)^3 = \$665.50$$

This problem also may be solved using a compound interest table:

$$F = P(F/P, i, n) = 500(F/P, 10\%, 3)$$

From the 10% compound interest table, read $(F/P, 10\%, 3) = 1.331$.

$$F = 500(F/P, 10\%, 3) = 500(1.331) = \$665.50$$

Example 6.4

To raise money for a new business, a small startup company asks you to lend it some money. The entrepreneur offers to pay you \$3000 at the end of four years. How much should you give the company now if you want to realize 12% interest per year?

Solution

P = unknown, F = \$3000, n = 4 years, and i = 12%:

$$P = F(1 + i)^{-n} = 3000(1 + 0.12)^{-4} = \$1906.55$$

Alternative computation using a compound interest table:

$$P = F(P/F, i, n) = 3000(P/F, 12\%, 4) = 3000(0.6355) = \$1906.50$$

Note that the solution based on the compound interest table is slightly different from the exact solution using a hand-held calculator. In engineering economics, the compound interest tables are considered to be sufficiently accurate.

Uniform Payment Series Formulas

Consider the situation shown in Figure 6.2. Using the single-payment compound amount factor, we can write an equation for F in terms of A:

$$F = A + A(1 + i) + A(1 + i)^2 \qquad \textbf{(i)}$$

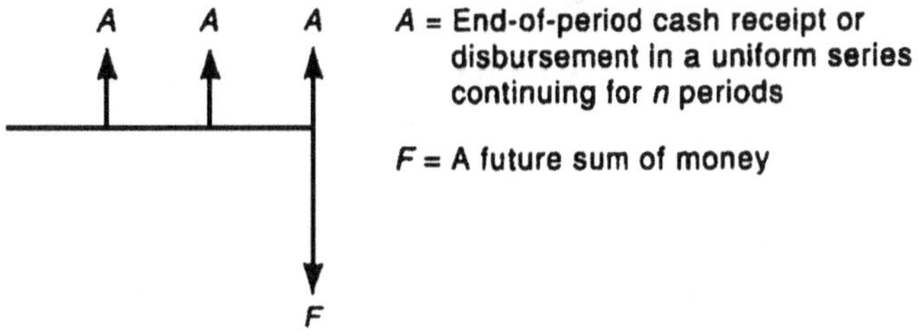

Figure 6.2 Cash flow diagram—uniform payment series

In this situation, with n = 3, Equation (i) may be written in a more general form:

$$F = A + A(1 + i) + A(1 + i)^{n-1} \qquad \textbf{(ii)}$$

Multiply Eq. (ii) by $(1 + i)$ $\quad (1 + i)F = A(1 + i) + A(1 + i)^{n-1} + A(1 + i)^n$ **(iii)**

Subtract Eq. (ii) yields: $\quad iF = -A + A(1 + i)^n$

This produces the **uniform series compound amount formula**:

$$F = A\left[\frac{(1+i)^n - 1}{i}\right].$$

Solving this equation for A produces the **uniform series sinking fund formula**:

$$R = \frac{8.31}{\text{m.w.}} = \frac{8.31}{18} =$$

Since $F = P(1 + i)^n$, we can substitute this expression for F in the equation and obtain the **uniform series capital recovery formula**:

$$A = P\left[\frac{i(1+i)^n}{(1+i)^n - 1}\right].$$

Solving the equation for P produces the **uniform series present worth formula**:

$$P = A\left[\frac{(1+i)^n - 1}{i(1+i)^n}\right].$$

In functional notation, the uniform series factors are:

Compound amount (F/A, i, n)

Sinking fund (A/F, i, n)

Capital recovery (A/P, i, n)

Present worth (P/A, i, n)

Example 6.5

If \$100 is deposited at the end of each year in a savings account that pays 6% interest per year, how much will be in the account at the end of five years?

Solution

$A = \$100$, F = unknown, $n = 5$ years, and $i = 6\%$:

$$F = A(F/A, i, n) = 100(F/A, 6\%, 5) = 100(5.637) = \$563.70$$

Example 6.6

A fund established to produce a desired amount at the end of a given period, by means of a series of payments throughout the period, is called a **sinking fund**. A sinking fund is to be established to accumulate money to replace a \$10,000 machine. If the machine is to be replaced at the end of 12 years, how much should be deposited in the sinking fund each year? Assume the fund earns 10% annual interest.

Solution

$$\text{Annual sinking fund deposit } A = 10{,}000(A/F, 10\%, 12)$$
$$= 10{,}000(0.0468) = \$468$$

Example 6.7

An individual is considering the purchase of a used automobile. The total price is \$6200. With \$1240 as a down payment, and the balance paid in 48 equal monthly payments with interest at 1% per month, compute the monthly payment. The payments are due at the end of each month.

Solution

The amount to be repaid by the 48 monthly payments is the cost of the automobile *minus* the \$1240 down payment.

$P = \$4960$, A = unknown, $n = 48$ monthly payments, and $i = 1\%$ per month:

$$A = P(A/P, 1\%, 48) = 4960(0.0263) = \$130.45$$

Example **6.8**

A couple sell their home. In addition to cash, they take a mortgage on the house. The mortgage will be paid off by monthly payments of \$450 for 50 months. The couple decides to sell the mortgage to a local bank. The bank will buy the mortgage, but it requires a 1% per month interest rate on its investment. How much will the bank pay for the mortgage?

Solution

$A = \$450$, $n = 50$ months, $i = 1\%$ per month, and $P =$ unknown:

$$P = A(P/A, i, n) = 450(P/A, 1\%, 50) = 450(39.196) = \$17{,}638.20$$

Uniform Gradient

At times, one will encounter a situation where the cash flow series is not a constant amount A; instead, it is an increasing series. The cash flow shown in Figure 6.3 may be resolved into two components (Figure 6.4). We can compute the value of P^* as equal to P' plus P, and we already have the equation for P':$P' = A(P/A, i, n)$.

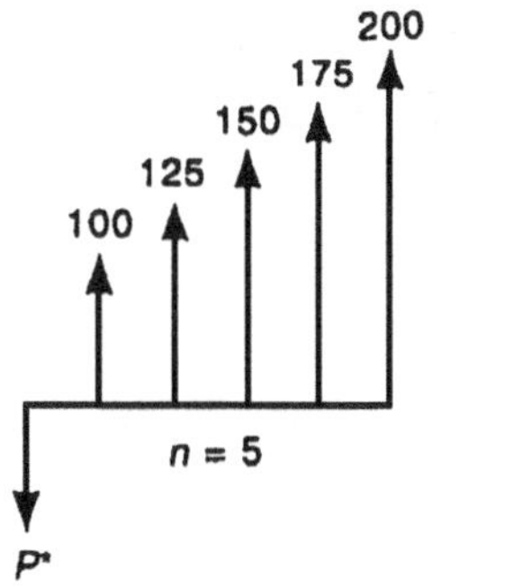

Figure 6.3 Cash flow diagram—uniform gradient

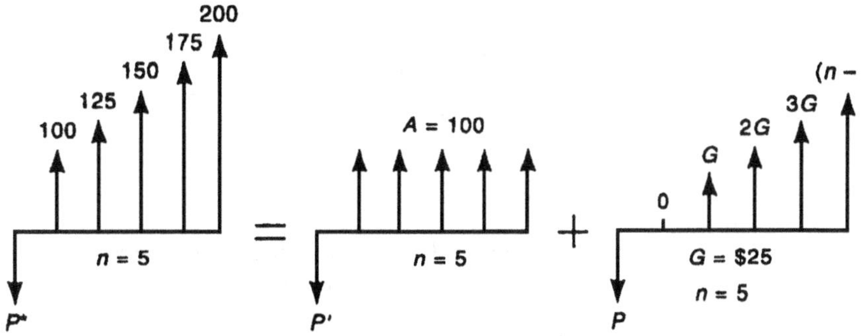

Figure 6.4 Uniform gradient diagram resolved

The value for P in the right-hand diagram is

$$P = G\left[\frac{(1+i)^n - 1}{i^2(1+i)^n} - \frac{n}{i(1+i)^n}\right].$$

This is the **uniform gradient present worth formula**. In functional notation, the relationship is $P = G(P/G, i, n)$.

Example **6.9**

The maintenance on a machine is expected to be \$155 at the end of the first year, and it is expected to increase \$35 each year for the following seven years (Exhibit 1). What sum of money should be set aside now to pay the maintenance for the eight-year period? Assume 6% interest.

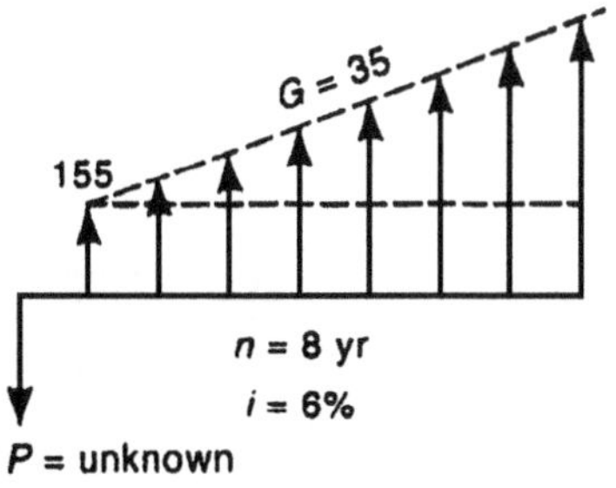

Exhibit 1

Solution

$$P = 155(P/A, 6\%, 8) + 35(P/G, 6\%, 8)$$
$$= 155(6.210) + 35(19.841) = \$1656.99$$

In the gradient series, if—instead of the present sum, P—an equivalent uniform series A is desired, the problem might appear as shown in Figure 6.5. The relationship between A' and G in the right-hand diagram is

$$A' = G\left[\frac{1}{i} - \frac{n}{(1+i)^n - 1}\right]$$

In functional notation, the uniform gradient (to) uniform series factor is: $A' = G(A/G, i, n)$.

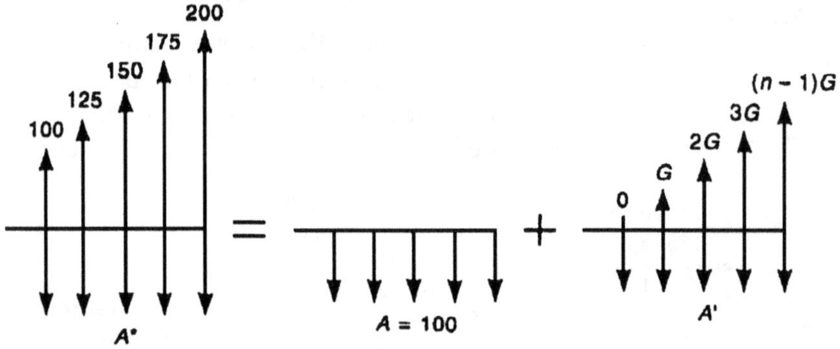

Figure 6.5 Uniform series, uniform gradient cash flow diagram

The **uniform gradient uniform series factor** may be read from the compound interest tables directly, or computed as

$$(A/G, i, n) = \frac{1 - n(A/F, i, n)}{i}$$

Note carefully the diagrams for the uniform gradient factors. The first term in the uniform gradient is zero and the last term is $(n - 1)G$. But we use n in the equations and function notation. The derivations (not shown here) were done on this basis, and the uniform gradient compound interest tables are computed this way.

Example 6.10

For the situation in Example 6.9, we wish now to know the uniform annual maintenance cost. Compute an equivalent A for the maintenance costs.

Solution

Refer to Exhibit 2. The equivalent uniform annual maintenance cost is

$$A = 155 + 35(A/G, 6\%, 8) = 155 + 35(3.195) = \$266.83$$

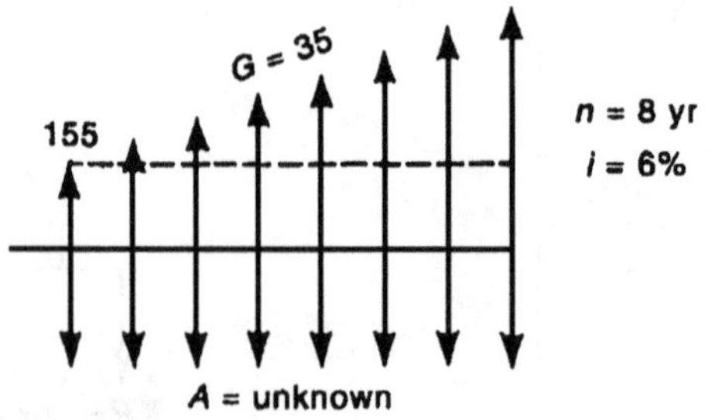

Exhibit 2

Standard compound interest tables give values for eight interest factors: two single payments, four uniform payment series, and two uniform gradients. The tables do *not* give the uniform gradient future worth factor, $(F/G, i, n)$. If it is needed, it may be computed from two tabulated factors:

$$(F/G, i, n) = (P/G, i, n)(F/P, i, n)$$

For example, if $i = 10\%$ and $n = 12$ years, then $(F/G, 10\%, 12) = (P/G, 10\%, 12)\ (F/P, 10\%, 12) = (29.901)(3.138) = 93.83$.

A second method of computing the uniform gradient future worth factor is

$$(F/G,i,n) = \frac{(F/G,i,n) - n}{i}$$

Using this equation for $i = 10\%$ and $n = 12$ years, $(F/G, 10\%, 12) = [(F/A, 10\%, 12) - 12]/0.10 = (21.384 - 12)/0.10 = 93.84$.

Table 6.2 Continuous compounding: Functional notation and formulas

Factor	Given	To Find	Functional Notation	Formula
Single payment				
Compound amount factor	P	F	$(F/P, r\%, n)$	$F = P\,[e^{rn}]$
Present worth factor	F	P	$(P/F, r\%, n)$	$P = F\,[e^{-rn}]$
Uniform payment series				
Sinking fund factor	F	A	$(A/F, r\%, n)$	$A = F\left[\frac{e^r - 1}{e^{rn} - 1}\right]$
Capital recovery factor	P	A	$(A/P, r\%, n)$	$A = P\left[\frac{e^r - 1}{1 - e^{-rn}}\right]$
Compound amount factor	A	F	$(F/A, r\%, n)$	$F = A\left[\frac{e^{rn} - 1}{e^r - 1}\right]$
Present worth factor	A	P	$(P/A, r\%, n)$	$P = A\left[\frac{1 - e^{-rn}}{e^r - 1}\right]$

r = nominal annual interest rate, n = number of years.

Example 6.11

Five hundred dollars is deposited each year into a savings bank account that pays 5% nominal interest, compounded continuously. How much will be in the account at the end of five years?

Solution

$A = \$500$, $r = 0.05$, $n = 5$ years.

$$F = A(F/A, r\%, n) = A\left[\frac{e^{rn} - 1}{e^r - 1}\right] = 500\left[\frac{e^{0.05(5)} - 1}{e^{0.05} - 1}\right] = \$2769.84$$

NOMINAL AND EFFECTIVE INTEREST

Nominal interest is the annual interest rate without considering the effect of any compounding. **Effective interest** is the annual interest rate taking into account the effect of any compounding during the year.

Non-annual Compounding

Frequently an interest rate is described as an annual rate, even though the interest period may be something other than one year. A bank may pay 1% interest on the amount in a savings account every three months. The *nominal* interest rate in this situation is $4 \times 1\% = 4\%$. But if you deposited \$1000 in such an account, would you have 104%(1000) = \$1040 in the account at the end of one year? The answer is no, you would have more. The amount in the account would increase as follows.

Amount in Account

Beginning of year:	1000.00
End of three months:	1000.00 + 1%(1000.00) = 1010.00
End of six months:	1010.00 + 1%(1010.00) = 1020.10
End of nine months:	1020.10 + 1%(1020.10) = 1030.30
End of one year:	1030.30 + 1%(1030.30) = 1040.60

At the end of one year, the interest of \$40.60, divided by the original \$1000, gives a rate of 4.06 percent. This is the *effective* interest rate.

$$\text{Effective interest rate per year:} \quad i_{eff} = (1 + r/m)^m - 1$$

where r = nominal annual interest rate
m = number of compound periods per year
r/m = effective interest rate per period

Example 6.12

A bank charges 1.5% interest per month on the unpaid balance for purchases made on its credit card. What nominal interest rate is it charging? What is the effective interest rate?

Solution

The nominal interest rate is simply the annual interest ignoring compounding, or 12(1.5%) = 18%.

$$\text{Effective interest rate} = (1 + 0.015)^{12} - 1 = 0.1956 = 19.56\%$$

SOLVING ENGINEERING ECONOMICS PROBLEMS

The techniques presented so far illustrate how to convert single amounts of money, and uniform or gradient series of money, into some equivalent sum at another point in time. These compound interest computations are an essential part of engineering economics problems.

The typical situation is that we have a number of alternatives; the question is, which alternative should we select? The customary method of solution is to express each alternative in some common form and then choose the best, taking both the monetary and intangible factors into account. In most computations an interest rate must be used. It is often called the **minimum attractive rate of return (MARR)**, to indicate that this is the smallest interest rate, or rate of return, at which one is willing to invest money.

Criteria

Engineering economics problems inevitably fall into one of three categories:

1. *Fixed input.* The amount of money or other input resources is fixed. *Example*: A project engineer has a budget of $450,000 to overhaul a plant.
2. *Fixed output.* There is a fixed task or other output to be accomplished. *Example*: A mechanical contractor has been awarded a fixed-price contract to air-condition a building.
3. *Neither input nor output fixed.* This is the general situation, where neither the amount of money (or other inputs) nor the amount of benefits (or other outputs) is fixed. *Example*: A consulting engineering firm has more work available than it can handle. It is considering paying the staff to work evenings to increase the amount of design work it can perform.

There are five major methods of comparing alternatives: present worth, future worth, annual cost, rate of return, and benefit-cost analysis. These are presented in the sections that follow.

Present Worth

Present worth analysis converts all of the money consequences of an alternative into an equivalent present sum. The criteria are:

Category	Present Worth Criterion
Fixed input	Maximize the present worth of benefits or other outputs
Fixed output	Minimize the present worth of costs or other inputs
Neither input nor output fixed	Maximize present worth of benefits minus present worth of costs, or maximize net present worth

Appropriate Problems

Present worth analysis is most frequently used to determine the present value of future money receipts and disbursements. We might want to know, for example, the present worth of an income-producing property, such as an oil well. This should provide an estimate of the price at which the property could be bought or sold.

An important restriction in the use of present worth calculation is that there must be a common analysis period for comparing alternatives. It would be incorrect, for example, to compare the present worth (PW) of cost of pump *A*, expected to last 6 years, with the PW of cost of pump *B*, expected to last 12 years (Figure 6.6). In situations like this, the solution is either to use some other analysis technique (generally, the annual cost method is suitable in these situations) or to restructure the problem so that there is a common analysis period.

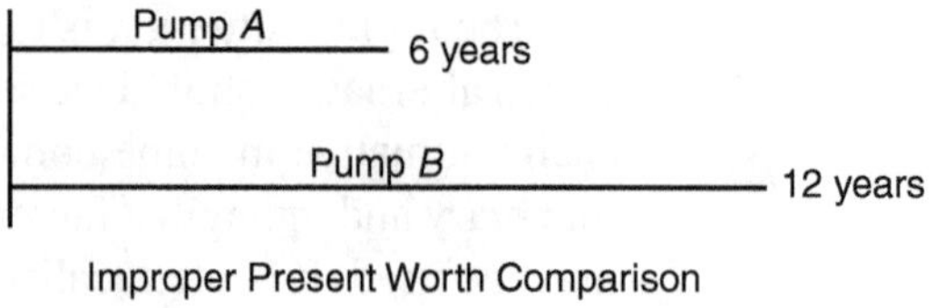

Figure 6.6 Improper present worth comparison

In this example, a customary assumption would be that a pump is needed for 12 years and that pump A will be replaced by an identical pump A at the end of 6 years. This gives a 12-year common analysis period (Figure 6.7). This approach is easy to use when the different lives of the alternatives have a practical least-common-multiple life. When this is not true (for example, the life of *J* equals 7 years and the life of *K* equals 11 years), some assumptions must be made to select a suitable common analysis period, or the present worth method should not be used.

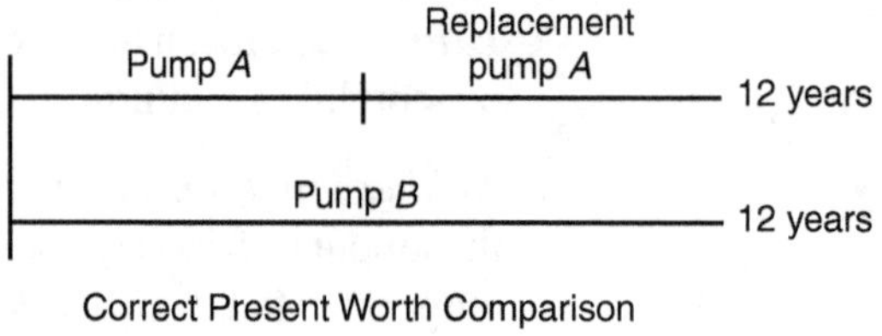

Figure 6.7 Proper present worth comparison

Example **6.13**

Machine *X* has an initial cost of \$10,000, an annual maintenance cost of \$500 per year, and no salvage value at the end of its 4-year useful life. Machine *Y* costs \$20,000, and the first year there is no maintenance cost. Maintenance is \$100 the second year, and it increases \$100 per year thereafter. The machine has an anticipated \$5000 salvage value at the end of its 12-year useful life. If the minimum attractive rate of return (MARR) is 8%, which machine should be selected?

Solution

The analysis period is not stated in the problem. Therefore, we select the least common multiple of the lives, or 12 years, as the analysis period.

Present worth of cost of 12 years of machine *X*:

$$\begin{aligned}\text{PW} &= 10{,}000 + 10{,}000(P/F, 8\%, 4) + 10{,}000(P/F, 8\%, 8) + 500(P/A, 8\%, 12)\\ &= 10{,}000 + 10{,}000(0.7350) + 10{,}000(0.5403) + 500(7.536) = \$26{,}521\end{aligned}$$

Present worth of cost of 12 years of machine *Y*:

$$\begin{aligned}\text{PW} &= 20{,}000 + 100(P/G, 8\%, 12) - 5000(P/F, 8\%, 12)\\ &= 20{,}000 + 100(34.634) - 5000(0.3971) = \$21{,}478\end{aligned}$$

Choose machine *Y*, with its smaller PW of cost.

Example **6.14**

Two alternatives have the following cash flows:

	Alternative	
Year	***A***	***B***
0	–$2000	–$2800
1	+800	+1100
2	+800	+1100
3	+800	+1100

At a 4% interest rate, which alternative should be selected?

Solution

The net present worth of each alternative is computed:

Net present worth (NPW) = PW of benefit – PW of cost

$NPW_A = 800(P/A, 4\%, 3) - 2000 = 800(2.775) - 2000 = \$220.00$

$NPW_B = 1100(P/A, 4\%, 3) - 2800 = 1100(2.775) - 2800 = \$252.50$

To maximize NPW, choose alternative *B*.

Infinite Life and Capitalized Cost

In the special situation where the analysis period is infinite ($n = \infty$), an analysis of the present worth of cost is called **capitalized cost**. There are a few public projects where the analysis period is infinity. Other examples are permanent endowments and cemetery perpetual care.

When n equals infinity, a present sum P will accrue interest of Pi for every future interest period. For the principal sum P to continue undiminished (an essential requirement for n equal to infinity), the end-of-period sum A that can be disbursed is Pi (Figure 6.8).

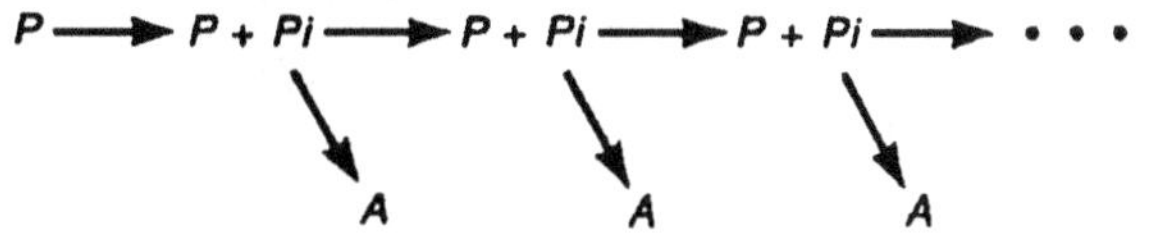

Figure 6.8 Infinite life, capitalized cost diagram

When $n = \infty$, the fundamental relationship is

$$A = Pi$$

Some form of this equation is used whenever there is a problem involving an infinite analysis period.

Example **6.15**

In his will, a man wishes to establish a perpetual trust to provide for the maintenance of a small local park. If the annual maintenance is $7500 per year and the trust account can earn 5% interest, how much money must be set aside in the trust?

Solution

When $n = \infty$, $A = Pi$ or $P = A/i$. The capitalized cost is $P = A/i = \$7500/0.05 = \$150{,}000$.

Future Worth or Value

In present worth analysis, the comparison is made in terms of the equivalent present costs and benefits. But the analysis need not be made in terms of the present—it can be made in terms of a past, present, or future time. Although the numerical calculations may look different, the decision is unaffected by the selected point in time. Often we do want to know what the future situation will be if we take some particular course of action now. An analysis based on some future point in time is called **future worth analysis.**

Category	Future Worth Criterion
Fixed input	Maximize the future worth of benefits or other outputs
Fixed output	Minimize the future worth of costs or other inputs
Neither input nor output fixed	Maximize future worth of benefits minus future worth of costs, or maximize net future worth

Example 6.16

Two alternatives have the following cash flows:

	Alternative	
Year	*A*	*B*
0	–\$2000	–\$2800
1	+800	+1100
2	+800	+1100
3	+800	+1100

At a 4% interest rate, which alternative should be selected?

Solution

In Example 6.14, this problem was solved by present worth analysis at year 0. Here it will be solved by future worth analysis at the end of year 3.

Net future worth (NFW) = FW of benefits – FW of cost

$$\begin{aligned} NFW_A &= 800(F/A, 4\%, 3) - 2000(F/P, 4\%, 3) \\ &= 800(3.122) - 2000(1.125) = +\$247.60 \end{aligned}$$

$$\begin{aligned} NFW_B &= 1100(F/A, 4\%, 3) - 2800(F/P, 4\%, 3) \\ &= 1100(3.122) - 2800(1.125) = +\$284.20 \end{aligned}$$

To maximize NFW, choose alternative *B*.

Annual Cost

The annual cost method is more accurately described as the method of equivalent uniform annual cost (EUAC). Where the computation is of benefits, it is called the method of equivalent uniform annual benefits (EUAB).

Criteria

For each of the three possible categories of problems, there is an annual cost criterion for economic efficiency.

Category	Annual Cost Criterion
Fixed input	Maximize the equivalent uniform annual benefits (EUAB)
Fixed output	Minimize the equivalent uniform annual cost (EUAC)
Neither input nor output fixed	Maximize EUAB – EUAC

Application of Annual Cost Analysis

In the section on present worth, we pointed out that the present worth method requires a common analysis period for all alternatives. This restriction does not apply in all annual cost calculations, but it is important to understand the circumstances that justify comparing alternatives with different service lives.

Frequently, an analysis is done to provide for a more-or-less continuing requirement. For example, one might need to pump water from a well on a continuing basis. Regardless of whether each of two pumps has a useful service life of 6 years or 12 years, we would select the alternative whose annual cost is a minimum. And this still would be the case if the pumps' useful lives were the more troublesome 7 and 11 years. Thus, if we can assume a continuing need for an item, an annual cost comparison among alternatives of differing service lives is valid. The underlying assumption in these situations is that the shorter-lived alternative can be replaced with an identical item with identical costs, when it has reached the end of its useful life. This means that the EUAC of the initial alternative is equal to the EUAC for the continuing series of replacements.

On the other hand, if there is a specific requirement to pump water for ten years, then each pump must be evaluated to see what costs will be incurred during the analysis period and what salvage value, if any, may be recovered at the end of the analysis period. The annual cost comparison needs to consider the actual circumstances of the situation.

Examination problems are often readily solved using the annual cost method. And the underlying *continuing requirement* is usually present, so an annual cost comparison of unequal-lived alternatives is an appropriate method of analysis.

Example 6.17

Consider the following alternatives:

	A	*B*
First cost	\$5000	\$10,000
Annual maintenance	500	200
End-of-useful-life salvage value	600	1000
Useful life	5 years	15 years

Based on an 8% interest rate, which alternative should be selected?

Solution

Assuming both alternatives perform the same task and there is a continuing requirement, the goal is to minimize EUAC.

Alternative *A*:

$$\begin{aligned} \text{EUAC} &= 5000(A/P, 8\%, 5) + 500 - 600(A/F, 8\%, 5) \\ &= 5000(0.2505) + 500 - 600(0.1705) = \$1650 \end{aligned}$$

Alternative *B*:

$$\begin{aligned} \text{EUAC} &= 10{,}000(A/P, 8\%, 15) + 200 - 1000(A/F, 8\%, 15) \\ &= 10{,}000(0.1168) + 200 - 1000(0.0368) = \$1331 \end{aligned}$$

To minimize EUAC, select alternative *B*.

Rate of Return Analysis

A typical situation is a cash flow representing the costs and benefits. The rate of return may be defined as the interest rate where PW of cost = PW of benefits, EUAC = EUAB, or PW of cost – PW of benefits = 0.

Example 6.18

Compute the rate of return for the investment represented by the following cash flow table.

Year:	0	1	2	3	4	5
Cash flow:	–\$595	+250	+200	+150	+100	+50

Solution

This declining uniform gradient series may be separated into two cash flows (Exhibit 3) for which compound interest factors are available.

Note that the gradient series factors are based on an *increasing* gradient. Here the declining cash flow is solved by subtracting an increasing uniform gradient, as indicated in Exhibit 3.

PW of cost – PW of benefits = 0

$$595 - [250(P/A, i, 5)] - 50(P/G, i, 5) = 0$$

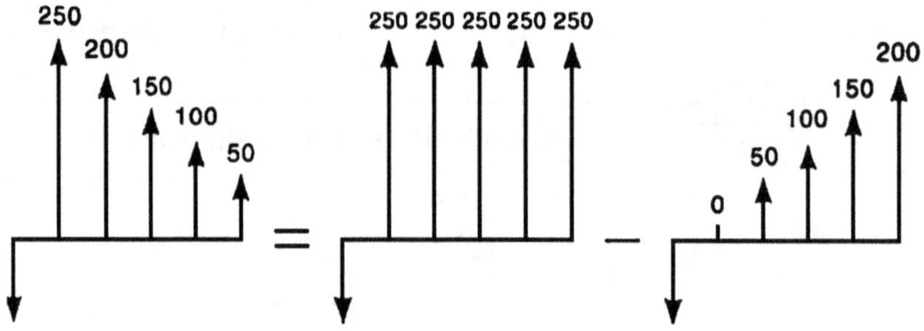

Exhibit 3

Try $i = 10\%$:

$$595 - [250(3.791) - 50(6.862)] = -9.65$$

Try $i = 12\%$:

$$595 - [250(3.605) - 50(6.397)] = +13.60$$

The rate of return is between 10 and 12%. It may be computed more accurately by linear interpolation:

$$\text{Rate of return} = 10\% + (2\%)\left(\frac{9.65 - 0}{13.60 + 9.65}\right) = 10.83\%$$

Two Alternatives

Compute the incremental rate of return on the cash flow representing the difference between the two alternatives. Since we want to look at increments of *investment*, the cash flow for the difference between the alternatives is computed by taking the higher initial-cost alternative minus the lower initial-cost alternative. If the incremental rate of return is greater than or equal to the predetermined minimum attractive rate of return (MARR), choose the higher-cost alternative; otherwise, choose the lower-cost alternative.

Example **6.19**

Two alternatives have the following cash flows:

	Alternative	
Year	***A***	***B***
0	–$2000	–$2800
1	+800	+1100
2	+800	+1100
3	+800	+1100

If 4% is considered the minimum attractive rate of return (MARR), which alternative should be selected?

Solution

These two alternatives were previously examined in Examples 6.14 and 6.16 by present worth and future worth analysis. This time, the alternatives will be resolved using a rate-of-return analysis.

Note that the problem statement specifies a 4% MARR, whereas Examples 6.14 and 6.16 referred to a 4% interest rate. These are really two different ways of saying the same thing: the minimum acceptable time value of money is 4%.

First, tabulate the cash flow that represents the increment of investment between the alternatives. This is done by taking the higher initial-cost alternative minus the lower initial-cost alternative:

	Alternative		Difference between alternatives
Year	***A***	***B***	***B* – *A***
0	–$2000	–$2800	–$800
1	+800	+1100	+300
2	+800	+1100	+300
3	+800	+1100	+300

Then compute the rate of return on the increment of investment represented by the difference between the alternatives:

$$\text{PW of cost} = \text{PW of benefits}$$
$$800 = 300(P/A, i, 3)$$
$$(P/A, i, 3) = 800/300 = 2.67$$
$$i = 6.1\%$$

Since the incremental rate of return exceeds the 4% MARR, the increment of investment is desirable. Choose the higher-cost alternative *B*.

Before leaving this example, one should note something that relates to the rates of return on alternative *A* and on alternative *B*. These rates of return, if calculated, are:

	Rate of Return
Alternative *A*	9.7%
Alternative *B*	8.7%

The correct answer to this problem has been shown to be alternative *B*, even though alternative *A* has a higher rate of return. The higher-cost alternative may be thought of as the lower-cost alternative plus the increment of investment between them. Viewed this way, the higher-cost alternative *B* is equal to the desirable lower-cost alternative *A* plus the difference between the alternatives.

The important conclusion is that computing the rate of return for each alternative does *not* provide the basis for choosing between alternatives. Instead, incremental analysis is required.

Example 6.20

Consider the following:

	Alternative	
Year	***A***	***B***
0	–$200.0	–$131.0
1	+77.6	+48.1
2	+77.6	+48.1
3	+77.6	+48.1

If the MARR is 10%, which alternative should be selected?

Solution

To examine the increment of investment between the alternatives, we will examine the higher initial-cost alternative minus the lower initial-cost alternative, or *A* – *B*.

	Alternative		Increment
Year	***A***	***B***	***A* – *B***
0	–$200.0	–$131.0	–$69.0
1	+77.6	+48.1	+29.5
2	+77.6	+48.1	+29.5
3	+77.6	+48.1	+29.5

Solve for the incremental rate of return:

$$\text{PW of cost} = \text{PW of benefits}$$
$$69.0 = 29.5(P/A, i, 3)$$
$$(P/A, i, 3) = 69.0/29.5 = 2.339$$

From compound interest tables, the incremental rate of return is between 12 and 18%. This is a desirable increment of investment; hence we select the higher-initial-cost alternative *A*.

Three or More Alternatives

When there are three or more mutually exclusive alternatives, proceed with the same logic presented for two alternatives. The components of incremental analysis are listed below.

Step 1. Compute the rate of return for each alternative. Reject any alternative where the rate of return is less than the desired MARR. (This step is not essential, but helps to immediately identify unacceptable alternatives.)

Step 2. Rank the remaining alternatives in order of increasing initial cost.

Step 3. Examine the increment of investment between the two lowest-cost alternatives as described for the two-alternative problem. Select the better of the two alternatives and reject the other one.

Step 4. Take the preferred alternative from step 3. Consider the next higher initial-cost alternative, and proceed with another two-alternative comparison.

Step 5. Continue until all alternatives have been examined and the best of the multiple alternatives has been identified.

Example 6.21

Consider the following:

	Alternative	
Year	***A***	***B***
0	–$200.0	–$131.0
1	+77.6	+48.1
2	+77.6	+48.1
3	+77.6	+48.1

If the MARR is 10%, which alternative, if any, should be selected?

Solution

One should carefully note that this is a *three-alternative* problem, where the alternatives are *A*, *B*, and *Do nothing*. In this solution we will skip step 1. Reorganize the problem by placing the alternatives in order of increasing initial cost:

	Alternative		
Year	***Do Nothing***	***B***	***A***
0	0	– $131.0	–$200.0
1	0	+ 48.1	+77.6
2	0	+ 48.1	+77.6
3	0	+ 48.1	+77.6

Examine the *B – Do nothing* increment of investment:

Year	*B – Do Nothing*
0	–$131.0 – 0 = – $131.0
1	+ 48.1 – 0 = + 48.1
2	+ 48.1 – 0 = + 48.1
3	+ 48.1 – 0 = + 48.1

Solve for the incremental rate of return:

$$\text{PW of cost} = \text{PW of benefits}$$
$$131.0 = 48.1(P/A, i, 3)$$
$$(P/A, i, 3) = 131.0/48.1 = 2.723$$

From compound interest tables, the incremental rate of return is about 5%. Since the incremental rate of return is less than 10%, the *B – Do nothing* increment is not desirable. Reject alternative *B*.

Year	*A – Do Nothing*
0	–$200.0 – 0 = –$200.0
1	+77.6 – 0 = +77.6
2	+77.6 – 0 = +77.6
3	+77.6 – 0 = +77.6

Next, consider the increment of investment between the two remaining alternatives. Solve for the incremental rate of return:

$$\text{PW of cost} = \text{PW of benefits}$$
$$200.0 = 77.6(P/A, i, 3)$$
$$(P/A, i, 3) = 200.0/77.6 = 2.577$$

The incremental rate of return is 8%, less than the desired 10%. Reject the increment and select the remaining alternative: *Do nothing*.

If you have not already done so, you should go back to Example 6.20 and see how the slightly changed wording of the problem has radically altered it. Example 6.20 required a choice between two undesirable alternatives. This example adds the *Do nothing* alternative, which is superior to *A* and *B*.

BENEFIT-COST ANALYSIS

Generally, in public works and governmental economic analyses, the dominant method of analysis is the **benefit-cost ratio (B/C)**. It is simply the ratio of benefits divided by costs, taking into account the time value of money.

$$B/C = \frac{\text{PW of benefits}}{\text{PW of cost}} = \frac{\text{Equivalent uniform annual benefits}}{\text{Equivalent uniform annual cost}}$$

For a given interest rate, a B/C ratio ≥ 1 reflects an acceptable project. The B/C analysis method is parallel to rate-of-return analysis. The same kind of incremental analysis is required.

Example 6.22

Solve Example 6.20 by benefit-cost analysis.

Solution

	Alternative		Increment
Year	***A***	***B***	***A* – *B***
0	–\$200.0	–\$131.0	–\$69.0
1	+77.6	+48.1	+29.5
2	+77.6	+48.1	+29.5
3	+77.6	+48.1	+29.5

The benefit-cost ratio for the $A - B$ increment is

$$\mathrm{B/C} = \frac{\text{PW of benefits}}{\text{PW of cost}} = \frac{29.5(P/A, 10\%, 3)}{69.0} = \frac{73.37}{69.0} = 1.06$$

Since the B/C ratio exceeds 1, the increment of investment is desirable. Select the higher-cost alternative A.

Breakeven Analysis

In business, *breakeven* is defined as the point where income just covers costs. In engineering economics, the breakeven point is defined as the point where two alternatives are equivalent.

Example 6.23

A city is considering a new \$50,000 snowplow. The new machine will operate at a savings of \$600 per day compared with the present equipment. Assume that the MARR is 12%, and the machine's life is ten years with zero resale value at that time. How many days per year must the machine be used to justify the investment?

Solution

This breakeven problem may be readily solved by annual cost computations. We will set the equivalent uniform annual cost (EUAC) of the snowplow equal to its annual benefit and solve for the required annual utilization. Let X = breakeven point = days of operation per year.

$$\text{EUAC} = \text{EUAB}$$
$$50{,}000(A/P, 12\%, 10) = 600X$$
$$X = 50{,}000(0.1770)/600 = 14.8 \text{ days/year}$$

BONDS

A **bond** is a form of debt represented by a certificate. The bond will specify the amount of the debt, the interest rate of the bond, how often the interest is paid, and when the debt will be repaid.

Bond Value

Bond value is the present worth of all the future interest payments plus the future repayment of the debt, computed at some selected interest rate.

Example 6.24

A \$5000 bond is being offered for sale. It has a stated interest rate of 7%, paid annually. At the end of eight years the \$5000 debt will be repaid along with the last interest payment. It you want an 8% rate of return on this investment (bond yield), how much would you be willing to pay for the bond (bond value)?

Solution

The bond pays 7% × \$5000 = \$350 at the end of every year and will repay the \$5000 debt at the end of eight years.

$$\begin{aligned}\text{Bond value} &= \text{PW of all future benefits}\\ &= 350(\text{P/A},8\%,8) + 5000(\text{P/F},8\%,8)\\ &= 350(5.747) + 5000(0.5403) = \$4712.95\end{aligned}$$

Bond Yield

Bond yield is the interest rate at which the benefits of owning the bond are equivalent to the cost of the bond.

Example 6.25

If the bond in Example 6.24 can actually be purchased for \$4200, what is the bond yield?

Solution

Set the cost of the bond equal to the PW of the bond benefits and solve for the unknown interest rate. The resulting i^* is the bond yield.

$$\$4200 = 350(P/A,i,8) + 5000(P/F,i,8)$$

The equation must be solved by trial and error. Try $i = 10\%$.

$$\$4200 \stackrel{?}{=} 350(5.335) + 5000(0.467) = 4202.25$$

We see that i^* is very close to 10%. No further computations are required. The bond yield is very close to 10%.

PAYBACK PERIOD

Payback period is the period of time required for the profit or other benefits of an investment to equal the cost of the investment.

Example 6.26

A project has the following costs and benefits.

Year	Costs	Benefits
0	$1400	
1	500	$200
2	300	100
3–10		400/year

What is the payback period?

Solution

The total cost is $2200. At the end of year 6 the total benefits will be 200 + 100 + 400 + 400 + 400 + 400 = $1900. And at the end of year 7 benefits will be 1900 + 400 = $2300. The payback period is where benefits equal cost. Since a cash flow table is normally based on the end-of-year convention (See Example 6.1), the payback period is at the end of year 7 and the answer is 7 years.

If, on the other hand, the problem had been stated in words something like ". . .and the benefits from the third year on are $400/year," you would assume the benefits occur uniformly throughout the year. In this situation, the correct answer would be 6.75 years.

VALUATION AND DEPRECIATION

Depreciation of capital equipment is an important component of many after-tax economic analyses. For this reason, one must understand the fundamentals of depreciation accounting.

Notation

BV = book value
C = cost of the property (basis)
D_j = depreciation in year j
S_n = salvage value in year n

Depreciation is the systematic allocation of the cost of a capital asset over its useful life. **Book value** is the original cost of an asset minus the accumulated depreciation of the asset.

$$\text{Book value (BV)} = \text{C} - \Sigma(\text{D}_j)$$

In computing a schedule of depreciation charges four items are considered:

1. Cost of the property, C (called the *basis* in tax law)
2. Type of property. Property is classified either as **tangible** (such as machinery) or **intangible** (such as a franchise or a copyright) and as either **real property** (real estate) or **personal property** (everything not real property)
3. Depreciable life in years, n
4. Salvage value of the property at the end of its depreciable (usable) life, S_n

Straight-Line Depreciation

Depreciation charge in any year is given by

$$D_j = \frac{C - S_n}{n}$$

An alternate computation of the depreciation charge in year j is

$$D_j = \frac{C - \text{Depreciation taken to beginning of year } j - S_n}{\text{Remaining useful life at beginning of year } j}$$

Double-Declining-Balance Depreciation

DDB depreciation in any year, $D_j = \frac{2}{n}$ (C – depreciation in years prior to j).

For 150% declining-balance depreciation, replace the 2 in the equation with 1.5.

Modified Accelerated Cost Recovery System Depreciation

The modified accelerated cost recovery system (MACRS) depreciation method generally applies to property placed in service after 1986. To compute the MACRS depreciation for an item one must know the following:

1. Cost (basis) of the item
2. Property class. All tangible property is classified in one of six classes (3, 5, 7, 10, 15, and 20 years), based on the life over which it is depreciated (see Table 6.3). Residential real estate and nonresidential real estate are in two separate real property classes of 27.5 years and 39 years, respectively.
3. Depreciation computation
   - The 3-, 5-, 7-, and 10-year property classes use double-declining-balance depreciation with conversion to straight-line depreciation in the year that increases the deduction.
   - The 15- and 20-year property classes use 150% declining-balance depreciation with conversion to straight-line depreciation in the year that increases the deduction.
   - In MACRS the salvage value is assumed to be zero.

Half-Year Convention

Except for real property, a half-year convention is used. Under this convention all property is considered to be placed in service in the middle of the tax year, and a half year of depreciation is allowed in the first year. For each of the remaining years, one is allowed a full year of depreciation. If the property is disposed of prior to the end of the recovery period (property class life), a half year of depreciation is allowed in that year. If the property is held for the entire recovery period, a half year of depreciation is allowed for the year following the end of the recovery period (see Table 6.3).

Table 6.3 Modified ACRS (MACRS) depreciation for personal property—half-year convention

		Applicable Percentage for the Class of Property		
Recovery Year	**3-year Recovery**	**5-year Recovery**	**7-year Recovery**	**10-year Recovery**
1	33.33	20.00	14.29	10.00
2	44.45	32.00	24.49	18.00
3	14.81†	19.20	17.49	14.40
4	7.41	11.52†	12.49	11.52
5		11.52	8.93†	9.22
6		5.76	8.92	7.37
7			8.93	6.55†
8			4.46	6.55
9				6.56
10				6.55
11				3.28

† Use straight-line depreciation for the year marked and all subsequent years.

Example 6.27

A \$5000 computer has an anticipated \$500 salvage value at the end of its five-year depreciable life. Compute the depreciation schedule by MACRS depreciation. Do the MACRS computation by hand, and then compare the results with the values from Table 6.3.

Solution

The depreciation method is double declining balance with conversion to straight line for the computer's five-year property class and the half-year convention is used. Salvage value S_n is assumed to be zero for MACRS. Using the equation for DDB depreciation in any year:

Year

$$1\left(\frac{1}{2}\text{ year}\right) \quad D_1 = \frac{1}{2}\times\frac{2}{5}(5000-0) = \$1000$$

$$2 \quad D_2 = \frac{2}{5}(5000-1000) = 1600$$

$$3 \quad D_3 = \frac{2}{5}(5000-2600) = 960$$

$$4 \quad D_4 = \frac{2}{5}(5000-3560) = 576$$

$$5 \quad D_5 = \frac{2}{5}(5000-4136) = 346$$

$$6\left(\frac{1}{2}\text{ year}\right) \quad D_6 = \frac{1}{2}\times\frac{2}{5}(5000-4482) = 104$$

$$\$4586$$

The computation must now be modified to convert to straight-line depreciation at the point where the straight-line depreciation will be larger. Using the alternate straight-line computation,

$$D_5 = \frac{5000 - 4136 - 0}{1.5 \text{ years remaining}} = \$576$$

This is more than the \$346 computed using DDB; hence, switch to the straight-line method for year 5 and beyond.

$$D_6\left(\frac{1}{2}\text{year}\right) = \frac{1}{2}(576) = \$288$$

Answers:

Year	Depreciation (MACRS)
1	\$1000
2	1600
3	960
4	576
5	576
6	288
	\$5000

The computed MACRS depreciation is identical with that obtained from Table 6.3.

INFLATION

Inflation is characterized by rising prices for goods and services, while deflation produces a decrease in prices. An inflationary trend makes future dollars have less purchasing power than present dollars. This benefits long-term borrowers of money because they may repay a loan of present dollars in the future with dollars of reduced buying power. The help to borrowers is at the expense of lenders. Deflation has the opposite effect. Money borrowed at a point in time followed by a deflationary period subjects the borrower to loan repayment with dollars of greater purchasing power than those he borrowed. This is to the lenders' advantage at the expense of borrowers.

Price changes occur in a variety of ways. One method of stating a price change is a uniform rate of price change per year.

f = general inflation rate per interest period
i = effective interest rate per interest period

The following example problem will illustrate the computations.

Example 6.28

A mortgage will be repaid in three equal payments of \$5000 at the end of years 1, 2, and 3. If the annual inflation rate, f, is 8% during this period, and the investor wishes a 12% annual interest rate (i), what is the maximum amount he would be willing to pay for the mortgage?

Solution

The computation is a two-step process. First, the three future payments must be converted into dollars with the same purchasing power as today's (year 0) dollars.

Year	Actual Cash Flow		Multiplied by		Cash Flow Adjusted to Today's (Year 0) Dollars
0	—	×	—	=	—
1	+5000	×	$(1 + 0.08)^{-1}$	=	+ 4630
2	+5000	×	$(1 + 0.08)^{-2}$	=	+ 4286
3	+5000	×	$(1 + 0.08)^{-3}$	=	+ 3969

The general form of the adjusting multiplier is

$$(1 + f)^{-n} \text{ or } (P/F, f, n)$$

Now that the problem has been converted to dollars of the same purchasing power (today's dollars in this example), we can proceed to compute the present worth of the future payments at the desired 12% interest rate.

Year	Actual Cash Flow		Multiplied by		Present Worth
0	—	×	—	=	—
1	+4630	×	$(1 + 0.12)^{-1}$	=	+4134
2	+4286	×	$(1 + 0.12)^{-2}$	=	+3417
3	+3969	×	$(1 + 0.12)^{-3}$	=	+2825
					\$10,376

The investor would pay \$10,376.

Alternate Solution

Instead of doing the inflation and interest rate computations separately, one can compute a combined equivalent interest rate per interest period, d.

$$d = (1 + f)(1 + i) - 1 = i + f + (i \times f)$$

For this cash flow, $d = 0.12 + 0.08 + 0.12(0.08) = 0.2096$. Since we do not have 20.96% interest tables, the problem must be calculated using present-worth equations.

$$\begin{aligned} \text{PW} &= 5000(1 + 0.2096)^{-1} + 5000(1 + 0.2096)^{-2} + 5000(1 + 0.2096)^{-3} \\ &= 4134 + 3417 + 2825 = \$10{,}376 \end{aligned}$$

Example 6.29

One economist has predicted that there will be a 7% per year inflation of prices during the next ten years. If this proves to be correct, an item that presently sells for \$10 would sell for what price ten years hence?

Solution

$f = 7\%, P = \$10$

$F = ?, n = 10$ years

Here, the computation is to find the future worth F, rather than the present worth, P.

$$F = P(1 + f)10 = 10(1 + 0.07)10 = \$19.67$$

Effect of Inflation on a Rate of Return

The effect of inflation on the computed rate of return for an investment depends on how future benefits respond to the inflation. If benefits produce constant dollars, which are not increased by inflation, the effect of inflation is to reduce the before-tax rate of return on the investment. If, on the other hand, the dollar benefits increase to keep up with the inflation, the before-tax rate of return will not be adversely affected by the inflation.

This is not true when an after-tax analysis is made. Even if the future benefits increase to match the inflation rate, the allowable depreciation schedule does not increase. The result will be increased taxable income and income tax payments. This reduces the available after-tax benefits and, therefore, the after-tax rate of return.

Example **6.30**

A man bought a 5% tax-free municipal bond. It cost $1000 and will pay $50 interest each year for 20 years. The bond will mature at the end of 20 years and return the original $1000. If there is 2% annual inflation during this period, what rate of return will the investor receive after considering the effect of inflation?

Solution

$$d = 0.05,\ i = \text{unknown},\ f = 0.02$$

Combined effective interest rate/interest period,

$$d = i + f + (i \times f)$$
$$0.05 = i + 0.02 + 0.02i$$
$$1.02i = 0.03,\ i = 0.294 = 2.94\%$$

REFERENCE

Newnan, D. G., et al. *Engineering Economic Analysis*, 6th ed. San Jose, CA: Engineering Press, 2000.

PROBLEMS

6.1 A retirement fund earns 8% interest, compounded quarterly. If \$400 is deposited every three months for 25 years, the amount in the fund at the end of 25 years is nearest to:

a. \$50,000 c. \$100,000
b. \$75,000 d. \$125,000

6.2 The repair costs for some handheld equipment are estimated to be \$120 the first year, increasing by \$30 per year in subsequent years. The amount a person needs to deposit into a bank account paying 4% interest to provide for the repair costs for the next five years is nearest to:

a. \$500 c. \$700
b. \$600 d. \$800

6.3 One thousand dollars is borrowed for one year at an interest rate of 1% per month. If this same sum of money were borrowed for the same period at an interest rate of 12% per year, the saving in interest charges would be closest to:

a. \$0 c. \$5
b. \$3 d. \$7

6.4 How much should a person invest in a fund that will pay 9%, compounded continuously, if he wishes to have \$10,000 in the fund at the end of ten years?

a. \$4000 c. \$6000
b. \$5000 d. \$7000

6.5 A store charges 1.5% interest per month on credit purchases. This is equivalent to a nominal annual interest rate of:

a. 1.5% c. 18.0%
b. 15.0% d. 19.6%

6.6 A small company borrowed \$10,000 to expand its business. The entire principal of \$10,000 will be repaid in two years, but quarterly interest of \$330 must be paid every three months. The nominal annual interest rate the company is paying is closest to:

a. 3.3% c. 6.6%
b. 5.0% d. 13.2%

6.7 A store's policy is to charge 3% interest every two months on the unpaid balance in charge accounts. The effective interest rate is closest to:

a. 6% c. 15%
b. 12% d. 19%

6.8 The effective interest rate on a loan is 19.56%. If there are 12 compounding periods per year, the nominal interest rate is closest to:

a. 1.5% c. 9.0%
b. 4.5% d. 18.0%

6.9 A deposit of \$300 was made one year ago into an account paying monthly interest. If the account now has \$320.52, the effective annual interest rate is closest to:

a. 7% c. 12%
b. 10% d. 15%

6.10 If the effective interest rate per year is 12%, based on monthly compounding, the nominal interest rate per year is closest to:

a. 8.5% c. 10.0%
b. 9.3% d. 11.4%

6.11 If 10% nominal annual interest is compounded daily, the effective annual interest rate is nearest to:

a. 10.00% c. 10.50%
b. 10.38% d. 10.75%

6.12 An individual wishes to deposit a certain quantity of money now so that he will have \$500 at the end of five years. With interest at 4% per year, compounded semiannually, the amount of the deposit is nearest to:

a. \$340 c. \$410
b. \$400 d. \$416

6.13 A steam boiler is purchased on the basis of guaranteed performance. A test indicates that the operating cost will be \$300 more per year than the manufacturer guaranteed. If the expected life of the boiler is 20 years, and the time value of money is 8%, the amount the purchaser should deduct from the purchase price to compensate for the extra operating cost is nearest to:

a. \$2950 c. \$4100
b. \$3320 d. \$5520

6.14 A consulting engineer bought a fax machine with one year's free maintenance. In the second year the maintenance cost is estimated at \$20. In subsequent years the maintenance cost will increase \$20 per year (that is, third year maintenance will be \$40, fourth year maintenance will be \$60, and so forth). The amount that must be set aside now at 6% interest to pay the maintenance costs on the fax machine for the first six years of ownership is nearest to:

a. \$101 c. \$229
b. \$164 d. \$284

6.15 An investor is considering buying a 20-year corporate bond. The bond has a face value of \$1000 and pays 6% interest per year in two semiannual payments. Thus the purchaser of the bond will receive \$30 every six months, and in addition he will receive \$1000 at the end of 20 years, along with the last \$30 interest payment. If the investor believes he should receive 8% annual interest, compounded semiannually, the amount he is willing to pay for the bond (bond value) is closest to:

a. \$500 c. \$700
b. \$600 d. \$800

6.16 Annual maintenance costs for a particular section of highway pavement are \$2000. The placement of a new surface would reduce the annual maintenance cost to \$500 per year for the first five years and to \$1000 per year for the next five years. The annual maintenance after ten years would again be \$2000. If maintenance costs are the only saving, the maximum investment that can be justified for the new surface, with interest at 4%, is closest to:

a. \$5500 c. \$10,000
b. \$7170 d. \$10,340

6.17 A project has an initial cost of \$10,000, uniform annual benefits of \$2400, and a salvage value of \$3000 at the end of its ten-year useful life. At 12% interest the net present worth (NPW) of the project is closest to:

a. \$2500 c. \$4500
b. \$3500 d. \$5500

6.18 A person borrows \$5000 at an interest rate of 18%, compounded monthly. Monthly payments of \$167.10 are agreed upon. The length of the loan is closest to:

a. 12 months c. 24 months
b. 20 months d. 40 months

6.19 A machine costing \$2000 to buy and \$300 per year to operate will save labor expenses of \$650 per year for eight years. The machine will be purchased if its salvage value at the end of eight years is sufficiently large to make the investment economically attractive. If an interest rate of 10% is used, the minimum salvage value must be closest to:

a. \$100 c. \$300
b. \$200 d. \$400

6.20 The amount of money deposited 50 years ago at 8% interest that would now provide a perpetual payment of \$10,000 per year is nearest to:

a. \$3000 c. \$50,000
b. \$8000 d. \$70,000

6.21 An industrial firm must pay a local jurisdiction the cost to expand its sewage treatment plant. In addition, the firm must pay \$12,000 annually toward the plant operating costs. The industrial firm will pay sufficient money into a fund that earns 5% per year to pay its share of the plant operating costs forever. The amount to be paid to the fund is nearest to:

a. \$15,000 c. \$60,000
b. \$30,000 d. \$240,000

6.22 At an interest rate of 2% per month, money will double in value in how many months?

a. 20 months c. 24 months
b. 22 months d. 35 months

6.23 A woman deposited $10,000 into an account at her credit union. The money was left on deposit for 80 months. During the first 50 months the woman earned 12% interest, compounded monthly. The credit union then changed its interest policy so that the woman earned 8% interest compounded quarterly during the next 30 months. The amount of money in the account at the end of 80 months is nearest to:

a. $10,000
b. $12,500
c. $15,000
d. $20,000

6.24 An engineer deposited $200 quarterly in her savings account for three years at 6% interest, compounded quarterly. Then for five years she made no deposits or withdrawals. The amount in the account after eight years is closest to:

a. $1200
b. $1800
c. $2400
d. $3600

6.25 A sum of money, Q, will be received six years from now. At 6% annual interest the present worth of Q is $60. At this same interest rate the value of Q ten years from now is closest to:

a. $60
b. $77
c. $90
d. $107

6.26 If $200 is deposited in a savings account at the beginning of each year for 15 years and the account earns interest at 6%, compounded annually, the value of the account at the end of 15 years will be most nearly:

a. $4500
b. $4700
c. $4900
d. $5100

6.27 The maintenance expense on a piece of machinery is estimated as follows:

Year	1	2	3	4
Maintenance	$150	$300	$450	$600

If interest is 8%, the equivalent uniform annual maintenance cost is closest to:

a. $250
b. $300
c. $350
d. $400

6.28 A payment of $12,000 six years from now is equivalent, at 10% interest, to an annual payment for eight years starting at the end of this year. The annual payment is closest to:

a. $1000
b. $1200
c. $1400
d. $1600

6.29 A manufacturer purchased $15,000 worth of equipment with a useful life of six years and a $2000 salvage value at the end of the six years. Assuming a 12% interest rate, the equivalent uniform annual cost (EUAC) is nearest to:

a. $1500
b. $2500
c. $3500
d. $4500

6.30 Consider a machine as follows:

Initial cost: $80,000
End-of-useful-life salvage value: $20,000
Annual operating cost: $18,000
Useful life: 20 years

Based on 10% interest, the equivalent uniform annual cost for the machine is closest to:

a. $21,000 c. $25,000
b. $23,000 d. $27,000

6.31 Consider a machine as follows:

Initial cost: $80,000
Annual operating cost: $18,000
Useful life: 20 years

What must be the salvage value of the machine at the end of 20 years for the machine to have an equivalent uniform annual cost of $27,000? Assume a 10% interest rate. The salvage value S_{20} is closest to:

a. $10,000 c. $30,000
b. $20,000 d. $40,000

6.32 Twenty-five thousand dollars is deposited in a savings account that pays 5% interest, compounded semiannually. Equal annual withdrawals are to be made from the account beginning one year from now and continuing forever. The maximum amount of the equal annual withdrawals is closest to:

a. $625 c. $1250
b. $1000 d. $1265

6.33 An investor is considering the investment of $10,000 in a piece of land. The property taxes are $100 per year. The lowest selling price the investor must receive if she wishes to earn a 10% interest rate after keeping the land for ten years is:

a. $20,000 c. $23,000
b. $21,000 d. $27,000

6.34 The rate of return for a $10,000 investment that will yield $1000 per year for 20 years is closest to:

a. 1% c. 8%
b. 4% d. 12%

6.35 An engineer invested $10,000 in a company. In return he received $600 per year for six years and his $10,000 investment back at the end of the six years. His rate of return on the investment was closest to:

a. 6% c. 12%
b. 10% d. 15%

6.36 An engineer made ten annual end-of-year purchases of \$1000 of common stock. At the end of the tenth year, just after the last purchase, the engineer sold all the stock for \$12,000. The rate of return received on the investment is closest to:

a. 2% c. 8%
b. 4% d. 10%

6.37 A company is considering buying a new piece of machinery.

Initial cost: \$80,000
End-of-useful-life salvage value: \$20,000
Annual operating cost: \$18,000
Useful life: 20 years

The machine will produce an annual saving in material of \$25,700. What is the before-tax rate of return if the machine is installed? The rate of return is closest to:

a. 6% c. 10%
b. 8% d. 15%

6.38 Consider the following situation: Invest \$100 now and receive two payments of \$102.15—one at the end of year 3 and one at the end of year 6. The rate of return is nearest to:

a. 6% c. 10%
b. 8% d. 18%

6.39 Two mutually exclusive alternatives are being considered:

Year	A	B
0	–\$2500	–\$6000
1	+746	+1664
2	+746	+1664
3	+746	+1664
4	+746	+1664
5	+746	+1664

The rate of return on the difference between the alternatives is closest to:

a. 6% c. 10%
b. 8% d. 12%

6.40 A project will cost \$50,000. The benefits at the end of the first year are estimated to be \$10,000, increasing \$1000 per year in subsequent years. Assuming a 12% interest rate, no salvage value, and an eight-year analysis period, the benefit-cost ratio is closest to:

a. 0.78 c. 1.28
b. 1.00 d. 1.45

6.41 Two alternatives are being considered:

	A	B
Initial cost	$500	$800
Uniform annual benefit	$140	$200
Useful life, years	8	8

The benefit-cost ratio of the difference between the alternatives, based on a 12% interest rate, is closest to:

a. 0.60 c. 1.00
b. 0.80 d. 1.20

6.42 An engineer will invest in a mining project if the benefit-cost ratio is greater than 1.00, based on an 18% interest rate. The project cost is $57,000. The net annual return is estimated at $14,000 for each of the next eight years. At the end of eight years the mining project will be worthless. The benefit-cost ratio is closest to:

a. 0.60 c. 1.00
b. 0.80 d. 1.20

6.43 A city has retained your firm to do a benefit-cost analysis of the following project:

Project cost: $60,000,000
Gross income: $20,000,000 per year
Operating costs: $5,500,000 per year
Salvage value after ten years: None

The project life is ten years. Use 8% interest in the analysis. The computed benefit-cost ratio is closest to:

a. 0.80 c. 1.20
b. 1.00 d. 1.60

6.44 A piece of property is purchased for $10,000 and yields a $1000 yearly profit. If the property is sold after five years, the minimum price to break even, with interest at 6%, is closest to:

a. $5000 c. $7700
b. $6500 d. $8300

6.45 Given two machines:

	A	B
Initial cost	$55,000	$75,000
Total annual costs	$16,200	$12,450

With interest at 10% per year, at what service life do these two machines have the same equivalent uniform annual cost? The service life is closest to:

a. four years c. six years
b. five years d. eight years

6.46 A machine part that is operating in a corrosive atmosphere is made of low-carbon steel. It costs $350 installed, and lasts six years. If the part is treated for corrosion resistance it will cost $700 installed. How long must the treated part last to be as economical as the untreated part, if money is worth 6%?

a. 8 years
b. 11 years
c. 15 years
d. 17 years

6.47 A firm has determined that the two best paints for its machinery are Tuff-Coat at $45 per gallon and Quick at $22 per gallon. The Quick paint is expected to prevent rust for five years. Both paints take $40 of labor per gallon to apply, and both cover the same area. If a 12% interest rate is used, how long must the Tuff-Coat paint prevent rust to justify its use?

a. Five years
b. Six years
c. Seven years
d. Eight years

6.48 Two alternatives are being considered:

	A	B
Cost	$1000	$2000
Useful life in years	10	10
End-of-useful-life salvage value	$100	$400

The net annual benefit of alternative A is $150. If interest is 8%, what must be the net annual benefit of alternative B for the two alternatives to be equally desirable?

a. $150
b. $200
c. $225
d. $275

6.49 A $5000 municipal bond is offered for sale. It will provide 8% annual interest by paying $200 to the bondholder every six months. At the end of ten years, the $5000 will be paid to the bondholder along with the final $200 interest payment. If you consider 12% nominal annual interest, compounded semiannually, an appropriate bond yield, the amount you would be willing to pay for the bond is closest to:

a. $2750
b. $3850
c. $5000
d. $7400

6.50 A municipal bond is being offered for sale for $10,000. It is a zero-coupon bond, that is, the bond pays no interest during its 15-year life. At the end of 15 years the owner of the bond will receive a single payment of $26,639. The bond yield is closest to:

a. 4%
b. 5%
c. 6%
d. 7%

6.51 A firm is considering purchasing $8000 of small hand tools for use on a production line. It is estimated that the tools will reduce the amount of required overtime work by $2000 the first year, with this amount increasing by $1000 per year thereafter. The payback period for the hand tools is closest to:

a. 2.00 years c. 2.75 years
b. 2.50 years d. 3.00 years

6.52 Special tools for the manufacture of finished plastic products cost $15,000 and have an estimated $1000 salvage value at the end of an estimated three-year useful life and recovery period. The third-year straight-line depreciation is closest to:

a. $3000 c. $4000
b. $3500 d. $4500

6.53 Refer to the facts of Problem 6.52. The first-year MACRS depreciation is closest to:

a. $3000 c. $4000
b. $3500 d. $5000

6.54 An engineer is considering the purchase of an annuity that will pay $1000 per year for ten years. The engineer feels he should obtain a 5% rate of return on the annuity after considering the effect of an estimated 6% inflation per year. The amount he would be willing to pay to purchase the annuity is closest to:

a. $1500 c. $4500
b. $3000 d. $6000

6.55 An automobile costs $20,000 today. You can earn 12% tax-free on an *auto purchase account.* If you expect the cost of the auto to increase by 10% per year, the amount you would need to deposit in the account to provide for the purchase of the auto five years from now is closest to:

a. $12,000 c. $16,000
b. $14,000 d. $18,000

6.56 An engineer purchases a building lot for $40,000 cash and plans to sell it after five years. If he wants an 18% before-tax rate of return, after taking the 6% annual inflation rate into account, the selling price must be nearest to:

a. $55,000 c. $75,000
b. $65,000 d. $125,000

6.57 A piece of equipment with a list price of $450 can actually be purchased for either $400 cash or $50 immediately plus four additional annual payments of $115.25. All values are in dollars of current purchasing power. If the typical customer considered a 5% interest rate appropriate, the inflation rate at which the two purchase alternatives are equivalent is nearest to:

a. 5% c. 8%
b. 6% d. 10%

SOLUTIONS

6.1 d.

$$F = A(F/A,i,n) = 400(F/A,2\%,100)$$
$$= 400(312.23) = \$124,890$$

6.2 d.

$$P = A(P/A,i,n) + G(P/G,i,n)$$
$$= 120(P/A,4\%,5) + 30(P/G,4\%,5)$$
$$= 120(4.452) + 30(8.555) = \$791$$

6.3 d.

At $i = 1\%$/month: $F = 1000(1 + 0.01)^{12} = \$1126.83$
At $i = 12\%$/year: $F = 1000(1 + 0.12)^{1} = 1120.00$
Saving in interesting charges = 1126.83 – 1120.00 = \$6.83

6.4 a.

$$P = Fe^{-rn} = 10{,}000e^{-0.09(10)} = 4066$$

6.5 c. The nominal interest rate is the annual interest rate ignoring the effect of any compounding. Nominal interest rate = 1.5% × 12 = 18%.

6.6 d. The interest paid per year = 330 × 4 = 1320. The nominal annual interest rate = 1320/10,000 = 0.132 = 13.2%.

6.7 d.

$$i_e = (1 + r/m)^m - 1 = (1 + 0.03)6 - 1 = 0.194 = 19.4\%$$

6.8 d.

$$i_e = (1 + r/m)^m - 1$$
$$r/m = (1 + i^e)^{1/m} - 1 = (1 + 0.1956)1/12 - 1 = 0.015$$
$$r = 0.015(m) = 0.015 \times 12 = 0.18 = 18\%$$

6.9 a.

$$i_e = 20.52/300 = 0.0684 = 6.84\%$$

6.10 d.

$$i^e = (1 + r/m)^m - 1$$
$$0.12 = (1 + r/12)12 - 1$$
$$(1.12)1/12 = (1 + r/12)$$
$$1.00949 = (1 + r/12)$$
$$r = 0.00949 \times 12 = 0.1138 = 11.38\%$$

6.11 c.

$$i^e = (1 + r/m)^m - 1 = (1 + 0.10/365)^{365} - 1 = 0.1052 = 10.52\%$$

6.12 c.

$$P = F(P/F,i,n) = 500(P/F,2\%,10) = 500(0.8203) = \$410$$

6.13 a.

$$P = 300(P/A,8\%,20) = 300(9.818) = \$2945$$

6.14 c. Using single payment present worth factors:

$$P = 20(P/F,6\%,2) + 40(P/F,6\%,3) + 60(P/F,6\%,4) + 80(P/F,6\%,5) + 100(P/F,6\%,6) = \$229$$

Alternate solution using the gradient present worth factor:

$$P = 20(P/G,6\%,6) = 20(11.459) = \$229$$

6.15 d.

$$PW = 30\,(P/A,4\%,40) + 1000(P/F,4\%,40) = 30(19.793) + 1000(0.2083) = \$802$$

6.16 d. Benefits are $1500 per year for the first five years and $1000 per year for the subsequent five years.

As Exhibit 6.16 indicates, the benefits may be considered as $1000 per year for ten years, plus an additional $500 benefit in each of the first five years.

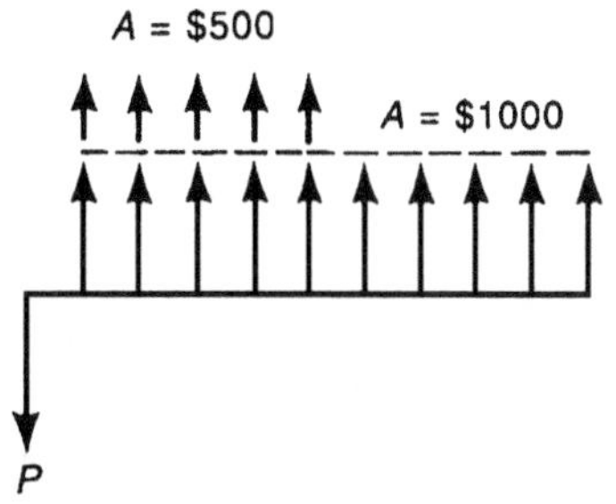

Exhibit 6.16

$$\begin{aligned}\text{maximum investment} &= \text{present worth of benefits}\\ &= 1000(P/A,4\%,10) + 500(P/A,4\%,5)\\ &= 1000(8.111) + 500(4.452) = \$10{,}337\end{aligned}$$

6.17 c.

$$\begin{aligned}NPW &= \text{PW of benefits} - \text{PW of cost}\\ &= 2400(P/A,12\%,10) + 3000(P/F,12\%,10) - 10{,}000 = \$4526\\ &= 2400(5.65) + 3000(.32) - 10{,}000 = \$4526\end{aligned}$$

6.18 d.

$$\begin{aligned}\text{PW of benefits} &= \text{PW of cost}\\ 5000 &= 167.10(P/A,1.5\%,n)\\ (P/A,1.5\%,n) &= 5000/167.10 = 29.92\end{aligned}$$

From the $1\frac{1}{2}\%$ interest table, $n = 40$.

6.19 c.

$$\begin{aligned} \text{NPW} &= \text{PW of benefits} - \text{PW of cost} = 0 \\ &= (650 - 300)(P/A,10\%,8) + S_8\,(\text{P/F},10\%,8) - 2000 = 0 \\ &= 350(5.335) + S_8(0.4665) - 2000 = 0 \\ S_8 &= 132.75/0.4665 = \$285 \end{aligned}$$

6.20 a. The amount of money needed now to begin the perpetual payments is $P' = A/i = 10{,}000/0.08 = 125{,}000$. From this we can compute the amount of money, P, that would need to have been deposited 50 years ago:

$$P = 125{,}000(P/F,8\%,50) = 125{,}000(0.0213) = \$2663$$

6.21 d.

$$P = A/i = 12{,}000/0.5 = \$240{,}000$$

6.22 d.

$$\begin{aligned} 2 &= 1(F/P,i,n) \\ (F/P,2\%,n) &= 2 \end{aligned}$$

From the 2% interest table, n = about 35 months.

6.23 d. At the end of 50 months

$$F = 10{,}000(F/P,1\%,50) = 10{,}000(1.645) = \$16{,}450$$

At the end of 80 months

$$F = 16{,}450(F/P,2\%,10) = 16{,}450(1.219) = \$20{,}053$$

6.24 d.

$$\begin{aligned} \text{FW} &= 200(\text{F/A},1.5\%,12)(F/P,\ 1.5\%,20) \\ &= 200(13.041)(1.347) = \$3513 \end{aligned}$$

6.25 d. The present amount $P = 60$ is equivalent to Q six years hence at 6% interest. The future sum F may be calculated by either of two methods:

$$F = Q(F/P,6\%,4) \text{ and } Q = 60(F/P,6\%,6)$$

or

$$F = P(F/P,6\%,10)$$

Since P is known, the second equation may be solved directly.

$$F = P(F/P,6\%,10) = 60(1.791) = \$107$$

6.26 c.

$$F' = A(F/A,i,n) = 200(F/A,6\%,15) = 200(23.276) = \$4655.20$$
$$F = F'(F/P,i,n) = 4655.20(F/P,6\%,1) = 4655.20(1.06) = \$4935$$

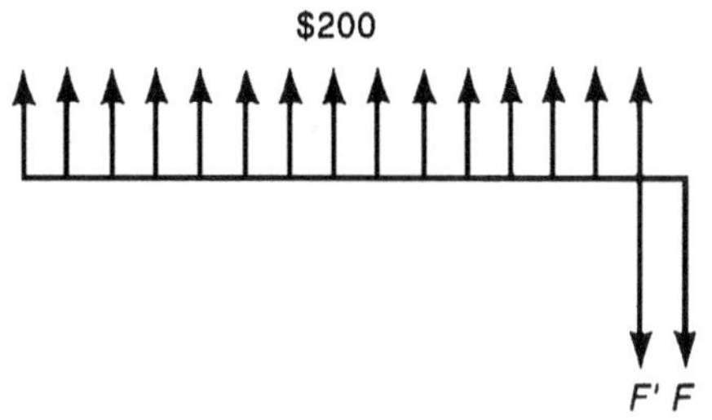

Exhibit 6.26

6.27 c.

$$\text{EUAC} = 150 + 150(A/G,8\%,4) = 150 + 150(1.404) = \$361$$

6.28 b.

$$\text{Annual payment} = 12{,}000(P/F,10\%,6)(A/P,10\%,8)$$
$$= 12{,}000(0.5645)(0.1874) = \$1269$$

6.29 c.

$$\text{EUAC} = 15{,}000(A/P,12\%,6) - 2000(A/F,12\%,6)$$
$$= 15{,}000(0.2432) - 2000(0.1232) = \$3402$$

6.30 d.

$$\text{EUAC} = 80{,}000(A/P,10\%,20) - 20{,}000(A/F,10\%,20)$$
$$+ \text{annual operating cost}$$
$$= 80{,}000(0.1175) - 20{,}000(0.0175) + 18{,}000$$
$$= 9400 - 350 + 18{,}000 = \$27{,}050$$

6.31 b.

$$\text{EUAC} = \text{EUAB}$$
$$27{,}000 = 80{,}000(A/P,10\%,20) + 18{,}000 - S_{20}(A/F,10\%,20)$$
$$= 80{,}000(0.1175) + 18{,}000 - S_{20}(0.0175)$$
$$S_{20} = (27{,}400 - 27{,}000)/0.0175 = \$22{,}857$$

6.32 d. The general equation for an infinite life, $P = A/i$, must be used to solve the problem.

$$ie = (1 + 0.025)2 - 1 = 0.050625$$

The maximum annual withdrawal will be $A = Pi = 25{,}000(0.050625)$ = \$1266.

6.33 d.

$$\text{Minimum sale price} = 10{,}000(F/P,10\%,10) + 100(F/A,10\%,10)$$
$$= 10{,}000(2.594) + 100(15.937) = \$27{,}530$$

6.34 c.

$$\text{NPW} = 1000(P/A,i,20) - 10{,}000 = 0$$
$$(P/A,i,20) = 10{,}000/1000 = 10$$

From interest tables: $6\% < i < 8\%$.

6.35 a. The rate of return was 600/10,000 = 0.06 = 6%.

6.36 b.

$$F = A(F/A,i,n)$$
$$12{,}000 = 1000(F/A,i,10)$$
$$(F/A,i,10) = 12{,}000/1000 = 12$$

In the 4% interest table: $(F/A,4\%,10) = 12.006$, so $i = 4\%$.

6.37 b.

$$\text{PW of cost} = \text{PW of benefits}$$
$$80{,}000 = (25{,}700 - 18{,}000)(P/A,i,20) + 20{,}000(P/F,i,20)$$

Try $i = 8\%$.

$$80{,}000 \stackrel{?}{=} 7700(9.818) + 20{,}000(0.2145) = 79{,}889$$

Therefore, the rate of return is very close to 8%.

6.38 d.

$$\text{PW of cost} = \text{PW of benefits}$$
$$100 = 102.15(P/F,i,3) + 102.15(P/F,i,6)$$

Solve by trial and error. Try $i = 12\%$.

$$100 \stackrel{?}{=} 102.15(0.7118) + 102.15(0.5066) = 124.46$$

The PW of benefits exceeds the PW of cost. This indicates that the interest rate i is too low. Try $i = 18\%$.

$$100 \stackrel{?}{=} 102.15(0.6086) + 102.15(0.3704) = 100.00$$

Therefore, the rate of return is 18%.

6.39 c. The difference between the alternatives:

$$\text{Incremental cost} = 6000 - 2500 = \$3500$$

$$\text{Incremental annual benefit} = 1664 - 746 = \$918$$
$$\text{PW of cost} = \text{PW of benefits}$$
$$3500 = 918(P/A,i,5)$$
$$(P/A,i,5) = 3500/918 = 3.81$$

From the interest tables, i is very close to 10%.

6.40 c.

$$B/C = \frac{\text{PW of benefits}}{\text{PW of cost}} = \frac{10{,}000\ (P/A,\ 12\%,\ 8) + 1000\ (P/G,\ 12\%,\ 8)}{50{,}000}$$

$$= \frac{10{,}000\ (4.968) + 1000\ (14.471)}{50{,}000} = 1.28$$

6.41 c.

$$B/C = \frac{\text{PW of benefits}}{\text{PW of cost}} = \frac{60(P/A,12\%,8)}{300} = \frac{60(4.968)}{300} = 0.99$$

Alternate solution:

$$B/C = \frac{\text{EUAB}}{\text{EUAC}} = \frac{60}{300(A/P,12\%,8)} = \frac{60}{300(0.2013)} = 0.99$$

6.42 a.

$$B/C = \frac{\text{PW of benefits}}{\text{PW of cost}} = \frac{14,000(P/A,18\%,8)}{57,000} = \frac{14,000(4.078)}{57,000} = 1.00$$

6.43 d.

$$B/C = \frac{\text{EUAB}}{\text{EUAC}} = \frac{20,000,000 - 5,500,000}{60,000,000(A/P,8\%,10)} = 1.62$$

6.44 c.

$$\begin{aligned} F &= 10,000(F/P,6\%,5) - 1000(F/A,6\%,5) \\ &= 10,000(1.338) - 1000(5.637) = \$774 \end{aligned}$$

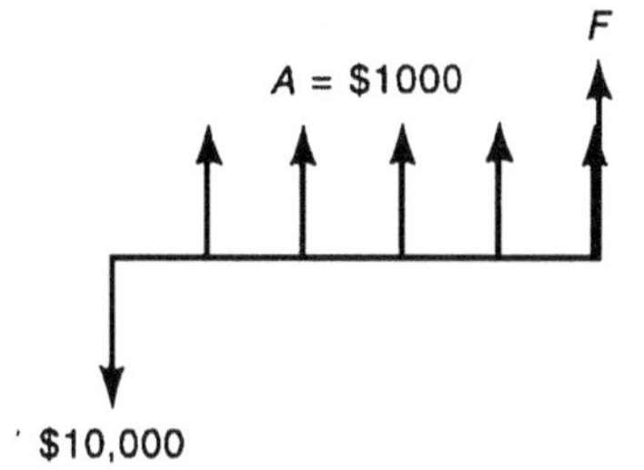

Exhibit 6.44

6.45 d.

$$\begin{aligned} \text{PW of cost}_A &= \text{PW of cost}_B \\ 55,000 + 16,200(P/A,10\%,n) &= 75,000 + 12,450(P/A,10\%,n) \\ (P/A,10\%,n) &= (75,000 - 55,000)/(16,200 - 12,450) \\ &= 5.33 \end{aligned}$$

From the 10% interest tables, n = 8 years.

6.46 c.

$$\begin{aligned} \text{EUAC}_{\text{untreated}} &= \text{EUAC}_{\text{treated}} \\ 350(A/P,6\%,6) &= 700(A/P,6\%,n) \\ 350(0.2034) &= 700(A/P,6\%,n) \\ (A/P,6\%,n) &= 71.19/700 = 0.1017 \end{aligned}$$

From the 6% interest table, n = 15+ years.

6.47 d.

$$\text{EUAC}_{\text{T-C}} = \text{EUAC}_{\text{Quick}}$$
$$(45 + 40)(A/P,12\%,n) = (22 + 40)(A/P,12\%,5)$$
$$(A/P,12\%,n) = 17.20/85 = 0.202$$

From the 12% interest table, $n = 8$.

6.48 d. At breakeven,

$$\text{NPWA} = \text{NPWB}$$
$$150(P/A,8\%,10) + 100(P/F,8\%,10) - 1000 = \text{NAB}(P/A,8\%,10) + 400(P/F,8\%,10) - 2000$$
$$52.82 = 6.71(\text{NAB}) - 1814.72$$

Net annual benefit (NAB) = (1814.72 + 52.82)/6.71 = \$278

6.49 b. The number of six-month compounding periods in this problem is 20. So $n = 20$ and 12%/2 = 6% is the interest rate for the six-month interest period.

$$\text{Bond value} = \text{PW of all future benefits}$$
$$= 200(P/A,6\%,20) + 5000(P/F,6\%,20)$$
$$= 200(11.470) + 5000(0.3118) = \$3853$$

6.50 d. We know $P = 10{,}000$, $F = 26{,}639$, $n = 15$, and i = bond yield. Using the equation for the single payment compound amount:

$$F = P(1 + i)^n$$
$$26{,}639 = 10{,}000(1 + i)^{15}$$
$$2.66391/15 = (1 + i)$$
$$1.0675 = 1 + i$$
$$i = 0.0675 = 6.75\%$$

6.51 c. The annual benefits are \$2000, \$3000, \$4000, \$5000, and so on. The payback period is the time when \$8000 of benefits are received. This will occur in 2.75 years.

6.52 d.

$$D_3 = (C - S)/n = (15{,}000 - 1000)/3 = \$4666$$

6.53 d. From the modified ACRS table (Table 6.3) read for the first recovery year and three-year recovery the MACRS depreciation is 33.33% × 15,000 = \$5000.

6.54 d.

$$d = i + f + (i \times f) = 0.05 + 0.06 + 0.05(0.06) = 0.113 = 11.3\%$$

$$P = A(P/A,11.3\%,10) = 1000\left[\frac{(1+0.113)^{10} - 1}{0.113(1+0.113)^{10}}\right]$$

$$= 1000\left[\frac{1.9171}{0.3296}\right] = \$5816$$

6.55 d.

Cost of auto five years hence $(F) = P(1 + \text{inflation rate})^n$

$= 20{,}000(1 + 0.10)5 = 32{,}210$

Amount to deposit now to have \$32,210 available five years hence:

$P = F(P/F,i,n) = 32{,}210\ (P/F,12\%,5) = 32{,}210(0.5674) = \$18{,}276$

6.56 d.

$$\text{Selling price } (F) = 40{,}000(F/P,18\%,5)(F/P,6\%,5)$$
$$= 40{,}000(2.288)(1.338) = \$122{,}500$$

6.57 b.

$$\text{PW of cash purchase} = \text{PW of installment purchase}$$
$$400 = 50 + 115.25(P/A,d,4)$$
$$(P/A,d,4) = 350/11.25 = 3.037$$

From the interest tables, $d = 12\%$.

$$d = i + f + i\,(f)$$
$$0.12 = 0.05 + f + 0.05\text{f}$$
$$f = 0.07/1.05 = 0.0667 = 6.67\%$$

CHAPTER 7

Properties of Electrical Materials

OUTLINE

All engineering products are made of materials. Thus, engineers become directly involved with materials, whether they be design engineers, production engineers, or applications engineers. Their familiarity with a wide spectrum of materials becomes particularly important as they advance through management and into administration, where they must oversee the activities of additional engineers on their technical staffs.

The way that an engineering product performs in service is a consequence of the combination of the components of the product. Thus, a cellular phone must have the diodes, resistors, capacitors, and other components that function together to meet its design requirements. Likewise, a competitively produced car must possess a carefully designed engine with its numerous parts, as well as safety features and operating characteristics that meet customer approval. Materials are pertinent to each and every design consideration.

Just as it is to be expected that the internal circuitry of a four-function hand calculator will differ from the internal circuitry of its multifunctional scientific counterpart, the internal structure of a steel gear differs from that of the sheet steel to be used in an automotive fender. Their roles, and therefore their properties, are designed to be different.

The variations in the internal structures of materials that lead to property differences include variations in atomic coordination and electronic energies, differences in internal geometries (microstructures), and the incorporation of larger structures, sometimes called macrostructures. Each of these is considered in the following sections, along with procedures for obtaining desired structures and properties.

ATOMIC ORDER IN ENGINEERING MATERIALS

Atoms, Ions, and Electrons

There is an order within atoms. Each atom has an integer number of protons. That number is called the **atomic number**. The natural elements possess, progressively, 1 to 92 of these protons, which carry a positive charge. A neutral atom has a number of electrons equal to the number of protons. Each electron is negative with a charge of 1.6×10^{-17} coulombs. Electrons are only allowed in given orbitals (called shells) that correspond to specific allowed energy levels.

With the exception of the principal isotope of hydrogen, each atom possesses neutrons. While these are charge-neutral, they add to the mass of each atom. The protons and neutrons reside in the nucleus of the atom. Figure 7.1 shows the Bohr model of a sodium atom. The lighter elements contain approximately equal numbers of protons and neutrons; however, in heavier elements the number of neutrons exceeds the number of protons. Furthermore, the number of neutrons per atom is not fixed. Thus, we encounter several **isotopes** for most atoms.

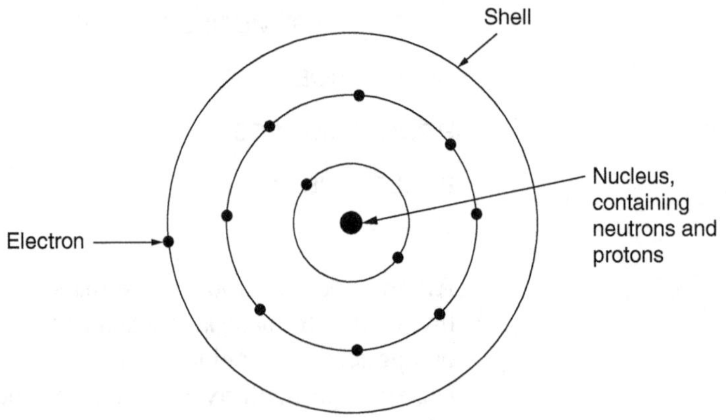

Figure 7.1 Bohr model of a sodium atom

Table 7.1 Data for selected atoms

Element	Protons Electrons Atomic No.	Neutrons (in natural isotopes)	Atomic Mass Unit	Grams per Avogadro's Number*
Hydrogen	1	0 or 1	1.008	1.008
Carbon	6	6 or 7	12.011	12.011
Oxygen	8	8, 9, or 10	15.995	15.995
Chlorine	17	18 or 20	35.453	35.453
Iron	26	28, 30, 31, or 32	55.847	55.847
Gold	79	118	196.97	196.97
Uranium	92	142, 143, or 146	238.03	238.03

*Avogadro's number = 6.022 × 1023

Since the mass of an electron is appreciably less than 1% of that of protons and neutrons, the mass of an atom is directly related to the combined number of the latter two. By definition, an **atomic mass unit** (amu) is 1/12 of the mass of a carbon isotope that has six protons and six neutrons, C^{12}. The **atomic mass** of an element is equal to the number of these atomic mass units. (Selected values are listed in Table 7.1.) Thus while there are integer numbers of neutrons, protons, and electrons in each atom, the mass generally is not an integer, because more than one isotope is typically present.

A limited number of electrons may be accepted or released by an atom, thus introducing a charge on the atom (due the difference in the number of protons and electrons). A charged atom is an **ion**. Negative ions that have accepted extra electrons are called **anions**. Positive ions that have released electrons are called **cations**. Because they are charged, ions respond to electric fields. These fields may involve macroscopic dimensions (in electroplating baths); or they may involve interatomic distances (in molecules). Unlike charges attract; like charges repel.

Energy is required to remove an electron from a neutral atom. Figure 7.2 shows this schematically for a sodium atom. Conversely, fixed quantities of energy are released when electrons are captured by a positive ion. These energy levels (**states**) associated with an atom are fixed. Furthermore each state may accept only two electrons, and these must have opposite magnetic characteristics. Electronic, magnetic, and optical properties of materials must be interpreted accordingly.

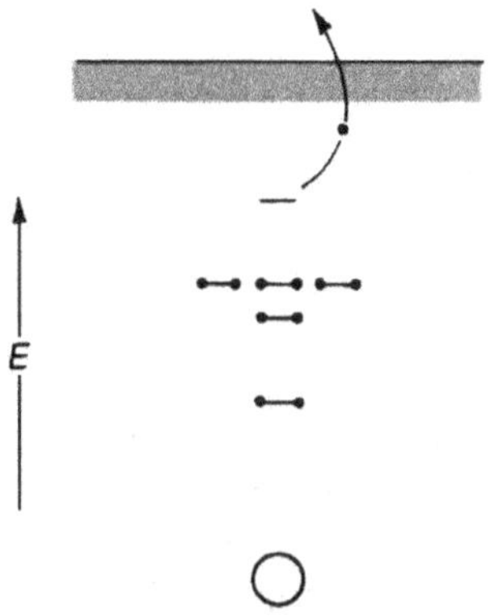

Figure 7.2 Ionization energy (schematic for sodium). Electrons reside at specific energy **states** (levels). Energy must be supplied to remove an electron from an atom, producing a positive ion. Two electrons (of opposite magnetic spins) may reside in each state.

Molecules

Atoms can join to one another; this is called **bonding**. Strong attractive forces can develop between atoms by three mechanisms; (1) coulombic attraction between oppositely charged ions, forming ionic bonds; (2) sharing of electrons to fill outer shells, creating covalent bonds; and (3) formation of ion cores surrounded by valence electrons that have been excited above the Fermi level and have become free electrons, forming metallic bonds. More detailed examples of these three primary types of bonds follow.

Ionic bonds form between metallic and nonmetallic atoms. The metallic atoms release their valence electrons to become cations (which are positively charged) and the nonmetallic atoms accept them to become anions. Ionic bonds are nondirectional. For example, a sodium ion that has lost an electron (Na^+) associates with as many negatively charged chlorine ions (Cl^-) as space will allow. And each

Cl^- ion will become *coordinated* with as many Na^+ ions as necessary to balance the charge. The resulting structure will continue to grow in three dimensions until all available ions are positioned. Energy is released with each added ion.

Covalent bonds form between atoms that share valence electrons in order to fill their outer shells. In the simplest case, two hydrogen atoms release energy as they combine to produce a hydrogen molecule:

$$2H \rightarrow H2 \quad \text{or} \quad 2H \rightarrow H\text{—}H \tag{7.1}$$

The bond between the two involves a pair of shared electrons. This mechanism is common among many atomic pairs. In this case only one pair of atoms is involved. The covalent bonds of molecules are stereospecific; that is, they are between specific atoms and are therefore directional bonds.

In polymers a string or network of thousands or millions of atoms is bonded together. Examples include polyethylene, which has the structure shown in Figure 7.3(a), in which there is a backbone of carbon atoms that are covalently bonded; that is, they share pairs of valence electrons. Since each carbon atom has four valence electrons, it can form four covalent bonds, thus adding two hydrogens at the side of the chain in addition to the two bonds along the chain. Polyvinyl chloride, Figure 7.3(b), is related but has one of the four hydrogen atoms replaced by a chlorine atom.

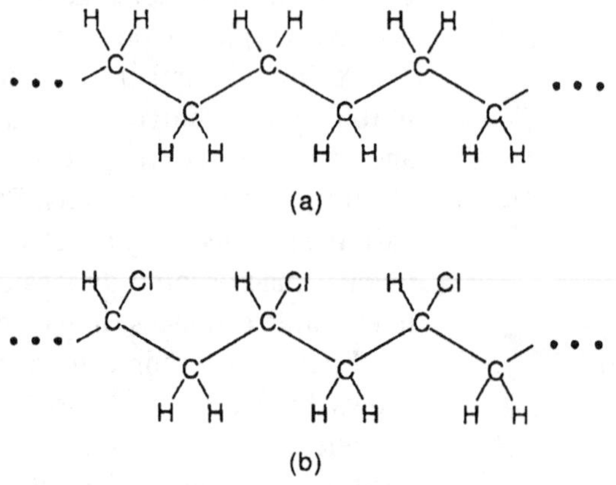

Figure 7.3 Covalent bonds: (a) polyethylene; (b) polyvinyl chloride

Metallic bonds form between the elements on the left side of the periodic table known as metals. Metallic bonds can form between atoms of the same element, to form a pure metal such as gold (Au), or between different metal atoms to form an alloy, such as brass, a mixture of copper (Cu) and zinc (Zn). The basis for the metallic bond is the formation of ion cores created when the metal's valence electrons are no longer associated with a specific atom. These electrons (called free electrons) move freely around surrounding metal ion cores, shielding them from each other. These freely moving electrons are often referred to as a *sea of electrons*. Metallic bonds are nondirectional.

The type and strength of bonding between atoms and molecules determines many properties of materials. As a general rule (and with other things being equal), the stronger the atomic bonding, the higher the melting temperature, hardness, and elastic modulus of materials. Ionically bonded materials are usually electrical and thermal insulators, while materials with metallic bonds have high electrical and thermal conductivities.

Crystallinity

The repetition of atomic coordinations in three dimensions produces a periodic structure that is called a **crystal**. The basic building block of a crystal is called a unit cell. Figure 7.4 illustrates the unit cell structure of iron. Each atom in this metal has eight nearest neighbors, which are symmetrically coordinated to give a **body-centered cubic** (BCC) crystal. About 30% of the metals have this structure. The atoms of aluminum and copper, among another 30% of the metals, become coordinated with 12 nearest neighbors with the result that **face-centered cubic** (FCC) crystal lattices are formed, as shown in Figure 7.5. A third group of metals form **hexagonal crystals** with **close packing** (HCP), as shown in Figure 7.6. As in the FCC crystals, each atom is coordinated with 12 nearest neighbors in HCP crystals.

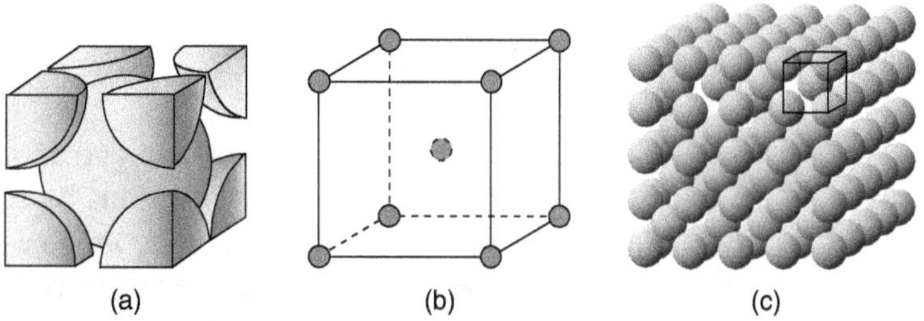

Figure 7.4 Body-centered cubic crystal structure: (a) a hard-sphere unit cell representation; (b) a reduced-sphere unit cell; (c) an aggregate of many atoms

It is possible to have a very high degree of perfection in crystals. For example, the repetition dimension (**lattice constant**) of the FCC lattice of pure copper is constant to the fifth significant figure (and to the sixth if the thermal expansion is factored in). This high degree of ordering provides a quantitative base for anticipating properties. Included are density calculations, certain thermal properties, and some of the effects of alloying.

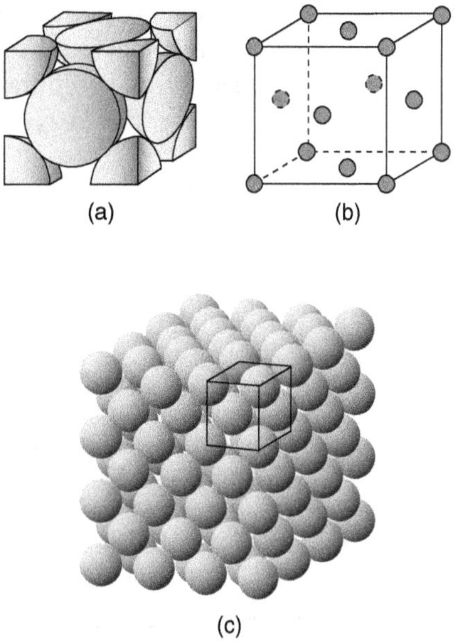

Figure 7.5 Face-centered cubic crystal structure: (a) a hard-sphere unit cell representation; (b) a reduced-sphere unit cell; (c) an aggregate of many atoms

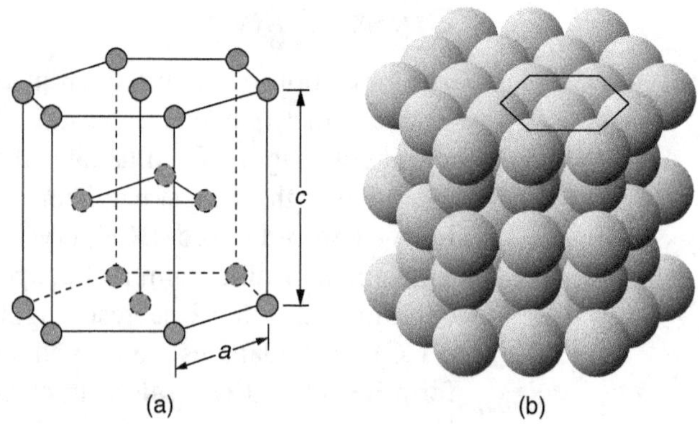

Figure 7.6 Hexagonal close-packed crystal structure: (a) a reduced-sphere unit cell (a and c represent the short and long edge lengths, respectively); (b) an aggregate of many atoms

Directions and Planes

Many properties are **anisotropic**; that is, they differ with direction and orientation. We can identify crystal directions by selecting any zero location (the origin) and determining the x, y, and z coordinates for any point along the direction ray. A corner of the unit cell is often used as the origin. The unit length is the edge length of the unit cell. The direction of easy magnetization in iron is parallel to one of the crystal axes. This is labeled the [100] direction, because that direction passes from the origin through a point that is one unit along the x-axis and zero units along the other two axes. Figure 7.7(a) shows a ray in the [120] direction and a ray in the $[1\bar{1}0]$ direction, where the overbar indicates a negative direction. Parallel directions carry the same label. We use square brackets, [ ], for closures for direction rays.

In cubic crystals, each of the four directions that are diagonal through the cube are identical (because the three axes are identical). We label these four directions as a *family* with pointed arrows for closures, <111>.

Figure 7.7(b) identifies the three shaded planes as (001), (210), and (111). Here the labeling procedure (known as indexing) is somewhat more complicated than for directions (but leads to simplified mathematics for complex calculations). As an example we will draw the (210) plane. We first invert the three indices, 1/**2**,

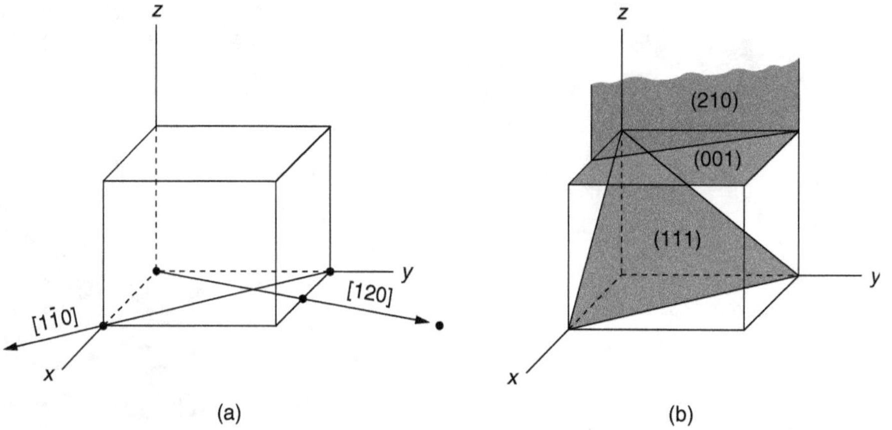

Figure 7.7 Crystal notation. (a) Directions, [120] and $[1\bar{1}0]$. The x, y, and z coordinates are used for crystal directions. Square brackets are used as closures. Negative coordinates are indicated with an overbar. (b) Planes, (001), (210), and (111). The reciprocals of the axial intercepts are used for crystal planes. Parentheses are used as closures. Any point may be selected as an arbitrary origin.

1/**1**, 1/**0**. These are the intercept dimensions of the plane across the three axes; specifically, 0.5 on the x-axis, 1.0 on the y-axis, and infinity along the z-axis. An adjacent parallel plane with intercepts of 1, 2, and ∞ carries the same (210) index. We use parentheses, ( ), as closures for the indices of individual planes, and braces, { }, as closures for a family of comparable planes. To index an unknown plane, the procedure is reversed: (1) Choose an origin that the plane does not pass through. (2) Determine the intercepts of the plane on the x, y, and z axes. (3) Take reciprocals of these intercepts. (4) Clear fractions and enclose in parentheses ( ).

Characteristics of Ordered Solids

There are several useful properties of unit cells that can be determined through geometric relations and 3-D visualization. These include:

- Number of atoms per unit cell
- Number of nearest-neighbor atoms (coordination number)
- Lattice parameter (spacing of atoms)
- Distance of nearest approach of atoms
- Atomic packing factor (the volume of atoms per unit volume of the solid)
- Density

Some of these relationships are given in Table 7.2 and in the NCEES *Fundamentals of Engineering Supplied-Reference Handbook* and therefore do not need to be memorized, but it is useful to see how these are determined. The following examples will illustrate these relationships.

Table 7.2 Characteristics of selected crystal structures

Unit Cell	Number of Atoms per Unit Cell	Coordination Number	Lattice Parameter	Packing Factor
BCC	2	8	$a = 4R/\sqrt{3}$	0.68
FCC	4	12	$a = 2R/\sqrt{2}$	0.72
HCP		12		0.72

Figure 7.4 showed a unit cell of α iron with an atom at its center. Inasmuch as each of the eight corner atoms is shared by the eight adjacent unit cells, we can note that there are ($1 + 8/8 = 2$) atoms per unit cell. From Table 7.1, each iron atom has a mass of 55.85 g per 0.6022×10^{24} atoms. Since iron forms a body-centered cubic crystal, its unit cell has a mass of 1.855×10^{-26} g. X-ray diffraction techniques give a lattice constant value of 2.866×10^{-18} m. As a result, the mass per unit volume, that is, the **density**, may be calculated to be nearly 7.88 g/cm^3. Careful density measurements give a value of slightly more than 7.87 g/cm^3 at ambient temperatures. The close agreement for the simple property of density implies that the concept of the crystal structure is valid.

The relationship between the size of the atoms (atomic radius, r) and lattice parameter (a) for BCC crystals is demonstrated in Figure 7.8. Note that the atoms touch along the body diagonal. By inspection this gives a known length of the body diagonal of $4r$.

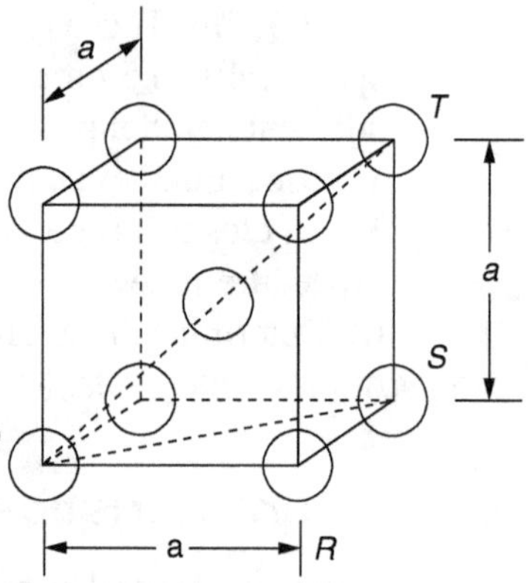

Figure 7.8 BCC unit cell

Using the triangle QRS

$$\|\overline{QS}^2\| = a^2 + a^2 = 2a^2$$

and for triangle QST

$$\|\overline{QT}^2\| = \|\overline{TS}^2\| + \|\overline{QS}^2\|$$

But $\overline{QT} = 4r$, r being the atomic radius. Also, $\overline{TS} = a$. Therefore,

$$(4r)^2 = a^2 + 2a^2$$

or

$$a = \frac{4r}{\sqrt{3}}$$

The relationship between r and a for FCC crystals can be similarly determined by noting that the atoms touch along the face diagonal as shown in Figure 7.9.

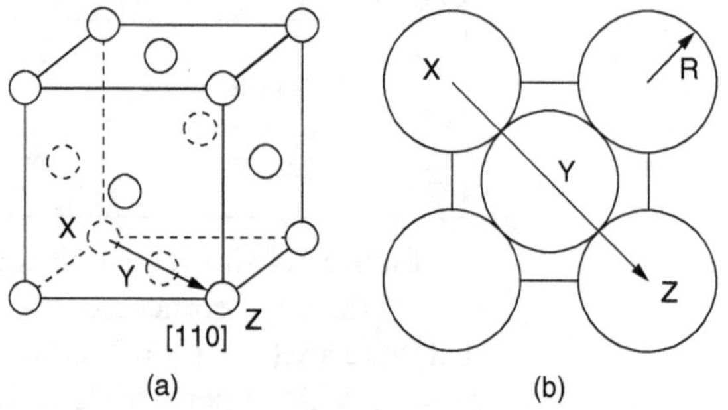

Figure 7.9 (a) Reduced-sphere FCC unit cell with the [110] direction indicated. (b) The bottom face-plane of the FCC unit cell in (a) on which is shown the atomic spacing in the [110] direction, through atoms labeled X, Y, and Z.

The plastic deformation of these solids is also related to crystal structure. To illustrate, in Figure 7.10 the {111} plane of an FCC structure is shown. The {111} planes of aluminum and other FCC metals are the most densely packed planes; each atom of those planes is surrounded by six other atoms in the same plane. There is no arrangement where more atoms could have been included. This is not true for other planes within the FCC crystal. Since there is a fixed number of

atoms per unit volume, it is apparent that the interplanar spacings between parallel (111) planes through the centers of atoms must be greater than between planes of other orientations. It is thus not surprising that sliding (**slip**) occurs there at lower stresses than on other planes.

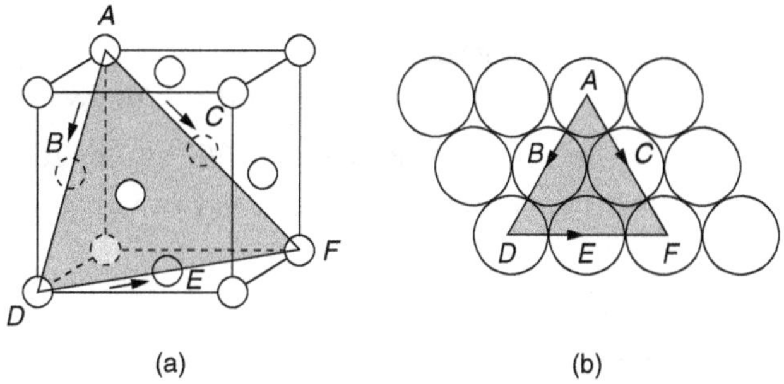

Figure 7.10 (a) A {111}<110> slip system shown within an FCC unit cell. (b) The (111) plane from (a) and three <110> slip directions (as indicated by arrows) within that plane comprise possible slip systems.

Not only is the required shear stress for slip low on the {111} planes, the <110> directions on those planes require less stress for slip than other directions. This is because the step distance between like crystal positions is the shortest, specifically, $2r$ where r is the atomic radius. We speak of the <110>{111} **slip system** for FCC metals. In a BCC metal, <111> {110} is the prominent slip system. Note especially that the {111} planes and the <110> directions are operative in FCC metals, whereas it is the {110} planes and the <111> directions in BCC metals. Hexagonal metals such as Mg, Zn, and Ti do not deform as readily as BCC and FCC metals because there are fewer combinations of directions and planes for slip by shear stresses.

Example 7.1

Carbon (12.011 amu) contains C^{12} and C^{13} isotopes with masses of 12.00000 amu and 13.00335 amu, respectively. What are the percentages of each?

Solution

$$12.011 = x\,(12.00000) + (1 - x)(13.00335)$$
$$1.00335\,x = 0.99335$$
$$x = 98.9\%$$

Carbon is 98.9% C^{12} and 1.1% C^{13}.

Example 7.2

Aluminum has a face-centered cubic unit cell, that is, an atom at each corner of the unit cell and an atom at the center of each face (see Figure 7.5). The Al–Al distance (= $2r$) is 0.2863 nm. Calculate the density of aluminum. (The mass of an aluminum atom is 26.98 amu.)

Solution

$$\text{Volume} = [2(0.2863 \times 10^{-9}\ \text{m})/\sqrt{2}]^3 = 6.638 \times 10^{-29}\ \text{m}^3$$

$$\text{Mass} = (8/8 + 6/2\ \text{atoms})(26.98\ \text{g}/6.022 \times 10^{23}\ \text{atoms}) = 1.792 \times 10^{-22}\ \text{g}$$

$$\text{Density} = (1.792 \times 10^{-22}\ \text{g})/(6.638 \times 10^{-29}\ \text{m}^3) = 2.700 \times 10^6\ \text{g/m}^3 = 2.700\ \text{g/cm}^3$$

$$\text{Actual density} = 2.699\ \text{g/cm}^3$$

Example 7.3

What is the repeat distance along a <211> direction of a copper crystal that is face-centered cubic and has a unit cell dimension (lattice constant) of 0.3615 nm?

Solution

Select the center of any atom as the origin. Make a sketch of a cubic unit cell with that origin arbitrarily set at the lower left rear corner, as shown in Exhibit 1. One of the <211> directions, with coefficients of 2, 1, and 1, exits the first unit cell through the center of its front face, where another atom is centered (with no other intervening atoms).

$$d^2 = a^2 + \left(\frac{a}{2}\right)^2 + \left(\frac{a}{2}\right)^2 = \frac{6}{4}(0.3615\ \text{nm})^2;\ d = 0.4427\ \text{nm}$$

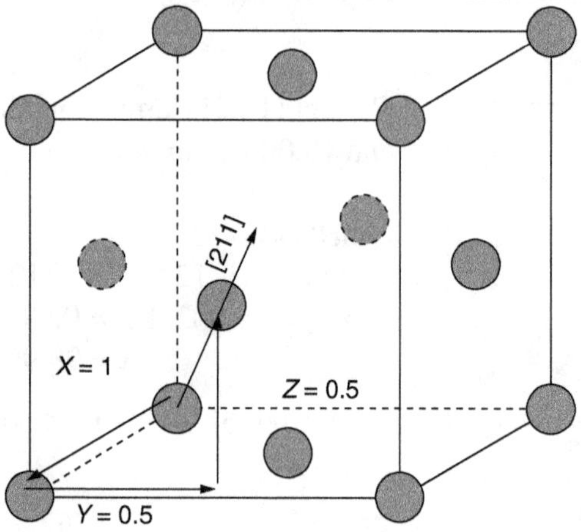

Exhibit 1 FCC unit cell

Example 7.4

Assuming spherical atoms, calculate the packing factor of a BCC metal.

Solution

The packing factor is the volume of atoms per unit volume of the solid. Based on Figure 7.4, there are (8/8 + 1) atoms/unit cell.

$$\text{Volume of 2 atoms in the BCC unit cell} = 2 \times (4\pi/3)r^3 = 8.38r^3$$

Since the cube diagonal is $4r$,

$$\text{Volume of unit cell} = a^3 = \left(\frac{4r}{\sqrt{3}}\right)^3 = 12.32r^3$$

$$\text{Packing factor} = \frac{8.38r^3}{12.32r^3} = 68\%$$

Example 7.5

How many atoms are there per mm^2 on one of the {110} planes of copper (FCC)?

Solution

From Example 7.3, $a_{Cu} = 0.3615$ nm. A {110} plane lies diagonally through the unit cell and is parallel to one of the axes. There are (4/4 + 2/2 atoms) in an area measuring a by $a\sqrt{2}$. The number of atoms is 2 atoms/[(0.3615 × 10^{-6} mm)^2 $\sqrt{2}$] = 10.8 × 10^{12}/mm2.

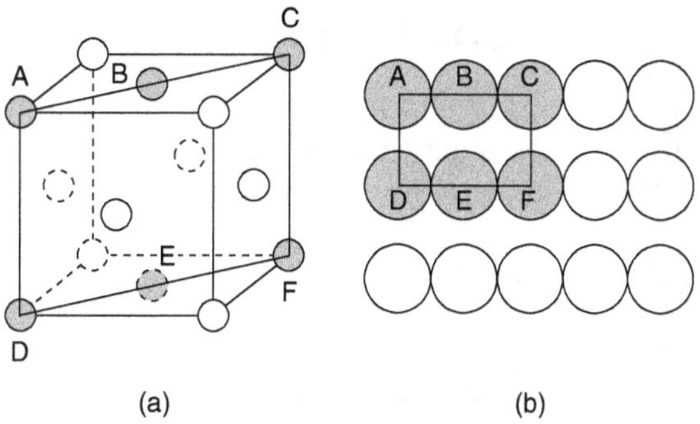

Exhibit 2 (a) Reduced-sphere FCC unit cell with (110) plane. (b) Atomic packing of an FCC (110) plane. Corresponding atom positions from (a) are indicated.

ATOMIC DISORDER IN SOLIDS

In the previous section, we paid attention to the orderly combinations that can exist in engineering materials. A variety of properties and behaviors are closely related to that ordering. Examples that were cited included density, slip systems, and molecular melting.

However, no solid has perfect order. There are always imperfections present, and these may be highly significant. A few missing potassium atoms in a compound such as KBr do not detectably affect the density; however, their absence introduces color. Likewise, the absence of a partial plane of atoms in a metal significantly modifies the shear stress required by a slip system for plastic deformation. Also, a rubber is vulcanized by the joining (**crosslinking**) of adjacent molecules

with only a minor compositional change (sulfur addition). As a final example, the thermal conductivity is doubled in diamond if the 1% of naturally present C^{13} has been removed.

Crystal defects can be characterized as point, line (one-dimensional), plane (two-dimensional), or volume (three-dimensional) defects.

Point Imperfections

Imperfections may be atomically local in nature. Missing atoms (**vacancies**), extra atoms (**interstitials**), **displaced** atoms, and impurity atoms are called **point imperfections** (Figure 7.11). Their existence facilitates the transport of atoms (**diffusion**), thus becoming important in materials processing. In service, the presence of point imperfections scatters internal waves and thus reduces energy transport. These include elastic waves for thermal conductivity, light waves for optical transparency, and electron waves for electrical conduction.

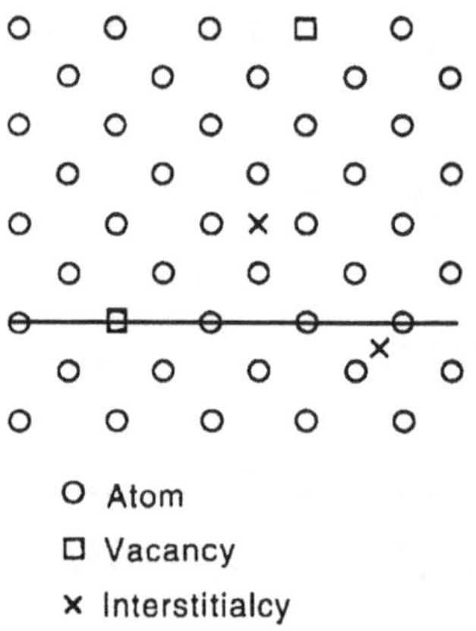

Figure 7.11 Point imperfections. These defects can originate from imperfect crystallization, or through a relocation of energized atoms.

Lineal Imperfections

The principal defect of this type is a **dislocation**. It is most readily visualized (Figure 7.12) as a partial displacement along a slip system or an extra half-plane of atoms. Dislocations facilitate plastic deformation by slip; however, increased numbers of dislocations lead to dislocation tangles or *traffic snarls* and therefore to interference of slip. Thus, ductility decreases and strength increases. Dislocations may develop during initial crystal growth as well as from plastic deformation.

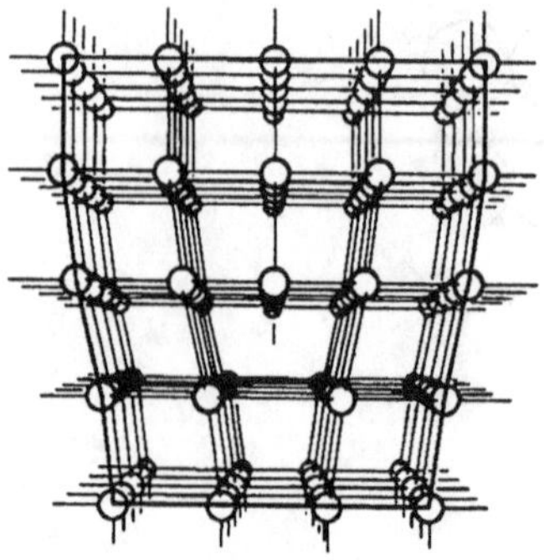

Figure 7.12 Dislocation, ⊥ (schematic). These lineal imperfections facilitate slip within crystals. Excessive numbers of defects, however, lead to their entanglement and a resistance to deformation. The resulting increase in strength is called **work hardening**.

Boundaries

No liquid or solid is infinite; each has a **surface**. The resulting two-dimensional boundary has a different structure and bonding than that encountered in the underlying material. Since atoms are absent from one side of the boundary, the atoms at these surfaces possess additional energy, and subsurface distortions are introduced.

Grain Boundaries

Boundaries also occur where two growing crystals meet. These are called grain boundaries. There are atoms on each side of the boundary; however, any misorientation between the two crystal grains leads to local inefficiencies in atomic packing. As a result some atom-to-atom distances are compressed; others are stretched. Both distortions increase the energy of the atoms along the grain boundaries. This **grain-boundary energy** introduces reactive sites for structural modification during processing and in service. The imperfect grain boundary is also an *avenue* for atomic diffusion within solid materials (Figure 7.13). Further, the mismatch at a grain boundary blocks slip that might otherwise occur, particularly at ambient temperatures where atom-by-atom mobility is limited.

Solutions

Both sugar and salt dissolve in water, each producing a **solution** (commonly called a syrup and a brine, respectively). There are many familiar solutions. Lower melting temperatures, increased conductivity, and altered viscosities commonly result.

Solid Solutions

Impurities, both unwanted and intentional, may also dissolve into a solid. A crystal cannot be perfect when foreign atoms are present. Common brass (70Cu–30Zn) is a familiar example. Zinc atoms simply substitute for copper atoms to produce a **substitutional solid solution**. It has the face-centered cubic crystal structure of pure copper; however, with approximately one-third of the copper atoms replaced by zinc atoms, we can anticipate certain changes. First, the size of the unit cell is increased because zinc atoms are approximately 4% larger than copper atoms. (Fifteen percent mismatch is the practical limit for extensive substitutional solid solution.) Second, charge transport is greatly reduced because the electrons are scattered as they travel toward the positive electrode through locally varying electrical fields. Thus, the electrical and thermal **conductivities** are decreased. Also, atoms of a different size immobilize dislocation movements and in turn produce **solution hardening**.

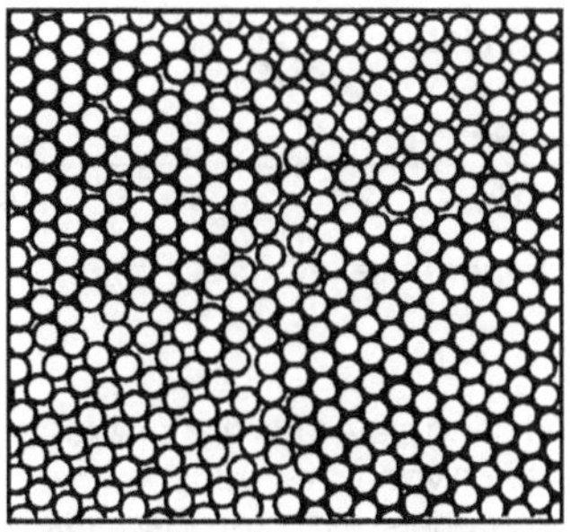

Figure 7.13 Grain boundaries (schematic). Most materials contain a multitude of grains, each of which is a separate crystal. The boundary between grains is a zone of mismatch. Atoms along grain boundaries possess added +energy because they are not as efficiently coordinated with their neighbors.

There are some important situations in which small atoms can be positioned among larger atoms. The most widely encountered example is the solution of carbon in face-centered cubic iron at elevated temperatures. The result is an **interstitial solid solution**. Iron changes to body-centered cubic at ambient temperatures. The BCC iron cannot accommodate many carbon atoms in its interstices. This loss of interstitial solubility plays a major role in the various heat treatments of steel.

Amorphous Solids

Materials lose their crystallinity when they melt. The long-range order of the crystals is not maintained. As a liquid, the material is amorphous (literally, without form). Those materials that are closely packed—for example, metals—will expand on melting [Figure 7.14(a)]. Being thermally agitated, the atoms do not maintain close coordination with neighboring atoms (or molecules). A few materials, such as ice, which has stereospecific bonds, lose volume on melting and become more dense [Figure 7.14(b)].

In certain cases, crystallization may be avoided during cooling. An amorphous solid can result. Two common examples are window glass and the candy part of peanut brittle. In neither case is there time for the relatively complex crystalline structures to form. Very rapid cooling rates are required to avoid crystallization when the crystalline structures are less complex. For example, metals must be quenched a thousand degrees in milliseconds to avoid crystallization. The amorphous materials that result are considered to be **vitreous**, or glass-like.

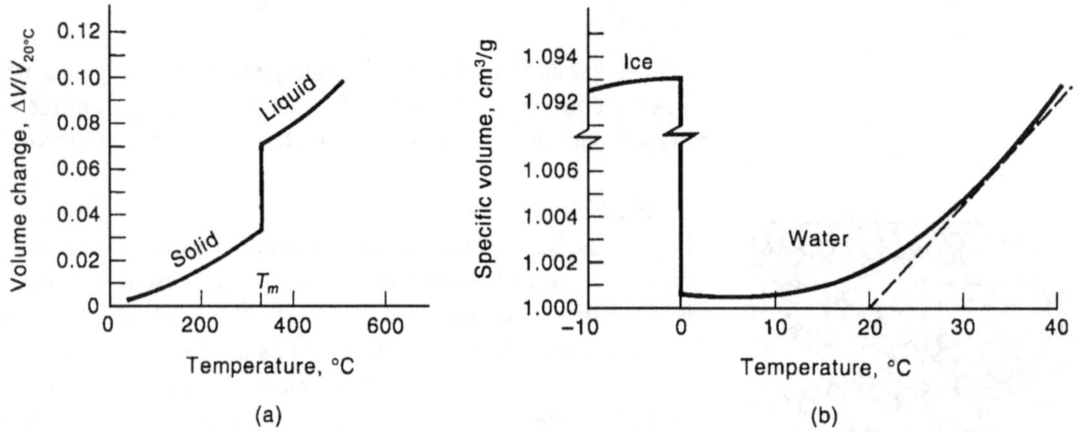

Figure 7.14 Volume changes during heating. (a) Lead (FCC); (b) H2O. Melting destroys the efficient packing of metallic atoms within solids, so most metals expand when melted. The crystalline structure of ice, silicon, and a number of related materials with stereospecific bonds have low, inefficient atomic packing within solids. Therefore, they lose volume when melted.

Example **7.6**

Sterling silver contains 92.5% silver and 7.5% copper by weight. What percentage of the atoms on a (111) plane are silver? Copper?

Solution

The alloy is a random solid solution; therefore the percentage of atoms on the (111) plane or any other plane will be the same as throughout the alloy. Change weight percent to atom percent. The atomic masses are 107.87 and 63.54 amu, respectively.

Basis: 1000 amu = 925 amu Ag + 75 amu Cu

Ag: 925 amu/(107.87 amu/Ag) = 8.58 Ag atoms

Cu: 75 amu/(63.54 amu/Cu) = 1.18 Cu atoms

Total: = 9.76 atoms

Ag atoms = 8.58/9.76 = 87.9%; Cu atoms = 12.1%

MICROSTRUCTURES OF SOLID MATERIALS

The atomic coordination within solids is on the nanometer scale. The resulting structures involve either crystalline solids, or amorphous solids such as the glasses. As discussed, certain properties arise from these atom-to-atom relationships. Other properties arise from longer-range structures, generally with micrometer to millimeter dimensions, called **microstructures**.

Atomic Movements in Materials

Our initial examination of crystals implied that an atom becomes permanently coordinated with adjacent atoms and remains fixed in position. This is not entirely true. In the first place, there is thermal vibration of the atoms within the crystal. Thus, while the lattice constant and the mean interatomic distances are fixed to several significant figures, the instantaneous interatomic distances vary. The

amplitude of vibration increases with temperature. At the melting temperature, the crystal is literally *shaken apart*. As the melting point is approached, a measurable fraction of atoms jump out of their crystalline positions. They may return, or they may move to other sites, producing the vacancies and interstitials discussed in the previous section.

Diffusion

Within a single-component material, such as pure copper, there is equal probability that like numbers of copper atoms will jump in each of the coordinate directions. Thus, there is no net change.

Imagine, however, one location, x_1, in nickel containing 2000 atoms of copper for every mm^3 of nickel, whereas 1 mm to the right at x_2 there are 1000 atoms of copper for every mm^3. Although all copper atoms have the same probability for jumping in either direction, there is a net movement of copper atoms to the right simply because there are unequal numbers of copper atoms in the two locations. There is a copper **concentration gradient**, $\Delta C/\Delta x$. In this case

$$\Delta C/\Delta x = (C_2 - C_1 \text{ Cu/mm}^3)/(x^2 - x^1 \text{ mm}) = -(1000 \text{ Cu/mm}^3)/\text{mm} \qquad \textbf{(7.2)}$$

The rate of diffusion, called the **flux**, J, is proportional to the concentration gradient

$$J = -D\frac{dC}{dx} \qquad \textbf{(7.3)}$$

where D is the *diffusivity*, also called the **diffusion coefficient**. (Its units are m^{2}s^{-1} since the units for flux and concentration gradient are m^{-2}s^{-1} and m^{-4}, respectively.)

The diffusion coefficient can be calculated by

$$D = D_o e^{-Q/(RT)}$$

where D_o (with units of m^{2}s^{-1}) is the proportionality constant, Q (with units of J(mole)$^{-1}$) is the activation energy, R is the gas constant, and T is absolute temperature.

Among the various factors that affect the diffusivity are (1) the size of the diffusing atom, (2) the crystal structure of the matrix, (3) bond strength, and (4) temperature. Comparisons are made in Table 7.3. The diffusivity of the C in Fe_{FCC} is higher than for the Fe in Fe_{FCC} because the diffusing carbon atom is smaller than the iron atom. The diffusivity of the C in Fe_{BCC} is higher than for the C in Fe_{FCC} because the latter contains more iron atoms per m^3. The FCC packing factor is higher than the BCC form. The diffusivity for Fe in Fe_{FCC} is lower than for Cu in Cu_{FCC} because the iron atoms are more strongly bonded than the copper atoms. (The melting temperatures provide evidence of this.) In each case, higher diffusion coefficients accompany higher temperatures.

The process engineer obtains many of the properties required of a material by heat-treating procedures. Diffusion plays the predominant role in achieving the required microstructures.

Table 7.3 Selected diffusion coefficients

Diffusing Atom	Host Structure	Diffusion Coefficient, D, m²/s	
		500°C (930°F)	1000°C (1830°F)
Fe	FCC Fe	2×10^{-23}	2×10^{-16}
C	FCC Fe	5×10^{-15}	3×10^{-11}
C	BCC Fe	1×10^{-12}	2×10^{-9}
Cu	FCC Cu	1×10^{-18}	2×10^{-13}

Structures of Single-Phase Solids

Many materials possess only one structure. Examples include copper wire, transparent polystyrene cups, and AI_2O_3 substrates for electronic circuits. The wire contains only face-centered-cubic crystals. The polystyrene is an amorphous solid with minimal crystallinity. The substrates have numerous crystals, all with the same crystalline structure. We speak of single phases because none of these materials contains a second structure.

Grains

Each of the individual crystals in a copper wire is called a **grain**. Recall from the previous section that adjacent crystals may be misoriented with respect to each other, and that there is a boundary between them. This is shown schematically in Figure 7.15.

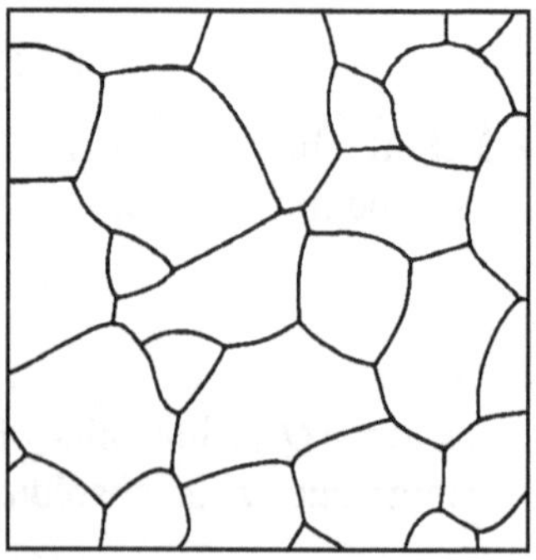

Figure 7.15 Grains (schematic). Each grain is a separate crystal. There is a surface of mismatch between grains because adjacent grains have unlike orientations. The **grain boundary area** is inversely related to grain size.

The **grain size** is an important structural parameter, because the grain boundary area varies inversely with the grain size. Diffusion is faster along grain boundaries because there is less-perfect packing of the atoms and, consequently, a more open structure. At ambient temperatures, grain boundaries interfere with plastic deformation, thus increasing the strength. At elevated temperatures the grain boundaries contribute to creep and therefore are to be minimized. Grain boundaries also serve as locations that initiate structural changes within a solid.

Grain growth may occur in a single-phase material. The driving force is the fact that the atoms at the grain boundary possess extra energy. Grain growth reduces this excess energy by minimizing the boundary area. Higher temperatures increase the rate of grain growth because the atoms migrate faster. However, since the growth rate is inversely related to grain size, we see a decrease in the rate of growth with time.

The texture of a single-phase solid can also depend on **grain shape** and **orientation**. Even a noncrystalline material may possess a structure. For example, the molecular chains within a nylon fiber have been aligned during processing to provide greater tensile strength.

Phase Diagrams

Many materials possess more than one phase. A simple and obvious example is a cup containing both ice and water. While ice and water have the same composition, the structures of the two phases are different. There is a **phase boundary** between the two phases. A less obvious, but equally important material is the steel used as a bridge beam. The steel in the beam contains two phases: nearly pure iron (body-centered cubic), and an iron carbide, Fe_3C.

In these two examples, we have a mixture of two phases. Solutions are phases with more than one component. In the previous section, we encountered brass, a solid solution with copper and zinc as its components.

Although the steel beam just cited contains a mixture of two phases at ambient temperatures, it contained only one phase when it was red-hot during the shaping process. At that temperature, the iron was face-centered-cubic and was thereby able to dissolve all of the carbon into its interstices. No Fe_3C remained. The phases within a material can be displayed on a **phase diagram** as a function of temperature and composition.

Phase diagrams are useful to the engineer because they indicate the temperature and composition requirements for attaining the required internal structures and accompanying service properties. The phase diagram shows us (1) *what* phases to expect, (2) the *composition* of each phase that is present, and (3) the *quantity* of each phase within a mixture of phases.

What Phases?

Sterling silver contains 92.5Ag–7.5Cu (weight percent). Using the Ag–Cu phase diagram of Figure 7.16, we observe that this composition is liquid above 910°C; below 740°C, it contains a mixture of the α and β solid structures. The former is a solid solution of silver plus a limited amount of copper; the latter is a solid solution of copper plus a limited amount of silver. Between 740 and 810°C, only one phase is present, α. In that temperature range, all of the copper can be dissolved in the α solid solution. From 810 to 910°C, the alloy changes from no liquid to all liquid.

Phase Compositions?

Pure silver has a face-centered-cubic structure. Copper forms the same crystalline structure. Not surprisingly, copper atoms can be substituted for silver. But the solid solution in α is limited, because the silver atom is 13% larger in diameter than is copper. However, the solubility increases with temperature to 8.8 weight-percent copper at 780°C. This is shown by the boundary of the silver-rich shaded area of Figure 7.16. Within that shaded area, we have a single phase called α.

Conversely, the FCC structure of copper can dissolve silver atoms in solid solution. At room temperature the solubility is very small. Again, as the temperature is raised the solubility limit increases to 8 weight-percent silver (92 wt. % Cu) at 780°C. This copper-rich phase is called β.

Silver and copper are mutually soluble in a liquid solution. Above 1100°C there is no limit to the solubility. As the temperature is reduced below the melting point of copper (1084°C), the copper solubility limit decreases from 100% to 28%. Excess copper produces the β phase. Likewise, below the melting point of silver (962°C), the silver solubility limit decreases from 100% to 72%. Excess silver produces the α phase. The two solubility curves cross at approximately 72Ag–28Cu and 780°C. We call this low-melting liquid **eutectic**.

How Much of Each Phase in a Mixture?

At 800°C, a 72Ag–28Cu alloy is entirely liquid. At the same temperature, but with added copper, the solubility limit is reached at 32% Cu. Beyond that limit, still at 800°C, any additional copper precipitates as β. Halfway across the two-phase field of (L + β), there will be equal quantities of the two phases. Additional copper in the alloy increases the amount of β. Within this two-phase region the liquid remains saturated with 32% Cu, and the solid β is saturated with 8% Ag (thus, 92% Cu).

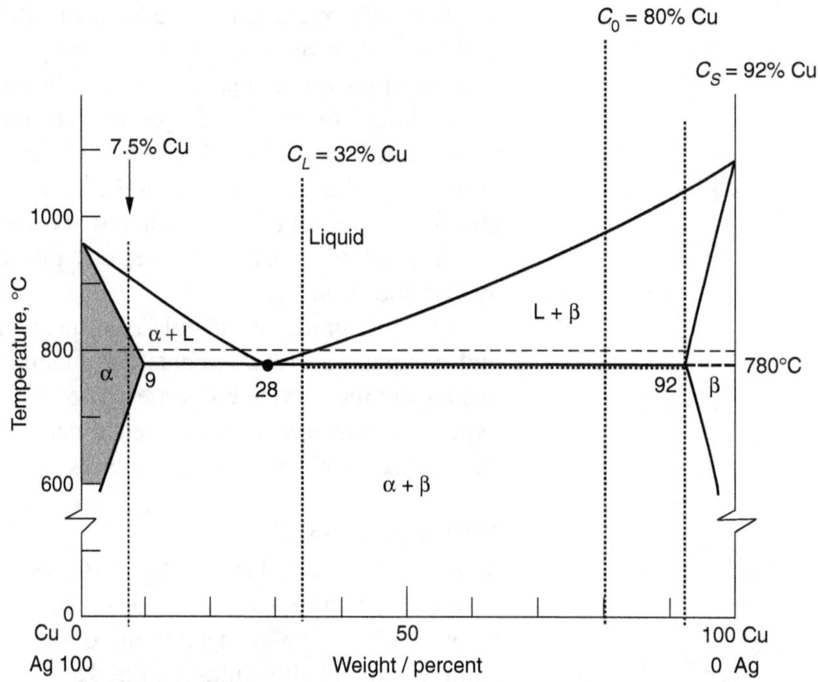

Figure 7.16 Silver-copper phase diagram. Sterling silver contains 7.5% copper; therefore, it has a single phase, α, in the 740–810°C range.

The *composition* of each phase is dictated by the solubility limits. (In a one-phase field, the solubility limits are not factors; the alloy composition and the phase composition are identical.) The *amount* of each phase in a two-phase field is determined by interpolation between the solubility limits using what is called the lever law. For example, at 800°C, an alloy consisting of 80% Cu and 20% Ag would consist of a liquid phase containing 32% Cu and a solid phase of 92% Cu. The weight fraction of liquid phase, W_L, and solid phase, W_s, is determined by

In addition $W_L + W_S = 1$.

$$W_L = \frac{C_s - C_O}{C_S - C_L} \quad \text{and} \quad W_S = \frac{C_O - C_L}{C_S - C_L}$$

Reaction Rates in Solids

A phase diagram is normally an equilibrium diagram; that is, all reactions have been completed. The time required to reach equilibrium generally increases with decreasing temperature. Thus, a material may not always possess the expected phases with predicted amounts or compositions. Even so, the phase diagram is valuable. For example, sterling silver (92.5Ag–7.5Cu) contains only one phase when equilibrated at 775°C (Figure 7.16). Slow cooling to room temperature precipitates β as a minor second phase, as would be expected when plenty of time is available. Rapid cooling, however, traps the copper atoms within the a solid solution. This situation is used to advantage, because the solid solution is stronger than the ($\alpha + \beta$) combination. Also, a single-phase alloy corrodes less readily. This explains why the *impure* sterling silver is commonly preferred over pure silver.

The selection of compositions and processing treatments is generally based on a knowledge of equilibrium diagrams plus a knowledge of how equilibrium is circumvented.

Microstructures of Multiphase Solids

The microstructure of a single-phase, crystalline solid includes the *size*, *shape*, and *orientation* of the grains. Variations in these properties are also found in multiphase solids. In addition, the microstructure of a multiphase solid may also vary in the *amount* of each phase and the *distribution* of the phases. In an equilibrated microstructure, the amounts of the phases may be predicted directly from the phase diagrams using the lever law. From Figure 7.17, a 1080 steel (primarily iron, with 0.80 percent carbon) will have twice as much Fe_3C (W_{Fe3C}) at room temperature as a 1040 steel (with 0.40 percent carbon). The Fe_3C is a hard phase. Therefore, with all other factors equal, we expect a 1080 steel to be harder than a 1040 steel, and it is.

$$W_{Fe_3C} = \frac{C_0 - C_\alpha}{C_{Fe_3C} - C_\alpha}$$

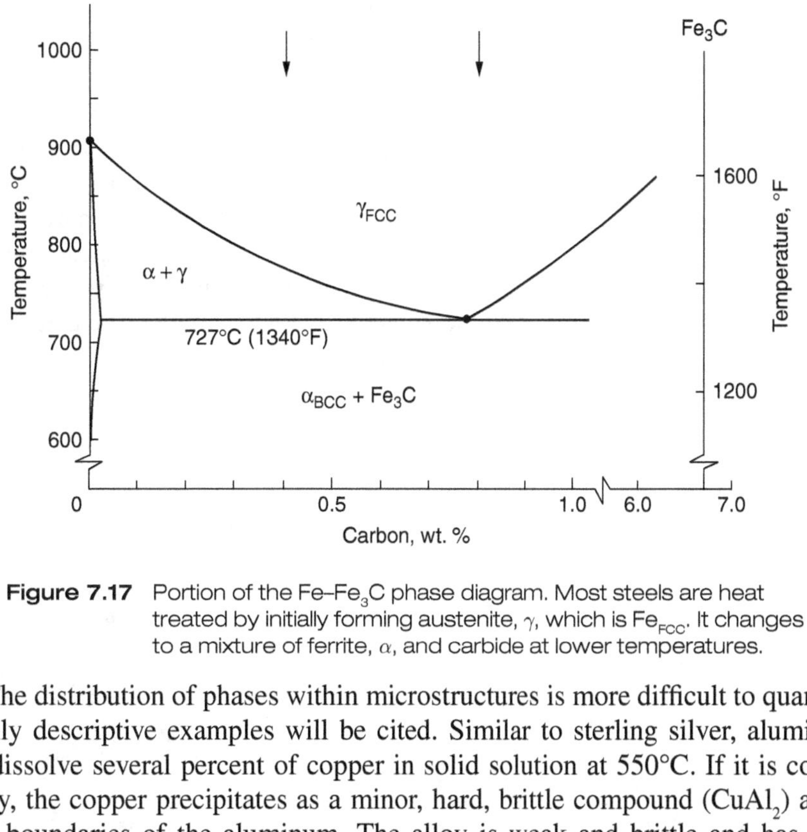

Figure 7.17 Portion of the Fe–Fe_3C phase diagram. Most steels are heat treated by initially forming austenite, γ, which is Fe_{FCC}. It changes to a mixture of ferrite, α, and carbide at lower temperatures.

The distribution of phases within microstructures is more difficult to quantify, so only descriptive examples will be cited. Similar to sterling silver, aluminum will dissolve several percent of copper in solid solution at 550°C. If it is cooled slowly, the copper precipitates as a minor, hard, brittle compound ($CuAl_2$) along grain boundaries of the aluminum. The alloy is weak and brittle and has little practical use. If the same alloy is cooled rapidly from 550°C, trapping the copper atoms within the aluminum grains as shown in Figure 7.18(a), the quenched solid solution is stronger and more ductile and has commercial uses. If the quenched alloy is reheated to 100°C, the $CuAl_2$ precipitates, as expected from the phase diagram shown in Figure 7.18(b) and (c). In this case, however, the precipitate is very finely dispersed within the grains of aluminum. The alloy retains its toughness, because the brittle $CuAl_2$ does not form a network for fracture paths. In addition, the strength is increased because the submicroscopic hard particles interfere with the deformation of the aluminum along slip planes. Alloys of this type are used in airplane construction because they are light, strong, and tough. Observe that all of

the examples in this paragraph are for the same alloy. The properties have been varied through microstructural control.

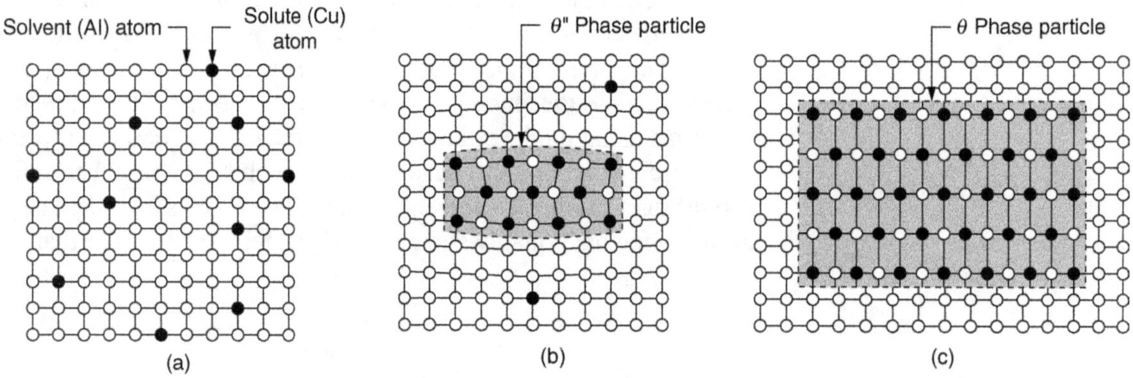

Figure 7.18 Schematic depiction of several stages in the formation of the equilibrium precipitate (*q*) phase. (a) A supersaturated a solid solution; (b) a transition, θ'', precipitate phase; (c) the equilibrium θ' phase, within the a-matrix phase. Actual phase particle sizes are much larger than shown here.

Two distinct microstructures may be produced in a majority of steels. In one, called **spheroidite**, the hard Fe_3C is present as rounded particles in a matrix of ductile ferrite (α). In the other, called **pearlite**, Fe_3C and ferrite form fine alternating layers, or lamellae. Spheroidite is softer but tougher; pearlite is harder and less ductile (Figure 7.19). The mechanical properties are controlled by the spacing of the Fe_3C, because the hard Fe_3C phase stops dislocation motion. The closer the spacing between Fe_3C particles, the greater the strength or hardness, but the lower the ductility.

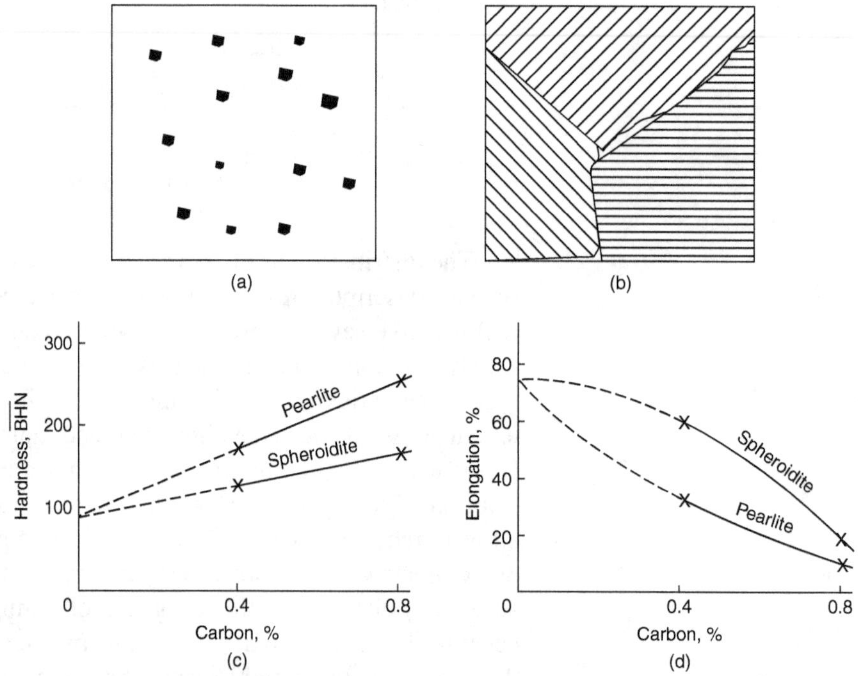

Figure 7.19 Phase distributions (schematic). The two samples are of the same steel, both containing ferrite (white) and carbide (black) but heat treated differently. Spheroidite is shown in (a), and pearlite in (b). The hardness of the two structures is shown in (c), and ductility is shown in (d).

Example 7.7

At 780°C, an Ag–Cu liquid of eutectic composition (Figure 7.16) solidifies to solid α and solid β. (i) What are the compositions of the two solid phases just below the eutectic temperature? (ii) How much of each of these two phases exists per 100 grams of alloy?

Solution

(i) From Figure 7.16, the α phase is 91Ag–9Cu, and the β phase is 8Ag–92Cu.

(ii) Interpolation along the 780°C tie-line between the solubility limits yields

$$\beta\text{: (using Cu) } [(28 - 9)/(92 - 9)](100\text{ g}) = 23\text{ g}$$

$$\alpha\text{: (using Cu) } [(92 - 28)/(92 - 9)](100\text{ g}) = 77\text{ g}$$

or

$$\alpha\text{: (using Ag) } [(72 - 8)/(92 - 9)](100\text{ g}) = 77\text{ g}$$

Example 7.8

The phases and microstructures of an SAE 1040 steel may be related to the Fe-Fe_3C phase diagram (Figure 7.17). (i) Assume equilibrium. What are the phases and their weight percents at 728°C? At 726°C? (ii) Pearlite has the eutectoid composition of 0.77% C. What percent of the steel will *not* be contained in the pearlite?

Solution

(i) At 728°:

$$\alpha\ (0.02\%\text{ C}): (0.77 - 0.40)/(0.77 - 0.02) = 49\%\ \alpha$$

$$\gamma\ (0.77\%\text{ C}): (0.40 - 0.02)/(0.77 - 0.02) = 51\%\ \gamma$$

$$Fe_3C\text{ contains } 12/[12 + 3(55.85)] = 6.7\%\text{ C}$$

At 726°:

$$\alpha\ (0.02\%\text{ C}): (6.7 - 0.40)/(6.7 - 0.02) = 94\%\ \alpha$$

$$Fe_3C\text{: } (0.40 - 0.02)/(6.7 - 0.02) = 6\%\ Fe_3C$$

(ii) All of the pearlite, $\alpha + Fe_3C$, comes from the γ. This FCC phase changes to pearlite at 727°C. The α that was present at 728°C remains unchanged. Therefore, the answer is $P = 51\%$; and unchanged $\alpha = 49\%$.

MATERIALS PROCESSING

For many engineers, materials are first encountered in terms of handbook data or stockroom inventories. However, materials always have a prior history. They must be obtained from natural sources, then subjected to compositional modifications and complex shaping processes. Finally, specific microstructures are developed to achieve the properties that are necessary for extended service.

Extraction and Compositional Adjustments

Few materials are used in their natural form. Wood is cut and reshaped into lumber, chipboard, or plywood; most metals must be extracted from their ores; rubber latex is useless unless it is vulcanized.

Extraction from Ores

Most ores are oxides or sulfides that require chemical reduction. Commonly, oxide ores are chemically reduced with carbon- or CO-containing gas. For example,

$$Fe_2O_3 + 3\,CO \rightarrow 2\,Fe + 3\,CO_2 \quad \textbf{(7.4)}$$

Elevated temperatures are used to speed up the reactions and more completely reduce the metal. If the metal is melted, it is more readily separated from the accompanying gangue materials. The reduced product is a carbon-saturated metallic iron. As such, it has only limited applications. Normally, further processing is required.

Refining

Dissolved impurities must be removed. Even if the above ore were of the highest quality iron oxide, it would be necessary to refine it, because the metallic product is saturated with carbon. In practice, small but undesirable quantities of silicon and other species are also reduced and dissolved in the iron. They are removed by closely controlled **reoxidation** at chemically appropriate temperatures (followed by **deoxidation**). The product is a **steel**. Alloying additions are made as specified to create different types of steel.

Chemicals from which a variety of plastics are produced are refined from petroleum. The principal step of petroleum refinement involves selective distillation of liquid petroleum. Lightweight fractions are removed first. Controlled temperatures and pressures distill the molecular fractions that serve as precursors for polymers. Residual fractions are directed to other products.

Polymerization makes macromolecules out of the smaller molecules that are the product of distillation. **Addition polymerization** involving a C=C→C—C reaction is encountered in the polymerization of ethylene, $H_2C{=}CH_2$; vinyl chloride, $H_2C{=}CHCl$; and styrene, $H_2C{=}CH(C_6H_5)$.

$$C{=}C \rightarrow C{-}C{-} \quad \textbf{(7.5)}$$

Shaping Processes

The earliest cultural ages of human activities produced artifacts that had been shaped from stone, bronze, or iron. In modern technology, we speak of casting, deformation, cutting, and joining in addition to more specialized shaping procedures.

Casting

The concept of casting is straightforward. A liquid is solidified within a mold of the required shape. For metal casting, attention must be given to volume changes; in most cases there is shrinkage. In order to avoid porosity, provision must be made for feeding molten metal from a **riser**. **Segregation** may occur at the solidifying front because of compositional differences in the $(\alpha + L)$ range. (See the earlier discussion of phase diagrams and the discussion of annealing processes in a following subsection.)

A number of ceramic products are made by **slip casting**. The slip is a slurry of fine powders suspended in a fluid, usually water. The mold is typically of gypsum plaster with a porosity that absorbs water from the adjacent suspension. When the shell forming inside the mold is sufficiently thick, the remaining slip is drained. Subsequent processing steps are **drying** and **firing**. The latter high-temperature step bonds the powder into a coherent product.

The casting process is also used in forming polymeric products. Here the solidification is accomplished by polymerization. There is a chemical reaction between the small precursor molecules of the liquid to produce macromolecules and a resulting solid.

Deformation Processes

Deformation processes include forging, rolling, extrusion, and drawing, plus a number of variants. In each case, a force is applied, and a dimensional change results. **Forging** involves shape change by impact. **Rolling** may be used for sheet products as well as for products with constant cross sections, for example, structural beams. **Extrusion** is accomplished through open or closed dies. The former requires that the product be of uniform cross section, such as plastic pipe or siderails for aluminum ladders. Closed dies are molds into which the material is forced. These forming processes can be done at ambient temperature (cold working) or elevated temperatures ($T > 0.4T_m$ in Kelvin; hot working). T_m is the melting temperature. The forming temperature has a strong effect on mechanical properties. Products formed at ambient temperature have high dislocation densities and hence greater strength and hardness but lower ductility than hot-worked products.

In general, ceramics do not lend themselves to the above deformation processes because they lack ductility. Major exceptions are the glasses, which deform not by crystalline slip but by viscous flow.

Cutting

Chiseling and sawing are cutting processes that predate history. Current technology includes **machining** in which a cutting tool and the product move with respect to each other. Depth and rates of cut are adjustable to meet requirements. **Grinding** is a variant of machining that is used for surface removal.

Joining

The process of **welding** produces a joint along which the abutting material has been melted and filled with matching metal. **Soldering** and **brazing** processes use fillers that have a lower melting point than the adjoining materials, which remain solid. There are glass solders as well as metallic ones. Adhesives have long been used for joining wood and plastic components, and many have now been developed to join metals and ceramics.

Annealing Processes

Annealing processes involve reheating a material sufficiently that internal adjustments may be made between atoms or between molecules. The temperature of annealing varies with (1) the material, (2) the amount of time available, and (3) the structural changes that are desired.

Homogenization

The dynamics of processing will produce segregation. For example, when an 80Cu–20Ni alloy starts to solidify at 1200°C, the first solid contains 30% Ni. When solidification is completed, the final liquid has only 12% Ni. Uniformity can be obtained if the alloy is reheated to a temperature at which the atoms can relocate by diffusion. There is a time-temperature relationship (log t vs. $1/T$). In this case an increase in temperature from 500 to 550°C reduces the necessary annealing time by a factor of eight.

Recrystallization

Networks of dislocations are introduced when most metals are plastically deformed at ambient temperatures (cold working). The result is a work hardening and loss of ductility. Whereas the resulting increase in strength is often desired, the property changes resulting from dislocations make further deformation processing more difficult. Annealing will remove the dislocations and restore the initial workable characteristics by forming new, strain-free crystals.

A one-hour heat treatment is a common shop practice because it allows for temperature equalization as well as scheduling requirements. For that time frame, it is necessary to heat a metal to approximately 40 percent of its melting temperature (on the absolute scale). Thus, copper that melts at 1085°C (1358 K) may be expected to recrystallize in the hour at 270°C (545 K). The recrystallization time is shorter at higher temperatures and longer at lower temperatures.

Grain Growth

Extended annealing, beyond that required for recrystallization, produces grain growth and therefore coarser grains. Normally, this is to be avoided. However, grain growth has merit in certain applications because grain boundaries hinder magnetic domain boundary movements, reducing creep. So, coarse grains are preferred in the sheet steel used in transformers, for example. At high temperatures, grain boundaries permit creep to occur under applied stresses, producing changes in dimensions.

Residual Stresses

Expansions and contractions occur within materials during heat-treating operations. These are isotropic for many materials; or they may vary with crystal orientation. Also, differential expansions exist between the two or more phases in a multiphase material. The latter, plus the presence of thermal gradients, introduce internal stresses, which can lead to delayed fracture if not removed.

It is generally desirable to eliminate these residual stresses by an annealing process called **stress relief**. The required temperature is less than that for recrystallization because atomic diffusion is generally not necessary; rather, adjustments are made through the local movement of dislocations. Stress relief is performed on metals before the final machining or grinding operation. Annealing is always performed on glass products, because any residual surface tension easily activates cracks in this nonductile material.

Induced Stresses

In apparent contradiction to the last statement, residual compressive stresses may be prescribed for certain glasses, since glass like most nonductile materials is strong in **compression** but weak in **tension**. As an example, a familiar dinnerware product is made from a *sandwich* glass sheet in which the *bread* layers have a

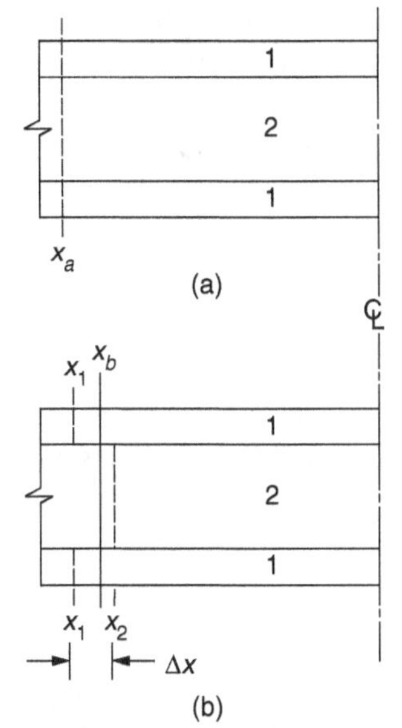

Figure 7.20 Induced stresses (sandwich glass). (a) The previously bonded composite containing glasses 1 and 2 is annealed. There are no internal stresses at x_a. (b) If the three layers were separate, the outer layers, which have a lower thermal coefficient, would contract less during cooling than the center glass (x_1 vs. x_2). Since the layers are bonded together, the restricted contraction of the center (x_a to x_b rather than x_a to x_2) induces compression within the surface layers (x_1 to x_b).

lower thermal expansion than does the *meat* layer. The processing involves heating the dinnerware to relieve all stresses (annealing). As the dinnerware pieces are cooled, the center layer tries to contract more than the surface layers, placing the surfaces under compression (Figure 7.20). Any tension encountered in service must overcome the residual compression before a crack can propagate.

Time-Dependent Processes

We have seen in a previous section that sterling silver is solution treated to dissolve all of the copper within the silver-rich α phase. The single phase is preserved by rapidly cooling the alloy. This avoids the precipitation of the copper-rich β phase, as required for equilibrium. The cooling rate need not be drastic for sterling silver because it takes a minute or more to nucleate and grow the precipitate, β.

Even more time is available for the production of a **silicate glass**—a supercooled liquid. The necessary bond breaking and rearrangements are very slow. The available processing times can approach an hour or more. However, in order to produce a **metallic glass**, the cooling rate must approach 1000°C per *millisecond*. Otherwise, individual metal atoms rapidly order themselves into one of the crystalline patterns described earlier.

Martensitic Reactions

Most steel processing treatments initially heat the steel to provide a single-phase microstructure of γ or **austenite** (Fe_{FCC}). This is face-centered-cubic and dissolves all of the carbon that is present. Normal cooling produces **pearlite**, a lamellar microstructure containing layers of α or ferrite (Fe_{BCC}) and **carbide** (Fe_3C), as shown previously on the Fe–Fe_3C phase diagram (Figure 7.17).

$$Fe_{FCC} \xrightarrow{\text{cooling}} Fe_{BCC} + Fe_3C \qquad \textbf{(7.6)}$$

If **quenched**, a different structure forms:

$$Fe_{FCC} \xrightarrow{\text{quenching}} \text{Martensite} \qquad \textbf{(7.7)}$$

Martensite is a transition phase. It offers an interesting possibility for many applications because it is much harder than pearlite. Unfortunately, martensite is also very brittle, and its usefulness in steel is severely limited. Martensite will exist almost indefinitely at ambient temperatures, but reheating the steel provides an opportunity for the completion of the reaction of Equation (7.6).

$$\text{Martensite} \xrightarrow{\text{tempering}} Fe_3C \qquad \textbf{(7.8)}$$

The reheating process is called **tempering**. The product, which has a microstructure of finely dispersed carbide particles in a ferrite matrix, is both hard and tough. It is widely used and is called **tempered martensite**.

Hardenability

Tempered martensite is the preferred microstructure of many high-strength steels. Processing requires a sufficiently rapid quench to obtain the intermediate martensite, Equation (7.7), followed by tempering, Equation (7.8). This means severe quenching for products of Fe–C steels that are larger than needles or razor blades. Even then, martensite forms only at the quenched surface. The subsurface metal transforms directly to the ferrite and carbide, Equation (7.6).

The reaction rate of Equation (7.6) can be decreased by the presence of various alloying elements in the steel. Thus, gears and similar products commonly contain fractional percentages of nickel, chromium, molybdenum, or other metals. Quenching severity can be reduced, and larger components can be hardened throughout. These alloying elements delay the formation of carbide because, not only must small carbon atoms relocate, it is also necessary for the larger metal atoms to choose between residence in the ferrite or in the carbide.

Surface Modification

Products may be treated so that their surfaces are modified and therefore possess different properties than the original material. Chrome plating is a familiar example.

Carburizing

Strength and hardness of a steel increase with carbon content. Concurrently, ductility and toughness decrease. With these variables, the engineer must consider trade-offs when specifying steels for mechanical applications. An alternate possibility is to alter the surface zone. A common example is the choice of a low-carbon, tough steel that has had carbon diffused into the subsurface (<1 mm) to produce hard carbide particles. Wear resistance is developed without decreasing bulk toughness.

Nitriding

Results similar to carburizing are possible for a steel containing small amounts of aluminum. Nitrogen can be diffused through the surface to form a subscale containing particles of aluminum nitride. Since AlN has structure and properties that are related to diamond, wear resistance is increased for the steel.

Shot Peening

Superficial deformation occurs when a ductile material is impacted by sand or by hardened shot. A process employing shot peening places the surface zone in local compression and therefore lowers the probability for fracture initiation during tensile loading.

Example 7.9

Assume a single spherical shrinkage cavity forms inside a 2-kg lead casting as it is solidified at 327°C. What is the initial diameter of the cavity after solidification? (The greatest density of molten lead is 10.6 g/cm^3.)

Solution

Refer to Figure 7.14(a). Based on a unit volume at 20°C, lead shrinks from 1.07 to 1.035 during solidification.

The volume of molten lead is (2000 g)/(10.6 g/cm^3) = 188.7 cm^3.

Volume of solid lead at 327°C: (188.7 cm^3)(1.035/1.07) = 182.5 cm^3

Shrinkage: 188.7 cm^3 – 182.5 cm^3 = $\pi d^3/6$; $d = 2.28$ cm

Example 7.10

How much energy is involved in polymerizing one gram of ethylene (C_2H_4) into polyethylene. The double carbon bond possesses 162 kcal/mole, and the single bond has 88 kcal/mole.

Solution

One double carbon bond changes to two single bonds/mer:

$$(1 \text{ g})/(24 + 4 \text{ g/mole}) = 0.0357 \text{ moles}$$

The energy required to break 0.0357 moles of double bonds is

$$(1)(0.0357)(162 \text{ kcal}) = 5.79 \text{ kcal}$$

The energy released in joining twice as many single bonds is

$$(2)(0.0357)(-88 \text{ kcal}) = -6.29 \text{ kcal}$$

The net energy change is –6.29 + 5.79 kcal = 500 cal released/g.

Example 7.11

There are 36 equiaxed grains per mm^2 observed at a magnification of 100 in a selected area of copper. The copper is heated to double the average grain diameter. (i) How many grains exist per mm^2? (ii) What will be the percentage (increase, decrease) in grain boundary area?

Solution

(i) Doubling a lineal dimension decreases the number of grains by a factor of four, so there are 9 grains per mm^2.

(ii) Surface area is a function of the lineal dimension squared:

$$a_1/a_2 \propto d_1^2/d_2^2$$

Thus, $a_1/a_2 = 0.25$, or a 75% decrease in grain boundary area.

MATERIALS IN SERVICE

Products of engineering are made to be used. Conditions that are encountered in service most often vary tremendously from those present in the stockroom: static and dynamic loads, elevated and subambient temperatures, solar and nuclear radiation exposure, and many other reactions with the surrounding environment. All of these situations can lead to deterioration and even to failure. The design engineer should be able to anticipate the conditions of failure.

Mechanical Failure

Under ambient conditions, excessive loads can lead to bending or to cracking, the principal modes of mechanical failure. The former depends upon geometry and the stress level. **Stress** is defined as load divided by cross-sectional area, $\sigma = F/A$. Cracking (and succeeding fracture) includes those two considerations, plus the loading rate.

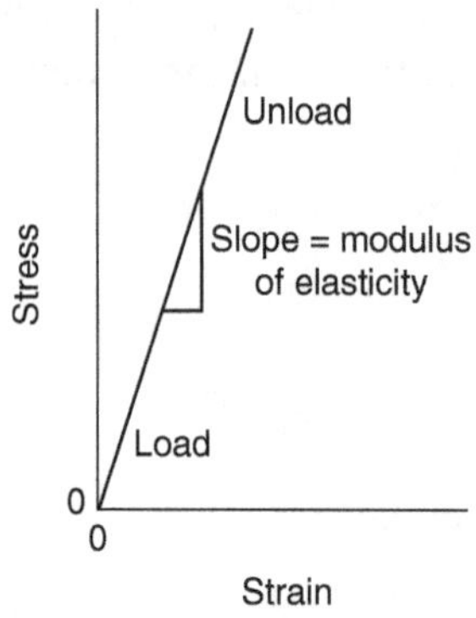

Figure 7.21 Schematic stress-strain diagram showing linear elastic deformation for loading and unloading cycles

Yield Strength

When solids are stressed, strain occurs. Strain is the change in length divided by the original length, $\varepsilon = \Delta L/L_0$. The ratio of stress to strain is called the **elastic modulus,** $E = \sigma/\varepsilon$, and is initially constant in most solids as shown in Figure 7.21. The interatomic spacings are altered as the load is increased. Initial slip starts at a threshold level called the **yield strength,** σ_y, shown in Figure 7.22. Higher stresses will produce a permanent distortion, which will be called failure if the product was designed to maintain its initial shape. The toughness of a material is related to the energy or work required for fracture, a product of both strength and ductility. In a tensile test, the energy is the area under the stress-strain curve. Ductile fracture involves significant plastic deformation and hence absorbs much more energy than brittle fracture, which has little or no plastic deformation. A complete stress-strain curve is shown in Figure 7.23.

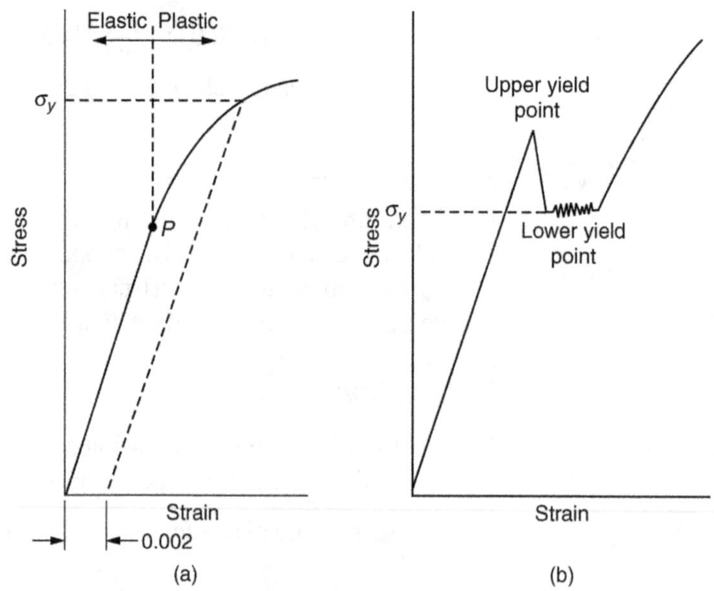

Figure 7.22 (a) Typical stress-strain behavior for a metal, showing elastic and plastic deformations, the proportional limit *P*, and the yield strength σ_y, as determined using the 0.002 strain offset method; (b) representative stress-strain behavior found for some steels, demonstrating the yield point phenomenon

Fracture

Breakage always starts at a location of **stress concentration**. This may be at a *flaw* of microscopic size, such as an abrasion scratch produced while cleaning eyeglasses, or it may be of larger dimensions, such as a hatchway on a ship.

With a crack, the **stress intensity factor**, K_I, is a function of the applied stress, σ, and of the square root of the crack length a:

$$K_I = y\sigma\sqrt{\pi a} \tag{7.9}$$

The proportionality constant, y, relates to cross-sectional dimensions and is generally near unity.

Fracture toughness is the **critical** stress intensity factor, K_{Ic}, to propagate fracture and is a property of the material. This corresponds to the yield strength, σ_y, being the critical stress to initiate slip. However, stronger materials generally have lower fracture toughness and *vice versa*.

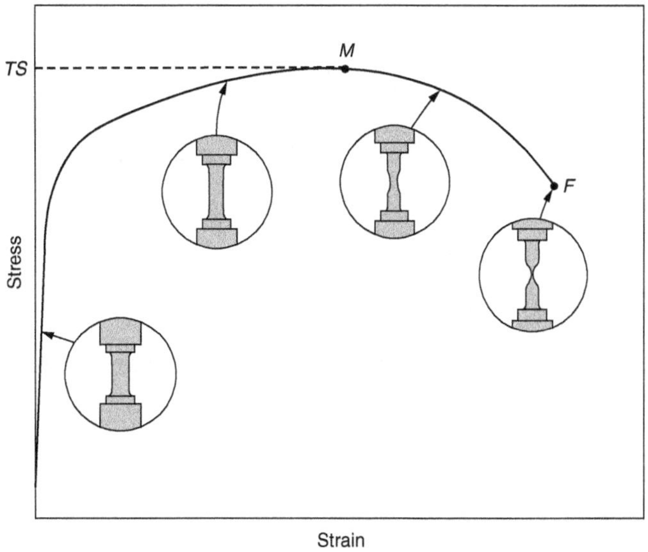

Figure 7.23 Typical engineering stress-strain behavior to fracture, point *F*. The tensile strength *TS* is indicated at point *M*. The circular insets represent the geometry of the deformed specimen at various points along the curve.

To illustrate the relationship between strength and toughness, consider a steel that has a yield strength, σ_y, of 1200 MPa, and a critical stress intensity factor, K_{Ic}, of 90 MPa • $m^{1/2}$.

In the presence of a 2-mm crack, a stress of 1135 MPa would be required to propagate a fracture, according to Equation (7.9). This is below the yield stress. If the value of K_{Ic} had been 100 MPa • $m^{1/2}$, fracture would not occur; rather, the metal would deform at 1200 MPa. A 2.2-mm crack would be required to initiate fracture without yielding.

Fatigue

Cyclic loading reduces permissible design stresses, as illustrated in Figure 7.24. Minute structural changes that introduce cracks occur during each stress cycle. The crack extends as the cycles accumulate, leading to eventual fracture. When this delayed behavior was first observed, it was assumed that the material got tired; hence the term *fatigue*. Steels and certain other materials possess an *endurance limit*, below which unlimited cycling can be tolerated.

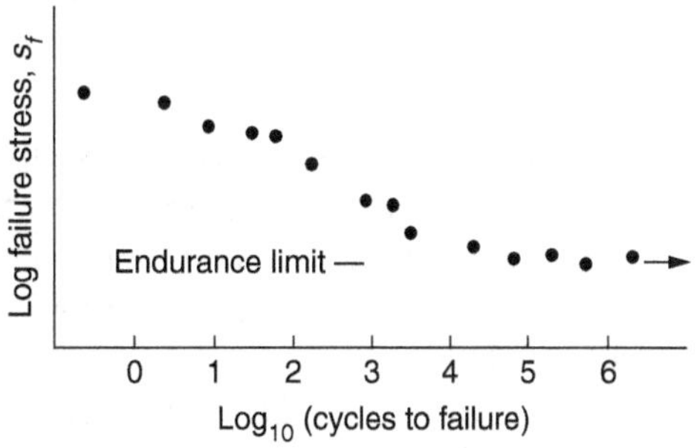

Figure 7.24 Cyclic fatigue. The stress for failure, *sf*, decreases as the number of loading cycles is increased. Most steels exhibit an endurance limit, a stress level for unlimited cycling. (A static tensile test is only one-fourth of a cycle.)

Example 7.12

(i) What is the maximum static force that can be supported without permanent deformation by a 2-mm-diameter wire that has a yield strength of 1225 MPa?

(ii) The elastic deformation at this threshold stress is 0.015 m/m. What is its elastic modulus?

Solution

(i) $\sigma_y = F/A$

$F = \pi(2\ \text{mm}/2)^2(1225\ \text{MPa}) = 3800\ \text{N}$

(ii) $E = \sigma/\varepsilon = 1225\ \text{MPa}/0.015\ \text{m/m} = 82{,}000\ \text{MPa}$

Example 7.13

The value of K_{Ic} for steel is 186 MPa•m$^{1/2}$. What is the maximum tolerable crack length, a, when the steel carries a nominal stress of 800 MPa? (Assume 1.1 as the proportionality constant.)

Solution

$$186\ \text{MPa}\bullet\text{m}^{1/2} = 800\ \text{MPa}\ (1.1)(\pi a)^{1/2}$$

$$a = 0.014\ \text{m} = 14\ \text{mm}$$

Thermal Failure

Melting is the most obvious change in a material at elevated temperatures. Overheating, short of melting, can also introduce microstructural changes. For example, the tempered martensite of a tool steel is processed so that it has a very fine dispersion of carbide particles in a tough ferrite matrix. It is both hard and tough and serves well for machining purposes. However, an excessive cutting speed raises the temperature of the cutting edge, causing the carbide particles to grow and softening the steel; if heating continues, failure eventually occurs by melting at the cutting edge. *High-speed* tools incorporate alloy additions, such as vanadium and chromium, that form carbides that are more stable than iron carbide. Thus, they can tolerate the higher temperatures that accompany faster cutting speeds.

Creep

As the name implies, **creep** describes a slow (<0.001%/hr) dimensional change within a material. It becomes important in long-term service of months or years. Slow viscous flow is commonly encountered in plastic materials. Refractories (temperature-resistant ceramics) will slowly slump when small amounts of liquid accumulate.

In metals, creep occurs when atoms become sufficiently mobile to migrate from compressive regions of the microstructure into tensile regions. Grain boundary areas are heavily involved. For this reason, coarser grained metals are advantageous for high-temperature applications. Three stages of creep are identified in Figure 7.25. Following the initial elastic strain, Stage 1 of creep is fairly rapid as stress variations are equalized. In Stage 2, the creep rate, dL/dt, is essentially

constant. Design considerations are focused on this stage. Stage 3, which accelerates when the cross-sectional area starts to be reduced, leads to eventual rupture.

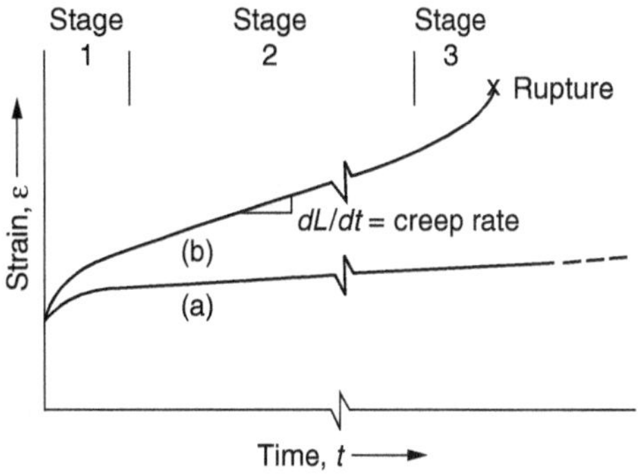

Figure 7.25 Creep. (*a*) Low stresses and/or low temperatures; (*b*) high stresses, high temperatures. The initial strain is elastic, followed by rapid strain adjustments (Stage 1). Design calculations are commonly based on the steady-state strain rate (Stage 2). Strain accelerates (Stage 3) when the area reduction becomes significant. Rupture occurs at *x*.

Spalling

Spalling is thermal cracking. It is the result of stress caused by differential volume changes during processing or service. As discussed earlier, stresses can be introduced into a material (1) by thermal gradients, (2) by anisotropic volume changes, or (3) by differences in expansion coefficients in multiphase materials. Cyclic heating and cooling lead to **thermal fatigue** when the differential stresses produce localized cracking.

The spalling resistance index (SRI) of a material is increased by higher thermal conductivities, k, and greater strengths, S; it is reduced with greater values of the thermal expansion coefficients, α, and higher elastic moduli. In functional form,

$$\text{SRI} = f(kS/\alpha E) \tag{7.10}$$

Low-Temperature Embrittlement

Many materials display an abrupt drop in ductility and toughness as the temperature is lowered. In glass and other amorphous materials, this change is at the temperature below which atoms or molecules cannot relocate in response to the applied stresses. This is the **glass-transition temperature**, T_g. Metals are crystalline and do not have a glass transition. However, steels and a number of other metals have a **ductility-transition temperature** below which fracture is nonductile. The impact energy required for fracture can drop by an order of magnitude at this transition temperature. Thus it becomes a very significant consideration in design for structural applications. The **ductile-to-brittle transition temperature** (DBTT) is often measured using the Charpy Impact test, with samples soaked at different temperatures immediately prior to testing. Representative curves and the influence of carbon content on the DBTT in steel are shown in Figure 7.26.

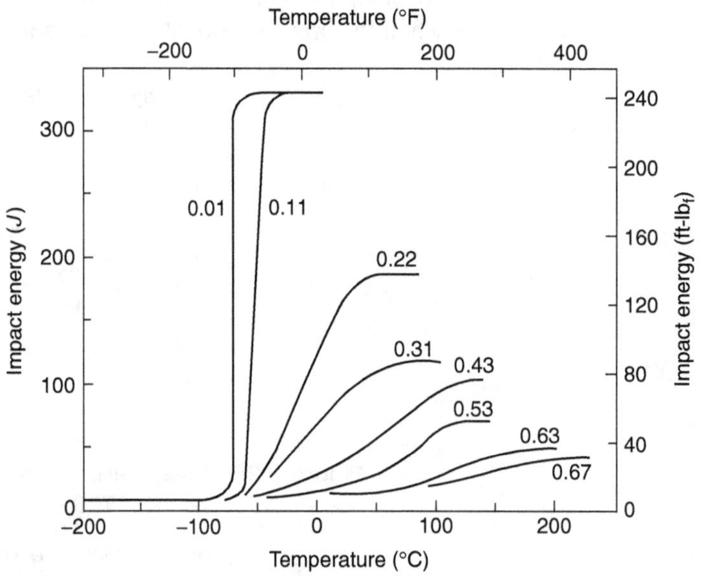

Figure 7.26 Influence of carbon content on the Charpy V-notch energy-versus-temperature behavior for steel

Radiation Damage

Unlike heat, which energizes all of the atoms and molecules within a structure, radiation introduces energy at *pinpoints* called **thermal spikes**. Individual bonds are broken, specific atoms are dislodged, molecules are ruptured, and electrons are energized. Each of these actions disorders the structure and alters the properties of the material. As expected, slip and deformation are resisted. Therefore, while strength and hardness increase, ductility and toughness decrease. Electrical and thermal conductivities drop within metals, because there is more scattering of the electrons as they move along the voltage or thermal gradient. These property changes, among others, are considered to be damaging changes, especially when they contradict carefully considered design requirements.

Damage Recovery

Partial correction of radiation damage is possible by annealing. Reheating a material allows internal readjustments, since atoms that have been displaced are able to relocate into a more ordered structure. It is similar to recrystallization after work hardening, where dislocations involving lineal imperfections composed of many atoms must be removed, except that radiation damage involves *pinpoint* imperfections, which means that it can be removed at somewhat lower temperatures than those required for recrystallization.

Chemical Alteration

Oxidation

Materials can be damaged by reacting chemically with their environments. All metals except gold oxidize in ambient air. Admittedly, some oxidize very slowly at ordinary temperatures. Others, such as aluminum, form a protective oxide surface that inhibits further oxidation. However, all metals—including gold—will oxidize significantly at elevated temperatures or in chemical environments that consume the protective oxidation.

Several actions are required for oxide scale to accumulate on a metal surface. Using iron as an example, the iron atom must be ionized to Fe^{2+} before it or the electrons move through the scale to produce oxygen ions, O^{2-}, at the outer surface. There, FeO or Fe_3O_4 accumulates. As the scale thickens, the oxidation rate decreases. However, exceptions exist. For example, the volume of MgO is less than the volume of the original magnesium metal. Therefore, the scale cracks and admits oxygen directly to the underlying metal. Also, an Al_2O_3 scale is insulating so the ionization steps are precluded.

Moisture

Moisture can produce chemical **hydration**. As examples, MgO reacts with water to produce $Mg(OH)_2$, and Fe_2O_3 can be hydrated to form $Fe(OH)_3$. Water can be absorbed into materials. Small H_2O molecules are able to diffuse among certain large polymeric molecules. Consequently, polymers such as the aramids, which we normally consider to be very strong, are weakened—a fact that the design engineer must consider in specifications.

Corrosion

Metallic corrosion is familiar to every reader who owns a car, since rust—$Fe(OH)_3$—is the most obvious product of corrosion. Oxidation produces positive ions and electrons:

$$M \rightarrow M^{n+} + ne^- \quad \textbf{(7.11)}$$

The reaction stops unless the electrons are removed. Oxygen accompanied by water (Figure 7.27) is a common consumer of the electrons:

$$O_2 + 2\,H_2O + 4e^- \rightarrow 4\,(OH)^- \quad \textbf{(7.12)}$$

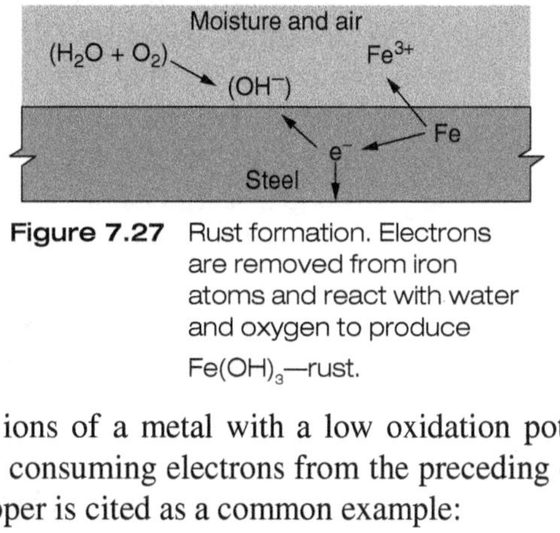

Figure 7.27 Rust formation. Electrons are removed from iron atoms and react with water and oxygen to produce $Fe(OH)_3$—rust.

Alternatively, if ions of a metal with a low oxidation potential are present, they can be reduced, consuming electrons from the preceding corrosion reaction, Equation (7.11). Copper is cited as a common example:

$$Cu^{2+} + 2e^- \rightarrow Cu^0 \quad \textbf{(7.13)}$$

Electroplating uses this reaction advantageously to deposit metals from a solution by the addition of electrons. The relative reactivity of metals with respect to standard electrodes is represented by the electromotive force (emf) series given in Table 7.4. However, in real environments such as sea water the galvanic series, as shown in Table 7.5, is more commonly used to determine the likelihood of corrosion.

Table 7.4 The standard emf series

	Electrode Reaction	Standard Electrode Potential V^0(V)
↑	$Au^{3+} + 3^{e-} \rightarrow Au$	+1.420
	$O_2 + 4H^- + 4e^- \rightarrow 2H_2O$	+1.229
	$Pl^2+ + 2e^- \rightarrow Pl$	+1.200
	$Ag^+ + e^- \rightarrow Ag$	+0.800
Increasingly	$Fe^{3+} + e^- \rightarrow Fe^{2+}$	+0.771
inert (cathodic)	$O_2 + 2H_2O + 4e^- \rightarrow 4(OH^-)$	+0.401
	$Cu^{2+} + 2e^- \rightarrow Cu$	+0.340
	$2H^+ + 2e^- \rightarrow H_2$	0.000
	$Pb^{2+} + 2e^- \rightarrow Pb$	–0.126
	$Sn^{2+} + 2e^- \rightarrow Sn$	–0.136
	$Ni^2+ + 2e^- \rightarrow Ni$	–0.250
	$Co^{2+} + 2e^- \rightarrow Co$	–0.277
	$Cd^{2+} + 2e^- \rightarrow Cd$	–0.403
	$Fe^{2+} + 2e^- \rightarrow Fe$	–0.440
Increasingly	$Cr^{3+} + 3e^- \rightarrow Cr$	–0.744
inert (cathodic)	$Zn^{2+} + 2e^- \rightarrow Zn$	–0.763
	$Al^{2+} + 3e^- \rightarrow Al$	–1.662
	$Mg^{2+} + 2e^- \rightarrow Mg$	–2.363
	$Na^+ + e^- \rightarrow Na$	–2.714
↓	$K^+ + e^- \rightarrow K$	–2.924

Corrosion Control

Corrosion is minimized by a variety of means. Some involve the avoidance of one or more of the above reactions. Feed water for steam-power boilers is deaerated; surfaces are painted to limit the access of water and air; junctions between unlike metals are electrically insulated. Other control procedures induce a reverse reaction: sacrificial anodes such as magnesium are attached to the side of a ship; iron sheet is galvanized with zinc. Each corrodes preferentially to the underlying steel and forces the iron to assume the role of Equation (7.13). Corrosion may also be restricted by an impressed voltage. Natural gas lines utilize this procedure by connecting a negative dc voltage to the pipe.

COMPOSITES

Composites are not new. Straw in brick and steel reinforcing rods in concrete have been used for a long time. But there is current interest in the development of new composites by designing materials appropriately. It is possible to benefit from the positive features of each of the contributors in order to optimize the properties of the composite.

The internal structures of composites may be viewed as enlarged poly-component micro-structures, which were previously discussed. Attention is given to size, shape, amounts, and distribution of the contributing materials. However, there is commonly a significant difference in processing composites. Typically, the internal structure of a composite is a function of mechanical processing steps—mixing, emplacement, surface deposition, and so on—rather than thermal processing. These processing differences suggest a different approach in examining property-structure relationships.

Table 7.5 The galvanic series

↑ Increasingly inert (cathodic)	Platinum
	Gold
	Graphite
	Titanium
	Silver
	316 Stainless steel (passive)
	304 Stainless steel (passive)
	Inconel (80Ni–13Cr–7Fe) (passive)
	Nickel (passive)
	Monel (70Ni–30Cu)
	Copper–nickel alloys
	Bronzes (Cu–Sn alloys)
	Copper
	Brasses (Cu–Zn alloys)
	Inconel (active)
	Nickel (active)
	Tin
	Lead
Increasingly inert (cathodic) ↓	316 Stainless steel (active)
	304 Stainless steel (active)
	Cast iron
	Iron and steel
	Aluminum alloys
	Cadmium
	Commercially pure aluminum
	Zinc
	Magnesium and magnesium alloys

Reinforced Materials

In familiar composites, such as reinforced concrete, the steel carries the tensile load. Also, there must be bonding between the reinforcement and the matrix. In a *glass* fishing rod, the glass fibers are all oriented longitudinally within the polymer matrix. If it is fractured, the break exhibits a splintered appearance with a noticeable amount of fiber pull-out.

Steel reinforcing bars (rebar) are used to reinforce concrete to meet strength and cost factors. Positioning is dictated by stress calculations. Rebar surfaces are commonly merloned (ridged circumferentially) for better anchorage.

Glass is widely used in fiber-reinforced plastics (FRP). The positioning of the fibers varies with the product. Continuous fibers are used in such structures as fuel storage tanks or rocket casings. However, chopped fibers are required when FRP are processed within molds. A matrix-to-glass bond must be achieved through chemical coatings at the interfaces.

Silicon carbide (SiC) and alumina (Al_2O_3) fibers are used increasingly in high-temperature composites with either metallic or ceramic matrices.

Inert fillers such as silica flour and wood flour serve multiple purposes in many polymers. They add strength, rigidity, and hardness to the product. In addition, they generally are less expensive than the matrix polymer.

Reinforcing bars or fibers are expected to carry the bulk of the tensile load. To be effective, the reinforcement must have a higher elastic modulus, E_r, than does the matrix because the reinforcement and the matrix undergo the same tensile strain when loaded ($\varepsilon_r = \varepsilon_m$). Therefore, $(E/\sigma)_r = (E/\sigma)_m$; and

$$\sigma_r / \sigma_m = E_r / E_m \quad \textbf{(7.14)}$$

Mixture Rules

We commonly study and analyze properties of composites in terms of the properties of the contributing materials. Mixture rules can then be formulated in which the properties are a function of the amounts and geometric distributions of each of the contributors. The simplest mixture rules are based on volume fraction, f. For example, the density of the mixture, ρ_m, is the volume-weighted average:

$$\rho_m = f_1\rho_1 + f_2\rho_2 + \ldots \quad \textbf{(7.15a)}$$

or simply

$$\rho_m = \sum f_i\rho_i \quad \textbf{(7.15b)}$$

Likewise, for *heat capacity*, c:

$$c_m = \sum f_i c_i \quad \textbf{(7.16)}$$

Directional Properties

Many composites are anisotropic. Laminates of two or more layers are bidirectional, as is a matted FRP that uses chopped fibers. The previously cited *glass* fishing rod has a structure with uniaxial anisotropy.

When considering conductivity, elastic moduli, strength, or other properties that are directional, attention must be given to the anisotropy of the composite. Consider the electrical resistance across a laminate that contains alternate layers of two materials with different resistances, R_1 and R_2. In a direction perpendicular to the laminate, the plies are in series. Thus the relationship is

$$R_\perp = L_1R_1 + L_2R_2 + \cdots \quad \textbf{(7.17)}$$

where L_i is the thickness of each ply. For unit dimensions, volume fractions, f_i, and the resistivities, ρ_i, are applicable:

$$\rho_\perp = f_1\rho_1 + f_2\rho_2 + \cdots \quad \textbf{(7.18)}$$

In contrast, for directions parallel to the laminate, resistivities follow the physics analog for parallel circuits:

$$\frac{1}{\rho_\parallel} = \frac{f_1}{\rho_1} + \frac{f_2}{\rho_2} + \cdots \quad \textbf{(7.19)}$$

The mixture rules for conductivities, either thermal, k, or electrical, σ, are inverted to those for resistivities:

$$\frac{1}{k_\perp} = \frac{f_1}{k_1} + \frac{f_2}{k_2} + \cdots \quad \textbf{(7.20)}$$

and

$$k_{\parallel} = f_1 k_1 + f_2 k_2 + \cdots \qquad \textbf{(7.21)}$$

More elaborate mixture rules must be used when the structure of the composite is geometrically more complex, such as the use of particulate fillers or chopped fibers. In general, however, the property of the composite falls between the calculated values using the parallel and series versions of the preceding equations.

Preparation

Composites receive their name from the fact that two or more distinct starting materials are combined into a unified material. The application of a protective coating to metal or wood is one form of composite processing. The process is not as simple as it first appears because priming treatments are commonly required after the surface has been initially cleared of contaminants and moisture; otherwise, peeling and other forms of deterioration may develop. Electroplating, Equation (7.13), commonly requires several intermediate surface preparations so that the final plated layer meets life requirements.

Wood paneling combines wood and polymeric materials into large sheets. **Plywood** not only has dimensional merit, it transforms the longitudinal anisotropy into a more desirable two-dimensional material. Related products include chipboard and similar composites. Composite panels include those with veneer surfaces where appearance and technical properties are valued.

The concept of uniformly mixing particulate **fillers** into a composite is simple. The resulting product is isotropic.

Several considerations are required for the use of **fibers** in a composite. Must the fiber be continuous? What are the directions of loading? What is the shear strength between the fiber and the matrix? Chopped fibers provide more reinforcement than do particles, and at the same time permit molding operations. The **aspect ratio** (*L*/*D*) must be relatively low for die molding. Higher ratios, and therefore more reinforcement, are used in sheet molding. (Sheet molded products are used where strength is not critical in the third dimension.) **Continuous fibers** maximize the mechanical properties of FRP composites. Their uses, however, are generally limited to products that permit parallel layments.

Example **7.14**

A rod contains 40 volume percent longitudinally aligned glass fibers within a plastic matrix. The glass has an elastic modulus of 70,000 MPa; the plastic, 3500 MPa. What fraction of a 700-N tensile load is carried by the glass?

Solution

Based on Equation (7.14):

$$(F_{gl}/0.4A)/(F_p/0.6A) = (70{,}000 \text{ MPa} / 3500 \text{ MPa}) = 20$$

$$F_{gl} = 20(0.4/0.6)\, F_p = 13.3\, F_p$$

$$F_{gl}/(F_{gl} + F_p) = (13.3\, F_p)/(13.3\, F_p + F_p) = 93\%$$

Example 7.15

An electric highline cable contains one cold-drawn steel wire and six annealed aluminum wires, all with a 2-mm diameter. (The steel provides the required strength; the aluminum, the conductivity.) Using the following data, calculate (i) the resistivity and (ii) the elastic modulus of the composite wire.

Steel: $\rho = 17 \times 10^{-6}\ \Omega \bullet \text{cm}$, $E = 205{,}000$ MPa

Aluminum: $\rho = 3 \times 10^{-6}\ \Omega \bullet \text{cm}$, $E = 70{,}000$ MPa

Solution

(i) From Equation (7.19):

$$1/\rho_{\|} = (1/7)/(17 \times 10^{-6}\ \Omega \bullet \text{cm}) + (6/7)/(3 \times 10^{-6}\ \Omega \bullet \text{cm})$$
$$= 0.294 \times 10^{6}\ \Omega^{-1} \bullet \text{cm}^{-1}$$

$$\rho_{\|} = 3.4 \times 10^{-6}\ \Omega \bullet \text{cm}$$

(ii) We must write a mixture rule for the elastic modulus of a composite in parallel. Let A be the area of one wire.

Since $\varepsilon_c = \varepsilon_{Al} = \varepsilon_{St}$, $[(F/A)/E]_C = [(F/A)/E]_{Al} = [(F/A)/E]_{St}$

Also, $F_C = F_{Al} + F_{St} = F_C(f_{Al}A_C/A_C)(E_{St}/E_C) + F_C(f_{St}A_C/A_C)(E_{St}/E_C)$

Canceling,

$$E_C = f_{Al}E_{Al} + f_{St}E_{St} = (6/7)(70{,}000\text{ MPa}) + (1/7)(205{,}000\text{ MPa}) = 89{,}000\text{ MPa}$$

The apparent modulus will be lower because there will also be cable extension by the straightening of the cable wire.

SELECTED SYMBOLS AND ABBREVIATIONS

Symbol or Abbreviation	Definition
A	area
a	unit cell length
a	crack length
amu	atomic mass unit
D	diffusion coefficient
D_o	proportionality constant
E	elastic modulus
ε	engineering strain
F	force
f	volume fraction
K_I	stress intensity factor
P	density
Q	activation energy
R	gas constant
r	atomic radius
σ	stress
σ_y	yield strength
SRI	Spalling Resistance Index
Tg	glass-transition temperature
Tm	melting temperature
V^0	standard electrode potential
W_L	weight fraction of liquid phase
W_S	weight fraction of solid phase
y	proportionality constant

REFERENCE

Van Vlack, L. *Elements of Materials Science and Engineering*, 6th ed. Addison-Wesley, 1989.

PROBLEMS

7.1 For a neutral atom:

a. the atomic mass equals the mass of the neutrons plus the mass of the protons
b. the atomic number equals the atomic mass
c. the number of protons equals the atomic number
d. the number of electrons equals the number of neutrons

7.2 All isotopes of a given element have:

a. the same number of protons
b. the same number of neutrons
c. equal numbers of protons and neutrons
d. the same number of atomic mass units

7.3 Which of the following statements is *FALSE*?

a. An anion has more electrons than protons.
b. Energy is released when water is solidified to ice.
c. Energy is required to remove an electron from a neutral atom.
d. Energy is released when a H_2 molecule is separated into two hydrogen atoms.

7.4 Select the correct statement.

a. Crystals possess long-range order.
b. Within a crystal, like ions attract and unlike ions repel.
c. A body-centered cubic metallic crystal (for example, iron) has nine atoms per unit cell.
d. A face-centered cubic metallic crystal (for example, copper) has 14 atoms per unit cell.

7.5 In a cubic crystal, a is the edge of a unit cell. The shortest repeat distance in the [111] direction of a body-centered cubic crystal is:

a. $a\sqrt{2}$ c. $a\sqrt{3}/2$
b. $2a$ d. $a\sqrt{3}/4$

7.6 All but which of the following data are required to calculate the density of aluminum in g/m^3?

a. Avogadro's number, which is 6.0×10^{23}
b. atomic number of Al, which is 13
c. crystal structure of Al, which is face-centered cubic
d. atomic mass of Al, which is 27 amu

7.7 The atomic packing factor of gold, an FCC metal, is:

a. $(4\pi r^3/3)/(4r/\sqrt{3})^3$
b. $4(4\pi r^3/3)/(4r/\sqrt{2})^3$
c. $4(4\pi r^3/3)/(r/\sqrt{2})^3$
d. $4(2r/\sqrt{2})^3/(4\pi r^3/3)$

7.8 Ethylene is C_2H_4. To meet bonding requirements, how many bonds are present?

a. 6 single
b. 4 single and 2 double
c. 1 double and 4 single
d. 12 single

7.9 Gold is FCC and has a density of 19.3 g/cm³. Its atomic mass is 197 amu. Its atomic radius, *r*, may be calculated using which of the following?

a. $19.3\ \text{g/cm}^3 = (197)(6.02 \times 10^{23})/[(4r/)\sqrt{2^3}]$
b. $19.3\ \text{g/cm}^3 = 2\ (197/6.02 \times 10^{23})/[(4r/)\sqrt{2^3}]$
c. $19.3\ \text{g/cm}^3 = 4\ (197/6.02 \times 10^{23})/[(4r/)\sqrt{2^3}]$
d. $19.3\ \text{g/cm}^3 = 6\ (197)(6.02 \times 10^{23})/[(4r/)\sqrt{2^3}]$

7.10 Each of the following groups of plastics is thermoplastic *EXCEPT*:

a. polyvinyl chloride (PVC) and a polyvinyl acetate
b. phenolics, melamine, and epoxy
c. polyethylene, polypropylene, and polystyrene
d. acrylic (Lucite) and polyamide (nylon)

7.11 Styrene resembles vinyl chloride, C_2H_3C1, except that the chlorine is replaced by a benzene ring. The mass of each mer is:

a. 8(12) + 9(1) amu
b. 26 + 78 amu
c. 27 + 6(12) + 6(1) amu
d. 2(12) + 3(1) + 77 amu

7.12 The $\langle 1\bar{1}0 \rangle$ family of directions in a cubic crystal include all but which of the following? (An overbar is a negative coefficient.)

a. [110]
b. $[0\bar{1}1]$
c. [101]
d. $[1\bar{1}1]$

7.13 The {112} family of planes in a cubic crystal includes all but which of the following directions?

a. (212)
b. (211)
c. $(1\bar{1}2)$
d. (121)

7.14 Crystal imperfections include all but which of the following?

a. Dislocations
b. Displaced atoms
c. Interstitials
d. Dispersions

7.15 A dislocation may be described as a:

a. displaced atom
b. shift in the lattice constant
c. slip plane
d. lineal imperfection

7.16 A grain within a microstructure is:
a. a particle the size of a grain of sand
b. the nucleus of solidification
c. a particle the size of a grain of rice
d. an individual crystal

7.17 Which of the following does *NOT* apply to a typical brass?
a. An alloy of copper and zinc
b. A single-phase alloy
c. An interstitial alloy of copper and zinc
d. A substitutional solid solution

7.18 Sterling silver, as normally sold:
a. is pure silver
b. is a supersaturated solid solution of 7.5% copper in silver
c. is 24-carat silver
d. has higher conductivity than pure silver

7.19 Atomic diffusion in solids matches all but which of the following generalities?
a. Diffusion is faster in FCC metals than in BCC metals.
b. Smaller atoms diffuse faster than do larger atoms.
c. Diffusion is faster at elevated temperatures.
d. Diffusion flux is proportional to the concentration gradient.

7.20 The proportionality constant for a particular gas diffusing through copper at 1000°C is 0.022 cm^2/s and the activation energy is 97 kJ/mole. Find the diffusion coefficient.
a. 1.6×10^{-6} cm^2/s
b. 1.9×10^{-6} cm^2/s
c. 2.3×10^{-6} cm^2/s
d. 4.4×10^{-6} cm^2/s

7.21 Grain growth involves all but which of the following?
a. Reduced growth rates with increased time
b. An increase in grain boundary area per unit volume
c. Atom movements across grain boundaries
d. A decrease in the number of grains per unit volume

7.22 Imperfections within metallic crystal structures may be any but which of the following?
a. Lattice vacancies and extra interstitial atoms
b. Displacements of atoms to interstitial site (Frenkel defects)
c. Lineal defects or slippage dislocations caused by shear
d. Ion pairs missing in ionic crystals (Shottky imperfections)

7.23 All but which of the following statements about solid solutions are correct?

a. In metallic solid solutions, larger solute atoms occupy the interstitial space among solvent atoms in the lattice sites.
b. Solid solutions may result from the substitution of one atomic species for another, provided radii and electronic structures are compatible.
c. Defect structures exist in solid solutions of ionic compounds when there are differences in the oxidation state of the solute and solvent ions, because vacancies are required to maintain an overall charge balance.
d. Order-to-disorder transitions that occur at increased temperatures in solid solutions result from thermal agitation that dislodges atoms from their preferred neighbors.

7.24 In ferrous oxide, $Fe_{1-x}O$, 2% of the cation sites are vacant. What is the Fe^{3+}/Fe^{2+} ratio?

a. 2/98
b. 0.04/0.94
c. 0.04/0.96
d. 0.06/0.94

7.25 A solid solution of MgO and FeO contains 25 atomic percent Mg^{2+} and 25 atomic percent Fe^{2+}. What is the weight fraction of MgO? (Mg: 24; Fe: 56; and O: 16 amu)

a. 40/(40 + 72)
b. 24/(24 + 56), or 4/80
c. 25/(25 + 25)
d. (25 + 25)/(50 + 50)

7.26 The boundary between two metal grains provides all but which of the following?

a. An impediment to dislocation movements
b. A basis for an increase in the elastic modulus
c. A site for the nucleation of a new phase
d. Interference to slip

7.27 If 5% copper is added to silver:

a. the hardness is decreased
b. the strength is decreased
c. the thermal conductivity is decreased
d. the electrical resistivity is decreased

7.28 All but which of the following statements about diffusion and grain growth are correct?

a. Atoms can diffuse both within grains and across grain (crystal) boundaries.
b. The activation energy for diffusion through solids is inversely proportional to the atomic packing factor of the lattice.
c. Grain growth results from local diffusion and minimizes total grain boundary area. Large grains grow at the expense of small ones, and grain boundaries move toward their centers of curvature.
d. Net diffusion requires an activation energy and is irreversible. Its rate increases exponentially with temperature. It follows the diffusion equation, in which flux equals the product of diffusivity and the concentration gradient.

7.29 Refer to the accompanying Mg-Zn phase diagram, Exhibit 7.29. Select an alloy of composition C (71Mg–29Zn) and raise it to 575°C so that only liquid is present. Change the composition to 60Mg–40Zn by adding zinc. When this new liquid is cooled, what will be the first solid to separate?

a. A solid intermetallic compound
b. A mixture of solid intermetallic compound and solid eutectic C (71Mg–29Zn)
c. A solid eutectic C (71Mg–29Zn)
d. A solid solution containing less than 1% intermetallic compound dissolved in Mg

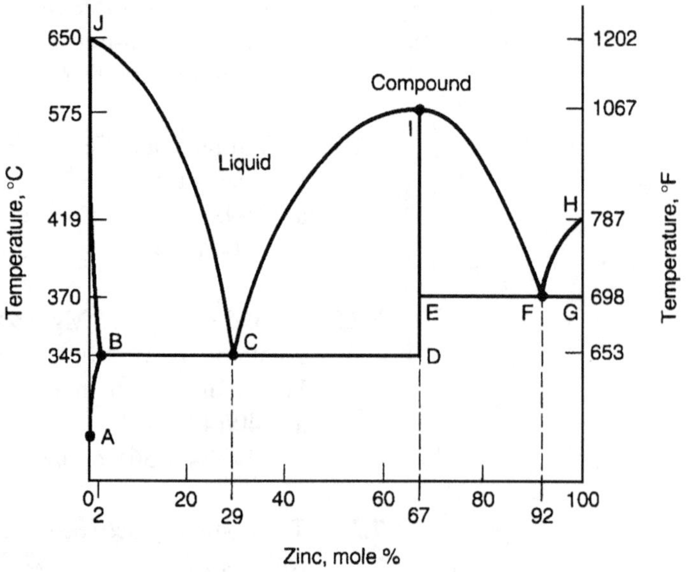

Exhibit 7.29 Magnesium-zinc phase diagram

7.30 Refer to the Mg-Zn phase diagram of Exhibit 7.29. Which of the following compounds is present?

a. Mg_3Zn_2
b. Mg2Zn3
c. MgZn
d. MgZn2

7.31 Refer to Exhibit 7.31, a schematic sketch of the Fe-Fe_3C phase diagram. All but which of the following statements are *TRUE*?

a. A eutectoid reaction occurs at location C, 727°C (1340°F).
b. The eutectic composition is 99.2 weight percent Fe and 0.8 weight percent C.
c. A peritectic reaction occurs at K, 1500°C (2732°F).
d. A eutectic reaction occurs at G, 1130°C (2202°F).

7.32 Refer to Exhibit 7.31, the Fe-Fe_3C phase diagram. Pearlite contains ferrite (α) and carbide (Fe_3C). The weight fraction of carbide in pearlite is:

a. 0.8%
b. BC/CD
c. CD/BD
d. BC/BD

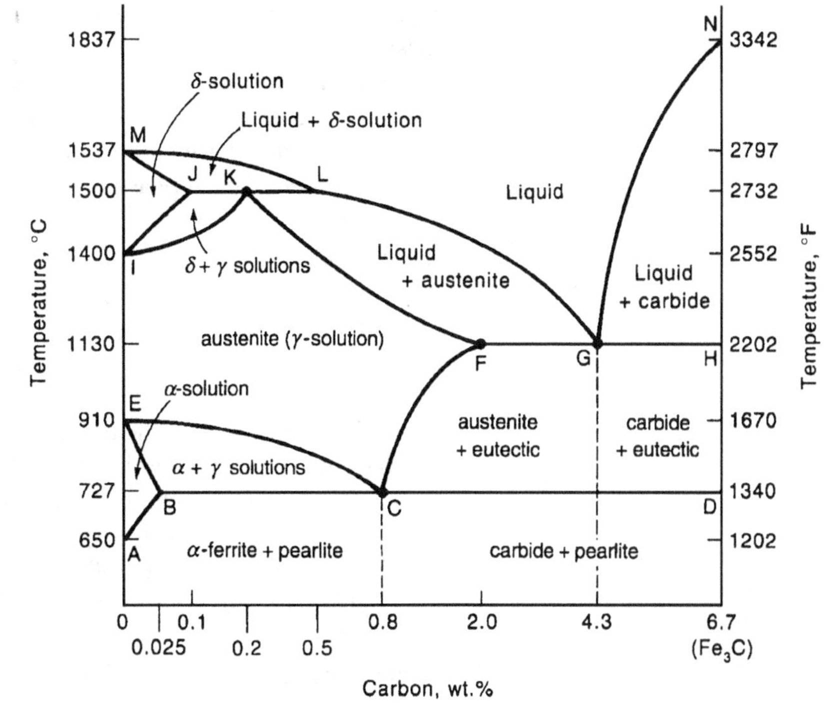

Exhibit 7.31 Iron-iron carbide phase diagram (schematic)

7.33 Consider the Ag-Cu phase diagram (Figure 7.16). Silver-copper alloys can contain *approximately* half liquid and half solid at all but which of the following situations?

a. 40Ag–60Cu at 781°C
b. 81Ag–19Cu at 781°C
c. 20Ag–80Cu at 910°C
d. 50Ag–50Cu at 779°C

7.34 Refer to the Ag-Cu phase diagram of Figure 7.16. Which of the following statements is *FALSE*?

a. The solubility limit of copper in the liquid at 900°C is approximately 62%.
b. The solubility limit of silver in b at 700°C is approximately 5%.
c. The solubility limit of silver in b at 900°C is approximately 7%.
d. The solubility limit of copper in b at 800°C is approximately 92%.

7.35 Other factors being equal, diffusion flux is facilitated by all but which of the following?

a. Smaller grain sizes
b. Smaller solute (diffusing) atoms
c. Lower concentration gradients
d. Lower-melting solvent (host structure)

7.36 Consider copper. All but which of the following statements are applicable for grain growth?

a. Atoms jump the boundary from large grains to small grains.
b. Grain size varies inversely with boundary area.
c. Grain growth occurs because the boundary atoms possess higher energy than interior atoms.
d. Grain growth occurs because larger grains have less boundary area.

7.37 A phase diagram can provide answers for all but which of the following questions?

a. What are the direction of the planes at a given temperature?
b. What phases are present at a given temperature?
c. What are the phase compositions at a given temperature?
d. How much of each phase is present at a given temperature?

7.38 In the Ag-Cu system (Figure 7.16), three equilibrated phases may be present at:

a. 930°C c. 830°C
b. 880°C d. 780°C

7.39 During heating, a 72Ag–28Cu alloy (Figure 7.16) may have any but which of the following equilibrium relationships?

a. ~25% β at 600°C, where β contains ~2% Ag
b. less than 50% β (95Cu–5Ag) at 700°C
c. ~74% α(93Ag–7Cu) at 750°C
d. α(26% Cu) and β(32% Cu) at 800°C

7.40 During cooling, a (20Ag–80Cu) alloy (Figure 7.16) has all but which of the following equilibrium situations?

a. The first solid forms at 980°C
b. The first solid contains 5% Ag
c. The second solid appears at 780°C
d. The last liquid contains 32% Cu

7.41 Add copper to 100 g of silver at 781°C (Figure 7.16). Assume equilibrium. Which statement is *TRUE*?

a. Liquid first appears with the addition of exactly 9 g of copper.
b. The last α disappears when approximately 39 g of copper has been added.
c. The solubility limit of copper in solid silver (α) is 28% copper.
d. Solid β first appears with the addition of 92 g of copper.

7.42 All but which of the following statements about strain hardening is correct?

a. Strain hardening is produced by cold working.
b. Strain hardening is relieved during annealing above the recrystallization temperature.
c. With more strain hardening, more time-temperature exposure is required for relief.
d. Strain hardening is relieved during recrystallization. Recrystallization produces less strained and more ordered structures.

7.43 Which process is used for the high-temperature shaping of many materials?

a. Reduction c. Polymerization
b. Recrystallization d. Extrusion

7.44 All but which of the following processes strengthens metals?

a. Precipitation processes that produce submicroscopic particles during a low-temperature heat treatment
b. Increasing the carbon content of low-carbon steels
c. Annealing above the recrystallization temperature
d. Mechanical deformation below the recrystallization temperature (cold working)

7.45 All but which of the following statements about the austentite-martensite-bainite transformations are correct?

a. Pearlite is a stable lamellar mixture consisting of BCC ferrite (α) plus carbide (Fe_3C). It forms through eutectoid decomposition during slow cooling of austenite. Most alloying elements in steel retard this transformation.
b. Martensite has a body-centered structure of iron that is tetragonal and is supersaturated with carbon. It forms by shear during the rapid quenching of austenite (FCC iron).
c. Tempering of martensite is accomplished by reheating martensite to precipitate fine particles of carbide within a ferrite matrix, thus producing a tough, strong structure.
d. Bainite and tempered martensite have distinctly different microstructures.

7.46 Steel can be strengthened by all but which of the following practices?

a. Annealing
b. Quenching and tempering
c. Age or precipitation hardening
d. Work hardening

7.47 Residual stresses can produce any but which of the following?

a. Warpage
b. Distortion in machined metal parts
c. Cracking of glass
d. Reduced melting temperatures

7.48 The reaction ($\gamma \rightarrow \alpha + Fe_3C$) is most rapid at:

a. the eutectoid temperature
b. 10°C above the eutectoid temperature
c. the eutectic temperature
d. 100°C below the eutectoid temperature

7.49 Grain growth, which reduces boundary area, may be expected to:

a. decrease the thermal conductivity of ceramics
b. increase the hardness of a solid
c. decrease the creep rate of a metal
d. increase the recrystallization rate

7.50 Rapid cooling can produce which one of the following in a material such as sterling silver?
a. Homogenization
b. Phase separation
c. Grain boundary contraction
d. Supersaturation

7.51 Martensite, which may be obtained in steel, is a:
a. supersaturated solid solution of carbon in iron
b. supercooled iron carbide, Fe_3C
c. undercooled FCC structure of austenite
d. superconductor with zero resistivity at low temperature

7.52 Alloying elements produce all but which one of the following effects in steels?
a. They alter the number of atoms in a unit cell of austenite.
b. They increase the depth of hardening in quenched steel.
c. They increase the hardness of ferrite in pearlite.
d. They retard the decomposition of austenite.

7.53 Hardenability may be defined as:
a. resistance to indentation
b. the hardness attained for a specified cooling rate
c. another measure of strength
d. rate of increased hardness

7.54 The linear portion of the stress-strain diagram of steel is known as the:
a. irreversible range
c. modulus of elasticity
b. scant modulus
d. elastic range

7.55 The ultimate (tensile) strength of a material is calculated from:
a. the applied force divided by the true area at fracture
b. the applied force times the true area at fracture
c. the tensile force at the initiation of slip
d. the applied force and the original area

7.56 All but which one of the following statements about slip are correct?
a. Slip occurs most readily along crystal planes that are least densely populated.
b. Slip, or shear along crystal planes, results in an irreversible plastic deformation or permanent set.
c. Ease of slippage is directly related to the number of low-energy slip planes within the lattice structure.
d. Slip is impeded by solution hardening, with odd-sized solute atoms serving as anchor points around which slippage does not occur.

7.57 When a metal is cold worked more severely, all but which one of the following generally occur?

a. The recrystallization temperature decreases.
b. The tensile strength increases.
c. Grains become equiaxed.
d. Slip and/or twinning occur.

7.58 All but which of the following statements about the rusting of iron are correct?

a. Contact with water or oxygen is required for rusting to occur.
b. Halides aggravate rusting, a process that involves electrochemical oxidation-reduction reactions.
c. Contact with a more electropositive metal restricts rusting.
d. Corrosion occurs in oxygen-rich areas.

7.59 All but which of the following statements about mechanical and thermal failure is *TRUE*?

a. Creep is time-dependent, plastic deformation that accelerates at increased temperatures. Stress rupture is the failure following creep.
b. Ductile fracture is characterized by significant amounts of energy absorption and plastic deformation (evidenced by elongation and reduction in cross-sectional area).
c. Fatigue failure from cyclic stresses is frequency-dependent.
d. Brittle fracture occurs with little plastic deformation and relatively low energy absorption.

7.60 The stress intensity factor is calculated from:

a. yield stress and crack depth
b. applied stress and crack depth
c. tensile stress and strain rate
d. crack depth and strain rate

7.61 Service failure from applied loads can occur in all but which of the following cases?

a. Cyclic loading, tension to compression
b. Glide normal to the slip plane
c. Cyclic loading, low tension to higher tension
d. Stage 2 creep

7.62 Brittle failure becomes more common when:

a. the endurance limit is increased
b. the glass-transition temperature is decreased
c. the critical stress intensity factor is increased
d. the ductility-transition temperature is increased

7.63 Where applicable, all but which of the following procedures may reduce corrosion?

a. Avoidance of bimetallic contacts
b. Sacrificial anodes
c. Aeration of feed water
d. Impressed voltages

7.64 A fiber-reinforced rod contains 50 volume percent glass fibers ($E = 70$ GPa, $\sigma_y = 700$ MPa) and 50 volume percent plastic ($E = 7$ GPa). The glass carries what part of a 5000-N tensile load?

a. [(7000 MPa)(0.5)]/[70,000 MPa)(0.5)] = 0.1; $F_{gl} = (0.1)(5000\text{ N}) = 500\text{ N}$

b. [(70,000)(0.5) + 7000(0.5)] = 5000/x; $x = 0.0002$

c. $[(F_{gl}/0.5A)/(F_p / 0.5A)] = (70/7) = 10$; $F_{gl}/(F_p + F_{gl}) = 10F_p/(10F_p + F_p) = 0.91$

d. (70)/[70 + 2(7)] = 0.83

SOLUTIONS

7.1 c. Each step through the periodic table introduces an additional proton and electron to a neutral atom.

7.2 a. The number of protons are fixed for an individual element. If the number of protons (and electrons) were varied, the chemical properties would be affected.

7.3 d. To separate H_2 into hydrogen atoms, the H-to-H bond would have to be broken, thus requiring energy.

7.4 a. Unlike ions attract. FCC metals possess four atoms per unit cell; BCC metals have two.

7.5 c. The [111] direction passes diagonally through the unit cell. The distance is $a\sqrt{3}$, which equals two repeat distances.

7.6 b. The mass is determined from 27 amu per 6.0×10^{23} atoms. Each cell of four atoms has a volume of $(4r/\sqrt{2})^3$.

7.7 b. Assuming spherical atoms, there are four atoms of radius r per unit cell. The cube edge is $4r/\sqrt{2}$.

7.8 c. There is a double bond between the two carbons. Each hydrogen is held with a single bond.

7.9 c. Density is mass/volume. The mass per FCC unit cell is 4 Au $\times$ (197 g/6.02×10^{23} Au). The volume per FCC unit cell of a metal is (face diagonal/$\sqrt{2}$)^3 or $(4r/\sqrt{2})^3$.

7.10 b. Thermoplastic materials are polymerized but soften for molding at elevated temperatures. The polymeric molecules are linear. Thus they include the ethylene-type compounds that are bifunctional (two reaction sites per mer).

Thermosetting materials develop three-dimensional structures that become rigid during processing. For example, phenol is trifunctional and thus forms a network structure. Reheating does not soften them.

7.11 d. Benzene is C_6H_6; however, in styrene, one hydrogen is absent at the connection to the C_2H_3–base.

7.12 d. Since a cubic crystal has interchangeable x-, y-, and z-axes, the <110> family includes all directions with permutations of 1, 1, and 0 (either + or –). (This is not necessarily true for noncubic crystals.)

7.13 a. Since a cubic crystal has interchangeable x-, y-, and z-axes, the {112} family includes all planes with index permutations of 1, 1, and 2 (either + or –). (This is not necessarily true for noncubic crystals.)

7.14 d. (b) and (c) involve individual atoms (point imperfections). (a) is a lineal imperfection. Boundaries result from a two-dimensional mismatch of crystal structures.

7.15 d. There are two types of dislocations: (1) an edge dislocation may be described as an edge of a missing half-plane of atoms; (2) a screw dislocation is the core of a helix.

7.16 d. Unless special efforts are made to grow single crystals, many crystals are nucleated and grow until they encounter neighboring crystals. Each grain is individually oriented.

7.17 c. Zinc is sufficiently near copper in size and electrical behavior to proxy for copper in the crystal structure. It is too big for the interstices.

7.18 b. The 7.5% copper replaces silver atoms. If it is cooled rapidly, the copper is retained in solid solution. The copper atoms interfere with electron movements within the silver.

7.19 a. FCC metals have a higher packing factor than do BCC metals; therefore, with other factors equal, diffusion is reduced.

7.20 c.

$$D = D_o e^{-Q/(RT)} = \left(0.022\ \text{cm}^2/\text{s}\right) e^{\frac{-97000\ \text{J/mol}}{8.314\ \text{J/(mol-K)}(1000+273\ \text{K})}} = 2.3 \times 10^{-6}\ \text{cm}^2/\text{s}$$

7.21 b. As the grains grow, their volume increases by the third power. Their surface area increases by the square.

7.22 d. Metallic crystals are not ionic and do not have discrete ions.

7.23 a. The interstitial sites are smaller than the atoms in metals.

7.24 b. To balance the charge, each missing Fe^{2+} ion must be compensated by two Fe^{3+} ions. Therefore, out of 100 cation sites, two are vacant, four are Fe^{3+}, and thus 94 are Fe^{2+}.

7.25 a. Using a computational basis of four atoms, (1 Mg^{2+} + 1 O^{2-}) + (1 Fe^{2+} + 1 O^{2-}) = (24 + 16) + (56 + 16) = (40 + 72).

7.26 b. The elastic strains between atoms along the boundary follow the same relationships as the strains among atoms within the grains.

7.27 c. Solid solution increases strength (solution hardening). It also decreases conductivity (and increases resistivity). Sterling silver is 92.5Ag–7.5Cu.

7.28 **b.** When atoms are moved from one site to another, bonds are broken and reconstituted. During transition, an activation energy is required to distort the lattice. Small solute atoms, low-melting-point solvents, and lower atomic packing factors in a lattice all require a lower activation energy. Hence activation energy for diffusion is *directly* proportional to the packing factor.

7.29 **a.** On cooling, curve CI is encountered at approximately 420°C (790°F). That curve is the solubility limit of Zn in that liquid. Zinc in excess of the solubility limit separates as the intermetallic compound, $MgZn_2$, which is plotted as the vertical line EI.

7.30 **d.** A ratio of 67 Zn atoms to 33 Mg atoms is 2-to-1; therefore, $MgZn_2$.

7.31 **b.** The eutectic composition is that of a low-melting liquid saturated with two solids. The 0.8 weight percent composition is a solid, not a liquid, at 727°C.

7.32 **d.** The (ferrite + carbide) area extends across the lower part of the phase diagram from nil carbon to 6.7 carbon. At the left side there is no Fe_3C; at the right side there is only carbide (Fe_3C contains 6.7% carbon). The amount of carbide between the two extremes may be determined by linear interpolation.

7.33 **d.** The eutectic temperature is 780°C (1445°F). That is the lowest temperature at which liquid can exist of equilibrium. At 779°C there are approximately equal amounts of α and β, the two solid solutions.

7.34 **d.** The curves of a phase diagram are solubility limits for the phases within the single-phase regions. Since copper is the solvent for the β structure, β has no upper limit of copper solubility (other than 100%).

7.35 **c.** The diffusion flux is proportional to the concentration gradient. (The other choices cited reduce the activation energy needed for diffusion.)

7.36 **a.** Boundary atoms possess higher energy. Therefore, the boundary is reduced and the grain size is increased at temperatures where the atoms can move. The net movement of the atoms is to the larger grains (with less boundary area).

7.37 **a.** Phase diagrams cannot be used to predict crystalline properties.

7.38 **d.** Above the eutectic temperature, (α + L) can be present concurrently, as can (L + β), but not (α + β). Below the eutectic temperature, (α + β) may be present, but no liquid. As the eutectic temperature is passed during cooling or heating, all three phases may coexist.

7.39 **d.** At 800°C, a 72Ag–28Cu alloy is fully liquid, which therefore has 72–28 composition.

7.40 d. During equilibrium cooling, the final liquid for this alloy does not disappear until the eutectic temperature is reached at 780ºC. At that temperature, the liquid composition is 72Ag–28Cu.

7.41 b. All α disappears on the right side of the (α + L) field, where the composition is 72Ag–28Cu, or 100g Ag to 39 g Cu.

7.42 c. As the temperature is increased, the atoms gain additional energy and can relocate, eliminating the strain energy that accompanies dislocations. *Less time* is required at higher temperature. *Less time* is also required for a highly cold-worked material because there is additional stored energy present.

7.43 d. Reduction and polymerization involve chemical reactions. Tempering and recrystallization involve reheating but no shape change.

7.44 c. Strength and hardness are increased at the expense of ductility and toughness (opposite of brittleness). The increase is facilitated by microstructures that interfere with dislocation movements. These include a high density of dislocations from plastic deformation, and the presence of many fine, hard particles. Annealing removes dislocations and permits the agglomeration of particles into fewer large particles.

7.45 d. The production of tempered martensite is indicated in (c) above. Bainite is formed by isothermally decomposing austenite directly to a microstructure of fine carbide particles within a ferrite matrix. Although the processing differs, the resulting microstructure and properties are nearly identical.

7.46 a. Annealing removes the hardness that was introduced by cold work. Quenched and tempered steels are harder with higher carbon contents, because more hard carbide particles are present. Alloying elements perform several hardening functions: They solution-harden the ferrite matrix; they slow down grain growth; and they delay the formation of pearlite, thus permitting more martensite with slower cooling rates (in turn, more tempered martensite may be realized farther below the quenched surface).

7.47 d. Stresses will relax below the melting temperature. Tensile stresses facilitate the cracking of brittle materials; compression limits cracking.

7.48 d. The reaction occurs only below the eutectoid temperature.

7.49 c. While grain boundaries interfere with slip at low temperatures, they facilitate creep at elevated temperatures.

7.50 d. The processing step of rapid cooling, such as quenching, retains the structures that existed at higher temperatures, even though a solubility limit is exceeded.

7.51 **a.** Martensite is a transition phase between austenite and ferrite, which retains carbon interstitially. Given an opportunity, the carbon separates as Fe_3C.

7.52 **a.** Alloying elements can dissolve substitutionally in austenite, which remains FCC.

7.53 **b.** Hardenability may be described as the ability, or the ease, by which martensitic hardness is obtained at various cooling rates (as located on an end-quenched, or Jominy, test).

7.54 **d.** The ratio of stress-to-strain is defined as the elastic modulus.

7.55 **d.** $\sigma_u = F/A_0$

7.56 **a.** Slip occurs most readily in directions that have the shortest steps, and along planes that are farthest apart. The latter are automatically the planes that are most densely populated.

7.57 **c.** Cold working—such as rolling, forging, drawing, or extrusion—deforms the material at temperatures below the recrystallization temperature. Strain hardening occurs, increasing both the yield and ultimate strength. Internal strains and minute cracks are introduced as slip or twinning occurs. Ductility, elongation, and the recrystallization temperature are decreased. A preferred grain orientation is introduced in the direction of elongation, and the grains are flattened.

7.58 **d.** Since oxygen is required for rust formation, oxygen-depleted areas become the anode and are corroded. This may lead to pitting, particularly if rust or other corrosion products are accumulated locally to prevent the access of oxygen. Iron and other metals may be protected from corrosion by the presence of a more electropositive metal such as magnesium or zinc. This is the reason for coating steel with zinc to produce galvanized sheet.

7.59 **c.** Although fatigue strength is not sensitive to temperature or loading rates, it is very sensitive to surface imperfections from which cracks originate and propagate.

7.60 **b.** The stress intensity factor is proportional to the applied stress and the square root of the crack depth.

7.61 **b.** Glide occurs parallel to the slip plane.

7.62 **d.** Brittleness exists below T_{DT}.

7.63 **c.** Corrosion commonly occurs in the combined presence of oxygen and water. Protection may be obtained by making a cathode out of the critical part or by avoiding air.

7.64 **c.** With equal strains, $(\sigma_{gl}/\sigma_p) = E_{gl}/E_p = 10$. Likewise with equal areas, $F_{gl} = 10F_p$, and $F_{gl}/(F_{gl} + F_p) = 10/(10 + 1)$.

CHAPTER 8

Engineering Sciences

OUTLINE

This chapter assumes the reader completed an introductory electrical engineering or circuits course but needs to review points of theory and application. For instance, the solution for a single voltage source in a series circuit might easily come to mind, but if one changed the circuit by inserting another source (multiple source network) that may be acting as a load, the method of solution may not be readily apparent without a short review.

This chapter presents the portions of theory that are relevant to the FE/EIT exam. An attempt is made to reduce the more detailed theory to the level for the expected problem and to leave out the more abstract formal development of a solution. For example, rather than setting up a three-phase ac problem for a complete solution—including possibly an unbalanced network—this review will assume the more likely case of all three legs of the circuit being part of a balanced network and proceed with a much simpler method of solution.

The objective of this presentation will be to jog the memory so that the reader can feel comfortable with the simpler type of *quick solution* problems expected on the examination. It should be noted that multiple-choice answers for any such problems are significantly different, which allows one to quickly locate the correct answer if the simplest possible solution can be found. As an example, in a series ac circuits problem one can frequently plot a phasor solution with ruler and protractor that is accurate enough to pick the correct answer. One needs to be careful to not solve for more than what is asked.

ELECTRICAL QUANTITIES AND DEFINITIONS

Electrostatics

The subject of electric fields is sometimes omitted in a formal course in electrical engineering (the knowledge is frequently assumed from a prerequisite physics course). Thus, one needs to review electric fields and flux densities attributable to electrical charges. These fields, forces, and flux densities require three-dimensional vector notation. However, most problems will reduce in complexity to two dimensions; this reduction will permit quick graphical solutions.

Whereas the forces exerted between charges depend on whether the charges are in motion, one may start with stationary electric charges that produce electric fields. These fields may be defined in terms of the forces they produce on one another.

The smallest amount of charge that can exist is the charge of one electron, which is 1.602×10^{-19} coulombs (C). One coulomb of charge is thus equivalent to 6.24×10^{18} electrons. This is the amount of charge that is necessary to develop a force of one newton in an electric field of one volt per meter. An electric field, **E** (boldface for vector quantity), is the amount of force (F) that would be exerted on a *positive charge* (assuming it is concentrated at a point) *of one coulomb* if it were placed in that field:

$$\mathbf{F} = Q\mathbf{E}$$

The electric field is not thought of as a point but rather as being distributed throughout a small region. This is a vector quantity; the direction of force on the one coulomb would be toward the point source of the field if that point were a negative charge. The units of measurement are newtons per unit of charge; alternately, it may be given in terms of volts/meter since

$$\frac{\text{force}}{\text{charge}} = \frac{\text{force} \times \text{distance}}{\text{charge} \times \text{distance}} = \frac{\text{energy}}{\text{charge} \times \text{distance}} = \frac{\text{voltage}}{\text{distance}}$$

For point charges, the force is directly proportional to the product of the two charges and inversely proportional to the square of the distance between them (similar to the laws of gravity).

$$\mathbf{F}_2 = \frac{Q_1 Q_2}{4\pi\varepsilon r^2}\mathbf{a}_{r12}, \quad \text{where} \tag{8.1a}$$

$\mathbf{F}_2$ = the force on charge 2 due to charge 1

Q_i = the *i*th point charge

r = the distance between charges 1 and 2

$\mathbf{a}_{r12}$ = a unit vector directed from 1 to 2

ε = the permittivity (or dielectric constant) of the medium

The constant of proportionality depends on the medium between the two charges. This constant is $1/(4\pi\varepsilon)$ or approximately 9×10^9 for free space. If the medium is not free space, the 9×10^9 is merely divided by the relative permittivity to give the simplified *in line* form as

$$F = (9 \times 10^9/\varepsilon_{rel})Q_1Q_2/r^2 \text{ newtons} \tag{8.1b}$$

$$\varepsilon = \varepsilon_{rel}\varepsilon_0 \text{ F/m} \tag{8.2}$$

and ε_0 = permittivity of free space = 8.85 × 10^{-12} farads/meter. Permittivity of air is approximately the same as that of free space or a vacuum (that is, ε_{rel} = 1.0006), but if the medium happens to be caster oil, ε_{rel} is almost 5.

A convenient way of thinking of these fields is to imagine flux lines radiating either away from or toward a point source, as shown in Figure 8.1. If one imagines a positive point source charge at the center of a sphere and arrows pointed away from the center, these arrows would be the flux lines (the bigger the charge, the more arrows).

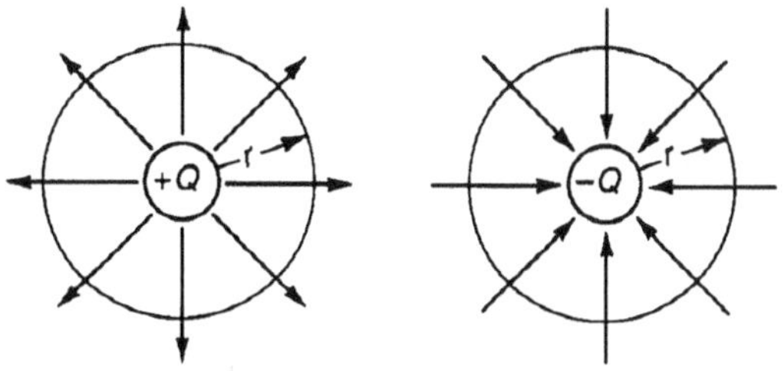

Figure 8.1 Electric flux lines around a charge

The flux density on the surface of the sphere (whose center is located at the point charge) would then be the number of arrows through a unit area on the sphere.

$$D = Q/A \tag{8.3a}$$

$$Q = \mathbf{D} \bullet \mathbf{A} \tag{8.3b}$$

where A is the area of the sphere ($4\pi r^2$) and Q is the quantity of charge in coulombs (assuming the area is normal to the flux). Equation (8.3b) is presented for those familiar with the dot and cross product vector notation (this notation guarantees the portion of the surface being considered is normal to the flux). If one were to divide the area of the sphere into very small areas, dA's, the sum of areas times the amount of flux through each area would be the amount of charge at the center of the sphere. More formally, as the size of each area approaches zero, and as one integrates over the entire area of the sphere, the total charge enclosed is Q; this is known as Gauss's Law, Equations (8.4a) and (8.4b). But, by using the dot-product notation, one is not limited to a spherical shape with the charge at the center; the formal law is then given as Equation (8.4b) or (8.4c):

$$Q = \sum D \; dA \text{ (for entire surface)} \tag{8.4a}$$

$$Q = \oint_s \mathrm{D} \bullet dA \tag{8.4b}$$

$$Q/\varepsilon = \oint_s \mathrm{E} \bullet dA \tag{8.4c}$$

The field strength, **E**, at the sphere's surface is then proportional to D,

$$\mathbf{E} = (D/\varepsilon)\mathbf{a}_r \tag{8.5}$$

where $\mathbf{a}_r$ is a unit radial vector direction. If there are a number of charges throughout a region, it is usually easier to use the flux density concept in solving problems. In this chapter, unit vectors will be denoted as **a** so that e can be reserved for other purposes.

Example 8.1

Assume three point charges, A, B, and C, as shown in Exhibit 1. Points A and B are 2 meters apart; Point C is on a perpendicular bisector between A and B and is 1 meter lower. Point A has 4×10^{-6} coulombs of negative charge, Point B has 10×10^{-6} coulombs of positive charge, and Point C has no charge yet. Determine the force and the field on B (in this case, due only to the charge on A) and the flux density at Point C.

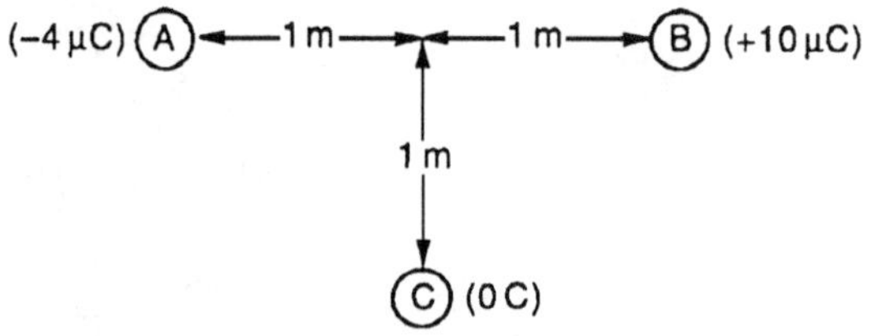

Exhibit 1 Point charge locations

Solution

The force on B due to A is directly proportional to the charges on A and B and inversely proportional to the square of the distance of separation. Using Equation (8.1),

$$\mathbf{F} = (9 \times 10^{9})(-4 \times 10^{-6})(10 \times 10^{-6})/(2^{2}) = -9 \times 10^{-2} \text{ newtons}$$

with the direction of the force toward each other.

$$\mathbf{E} \text{ (at B)} = \mathbf{F}/Q_{B} = 9 \times 10^{-2}/10^{-5} = 9 \times 10^{3} \text{ V/m}$$

(If the medium happened to be a special oil with relative permittivity 5.0, both **F** and **E** would only be one-fifth as large.) A more orderly solution (especially if several charges are involved—or none at C in this case) is to use the flux density relationship to find the individual Ds, then convert to Es. All that is now necessary to find the net **E** is to use vector summation of the flux densities and divide by ε. To find the flux density at C attributable to charge A, imagine a sphere passing through C with its center at A; repeat for B.

$$D_{CA} \text{ (at C attributable to A)} = Q_{A}/(4\pi r^{2})$$

$$\mathbf{E}_{CA} = (D/\varepsilon)\mathbf{a}_{rCA} = (Q_{A}/r^{2})(1/4\pi\varepsilon)\mathbf{a}_{rCA} \text{ V/m}$$

Recall that $1/(4\pi\varepsilon)$ for free space is 9×10^{9}, then

$$\mathbf{E}_{CA} = \left[(4 \times 10^{-6})/\sqrt{2^{2}}\right](9 \times 10^{9})\mathrm{a}_{,CA} = 1.8 \times 10^{4}\,\mathbf{a}_{,rCA} \text{ V/m}$$

$$\mathbf{E}_{CB} = \left[(10 \times 10^{-6})/\sqrt{2^{2}}\right](9 \times 10^{9})\mathrm{a}_{,CA} = 4.5 \times 10^{4}\,\mathbf{a}_{,rCA} \text{ V/m}$$

To find the E_{C} net one may use the more formal procedure of finding the rectangular components of each of the field vectors since only two dimensions are involved. Then, summing the horizontal and vertical components, the net field vector is the square root of the sum of the squares. If one assumes the reference vector,

$\mathbf{a}_r$, has the horizontal component a and the vertical component jb (the j implies the 90° or vertical axis), then

$$\mathbf{E}_{CA} = |\mathbf{E}_{CA}|(\cos\theta + j\sin\theta) = 1.8 \times 10^4 (\cos 135° + j \sin 135°)$$
$$= (-1.27 + j1.27) \times 10^4 \text{ V/m}$$
$$\mathbf{E}_{CB} = 4.5 \times 10^4 (\cos 225° + j \sin 225°) = (-3.18 - j3.18) \times 10^4 \text{ V/m}$$
$$\mathbf{E}_{Cnet} = (-4.45 - j1.91) \times 10^4 = 4.84 \times 10^4 \angle 203.2° \text{ V/m}$$

where the angle θ is the angle between the vector **E** and a horizontal reference line. However, solving for the vector field at C may be done faster by using a graphical solution, assuming reasonable accuracy. The points A, B, and C are set up (to their own scale); then, working with Point C, one places the vectors (using any suitable scale) that represent the two other fields. The reference direction and magnitude is then pictured as shown in Exhibit 2.

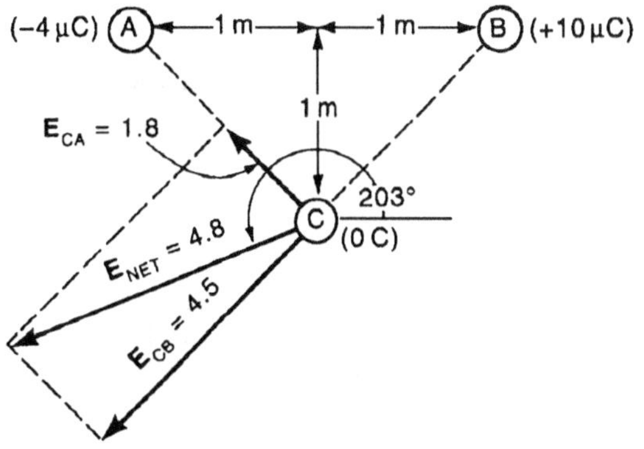

Exhibit 2 Sample problem vector fields (×10[4]) at C

Now, assume the charge at C is $+5 \times 10^{-6}$ coulombs; find the net vector field at Point B. To find this field at Point B, merely remove the charge at B.

$$\mathbf{E}_{BA} = (Q_A/r^2)(9 \times 10^9)\mathbf{a}_{rBA} = 0.90 \times 10^4 \, \mathbf{a}_{rBA} \text{ V/m}$$
$$\mathbf{E}_{BC} = (Q_C/r^2)(9 \times 10^9)\mathbf{a}_{rBC} = 2.25 \times 10^4 \, \mathbf{a}_{rBC} \text{ V/m}$$

Again, solve graphically for the solution (Exhibit 3).

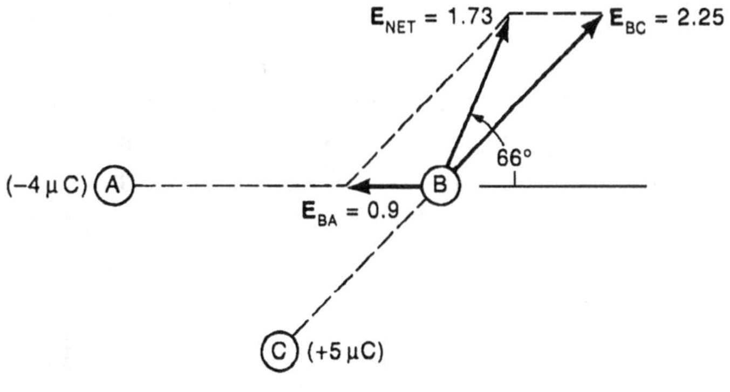

Exhibit 3 The electric field at B (×10[4])

The actual solution, using vector notation, is found to be **E** (at B) = $1.73 \times 10^4 \angle 66.5°$ volts/meter.

Electric field intensity, E (a vector quantity in volts/meter) at point 2 due to a point charge Q_1 at point 1 is

$$E = \frac{Q_1}{4\pi\varepsilon r^2}\hat{a}_{r12}$$

where $\hat{a}_{r12}$ is a unit vector from point 1 to point 2.

For a line charge of density ρ_L coulomb/meter on the z-axis,

$$E_L = \frac{\rho_L}{2\pi\varepsilon r}\hat{a}_r$$

where $\hat{a}_r$ is a unit vector from the line of charge to a distance r from the line of charge.

For a sheet charge of density ρ_s coulomb/meter^2 in the x-y plane:

$$E_S = \frac{\rho_s}{2\varepsilon}\hat{a}_z,\ z > 0$$

where $\hat{a}_z$ is a unit vector from the surface of the sheet charge to a distance z.

The electric flux density is defined as $D = \varepsilon E$.

CAPACITANCE

A more complex problem involving the x, y, and z axes is no more complicated except for the bookkeeping difficulty of solving a three-dimensional problem.

Before leaving the subject of static electric fields, the subject of energy storage in a capacitor (a pair of parallel plates separated by a distance, d) will be introduced. Capacitance is the ratio of the total stored charge uniformly distributed on the plates to the voltage difference between the plates. The separation distance, d, between plates will be considered to be small compared to the plate area (so that fringing may be neglected), then the field and flux lines will be perpendicular to the plates. The capacitance is

$$C = q_c(t)/v_c(t) \text{ farads (coulombs/volt)} \quad \textbf{(8.6a)}$$

and for non-time-varying quantities

$$C = Q/(Ed) = AD/(Ed) = A(E\varepsilon)/(Ed) = A\varepsilon/d \quad \textbf{(8.6b)}$$

Permittivity may now be defined in a slightly different manner, where ε equals the charge induced on one square meter of the capacitor plates by an electric field intensity of one volt/meter. Thus, for a free space separation of the plates, 8.85×10^{-12} coulombs is induced on one square meter of a conducting plate by an electric field having an intensity of one volt per meter.

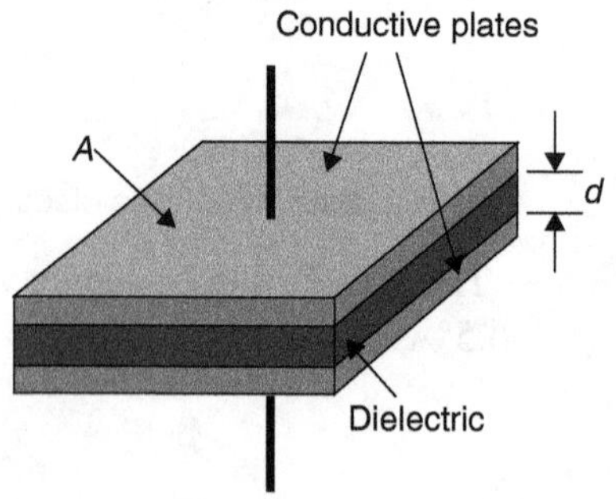

Figure 8.2 Parallel plate capacitor

Permittivity of free space separation of the plates is $\varepsilon = \varepsilon_o = 8.85 \times 10^{-12}$ coulombs/meter. Dielectrics other than air or free space have a relative permittivity of ε_r (a unitless number) so that the overall permittivity of that material is $\varepsilon = \varepsilon_r \varepsilon_o$.

In summary, the voltage difference between the two conductors is proportional to the charge:

$$q = Cv$$

The proportionality constant C is called *capacitance* with units of Farads (F), which is equivalent to coulomb/volt.

The current voltage relationship of the capacitor is:

$$i(t) = C\frac{dv(t)}{dt}$$

where $i(t)$ is the current through the capacitor, and $v(t)$ is the voltage across the capacitor as shown in Figure 8.3.

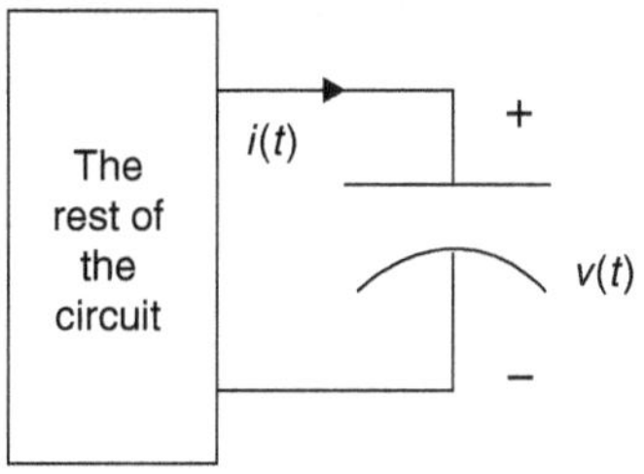

Figure 8.3

where $v(t)$ is a time varying current through the capacitor. If a DC source is connected to a capacitor, the $v(t)$ is a constant so the current through the capacitor is zero.

Alternate definitions of the current-voltage relationship of a capacitor are:

$$v(t) = \frac{1}{C}\int_{-\infty}^{t} i(x)dx$$

or

$$v(t) = v(t_0) + \frac{1}{C}\int_{t_0}^{t} i(x)dx$$

where $v(t_o)$ is the initial voltage stored in the capacitor (a DC current).

The energy stored in a capacitor is

$$w_C(t) = \frac{1}{2}Cv^2(t)$$

INDUCTANCE

Inductance occurs when current flows through a (real) conductor. The current flowing through the conductor sets up a magnetic field that is proportional to the current. The voltage difference across the conductor is proportional to the rate of change of the magnetic field. The voltage difference across the inductor is proportional to the rate of the current's change.

The proportionality constant is called the inductance, denoted L with Units of Henrys (H), which is equal to Volt•Seconds/Ampere.

The voltage across an inductor is

$$v(t) = L\frac{di(t)}{dt}$$

where $i(t)$ is a time varying current through the inductor. If a DC source is connected to an inductor, $i(t)$ is a constant so $v(t)$ across an inductor is zero.

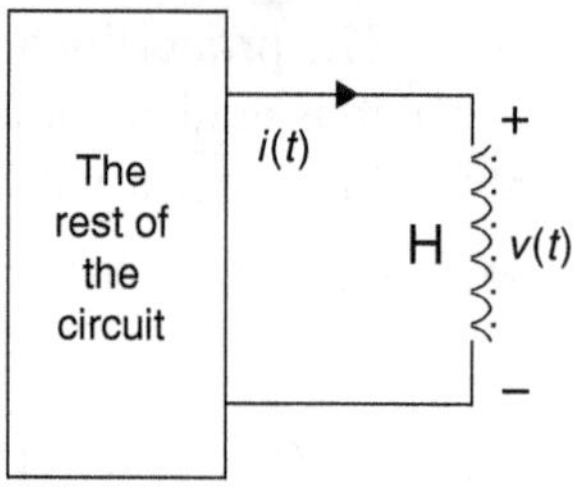

Figure 8.4

The current through the inductor can also be defined as:

$$i(t) = \frac{1}{L}\int_{-\infty}^{t} v(x)dx$$

or

$$i(t) = i(t_0) + \frac{1}{L}\int_{t_0}^{t} v(x)dx$$

where $i(t_o)$ is the initial current stored in the inductor (a DC current).

The energy stored in an inductor is

$$w_L(t) = \frac{1}{2}Li^2(t)$$

Series inductors combine like series resistors

$$L_{ser} = L_1 + L_2 + L_3 + \bullet\bullet\bullet.$$

Parallel inductors combine like parallel resistors

$$1/L_{par} = 1/L_1 + 1/L_2 + 1/L_3 + \bullet\bullet\bullet.$$

Magnetic Quantities and Definitions

Magnetic effects are related to the motion of charges, or currents. From the previous section on electrostatics, a force of one newton is produced by a charge of one coulomb in an electric field intensity of one volt per meter. Electric current, on the other hand, can be thought of as moving charges. **Current** is the time rate of change of the electric charge passing through a surface area. This definition is expressed as

$$i = dq/dt \tag{8.7}$$

The unit of current is the **ampere**, A, which equals one coulomb per second.

From the concept of moving charges, one can begin to understand magnetic fields. For permanent magnets (due to *static* magnetic fields) one recalls from physics that for some materials the molecular structure has the electron orbits of

the atoms aligned. These tiny moving charges of electrons produce tiny currents. This alignment results in magnetic fields; actually ferromagnetic materials can be thought of as a large number of magnetic domains, with the domains being mostly aligned. However, when these (magnetic) domains are in disarray or randomly aligned, the material is unmagnetized.

Oersted, in 1819, observed that a magnetic flux existed about a wire carrying an electric current. (Flux lines can almost be visualized by observing the pattern of sprinkled iron filings on a piece of paper held over one pole of a magnet.) A few years after Oersted observed the effect of magnetic flux, Ampere found that wire coils carrying a current acted in the same manner as magnets. Simply stated, a coil of several turns of wire produced a stronger magnetic flux than only one turn of wire for the same current. And, if there were a ferromagnetic material to carry (or to provide a path for) the magnetic flux, the flux strength would be much greater.

Consider a toroidal ferromagnetic ring wrapped with a coil of several turns of wire, with the coil connected to a variable current source. Assume the current is zero and the material is not magnetized to begin with, then with an increase of current, an increase in flux results. One tends to think that the relationship would be linear; but the relationship is actually rather complex for a ferromagnetic material. As the current is further increased, the flux tends to level off. The leveling off is caused by most of the magnetic domains in the material aligning themselves in the same direction; consequently, increasing the current beyond the *knee of the bend* does not significantly increase the flux. If the current is decreased, most (but not all) of the magnetic domains return to random directions for zero current. The *going up* path is not necessarily the same as the *going down* path; these paths are known as the hysteresis curve for a particular material. When the current reaches zero on the *coming down* side, the material is left partially magnetized; this is called the residual magnetism. Again, assuming the material is unmagnetized to begin with, the flux is caused by the current through the number of turns of wire. This product of the current and the number of turns of wire, or amp-turns ($A \bullet t$), is frequently called the magneto-motive force (mmf) and indicated with a script F. The mmf is the source that causes the magnetic flux (ϕ). A plot of these two quantities is given in Figure 8.5(b); this plot is referred to as the hysteresis curve.

If the width of the hysteresis curve were small (that is, the residual magnetic flux is small), only the first quadrant of the hysteresis curve is needed and can be drawn as a single line; then, only one curve per kind of magnetic material is needed.

Before a numerical problem can be solved, one needs to quantify and further define several terms. Rather than using flux, ϕ (units of webers), it is more appropriate to use flux density, B (units of tesla or webers/unit area). Flux density is the amount of flux passing through a unit area (normal to the flux). Also, rather than using the straight magneto-motive force designation, a more useful one is mmf/length, called the magnetic field intensity, H. These standardized quantities will allow a plot of B vs. H; this plot is always given for solid magnetic materials (that is, before any air gap might be cut into them).

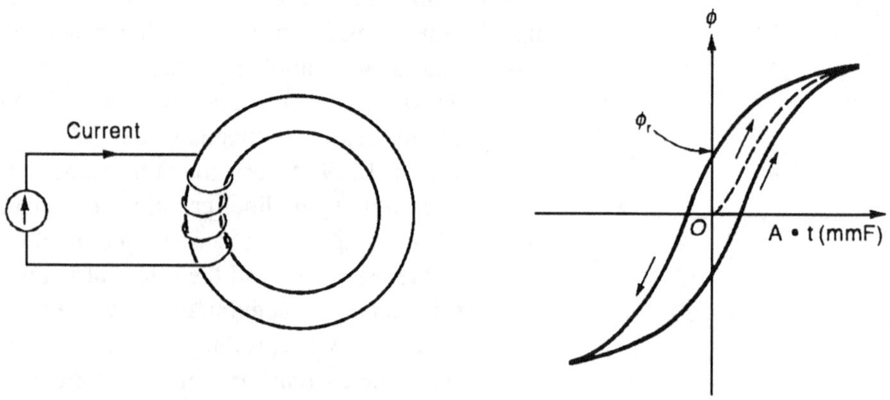

(a) Magnetic circuit (b) Hysteresis curve

Figure 8.5 Magnetic characteristics

One needs to define further the direction of magnetic flux and fields; this is difficult to do without the concept of magnetic poles. To show this effect, consider an air gap cut into the ferromagnetic material. However, analogous to electrical charges being positive or negative, one can think of magnetic poles (they always occur in pairs) as north and south (recall, like poles repel and unlike ones attract). As an example, consider a freely suspended magnet (say, a magnetized needle in a compass) in the earth's magnetic field; one end of the magnet points toward the geographical north. By common usage, this end of the magnet is referred to as the *north-seeking pole.* For the toroidal ring with the air gap cut in it, if the positive direction of the current enters the top end of the coil, the direction of the flux in the ring will be clockwise, and the top of the air gap is the north pole, whereas the bottom is the south pole.

In the previous example, the magnetic flux in the air gap is concentrated and may be very high. The lines of magnetic flux produced in the material and the air gap are the same and continuous when there is a current in the wire. Without the ferromagnetic material in the path, the relationship between the current (causing the magnetic flux) and the resulting magnetic field would be linear but very weak. The linear constant of proportionality is called the permeability of free space, μ_0 (as in the air gap). This constant is

$$\mu_0 = 4\pi \times 10^{-7} \text{ F/m} \tag{8.8a}$$

For ferromagnetic materials, the relative permeability is nonlinear; for approximate calculations, it is sometimes linearized in the region of the curve before magnetic saturation is reached. The slope of the curve in the saturation region approaches that of free space or air, thus

$$\mu_r \mu_0 \rightarrow \mu_0 \tag{8.8b}$$

The relationship between B and H may then be expressed as the slope of a B vs. H curve:

$$\mu = \mu_r \mu_0 = B/H \tag{8.8c}$$

when B and H are normal to each other.

As stated previously, flux lines are continuous (that is, the lines of flux in the ring and air gap are the same), whereas the flux density in the ring may or may not be the same as that in the air gap—frequently they are considered the same

by neglecting the fringing effect in the gap. Also, the cause of the flux (that is, the amp-turns) is thought of as being distributed along the whole ring, thus it is appropriate to use field intensity, H (amp-turns/meter or mmf/m). The length for this example is merely the mean circumference of the ring (the width of the air gap usually being negligible). Kirchhoff's voltage law in electrical series circuits states that the net voltage drop in a loop equals zero; one may use the same analogy for series magnetic circuits. That is, the net mmf in a magnetic series loop equals zero. Stated another way, the mmf source must equal the sum of the mmf drops (or losses) in the series circuit. Thus, summing these mmf drops in the iron and the air gap is all that is needed to find the mmf for the source.

Although the previous example involved a coil of wire, a more fundamental problem is one involving a long straight wire.

For a wire on the z-axis carrying a current,

$$\boldsymbol{H} = \frac{\boldsymbol{B}}{\mu} = \frac{\boldsymbol{I}\mathbf{a}_\theta}{2\pi r} \quad \textbf{(8.9a)}$$

where

$\boldsymbol{H}$ = the magnetic field strength (amps/meter)
$\boldsymbol{B}$ = the magnetic flux density (tesla)
$\mathbf{a}_\theta$ = the unit vector in positive θ direction in cylindrical coordinates
$\boldsymbol{I}$ = the current
μ = the permeability of the medium (for air, $\mu = \mu_0 = 4\pi \times 10^{-7}$ H/m)

The flux density at some radial distance, r, from the center line of the wire is given in Equation (8.9b).

$$B = (\mu i)(2\pi r) \quad \textbf{(8.9b)}$$

For the direction of the current shown in Figure 8.6, the flux density direction is shown with the head of an arrow as $(\odot)$ and the tail of an arrow as $(\otimes)$; this notation will be the same for current.

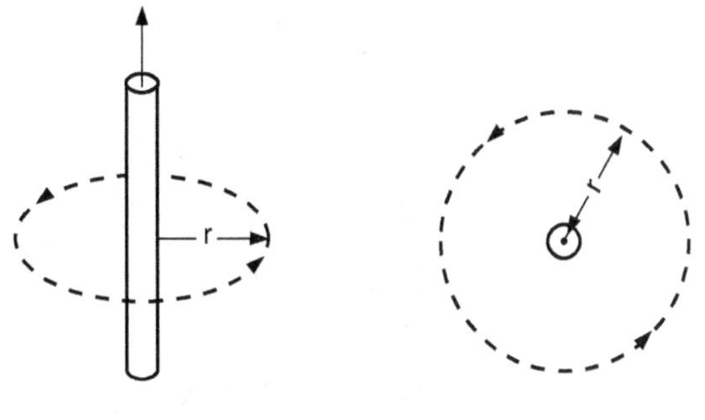

(a) Side view (b) Top view

Figure 8.6 The flux density around a wire

The direction of the flux may be remembered by using the right-hand rule: place the thumb in the direction of the current; the partially closed fingers will point in the direction of the magnetic flux. Now, if the long wire were formed into a circular coil of radius r, one could use calculus to consider a differential length of the wire and integrate around the closed loop to find the flux density within the loop. If there were several turns, N, for the loop, the equation for the flux density would be

$$B = (\mu N i)/r \quad \textbf{(8.10)}$$

The right-hand rule may also be used to find the direction that a current would flow if a voltage is induced (or generated) in a wire by the relative motion of a magnetic field and a wire (see Figure 8.7). Consider a straight wire being moved within a magnetic field (assume the wire and motion is normal to the magnetic field). A voltage induced in the wire will be proportional to the strength of the field, the length (l) of wire within the field, and the velocity, v, of the wire.

$$e \text{ (induced voltage)} = Blv \qquad \textbf{(8.11a)}$$

For a coil of N turns enclosing flux ϕ

$$e = -N\, d\phi/dt \qquad \textbf{(8.11b)}$$

where ϕ = the flux (webers) enclosed by the N conductor turns and

$$\phi = \int_A B \cdot dA$$

The direction of the flux is from the north pole face to the south pole face. It will help to think of the wire within the field as being a voltage generator (the induced voltage); then if there is a closed path (perhaps through an external resistive load) so that a current could flow, the polarity of the *generator* must be plus where the current (thumb direction) leaves the magnetic field and minus where it enters the field.

In this section, vector notation involving three-dimensional space has been kept to a minimum; the FE examination will probably not include this added complication for magnetic fields. Should such a problem occur, one could still attempt to tailor the problem using vector components. As an example, assume one is asked to find an induced voltage for the motion of a wire in a magnetic field as depicted in Figure 8.7 using Equation (8.11a). However, assume also that the wire velocity direction is not normal to the magnetic field but at an angle θ from the horizontal. The solution and the equation would be the same, except that one must use the vertical component of the velocity rather than the magnitude of the entire velocity.

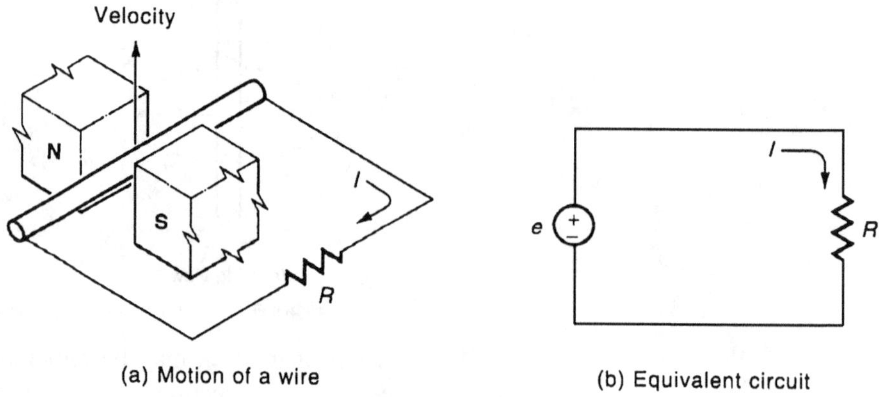

Figure 8.7 Induced voltage

Power, Energy, and Measurements

Before the discussion of power, energy, and measurements is undertaken, three items need to be reviewed. The first is notation, the second is the calculation of resistance, and the third is a more complete definition of voltage.

Notation

In this section, the notation for time-dependent quantities will normally be given by lowercase, italic letters (for example, for voltage, current, and such, $v(t)$, $i(t)$, where the (t) may or may not be included). A constant value, such as a battery voltage, will be given in uppercase, italic letters (for example, V and I); the effective or rms (root mean square) values and other quantities that have a nonvarying value (such as the average power) will also be expressed as an uppercase letter. Where confusion is possible, a subscript is normally used. Further discussion of notation will be presented where appropriate.

Resistance

Most reviews assume that one is familiar with simple wire resistance. Although the actual resistance of a wire conductor is usually considered to be negligible in circuit analysis, it is easily calculated. The parameters are shown in Figure 8.8.

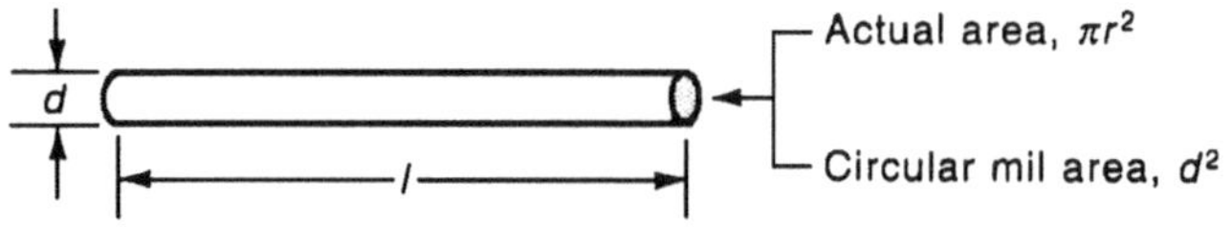

Figure 8.8 Wire resistance parameters

The resistance is proportional to its length and inversely proportional to its cross-sectional area; the constant of proportionality is the resistivity, ρ:

$$R = \frac{\rho L}{A} \tag{8.12}$$

The resistivity of a particular conductor is normally given for a standard temperature of 20°C. However, the units depend on the length and area. For the MKS system of units, the value of ρ for copper is $1.7 \times 10^{-8}\ \Omega \bullet \text{m}$ (for aluminum, it is almost twice this value).

Example 8.2

As an example, for a 5-meter length of 12-gauge (approximate diameter of 2 mm) copper wire at room temperature (near 20°C) find the resistance, R.

Solution

$$R = (1.7 \times 10^{-8})(5/[\pi(0.001)^2]) = 0.027\ \Omega$$

On the other hand, for another temperature, the resistivity is modified by the temperature coefficient, α, to be

$$\rho = \rho_0[1 + \alpha(\mathrm{T} - \mathrm{T}_0)] \tag{8.13a}$$

or

$$R = R_0[1 + \alpha(\mathrm{T} - \mathrm{T}_0)] \tag{8.13b}$$

where $(\mathrm{T} - \mathrm{T}_0)$ is the change of temperature from 20°C.

Generally, these two equations will solve most resistive type problems. However, here is one note of caution: unfortunately, the inch, foot, and circular mil units for area are still in use. These units can be confusing since the area of the wire may be given in circular mils; this area omits π in the true area, πr^2, computation and, instead, includes it in the resistivity constant. In this case, the resistivity for copper

wire is 10.4 Ω circ-mils/foot. Actually, the computation is made easier; assume a length of 5 feet for a wire diameter of 0.03 inches (or 30 mils):

$$R = (10.4)(5)/(30)^2 = 0.0578\ \Omega$$

The key to this type of problem is to check carefully by dimensional analysis to determine what units are being used. Wire tables, listing these parameters, should be furnished with the EIT examination when they are needed.

Power and Energy

Power (instantaneous, i.e., lowercase italic notation) is the rate of change of energy, dw/dt, or

$$p(t) = dw/dt = (dw/dq)(dq/dt) = v(t)(i) \quad \textbf{(8.14)}$$

The total energy is then given in Equation (8.16). (The function of time, t, is implied and will be dropped for simplicity.)

$$w = \int_0^T p\,dt = \int_0^T vi\,dt \quad \textbf{(8.15)}$$

Energy Storage

Energy may be stored in some electrical circuit elements. For electrical circuits, there are three basic elements: resistance, inductance, and capacitance. For the resistor, electrical energy cannot be stored since it is turned into heat; however, both the inductor and capacitor are capable of energy storage (see Figure 8.9).

$$w_L = (1/2)Li_L^2 \quad \textbf{(8.16a)}$$

$$w_C = (1/2)Cv_C^2 \quad \textbf{(8.16b)}$$

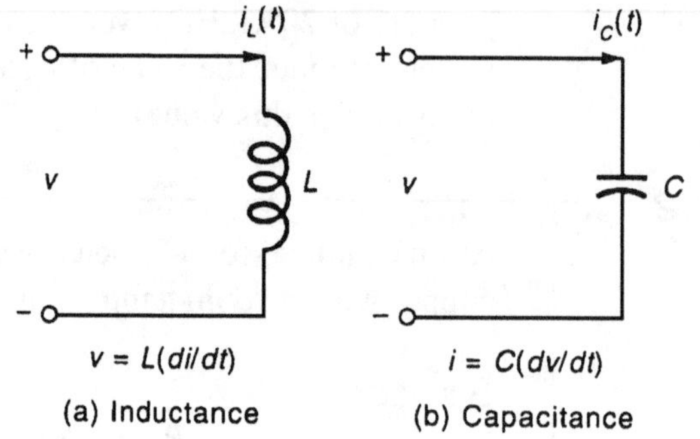

Figure 8.9 Energy storage elements

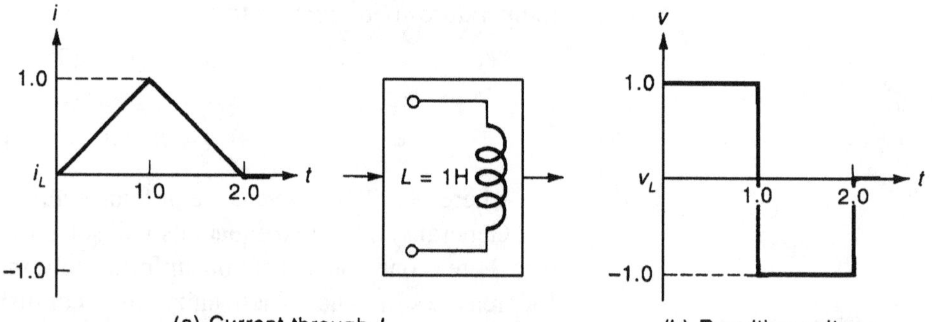

Figure 8.10 Inductor current-voltage relationship

The voltage across an inductor is a function of the rate of change of current. If there is no rate of change (or direct current), then the voltage must be zero, and the inductor acts like a short circuit or zero resistance. Actually, there is always some wire resistance, but usually this is negligible. For current to flow in a capacitor, there must be a rate of change of voltage. If there is no rate of change, there is no current, and the capacitor acts like an open circuit (this will be discussed in more detail later). As an example, assume the current (from a variable current source) through an inductor is as given in Figure 8.10(a); then the voltage across the inductor must be as shown in Figure 8.10(b).

As shown in Figure 8.11, the power *taken* (absorbed or stored) by the inductor is a function of time until $t = 1$ second and is positive; for the current with a negative slope, power is *given up* (or returned to the circuit source) from $t = 1$ second until $t = 2$ seconds. On the other hand, the energy stored (also a function of time) follows the square law given directly in Equation (8.16a). The resulting curves are found by splitting Equation (8.15):

$$w = \int_0^2 p\,dt = \int_0^1 vi\,dt + \int_1^2 vi\,dt$$

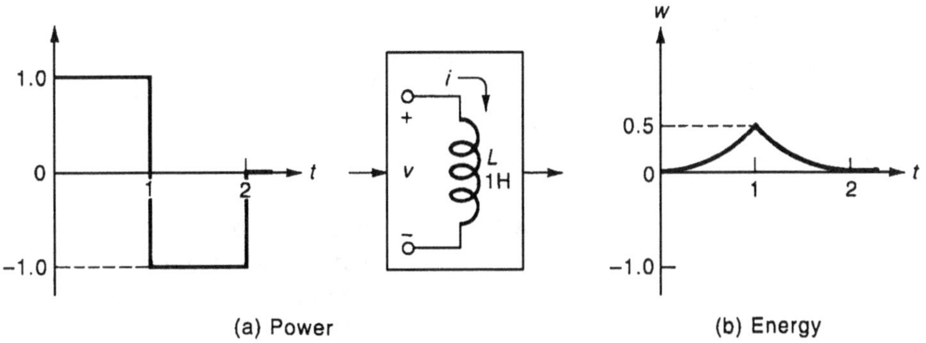

Figure 8.11 Power and energy plot for the current/voltage curves of Figure 8.10

PROBLEMS

8.1 For a parallel plate capacitor separated by an air gap of 1 cm and with an applied dc voltage across the plates of 500 volts, determine the force on an electron mass of 18.2×10^{-31} kg inserted in the space. The mass of an electron is 9.1×10^{-31} kg.

a. 3.2×10^{-14} N
b. 1.6×10^{-14} N
c. 9.1×10^{-31} N
d. 1.6×10^{-19} N

8.2 Assume a point charge of 0.3×10^{-3} C at an origin. What is the magnitude of the electric field intensity at a point located 2 meters in the x-direction, 3 meters in the y-direction, and 4 meters in the z-direction from the origin?

a. 500 kV/m
b. 5 kV/m
c. 93 kV/m
d. 9.3 MV/m

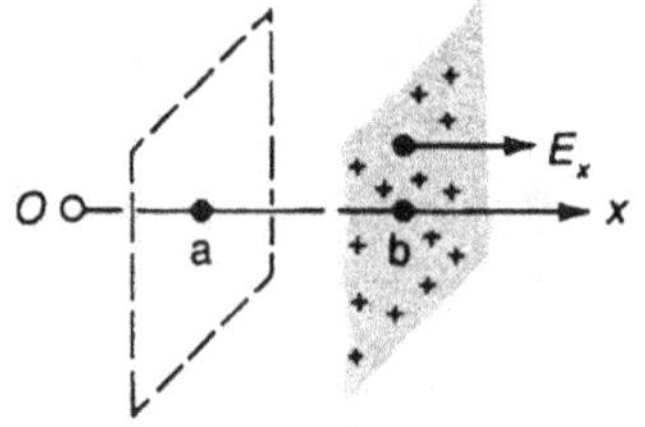

Exhibit 8.3 Charge placement

8.3 An infinite sheet of charge with a positive charge density, σ, has an electric field of:

$$\mathbf{E} = [\sigma/(2\varepsilon_0)]_{ax} \text{ for } x > b$$

If a second sheet of charge with a charge density of $-\sigma$ is then placed (see Exhibit 8.3), what is the electric field for $a < x < b$?

a. $(\sigma/\varepsilon_0)_{ax}$
b. 0
c. $(-\sigma/\varepsilon_0)_{ax}$
d. $(\sigma/2\varepsilon_0)_{ax}$

8.4 Two equal charges of 10 μC are located one meter apart on a horizontal line, and another charge of 5 μC is placed one meter below the first charge (forming a right triangle). What is the magnitude of the force on the 5 μC charge?

a. 0.09×10^6 N
b. 12.6×10^4 N
c. 6.39×10^4 N
d. 63×10^{-2} N

8.5 For a coil of 100 turns wound around a toroidal core of iron with a relative permeability of 1000, find the current needed to produce a magnetic flux density of 0.5 tesla in the core. The dimensions of the core are given in Exhibit 8.5.

a. 390 A
b. 39 A
c. 1.2 A
d. 12.2 A

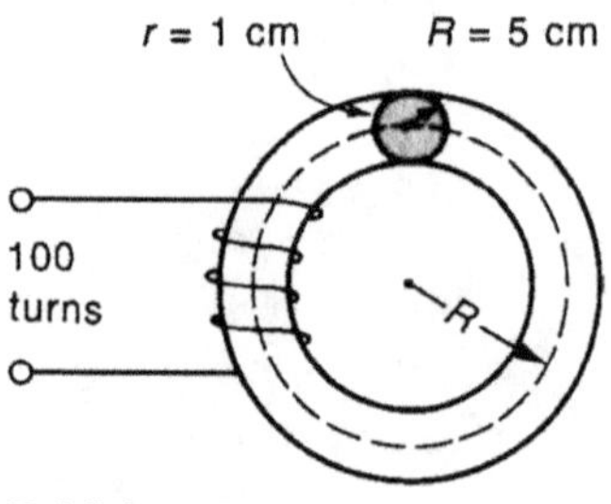

Exhibit 8.5

8.6 Two long straight wires, bundled together, have a magnetic flux density around them. One wire carries a current of 5 amperes, and the other carries a current of 1 ampere in the opposite direction. Determine the magnitude of the flux density at a point 0.2 meters away (i.e., normal to the wires).

a. $2\pi \times 10^{-6}$ T
c. 4×10^{-6} T
b. $4\pi \times 10^{-6}$ T
d. $16\pi \times 10^{-6}$ T

8.7 The root mean square of $i(t)$ for Exhibit 8.7 is:

a. 1.6 A
b. 3.0 A
c. 2.0 A
d. 0.0 A

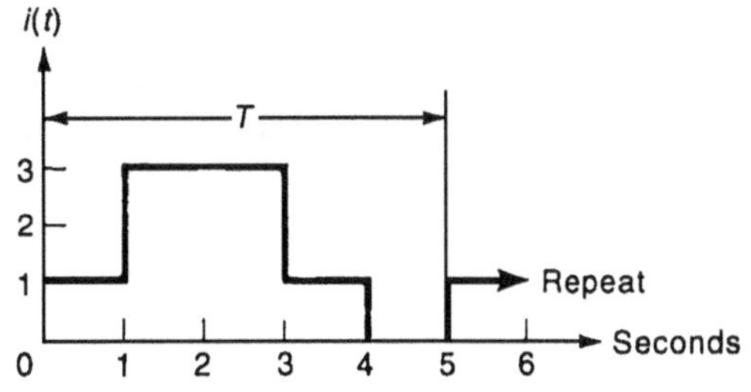

Exhibit 8.7 A current wave

8.8 A current phases through a 0.2-henry inductor. The current increases in a linear fashion from a value of zero at $t = 0$ to 20 A at $t = 20$ seconds. What is the amount of energy stored in the inductor at 10 seconds?

a. 0 J
c. 40 J
b. 10 J
d. 1 J

8.9 Two resistors of 2 ohms each are connected in parallel, another resistor of 1 ohm is connected in series with the parallel combination, and the resistive combination is connected to a 2-volt source. How much power is dissipated in either one of the parallel resistors?

a. 0.25 W
c. 1.0 W
b. 0.5 W
d. 1.5 W

8.10 A current source of 2 amperes is connected to four resistors, all in parallel. The resistors have values of 1, 2, 3, and 4 ohms, respectively. How much power is dissipated in the 2-ohm resistor?

a. 8.0 W
c. 2.0 W
b. 4.0 W
d. 0.46 W

8.11 Three resistors of 2 ohms each are connected in a "T" arrangement, and each side of the T is connected to its own battery voltage source. The battery on the left side is 1 volt (+ on top) and the battery on the right side is 2 volts (– on top). What is the power dissipated in the resistor in the middle leg?

a. 0 W
b. 4.5 W
c. 0.056 W
d. 0.89 W

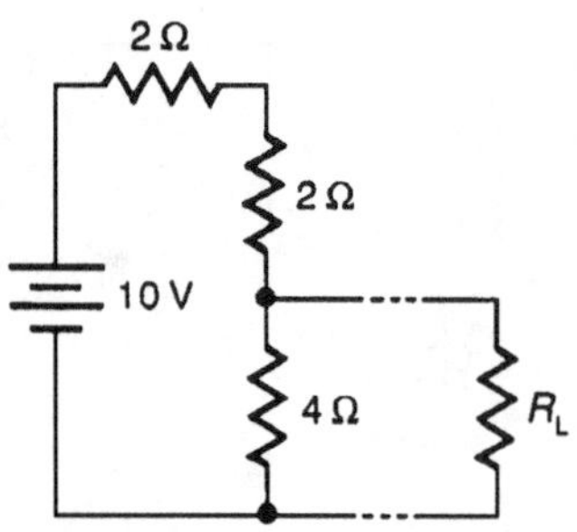

Exhibit 8.12 Original circuit

8.12 For the circuit in Exhibit 8.12, the load resistor, R_L, might "see" a Thevenin equivalent circuit in its place. What are the values of the equivalent circuit?

a. $V_{oc} = 5$ V, $R_{eq} = 2\ \Omega$
b. $V_{oc} = 5$ V, $R_{eq} = 1\ \Omega$
c. $V_{oc} = 4$ V, $R_{eq} = 2\ \Omega$
d. $V_{oc} = 1$ V, $R_{eq} = 2\ \Omega$

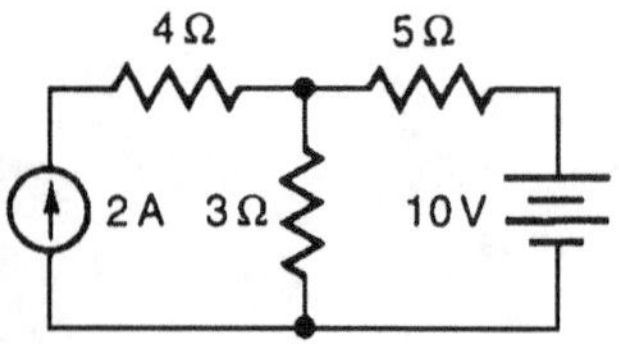

Exhibit 8.13 Circuit diagram

8.13 For the circuit shown in Exhibit 8.13, determine the magnitude of the voltage across the current source.

a. 16 V
b. 30 V
c. 20 V
d. 23 V

SOLUTIONS

8.1 b. The "mass" of 2 electrons has a charge $Q = 3.2 \times 10^{-19}$ C, thus the electric field is $\mathbf{E} = 500$ V/0.01 m $= 50 \times 10^3$ V/m. The force is then $\mathbf{F} = Q\mathbf{E} = (3.2 \times 10^{-19}) \times (50 \times 10^3) = 1.6 \times 10^{-14}$ N.

8.2 c. The magnitude of the length of the resultant vector, R, in the x, y, z plane is

$$R = \sqrt{2^2 + 3^2 + 4^2} = \sqrt{29}$$

The magnitude of the electric field, **E**, is $Q/(4\pi\varepsilon R^2) = (0.3 \times 10^{-3})/(4\pi \times 8.85 \times 10^{-12} \times 29) = 93{,}000$ V/m.

8.3 c. On the b plane (for that plane alone), $E^+ = (-\sigma/2e)_{ax}$, and for the negatively charged plane at the a plane (again for that plane alone, but acting to the right of a), is the same as before, therefore:

$$\mathbf{E} = \mathbf{E}^+ + \mathbf{E}^- = (-\sigma/\varepsilon_0)_{ax} \text{ V/m}$$

8.4 d. From a sketch of the vectors in Exhibit 8.4, the value of $\mathbf{E}_{net}$ is 12.6×10^4 V/m. **F** is then found to be

$$\mathbf{E} = \frac{10 \times 10^{-6}}{4\pi(8.85 \times 10^{-12})\, r^2}$$

$$\mathbf{F} = Q_C \mathbf{E}_{net} = 5 \times 10^{-6}\,(12.6 \times 10^4) = 63 \times 10^{-2} \text{ N}$$

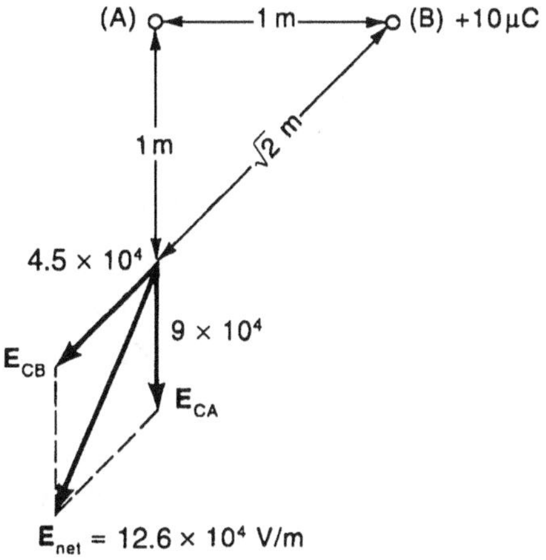

Exhibit 8.4 Vector field

8.5 c. The cross-sectional area of the iron core is $\pi r^2 = \pi \times 10^{-4}$ m². The path length is $l = 2\pi R = 2\pi \bullet 5 \times 10^{-2} = 0.1\pi$ m. The permeability is $\mu = \mu_0\mu_r = 4\pi \bullet 10^{-7} \times 10^3 = 4\pi \bullet 10^{-4}$.

Hence, $H = B/\mu = 0.5/(4\pi \bullet 10^{-4}) = 390$ A • t/m, and since H = mmf/length, mmf = $H \times$ length = 390 (0.1π) = 122.5 A • t. Thus, I = mmf/turns = 122.5/100 = 1.225 A.

8.6 c. Assume the two wires are bundled close together (with respect to the 0.2-meter position); then the net current to the right is $I_{net} = 5 - 1 = 4$ A. The flux density is given by $B = (\mu I)/(2\pi r) = (4\pi \times 10^{-7})(4)/(2\pi\ 0.2) = 4 \times 10^{-6}$ tesla.

8.7 c.

$$I_{rms} = \sqrt{(1/T)\int_0^T i^2\,dt} = \sqrt{(1/5)[(1)^2(1) + (3)^2(2) + (1)^2(1) + 0]} = 2 \text{ A}$$

8.8 b. The current at 10 seconds is 10 A. And from the equation for energy storage in an inductor, it is found that $W = (1/2)\,Li^2 = (1/2)(0.2)(10)^2 = 10$ J.

8.9 b. In the Exhibit 8.9, the resistance of the parallel combination is 1 Ω; then the series combination is 2 Ω. The current I_1 is $V/R = 2/2 = 1$ A, and the current for the parallel branch is

$$I_2 = \left[G_2/\left(\sum G\right)\right]I_1 = (1/2)/[(1/2)(1/2)]1$$

$$= 0.5 \text{ A},\ P_2 = I_2^2 R = (0.5)^2\ 2 = 0.5 \text{ watts}$$

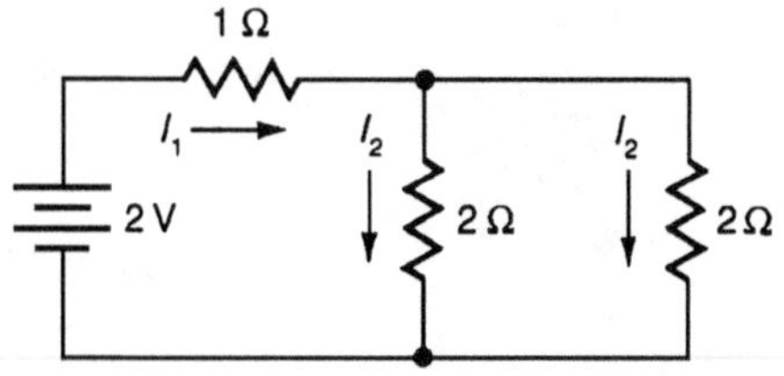

Exhibit 8.9 Circuit configuration

8.10 d. Refer to Exhibit 8.10. The current is given by $I_2 = [G_2/\Sigma G)]I_{total} = [(1/2)/(1 + 1/2 + 1/3 + 1/4)](2) = 0.48$ A, $P_2 = I^2R = (0.48)^2(2) = 0.46$ watts.

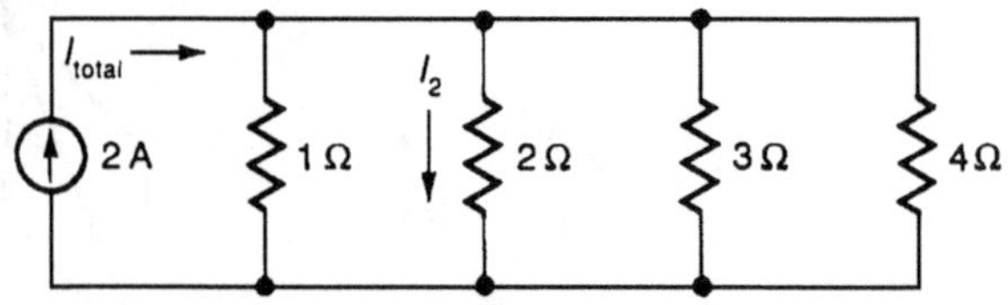

Exhibit 8.10 Circuit configuration

8.11 **c.** From the Exhibit 8.11, set up mesh currents, I_1 and I_2, then sum voltages around each loop:

Loop 1: $1 = 2I_1 + 2(I_1 - I_2)$;
Loop 2: $2 = 2(I_2 - I_1) + 2I_2$

By Cramer's Rule,

$$I_1 = \frac{\begin{vmatrix} 1 & -2 \\ 2 & 4 \end{vmatrix}}{\begin{vmatrix} 4 & -2 \\ -2 & 4 \end{vmatrix}} = 2/3\ A \qquad I_2 = \frac{\begin{vmatrix} 4 & 1 \\ -2 & 2 \end{vmatrix}}{\begin{vmatrix} 4 & -2 \\ -2 & 4 \end{vmatrix}} = 5/6\ A$$

$I_{\text{mid-leg}} = I_1 - I_2 = -1/6$ A; $\quad P_{\text{mid-leg}} = I^2R = (-1/6)^2 2 = 0.056$ W

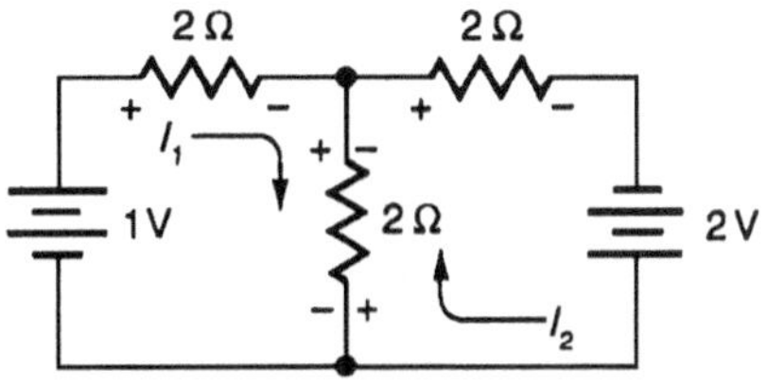

Exhibit 8.11 Circuit configuration

8.12 **a.** To find the Thevenin voltage, find the voltage across the 4-ohm resistor with R_L removed, which yields 5 volts. Thevenin resistance may be found by either of two methods. One method is to look back into the circuit with all active sources replaced with their own impedances and to calculate this output impedance; the other method is to short out the terminals of interest. For this second method, the impedance is

$$R_{eq} = V_{oc}/I_{sc} = 5/(10/4) = 2\ \Omega$$

8.13 **a.** First find the node voltage, V_1, at the intersection of the three resistors by summing the currents (start by assuming all currents flow away from the node). Assume that I_1 is to the left, I_3 to the right, and I_2 down.

$$\sum I = 0\text{: } (-2) + V_1/3 + (V_1 - 10)/5 = 0,\ 8V_1 = 60,\ V_1 = 7.5\text{ V};$$
$$V_A = V_1 - I_1R_4 = 7.5 - (-2)4 = 15.5\text{ V}$$

CHAPTER 9

Circuit Analysis (DC and AC Steady State)

OUTLINE

Average Power

Since power is defined as the product of voltage and current, then for simple DC voltage or current sources, the average power is simply the product of the current and voltage. This is written as uppercase, italic P (without subscript) as $P = VI$. (Generally, use this equation only for DC quantities, as ac or other types of wave forms may have a phase shift. This will be discussed later.)

Effective Values

For most wave forms, other than straight DC, one must define an effective or rms value of current and voltage since an average value of current or voltage could be zero for a sinusoidal signal. Another way of stating this is the following: "What equivalent value of current will cause the same heating power in a resistor as would a DC current?" The effective (or rms) value of current or voltage is defined as

$$I_{eff} = I_{rms} = I = \sqrt{(1/T)\int_0^T i^2\,dt} \quad \textbf{(9.1)}$$

If $i = I_{max} \sin \omega t$ or $i = I_{max} \cos \omega t$, then

$$I = 0.707 I_{max} = I_{max}/\sqrt{2} \quad \textbf{(9.2a)}$$

$$V = 0.707 V_{max} = V_{max}/\sqrt{2} \quad \textbf{(9.2b)}$$

Although Equation (9.1) and Figure 9.1 are for sinusoids, the effective or rms values may be found for any periodic wave form.

For sinusoids, the average power may involve phase angles (more on this later); however, one is safe in finding the power developed as heat in a resistor by using

$$P_{avg} = P = I^2 R = \left(\mathrm{I_m} / \sqrt{2}\right)^2 R \text{ watts} \quad \textbf{(9.3)}$$

For a short example, assume a known sinusoidal current of $i = 14.1 \cos \omega t$ flows through a resistor of 25 ohms. The effective, or rms, current is easily computed from Equation (9.1) or (9.2) and the power by Equation (9.3):

$$P = \left(14.1/\sqrt{2}\right)^2 (25) = 2500 \text{ watts}$$

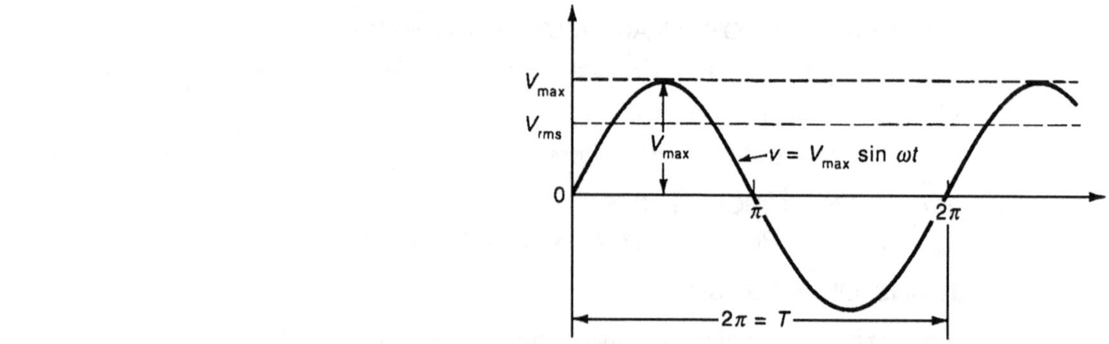

Figure 9.1 Effective or rms value for a sinusoid

If the sinusoid is replaced with another kind of periodic wave form, Equation (9.1) would, of course, still be used. However, sometimes a table of *standard wave forms* with a list of effective or rms values is available.

Average Voltage and Current

All DC quantities, being constant values, are represented by uppercase letters. However, for changing quantities one must be careful with notation. The formal

definition involves the time period of interest, T. The average voltage (or current) is given by

$$V_{avg} = (1/T)\int_0^T v\,dt \tag{9.4}$$

or the area under the voltage curve divided by the period of time. Of course, the same holds for current.

If the positive and negative areas balance over a specific period of time, then the net area is zero. It should then be obvious that the average voltage from a sine wave generator over a full period, T (or 2π), is zero:

$$V_{avg} = (1/T)\int_0^T V_{max} \sin \omega t\,dt = 0$$

Over a *half period*, $(1/2)T$, the average voltage is

$$V_{avg} = (2/T)\int_0^{T/2} V_{max} \sin \omega t\,dt = 2V_{max}/\pi$$

(*Caution*: a half wave over a full period has an average value of V_{max}/π.)

For a sinusoidal voltage or current of frequency f (Hz) and period T (seconds),

$$f = 1/T = \omega/(2\pi)$$

where

ω = the angular frequency in radians/s.

Average Value

For a periodic waveform (either voltage or current) with period T,

$$X_{ave} = \left(1/T\right)\int_0^T x(t)dt$$

The average value of a full-wave rectified sinusoid is

$$X_{ave} = (2X_{max})/\pi$$

and half this for half-wave rectification, where

X_{max} = the peak amplitude of the sinusoid.

Effective or RMS Values

For a periodic waveform with period T, the rms or effective value is

$$X_{eff} = X_{rms}\left[\left(1/T\right)\int_0^T x^2(t)dt\right]^{1/2}$$

For a sinusoidal waveform and full-wave rectified sine wave,

$$X_{eff} = X_{rms} = X_{max}/\sqrt{2}$$

For a half-wave rectified sine weave,

$$X_{eff} = X_{rms} = X_{max}/2$$

For a periodic signal,

$$X_{rms} = \sqrt{X_{dc}^2 + \sum_{n=1}^{\infty} X_n^2}$$

where

X_{dc} = dc component of $x(t)$

X_n = rms value of the nth harmonic

Example 9.1

For the periodic waveform shown, find the average value.

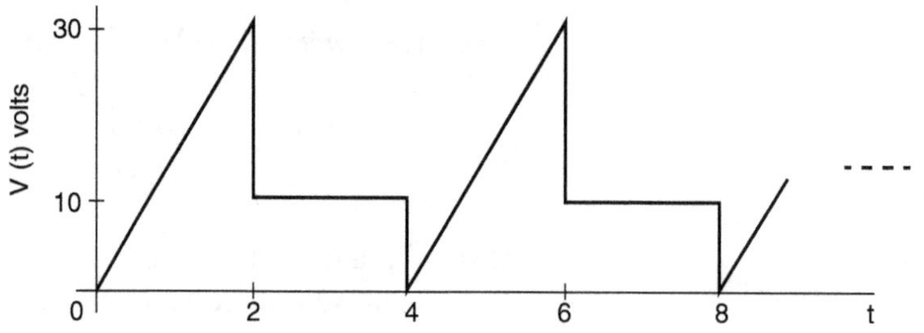

Exhibit 1

a. 25.0 V
b. 14.1 V
c. 12.5 V
d. 6.5 V

T = 4

Discrete integration:	find the area under the waveform
Area of rectangle:	base = 2 s; height = 10 V; (2 s)(10 V) = 20 V–s
Area of triangle:	base = 2 s; height = 30 V; (1/2)(2 s)(30 V) = 30 V–s
Integral total:	50 V–s

$$X_{ave} = \frac{1}{4s}[50V \cdot s]$$

Solution

The correct answer is c. 12.5V

DC CIRCUITS AND RESISTANCE

Ohm's and Kirchhoff's Laws for a Single Source Network

The solutions of all circuits problems whether they are dc, ac, single source, or multiple source, involve the use of these laws. The first is Kirchhoff's voltage law (KVL):

For any closed loop in a circuit, the voltage algebraically sums to zero. $\Sigma v = 0$	or	The voltage rises equal the voltage drops in a closed loop. $\Sigma V_{\text{rises}} = \Sigma V_{\text{drops}}$

Another way of stating this relationship is to say the sum of the voltage rises is equal to the sum of the voltage drops in any loop. Both of these statements are true of both dc and instantaneous values. However, one needs to be careful when dealing with ac analysis with possibly different phase angles; this relationship will be discussed later.

The second is Kirchhoff's current law (KCL); this law involves any junction, or node, in an electrical circuit:

For any node in an electrical circuit, the net current algebraically sums to zero. $\Sigma i = 0$	or	The total current entering a junction equals the total current leaving. $\Sigma I_{\text{in}} = \Sigma I_{\text{out}}$

Restated, the sum of the currents entering a junction must equal the sum of the currents leaving the junction. Again, this is true of both dc and instantaneous values; however, for ac circuit analysis care is required in its application.

Ohm's law for resistance ($R = v/i$) is well known and is the same for dc, instantaneous quantitities, and ac values. For a series circuit (where the current is the same in every element) the equivalent resistance merely becomes

$$R_T = R_1 + R_2 + \cdots + R_n = \sum R \tag{9.5a}$$

For parallel circuits (where the voltage across every element is the same) the equivalent resistance, R_T, is

$$1/R_T = 1/R_1 + 1/R_2 + \cdots + 1/R_n = \sum G \tag{9.5b}$$

The conductance G is simply the inverse of the resistance (whose units are siemens or mhos, $1/\Omega$). From Equation (9.5b), one can quickly determine that the equivalent resistance for two resistors (or impedances) in parallel is $R_T = R_1R_2/(R_1 + R_2)$.

Example 9.2

A simple example follows; for this type of circuit problem, it is usually quicker to convert the parallel resistors to an equivalent value. The simpler series circuit is easily solved: by finding the voltage drop across any element, the voltage across the equivalent resistance is found. Assume the question is to find the power dissipated in the 6-Ω resistor in Exhibit 2.

Solution

The equivalent parallel resistance is found to be 3/2 Ω. This value yields a total series resistance of 4 Ω as shown in Exhibit 2b. The series current is easily found to be 3 A; the voltage drop across the parallel resistance is $V_{eq} = I(R_T) = (3)(3/2) = 9/2$ volts. The current through the 6-Ω resistor is $I = V_{eq}/R_6 = (9/2)/6 = 3/4$ A. The power dissipated in the 6-Ω resistor is $P_{6\Omega} = I^2R = (3/4)^2 6 = 27/8 = 3.375$ watts.

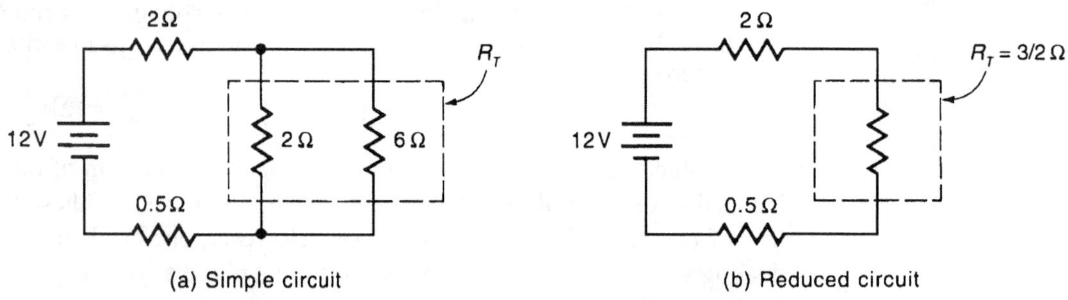

Exhibit 2 A simple voltage source circuit

Here, the power from the source equals the sum of the power dissipated in each of the resistors. It is instructive to compute the sum of the power lost; this is

$$P_{source} = V_{source} I = (12)(3) = 36 \text{ watts}$$

$$\sum P_{lost} = I^2 \left(\sum R_{ser}\right) = 9(2 + 3/2 + 1/2) = 36 \text{ watts}$$

For this problem, a somewhat more formal method is to use the voltage dividing equation after R_T is found (all elements are now in series). The voltage across R_T may be calculated to be $V_T = (R_T / \Sigma R)V_{bat}$; then, the current through R_6 is determined as before.

Example 9.3

Consider another example with a current source: here, the series portion of the circuit should be reduced to one resistor; with all of the resistors now in parallel, the voltage across this group is easily found. Now the question is to find the amount of power dissipated in the 2-ohm resistor in Exhibit 3.

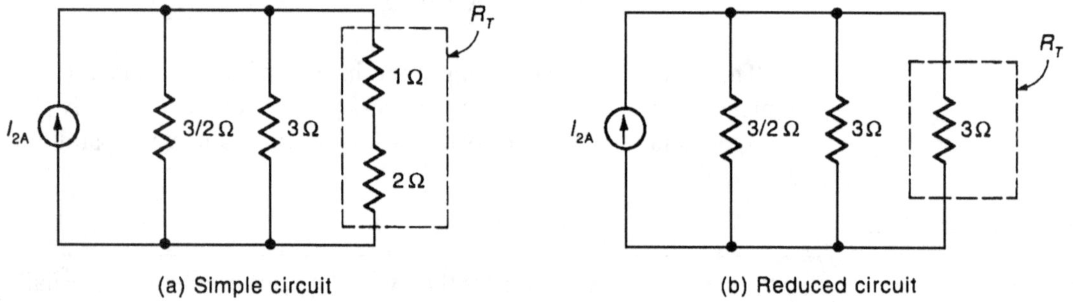

Exhibit 3 A simple single current source circuit

Solution

After finding the one series resistor, R_s, that is equivalent to the two resistances in series, all resistances are now in parallel. Then using Equation (9.4b), or merely taking two resistors at a time, one easily computes the total equivalent one resistance to be 3/4 Ω. The voltage across the parallel circuit is $RI = (3/4)(2) = 3/2$ volts. The current through the series equivalent branch is $I_{se} = V_{par} / R_{se} = (3/2)/3 = 1/2$ amperes; the power dissipated in the 2-Ω resistor is $P = I^2R = (1/2)^2 2 = 0.5$ watts.

Again, a quick check is to find if the power taken from the source ($P_s = VI = (3/2)2 = 3$ watts) and the power dissipated in the resistors are equal:

$$\sum P_{\text{lost}} = V^2(1/R_{3/2} + 1/R_3 + 1/R_{se}) = (3/2)^2(2/3 + 1/3 + 1/3) = 3 \text{ watts}$$

For this problem, as before, there is a somewhat more formal method of finding the current through R_{se} directly; $I_{se} = (G_{se}/\Sigma G)I_{tot}$. Knowing the branch current, the power is easily found.

Multiple Source Networks and Theorems

Although the term *multiple source circuits* implies multiple power output, this implication may be incorrect as the voltage or current source may actually absorb power. If the current is flowing into a voltage *source*—from plus to minus—the *source* is actually a *load* taking power (that is, a battery being charged). Therefore, it is very important to determine the direction of current (or voltage polarity as the case may be). The procedure is to assume current directions and carefully label these on a circuit diagram; then let the mathematics determine the actual direction. One way to do this is to assume a current through each element (of course series elements will have the same current) of a circuit. This is in contrast to assuming loop or mesh currents; however, both methods amount to the same thing. A short example (see Figure 9.2) will show the method. (To keep the circuit diagrams uniform and to later allow for time varying voltage sources, a circle is used to indicate the voltage source rather than showing a battery.)

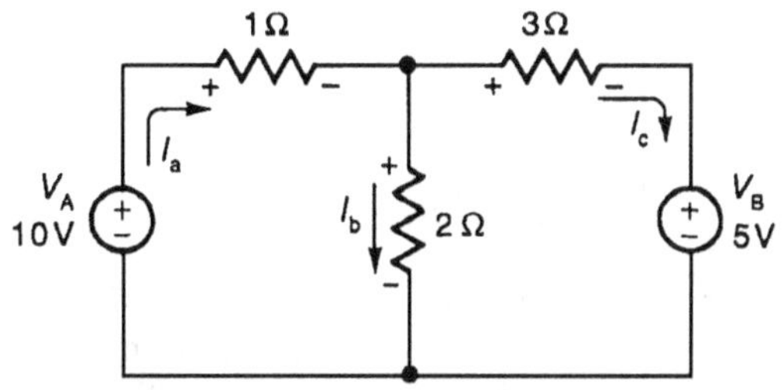

Figure 9.2 A two-loop network

After labeling the assumed current directions, place a plus sign where the current enters the resistor and a negative sign where it leaves. Then, by Kirchhoff's voltage law, sum the voltages around each loop:

$$V_A - R_1 I_a - R_2 I_b = 0 \quad \textbf{(9.6a)}$$
$$V_B + R_3 I_c - R_2 I_b = 0 \quad \textbf{(9.6b)}$$

Since three variables are present, another equation is needed; Kirchhoff's current law will produce the third equation (actually J – 1 node junction equations are needed; here J = 2). Summing currents at one junction (say, the upper middle node) gives $I_a = I_b + I_c$.

Rewriting the equations for loops one and two (here, replacing all I_a), yields

$$V_A = R_1(I_b + I_c) + R_2 I_b, \qquad 10 = 3I_b + I_c \quad \textbf{(9.7a)}$$
$$V_B = R_2 I_b - R_3 I_c, \qquad 5 = 2I_b - 3I_c \quad \textbf{(9.7b)}$$

Solving for the currents, the results are

$$I_a = 3.64 \text{ A}, \quad I_b = 3.18 \text{ A}, \quad I_c = 0.455 \text{ A}$$

Since all of the currents are positive, the assumed directions of the currents are correct; therefore, the voltage *source* B is really a load (perhaps a battery being charged). As a check, the sum of the voltages around the outside loop should equal zero (starting at the upper left-hand corner): Does 1(3.64) + 3(0.455) + 5 – 10 = 0? Or, 3.64 + 1.365 + 5 – 10 = 0.005 (acceptable).

Another way of analyzing the circuit is to use the *mesh* technique of analysis. Notice in the previous two-loop problem, the current through the middle resistance that was identified as I_b is nothing more than $I_a - I_c$. If we now consider going around the entire left loop as I_a and around the entire right loop as I_c, the currents mesh at the middle resistance. Because voltages are summed around each loop, the net voltage across the middle resistor (when going around the left loop) is $RI_a - RI_c$; the loop currents are in opposite directions. The same kind of equation is written for the right-hand loop. Thus one current variable (I_b) is eliminated. There are still other ways of analyzing the circuit, as will be pointed out later.

Example 9.4

Another example that involves mixed sources of current and voltages is shown in Exhibit 4. Find the voltage across the current source for this circuit configuration.

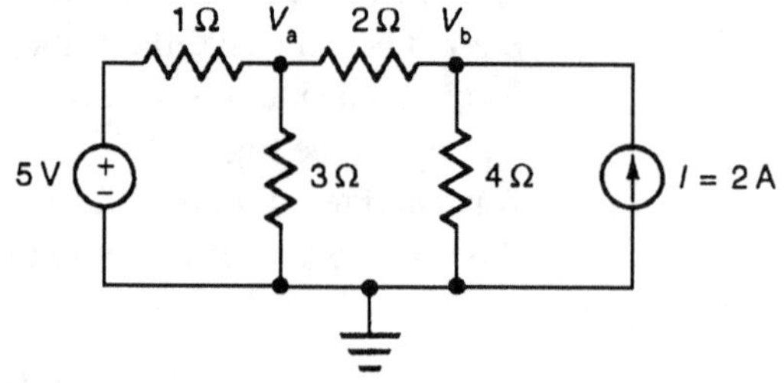

Exhibit 4 Mixed source circuit

Solution

Here, the node-voltage method of analysis will be used. This method finds voltages with respect to some common reference point called a ground node (see Exhibit 4). By wisely selecting this common point to include as many junctions as possible, the number of simultaneous equations may be reduced. The node voltage will be considered as a voltage rise from the common reference node (that is, current directions may then be assumed away from the node while writing the equations for that particular node).

$$\text{At } V_a, \sum I \qquad 0 = (V_a - 5)/1 + (V_a - V_b)/2 + (V_a - 0)/3$$

$$\text{At } V_b, \sum I \qquad 0 = (V_b - V_a)/2 + (V_b - 0)/4 + (-2)$$

Simplifying (multiplying through by 6 and 4, respectively) and collecting terms,

$$30 = 11V_a - 3V_b$$
$$8 = -2V_a + 3V_b$$

Solving these equations for the node voltages gives $V_a = 4.22$ V and $V_b = 5.48$ V. From these voltages, any desired currents or powers may be found. To check the solution, find the sum of the power for the current and voltage sources and compare this result with the sum of the power dissipated by the resistors ($P_{\text{sources}} = 14.9$

watts = $\Sigma P_{resistors}$). Either of the apparent sources could actually be a load by taking power from the other source. If the voltage source is a battery and it is found that the actual current flows through the battery from plus to minus, then the battery is being charged and acts as a load.

Network Reduction, Thévenin and Norton Equivalents

Replacing a complicated circuit by its electrical equivalent is a powerful tool used in electrical engineering. We already used this idea when we replaced resistor combinations with an equivalent resistance. Thévenin's theorem provides a means of reducing a complicated linear network into an equivalent circuit when there are two terminals of special interest (a and b in Figure 9.3). This equivalent Thévenin circuit is composed of a voltage source and a resistor in series. If either the original network or its Thévenin equivalent is connected to another electrical network, the response (i.e., voltage and current) at the terminals a and b will be identical. In other words, one could not tell the difference between the original network and its Thévenin equivalent.

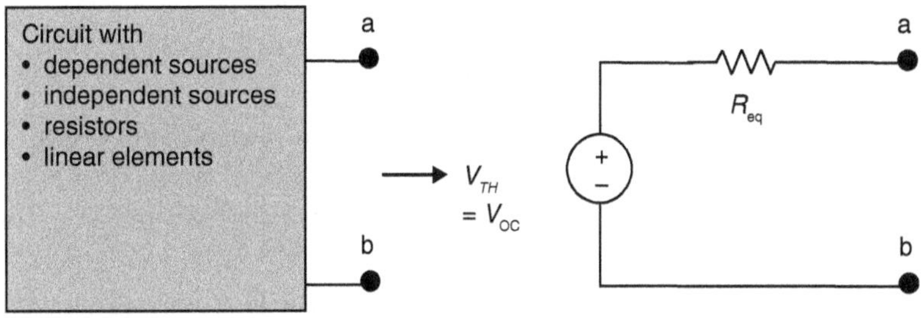

Figure 9.3 Replacing a "Black Box Circuit" with its Thévenin Equivalent

To determine the Thévenin equivalent of a linear electrical network, we need the value of the voltage source, V_{OC}, and the resistor, R_{th}. (Note that since R_{OC} appears at the output of the circuit, it is sometimes called the output resistance, R_{out}.) V_{OC} can be determined by measuring the voltage at the terminals of the network when the terminals are open-circuited (no load connected). Determining the Thévenin resistance value is more difficult. If the terminals of the network are shorted together and the current measured through the short, the Thévenin resistance can be determined as:

$$\text{Thevenin resistance} = R_{eq} = \frac{\text{open-circuit voltage}}{\text{short-circuit current}}$$

However, sometimes it is not possible to measure either the open-circuit voltage and/or the short-circuit current without damaging the original circuit. Hence, one can plot the terminal voltage (V_{ab}) vs. current ($I_{ab} = I_{load}$) with varying load resistances and use this to determine R_{eq} and V_{OC}.

Most circuits may be greatly reduced in complexity and thus yield a simpler solution. This is especially so if a variable load is involved and requires a number of repeated calculations. Consider the circuit shown in Figure 9.4; many calculations would be involved if one were asked to compute the power dissipated in R_L for several different values of R_L. If one could reduce the network (all of that circuitry to the left of × – ×) to one simple voltage source in series with one resistance [see Figure 9.4(b)], then calculating the current to R_L would be simple and easy.

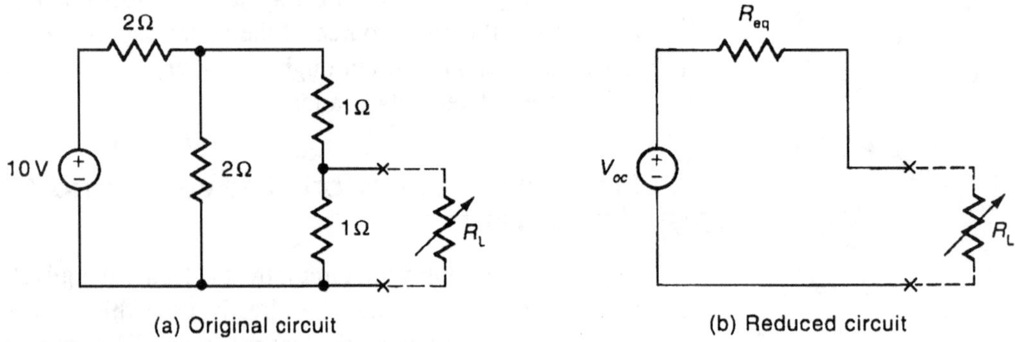

Figure 9.4 Circuit for Thevenin's reduction

Reducing the network is done with Thevenin's theorem. One can find the Thevenin voltage by merely opening the network at the point of interest (that is, temporarily removing R_L) and measuring the open circuit voltage at × – ×; the open circuit voltage is the Thevenin voltage. Next, place a short circuit (an ammeter, assumed to have zero resistance) across this section and measure the short circuit current. The Thevenin resistance is given as

$$R_{eq} = \frac{V_{OC}}{I_{SC}}$$

To find a Thevenin equivalent circuit on an examination, one cannot measure the various voltages or currents but must calculate them. Calculating the open circuit voltage does not present a problem, but more needs to be said about calculating the resistance.

There are at least two ways to calculate the Thevenin resistance. One is to calculate the short circuit current and proceed as before. The other method is to replace all voltage sources with their internal resistance (usually zero) and any current source with its internal resistance (usually infinity) and then calculate the resistance one would see looking back into the circuit (to the left of × – × in Figure 9.4). However, caution is needed if any dependent sources are present. For the values given in Figure 9.4, the calculated open circuit voltage is 5/3 volts, and the short circuit current is 5/2 amperes; thus the Thevenin equivalent circuit is as given in Figure 9.5(a).

The current source that is equivalent to the Thevenin circuit is Norton's equivalent circuit. Norton's circuit is the current source equivalency for Thevenin's voltage source [see Figure 9.5(b)]. The value of the resistance is the same except that it is usually stated in terms of conductance ($1/R$) and the units are mho (old) or siemens (new). The current source may be found directly from Thevenin's circuit by finding the short circuit current directly from Thevenin's circuit. If one is asked for a Norton equivalent circuit, one can first find Thevenin's circuit then convert to Norton's circuit.

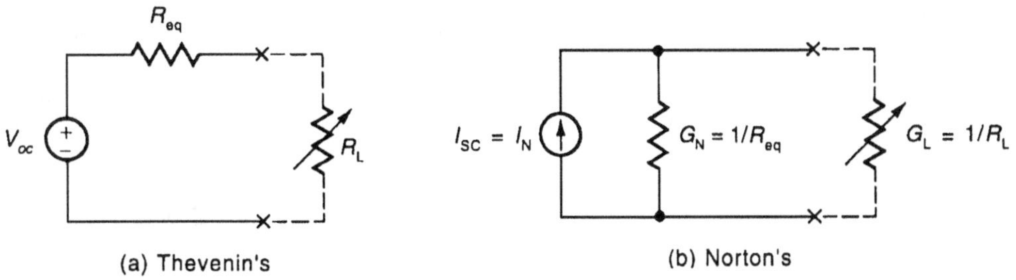

Figure 9.5 Equivalent circuits

Thévenin's Theorem states that we can replace the entire network, exclusive of the load, by an equivalent circuit that contains only an independent voltage source in series with an impedance (resistance) such that the current-voltage relationship at the load is unchanged.

Norton's Thereom is identical to Thévenin's Theorem except that the equivalent circuit is an independent current source in parallel with an impedance (resistor). Hence, the Norton equivalent circuit is a source transformation of the Thévenin equivalent circuit.

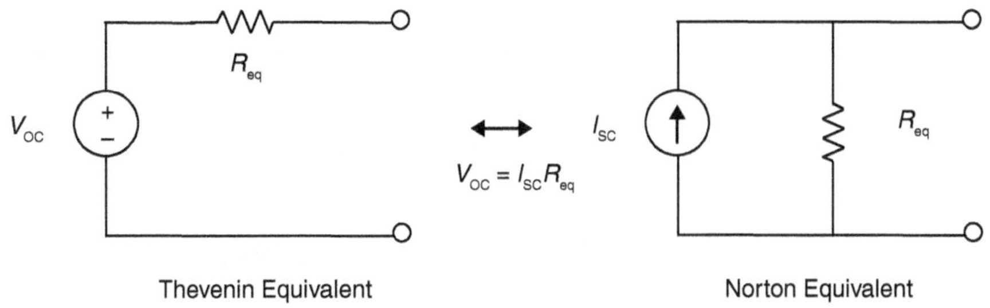

Figure 9.6

Procedure for determining Thevenin or Norton equivalent circuits

1. Pick a good breaking point in the circuit (cannot split a dependent source and its control variable).
2. **Thevenin**: Compute the open circuit voltage, V_{OC}.
   Norton: Compute the short circuit current, I_{SC}.
3. Compute the Thevenin equivalent resistance, R_{eq}.
   a). If there are only independent sources, then short circuit all the voltage sources and open circuit the current.
   b). If there are only dependent sources, use a test voltage or current source in order to calculate $R_{eq} = V_{Test} / I_{Test}$.
   c). If there are both independent and dependent sources, then compute R_{eq} from $R_{eq} = V_{OC} / I_{SC}$.
4. Replace circuit with Thevenin/Norton equivalent.
   Thevenin: V_{OC} in series with R_{eq}
   Norton: I_{SC} in parallel with R_{eq}

Note: For 3(b), the equivalent network is merely R_{eq}, that is, no current or voltage sources.

Example 9.5

Find the Thévenin equivalent voltage and resistance of the following circuit:

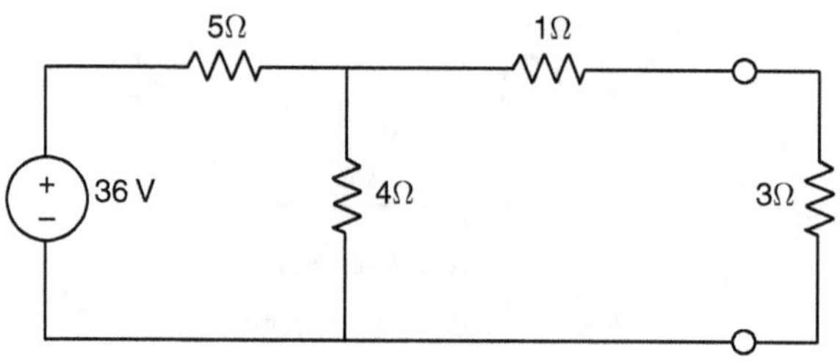

Exhibit 5

Solution

$$R_{TH} = 1\Omega + 4\Omega \,||\, 5\Omega = 3.22\Omega$$

$$R_{TH} = 1 + \frac{1}{\frac{1}{5} + \frac{1}{4}} = 1 + \frac{20}{9} = \frac{20}{9}\Omega = 3.222\Omega$$

The voltage across the 4 ohm resistor is the open circuit voltage, V_{oc}:

$$V = \left(\frac{4}{4+5}\right) 36 = 16 \text{ V}$$

Source Transforms

The equivalent circuits called the source transformation can be defined as follows: A portion of a circuit where we have a voltage source in series with a resistance is equivalent to current source in parallel with a resistance. The resistances for these two equivalents are equal. These two cases are equivalent as long as the resistances are equal and if the voltage source and current source are related by

$$v_S = i_S R_{EQ}.$$

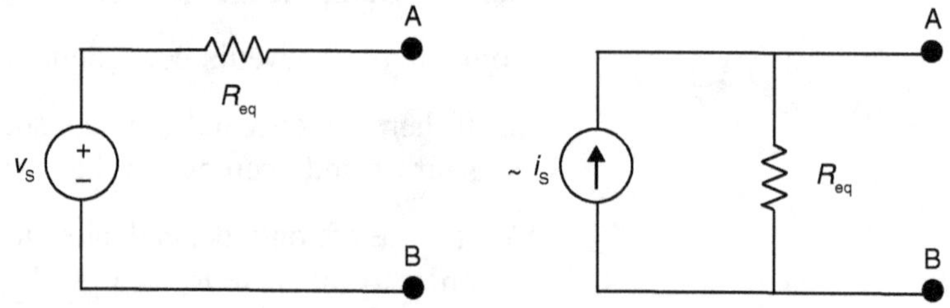

Figure 9.7

This equivalence can go in either direction. That is, we can replace the circuit on the right with the one on the left, or the other way around. Neither one is simpler; we just prefer one or the other in some situations.

Source Transformation Hints:

- These equivalent circuits can go in either direction. That is, we can replace the circuit on the right with the one on the left, or the other way around.
- The polarities of the sources with respect to the terminals are important. This is one good reason for naming the terminals of these equivalents.
- As with all equivalent circuits, these are equivalent only with respect to the things connected to the equivalent circuits.
- These equivalent circuits hold for dependent sources as well as independent sources. The key is that the variable, which the dependent sources depend on, must remain intact. That is, the voltage or current that the dependent sources use must be outside of the circuit being replaced.

Example **9.6**

Solve for the voltage v_X in the circuit given below. We could certainly solve this circuit using Kirchoff's laws. However, we are going to solve it instead by using a series of equivalent circuits and simplify the circuit down step by step.

We wish to solve for the voltage v_X in the circuit Exhibit 6. We note that we have a voltage source, v_S, in series with a resistor, R_1. We can replace them with a current source in parallel with a resistor. When we do, we will have current sources in parallel and resistors in parallel, which we can simplify further. So, let's take the first step.

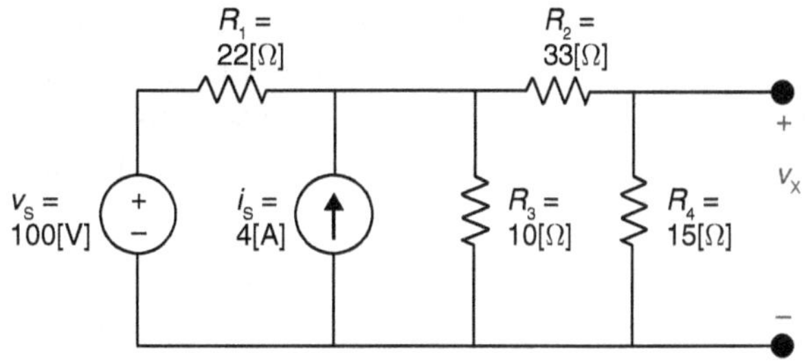

Exhibit 6

We wish to solve for the voltage v_X in the circuit Exhibit 7. We note that we have a voltage source, v_S, in series with a resistor, R_1. We can replace them with a current source in parallel with a resistor. When we do, we will have current sources in parallel and resistors in parallel, which we can simplify further. So, let's take the first step.

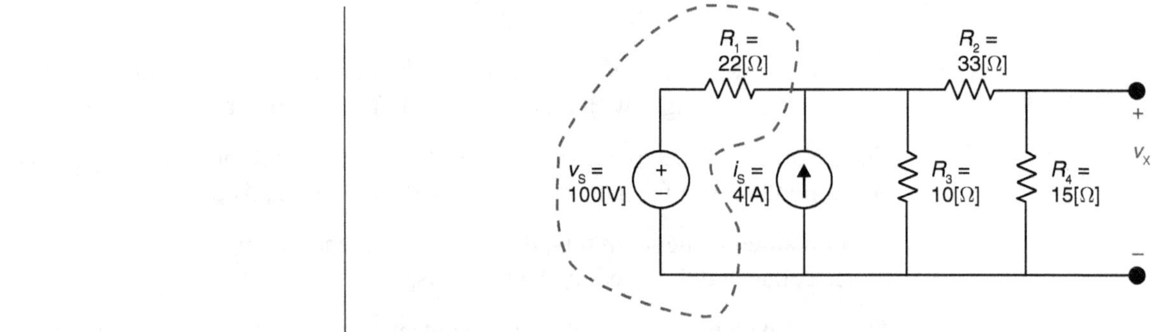

Exhibit 7

We want to replace the voltage source in series with a resistor, with a current source in parallel with a resistor. Here, we have made this replacement. Note that we now have two current sources in parallel and two resistors in parallel. Since the voltage we are looking for is outside these combinations, we can replace them with their equivalents. That is our next step.

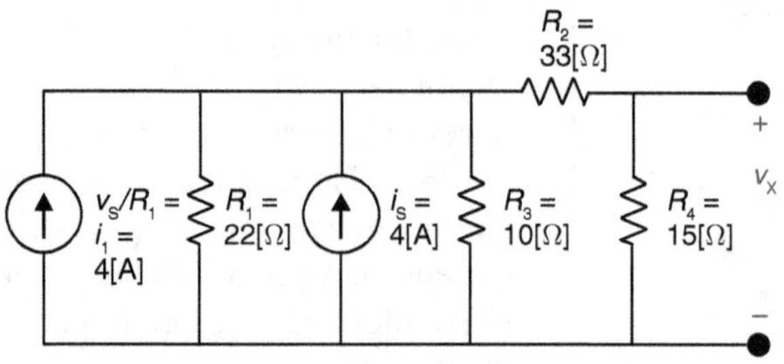

Exhibit 8

We have replaced the parallel current sources and parallel resistors with their equivalents. Now we can note that we have a current source in parallel with a resistor. We could replace this with a voltage source in series with a resistor, and then we could simplify the circuit further.

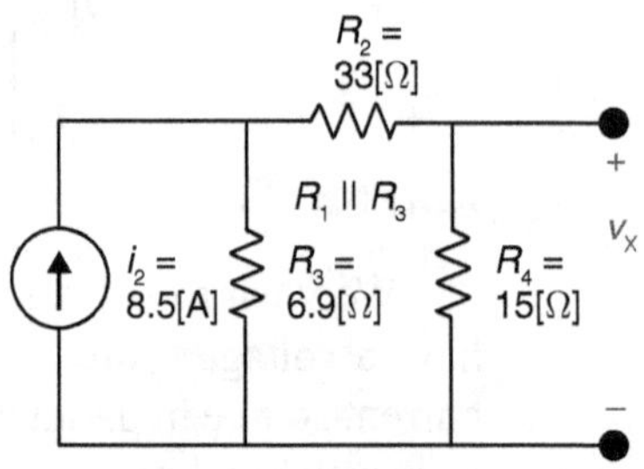

Exhibit 9

The current source in parallel is in a Norton source configuration. Using source transformation, the Norton-configured current source in parallel with R_3 can be transformed into an equivalent Thevenin voltage in series with the resistor R_3. At this point, we have three resistors in series (R_3, R_2, R_4, and so on), and we want the

voltage across one of them. This means that we use the voltage divider rule, and write,

$$v_X = v_3 \frac{R_4}{R_4 + R_1 \parallel R_3 + R_2} =$$

$$v_X = 59[\text{V}]\frac{15[\Omega]}{15[\Omega] + 6.9[\Omega] + 33[\Omega]} = 16[\text{V}].$$

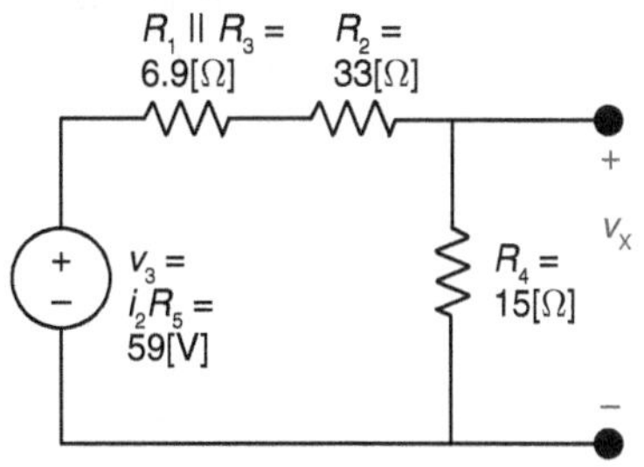

Exhibit 10

Maximum Power Transfer

Assume one wishes to determine the maximum power that could be dissipated in a variable load resistor that is nested in a multiple source circuit. First, it is necessary to know the size of the resistor. The **maximum power transfer theorem** (for dc circuits) states that maximum power is extracted from a circuit when the circuit is converted to Thevenin's equivalent circuit and the load resistance is equal to Thevenin's resistance. A consequence of this theorem is that half of the power is dissipated in the load and the other half in Thevenin's equivalent resistance. Consider the circuit of Figure 9.8; all that is necessary is to isolate the load resistor from being *buried* in the circuit. This is done by rearranging the circuit as shown in Figure 9.8(b). One way is to move the load resistor to the right side of the circuit and then find Thevenin's equivalent circuit for the portion on the left.

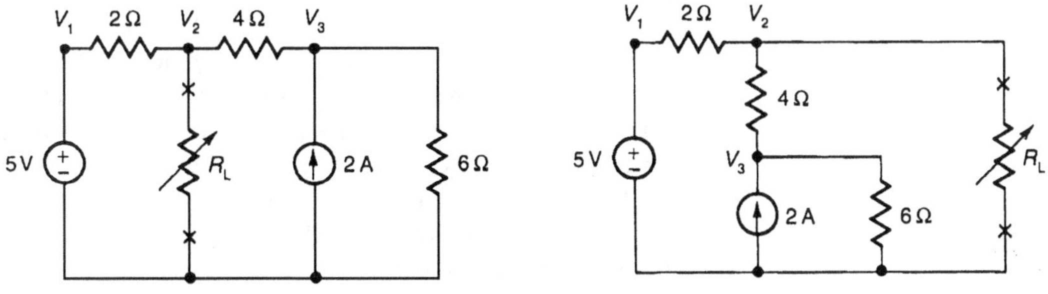

(a) Original circuit (b) Rearranged circuit

Figure 9.8 A maximum power transfer problem

For the rearranged circuit of Figure 9.8, the open circuit voltage (that is, with R_L temporarily disconnected) will be found by the node method of analysis:

$$\text{At } V_2, \sum I = (V_2 - V_1)/2 + (V_2 - V_3)/4 = 0$$

$$\text{At } V_3, \sum I = (V_3 - V_2)/4 - 2 + V_3/6 = 0$$

Solving (with $V_1 = 5$ volts) for $V_2 = V_T$ yields 6.116 volts. Thevenin's resistance can now be found by using the simpler method of merely replacing all independent voltage sources with zero and all independent current sources with an open circuit; then, looking back into the circuit × – ×, the equivalent resistance can now be found. This resistance yields R_{oc} = 1.667 Ω. From the maximum power relationship, $R_L = R_{oc}$. The power dissipated in R_L = 5.61 watts; see Figure 9.9.

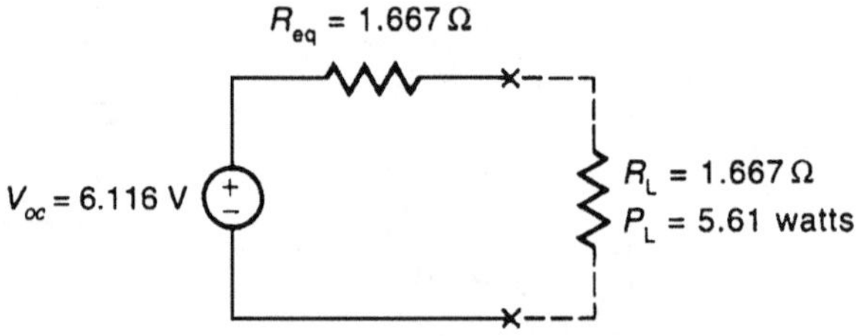

Figure 9.9 Final load resistance using Thevenin's circuit

Transient Response for a Single Energy Storage Element

If an energy storage element, such as a capacitor or inductor, is present in a circuit with one or more resistors, the problem solution will be a function of time. The voltage across a capacitor or current through an inductor cannot change instantaneously but takes time (unless infinite pulses are involved). It is assumed that the circuit is connected to either a voltage or current source or has some initial values.

Capacitive Circuits

If a capacitor (assume initially uncharged) is being charged from a voltage source through a resistor as shown in Figure 9.10(a), then it takes time for it to reach the charging voltage. The voltage vs. time solution is plotted in Figure 9.10(b). Here it is obvious that the amount of time for the capacitor voltage to reach its final value is infinite. On the other hand, if the capacitor already has an initial charge (or voltage) and is being discharged through a resistor, it again takes time for it to discharge [refer to Figure 9.11(b)]; this amount of time is also infinite.

Rather than use infinity as the changing time, it is more convenient to define a time constant, τ, to obtain a practical result. The time constant is some value of t that makes the exponent, x, of e^x, equal to –1. As an example, if $x = -t/RC$, then

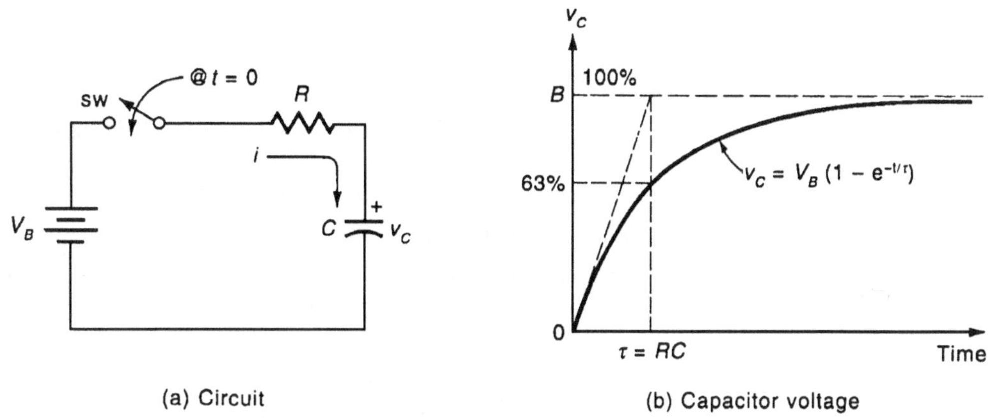

Figure 9.10 The charging of a capacitor, $\tau = RC$

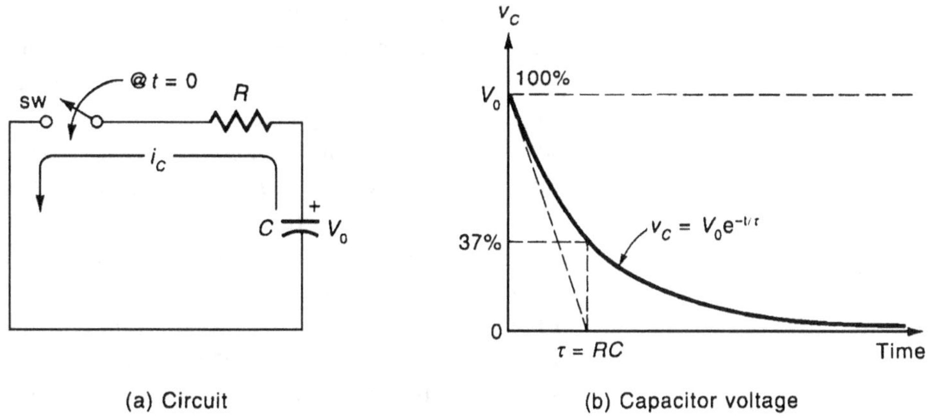

Figure 9.11 The discharging of a capacitor, $\tau = RC$

the time constant is equal to the value of RC. This value of e^{-1} is 0.3679, or approximately 37%; it is so often used in electrical transient analysis that it probably should be committed to memory. In Figure 9.10, V_B is the final value of the voltage, and at $t = \tau$ the parenthetical quantity is approximately 63% so the variable is within 37% of its final value. Also note that in Figure 9.11, the voltage decreases from the initial value, V_0, by 63% (or is within 37% of the final value) at $t = \tau$. If the initial slope of the curves in both Figures 9.10 and 9.11 were extrapolated forward, the intersection of the asymptotes with the horizontal axis would occur at $t = \tau$. To be realistic, *within* 37% is not good enough for engineering purposes, and a more practical approach is to consider the voltage at *almost* its final value in five time constants (well within 1%).

The equations in Figure 9.10 and Figure 9.11 are the solutions of the integral-differential equations that describe the circuit(s). Kirchhoff's voltage law states that sums of voltages around any closed loop must be equal to zero at *any* instant of time. In Figure 9.10, the switch closes at $t = 0$; the voltage around the loop (for $t > 0$) is $V_B = Ri + v_c$, where v_c is q/C. Since current is defined as dq/dt, v_c is the integral of the present expression. If the initial voltage (or charge) on the capacitor was zero at the instant before the switch was closed, then $V_B = Ri + q/C = Ri + (I/C)\int_0^t i\,dt$.

The solution to this equation is

$$v_c(t) = v_c(0)e^{-t/RC} + V(I - e^{-t/RC}) \quad \textbf{(9.8a)}$$

and Equation (9.8a) frequently reduces to Equation (9.8b):

$$v_C = v_B(1 - e^{-t/\tau}) \quad \textbf{(9.8b)}$$

where $\tau = RC$. If t goes to infinity, then $v_C \rightarrow V_B$. If the initial value was not zero, as in Figure 9.11, it must also be considered. The differential equation used to obtain the solution for Figure 9.11(b) may be found by the node voltage method; use the lower junction of RC as the reference node, and the currents to the top voltage node are given by $i_C + i_R = 0 = C(dv/dt) + v/R$. Knowing the initial voltage, $V_C(0^-)$, the voltage across the capacitor just before the switch was closed, and that $V_C(0^-) = V_C(0) = V_C(0^+)$, the differential equation is easily solved. The solution, where $\tau = RC$, is $v_C = V_C(0)e^{-t/\tau}$.

A somewhat more comprehensive example involving a multiple time constant circuit is presented in Figure 9.12. The switch is assumed to be open for a long time (so long that any previous voltage across the capacitor has been reduced to zero because of R_3). The switch is then moved to the middle position for five seconds ($0 < t < 5$); it will then be switched to the lower position and remain there; this lower position will have a time, t', that starts at the time of switching to this new position. It is desired to know the current through the capacitor at $t = 9.8$ s ($t' = 4.8$ s). Although this problem may seem more comprehensive than most, the reader should follow the details of the solution to note simplification techniques. First, it should be obvious that the problem may be broken into two parts. The first part spans the first 5 seconds, and the second runs from $t = 5$ (or $t' > 0$) seconds. When the switch is in the middle position, one needs to make a Thevenin equivalent circuit (refer to Figure 9.13) to the left of $\times - \times$ and then solve for the capacitor voltage at $t = 5$s as done on the previous problem. This voltage at $t = 5$ s is easily computed from the capacitor charge equation as $v_C(t = 5) = 7.5(1 - e^{-5/3}) = 6.083$ volts.

One could almost obtain this value from a sketch, as at one time constant (3 seconds) the voltage would be 63% of 7.5 volts (4.72 volts), and at two time constants (6 seconds) the voltage would be 87% of 7.5 volts (6.49 volts). Thus at 5/3 time constant, a plot would yield about 6.1 volts. Of course the final voltage of Figure 9.13 is the initial voltage when the switch is moved from the middle to the bottom position in Figure 9.14. The voltage at $t' = 4.8$ ($t = 9.8$) seconds is 37% of the initial value, $0.37 \times 6.08 = 2.25$ volts. The current at this instant of time is $v_C/R_{Eq} = 1.87$ μA.

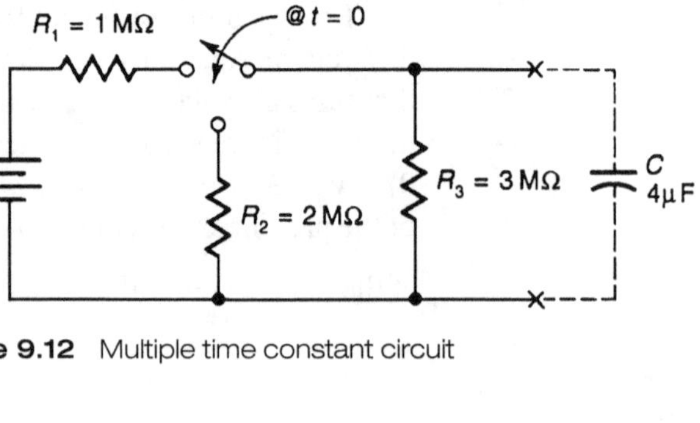

Figure 9.12 Multiple time constant circuit

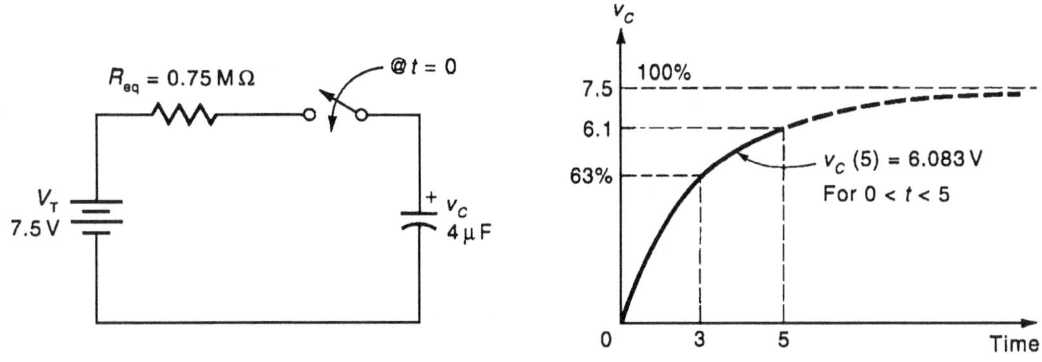

(a) Thevenin's equivalent (b) Capacitor voltage

Figure 9.13 The charging of a capacitor during $0 < t < 5$ seconds, for $\tau = 3$

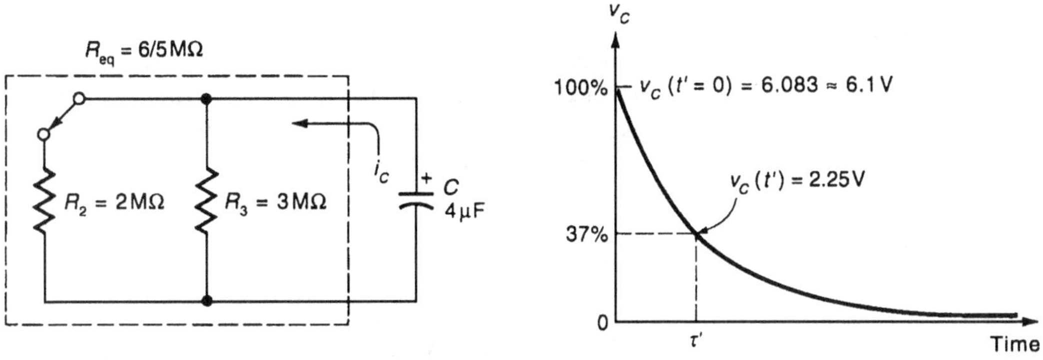

(a) Equivalent circuit (b) Capacitor voltage

Figure 9.14 The discharging of a capacitor for $t > 5$ (or $t' > 0$) seconds, $\tau' = 4.8$

Inductive Circuits

When an inductor (instead of a capacitor) is in a circuit, the current through the inductor takes time to change (like a voltage across a capacitor) and the circuit may be treated much like the previous voltage-capacitor relationship,

$$i(t) = i(0)e^{-Rt/L} + V/R(1 - e^{-Rt/L}) \tag{9.9}$$

An example *RL* circuit problem is presented in Figure 9.15. Here, the time constant, τ, is L/R. Assume zero initial current in the inductor. A voltage will be induced across an inductor equal to $L(di/dt)$ because of the rate of change of magnetic flux through a coil or around a wire. The polarity of this voltage depends on whether the flux is increasing or decreasing. Unlike a capacitor, where the capacitor acts as an open circuit (that is, no current flow) after the *voltage* stabilizes, the inductor acts like a short circuit after the *current* stabilizes. Thus the final value of the current in Figure 9.15 is the applied voltage divided by the series resistance.

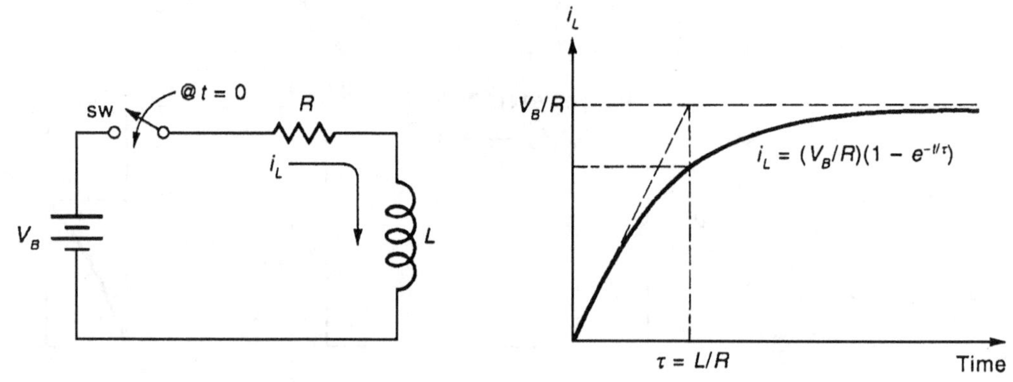

(a) Circuit (b) Inductor current

Figure 9.15 An RL circuit, $\tau = L/R$

Example 9.7

An inductor has an initial current caused by the switch in Exhibit 11 being connected to a voltage source for a long period of time and then suddenly switched to the open position at $t = 0$. Find the current at $t = 0.1$ seconds and the voltage across the inductor at the same time.

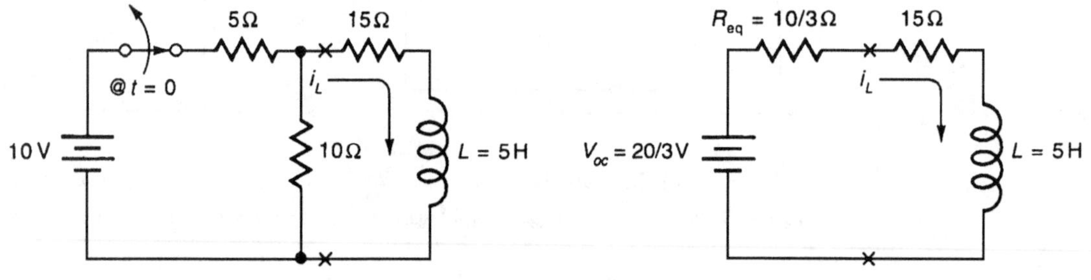

(a) Circuit (b) Thevenin's equivalent

Exhibit 11 Inductor problem before the switch opens

Solution

Before the switch is open, the easy way to solve the problem is to make a Thevenin equivalent circuit of that portion of the circuit to the left of × – ×. While the switch is connected to the voltage source, the polarity of the voltage across the inductor is positive at the upper terminal of the inductor (while the voltage source is providing an increasing current in the inductor). Just before the switch opens the current in the inductor is $I(0^-)$. Because current cannot change instantaneously, $I_0(0^+)$ is the same current immediately after the switch is opened. However, the voltage polarity switches immediately as the energy stored in the inductor causes the current to continue to flow in the same direction [that is, $L(di/dt)$ acts like a voltage source that is strong enough to keep the current flowing]. The current plot is given in Exhibit 12. The voltage is applied for a long period of time, so any rates of change, $L(di/dt)$, are completed; the inductor acts like a short circuit current and is easily found to be 0.3636. At $t(0)$, this current is the initial current $I(0) = I_0$ for the equation in Exhibit 12(c). The current at $t = 0.1$ second is found directly from the exponential equation where the time constant, $\tau = L/R$, has a resistance equal to the sum of the two resistors in series, $R = 25\ \Omega$, so $\tau = (5/25) = 0.2$ second. This current is $i = I_0 e_{-t/\tau} = 0.3636e^{-(0.1/0.2)} = 0.220$ A.

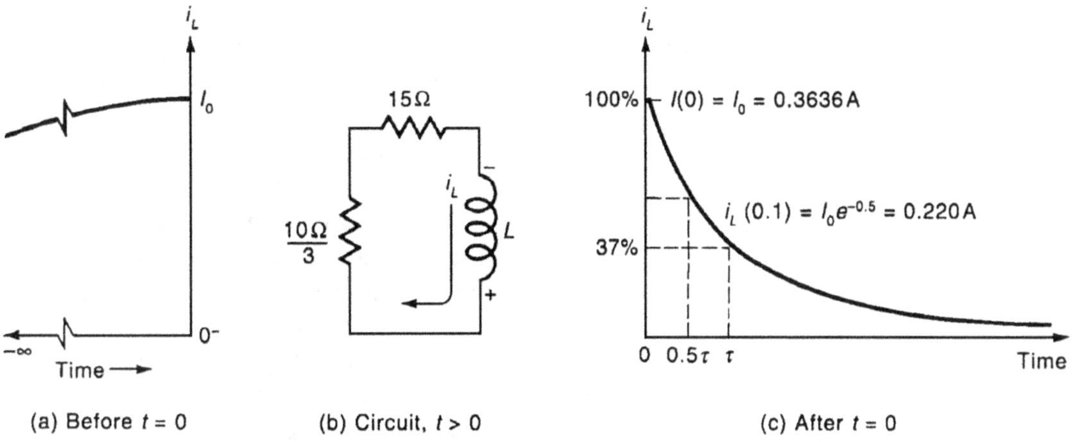

Exhibit 12 Current relationship in an inductor

The voltage across $L(di/dt)$ must be the same as the voltage drop across the resistors, since the loop is closed. Thus at $t = 0.2$ second, the voltage is $iR = 5.50$ volts; the polarity of this voltage is with the plus sign at the bottom of the inductance.

For an *RLC* circuit that involves two energy storage elements, *L* and *C*, the solution is complex. The governing equation is a second order differential equation whose solution may involve complex conjugate parameters.

AC CIRCUITS

In this review, the emphasis is on easily visualized graphical solutions rather than formal mathematical techniques. The review is based on assumptions that should be understood before the material is presented. The assumptions are the following:

- All sources are sinusoidal and are of the same frequency in any circuit unless specifically noted. For certain kinds of circuits, such as filters and resonant circuits, frequency changes will be made and will be considered in steady state and of the same frequency.
- Voltages and/or currents are considered at steady state. Any transients that may have resulted from the sudden closing of a switch are not considered. This assumption greatly simplifies the analysis; differential equation solutions will be bypassed and are replaced with phase-shifting operators. Although switch closing may be part of a circuit, it is assumed that one waits a short period of time (actually five time constants or more) for any transient or nonsinusoidal effects to die out before analyzing the circuit.
- Current or voltage sources are single phase unless otherwise noted (such as in three-phase circuit analysis).
- Circuits are linear. If a sinusoidal signal is applied to a circuit, then a current or voltage measured anyplace in the circuit will also be sinusoidal (with no harmonics). The only difference between an input and an output sinusoid will be a possible change in magnitude and phase.

An oversimplified pictorial (see Figure 9.16) will help one visualize a sinusoidal voltage source along with some of the above assumptions. The oversimplification is that of showing only one loop of wire in a magnetic field producing a pure

sine wave. The frequency of the sine wave is directly proportional to shaft speed. And, the time for one revolution for a single pair of poles (called the period, T) is the inverse of the frequency. The wave is periodic and continuous and may be represented with a phasor.

Consider how one could draw a sine wave rather accurately by placing the tip of a pencil at the center of an X–Y plot (start with it laying horizontally to the right of the origin) and then allowing it to rotate counterclockwise through 360°. If one were to view the eraser from afar to the left and then to project horizontally the tip of the eraser onto the vertical axis of a time plot, the projection would trace out a pure sine wave (see Figure 9.17); the pencil could be thought of as a phasor, a two-dimensional vector. This phasor (length) represents the maximum value (height) of the sine wave (it is usually more convenient to substitute the rms value rather than the maximum value for the length). This maximum value will, at first, be used to demonstrate how the rotating phasor is visualized. When using these phasors, one's real concern is a time *snapshot* of the relative positions of the phasors. Also, rather than plotting the voltage vs. θ as in Figures 9.16 and 9.17, it is more convenient to plot it against ωt or $2\pi ft$. The angle the phasor passes through, with respect to some reference position or another phasor, represents a phase angle.

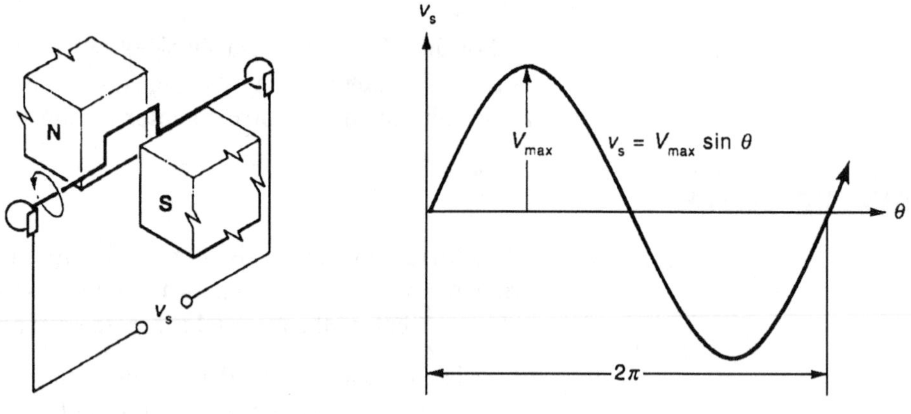

(a) Induced voltage (b) Wave shape

Figure 9.16 Simplified ac voltage source

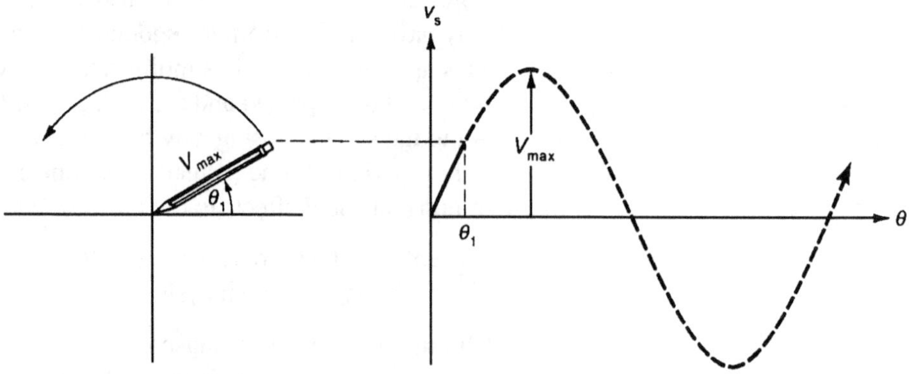

(a) Phasor concept (b) Sine wave

Figure 9.17 Graphical production of a sine wave

As an example of the simplicity of ac circuit analysis when using this phasor representation, consider summing two ac voltage sources graphically as in Figure 9.18(b). Here, one would sum the two voltages and continually draw the sum of the two waves; the result is

$$v_{total} = V_{max1} \sin \omega t + V_{max2} \sin(\omega t + \alpha) = V_{total} \sin(\omega t - \theta)$$

This graphic summing produces the desired total voltage and also displays the phase relationship with respect to either of the original sine waves. However, in Figure 9.18(c), the parallelogram formed from the two phasors yields the resulting phasor (the length is $v_{max\ total}$) much easier than summing the two sine waves. Furthermore, it gives the phase angle directly. The result is the same, in terms of relative magnitude and phase angle, for any instant of time. A formal mathematical description is

$$v_{total} = Im[V_{max\ total} e^{j(\omega t - \theta)}] \tag{9.10}$$

The notation *Im* implies the imaginary part of the expression that follows. A much simpler descriptive notation that most engineers use is to describe the representative phasor by a magnitude and its phase angle as $\mathbf{V}_{max\ total} \angle -\theta$. In electrical engineering, a positive rotation of the phasor is considered to be counterclockwise. Thus, in Figure 9.18, the parallelogram resultant phasor may be listed as being θ degrees behind (or lagging) the phasor V_1 or as ϕ degrees ahead (or leading) V_2.

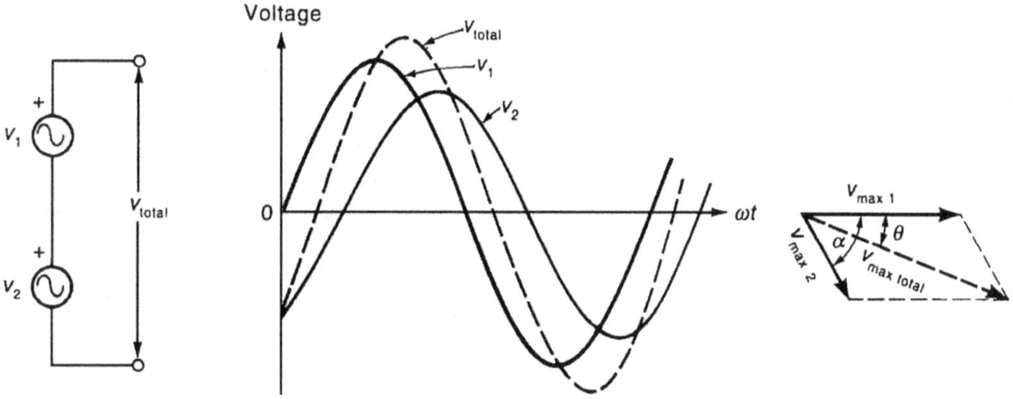

(a) Circuit (b) Graphical summing (c) Phasor addition

Figure 9.18 The addition of two voltage sources

Phasor Manipulation

Although adding two phasors is easily accomplished with the parallelogram, adding more than two might better be done by breaking each phasor into its x and y components and then summing the components. Multiplying phasors is done by multiplying the magnitudes and summing the angles, and division is done by dividing the magnitudes and subtracting the angles. As an example, two phasors $\mathbf{A} = 10\angle 0°$ and $\mathbf{B} = 5\angle 90°$ sum to $\mathbf{A}+\mathbf{B} = 11.2\angle 26.6°$. And $\mathbf{AB} = 50\angle 90°$; or $\mathbf{A}/\mathbf{B} = 2\angle -90°$. The concept of rotation is important. Assigning phasor **B** to be **B** $10\angle 180°$, then $\mathbf{B} = -\mathbf{A}$; one could say that **B** is the same as **A** if **A** were rotated through 180°. Here, multiplying phasor **A** by –1 is considered as operating on **A** to rotate it through 180°. One could then say that multiplying a phasor by the square root of –1 is also an operator that rotates the phasor through 90°. This imaginary value, the square root of –1, is referred to as j. The operator j then rotates the pha-

sor by 90°. As an example, the only difference between a sine wave and a cosine wave (for the same amplitude) is that a sine wave is shifted through 90° to become a cosine wave,

$$\cos\theta = \sin(\theta + 90°) = j\sin\theta \tag{9.11}$$

Because of the effect of Equation (9.11), it will be more convenient to use the real (x-axis) and imaginary j (y-axis) notation when dealing with phasors.

For most ac voltages or currents, one is usually interested in rms values rather than peak or maximum quantities. It was previously shown that the rms [or in *what a meter would read*] value of a sine wave is its maximum value divided by the square root of two (or $V_{rms} = 0.707V_{max}$). Thus, one usually begins with rms magnitudes when using phasors. This makes voltage, current, and (especially) power calculations much simpler; the notation is even easier (the rms subscripts are dropped). In ac circuits there are really only three important devices: resistors (energy dissipating element), capacitors (energy storage element), and inductors (also an energy storage element).

> Since all phasors are relative, plot phasor lengths as rms values rather than peak values.

Resistors

As in dc circuits, this resistive element dissipates power equal to the current squared times the resistance. This is not the only equation for power, but *it is the safest equation to use in ac circuits* unless one is very careful with notation and is experienced in ac circuit theory. Also, the voltage across a resistor is always in phase with the current through the resistor. The resistor stores no energy but dissipates the power in terms of heat.

> Current and voltage are in phase for a resistor: $\mathbf{V}_R = R\mathbf{I}$.

By this notation, voltages and currents in bold indicate that they may be complex values.

CAPACITORS

The capacitor stores energy for half a cycle and gives it up on the other half, the net (real) energy is zero. However, it is sometimes convenient to refer to the product of voltage and current as imaginary power (using the symbol Q and calling it reactive power). The result of this energy interchange is that the current through the capacitor has a 90° phase difference for the two phasors; the current is ahead of the voltage (or leads the voltage). Whereas the resistance, R, impedes the flow of current, the impending quantity for a capacitor is the reactance, called X_c. Not only does X_c impede the current, but it also causes a phase shift of –90° so that the voltage across the capacitor is lagging the current by 90°. These descriptive words may be replaced by the symbol $-j$.

> The voltage drop across a capacitor is 90° behind the current.
>
> $$\mathbf{V}_C = -jX_C\mathbf{I}, \qquad \text{where } X_C = \frac{1}{2\pi fC}$$

The instantaneous voltage across a capacitor for a given current is

$$v = 1/C \int i \, dt \quad \textbf{(9.12a)}$$

and if the given current is $i = I_{max} \sin \omega t$ then

$$v = 1/C \int I_{max} \sin \omega t \, dt \quad \textbf{(9.12b)}$$

and the solution is

$$v = [-1/(\omega C)] I_{max} \cos \omega t = [1/(\omega C)] I_{max} (-j) \sin \omega t \quad \textbf{(9.12c)}$$

Using phasor notation, one can show that Equation (9.12c) is equivalent to

$$\mathbf{V}_C = -jX_C\mathbf{I}, \quad \text{where } X_C = 1/(\omega C) \quad \textbf{(9.13)}$$

It is obvious that a numerical value of X_C is a function of frequency. In fact, if the frequency is infinite, X_C is zero as in a short circuit; and if the frequency is zero, X_C is infinity as in an open circuit. This relationship between current and voltage is shown graphically in Figure 9.19.

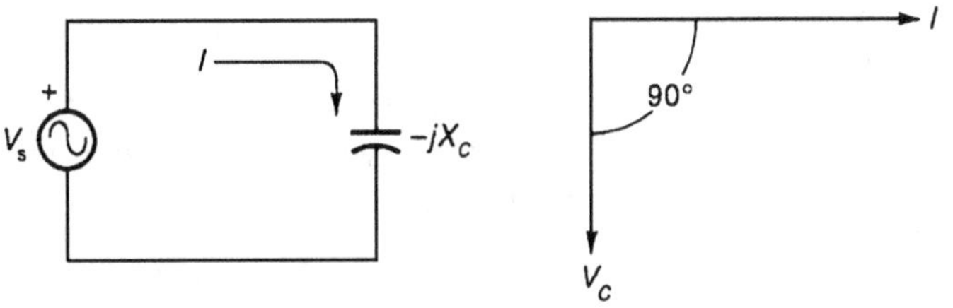

(a) Circuit (b) Phasor relationship

Figure 9.19 Voltage-current relationship for a capacitor. (The voltage and current are not to the same scale.)

Example **9.8**

Consider a series *R–C* circuit whose measured current is 5 amperes (rms). Determine the voltage source required to produce this current. Assume that the voltage source is known to have a frequency of 60 Hz, with $R = 10$ ohms and $C = (0.1/377)$ farads. The factor $2\pi f$ for 60 Hz is 377.

Solution

The effect of the capacitor is to create a 90° phase shift between the current and voltage while the resistor produces no phase shift. The instantaneous Kirchhoff voltage equation is

$$v_{total} = Ri + v_C = Ri + (1/C) \int i \, dt \quad \textbf{(9.14a)}$$

Rather than solving the above equation, phasors will be used here in the form

$$\mathbf{V}_s = \mathbf{V}_R + \mathbf{V}_C = R\mathbf{I} - jX_C\mathbf{I} \quad \textbf{(9.14b)}$$

Now R and jX_C should be viewed as operators (they operate on the current to produce a voltage—and the j is to produce a 90 degree phase shift). Then X_C is calculated from $1/(2\pi fC)$ to be 10 ohms.

$$\mathbf{V}_s = 10\mathbf{I} - j10\mathbf{I} \qquad \textbf{(9.14c)}$$

Remember, the $-j10$ operator multiplies the current phasor by ten and shifts it through $-90°$. With the two voltage phasors, one only needs the parallelogram construction to get the voltage source phasor along with its angular relationship to the current, as shown in Exhibit 13.

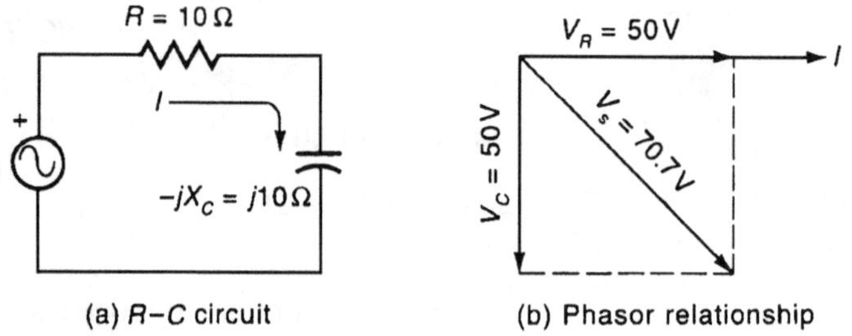

Exhibit 13 Voltage relationship for an *R–C* circuit

The voltage source is 70.7 volts with the voltage phasor lagging 45° behind the current. Or if the voltage source is considered to be the reference, one could say that the current leads the voltage by 45°. Observe that all of the (real) power from the source is dissipated by heat loss in the resistor (no real power is dissipated in the capacitor):

$$P_R = I^2R = 5^2(10) = 250 \text{ watts}$$

The power from the source, P_s, is the product of voltage and current times the power factor, which is defined as the cosine of the angle between the voltage and current. Thus

$$P_s = VI\cos 45° = 70.7 \times 5 \times 0.707 = 250 \text{ watts}$$

The reactive power, Q, is calculated as follows:

$$P_{\text{reactive}} = Q = VI\sin\theta = 70.7 \times 5 \times 0.707 = 250 \text{ VARs}$$

(*Note*: P_s and Q match only because θ is 45°.)

Inductors

Like the capacitor, the inductor stores energy for half a cycle and returns it to the circuit for the next half cycle. In circuit analysis, the inductor behaves in a similar manner as a capacitor except the sign is reversed; here the term is $+jX_L$ where X_L is directly proportional to the frequency and is equal to $\omega_L = 2\pi fL$. For the inductor, the voltage leads the current by 90°, or the current lags the voltage.

> A voltage drop across an inductor leads the current by 90°.
>
> $\mathbf{V}_L = jX_L\mathbf{I}, \quad \text{where } X_L = 2\pi fL$

Also, at zero frequency, the reactance is zero; and for an infinite frequency, the reactance is infinite. The phase relationship is shown in Figure 9.20.

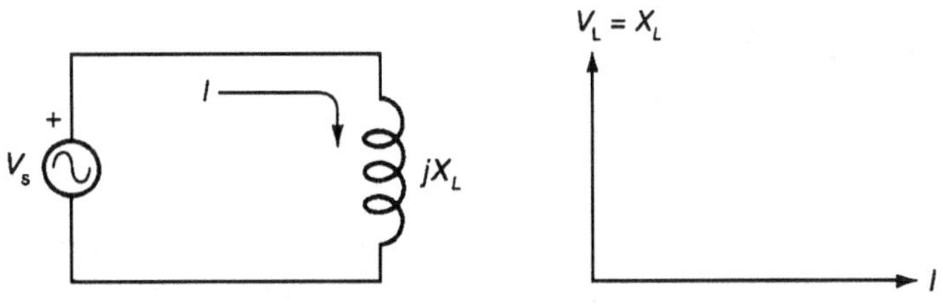

(a) Circuit (b) Phasor relationship

Figure 9.20 Voltage-current relationship for an inductor

Example 9.9

Consider the circuit of Exhibit 14, where the current is, as before, 5 amperes, R is 10 Ω, and $L = 10/377$ henries.

Solution

Here X_L is ohms (Exhibit 14). The answers are unchanged from Example 9.8 except for the phase relationships.

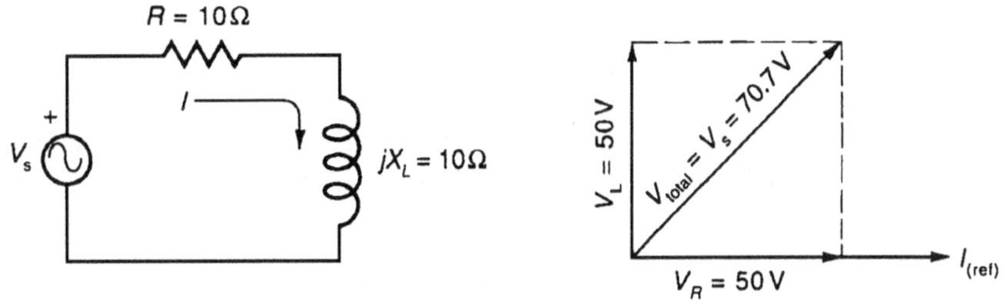

(a) Circuit (b) Phasor relationship

Exhibit 14 An *R–L* circuit voltage-current relationship

Impedance Relationship

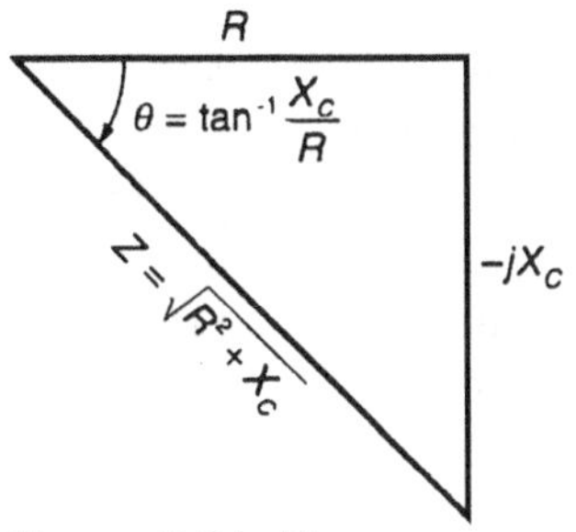

Figure 9.21 The impedance relationship

In general, ac voltages and currents are related by a quantity called impedance (Z). It is usually complex, and it is sometimes referred to as Ohm's law for ac circuits. This association is easily explained by reference to either of the two previous example problems. For instance, in Exhibit 13 and Equation (9.14), the current was assumed to be known. If the current were unknown and the source voltage was given as 70.7 volts, then $\mathbf{V}_s = 70.7\angle 0°$ volts can be the known reference phasor. From Equation (9.14b), the unknown current is easily factored out of the expression to give $\mathbf{V}_s = (R - jX_C)\mathbf{I}$.

The parenthetical quantity—or the operators—for this problem, as in Equation (9.14c), is the complex impedance. It has a right-triangle relationship as in Figure 9.21 and is given by $\mathbf{Z} = R - jX_C = 10 - j10 = 10\sqrt{2}\angle -45°$.

The $10 - j10$ is known as the rectangular form, and the $10\sqrt{2}\angle - 45°$ is known as the polar form. The rectangular form is usually used when adding or subtracting is involved, and the polar form is used when one is multiplying or dividing. To finish the problem, the current is found as $\mathbf{I} = \mathbf{V}_s/\mathbf{Z} = (70.7\angle 0°)/(10\sqrt{2}\angle - 45°) = \angle + 45°$ A.

Example 9.10

Another series circuit problem will expand on the complex impedance concept; see Exhibit 15. Here, all of the resistances and reactances and the source voltage are given for a particular frequency. It is desired to find the power dissipated in the 20-ohm load resistance and also to find the total power from the source voltage. Since the circuit is a series one, the current is common for all elements; therefore the current should be found. The voltage source is 100 volts.

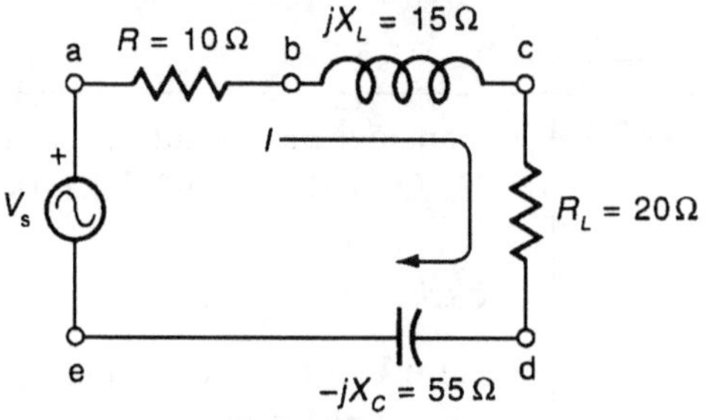

Exhibit 15 A series circuit with known parameters

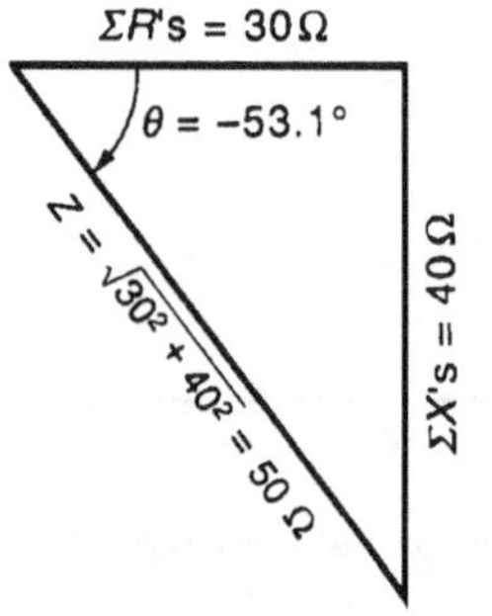

Exhibit 16 Impedance triangle

Solution

Find the total impedance to find the current (see Exhibit 16): $\mathbf{Z} = 10 + j15 + 20 - j55 = (10 + 20) + j(15 - 55) = 30 - j40 = 50 \angle -53.1°\Omega$.

From this complex impedance, current and power can be found directly:

$$\mathbf{I} = \mathbf{V}/\mathbf{Z} = (100\angle 0°)/(50\angle -53.1°) = 2 \angle +53.1° \text{ amperes}$$

$$P_{RL} = I^2R_L = 2^2(20) = 80 \text{ watts}$$

$$P_s = V_sI \cos\theta = 100 \times 2 \cos(-53.1°) = 120 \text{ watts}$$

Check: $P_s = \Sigma I^2R = 2^2(10 + 20) = 120$ watts.

Example 9.11

Suppose, in Example 9.10, one is asked to find the magnitude and phase of the voltage across two points—say the voltage from point b to point d.

Solution

The phasor plot readily yields this answer. Since the current is common to all elements, the current should be made the reference phasor. Again, the currents and voltages are not necessarily plotted to the same scale. Rather than having all phasors emanating from the origin, it is convenient to plot the voltages in a cumulative fashion, from head to tail (see Exhibit 17).

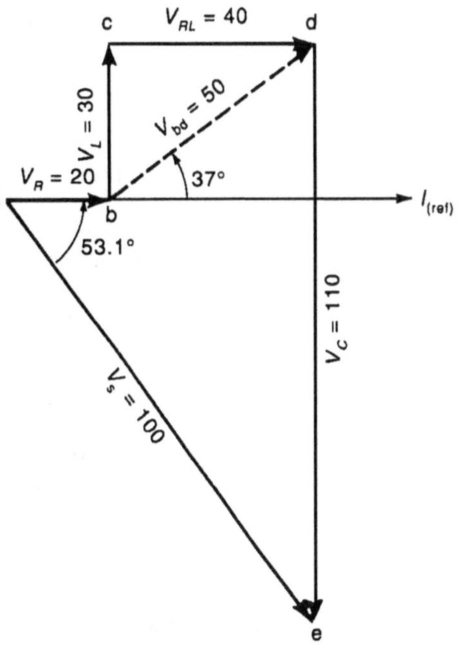

Exhibit 17 Plot of voltages vs. current

The voltage, V_{bd}, may be read directly from the plot to be 50 volts at an angle of 37° ahead of the current. An interesting aspect of this problem is brought out if the frequency of the source is doubled. Doubling the frequency causes no change in the resistive elements but dramatic changes in the reactive ones. For the inductor, X_L is 15 × 2 = 30 ohms and for the capacitor $X_C = 0.5 \times 55 = 27.5$ ohms. The impedance then becomes $\mathbf{Z} = 10 + j30 + 20 - j27.5 = 30 + j2.5 = 30.1\angle 4.76°$ ohms. The current is $\mathbf{I} = (100\angle 0°)/30.1\angle 4.76° = 3.32\angle{-4.76°}$ A, and the power dissipated in the 20-ohm resistor is

$$P_{RL} = I^2R_L = 3.32^2 \times 20 = 220 \text{ watts}$$

At this point, several practical observations are in order. For approximate answers, if either the real or imaginary part is more than ten times the other, the hypotenuse is almost equal to the longest leg, and the angle is within a few degrees of being zero. Using this approximation for impedance, the approximate current is 3.3 amperes and P_{RL} is 222 watts. Another observation is that by changing the frequency, the power output has gone from only 80 watts to well over 200. There is a specific frequency to get maximum current and power; this is called the resonant frequency.

SUMMARY OF AC CIRCUITS

- Any steady-state voltage or current in a linear circuit with a sinusoidal source is also a sinusoid.
  - This is a consequence of the nature of particular solutions for sinusoidal forcing functions.
  - All steady-state voltages and currents have the same frequency as the source.

- In order to find a steady-state voltage or current, all we need to know is its *magnitude* and its *phase* relative to the source. (We already know its frequency.)
- Usually, an AC steady-state voltage or current is given by the particular solution to a differential equation.
- We do not have to find this differential equation from the circuit, and we don't have to solve it.
- Instead, we use the concepts of *phasors* and complex impedances.
- Phasors and complex impedances convert problems involving differential equations into simple circuit analysis problems.
- Recall that a *phasor* is a complex number that represents the magnitude and phase of a sinusoidal voltage or current.

$$\underset{\text{Time domain}}{x(t) = X_M \cos(\omega t + \theta)} \quad \leftrightarrow \quad \underset{\text{Frequency Domain}}{\mathrm{X} = X_M \angle \theta}$$

- For AC steady-state analysis, this is all we need; we already know the frequency of any voltage or current.
- AC steady-state analysis using phasors allows us to express the relationship between current and voltage using a formula that looks like Ohm's law:

$$\mathrm{V} = \mathrm{I}\,\mathrm{Z}$$

- Z is called *impedance* (units of ohms, W).
- Impedance is (often) a complex number, but is not technically a phasor.
- Impedance depends on frequency, ω.
- Phasors allow us to express current-voltage relationships for inductors and capacitors much like we express the current-voltage relationship for a resistor.
- A complex exponential is the mathematical tool needed to obtain this relationship.
- Phasors are expressed as cosine terms; therefore, we must remember the following phasor trignometric relationships:

Sine - Cosine Relations

$$\cos(\omega t) = \sin(\omega t + \pi/2) = -\sin(\omega t - \pi/2)$$
$$\sin(\omega t) = \cos(\omega t - \pi/2) = -\cos(\omega t + \pi/2)$$

Phasor Transforms of Sinusoids

$$P\left[v_{\max} \cos(\omega t + \phi)\right] = V_{\text{rms}} \angle \phi = \mathrm{V}$$
$$P\left[I_{\max} \cos(\omega t + \phi)\right] = I_{\text{rms}} \angle \phi = \mathrm{I}$$

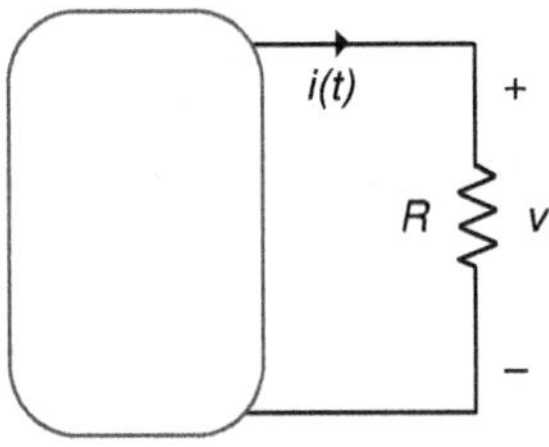

$v(t) = R\,i(t)$

$V = I\,R$

$V = I\,Z \;\Rightarrow\; Z_R = R$

I-V Relationship for a Resistor

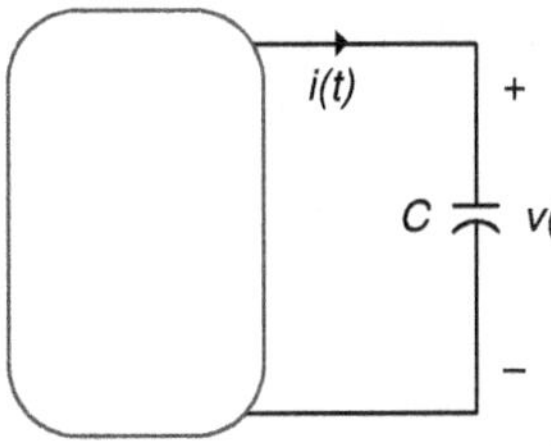

$i(t) = C\dfrac{dv(t)}{dt}$

$V = I\dfrac{1}{j\omega C}$

$V = I\,Z \;\Rightarrow\; Z_C = \dfrac{1}{j\omega C}$

I-V Relationship for a Capacitor

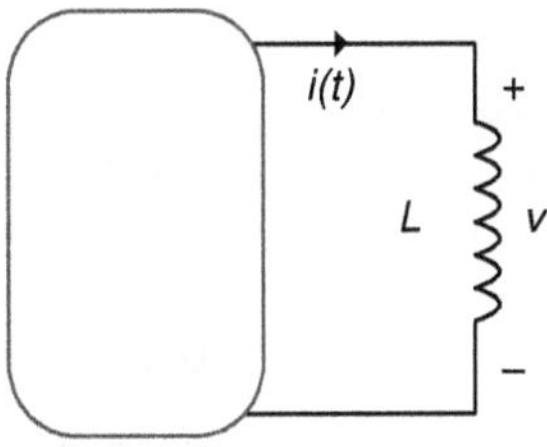

$v(t) = L\dfrac{di(t)}{dt}$

$V = j\omega L I$

$V = I\,Z \;\Rightarrow\; Z_L = j\omega L$

I-V Relationship for an Inductor

Table 9.1 Impedance Summary Table

Component	Impedance	Phasor
Resistor 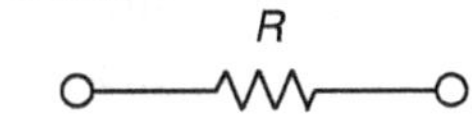	$Z_R = R$	$Z_R = R\angle 0°$
Capacitor 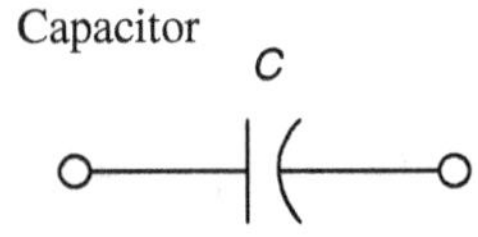	$Z_C = \dfrac{1}{j\omega C} = \dfrac{j}{\omega C}$	$Z_C = \dfrac{1}{\omega C}\angle -90°$
Inductor 	$Z_L = j\omega L$	$Z_C = \omega L\angle +90°$

Example 9.12

Find the phasor current / in polar form for the following circuit using the voltage source as the reference angle.

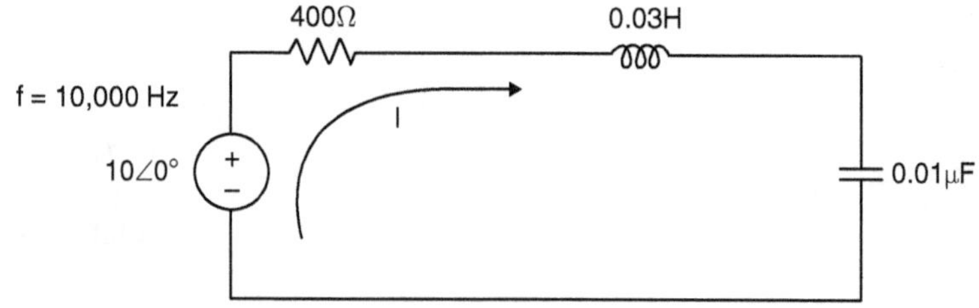

a. 0.0250 ∠ 0° A
b. 0.0202 ∠ –36.27° A
c. 0.0578 ∠ 53.73° A
d. 0.0500 ∠ 0° A

Solution

From Ohm's Law: $I = V/Z$ (where Z is impedance)

$Z_R = R = 400\ \Omega$

$Z_C = 1/(j\omega C) = 1/[j(2\pi)(10{,}000\ \text{s}^{-1})(0.01\ \mu\text{F})] = -j1591.5\ \Omega$

$Z_L = j\omega L = [j(2\pi)(10{,}000\ \text{s}^{-1})(0.03\text{H})] = j1885.0\ \Omega$

From KVL: $V = Z_R(I) + Z_C(I) + Z_L(I) = (Z_R + Z_C + Z_L)(I)$

$V = 10 \angle 0°\ \text{V}$

$I = V/Z_{\text{Total}} = 10 \angle 0°\ \text{V}/(400\ \Omega + -j1591.5\ \Omega + j1885.0\ \Omega)$

$$I = \frac{10}{400 + j293.5} A = \frac{10\angle 0^{\circ}}{496.1\angle 36.27^{\circ}} = 0.0202\angle -36.27^{\circ}$$

The correct answer is b. 0.0202 ∠ –36.27° A.

IMPEDANCE MATCHING WITH IDEAL TRANSFORMERS

Transformers are often used for impedance matching. Here we will examine only the sinusoidal steady state and will assume the transformer to be ideal (which means that it has no P or Q loss or phase shift).

Consider an ideal, lossless transformer, with a turns ratio a, used to match a load to an ac source. Such a transformer is shown imbedded in the example circuit of Figure 9.22a. Ideal transformer theory (in terms of Faraday's law and Ampere's circuital law) gives

$$a = N_1/N_2 = |V_p/V_s| = |V_1/V_2| = |I_s/I_p| = |I_2/I_1|\ . \qquad \textbf{(9.15)}$$

Although shown for magnitudes, these relationships hold for phasor voltages and currents as well.

It is easy to show that the impedance of the load, as seen when "looking" into the primary (energized) side, is

$$\mathbf{Z}_p = \mathbf{a}^2\mathbf{Z}_s \qquad \textbf{(9.16)}$$

where $\mathbf{Z}_s$ is the load impedance, or impedance on the secondary side (equal to 10 – j5 Ω *in Figure 9.22a*). We say that impedances, voltages, and currents can be referred across a transformer. An important point to remember: *Voltages refer*

as the turns ratio, currents refer as the inverse of the turns ratio, and impedances refer as the turns ratio squared. As with voltages and currents, the impedances $\mathbf{Z}_s$ and $\mathbf{Z}_p$ in Equation 9.16 may be expressed as complex numbers, and, since turns ratio a is real, the angle of the secondary impedance is the same as the angle of the secondary impedance referred to the primary.

As a short example, assume that a voltage source of 50 V (rms) with an internal impedance of 100 + j 50 Ω is connected to a load impedance of 10 – j5 Ω through the ideal transformer as shown in Figure 9.22a. Assume a transformer turns ratio of $a = \sqrt{10}$. Let us compare the power dissipations in the circuit with those that would occur if the same load were connected to the same Thevenin source *without* the transformer present.

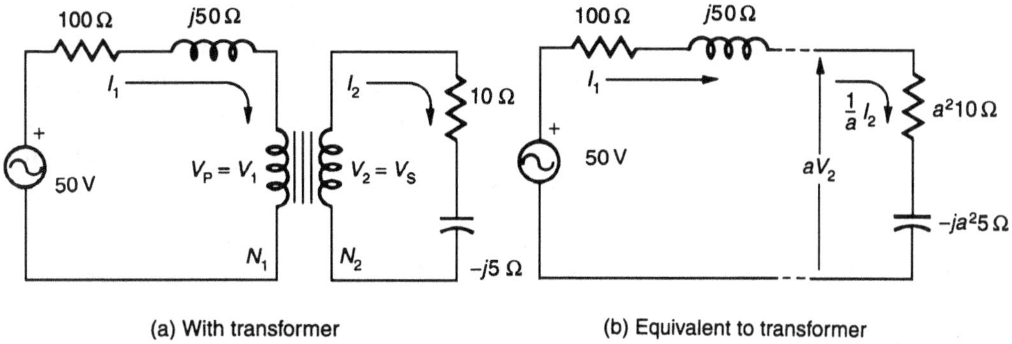

Figure 9.22 Simple ac circuit with transformer and the equivalent circuit referred to primary

When load and source are connected together *without* the transformer, the two are in a simple series loop. The power dissipation in the source (i.e., in its internal impedance) and in the load, respectively, may be found by first finding the current

$$\mathbf{I} = 50\angle 0°/(100 + j50 + 10 - j5) = 0.421\angle{-22.4°}\text{A}$$

giving a power dissipation in the source of

$$P_{\text{source loss}} = I^2(100) = 17.7 \text{ W}$$

Similarly, for this case the power supplied to the load is

$$P_{\text{load}} = I^2(10) = 1.77 \text{ W}$$

Note that, in this small, numerically contrived problem, the power loss in the source (which might include a transmission network) is ten times the power supplied to the load. This does *not* represent a very good (certainly not an efficient) power transmission system!

On the other hand, if we interpose a step-down transformer with turns ratio $a = \sqrt{10}$ as shown in the figure, the load impedance, as referred to the source side, is $a^2\mathbf{Z}_L$, or $(\sqrt{10})^2(10 - j5) = 100 - j50$ Ω, and the current out of the source is now

$$\mathbf{I}_1 = 50\angle 0°/(100 + j50 + 100 - j50) = 0.25\angle 0° \text{ A},$$

from which the power dissipated in the source is found as

$$P_{\text{source}} = I_1^2 R_{\text{source}} = 6.25 \text{ W}$$

and the power supplied to the load is

$$P_{\text{load}} = I_1^2 R_{\text{load/referred}} = 6.25 \text{ W}$$

(Alternatively, we could have obtained P_{load} by first finding $\boldsymbol{I}_2$ in Figure 9.22a from Equation 9.15 and then finding $P_{\text{load}} = I_2^2 R_{\text{load}} = 6.25$ W.)

This example points out how a transformer can be used to better match a load to a source for the purpose of power transfer. Even with the transformer shown above, this example network still does not represent a good power system from a power transfer standpoint (the transmission efficiency is 50%), but the power delivery to the load has been greatly improved by adding the transformer. Of course, in real networks, the different voltage levels produced by the inclusion of transformers in the circuit must be considered carefully.

In electric power networks, transformers are used widely to enable the transfer of energy at higher voltages, minimizing loss. In large ac power systems, transmission-line efficiencies might be in the mid-90% range, and transformers may have efficiencies of 98–99%. In such systems, of course, the objective is not to maximize power but to transmit power to the customer with as low a loss as possible (i.e., with the greatest efficiency). This is in distinction to problems such as transferring data to and from satellites, where maximizing the power of the signal is more important and loss considerations (at least in the ground-based stations) are secondary.

IMPEDANCE MATCHING AND MUTUAL COUPLING

A somewhat more comprehensive situation is involved for a non-ideal transformer or for an air-core, coupled-coil system with mutual inductance M, whose *coefficient of coupling* k is less than unity. (Recall that, for a pair of coupled coils, the mutual inductance is given, in terms of the individual coil inductances L_1 and L_2, as $M = k\sqrt{(L_1 L_2)}$. Also, recall the dot notation (or *dot convention*) used to show relative polarity: voltages at dotted terminals are simultaneously in phase with respect to their undotted counterparts.)

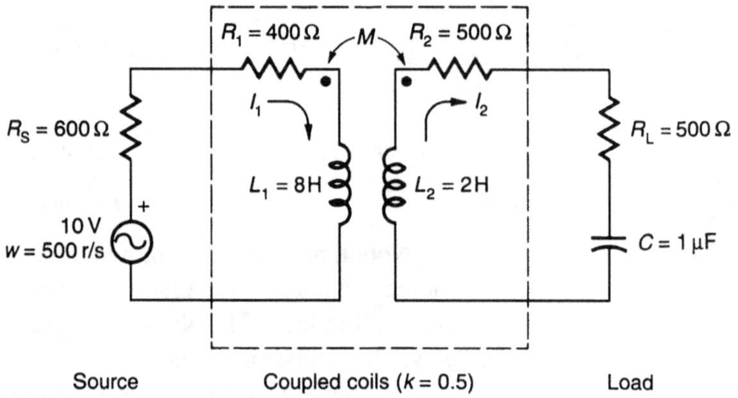

Figure 9.23 Coupled circuit example

In such a high-loss, coupled-coil system, the secondary impedance, as reflected to the primary (which we shall call $\mathbf{Z}_p$), is no longer just $a^2\mathbf{Z}_s$ in terms of the secondary (load) impedance, but is now a function of k, ω, L_1, L_2, and the load impedance.

In general, the coefficient of coupling can take on the values $0 \le k \le 1$. The following example will illustrate the calculations involved for a system where $k < 1$. We will assume the self-inductances to have real values.

Assume that an ac voltage source with an internal resistance R_s is coupled to a load impedance $\mathbf{Z}_L$ by two air-core coils with a coupling coefficient $k = 0.5$, as

shown in Figure 9.23. Determine the power dissipated in the load and whether the load is matched to the source. The angular frequency $\omega = 500$ rad/sec.

The mutual inductance is given by

$$M = k\sqrt{L_1 L_2} \text{ H}$$

and the mutual impedance is

$$jX_M = j\omega M \ \Omega$$

Then,

$$M = 0.5\sqrt{8 \times 2} = 2\text{H}; \qquad jX_M = j500 \times 2 = j1000\Omega$$
$$jX_{L1} = j\omega L_1 = j500\times 8 = j4000\Omega; \qquad jX_{L2} = j500 \times 2 = j1000\Omega$$
$$jX_c = -j\frac{1}{\omega C} = -j\frac{1}{500\times 1\times 10^{-6}} = -j2000\Omega$$
$$\mathbf{Z}(Primary) = \mathbf{Z}_{11} = 600 + 400 + j4000 = (1+4)\times 10^3\Omega$$
$$\mathbf{Z}(Secondary) = \mathbf{Z}_{22} = 500 + 500 + j1000 - j2000 = (1 - j1)10^3\Omega$$

The reflected impedance $\mathbf{Z}_r$ (from the load side to the primary side) is referred not by a^2, but by the quantity $X_M^2/|\mathbf{Z}_{22}|^2$, which is then multiplied by the conjugate of $\mathbf{Z}_{22}$ in order to obtain maximum power:

$$\mathbf{Z}_r = \left|\frac{X_M}{\mathbf{Z}_{22}}\right|^2 \mathbf{Z}_{22}(\text{conj}) = \left|\frac{10^3}{\sqrt{2}\times 10^3}\right|^2 (1+j1)\times 10^3 = (0.5 + j0.5)\times 10^3$$
$$= \sqrt{2}\times 0.5\times 10^3\angle 45°$$

The primary and secondary currents may be found directly as

$$\mathbf{I}_1 = \frac{V\angle 0°}{\mathbf{Z}_{11} + \mathbf{Z}_r} = \frac{10\angle 0°}{(1 + j4 + 0.5 + j0.5)\times 10^3} = \frac{10\angle 0°}{(1.5 + j4.5)10^3} = 2.11\angle -71.6° \text{mA}$$
$$\mathbf{I}_2 = \frac{jX_M}{\mathbf{Z}_{22}}\mathbf{I}_1 = \left(\frac{10^3\angle 90°}{\sqrt{2}\times 10^3\angle -45°}\right)(2.11\angle -71.6°) = 1.5\angle -26.6° \text{ mA}$$

One would like the efficiency of the circuit (in transferring power to the load) to approach 50% for maximum power transfer (i.e., $\mathbf{P}_L/\mathbf{P}_{\text{source}}$ 1.0), but, of course, this can never be achieved here because of the real impedance parameters of the coils, and the fact that k is less than unity. The power values for the source and load sides are

$$P_L = I_2^2 R_L = (1.5 \times 10^{-3})^2 \times 500 = 1.12 \times 10^{-3} \text{ W}$$
$$P_S = V_1 I_1 \cos\phi = (10)(2.11 \times 10^{-3}) \cos 71.6° = 6.67 \times 10^{-3} \text{ W}$$

And, thus, the efficiency is

$$Eff = \frac{P_L}{P_S} = \frac{1.12\times 10^{-3}}{6.67\times 10^{-3}} = 16.8\%$$

When mutual coupling is involved in situations where $k < 1$, impedance matching becomes difficult. However, if the real parts of both the source and load impedance cannot be altered, the series reactance of the load can usually be changed to cancel the source reactance. The objective is usually to maximize the current and thus maximize the power in the load.

Resonant Frequency

For series circuits, the resonant frequency occurs when all of the reactive components cancel so that $X_L = X_C$, $\omega L = 1/\omega C$. For this particular frequency, the subscript notation may be given as *res*, *0*, or *n*.

Series Resonant Frequency

$$\omega_0 = 2\pi f_0 = \frac{1}{\sqrt{LC}}$$

The series resonant frequency concept leads directly to the maximum power transfer theorem, which should now be obvious. Maximum power occurs when the reactive components in an ac series circuit cancel.

Parallel ac circuits are no more difficult than series ones but may require slightly more bookkeeping; also, since many reciprocals are involved, additional definitions may be used to identify these reciprocals. As an example, the reciprocal of impedance, Z, is admittance, Y; the units of Y are siemens (old notation mhos) abbreviated S. The admittance may be further expanded to have a real and imaginary part. The real part is called the conductance, G, and the imaginary part is called the susceptance, B; both parts have the units of siemens. However, for simple problems, these definitions are optional; consider the example shown in Figure 9.24.

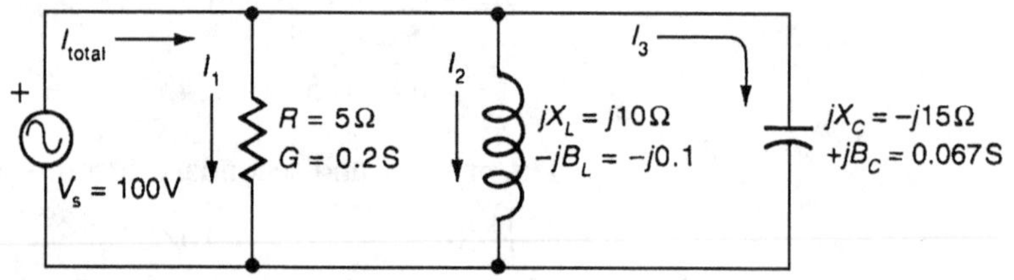

Figure 9.24 A parallel circuit

Example 9.13

Solution

The equivalent impedance for this problem may be found by either dividing the source voltage by the total current (see Exhibit 18) or by taking the reciprocal of the total admittance.

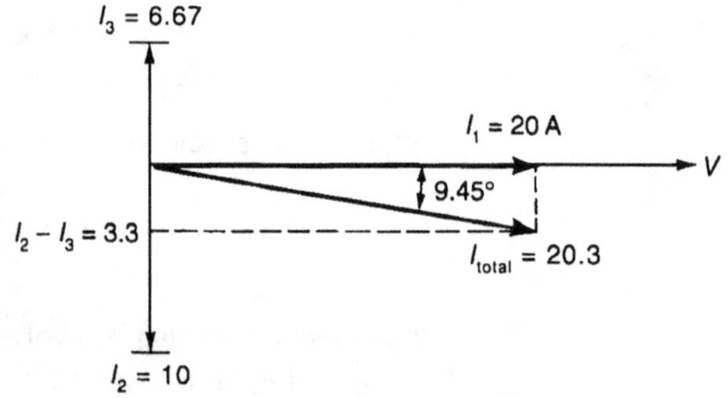

Exhibit 18 The phasor relationship for Figure 9.24

$$\mathbf{I}_{total} = \mathbf{I}_1 + \mathbf{I}_2 + \mathbf{I}_3$$

where

$\mathbf{I}_1 = \mathbf{V}/R = (100\angle 0°)/5 = 20\angle 0°$ A
$\mathbf{I}_2 = \mathbf{V}/(jX_L) = (100\angle 0°)/(10\angle 90°) = 10\angle -90°$ A
$\mathbf{I}_3 = \mathbf{V}/(-jX_C) = (100\angle 0°)/(15\angle -90°) = 6.67\angle 90°$ A
$\mathbf{I}_{total} = 20 - j10 + j6.67 = 20 - j3.33 = 20.28\angle -9.46°$

$$\mathbf{Z} = \mathbf{V}/\mathbf{I} = (100\angle 0°)/(20.28\angle -9.46°) = 4.93\angle 9.46° \text{ ohms}$$

However, using admittances, Y may be found directly:

$$G = 0.20 \text{ S}, \quad -jB_L = -j0.10 \text{ S}, \quad jB_C = j0.066 \text{ S}$$
$$\mathbf{Y} = G - jX_L + jX_C = 0.20 - j0.10 + j0.066 = 0.20 - j0.03 = 0.203\angle -9.45° \text{ S}$$
$$\mathbf{Z} = 1/\mathbf{Y} = 1/(0.203\angle -9.45°) = 4.93\angle 9.45° \text{ ohms}$$

Example 9.14

A final example of a combined series and parallel circuit is given in Exhibit 19. For this kind of problem, the reader is urged to make two separate plots to find the individual branch currents, then add the two current phasors on a third plot to find the total current. Find the power taken from the source.

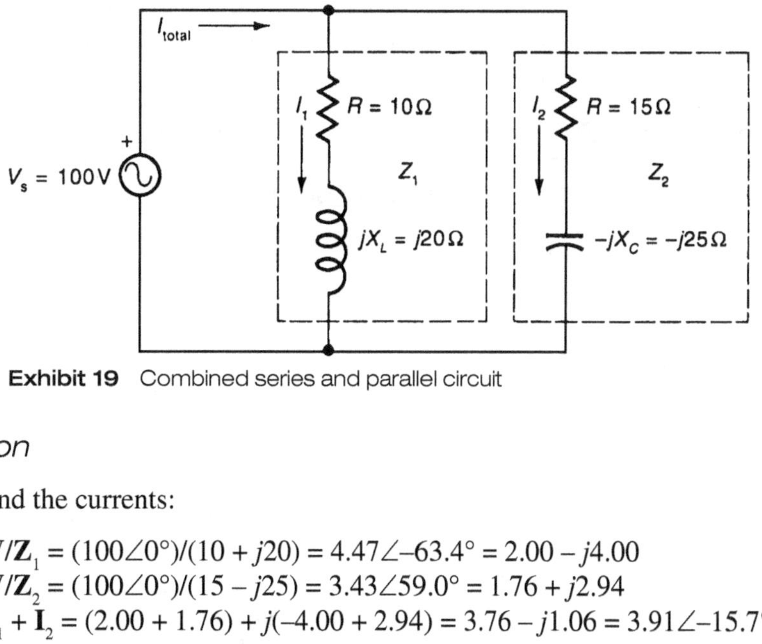

Exhibit 19 Combined series and parallel circuit

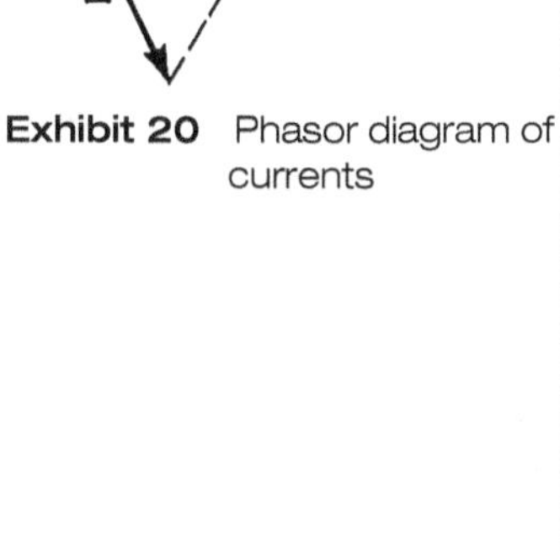

Exhibit 20 Phasor diagram of currents

Solution

First, find the currents:

$\mathbf{I}_1 = \mathbf{V}/\mathbf{Z}_1 = (100\angle 0°)/(10 + j20) = 4.47\angle -63.4° = 2.00 - j4.00$
$\mathbf{I}_2 = \mathbf{V}/\mathbf{Z}_2 = (100\angle 0°)/(15 - j25) = 3.43\angle 59.0° = 1.76 + j2.94$
$\mathbf{I}_{total} = \mathbf{I}_1 + \mathbf{I}_2 = (2.00 + 1.76) + j(-4.00 + 2.94) = 3.76 - j1.06 = 3.91\angle -15.7°$

See Exhibit 20 for the phasor diagram. The power from the source is now found to be

$$P_s = \mathbf{V}\mathbf{I}_{total} \cos\theta = 100 \times 3.91 \times \cos(-15.7) = 376 \text{ watts}$$

(*Check*: $P_{total} = (\mathbf{I}_1)^2 R_1 + (\mathbf{I}_2)^2 R_2 = 200 + 176 = 376$ watts.)

Although calculations are straightforward, the reader is urged to sketch the phasor diagram. Again, for a multiple-choice problem, the graphical solution may be sufficiently accurate for one to select the correct answer.

Quality Factor

For parallel resonance as for series resonance circuits, Z still equals R at resonant frequency. For the series circuit the inductive and capacitive reactances cancel; and for parallel circuits, the inductive and capacitive susceptances (in siemens) cancel. In describing the behavior of these resonant circuits another descriptive quantity is frequently used—especially so for parallel circuits—which is called the *quality factor*, Q, of the circuit. For a series circuit Q is a measure of the energy stored in an inductor compared to the energy dissipated in the resistance; this ratio may also be given as

$$Q_{\text{series}} = \omega_o L/R = 1/(\omega_o CR) \tag{9.17}$$

where Q is dimensionless and may be quite high for a sharp resonant peak as a narrow bandwidth circuit. On the other hand, for a parallel circuit, Q may be defined (see Figure 9.24) as

$$Q_{\text{parallel}} = 1/Q_{\text{series}} = \omega_o RC = R/(\omega_o L) \tag{9.18}$$

and the bandwidth, BW, may easily be found as

$$BW = \omega_o / Q_{\text{parallel}} \text{ (rad/s)} \tag{9.19}$$

Transfer Function

The transfer function is the ratio of desired response of a system to the input (or excitation) when all the initial conditions are zeros.

Example 9.15

Find the transfer function $T_{(s)} = \dfrac{V_2(s)}{V_1(s)}$ of the circuit shown in Exhibit 21.

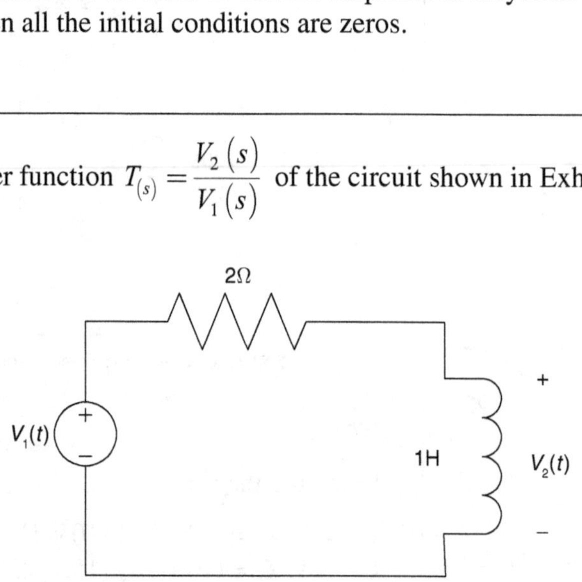

Exhibit 21

Solution

The s-domain circuit is drawn, as shown in Exhibit 22, by replacing the inductor with s •, the source by $V_1(s)$, and maintaining the resistor as such. Using voltage division, $T(s) = \dfrac{V_2(s)}{V_1(s)} = \dfrac{s}{s+2}$.

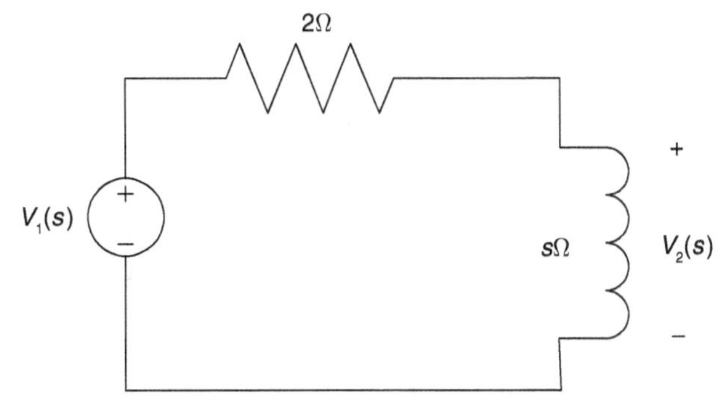

Exhibit 22

For a transfer function H(s), a plot of |H(jω)| versus ω and a plot of the phase angle of H(jω) versus ω are called the frequency response plots. For convenience, a plot of 20 log |H(jω)| dB (decibel) versus log ω, and a plot of the phase angle of H(jω) versus log ω are usually drawn. These are called Bode plots.

ELECTRIC MACHINES

AC Machines

The speed of rotation of a synchronous motor and that of a rotating magnetic field, in either a synchronous motor or an induction motor, are decided by the equation

$$n_s = \frac{120f}{p} \quad \textbf{(9.20)}$$

where f = line frequency in Hz, p = the number of poles, and the speed is in rpm. For three-phase induction motors, the actual speed of rotation will always be less than the speed of the rotating field. This difference is expressed by a factor called slip, as given by the equation

$$slip = \frac{n_s - n}{n_s} \quad \textbf{(9.21)}$$

DC Machines

For direct current machines, the voltage induced in the armature, E_a, is directly proportional to the product of speed, n, and the magnetic flux, ϕ, generated by the field. The magnetic flux is directly proportional to the field current, I_f. The relation between E_a and I_f is determined experimentally.

Example 9.16

Exhibit 23 shows the equivalent circuit of a separately excited DC generator where R_a is the armature resistance, R_L is the load resistance, and E_a is the induced EMF of the armature. It is determined experimentally that the induced EMF is 100 V for a field current of 1 A on no load at 1000 rpm. Find the load voltage, V_L, at 800 rpm if the field current is 1 A, R_a is 1 Ω, and R_L is 10 Ω.

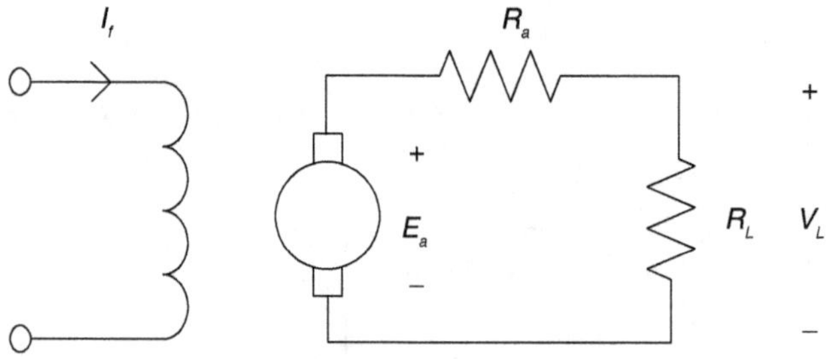

Exhibit 23

Solution

Since the induced EMF $E_a = K_a n\phi$, and flux $\phi = K_f I_f$, where K_a and K_f are constants, at any given I_f, E_a is proportional to speed n. As the field current is fixed, E_a is directly proportional to speed. Then, at 800 rpm, $E_a = 100\frac{800}{1000} = 80$ V.

Using KVL, $80 = I_a(1 + 10)$; $I_a = 7.27$ A; load voltage $V_L = 10I_a = 72.7$ V.

ELECTRONIC CIRCUITS

A thorough review of electronics is not undertaken here. But two topics—the solid state diode and the operational amplifier—have been selected as deserving attention. The complexity of certain aspects of both solid state theory and integrated circuit theory is well beyond the scope of this review, so only the idealized devices will be dealt with.

Diodes

The solid state theory of diode operation depends on the particular kind of diode being considered. For example, for the junction diode, knowledge of solid state theory and the behavior of majority and minority carriers in the presence of an electric field is desirable. But when an idealized diode is treated, the full theory is not essential. For a p–n junction diode, a very simplistic explanation of the operation at the junction between a p and an n type semiconductor is that in each type of material there are many free charges available; these are holes (p, positive) and electrons (n, negative), respectively. If the diode is biased in favor of forcing positive charges near the boundary (the positive voltage being connected to the p material and the negative terminal to the n material), a rapid recombining of the charges takes place [see Figure 9.25(a)]; this is the direction of easy current flow. On the other hand, if the diode is reverse biased [Figure 9.25(b)], the free charges are attracted toward their bias polarities, leaving a dearth of charges at the junction for very little recombination and almost no current flow. When the bias is in the forward direction, the voltage necessary to cause the charges to recombine is fairly small but still could be significant (see Figure 9.26). The voltage is near half of one volt (approximately 0.4 V for germanium and near 0.7 for silicon) and is nonlinear. In the reverse direction, the current is essentially zero until breakdown voltage is reached; this breakdown is referred to as Zener voltage, which ranges from a few volts to several hundred volts. When designing circuits that use these diodes, care must be taken to work well within the reverse peak breakdown voltage. If one ignores the nonlinearity by assuming that the

half volt is negligible for the forward direction, then the symbol shown in Figure 9.26(b) represents the ideal diode (the arrowhead side is the anode, and the other side is the cathode). These diodes, of course, have many applications; in this review, the applications will be limited to the ideal case in pure rectifying circuits.

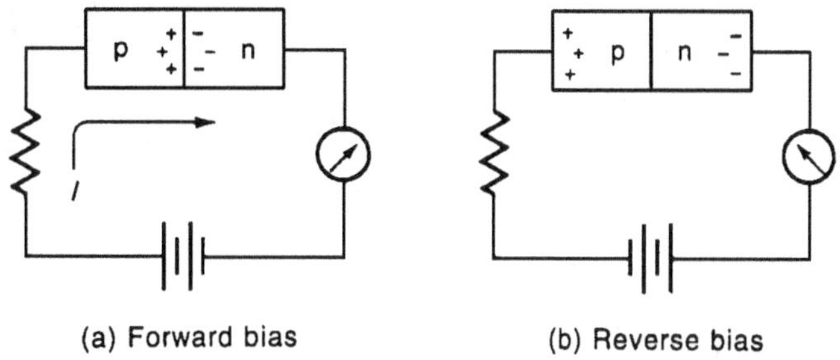

Figure 9.25 Charges inside a junction diode

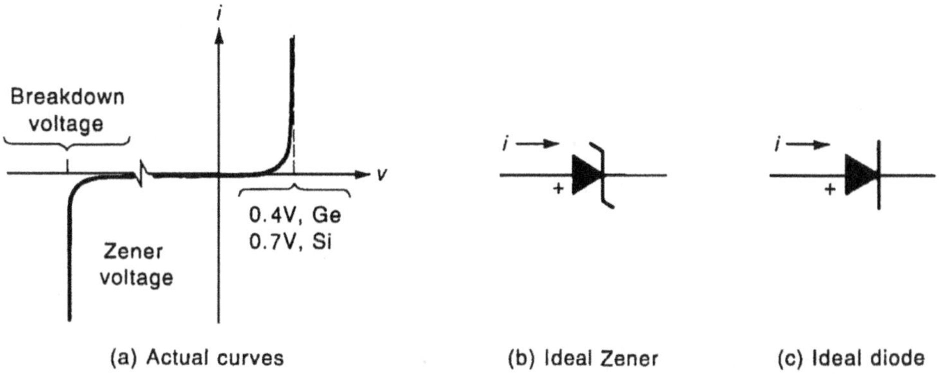

Figure 9.26 Junction diode voltage–current characteristics

Rectifying Circuits

Most diode rectifying circuits are used to convert ac voltages to *pulsed dc* voltages (see Figure 9.27). The diode is used to convert an ac voltage to a half-wave sinusoid so that the meter measurement found is the average current. Rectification is not limited to sinusoid; the following table (see Table 9.2) shows a sample of various kinds of signals and kinds of rectification, either full- or half-wave, relationships.

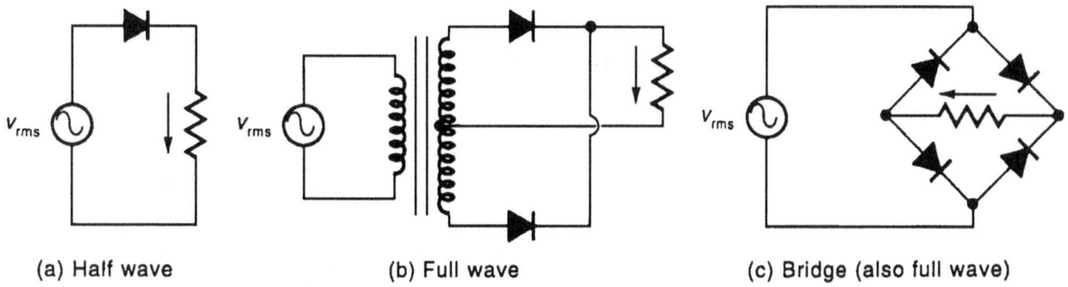

Figure 9.27 Rectifier circuits

Table 9.2 Rectified values for three signals

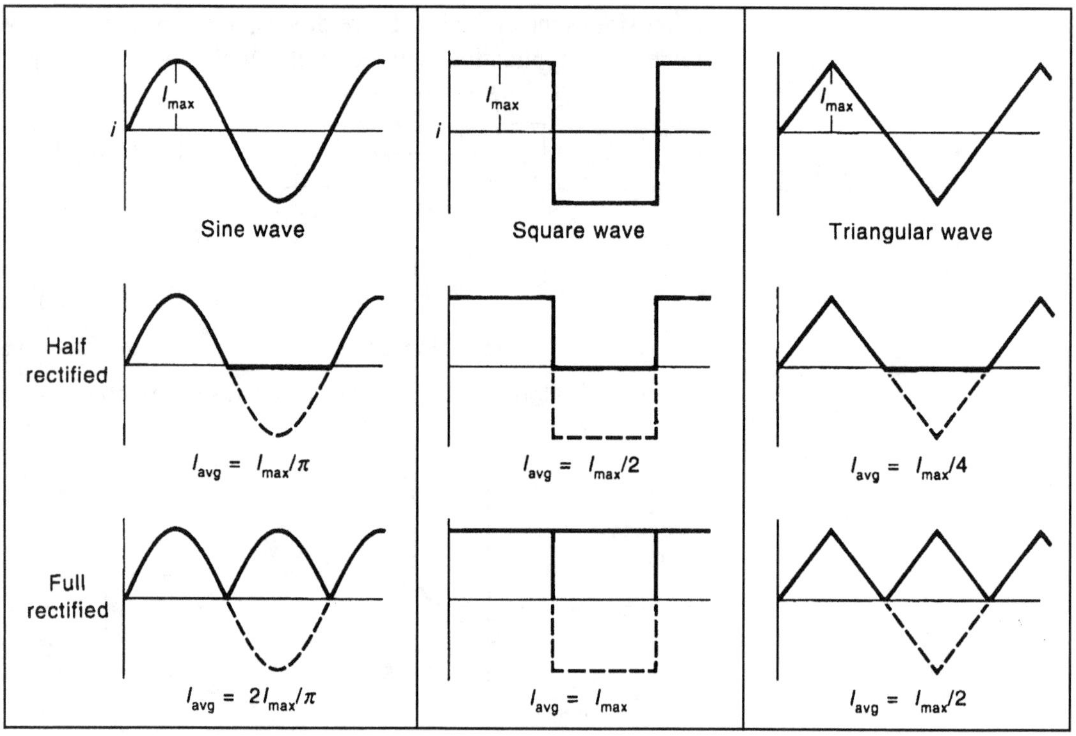

Example 9.17

A triangular wave form with a peak value of 50 volts is rectified by a half-wave rectifier and goes to a load resistor of 100 ohms (see Exhibit 24); the ammeter in the circuit is a dc type that measures average current. What is this current?

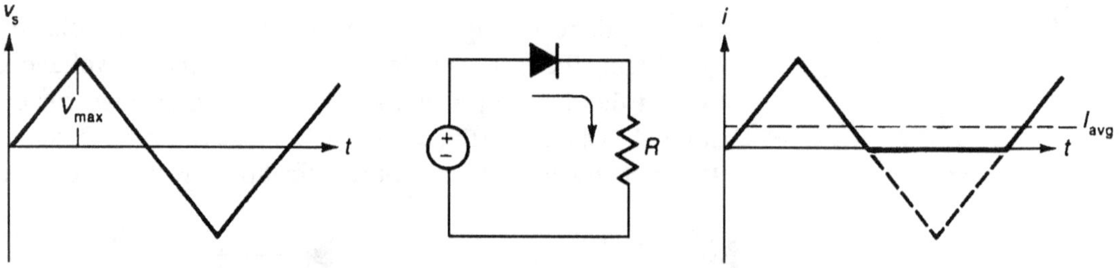

Exhibit 24 Half-wave rectifying circuit

Solution

The current is v/R and is found from the equation for average values as

$$I_{avg} = 1/R\left(1/T\int_0^T v\,dt\right) = 1/R\left[1/T\int_0^{T/2} v\,dt + 1/T\int_{T/2}^{T} 0\,dt\right] \qquad \textbf{(9.22)}$$

The integral is the area of the triangle over a half period divided by a full period, T.

$$I_{avg} = [(V_{max}/R)(0.5)(0.5T)]/T = (50/100)(1/4) = 0.125\text{ A}$$

Or, the current can be found by reading directly from Table 9.2; the average reading is one-quarter of the peak (or maximum) value of the current.

Operational Amplifiers

The operational amplifier is a high gain differential amplifier circuit (see the following list) that has been highly developed over the years. Since the cost has gone from a few hundred dollars (old vacuum tube era) to a few cents for highly developed integrated circuits, the applications for this device cover almost all areas of engineering instrumentation. This discussion focuses on an ideal operational amplifier that is treated externally as a black box. This operational amplifier (referred to as an *op-amp*) differs from a normal amplifier. For example, a home hi-fi audio amplifier's frequency response is considered good if it amplifies voltages over a frequency range from approximately 20 Hz to 20,000 Hz. An op-amp has much higher amplification. It also has several other significant characteristics:

- The amplification is usually of the order 100,000 or more. It is based on the input voltage being the difference between two very small voltages, $v_d = v_p - v_n = v_1 - v_2$. These small voltages are designated as positive and negative; however, the actual polarity of the applied voltages could be either. This implies that the output voltage is zero if the two small input voltages are equal.
- The amplification is flat over a frequency range from zero Hz (that is, *down to dc*) to some very high frequency (high compared to the highest frequency being amplified). Before the low-drift transistor, great care and clever circuit design were required to obtain a *dc amplification.*
- The currents to the actual input pins (both positive and negative) are very small and may usually be neglected; this means that the input resistance (or impedance) is very high. Also, the output resistance (or impedance) is very low; again, "low" means relatively small compared with the external circuitry values.
- The device is linear over a known range, which means that the superposition theorem applies over a range of voltages (for example, if the input voltage were doubled, the output voltage would double).

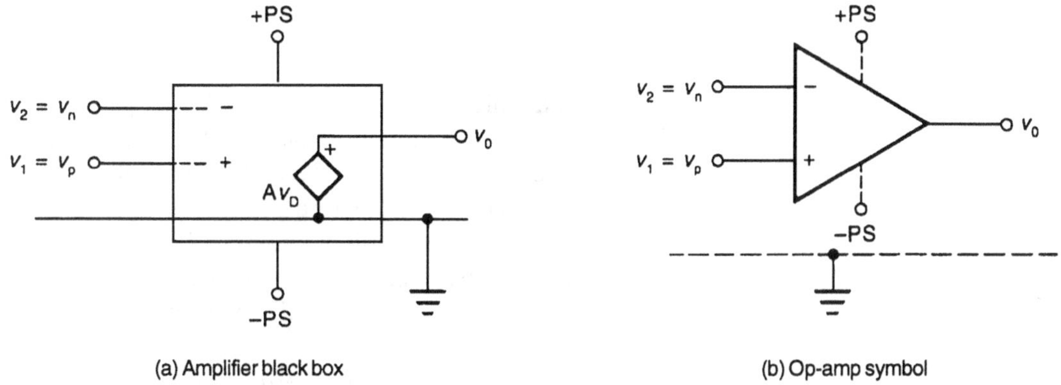

Figure 9.28 The operational amplifier

One may visualize an op-amp as the equivalent circuit shown in Figure 9.28(a). In this figure, the positive and negative power supply (+PS, –PS) connections are shown, but, as in Figure 9.28(b), they may not be shown. Since input voltages may be positive or negative, the power supply voltages are both relative to some common point, usually referred to as ground (signal ground). The power supply voltages must be larger than the largest expected output voltage within the limits

of the op-amp. These constraints are normally assumed and are not usually stated or even shown on a diagram [see Figure 9.28(b)]; the triangular symbol may have the vertical side shown as slightly rounded in some diagrams.

The op-amp is used in circuits designed for use in either the inverting or the noninverting mode. Consider the inverting mode circuit (see Figure 9.29); here, since the two voltage input pins are assumed to go to an open circuit, the input currents for both the plus and minus pins are zero, and the voltage difference between these two pins is essentially zero. Since the gain is so high and output voltages are in the several-volts range, the input voltages are in the microvolt range. This makes the circuit analysis especially easy because if one knows one input voltage, the other is essentially the same (actually only a few microvolts different). So, if one input happens to be grounded [as in Figure 9.29(a)], the other input is almost zero. The equations for the output voltage given in Figure 9.29(a) are easily obtained by realizing that the current into the op-amp itself is zero. By summing currents at Node 1, i_a must equal $-i_f$ and the voltage at the junction is near zero volts. Since the node voltage is essentially zero, i_1 is v_a/R_1 and i_f is v_0/R_f. Thus, the circuit amplifies (by a factor of $-R_f/R_1$) as it inverts and has a relatively low current input at v_a (to the external circuit if R_1 is high) and whose output acts almost like an ideal voltage source. For more than one input, one simply sums the currents at Node 1 to yield the equation in Figure 9.29(b).

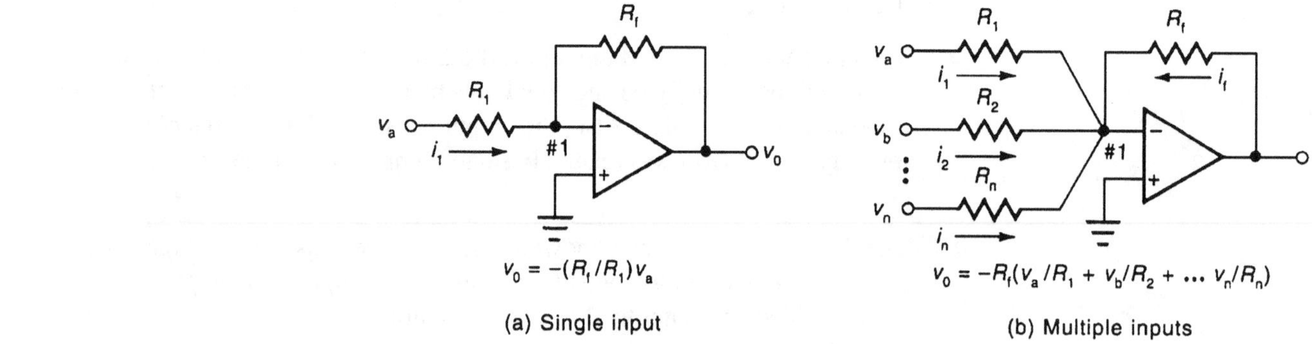

Figure 9.29 The op-amp in the inverting mode

As an example problem [for Figure 9.29(b)], four different transducers produce a possible maximum ac voltage of 0.1, 1.0, 5.0, and 10 volts, respectively. Each transducer is to be recorded on a one channel recorder whose desirable input signal level is one volt but whose input impedance will not allow a direct connection to the transducers. Since only one input at a time may be recorded, it is necessary only to determine each resistance ratio for a summing op-amp circuit. Summing is not required, but multiplying by a constant is. The ratios are easily found; in changing the level of the first voltage from 0.1 to 1, the ratio is ten. The common feedback resistor is arbitrarily chosen to be 100k ohms (the typical range of values runs from a few kilo-ohms to several megohms), then R_1 must be 10k ohms. Calculate the numerical values for the other resistor ratios shown in the circuit of Figure 9.30. When using the op-amp as a summer (all inputs connected at the same time), the instantaneous algebraic sum of the input voltages multiplied by their resistor ratio values will be summed together. They should not exceed the specified linear output voltage.

The other standard circuit configuration for the op-amp is the noninverting mode. For this, the negative input pin is normally fed from the output [perhaps through a resistive network as in Figure 9.31(b)], and the plus pin terminal is connected as an input. For the direct-feedback design [see Figure 9.31(a)], the output voltage—being also the minus terminal input—must be within a few microvolts of the plus terminal. Thus, this circuit has an output that is essentially the same as the input, and this circuit has a gain of unity with no change in polarity. The circuit is usually referred to as a buffer or voltage follower; the advantages are that it takes almost no power from an input source (that is, it does not "load" the input), and the output is almost as though it were an ideal voltage source. For the circuit shown in Figure 9.31(b), the minus input voltage must follow a certain percentage of the output and is considered a noninverting amplifier whose gain is v_0/v_{in} = Gain = $1 + R_2/R_1$. As an example, if a nonverting op-amp with a gain of three is desired, the resistor ratio must be two. If R_2 is 10 kΩ, then R_1 must be 5 kΩ.

The key to solving these operational amplifier circuits is that the current input to the op-amp itself is considered to be zero. And, if either the plus or minus input voltage is known (or is a ratio of some other voltage), the other input voltage is considered to be the same. The application of Kirchhoff's laws to the rest of the external circuit will usually yield the correct answer.

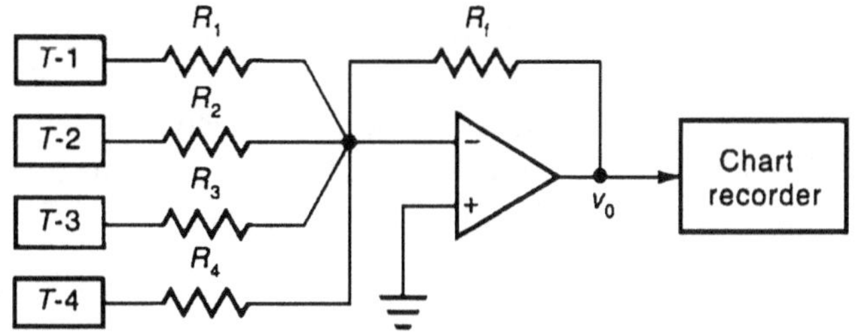

Figure 9.30 An op-amp circuit for matching voltage levels of various transducers. (*Caution*: only one switch to be closed at any one time.)

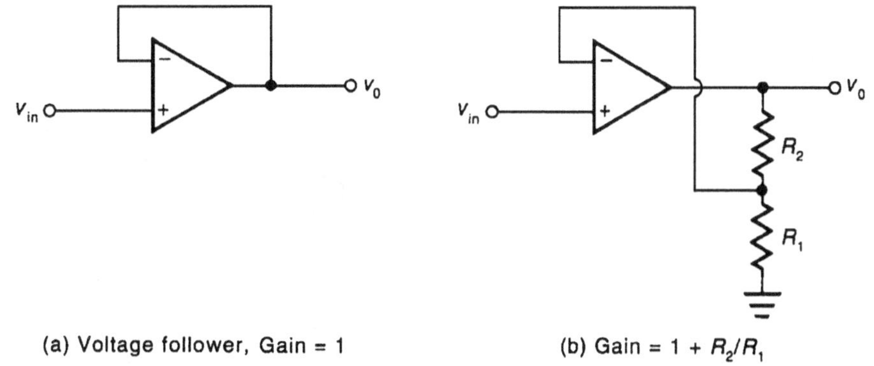

Figure 9.31 Noninverting op-amp circuits

TRANSFORMERS

The transformer is principally used in ac circuits to convert voltages from one level to another through the medium of magnetic fields. There are many other uses for the transformer, but they are specialized (such as pulse transformers). For ac circuits (implying sinusoidal wave forms), the ideal transformer is considered

as lossless with 100% efficiency; actually, the efficiency of a typical transformer is greater than 90%. For these ideal devices, the product of the input volt-amps equals the product of output volt-amps (for larger power transformers, $kVA_{in} = kVA_{out}$). The product is the apparent power (VA) rather than real power (watts). The nameplate rating of the transformer is important. The manufacturer gives the normal operating conditions; these nameplate ratings include the frequency, the voltage and the voltage ratio, and the kVA rating. The voltage ratios are the same as the turns ratio, a, and the current ratios are inversely related to the turns ratio. Whether a voltage is stepped up or down depends on which side one considers as primary and as secondary. For this discussion, assume the left side is primary (1) and the right side is secondary (2).

Example 9.18

For example, consider a transformer with a nameplate rating of 5 k*VA*, 60 Hz, and 880:220 V. The primary side might come from an 880-volt source, and the secondary would be at 220 volts.

Solution

The voltage/current rating is always given in rms values, and the turns ratio, of course, is 4:1. The current (or load) on the secondary side could be as high as $I_2 = VA/V_2 = 5000/220 = 22.7$ amperes, whereas the primary side would be $I_1 = 5000/880 = 5.68$ amperes, or 1/4 of 22.7 amperes. Note (from Exhibit 25) that a resistive load on the secondary side is $R_L = V/I = 220/22.7 = 9.69$ ohms, whereas it would be 880/5.68 = 155 ohms on the primary side. This equivalent resistance on the left side is a^2 times R_L:

$$R'_L = a^2R_L = (4)^2 \times 9.69 = 155\ \Omega$$

Here, $kVA_{in} = kVA_{out}$ and $kW_{in} = kW_{out}$ because the load is a pure resistive one (the power factor of the load is unity). If the load were $5 + j5$ (or $Z_L = \sqrt{2} \times 5\angle 45°$), the current would be

$$I_2 = V_2/Z_L = 220/\left(\sqrt{2} \times 5\angle 45°\right) = 31.1\angle -45°\text{ A}$$

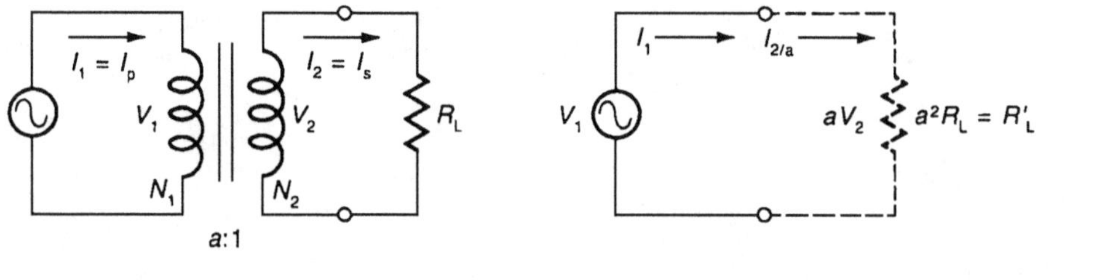

(a) Circuit with load (b) Circuit with equivalent load

Exhibit 25 A typical two-winding, loaded transformer

The current on the left side is $I_1 = I_2/a = 7.78$ amperes. These exceed the nameplate values, and a larger transformer would have to be selected. The equivalent impedance, Z'_L, of the load if reflected to the left side is

$$Z'_L = a^2Z_L = (4)^25 + j(4)^25 = 80 + j80\ \Omega$$

Caution is needed here because the power-in/power-out relationship is misleading, $P = VI\cos\theta = 220\,(31.1)\,(0.707) = 4837$ W, or less than 5 kW; the transformer rating is 40 kVA, not necessarily 40 kW.

This chapter has reviewed selected electrical fundamentals. The depth of coverage has been limited. The reader who has more study time should select a text written about electrical engineering for all engineers. Of the many books available, several stand out. Any edition of the following should be available at a library or bookstore:

- Carlson and Gisser, *Electrical Engineering Concepts and Applications,* Addison-Wesley.
- Clement and Johnson, *Electrical Engineering Science*, McGraw-Hill.
- Smith, *Circuits, Devices and Systems*, Wiley.

SELECTED SYMBOLS AND ABBREVIATIONS

Symbol or Abbreviation	Definition
A	area
A	amperes
A • t	amp-turns
ac	alternating current
B	magnetic flux density; susceptance
C	coulomb
C	capacitance
dc	direct current
E	electric field
e	induced voltage
ε	permittivity
F	farad
F	force
G	conductance
H	henry
H	magnetic field intensity
I_c	core loss
I_e	exciting current
I_f	field current
I_i	current
I_m	magnetizing current
K	dielectric constant
KCL	Kirchhoff's Current Law
KVL	Kirchhoff's Voltage Law
L	inductance
l	length
ma	milliamp
mv	millivolts
mmf	magneto-motive force
N	number of turns
N_{ag}	newton air gap
n	speed
n_s	synchronous speed
P_i, p	power

(Continued)

(Continued)

Symbol or Abbreviation	Definition
ϕ	magnetic flux
Q	point change, reactive power
R	resistance
R_{eq}	Thevenin's resistance
rms	root mean square
S	siemens
s	slip
T	tesla
T	period
T_d	developed torque
θ	angle
V, v	voltage
v	velocity
V_i, V_{oc}	terminal voltage, Thevenin's voltage
W	work
w	total energy
Y	admittance
Z, z	impedance
N_P	number of pole pairs

PROBLEMS

9.1 A charged 100-pF capacitor has initial voltage across it of 10 volts; a 100 kΩ resistor is suddenly connected across the capacitor (at $t = 0$) to discharge it. What is the magnitude of the instantaneous current at 20 microseconds?

a. 13.5 μA
b. 36.8 μA
c. 13.5 pA
d. 36.8 pA

9.2 Three 2-ohm resistors are arranged in "T" configuration. Connected to the left side is a 10-volt battery and switch; to the right is a 1-farad capacitor. The switch closes at $t = 0$. Find the time for the capacitor to reach 63% of its final voltage.

a. 0.2 s
b. 2.0 s
c. 0.3 s
d. 3.0 s

9.3 Three 2-ohm resistors are arranged in a "T" configuration. Connected to the left side is a 10-volt battery; to the right side is connected a switch and a 1-henry inductor. Assume the switch closes at $t = 0$. Find the amount of time for the inductor to reach 63% of its final current.

a. 0.2 s
b. 2.0 s
c. 0.3 s
d. 3.0 s

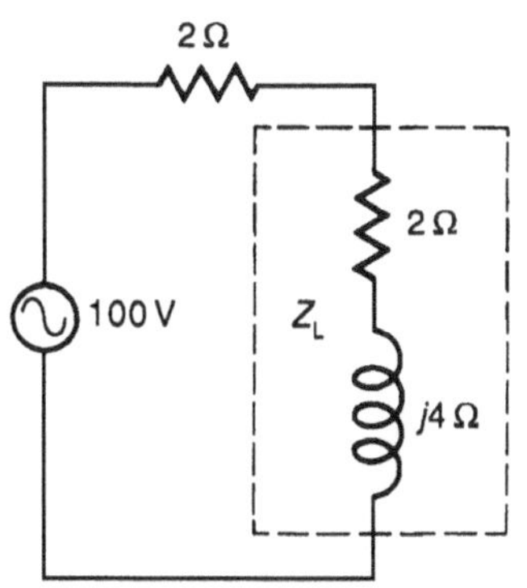

Exhibit 9.4 An ac circuit

9.4 For the circuit in the Exhibit 9.4, determine the power dissipated in the impedance, Z_L.

a. 1250 W
b. 625 W
c. 312 W
d. 1.7 kW

9.5 A resistance of 10 Ω, an inductor of 10/377 henries, and a capacitor of 20/377 farads are all connected in series to a 60-hertz, 100-volt source. Determine the magnitude of the current.

a. 3.3 A
b. 0.38 A
c. 10 A
d. $10\sqrt{2}$ A

9.6 If in Problem 9.19, all parameters were the same except that the frequency of the voltage source were doubled to 120 Hz, what would be the magnitude of the current?

a. 3.3 A
b. 0.38 A
c. 10 A
d. 5.5 A

9.7 A 10-ohm resistor and a capacitor with a capacitive reactance of $-j10$ Ω are connected in parallel. The parallel combination is connected in series through an inductive reactance of $+j10$ Ω to a 100-volt ac source. Determine the magnitude of the current from the source.

a. 6.7 A
b. 7.1 A
c. 10 A
d. $10\sqrt{2}$ A

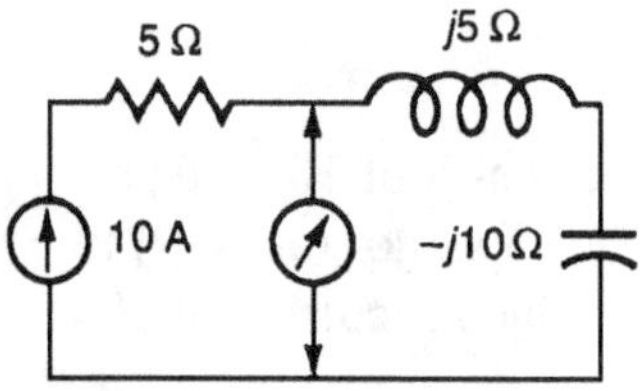

Exhibit 9.8 An ac circuit

9.8 An ac current source of 10 amperes is connected to a series circuit as shown in Exhibit 9.8. What would a voltmeter measure if the meter were connected across the inductor and capacitor combination?

a. 200 V
b. 150 V
c. 70 V
d. 50 V

9.9 For an *RLC* series circuit with $R = 10\ \Omega$, $L = 0.1$ henry, and $C = 0.1$ farad, all connected to an ac voltage source of 100 volts whose frequency could be varied, determine the frequency if maximum power is to be dissipated in R.

a. 10 Hz
b. 0 Hz
c. 1.6 Hz
d. 16 Hz

9.10 Find the transfer function $T(s) = \dfrac{V_2(s)}{V_1(s)}$ of the circuit shown in Exhibit 9.10.

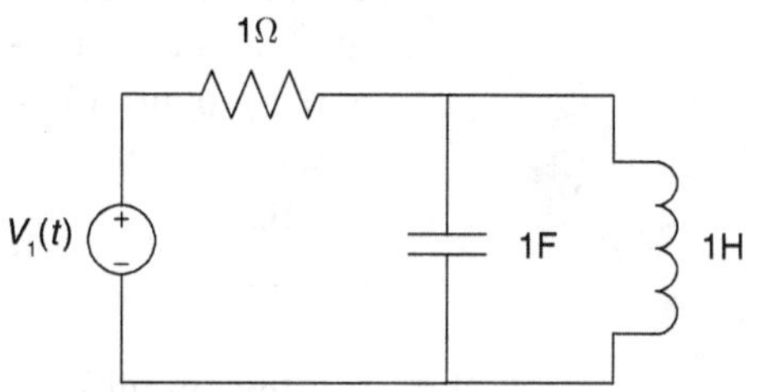

Exhibit 9.10

a. $\dfrac{s}{s^2+1}$

b. $\dfrac{s}{s^2+s+1}$

c. $\dfrac{1}{s^2+s+1}$

d. $\dfrac{1}{s^2+1}$

9.11 Find the transfer function $T(s) = \dfrac{V_0(s)}{V_{in}(s)}$ of the circuit shown in Exhibit 9.11. Assume that the op-amp is ideal.

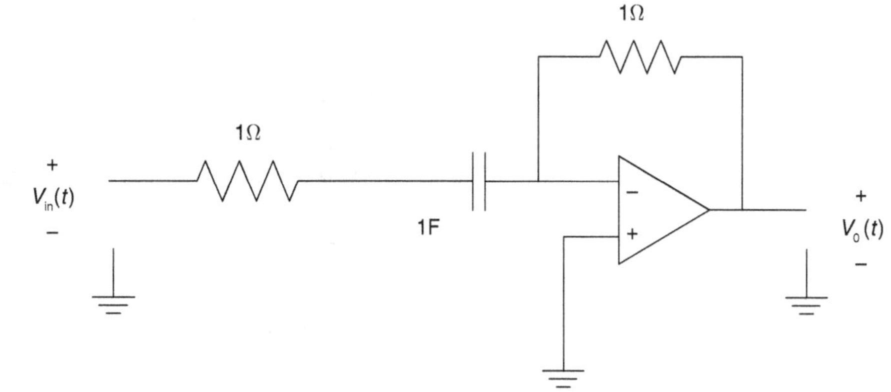

Exhibit 9.11

a. $-\dfrac{s}{s^2+1}$

b. $-\dfrac{1}{s^2+s+1}$

c. $-\dfrac{s}{s+1}$

d. $-\dfrac{1}{s+1}$

9.12 A low frequency ac voltage of 5 volts (rms) is applied to the input of the op-amp circuit in Exhibit 9.12. Determine the magnitude of the output voltage (rms).

a. 5 V
b. 2.5 V
c. 10 V
d. 20 V

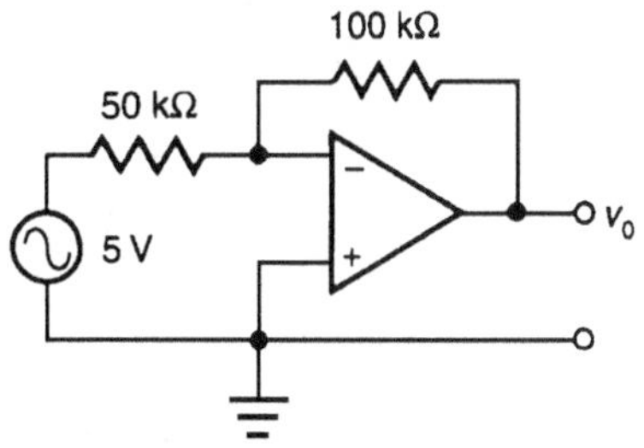

Exhibit 9.12 An op-amp circuit

9.13 A low frequency ac voltage of 5 volts (rms) is applied to the input of the op-amp circuit in Exhibit 9.13. Determine the magnitude of the output voltage (rms).

a. 5 V
b. 2.5 V
c. 10 V
d. 20 V

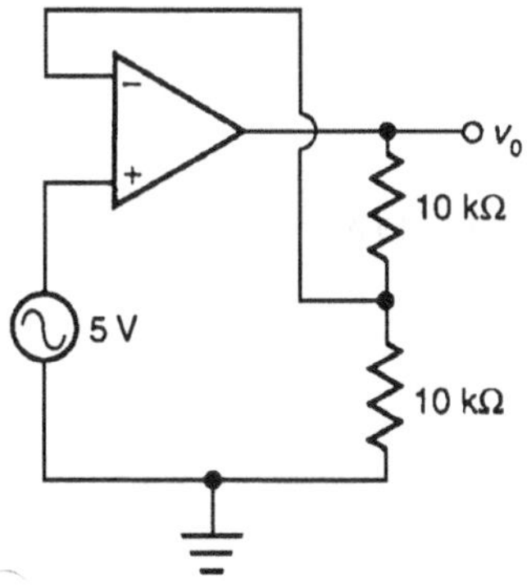

Exhibit 9.13 An op-amp circuit

9.14 The inputs for the op-amp circuits are given in Exhibit 9.14. What is the output voltage from the last op-amp?

a. +1 V c. +3 V
b. −1 V d. −3 V

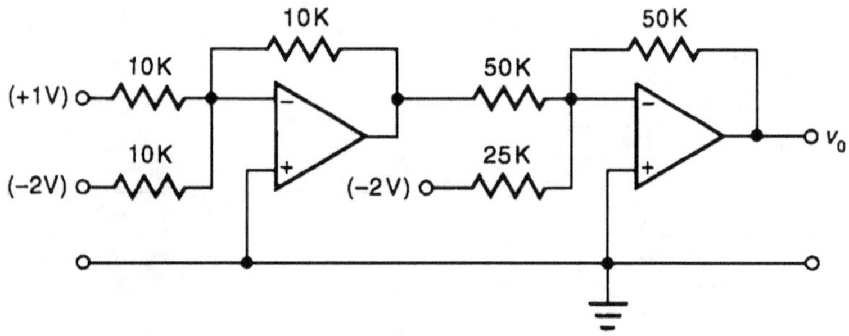

Exhibit 9.14 Summing circuits

9.15 A square wave of 1 V (or 2 V peak-to-peak) is applied to a bridge rectifier circuit where a 1-ohm resistor is connected to the output. What is the average current through the resistor?

a. 0.5 A c. πA
b. $\pi/2$ A d. 1.0 A

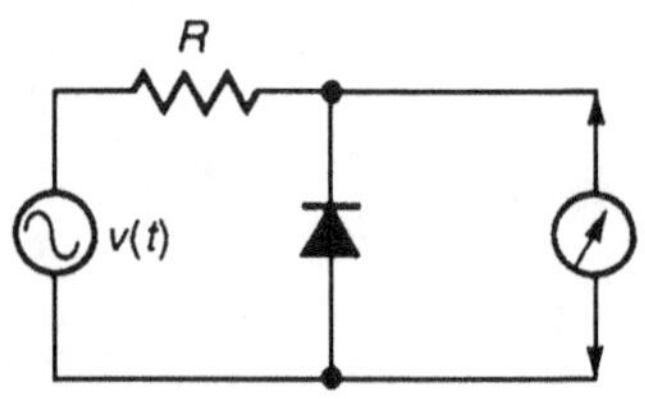

Exhibit 9.16 Clipping circuit

9.16 A sine wave voltage $v(t) = 14 \sin 2\pi ft$ is applied to the clipping circuit of Exhibit 9.16. A dc voltmeter (average reading instrument) is connected to the output. What does the meter read?

a. 2 V c. 7.5 V
b. 4.5 V d. 9 V

9.17 For an ideal, two-winding transformer whose nameplate reads 5 kVA, 400:200 V, and 60 Hz, determine the magnitude of a load that could be connected to the low voltage side for rated conditions. Assume the load impedance is $\mathbf{Z}_L = Z\angle 45°$, where Z is:

a. 4 Ω c. 16 Ω
b. 8 Ω d. 25 Ω

9.18 Determine the voltage across the 10A current source for the network shown in Exhibit 9.18.

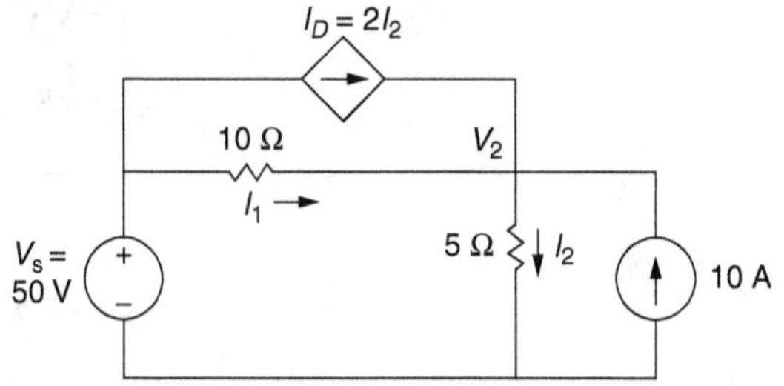

Exhibit 9.18 Circuit with two independent sources and one dependent source

9.19 An ideal linear transformer is used to match (for maximum power transfer) an amplifier with an output impedance of 100 Ω to a load of 5 Ω. Determine the turns ratio a of the transformer and the power dissipated in the load for a sinusoidal amplifier output current having a *peak* (zero-to-peak) value of 0.25 A.

9.20 The circuit in Exhibit 9.20 is in steady-state ac. Determine the magnitude of the current through the 50 Ω resistor.

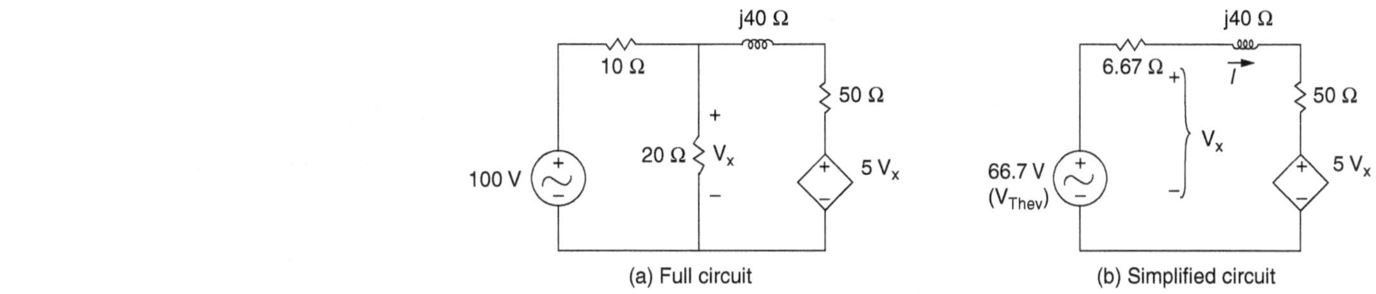

Exhibit 9.20 An ac circuit with one independent and one dependent voltage source (solved by using Thevenin's Theorem)

9.21 For the steady-state ac circuit in Exhibit 9.21 containing two energy storage elements, determine the power dissipated in the 4 Ω resistor.

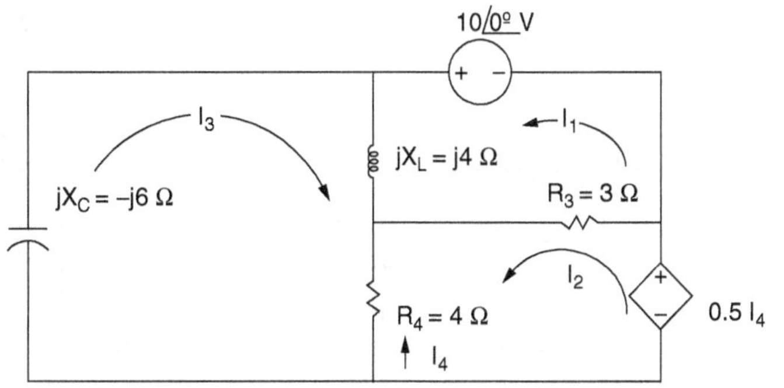

Exhibit 9.21 An ac circuit with two energy storage elements

SOLUTIONS

9.1 a. Refer to Exhibit 9.1. The time constant, τ, for an R–C circuit is RC. The voltage across the capacitor will discharge at a rate given by

$$v_C = V_C e^{-t/\tau} = 10\ e^{-20/10} = 1.35\ \text{V}, \quad i = v/R = 1.35/10^5 = 13.5 \times 10^{-6}\ \text{A}$$

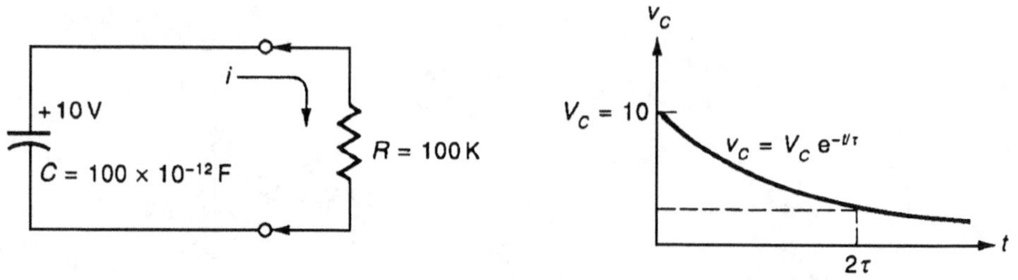

(a) R–C circuit (b) Voltage discharge curve

Exhibit 9.1 R–C circuit

9.2 d. First construct Thevenin's circuit so that all elements will be in series; this makes the R of the RC circuit especially easy to determine. Over one time constant, the voltage will build up to 63% of its final value.

$$V_{oc} = 5\ \text{V}, \quad R_{eq} = 5\ \Omega, \quad \tau = R_{ser}\ C = 3\ (1) = 3\ \text{s}$$

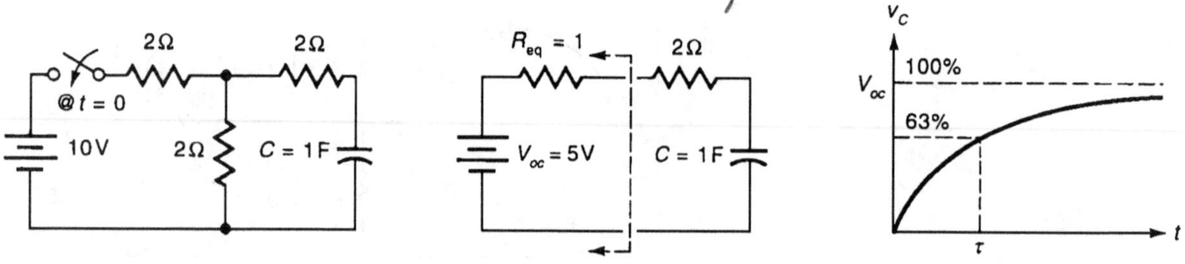

(a) Original circuit (b) Thevenin's circuit (c) Charging curve

Exhibit 9.2 Simplifying an R–C circuit

9.3 c. Make a Thevenin's equivalent circuit for finding the series resistance. The time constant for an LR circuit is $\tau = L/R = 1/3$ s. For a charging circuit, in one time constant, the current builds up to 63% of its final value.

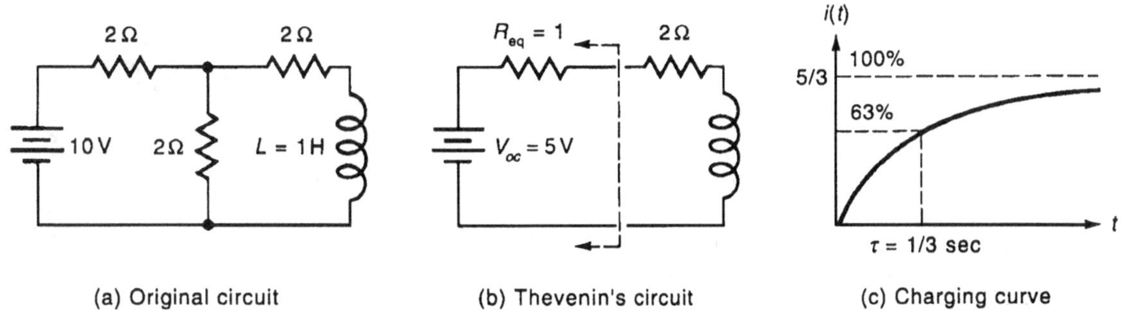

Exhibit 9.3 Simplifying an L-R circuit

9.4 b. For a series circuit, $\mathbf{Z}_{\text{total}} = R_2 + \mathbf{Z}_L$, then

$$\mathbf{I} = \mathbf{V}/\mathbf{Z} = 100\angle 0°/(4 + j4) = 100\angle 0°/\left[\sqrt{2}(4\angle 45°)\right] = 17.7\ \angle{-45°}$$

$$P_2 = I^2R = (17.7)^2(2) = 625 \text{ watts}$$

9.5 c. First it is necessary to compute the reactances (recall that $2\pi f = 377$ for 60 Hz): $X_L = 2\pi fL = (377)(10/377) = 10\ \Omega$, and $X_C = 1/(2\pi fC) = 10\ \Omega$. Thus

$$\mathbf{Z} = 10 + j10 - j10 = 10\angle 0°$$
$$\mathbf{I} = \mathbf{V}/\mathbf{Z} = 100\angle 0°/10\angle 0° = 10 \text{ A}$$

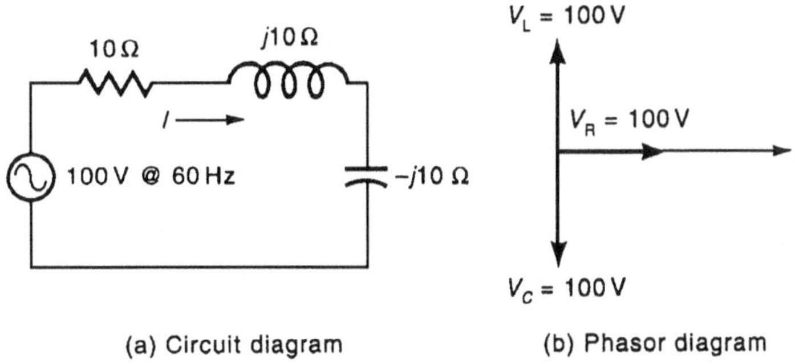

Exhibit 9.5 An R–L–C circuit

9.6 d. If the frequency is doubled, the reactances will change to $X_L = 2\ (10) = 20\ \Omega$, $X_C = 0.5\ (10) = 5\ \Omega$; hence, $Z = 10 + j20 - j5 = 18.2\angle 56.3°$. $|I| = |V/Z|$ (answer only requires magnitude) $= 100/18.2 = 5.5$ A.

9.7 **d.** First find the series equivalent to the parallel portion of the circuit:

$Z_P = (10)(-j10)/(10 - j10) = \left(10/\sqrt{2}\right)\angle -45° = 5\,j5\ \Omega;$

$Z_{total} = j10 + 5 - j5 = 5\sqrt{2}\angle 45°\ I = V/Z = 100/\left(5\sqrt{2}\right) = 10\sqrt{2}\ \text{A}$

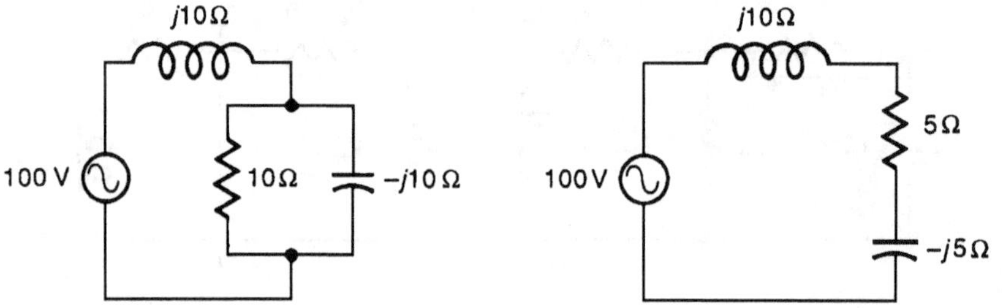

(a) Original circuit (b) Modified circuit

Exhibit 9.7 Reduced circuit

9.8 **d.** The impedance for the L–C portion of the circuit is $\mathbf{Z}_{L\text{-}C} = j5 - j10 = -j5 = 5\angle -90°$; $V_{L\text{-}C} = IZ_{L\text{-}C} = (10)(5) = 50$ V.

9.9 **c.** Maximum current occurs if X_L and X_C just cancel and Z is left with only resistance: $X_L = 2\pi fL$, $X_C = 1/(2\pi fC)$; $f_{res} = 1/(2\pi\sqrt{LC}) = 1.6$ Hz.

9.10 **b.** The frequency-domain circuit is shown in Exhibit 9.10.

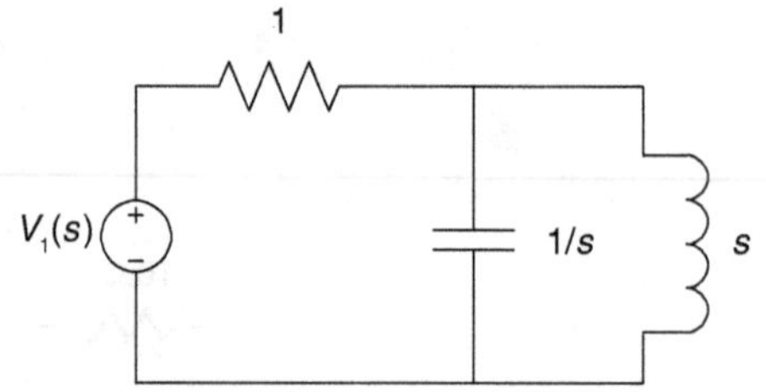

Exhibit 9.10

Combining the impedances in parallel, $Z_{eq} = \dfrac{s\left(\dfrac{1}{s}\right)}{s + \dfrac{1}{s}} = \dfrac{s}{s^2 + 1}$

Using voltage division rule, $T(s) = \dfrac{Z_{eq}}{1 + Z_{eq}} = \dfrac{s}{s^2 + s + 1}$

9.11 **c.** As the op-amp is ideal, $T(s) = \dfrac{V_0(s)}{V_{in}(s)} = -\dfrac{Z_2}{Z_1} = -\dfrac{1}{1 + 1/s} = -\dfrac{s}{s+1}$

9.12 **c.** The op-amp circuit produces a gain of $-(R_f/R_1)$ for an inverting amplifier; and here, only the magnitude is requested so the sign is not important.

$G = (100\text{k}/50\text{k}) = 2;\quad V_0 = 2V_{in},\quad V_0 = 2\,(5) = 10\ \text{V}$

9.13 **c.** This op-amp circuit produces a gain of $1 + (R_2/R_1)$ for a noninverting amplifier.

$$G = 1 + (10k/10k) = 2; \quad V_0 = 2\,(5) = 10\ V$$

9.14 **c.** The output from the first summing op-amp is $v_0 = -[(R_f/R_1)v_1 + (R_f/R_2)v_2] = -[(10k/10k)1 + (10k/10k)(-2)] = +1$ V. The output from the second summing op-amp is $v_0 = -[(R_f/R_3)v_3 + (R_f/R_4)v_4] = -[(50k/50k)1 + (50k/25k)(-2)] = +3$ V.

9.15 **d.** Refer to Exhibit 9.15. The bridge rectifier is a full-wave type, and, for a square wave, the result of taking the average is the maximum of the input itself. $I = V/R = 1/1 = 1$ A (average)

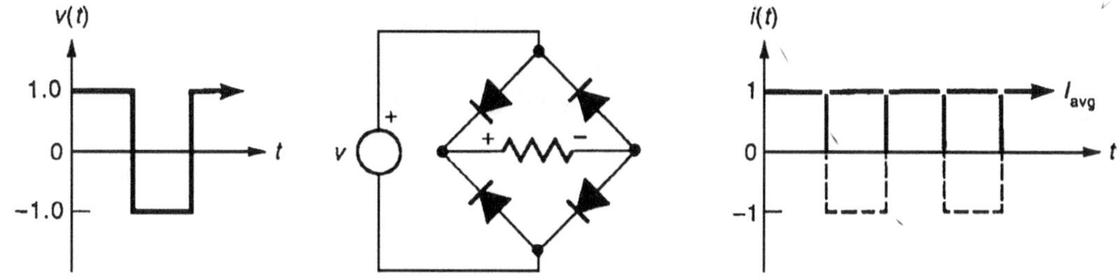

(a) Circuit (b) Full wave rectification

Exhibit 9.15 A full-wave bridge rectifier circuit

9.16 **b.** Since the output is unloaded (that is, the meter resistance is assumed to be >> R), the output is "shorted out" by the ideal diode for the negative half cycle; thus the output voltage appears as an average value. For a half-wave rectifier, the voltage is $V_{avg} = V_{max}/\pi = 14/\pi = 4.5$ V.

9.17 **b.** Assume the load side is V_2, then under full load conditions (rated current at rated voltage), the current is $I_2 = 5000$ VA/200 V = 25 A; $Z_L = 200$ V/25 A = 8 Ω regardless of phase.

9.18 Writing the loop voltage equation clockwise around the lower left loop,

$$50 = 10I_1 + 5I_2$$

Kirchhoff's Current law applied at node V_2 yields

$$I_1 + I_D + 10 = I_2, \quad \text{or} \quad I_1 + (2I_2) + 10 = I_2, \quad \text{from which } I_2 = -(10 + I_1)$$

Therefore,

$$50 = 10I_1 + 5(-10 - I_1), \quad \text{or} \quad 50 + 50 = 5I_1, \quad \text{and, thus, } I_1 = 100/5 = 20\text{A}$$

Also,

$$I_2 = -10 - (20) = -30\text{A}, \quad \text{and so } V_2 = 5(-30) = -150\text{V}$$

9.19 The primary will be assumed to be connected to the amplifier. Since a load impedance is reflected through the transformer as the turns ratio squared, the reflected load impedance "seen" by the amplifier is

$$Z_{\text{amp}} = a^2 Z_{\text{load}}$$

and, thus, the required turns ratio is

$$a = n_p/n_s = (Z_{\text{amp}}/Z_{\text{load}})^{1/2} = (100/5)^{1/2} = 4.47$$

Recalling that the rms voltage of a sinusoid is $1/\sqrt{2}$ times the peak voltage, the load current (rms) and power output are

$$I_{\text{load,rms}} = aI_{\text{amp,rms}} = 4.47(0.25/\sqrt{2}) = 0.79\text{ A}$$

$$P_{\text{load}} = I^2 R_L = (0.79)^2(5) = 3.13\text{ W}$$

You should verify that, since the transformer is ideal, this is the same value of power supplied by the *amplifier* (although at an rms current of 0.177 A flowing into a reflected impedance of 100 Ω). Thus,

$$P_{\text{amp}} = 0.177^2(100) = 3.13\text{ W}$$

In most problems like these, it may help to draw a simple circuit diagram.

9.20 The portion of the circuit to the left of the j40 Ω inductor in the original circuit has been simplified to the Thevenin equivalent shown in Exhibit 9.20 for you. (It is a good check to see if you can obtain these values.)

The equivalent circuit is now a simple series circuit and is easily solved by writing Kirchhoff's voltage law around the loop in Exhibit 9.20, as follows

$$66.7 = 6.67I + \text{j}40I + 50I + 5V_x, \quad \text{where } V_x = 66.7 - 6.67I$$
$$= [6.67 + 50 - 5(6.67)]I + \text{j}40I + 5(66.7)$$

$$66.7 - 333.5 = (23.27 + \text{j}40)I \equiv 46.5\ \angle 59.4°I$$

$$\therefore |\mathbf{I}| = (267\angle 0°)/(46.5\angle 59.4°)| = 5.74\text{A}$$

In some cases, a simplification such as that of Exhibit 9.20 may be given to you on the test as a part of the problem statement, making the problem much simpler for the careful reader!

9.21 First, it should be noted that the potential across the dependent voltage source (which is specified in terms of *branch* current I_4) is

$$0.5I_4 = 0.5(-I_3 - I_2)$$

in terms of *loop* currents I_3 and I_2.

The loop current I_2 is the *dependent* current; therefore,

$$I_2 = 0.5(-I_3 - I_2), \quad \text{giving } I_3 = -3I_2.$$

The loop currents can be established as follows. (Be careful to note that I_4 in Exhibit 9.21 is a branch current designation and, thus, does not enter into the loop-current formulation. You can consider it to be just a label on the diagram to identify a current through an element.)

Loop 1: $10\angle 0° = jX_L(I_1 + I_3) + R_3(I_1 - I_2)$

Loop 2: I_2 is that of the dependent source, $0.5I_4$

Loop 3: $R_4(I_3 + I_2) + jX_L(I_3 + I_1) + jX_C I_3 = 0$

Thus,

Loop 1: $10\angle 0° = j4(I_1 + I_3) + 3(I_1 - I_2)$, but $I_3 = -3I_2$

So,

$$10\angle 0° = (3 + j4)I_1 - (3 + j12)I_2$$
$$= 5\angle 53.1° I_1 - 12.3\angle 76.0° I_2$$

Loop 3: $$0 = 4(I_3 + I_2) + j4(I_3 + I_1) - j6I_3$$

or,

$$0 = 4(-3I_2 + I_2) + j4(-3I_2 + I_1) - j6(-3I_2)$$
$$= -8I_2 - j12I_2 + j18I_2 + j4I_1$$
$$= (j4)I_1 - (8 - j6)I_2$$

or,

$$0 = (-j4)I_1 + (8 - j6)I_2$$

which, in polar form, is

$$0 = 4\angle -90° I_1 + 10\angle -36.8° I_2$$

Then, using determinants,

$$\mathbf{I}_1 = \frac{\begin{vmatrix} 10\angle 0° & (-12.3\angle 76.0°) \\ 0 & (10\angle -36.9°) \end{vmatrix}}{\begin{vmatrix} 5\angle 53.1° & (-12.3\angle 76.0°) \\ 4\angle -90° & (10\angle -36.9°) \end{vmatrix}} = \frac{100\angle -36.9°}{50\angle 16.4° - 49.5\angle -14°}$$

$$= \frac{100\angle -36.9°}{96.0\angle 1.3°} = 1.04\angle -38.2° \mathbf{A}$$

$$\mathbf{I}_2 = \frac{\begin{vmatrix} 5\angle 53.1° & (10\angle 0°) \\ 4\angle -90° & 0 \end{vmatrix}}{96.0\angle 1.3°} = \frac{40\angle 90°}{96\angle 1.3°} = 0.417\angle 88.7° \mathbf{A}$$

The current through the 4Ω resistance is

$$I_4 = |I_4| = |I_3 + I_2| = |(-3I_2) + I_2| = 2I_2 = 2(0.417) = 0.834\text{A}$$

$$\therefore P_{4\text{ ohm}} = I^2R = (0.834)^2 4 = (0.696)(4) = 2.78\text{ W}$$

CHAPTER 10

Linear Systems

OUTLINE

FREQUENCY RESPONSE OF LINEAR SYSTEMS

If the relationship between the input and output can be expressed as

$x_{out}(t) = Kx_{in}(t)$ in the time domain, and $X_{out}(s) = KX_{in}(s)$ in the frequency domain

where K is a constant, we say the system is linear. Actually, the class of linear systems extends somewhat beyond the case where K is constant. The following definition defines a linear system: A system is linear if and only if

$$H(s)\,(a_1X_{in\,1}(s) + a_2X_{in\,2}(s)) = H(s)a_1X_{in\,1}(s) + H(s)a_2X_{in\,2}(s)$$

where a_1 and a_2 are any real numbers, and $X_{in\,1}$ and $X_{in\,2}$ are any two inputs.

Any linear system is characterized by a transfer function. A linear system also has transfer characteristics. However, if a system is not linear, the system does not have a transfer function.

Consider a linear system whose transfer function (in the Laplace domain) is known, being excited by an input signal having Laplace transform.

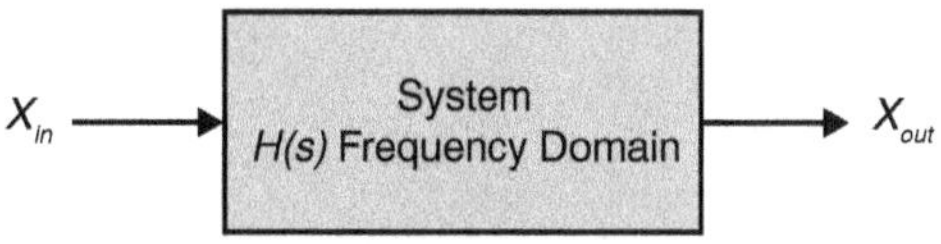

Figure 10.1 Single-Input, Single-Output System

The Laplace transform of the output signal, $X_{out}(s)$, is given by

$$X_{out}(s) = H(s)X_{in}(s) \tag{10.1}$$

In the time domain, $X_{out}(t)$ is called the impulse response. We have the equivalent expression in the time domain where * denotes a convolution in time.

$$x_{out}(t) = x_{in}(t) * h(t) \tag{10.2}$$

That is, the output signal is the convolution of the input signal with the impulse response of the system's transfer function. The convolution operation is defined as

$$x_{\text{in}}(t)\cdot h(t)=\int_{-\infty}^{\infty} x_{\text{in}}(\tau)h(t-\tau)d\tau \tag{10.3}$$

The merit of frequency-domain analysis is that for particular inputs, it is often easier to use Eqn. (10.1) and the inverse Laplace Transform to calculate the expected output of a circuit rather than Eqn. (10.3). Examples of this are when the inputs are pure sinusoids, or step inputs.

Sinusoidal Inputs

The output of an oscillator can often be characterized as a sinusoidal signal given by

$$x_{\text{in}}(t)=A_{\text{in}}\cos\left(\omega_{\text{in}}t\right)=A_{\text{in}}\frac{\left(e^{j\omega_{\text{in}}t}+e^{-j\omega_{\text{in}}t}\right)}{2} \tag{10.4}$$

where e^x is defined as

$$e^x=\cos(\omega t)+j\sin(\omega t) \tag{10.5}$$

and j is defined as

$$j=\sqrt{-1} \tag{10.6}$$

is a purely imaginary number of unit magnitude.

In the frequency domain, $X_{\text{in}}(s)$ consists of two impulses, one at

$$s=j\omega_{\text{in}} \tag{10.7}$$

and one at

$$s=-j\omega_{\text{in}} \tag{10.8}$$

with each impulse having a magnitude $A_{\text{in}}/2$.

After taking the inverse Laplace Transform of the output signal, it is seen that

$$\begin{aligned} x_{\text{out}}(t)&=\frac{A_{\text{in}}}{2}\left(e^{j\omega_{\text{in}}t}H(i\omega_{\text{in}})+e^{-j\omega_{\text{in}}t}H(-i\omega_{\text{in}})\right)\\ &=\frac{A_{\text{in}}}{2}\left|H(i\omega_{\text{in}})\right|\left(e^{j\omega_{\text{in}}t}e^{j\phi}+e^{-j\omega_{\text{in}}t}e^{-j\phi}\right)\\ &=\frac{A_{\text{in}}}{2}\left|H(i\omega_{\text{in}})\right|\left(e^{j(\omega_{\text{in}}t+\phi)}+e^{-j(\omega_{\text{in}}t+\phi)}\right)\\ &=\frac{A_{\text{in}}}{2}\left|H(i\omega_{\text{in}})\right|\cos\left(\omega_{\text{in}}t+\phi\right) \end{aligned} \tag{10.9}$$

where $H(j\omega_{\text{in}})$, the transfer function has been written in terms of its magnitude response and phase response; that is

$$H(j\omega_{\text{in}})=|H(j\omega_{\text{in}})|e^{j\phi} \tag{10.10}$$

and

$$\phi=\angle H(j\omega_{\text{in}}).$$

The development just presented has been given in terms of the Laplace Transform for the particular case where $s = j\omega_{in}$. It is often presented in terms of Fourier Transforms, which are equivalent to Laplace Transforms with $s = j\omega_{in}$, but in the notation, the j symbol denoting that the frequency is complex is usually not shown. For examaple, Eqn. (10.10) would normally be written as

$$H(\omega_{in}) = |H(\omega_{in})|e^{j\phi} \tag{10.11}$$

and

$$\phi = \angle H(\omega_{in}).$$

The interpretation of Eqn. (10.11) is as follows: when a linear electronic circuit is excited with the output of a sinusoidal oscillator, the output of the circuit will also be a sinusoid at the same frequency; however, its magnitude and phase will be different. In particular, the magnitude of the output sinusoid will be equal to the magnitude of the input sinusod multiplied by $|H(\omega_{in})|$ where $H(\omega_{in})$ is the Fourier Transform of the circuit or system commonly called the Transfer Function. In addition, the phase difference between the output sinusoid and the input sinusoid will be equal to ϕ where again $\phi = \angle H(j\omega_{in})$.

Example **10.1**

Consider a linear circuit having a transfer function given by

$$H(s) = \frac{A_0}{1 + \dfrac{s}{\omega_0}} \tag{10.12}$$

where $A_0 = 10$ and $\omega_0 = 2\pi \times 100$ rad/s. Find the magnitude and phase of the output sinusoid assuming the input sinusoid has a peak voltage of 1V for the frequencies 10Hz, 100Hz, and 1kHz.

Solution

The transfer function given by Eqn. (10.12) is often called a first-order, low-pass transfer function and is the most-commonly encountered transfer function in electronic circuits. It is an often-used model for an operational amplifier. We can rewrite Eqn. (10.12) with $s = j\omega$ using Fourier Transforms as

$$H(\omega) = \frac{A_0}{1 + j\dfrac{\omega}{\omega_0}} = \frac{A_0}{\sqrt{1 + \left(\dfrac{\omega}{\omega_0}\right)^2}} e^{j\phi} \tag{10.13}$$

where

$$\phi = -\tan^{-1}\left(\frac{\omega}{\omega_0}\right) \tag{10.14}$$

Note that

$$|H(\omega)| = \frac{A_0}{\sqrt{1 + \left(\dfrac{\omega}{\omega_0}\right)^2}} \tag{10.15}$$

Using Eqn. (10.14) and Eqn. (10.15), for the case f = 100 Hz, where $\omega = 2\pi f$ = 628.3 rad/s,

$$|H(\omega)| = \frac{10}{\sqrt{1+\left(\frac{2\pi f}{2\pi f_0}\right)^2}} = \frac{10}{\sqrt{1+\left(\frac{f}{f_0}\right)^2}}$$

$$= \frac{10}{\sqrt{1+\left(\frac{10}{100}\right)^2}} = 9.5 = 19.96\text{dB} \quad \textbf{(10.16)}$$

where converting a gain to dB implies taking the log (base 10) and multiplying by 20. The phase shift is also given by

$$\phi = -\tan^{-1}\left(\frac{10}{100}\right) = -0.00997 \text{ rad} = -5.7° \quad \textbf{(10.17)}$$

The fact that the phase difference between the input and output is negative implies the output sinusoid comes after the input sinusoid by –5.7°, or in other words, "lags" the input sinusoid. For f_{in} = 100Hz, we have

$$|H(\omega)| = \frac{10}{\sqrt{2}} = 0.7071\times 10 = 20\text{dB} - 3.01\text{dB} \quad \textbf{(10.18)}$$

and

$$\phi = -\tan^{-1}(1) = -0.785 \text{ rad} = -45° \quad \textbf{(10.19)}$$

Note that at $f_{in} = f_0$ or equivalently, for $\omega_{in} = \omega_0$, the magnitude gain is down by –3dB, and the phase is delayed by –45°. Finally, for f_{in} = 1 kHz ,we have

$$|H(\omega)| = \frac{10}{\sqrt{1+\left(\frac{f}{f_0}\right)^2}} = \frac{10}{\sqrt{1+\left(\frac{1000}{100}\right)^2}} = \frac{10}{10.05}$$

$$= 20\text{dB} - 20.04\text{dB} = -0.04\text{dB} \quad \textbf{(10.20)}$$

and

$$\phi = -\tan^{-1}\left(\frac{1000}{10}\right) = -1.47 \text{ rad} = -84° \quad \textbf{(10.21)}$$

Thus, the gain is approximately 20dB less than its low-frequency value, and the phase shift is approaching –90°.

Step Response of First-Order Circuits

Another common means of characterizing linear circuits is to excite them with step inputs. This would normally be done in practice by exciting them with a square wave having a low enough frequency (or equivalently long enough period) so the circuit settles between edges and, therefore, each edge effectively excites the circuit similar to a step input.

Consider a step input where $x_{in}(t) = A_{in}u(t)$, the step-input function $u(t)$, is defined as

$$u(t)=\begin{cases}0, & t\leq 0\\ 1, & t>0\end{cases} \tag{10.22}$$

The step function $u(t)$ has a Laplace Transform given by

$$U(s) = 1/s \tag{10.23}$$

Therefore, the Laplace Transform of the output of a linear system having transfer function $T(s)$, and a step input is given by

$$x_{out}(s)=A_{in}\frac{H(s)}{x} \tag{10.24}$$

Consider the special case where a first-order, low-pass filter has a transfer function given by

$$H(s)=\frac{A_0}{1+\dfrac{s}{\omega_0}} \tag{10.25}$$

Using Eqn. (10.24), we have

$$x_{out}(s)=\frac{A_{in}}{s}\frac{A_0}{1+\dfrac{s}{\omega_0}} \tag{10.26}$$

Eqn. (10.26) can be rewritten in terms of its residues as

$$x_{out}(s)=A_{in}A_{out}\left[\frac{1}{s}-\frac{1}{s+\omega_0}\right] \tag{10.27}$$

It is now simple to take the Inverse Laplace Transform to get

$$x_{out}(t) = u(t)A_{in}A_0[1 - e^{-t/\tau}] \tag{10.28}$$

where

$\tau = 1/\omega_0$.

In a similar manner, it is straightforward to show that the step response of a general first-order circuit having a transfer function given by

$$H(s)=A_0\left(\frac{1+\dfrac{s}{\omega_z}}{1+\dfrac{s}{\omega_0}}\right) \tag{10.29}$$

has an output having Laplace Transform

$$x_{out}(s)=\frac{A_{in}A_0}{s}\left(\frac{1+\dfrac{s}{\omega_z}}{1+\dfrac{s}{\omega_0}}\right) \tag{10.30}$$

and its step response is given by

$$x_{\text{out}}(t) = u(t)A_{\text{in}}A_0\left[1-\left(1-\frac{\omega_0}{\omega_z}\right)e^{-t/\tau}\right] \quad \textbf{(10.31)}$$

where

$\tau = 1/\omega_0$.

Note that the step response for very slightly greater than 0 is denoted by $x_{\text{out}}(0^+)$ and using Eqn. (10.31) is easily found to be given by

$$x_{\text{out}}(0^+) = A_{\text{in}}A_0\frac{\omega_0}{\omega_z} \quad \textbf{(10.32)}$$

This is easily verified using the Laplace Transform property:

$$x_{\text{out}}(0^+) = \lim_{s\to\infty} sX_{\text{out}}(s) = \lim_{s\to\infty} H(S)A_{\text{in}} = A_{\text{in}}A_0\frac{\omega_0}{\omega_z} \quad \textbf{(10.33)}$$

together with Eqn. (10.30). In a similar manner, it is easily found that after a long time, when the first-order circuit has settled, its response denoted $x_{\text{out}}(\infty)$ is given by

$$x_{\text{out}}(\infty) = A_{\text{in}}A_0 \quad \textbf{(10.34)}$$

Once again, this can be verified using the Laplace Transform property

$$x_{\text{out}}^{(\infty)} = \lim_{s\to 0} sX_{\text{out}}(s) = \lim_{s\to 0} H(S)A_{\text{in}} \quad \textbf{(10.35)}$$

together with Eqn. (10.30). Using Eqns. (10.31), (10.32), and (10.35), one can derive the general equation giving the step response of any first-order circuit as

$$x(t) = x(\infty) - [x(\infty) - x(0^+)]e^{-t/\tau} \quad \textbf{(10.36)}$$

s-Domain Circuit Analysis

The concept of transforming the time-domain circuit to the s-domain circuit is depicted in Figure 10.2. The s-domain circuit is topologically identical to the time-domain circuit; the only difference is how the circuit elements are modeled.

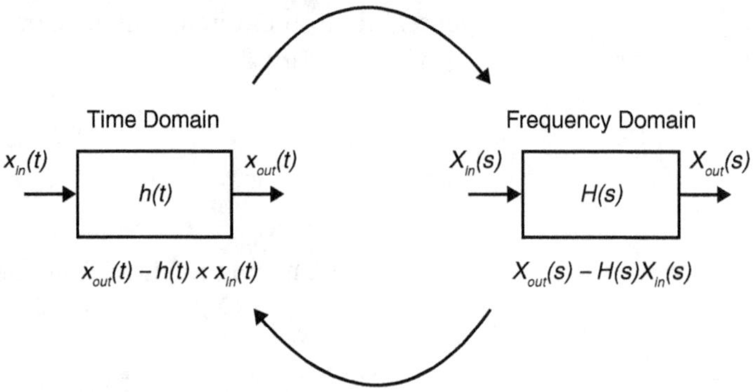

Figure 10.2 Transformation from Time-Domain Circuit to s-domain Circuit

All elements in the two circuits are identical except for the capacitors and inductors. The inductors and capacitors are simply replaced with impedances given in Figure 10.3.

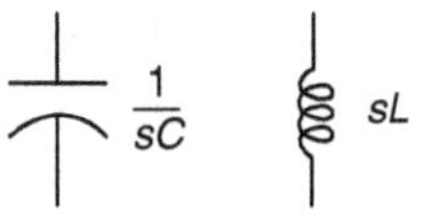

Figure 10.3 Impedances of Inductors and Capacitors in s-domain Network

Mathematically, these mappings of an element to an impedance can be expressed as

$$C \rightarrow 1/(sC) \quad \text{and} \quad L \rightarrow sL$$

After the s-domain circuit is obtained, it can be analyzed using standard circuit analysis techniques to obtain the transfer function $H(s)$. Once $H(s)$ is obtained, the sinusoidal steady state response can be found.

Phasor-Domain Circuit Analysis

The concept of transforming a circuit to the phasor-domain is shown in Figure 10.4.

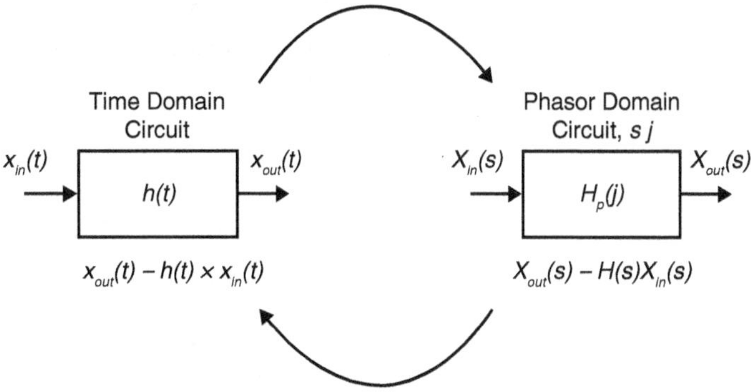

Figure 10.4 Impedances of Inductors and Capacitors in Phasor-Domain Network

Mathematically, these mappings of an element to an impedance can be expressed as

$$C \rightarrow \frac{1}{j\omega C} \quad \text{and} \quad L \rightarrow j\omega L.$$

After the phasor-domain circuit is obtained, it can be analyzed using standard circuit analysis techniques to obtain the phasor-domain transfer function $H_p(j\omega)$. Whereas the transfer function $H(s)$ includes the variable s and thus is neither a real or complex quantity until further information about s is given, the phasor-domain transfer function is a complex quantity, as are all impedances in the phasor-domain circuit. As such, manipulations of equations leading to $H_p(j\omega)$ can be made as part of the analysis process. Unfortunately this additional flexibility, when exercised, often causes unnecessary arithmetic calculations when calculating $H_p(j\omega)$.

Since the phasor-domain circuit and the s-domain circuits differ only in how the energy storage elements are characterized, and since this characterization is similar, it follows that

$$H(j\omega) = H(s)|_{s \rightarrow j\omega} = H_p(j\omega)$$

Example 10.2

Two approaches to sinusoidal steady state analysis

Consider the circuit in Exhibit 1. The sinusoidal steady state response will be obtained using two methods of analysis: the s-domain approach and the phasor-domain approach. In both cases, it will be assumed that

$$V_{in} = V_{out}\cos(\omega t + \phi)$$

and the goal is to obtain the steady state response $V_{out}(t)$.

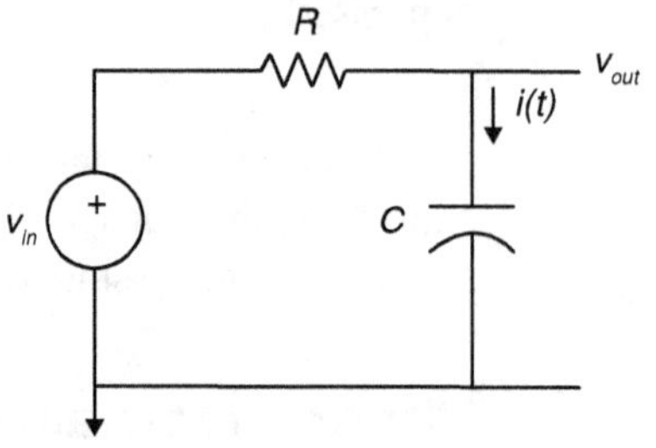

Exhibit 1 Example Time-Domain Circuit

s-Domain Analysis

The s-domain equivalent circuit is shown in Figure 10.5:

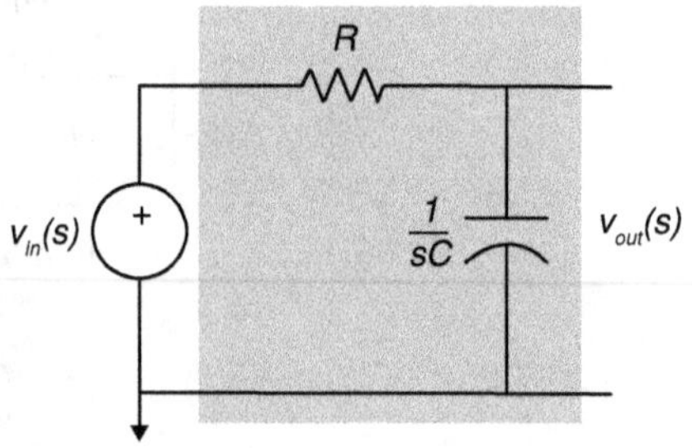

Figure 10.5 s Domain Circuit

It follows from KCL by summing currents at the output node that

$$V_{out}(s) = V_{in}(s)\left(\frac{\frac{1}{sC}}{\frac{1}{sC}+R}\right) = \frac{V_{in}(s)}{1+sCR}$$

Therefore, the transfer function is:

$$H(s) = \frac{V_{out}(s)}{V_{in}(s)} = \frac{1}{1+sCR}$$

Evaluating at s = jω,

$$|H(j\omega)| = \frac{1}{\sqrt{1+(\omega CR)^2}}, \qquad \angle H(j\omega) = -\tan^{-1}(\omega CR)$$

So the steady state output is

$$v_{out}(t) = V_m\left(\frac{1}{\sqrt{1+(\omega CR)^2}}\right)\cos\left(\omega t + \phi - \tan^{-1}(\omega CR)\right)$$

Phasor Domain Analysis

The phasor equivalent example circuit is shown in Figure 10.6.

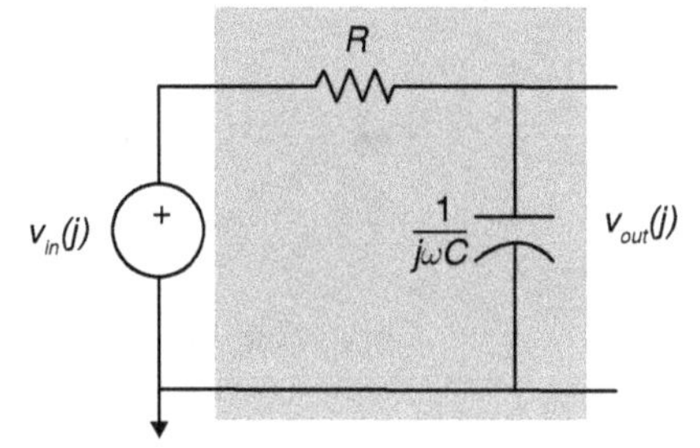

Figure 10.6

Phasor Domain Circuit

It follows from KCL by summing currents at the output node that

$$V_{out}(j\omega) = V_{in}(j\omega)V\left(\frac{\frac{1}{j\omega C}}{\frac{1}{j\omega C} + R}\right) = \frac{V_{in}(j\omega)}{1 + j\omega CR}$$

and the phasor domain transfer function is

$$H_p(s) = \frac{V_{out}(j\omega)}{V_{in}(j\omega)} = \frac{1}{1 + j\omega CR}.$$

The magnitude and phase of $H_p(j\omega)$ are

$$|H_p(j\omega)| = \frac{1}{\sqrt{1 + (\omega CR)^2}}, \qquad \angle H_p(j\omega) = -\tan^{-1}(\omega CR).$$

So the steady state output is,

$$v_{out}(t) = V_m\left(\frac{1}{\sqrt{1 + (\omega CR)^2}}\right)\cos\left(\omega t + \phi - \tan^{-1}(\omega CR)\right).$$

As expected, the phasor-domain and s-domain analysis results are identical.

Example 10.3

Consider the first-order, low-pass circuit shown in Exhibit 2. Assume $R = 1\text{k}\Omega$ and $C = 1\text{nF}$. Find the –3dB frequency of the circuit and the time constant of the circuit. Assuming the input signal is a 0.5V step input at time 0, what is the output voltage at 1.5μs?

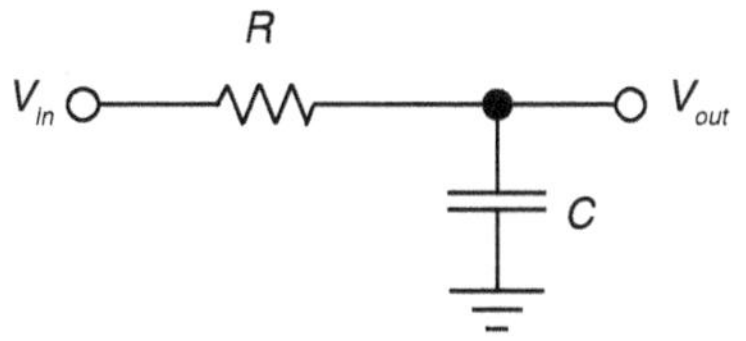

Exhibit 2

Solution

The transfer function of this circuit is easily found as

$$H(s)=\frac{1}{1+sCR}$$

The –3dB amplitude drop of the transfer function is equal to $H(s)=1/2$, so $=\frac{1}{CR}$.

This value of s –3dB of the amplitude is the cut off frequency ω_o

$$\omega_o=\frac{1}{RC}=\frac{1}{\left(1\times10^{-9}\right)\left(1\times10^{3}\right)}=1\times10^{6}\text{ rad}=1\text{ Mrad}$$

or
$$f_o=\frac{\omega_o}{2\pi}=\frac{1}{2\pi RC}=159\text{ Hz}$$

The time constant of the circuit is

$$\tau=\frac{1}{\omega_o}=RC=1\mu s.$$

Using Eqn. (10.36) the output voltage at 1.5 µs is found,

$$v_{out}(t)=0.5\left(1-e^{-1.5\times10^{-6}/1\times10^{-6}}\right)=0.39V.$$

Example 10.4

Consider an amplifier having a small signal transfer function that approximately is given by

$$A(s)=\frac{A_o}{1+\frac{s}{\omega_{-3\text{dB}}}}$$

What is the approximate unity gain frequency and phase shift at the unity gain frequency for $A_o = 1\times10^5$ and $\omega_{-3\text{dB}} = 1\times10^3$ radians?

Solution

At frequencies $s=j\omega >> j\omega_{-3\text{dB}}$, which is the case for most signal frequencies, the s term in the denominator dominates,

$$A(s)=\frac{A_o\omega_{-3\text{dB}}}{s}$$

and the open loop transfer function of the amplifier is very similar to that of an ideal integrator. The magnitude of the Fourier Transform is found by substituting $s=j\omega$. To find the unity gain frequency, this magnitude should be set to unity and then ω (often called ω_{ta}) should be solved.

$$\left|\frac{A_o\omega_{-3\text{dB}}}{\omega_{ta}}\right|=1$$

implying that

$$\omega_{ta} = A_o \omega_{-3\text{dB}}$$

the phase shift of the transfer function is

$$\angle A(\omega) = -\tan^{-1}\left(\frac{\omega}{\omega_{-3\text{dB}}}\right)$$

Since $A_o >> 1$, and $\frac{\omega}{\omega_{-3\text{dB}}} >> 1$,

$$\angle A(\omega_{ta}) = -90°$$

and $\omega_{ta} = 1 \times 10^8$ rad.

Resonance

Resonance in AC circuits implies a special frequency determined by the values of the resistance, capacitance, and inductance in an RLC second order circuit. For series resonance, the condition of resonance is straightforward and it is characterized by minimum impedance and zero phase. Parallel resonance, which is more common in electronic practice, requires a more careful definition.

The resonance of a series RLC circuit occurs when the inductive and capacitive reactances (X) are equal in magnitude but cancel each other because they are 180° in phase. The sharp minimum in impedance that occurs is useful in tuning applications. The sharpness of the minimum depends on the value of R and is characterized by the "Q" of the circuit.

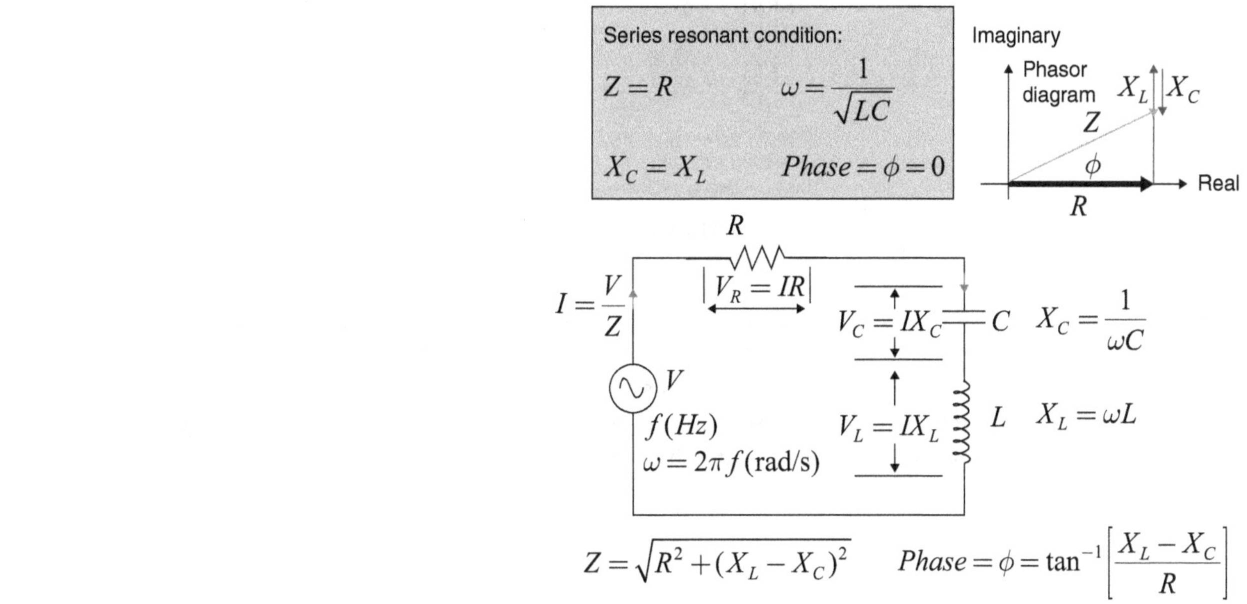

Figure 10.7

The RLC series circuit is a very important example of a resonant circuit. It has a minimum of impedance $Z = R + j0$ at the resonant frequency (the impedance is real at the resonant frequency), and the phase angle is equal to zero (because the imaginary component of the impedance is zero) at resonance. One way to visualize the behavior of the RLC series circuit is with the phasor diagram shown in Figure

10.7. The phasor diagram shown is at a frequency where the inductive reactance is greater than that of the capacitive reactance. This would occur at a frequency above the resonant frequency.

Resonant circuits are used to respond selectively to signals of a given frequency while discriminating against signals of different frequencies. If the response of the circuit is more narrowly peaked around the chosen frequency, we say that the circuit has higher "selectivity." A "quality factor" Q, as described in the following paragraph, is a measure of that selectivity. We speak of a circuit having a "high Q" if it is more narrowly selective.

An example of the application of resonant circuits is the selection of AM radio stations by the radio receiver. The selectivity of the tuning must be high enough to discriminate strongly against stations above and below in carrier frequency but not so high as to discriminate against the "sidebands" created by the imposition of the signal by amplitude modulation.

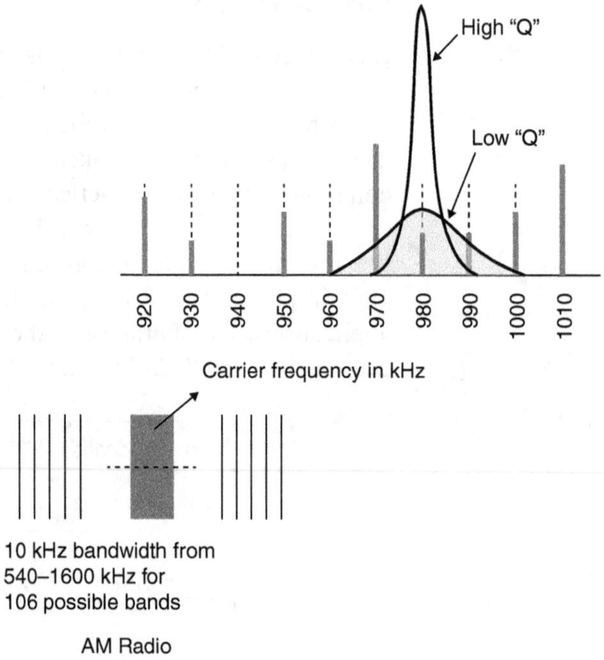

Figure 10.8

The selectivity of a circuit is dependent upon the amount of resistance in the circuit. The smaller the resistance, the higher the "Q" for given values of L and C; this implies that higher resistances incur higher loss in signal. The parallel resonant circuit is more commonly used in electronics, but the algebra necessary to characterize the resonance is much more involved.

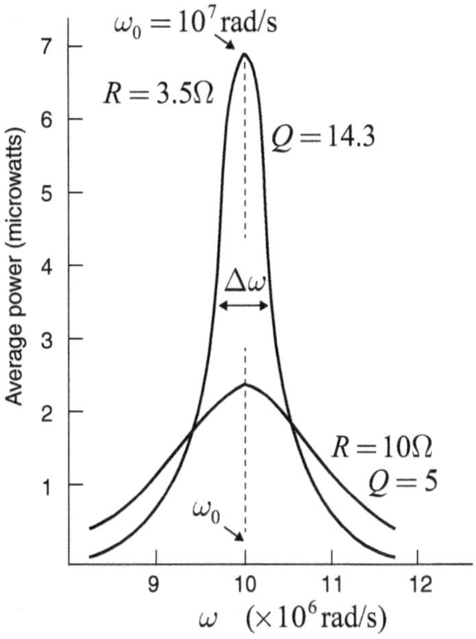

Figure 10.9

Using the same circuit parameters, Figure 10.10 shows the power dissipated in the circuit as a function of frequency. Since this power depends upon the square of the current, these resonant curves appear steeper and narrower than the resonance peaks for current above.

The quality factor Q is defined by

$$Q = \frac{\omega_0}{\Delta\omega}$$

where $\Delta\omega$ is the width of the resonant power curve at half maximum.

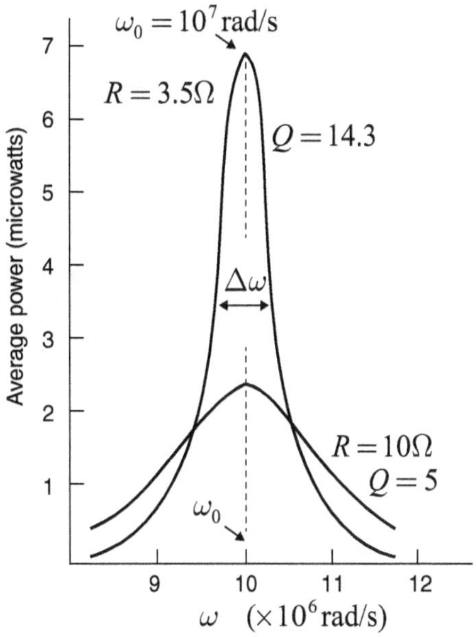

Figure 10.10

Since that width turns out to be $\Delta\omega = R/L$, the value of Q can also be expressed as

$$Q = \frac{\omega_0 L}{R}$$

The Q is a commonly used parameter in electronics, with values usually in the range of $Q = 10$ to 100 for circuit applications.

For series resonant circuits,

$$\omega_0 = \frac{1}{\sqrt{LC}} = 2\pi f_0 (\text{rad / s})$$

$$\omega_0 L = \frac{1}{\omega_0 C}$$

$Z = R$ at resonance.

$$Q = \frac{\omega_0 L}{R} = \frac{1}{\omega_0 CR}$$

$$BW = \omega_0 / Q (\text{rad / s})$$

The average power dissipated in a series resonant circuit can be expressed in terms of the rms voltage and current as follows:

$$P_{avg} = I_{rms}^2 R = \frac{V_{rms}^2}{Z^2} R = \frac{V_{rms}^2 R}{R^2 + (X_L - X_C)^2}$$

Using the forms of the inductive reactance and capacitive reactance, the term involving them can be expressed in terms of the frequency

$$(X_L - X_C)^2 = \left(\omega L - \frac{1}{\omega C}\right)^2 = \frac{L^2}{\omega^2}\left(\omega^2 - \omega_0^2\right)^2$$

where use has been made of the resonant frequency expression

$$\omega_0 = \frac{1}{\sqrt{LC}}$$

Substitution now gives the expression for average power as a function of frequency.

$$P_{avg} = \frac{V_{rms}^2 R\omega^2}{R^2\omega^2 + L^2\left(\omega^2 - \omega_0^2\right)^2}$$

This power distribution is plotted in Figure 10.11 using the same circuit parameters as were used in the example on the Q factor of the series resonant circuit. The average power at resonance is just

$$P_{avg} = \frac{V_{rms}^2}{R}$$

since at the resonant frequency ω_0, the reactive parts cancel so that the circuit appears as just the resistance R.

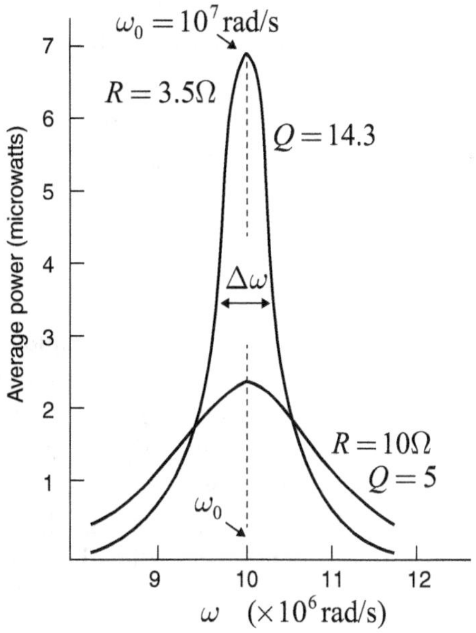

Figure 10.11

The resonance of a parallel RLC circuit is a bit more involved than the series resonance. The resonant frequency can be defined in three different ways, which converge on the same expression as the series resonant frequency if the resistance of the circuit is small.

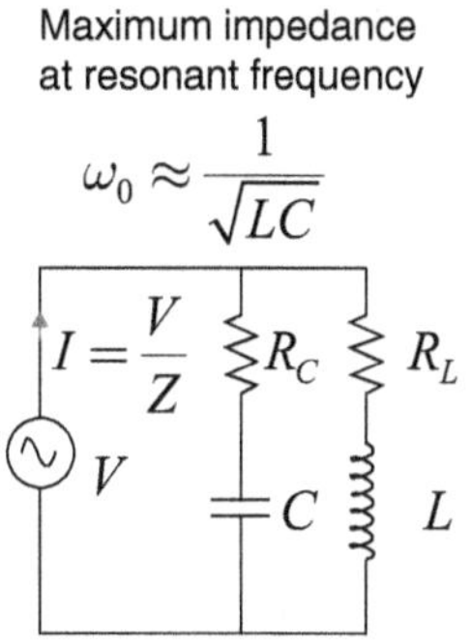

Figure 10.12 Parallel Resonance

For parallel resonance circuits,

$$\omega_0 = \frac{1}{\sqrt{LC}} = 2\pi f_0 (\text{rad / s})$$

$$\omega_0 L = \frac{1}{\omega_0 C} \text{ and}$$

$$Z = R \text{ at resonance.}$$

$$Q = \omega_0 RC = \frac{R}{\omega_0 L}$$

$$BW = \omega_0 / Q (\text{rad / s})$$

One of the ways to define resonance for a parallel RLC circuit is the frequency at which the impedance is maximum. The general case is rather complex, but the

special case where the resistances of the inductor and capacitor are negligible can be handled readily by using the concept of admittance.

Defining the parallel resonant frequency as the frequency at which the voltage and current are in phase, unity power factor, gives the following expression for the resonant frequency:

$$\omega_0 = \frac{1}{\sqrt{LC}}\left[\frac{R_L^2C - L}{R_C^2C - L}\right]^{\frac{1}{2}}$$

This resonant frequency expression is obtained by taking the impedance expressions for the parallel RLC circuit and setting the expression for X_{eq} equal to zero to force the phase to zero. After about a page of algebra, the previous expression emerges. Note that for small values of the resistances, this approaches the series resonant frequency.

Although the impedance Z is a far more common way to characterize the voltage-current relationships in an AC circuit, there are times when the admittance is a valuable construct. For a given circuit element, the admittance is just the reciprocal of the impedance.

The admittance has its most obvious utility in dealing with parallel AC circuits where there are no series elements. The equivalent admittance of parallel elements is the sum of the admittances of the components.

Example 10.5

Determine the resonant frequency for the circuit below.

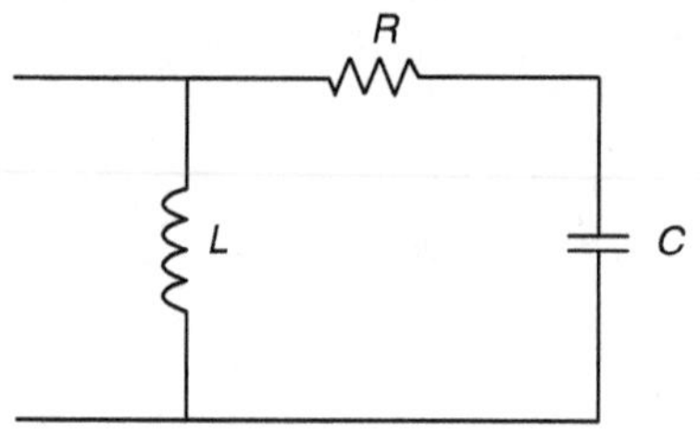

Exhibit 3

$$Z_{in} = \frac{j\omega L(R + \frac{1}{j\omega C})}{R + j\omega L + \frac{1}{j\omega C}} = \frac{(-\omega^2 LRC + j\omega L)}{(1 - \omega^2 LC) + j\omega RC}$$

At resonance, the phase angle of Z must be equal to zero
For zero phase,

$$\frac{\omega L}{(-\omega^2 LCR)} = \frac{\omega RC}{(1 - \omega^2 LC)}$$

This yields

$$\omega^2 LC - \omega^2 R^2 C^2 = 1$$

Solving for $\omega = \omega_o$,

$$\omega_o = \frac{1}{\sqrt{(LC - R^2C^2)}}$$

Example 10.6

A series RLC resonant circuit has a resonant frequency admittance of 2×10^{-2} *S*. The *Q* of the circuit is 50, and the resonant frequency is 10,000 rad/sec. Calculate the values of *R*, *L*, and *C*. Find the half-power frequencies and the bandwidth.

First, $R = 1/G = 1/(0.02) = 50$ ohms

Second, from $Q = \frac{w_O L}{R}$ we solve for *L*, knowing *Q*, *R*, and ω_o to find L = 0.25 H.

Third, we can use $C = \frac{Q}{w_O R} = \frac{50}{10{,}000x50} = 100\ \mu F$.

Fourth: We can use $\omega_{BW} = \frac{\omega_o}{Q} = \frac{1x10^4}{50} = 200\ \text{rad/sec}$

and fifth, use the approximations,

$$\omega_1 = \omega_o - 0.5\omega_{BW} = 10{,}000 - 100 = 9{,}900 \text{ rad/sec}$$
$$\omega_1 = \omega_o + 0.5\omega_{BW} = 10{,}000 + 100 = 10{,}100 \text{ rad/sec}$$

Two Port Networks

In a two-port electronic network, signals are fed into a pair of terminals, amplified and/or modified by the system, and finally extracted at another pair of terminals. Each pair of terminals is identified as a port: signals are fed into an *input port* and extracted from an *output port*. The modeling and analysis of transistor-based amplifiers, as well as feedback systems, is greatly simplified through the use of two-port network principles.

The items of interest in an electronic two-port network are the relationships between input port and output port voltages and currents. There are a few restrictions upon which two-port analysis techniques are based that must be identified:

- The network must be linear and time invariant.
- Connections may be made only to port terminals; no external connections can be made to any node internal to the port.
- All current entering one terminal of a port must exit the other terminal of that port.
- Sources and loads must be connected directly across the two terminals of a port.

As with all systems, it is important to define sign conventions. Figure 10.13 is a representation of a two-port network with appropriate voltage and current polarity definitions. As is standard in electronic systems, the voltage and current at each port obey the passive sign convention. Typically, the input port is identified as port #1 and the output port as port #2.

Three-terminal devices, such as transistors, can also be modeled using two-port techniques. One terminal is selected as a common terminal. That terminal is extended to both of the ports and becomes the reference (negative) terminal to each port.

Figure 10.13 Two-Port Network Sign Conventions

There are six basic sets of equivalent descriptive parameters for every two-port network:

1. Impedance parameters (z-parameters)—port voltages in terms of port currents.
2. Admittance parameters (y-parameters)—port currents in terms of port voltages.
3. Hybrid parameters (h-parameters)—input voltage and output current in terms of input current and output voltage.
4. Hybrid parameters (g-parameters)—input current and output voltage in terms of input voltage and output current.
5. Transmission parameters ($ABCD$-parameters)—input current and voltage in terms of output current and voltage.
6. Transmission parameters (**$\mathcal{ABCD}$** -parameters)—output current and voltage in terms of input current and voltage.

A short description of the first four two-port parameter set descriptions follows.

Impedance parameters (z-parameters)

The independent variables for this set of parameters are the port currents, and the dependent variables are the port voltages. Voltage as a function of current is an impedance. It is most common to write the equations in matrix form:

$$\begin{bmatrix} V_1 \\ V_2 \end{bmatrix} = \begin{bmatrix} z_{11} & z_{12} \\ z_{21} & z_{22} \end{bmatrix} \begin{bmatrix} I_1 \\ I_2 \end{bmatrix} \qquad \textbf{(10.37a)}$$

The parameters $\{z_{ij}\}$ are called the impedance (or z–) parameters of the network. For a linear, time-invariant network, the z-parameters can be obtained by performing simple tests on the network:

$$z_{ij} = \left.\frac{V_i}{I_j}\right|_{I_{k \neq j}=0} \qquad \textbf{(10.37b)}$$

For a nonlinear system that is operating in a region of linearity, a similar definition holds:

$$z_{ij} = \left.\frac{\partial V_i}{\partial I_j}\right|_{I_{k \neq j}=\text{Constant}}, \qquad \textbf{(10.37c)}$$

where the constant value of I_k is taken near the midpoint of the region of linearity. If a quiescent (zero-input) point exists, the constant value of I_k is chosen as its quiescent value.

Example 10.7

Determine the z-parameters for the given two-port network.

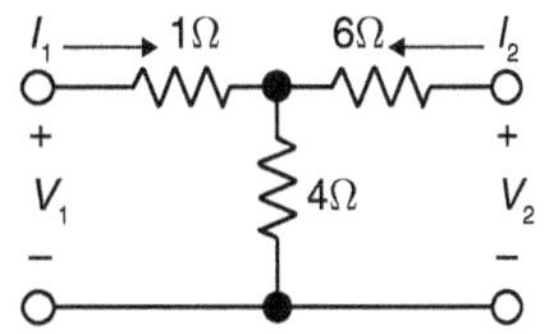

Exhibit 4

Solution

The z-parameters are defined for this linear system as open-circuit parameters; one of the currents is always set to zero. Zero current implies an open circuit in the appropriate path. Thus,

$z_{11} = 1 + 4 = 5\ \Omega$ (zero current in the 6 Ω resistor)
$z_{12} = 4\ \Omega$ (no voltage drop across the 1 Ω resistor)
$z_{21} = 4\ \Omega$ (no voltage drop across the 6 Ω resistor)
$z_{22} = 6 + 4 = 10\ \Omega$ (zero current in the 1 Ω resistor)

Admittance parameters (y-parameters)

Admittance parameters are defined with the independent variables that are the port voltages and the dependent variables that are the port currents; current as a function of voltage carries the units of admittance. The y-parameter equations are:

$$\begin{bmatrix} I_1 \\ I_2 \end{bmatrix} = \begin{bmatrix} y_{11} & y_{12} \\ y_{21} & y_{22} \end{bmatrix} \begin{bmatrix} V_1 \\ V_2 \end{bmatrix} \quad \textbf{(10.37d)}$$

The parameters can be determined by performing the tests:

$$y_{ij} = \left.\frac{I_i}{V_j}\right|_{V_{k\neq j}=0} \quad \textbf{(10.37e)}$$

or

$$y_{ij} = \left.\frac{\partial I_i}{\partial V_j}\right|_{V_{k\neq j}=\text{Constant}}. \quad \textbf{(10.37f)}$$

In a linear system, the test for finding y-parameters indicates that a voltage must be set to zero. Thus, the parameters are often called *short-circuit* admittance parameters.

Example 10.8

Determine the y-parameters for the network shown using standard phasor techniques, that is, find $Y(s)$.

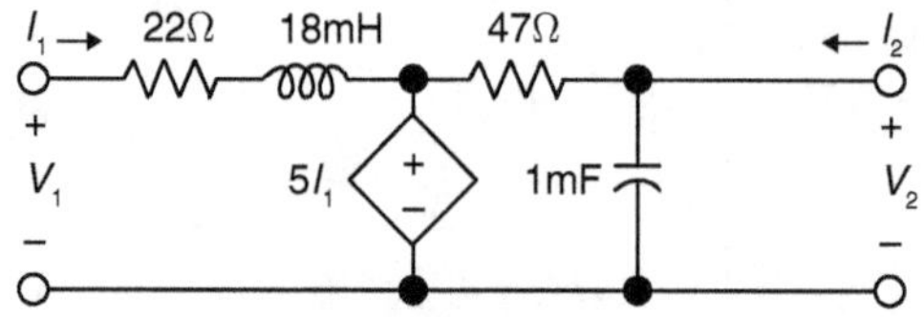

Exhibit 5

Solution

It can be seen that this network is a linear system. Both two-port and phasor techniques are appropriate for such a system. The phasor equivalent impedance of the inductor and the capacitor are:

$$Z_L = 0.018\text{s} \qquad Z_C = 1000/\text{s}$$

The y-parameter tests for a linear system are given by Eqn. (10.1e):

$$\psi_{\iota\varphi} = \left.\frac{I_\iota}{\varsigma_\varphi}\right|_{\varsigma_{\kappa\neq\varphi}=0}$$

In order to solve for $y11$ and $y21$, the output terminals are short-circuited ($V2 = 0$). A loop equation can then be written around the remaining left loop:

$$V_1 - 22\,I_1 - 0.018s\,I_1 - 5\,I_1 = 0$$

Which leads to:

$$\psi_{\iota\varphi} = \left.\frac{I_\iota}{\varsigma_\varphi}\right|_{\varsigma_{\kappa\neq\varphi}=0} = \frac{1}{27+0.018s}$$

Since the capacitor has been shorted out by setting $V_2 = 0$, a loop equation can be written around the remaining right loop:

$$5\,I_1 + 47\,I_2 = 0 \qquad \Rightarrow \qquad I_2 = -0.1064\,I_1$$

and

$$\psi_{21} = \left.\frac{I_2}{\varsigma_1}\right|_{\varsigma_2=0} = \frac{1}{253+0.1692s}$$

The other two parameters, y_{12} and y_{22}, are obtained by shorting the input terminal ($V_1 = 0$). A loop equation around the left loop of this configuration yields:

$$22\,I_1 + 0.018\text{s}\,I_1 - 5\,I_1 = 0 \qquad \Rightarrow \qquad I_1 = 0$$

Obviously

$$\psi_{12} = \left.\frac{I_1}{\varsigma_2}\right|_{\varsigma_1=0} = 0$$

With $I_1 = 0$, the current I_2 is the sum of the currents in the 47 Ω resistor and the capacitor (the dependent voltage source has zero value):

$$\psi_{22} = \left.\frac{I_2}{\varsigma_2}\right|_{\varsigma_1=0} = \psi_{47\Omega} + \psi_{1mF} = 0.02128 + 0.001s$$

The y-parameter matrix is then given by:

$$\Psi(\sigma)=\begin{bmatrix} \dfrac{1}{27+0.018s} & 0 \\ \dfrac{1}{253+0.1692s} & 0.02128+0.001s \end{bmatrix}$$

Hybrid parameters (h-parameters)

The independent variables are the input voltage and output current. The dependent variables are the input current and output voltage.

$$\begin{bmatrix} V_1 \\ I_2 \end{bmatrix}=\begin{bmatrix} h_{11} & h_{12} \\ h_{21} & h_{22} \end{bmatrix}\begin{bmatrix} I_1 \\ V_2 \end{bmatrix} \tag{10.37g}$$

Notice that these parameters, unlike the z- and y-parameters, do not all have the same dimensions. Each is different: h_{11} is the input port impedance, h_{12} is a dimensionless (input over output) voltage ratio, h_{21} is a dimensionless (output over input) current ratio, and h_{22} is output port admittance.

The parameters can be determined by performing the tests:

$$h_{11}=\left.\frac{V_1}{I_1}\right|_{V_2=0} \qquad h_{12}=\left.\frac{V_1}{V_2}\right|_{I_1=0} \tag{10.37h}$$

$$h_{21}=\left.\frac{I_2}{I_1}\right|_{V_2=0} \qquad h_{22}=\left.\frac{I_2}{V_2}\right|_{I_1=0}$$

or

$$h_{11}=\left.\frac{\partial V_1}{\partial I_1}\right|_{V_2=\text{Constant}} \qquad h_{12}=\left.\frac{\partial V_1}{\partial V_2}\right|_{I_1=\text{Constant}}$$

$$h_{21}=\left.\frac{\partial I_2}{\partial I_1}\right|_{V_2=\text{Constant}} \qquad h_{22}=\left.\frac{\partial I_2}{\partial V_2}\right|_{I_1=\text{Constant}} \tag{10.37i}$$

Hybrid parameters (g-parameters)

The independent variables are the input current and output voltage; the dependent variables are the input voltage and output current.

$$\begin{bmatrix} I_1 \\ V_2 \end{bmatrix}=\begin{bmatrix} g_{11} & g_{12} \\ g_{21} & g_{22} \end{bmatrix}\begin{bmatrix} V_1 \\ I_2 \end{bmatrix} \tag{10.37j}$$

Notice that these parameters, like the h-parameters, do not all have the same dimensions. Each is different: g_{11} is the input port admittance; g_{12} is a dimensionless (input over output) current ratio; g_{21} is a dimensionless (output over input) voltage ratio; and g_{22} is output port impedance.

The parameters can be determined by performing the tests:

$$g_{11}=\left.\frac{I_1}{V_1}\right|_{I_2=0} \qquad g_{12}=\left.\frac{I_1}{I_2}\right|_{V_1=0} \tag{10.37k}$$

$$g_{21}=\left.\frac{V_2}{V_1}\right|_{I_2=0} \qquad g_{22}=\left.\frac{V_2}{I_2}\right|_{V_1=0}$$

or

$$g_{11} = \left.\frac{\partial I_1}{\partial V_1}\right|_{I_2=\text{Constant}} \qquad g_{12} = \left.\frac{\partial I_1}{\partial I_2}\right|_{V_1=\text{Constant}} \tag{10.371}$$

$$g_{21} = \left.\frac{\partial V_2}{\partial V_1}\right|_{I_2=\text{Constant}} \qquad g_{22} = \left.\frac{\partial V_2}{\partial I_2}\right|_{V_1=\text{Constant}}$$

Circuit Representation of a Two-Port Network

It is often important to create a simple equivalent circuit for a two-port network where the network parameters are known. While there are several techniques for the creation of these equivalent networks, the most useful in electronic applications involves Thévenin and Norton input and output realizations. In general, network parameters are replaced by simple circuit elements as shown in Table 10.1. Relationships between currents and voltages at the same port are treated as impedances or admittances, while relationships at different ports are treated as dependent sources.

Table 10.1 Two-Port Network Replacement Circuit Elements for Network Parameters

Network Parameter	Replacement Circuit Element	
	Same Port	Opposite Port
impedance	impedance	current-controlled voltage source
admittance	admittance	voltage-controlled current source
current ratio	(not applicable)	current-controlled current source
voltage ratio	(not applicable)	voltage-controlled voltage source

Example 10.9

A two-port network has been found to have the following g-parameters:

$$g_{11} = 0.025\ S \quad g_{12} = 47\ mA/A$$
$$g_{21} = 14\ V/V \quad g_{22} = 270\ \Omega$$

Determine an equivalent circuit representation of the two-port network.

Solution

The matrix equation for the g-parameter representation of a two-port network can be written as two separate equations:

$$I_1 = g_{11}V_1 + g_{21}I_2 \quad \text{and} \quad V_2 = g_{21}V_1 + g_{22}I_2$$

The equation for I_1 reveals that two currents must be added together to make the input port current. Referring to Table 10.1, one finds that the currents emanate from an admittance and a current-controlled current source; they must be connected as a Norton source. The equation for V_2 implies that two voltages must be added together. Table 10.1 shows the elements are an impedance and a voltage-controlled voltage source; they are connected in Thévenin fashion. The equivalent circuit representation is shown in Exhibit 6. (Note: for clarity, g_{11} is shown as a resistance rather than a conductance).

Exhibit 6 Two-Port Realization

PROBLEMS

10.1 Find the inverse Laplace of the given transforms:

a. $\dfrac{2s+5}{s^2+5s+6}$

b. $\dfrac{(s+1)^2}{s^2-s-6}$

c. $\dfrac{5}{s^2\cdot(s+2)}$

d. $\dfrac{2s+1}{(s+1)\cdot(s^2+2s+2)}$

e. $\dfrac{s+2}{s\cdot(s+1)^2}$

10.2 Find the Laplace transform of $f_a(t) = t\cdot(u(t) - u(t-1))$.

10.3 Find the Laplace transform of $f_b(t) = \sin(t)\cdot(u(t) - u(t-\pi))$.

10.4 Find the Laplace transform of $f_c(t) = e^{-1}\cdot t\cdot(u(t) - u(t-1)) + e^{-t}\,u(t-1)$.

10.5 Find the current $y(t)$ for the two different $f(t)$ inputs. Assume initial conditions are 0.

$$u(t) = \Phi(t)$$

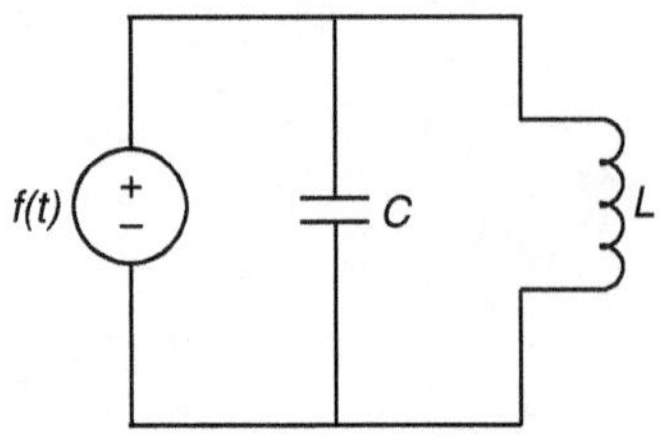

10.6 Find the two loop current in the circuit in Exhibit 10.6.

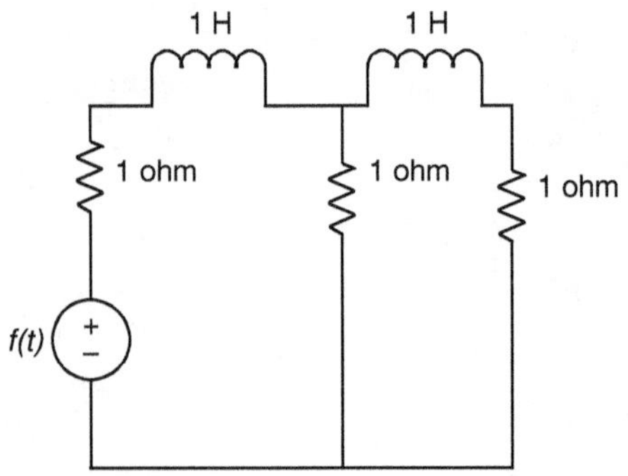

Exhibit 10.6

10.7 Find the output voltage $v_o(t)$ for the network given that $i_{L0} = 1\text{A}$ and $v_{c0} = 3\text{V}$.

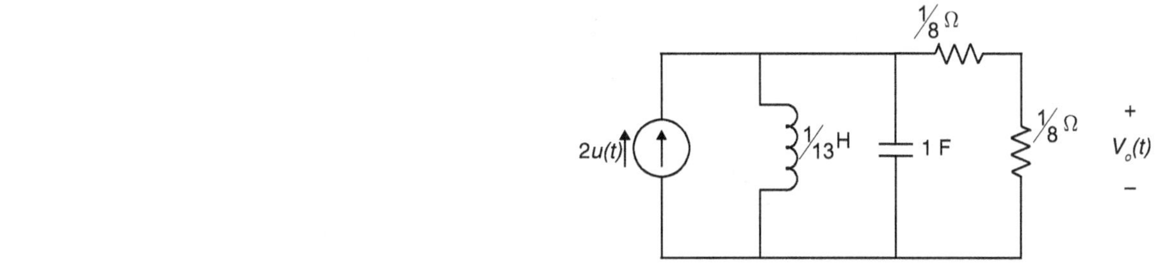

10.8 Find the canonical and cascade diagrams for

$$H(s) = \frac{3s \cdot (s+2)}{(s+1) \cdot (s^2 + 2s + 2)}.$$

10.9 Find the canonical and cascade diagrams for

$$H(s) = \frac{s \cdot (s+1) \cdot (s+2)}{(s+5) \cdot (s+6) \cdot (s+8)}.$$

10.10 Realize the following transfer function with Op Amp circuits.

$$H_i(s) = \frac{-10}{s+5}$$

10.11 Realize the following transfer function with Op Amp circuits.

$$H_{ii}(s) = \frac{10}{s+5}$$

10.12 Realize the following transfer function with Op Amp circuits.

$$H_{iii}(s) = \frac{s+2}{s+5}$$

SOLUTIONS

10.1

a. $$\frac{2s+5}{s^2+5s+6}=\frac{A}{s+2}+\frac{B}{s+3}=\frac{1}{s+2}+\frac{1}{s+3}$$

$$f_a(t)=\left(e^{-2t}+e^{-3t}\right)\cdot u(t)$$

b. $$\frac{(s+1)^2}{s^2-s-6}=\frac{(s+1)^2}{(s-3)\cdot(s+2)}=\frac{s^2+2s+1}{(s-3)\cdot(s+2)}$$

$$=1+\frac{A}{s-3}+\frac{B}{s+2}=1+\frac{\frac{16}{5}}{s-3}+\frac{\frac{1}{-5}}{s+2}$$

$$f_c(t)=\delta(t)+\left(3.2\cdot e^{3t}-0.2\cdot e^{-2t}\right)\cdot u(t)$$

c. $$\frac{5}{s^2\cdot(s+2)}=\frac{A}{s^2}+\frac{B}{s}+\frac{C}{s+2}=\frac{\frac{5}{2}}{s^2}+\frac{\frac{-5}{4}}{s}+\frac{\frac{5}{4}}{s+2}$$

$$\frac{d}{ds}\frac{5}{s+2}=\frac{-5}{(s+2)^2} \qquad \lim_{s\to 0}\frac{-5}{(s+2)^2}\to\frac{-5}{4}$$

$$f_d(t)=\left(\frac{5}{2}\cdot t-\frac{5}{4}+\frac{5}{4}\cdot e^{-2t}\right)\cdot u(t)$$

d. $$\frac{2s+1}{(s+1)\cdot(s^2+2s+2)}=\frac{A\cdot s+B}{s^2+2s+2}+\frac{C}{s+1}=\frac{A\cdot s+B}{s^2+2s+2}+\frac{-1}{s+1}$$

$$2s+1=A\cdot s\cdot(s+1)+B\cdot(s+1)-\left(s^2+2s+2\right)$$

$$1=B-2 \qquad B=3$$

$$2s+1=A\cdot s\cdot(s+1)+3\cdot(s+1)-\left(s^2+2s+2\right)$$

$$0\cdot s^2=A\cdot s^2-s^2 \qquad A=1$$

$$\frac{2s+1}{(s+1)\cdot(s^2+2s+2)}=\frac{s+3}{s^2+2s+2}+\frac{-1}{s+1}$$

$$A=1 \quad B=3$$

$$a=1 \quad c=2 \quad b=\sqrt{2-1} \qquad b=1$$

$$r=\frac{\sqrt{A^2c+B^2-2A\cdot B\cdot a}}{1} \qquad r=2.236$$

$$\theta=a\tan\left(\frac{A\cdot a-B}{A\cdot 1}\right) \qquad \theta=-63.435\,\text{deg}$$

$$f_e(t)=\left[2.236\cdot e^{-t}\cdot\cos(t+63.4\,\text{deg})+(-1)\cdot e^{-t}\right]\cdot u(t)$$

e. $$\frac{s+2}{s\cdot(s+1)^2}=\frac{A}{s}+\frac{B}{(s+1)^2}+\frac{C}{s+1}=\frac{2}{s}+\frac{-1}{(s+1)^2}+\frac{-2}{s+1}$$

$$\frac{d}{ds}\frac{s+2}{s}=\frac{1}{s}+\frac{s+2}{-s^2} \qquad \lim_{s\to-1}\left(\frac{1}{s}+\frac{s+2}{-s^2}\right)\to -2$$

$$f_f(t)=\left(2-t\cdot e^{-t}-2\cdot e^{-t}\right)\cdot u(t)$$

10.2 $f_a(t) = t\cdot u(t) - t\cdot u(t-1) = t\cdot u(t) - (t-1)\cdot u(t-1) + u(t-1)$

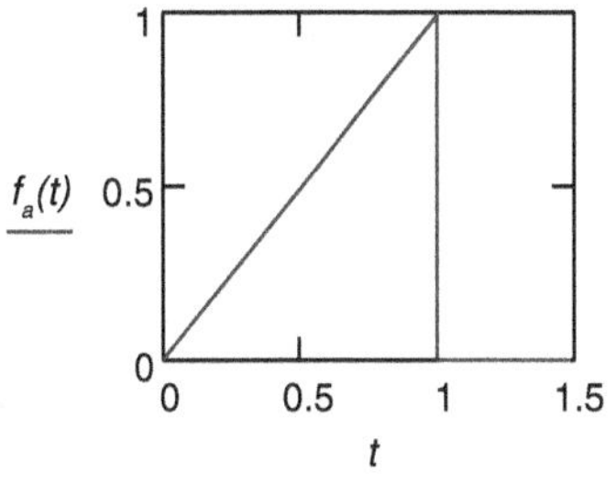

$$F_a(s)=\frac{1}{s^2}-\frac{1}{s^2}\cdot e^{-s}+\frac{1}{s}\cdot e^{-s}$$

10.3 $f_b(t) = \sin(t)\cdot(u(t) - u(t-\pi))$

$f_b(t) = \sin(t)\cdot u(t) - \sin(t)\cdot u(t-\pi)$
Use trig identity: $\sin(t-\pi) = -\sin(t)$
$f_b(t) = \sin(t)\cdot u(t) + \sin(t-\pi)\cdot u(t-\pi)$

$$F_b(s)=\frac{1}{s^2+1}+\frac{1}{s^2+1}\cdot e^{-s\cdot\pi}$$

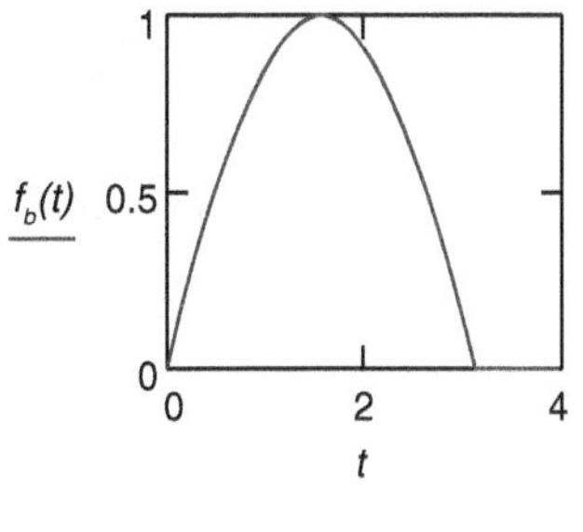

10.4

$$f_c(t)=e^{-1}\cdot t\cdot\left(u(t)-u(t-1)\right)+e^{-t}\cdot u(t-1)$$

$$f_c(t)=e^{-1}\cdot t\cdot u(t)-e^{-1}\cdot(t-1)\cdot u(t-1)-e^{-1}\cdot u(t-1)+e^{-1}\cdot e^{-(t-1)}u(t-1)$$

$$f_c(t)=e^{-1}\cdot\left[t\cdot u(t)-(t-1)\cdot u(t-1)-u(t-1)+e^{-(t-1)}u(t-1)\right]$$

$$F_c(s)=\frac{1}{e}\cdot\left(\frac{1}{s^2}-\frac{1}{s^2}\cdot e^{-s}-\frac{1}{s}\cdot e^{-s}+\frac{1}{s+1}\cdot e^{-s}\right)$$

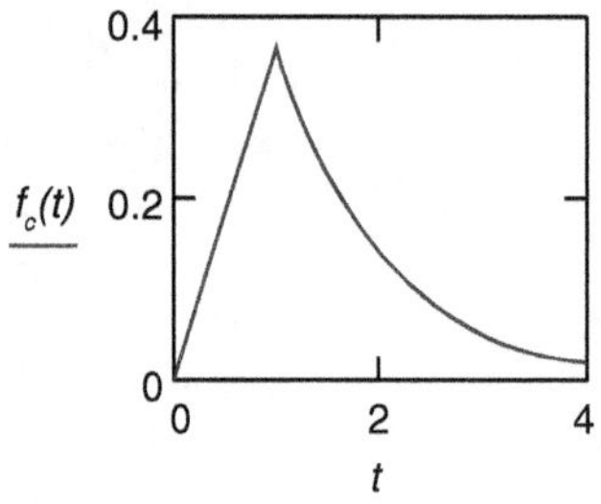

10.5

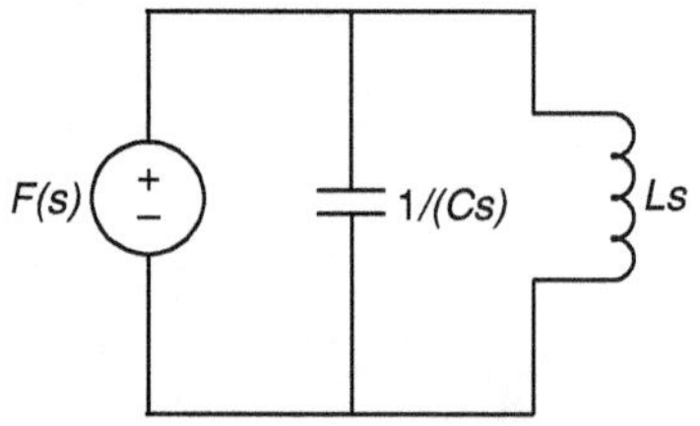

From circuit transform, we have $Y(s)$ (transform of current from source) is

$$Y(s)=\frac{F(s)}{Z(s)}=F(s)\cdot\left[\left(\frac{1}{C\cdot s}\right)^{-1}+\frac{1}{L\cdot s}\right]=F(s)\cdot\left(C\cdot s+\frac{1}{L\cdot s}\right)$$

$$f_a(t)=A\cdot\cos(\omega_0\cdot t)\cdot u(t)$$

$$F_a(s)=A\cdot\frac{s}{s^2+\omega_0{}^2}=A\cdot\frac{s}{s^2+\frac{1}{L\cdot C}}$$

$$Y_a(s)=\frac{s}{s^2+\frac{1}{L\cdot C}}\cdot\left(C\cdot s+\frac{1}{L\cdot s}\right)=\frac{C\cdot s+\frac{1}{L}}{s^2+\frac{1}{L\cdot C}}=\frac{C\cdot\left(s^2+\frac{1}{L\cdot C}\right)}{s^2+\frac{1}{L\cdot C}}=C$$

$$y_a(t)=A\cdot C\cdot\delta(t)$$

$$f_b(t)=A\cdot\sin(\omega_0\cdot t)\cdot u(t)$$

$$F_b(s)=A\cdot\frac{\omega_0}{s^2+\omega_0{}^2}=A\cdot\frac{\frac{1}{\sqrt{L\cdot C}}}{s^2+\frac{1}{L\cdot C}}$$

$$Y_b(s) = \frac{\frac{1}{\sqrt{L\cdot C}}}{s^2+\frac{1}{L\cdot C}}\cdot\left(C\cdot s+\frac{1}{L\cdot s}\right) = \frac{\sqrt{\frac{C}{L}}\cdot s+\frac{1}{L\cdot\sqrt{L\cdot C s}}}{s^2+\frac{1}{L\cdot C}}$$

$$= \frac{\sqrt{\frac{C}{L}}\cdot\left(s+\sqrt{\frac{L}{C}}\cdot\frac{1}{L\cdot\sqrt{L\cdot Cs}}\right)}{s^2+\frac{1}{L\cdot C}} = \ldots = \sqrt{\frac{C}{L}}\cdot\left(\frac{1}{s}\right)$$

$$y_b(t) = A\cdot\sqrt{\frac{C}{L}}\cdot u(t)$$

10.6 $f(t)$ is shown to be 3 before $t = 0$ and 6 after $t = 0$. This translates into telling us initial conditions are based upon 3V source and then $f(t) = 6\,u(t)$ $\Rightarrow F(s) = 6(1/s)$.

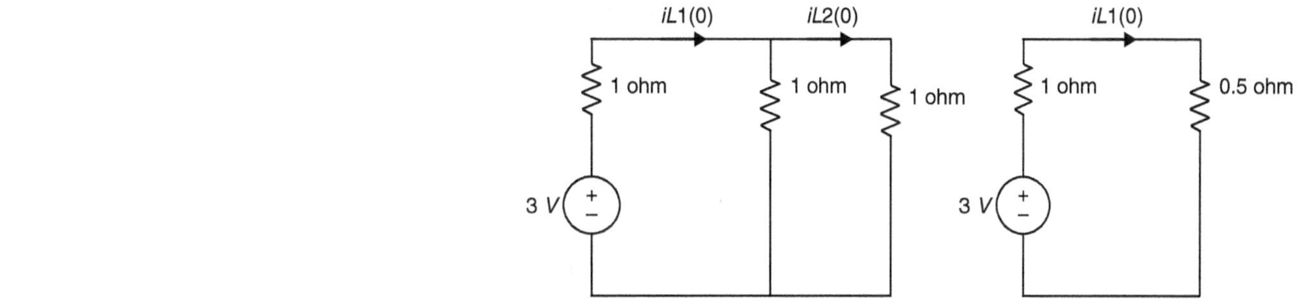

$$i_{L10} = \frac{3}{1.5} \qquad i_{L10} = 2$$

$$i_{L20} = \frac{3-2\cdot 1}{1} \qquad i_{L20} = 1$$

These initial conditions are then used for the circuit transformation:

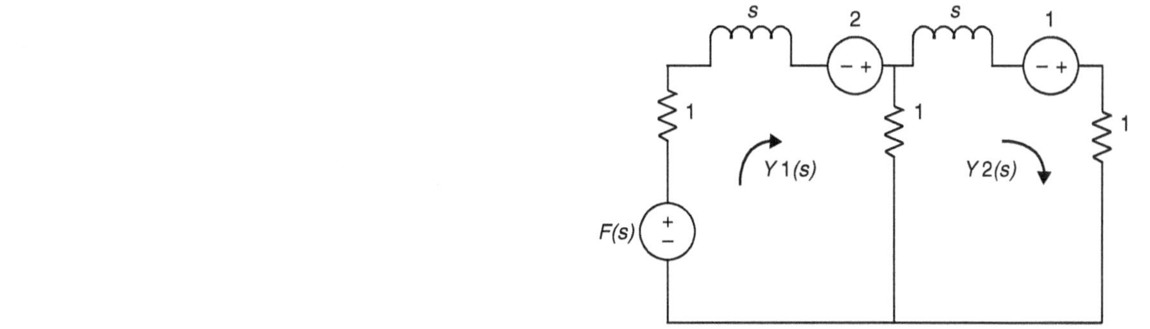

We can then do the loop equations, and, after gathering terms together, they look like this:

$$(s+2)\cdot Y_1(s) - 1\cdot Y_2(s) = F(s)+2 = \frac{6}{s}+2$$

$$-Y_1(s)+(s+2)\cdot Y_2(s) = 1$$

Rewriting into matrix form:

$$\begin{pmatrix} s+2 & -1 \\ -1 & s+2 \end{pmatrix} \cdot \begin{pmatrix} Y_1(s) \\ Y_2(s) \end{pmatrix} = \begin{pmatrix} \frac{6}{s}+2 \\ 1 \end{pmatrix} = \begin{pmatrix} \frac{2s+6}{s} \\ 1 \end{pmatrix}$$

Find matrix inverse:

$$\begin{pmatrix} s+2 & -1 \\ -1 & s+2 \end{pmatrix}^{-1} = \frac{1}{(s+2)^2-1} \cdot \begin{pmatrix} s+2 & 1 \\ 1 & s+2 \end{pmatrix}$$

$$= \frac{1}{s^2+4s+3} \cdot \begin{pmatrix} s+2 & 1 \\ 1 & s+2 \end{pmatrix}$$

Multiply both sides by this inverse:

$$\begin{pmatrix} s+2 & -1 \\ -1 & s+2 \end{pmatrix}^{-1} \cdot \begin{pmatrix} s+2 & -1 \\ -1 & s+2 \end{pmatrix} \cdot \begin{pmatrix} Y_1(s) \\ Y_2(s) \end{pmatrix} = \begin{pmatrix} s+2 & -1 \\ -1 & s+2 \end{pmatrix}^{-1} \cdot \begin{pmatrix} \frac{2s+6}{s} \\ 1 \end{pmatrix}$$

$$\begin{pmatrix} Y_1(s) \\ Y_2(s) \end{pmatrix} = \begin{pmatrix} s+2 & -1 \\ -1 & s+2 \end{pmatrix}^{-1} \cdot \begin{pmatrix} \frac{2s+6}{s} \\ 1 \end{pmatrix}$$

$$\begin{pmatrix} Y_1(s) \\ Y_2(s) \end{pmatrix} = \frac{1}{s^2+4s+3} \cdot \begin{pmatrix} s+2 & 1 \\ 1 & s+2 \end{pmatrix} \cdot \begin{pmatrix} \frac{2s+6}{s} \\ 1 \end{pmatrix} = \frac{1}{s^2+4s+3} \cdot \begin{bmatrix} \frac{(s+2)(2s+6)+s}{s} \\ \frac{2s+6+s^2+2s}{s} \end{bmatrix}$$

$$Y_1(s) = \frac{(s+2)(2s+6)+s}{s} \cdot \frac{1}{s^2+4s+3} = \frac{2s^2+11s+12}{s\cdot(s+1)\cdot(s+3)} = \frac{4}{s} + \frac{-1.5}{s+1} + \frac{-0.5}{s+3}$$

$$Y_2(s) = \frac{2s+6+s^2+2s}{s} \cdot \frac{1}{s^2+4s+3} = \frac{4s+6+s^2}{s\cdot(s+1)\cdot(s+3)} = \frac{2}{s} + \frac{-1.5}{s+1} + \frac{0.5}{s+3}$$

$$y_1(t) = \left(4 - \frac{3}{2}e^{-t} - \frac{1}{2}\cdot e^{-3t}\right)\cdot u(t)$$

$$y_2(t) = \left(2 - \frac{3}{2}e^{-t} + \frac{1}{2}\cdot e^{-3t}\right)\cdot u(t)$$

10.7 Using the current source versions of the sources that come from initial conditions, these need to point in same direction as current for inductor and toward + of voltage for cap:

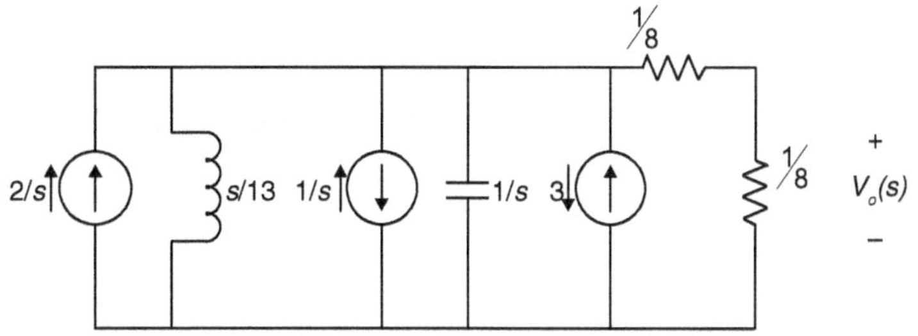

Parallel sources can be combined.

Now, there is a parallel L-C-R, the total impedence:

$$\frac{1}{Z_{TOT}}=\frac{1}{Z_L}+\frac{1}{Z_C}+\frac{1}{Z_R}=\frac{13}{s}+s+4$$

Total voltage

$$V_L=V_R=I_S\cdot Z_{TOT}=\frac{\frac{1}{s}+3}{s+4+\frac{13}{s}}=\frac{3s+1}{s^2+4s+13}$$

Output voltage is voltage just across the 1/8 ohm resistor:

$$V_o(s)=\frac{\frac{1}{8}}{\frac{1}{8}+\frac{1}{8}}\cdot\frac{3s+1}{s^2+4s+13}=\frac{1}{2}\cdot\frac{3s+1}{s^2+4s+13}$$

$$\frac{3s+5}{s^2+4s+13}$$

$$A=3 \quad B=1$$

$$a=2 \quad c=13 \quad b=\sqrt{13-4} \quad b=3$$

$$r=\frac{\sqrt{A^2c+B^2-2A\cdot B\cdot a}}{b} \qquad r=3.432$$

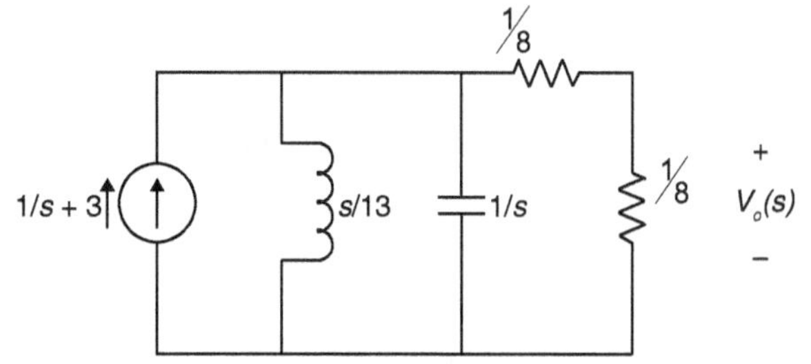

$$\theta = a\tan\left(\frac{A\cdot a - B}{A\cdot b}\right) \qquad \theta = 29.055\,\text{deg}$$

$$v_o(t) = \frac{1}{2}\cdot 3.43\cdot e^{-2t}\cdot\cos(3t + 30\,\text{deg})\cdot u(t)$$

10.8 For canonical, need polynomials multiplied out:

$$H(s) = \frac{3s\cdot(s+2)}{(s+1)\cdot(s^2+2s+2)} = \frac{3s^2+6s}{s^3+3s^2+4s+2}$$

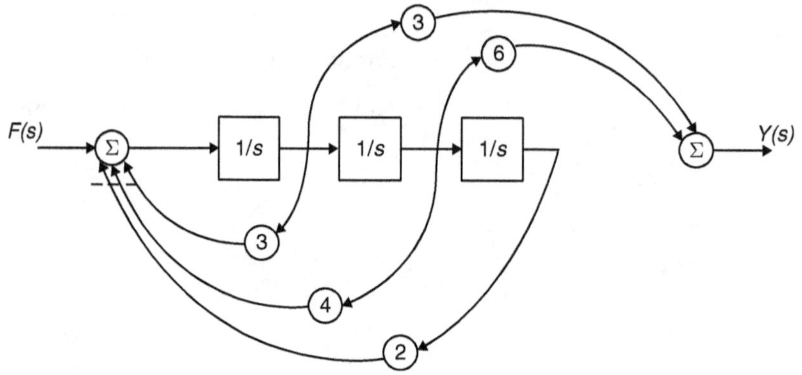

For cascade, need multiplicative factors

$$H(s) = \frac{3s}{s+1}\cdot\frac{s+2}{s^2+2s+2}$$

(Note that we can't get smaller than 2nd order when there is a complex pair.)

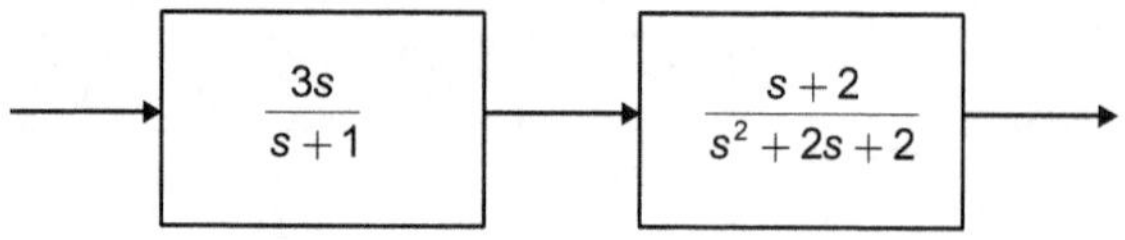

10.9 For canonical, we multiply out:

$$\frac{s^3+3s^2+2s}{s^3+19s^2+118s+240}$$

For cascade, we use multiplicative factors:

$$\frac{s}{s+5}\cdot\frac{s+1}{s+6}\cdot\frac{s+2}{s+8}$$

For parallel, we need to do partial fraction expansion. NOTE: Order of numerator is same as order of denominator.

$$\frac{s\cdot(s+1)\cdot(s+2)}{(s+5)(s+6)\cdot(s+8)} = \frac{s^3+3s^2+2s}{s^3+19s^2+118s+240} = 1 + \frac{A}{s+5} + \frac{B}{s+6} + \frac{C}{s+8}$$

$$\lim_{s\to-5}\frac{s\cdot(s+1)\cdot(s+2)}{(s+6)\cdot(s+8)}\to-20 \qquad \frac{-20}{s+5}$$

$$\lim_{s\to-6}\frac{s\cdot(s+1)\cdot(s+2)}{(s+5)\cdot(s+8)}\to 60 \qquad \frac{60}{s+6}$$

$$\lim_{s\to-8}\frac{s\cdot(s+1)\cdot(s+2)}{(s+5)\cdot(s+6)}\to-56 \qquad \frac{-56}{s+8}$$

The 1 needs to be combined into one of the other three terms.

$$\frac{s^3+3s^2+2s}{s^3+19s^2+118s+240}=1+\frac{-20}{s+5}+\frac{60}{s+6}+\frac{-56}{s+8}$$

$$=\frac{s+5}{s+5}+\left(\frac{-20}{s+5}+\frac{60}{s+6}+\frac{-56}{s+8}\right)$$

Canonical

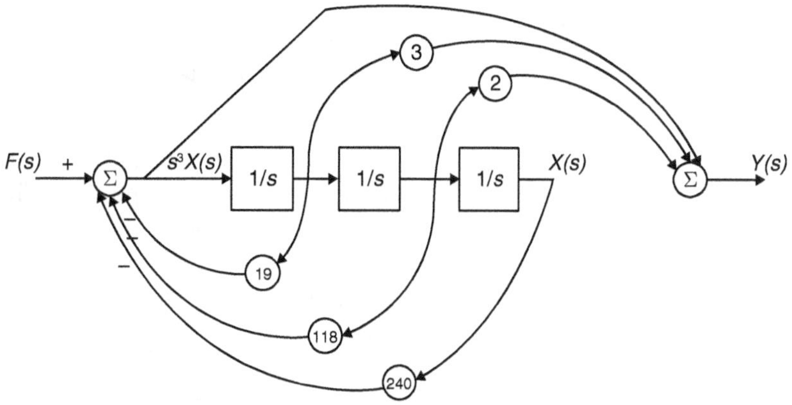

cascade:

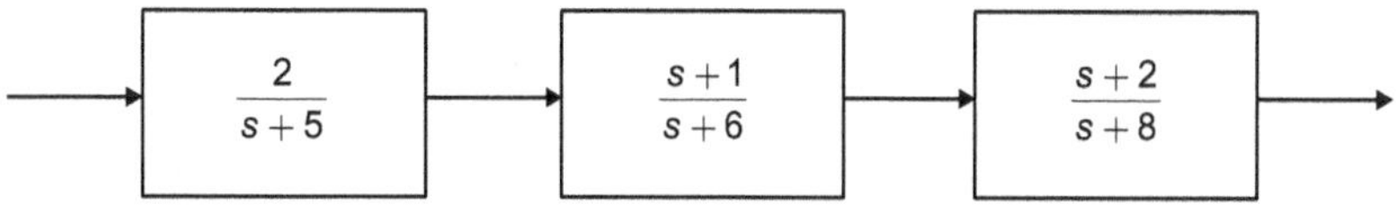

parallel:

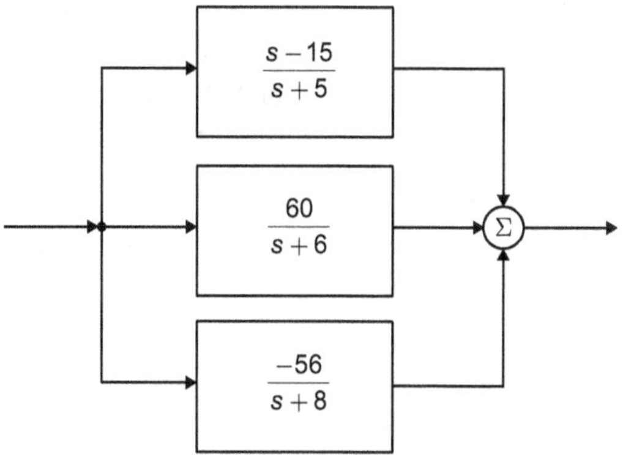

10.10

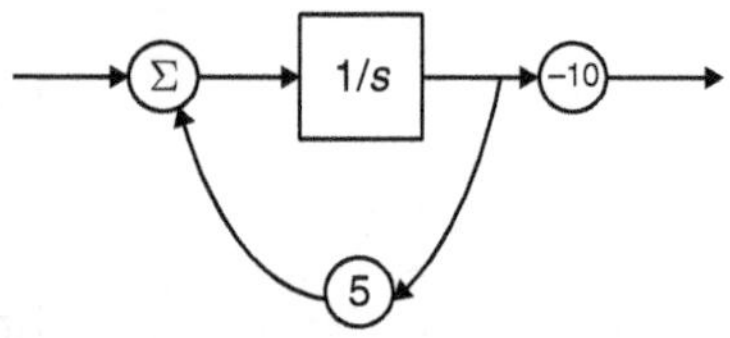

After getting canonical, substitute shorthand triangle notation for summers, integrators, and then remaining needed amplifiers:

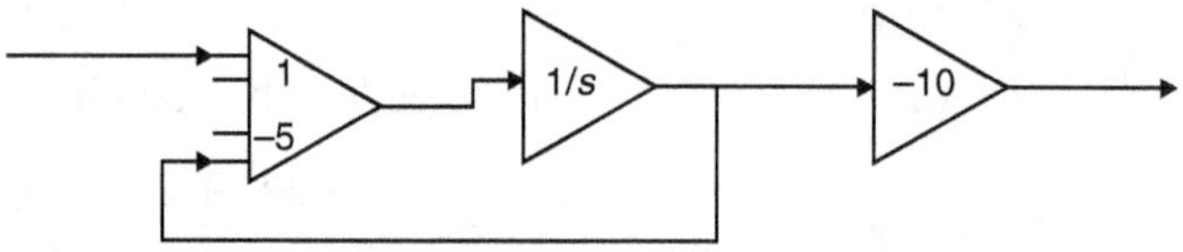

Need all gains to be negative, so replace positive ones with negative and add additional (–1) gain amplifier to cancel each time needed. (In this case, need to do that twice. Once on the first summer input and the second time for the integrator.)

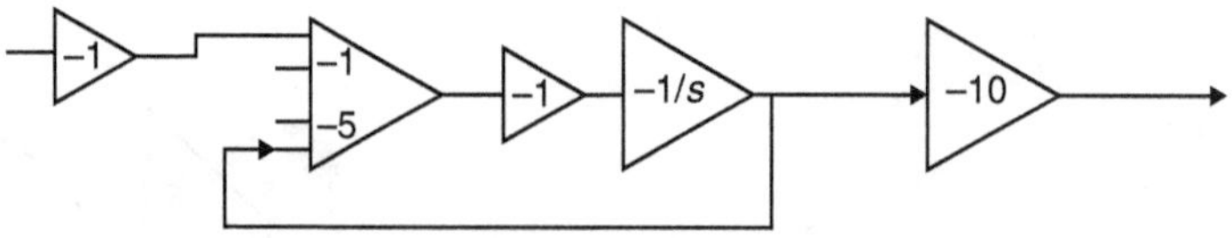

Now replace each triangle with its opamp equivalent circuit. Rf/R needs to be right ratio on amplifiers, 1/RC needs to be right value for integrator, and so forth. Values in Exhibit 10.10d used 1kohm Rf and 10 μF capacitor and then solved for other R values as needed. Other values for Rf and C could have also been used, and then different values for other Rs would have resulted.

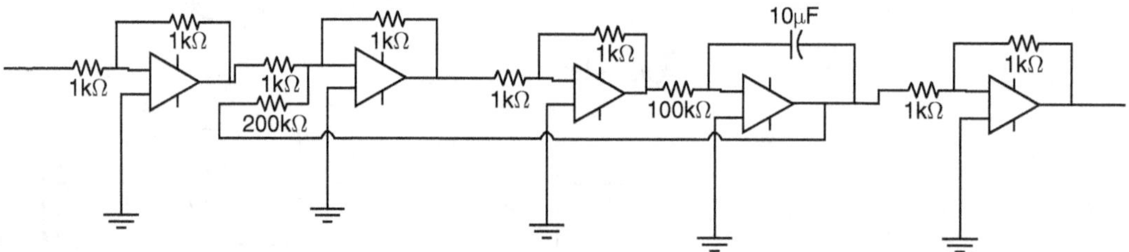

Exhibit 10.10d

10.11 For this next part, the only difference is overall $-1\text{x}H_i(s)$. This can be accomplished by adding a –1 amplifier at the beginning or at the end. By doing it at the beginning, we cancel out the –1 we had to put in during the last part, so we can just take that off for a realization of $H_{ii}(s)$.

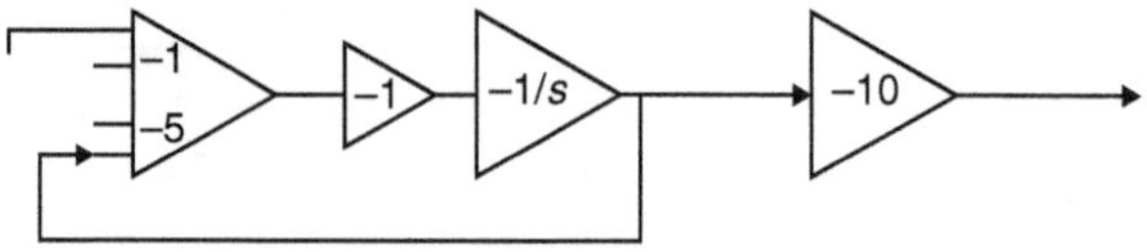

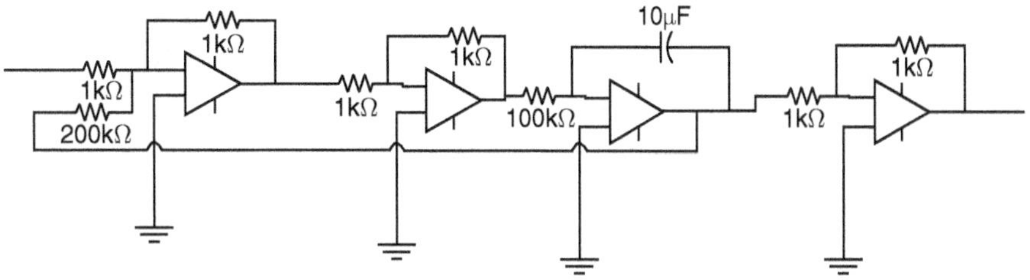
1kΩ
1kΩ
200kΩ
1kΩ
1kΩ
10μF
100kΩ
1kΩ
1kΩ

10.12

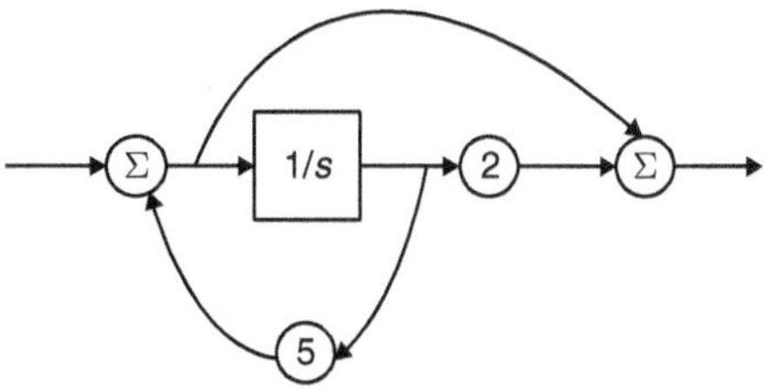
Σ
1/s
2
Σ
5

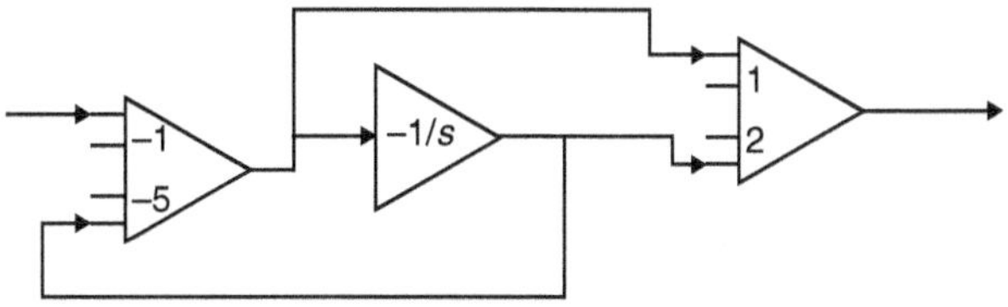
−1
−5
−1/s
1
2

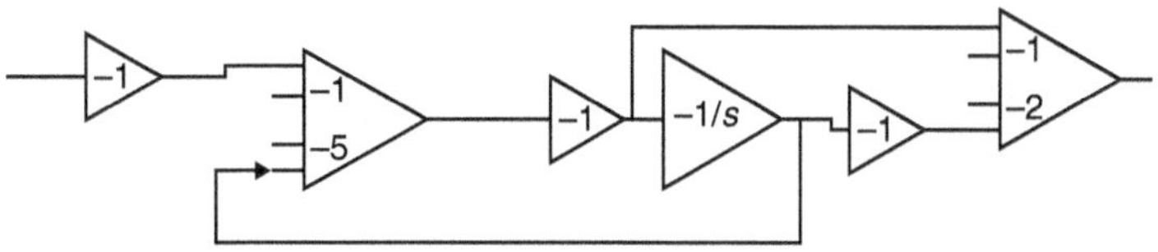
−1
−1
−5
−1
−1/s
−1
−1
−2

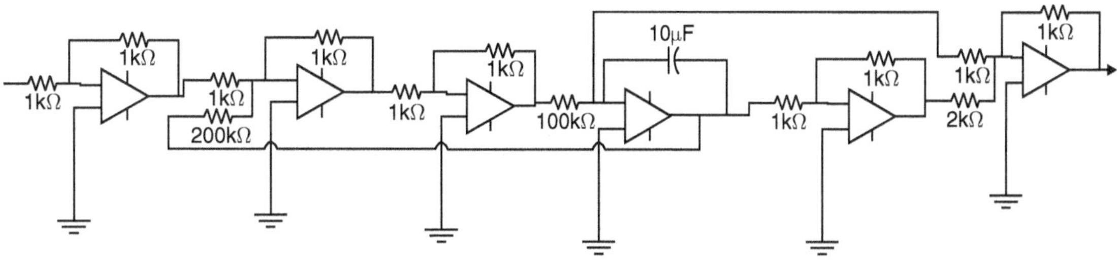
1kΩ
1kΩ
1kΩ
1kΩ
200kΩ
1kΩ
1kΩ
10μF
100kΩ
1kΩ
1kΩ
1kΩ
1kΩ
2kΩ

CHAPTER 11

Signal Processing

OUTLINE

CONVOLUTION OF DISCRETE-TIME SIGNALS

The *convolution sum* is:

$$y(kT) = x(kT) * y(kT) = \sum_{i=-\infty}^{\infty} x(iT)v(kT - iT).$$

If $x(kT) = 0$ and $v(kT) = 0$ for all $k<0$, then $x(iT) = 0$ for all $i<0$ and $v(kT - iT)$ for all integers $(k - i) < 0$ (or $k < i$).

$$\text{Then, } y(kT) = x(kT) * v(kT) = \begin{cases} 0 \ , & k = -1, -2, \dots \\ \sum_{i=0}^{k} x(iT)v(kT - iT), & k = 0, 1, 2, \dots \end{cases}.$$

⇒Any two signals that are 0 for all integers $k < 0$ can be convolved.
To compute the convolution sum,

- fold $v(iT)$ to be $v(-iT)$
- shift $v(-iT)$ by kT to $v(kT - iT)$
- if $k > 0$, $v(kT - iT)$ is kT shift right of $v(-iT)$ and if $k < 0$, $v(kT - iT)$ is left shift

Convolution Example

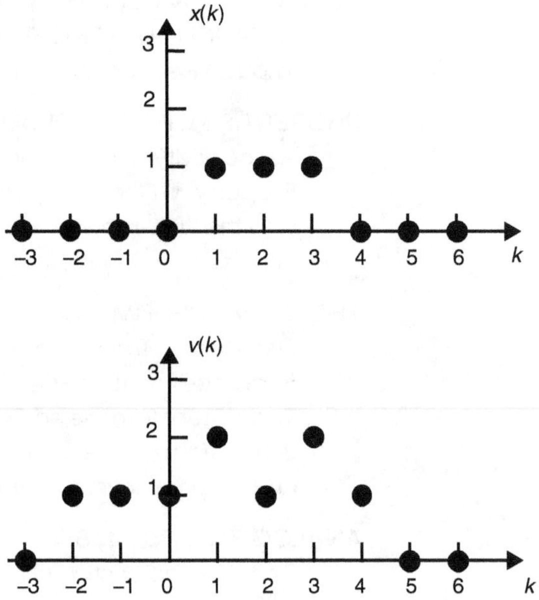

Figure 11.1

In this example, we wish to convolve the two functions, $x(kT)$ and $v(kT)$, shown on the left. To proceed, "fold" one of the functions about the vertical axis. It is best to fold the least complex function. In this case, the function $x(kT)$ is folded about the vertical axis.

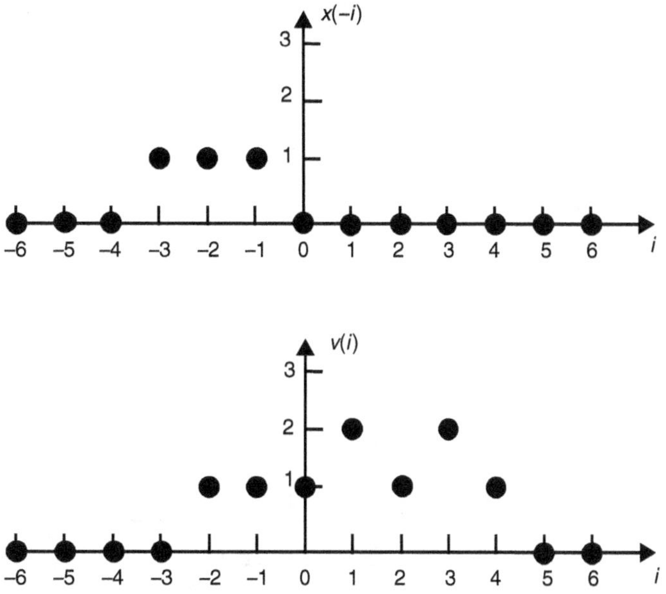

Figure 11.2

This is the folded version of the function $x(kT)$ or $x(-iT)$. Now we "slide" the function $x(-iT)$ over $v(iT)$ and see where the "overlaps" occur. At overlapping points, we multiply the value of $x(-iT)$ and $v(iT)$. We then sum up the results of the multiplication. Notice that we have folded $x(kT)$ instead of $v(kT)$. It does not matter which one we fold.

Also note that in order to get a good result, we must shift the function $x(-iT)$ by an amount $kT = -2$ so that the all of $x(-iT)$ eventually slides over $v(iT)$.

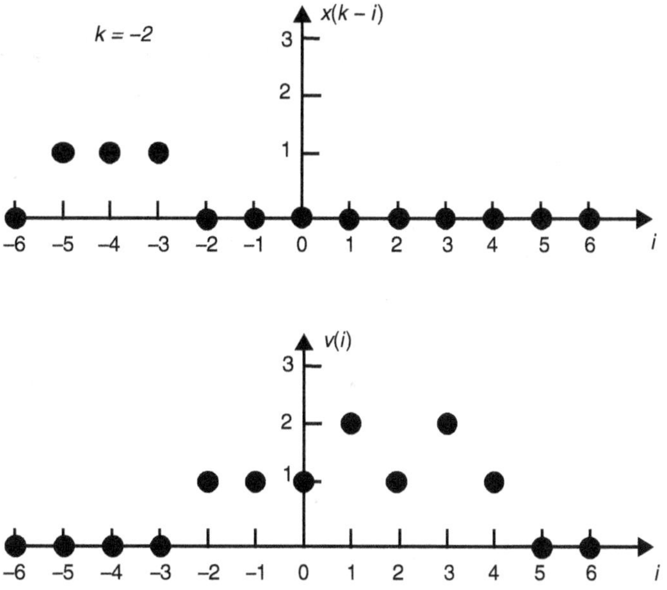

Figure 11.3

At this point, there is no overlap. We now create a table to help us tabulate the convolution.

Table 11.1

	v(iT)										
i *k* **shift**	**–3**	**–2**	**–1**	**0**	**1**	**2**	**3**	**4**	**5**	**6**	**Sum** **=** *y*(*kT*)
-2	0	0	0	0	0	0	0	0	0	0	0
-1											
0											
1											
2											
3											
4											
5											
6											
7											
8											

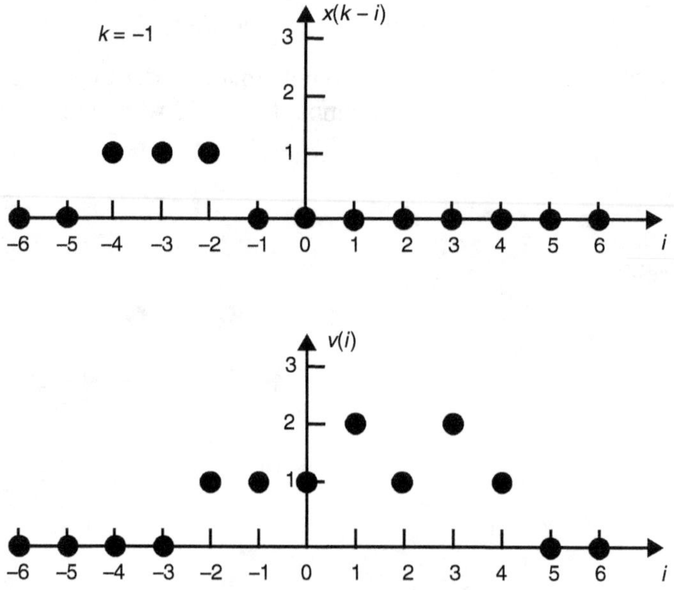

Figure 11.4

At this point, there is overlap at $i = -2$.

Table 11.2

i / *k* shift	−3	−2	−1	0	1	2	3	4	5	6	Sum = $y(kT)$
	$v(iT)$										
−2	0	0	0	0	0	0	0	0	0	0	0
−1	0	1	0	0	0	0	0	0	0	0	1
0											
1											
2											
3											
4											
5											
6											
7											
8											

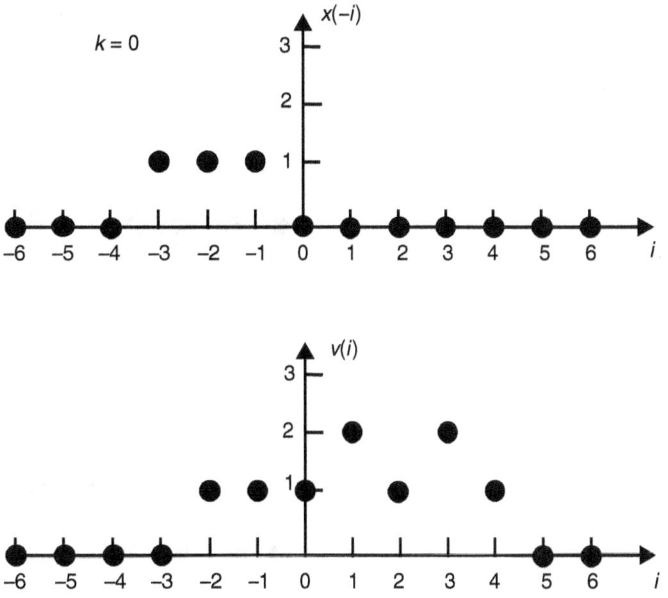

Figure 11.5

At this point, there is overlap at $i = -2$ and -1.

Table 11.3

					$v(iT)$						
i k **shift**	**–3**	**–2**	**–1**	**0**	**1**	**2**	**3**	**4**	**5**	**6**	**Sum** = $y(kT)$
–2	0	0	0	0	0	0	0	0	0	0	0
–1	0	1	0	0	0	0	0	0	0	0	1
0	0	1	1	0	0	0	0	0	0	0	2
1											
2											
3											
4											
5											
6											
7											
8											

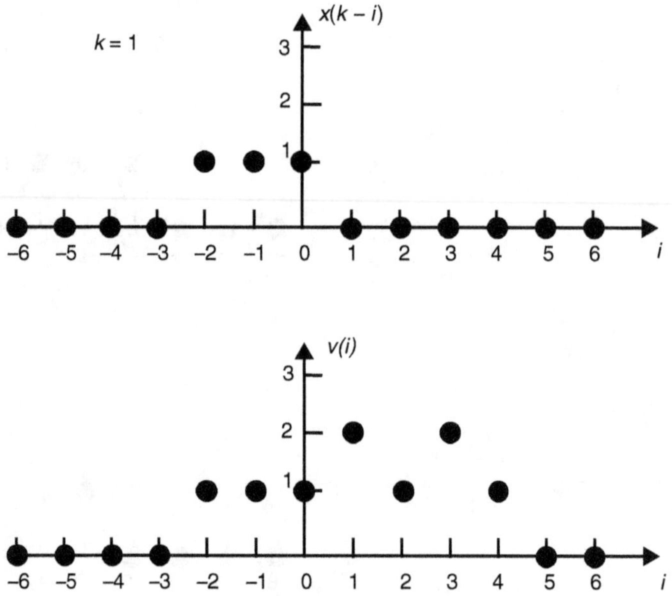

Figure 11.6

At this point, there are overlaps at $i = -2, -1$, and 0.

Table 11.4

	v(iT)										
i / *k* shift	**−3**	**−2**	**−1**	**0**	**1**	**2**	**3**	**4**	**5**	**6**	**Sum = y(kT)**
−2	0	0	0	0	0	0	0	0	0	0	0
−1	0	1	0	0	0	0	0	0	0	0	1
0	0	1	1	0	0	0	0	0	0	0	2
1	0	1	1	1	0	0	0	0	0	0	3
2											
3											
4											
5											
6											
7											
8											

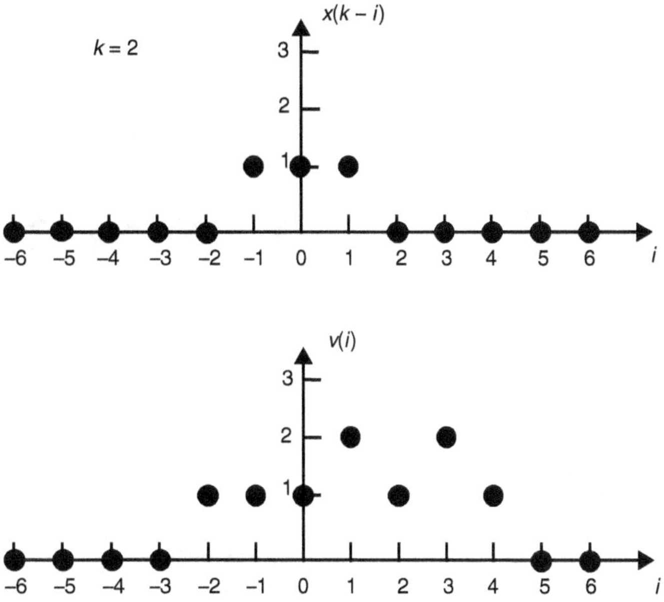

Figure 11.7

At this point, there are overlaps at $i = -1$, 0, and 1.

Table 11.5

					v(iT)						
i *k* **shift**	**−3**	**−2**	**−1**	**0**	**1**	**2**	**3**	**4**	**5**	**6**	**Sum** = *y*(*kT*)
−2	0	0	0	0	0	0	0	0	0	0	0
−1	0	1	0	0	0	0	0	0	0	0	1
0	0	1	1	0	0	0	0	0	0	0	2
1	0	1	1	1	0	0	0	0	0	0	3
2	0	0	1	1	2	0	0	0	0	0	4
3											
4											
5											
6											
7											
8											

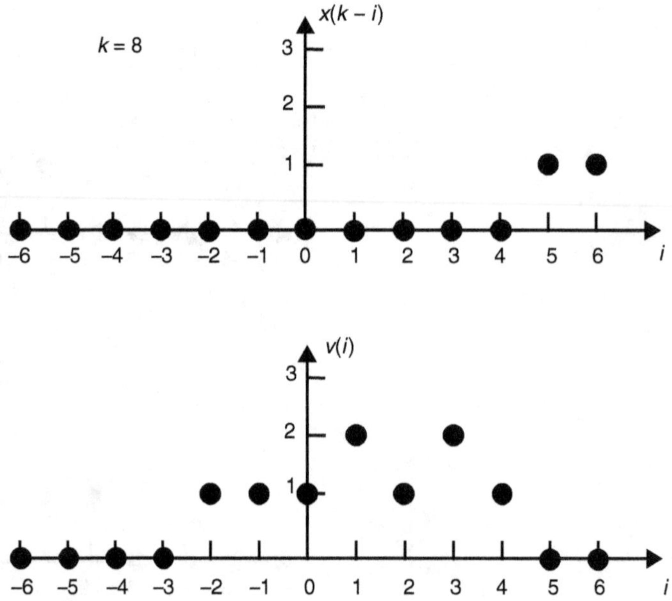

Figure 11.8

This is the point where the folded $x(iT)$ no longer overlaps $v(iT)$. The result is shown below with the table of results.

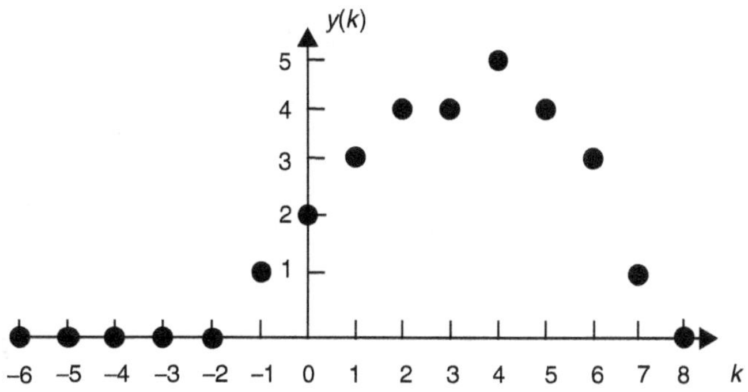

Figure 11.9

Table 11.6

i / k shift	$v(iT)$ –3	–2	–1	0	1	2	3	4	5	6	Sum = $y(kT)$
–2	0	0	0	0	0	0	0	0	0	0	0
–1	0	1	0	0	0	0	0	0	0	0	1
0	0	1	1	0	0	0	0	0	0	0	2
1	0	1	1	1	0	0	0	0	0	0	3
2	0	0	1	1	2	0	0	0	0	0	4
3	0	0	0	1	2	1	0	0	0	0	4
4	0	0	0	0	2	1	2	0	0	0	5
5	0	0	0	0	0	1	2	1	0	0	4
6	0	0	0	0	0	0	2	1	0	0	3
7	0	0	0	0	0	0	0	1	0	0	1
8	0	0	0	0	0	0	0	0	0	0	0

CONVOLUTION REPRESENTATION OF LINEAR TIME-INVARIANT CONTINUOUS-TIME SYSTEMS

Impulse Response

Recall the definition of an impulse function:

$$\delta(t) = 0,\ t \neq 0$$
$$\int \delta(\lambda)d\lambda = 1.$$

The impulse response is,

$$h(t) = \delta(t).$$

For a causal system, $h(t) = 0$ for all $t < 0$.

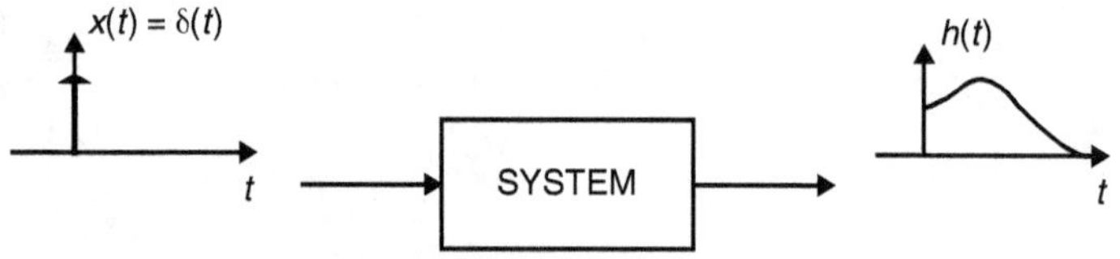

Figure 11.10 System impulse response

If $x(t)$ is a causal function [$x(t) = 0$ for all $t < 0$], by the sifting property,

$$x(t)=\int_{0^-}^{\infty} x(\lambda)\delta(t-\lambda)d\lambda.$$

The output is

$$y(t)=x(t)*h(t), t\geq 0$$

$$=\int_{0}^{\infty} x(\lambda)h(t-\lambda)d\lambda$$

which is the convolution representation.

Therefore,

$$x(t)*v(t)=\begin{cases}0, t<0\\ \int_{0}^{t} x(\lambda)v(t-\lambda)d\lambda,\ t>0\end{cases}$$

The integral exists if $x(t)$ and $v(t)$ are integrable. That is,

$$\int_{0}^{t} |x(\lambda)|d\lambda<\infty$$

$$\int_{0}^{t} |v(\lambda)|d\lambda<\infty, t>0.$$

The following steps are recommended when performing convolutions of two functions $x(t)$ and $v(t)$.

1. Graph $x(\lambda)$ and $v(-\lambda)$ (or vise-versa) as functions of λ. That is, fold $v(\lambda)$ about the vertical axis.
2. Upon folding $v(\lambda)$, denote the point where $\lambda = 0$ as t. All other points of $v(-\lambda)$ are relative to the reference point t. Remember, we're now in the λ-axis.
3. Define an interval for which the product $x(\lambda)v(t-\lambda)$ has the same analytical form (e.g., from $t = 0$ to $t = 1$).

4. Integrate the product $x(\lambda)v(t-\lambda)$ as a function of λ over the integral defined in step 3.
5. Repeat steps 3 and 4 as many times as necessary until $x(\lambda)*v(t)$ is computed for all $t > 0$.

Example 11.1

Convolve the following functions:

$$x(t) = \Pi\left(\frac{t-1}{2}\right)$$

$$v(t) = 2\Pi\left(t - \frac{1}{2}\right).$$

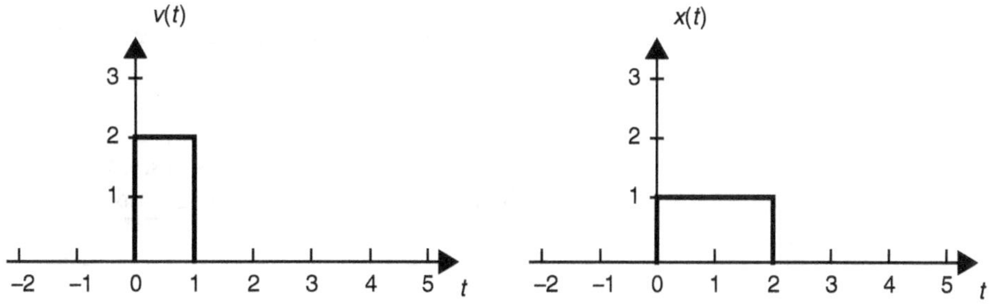

Exhibit 1

Choose to flip $v(t)$ about the y-axis. This will then be the convolution at $t = 0$.

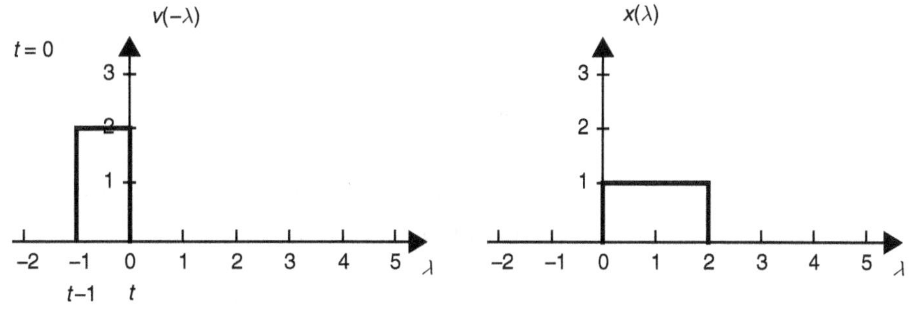

Exhibit 2

The first region of integration is $t < 0$ for which no overlapping area exists. We construct a table as follows:

Table 11.7

Time shift, t Region of Overlap	λ lower limit of integration	λ upper limit of integration	Area of Overlap (Integral)
$t < 0$	---	---	0

For ease of viewing the "overlap" intervals, the two functions are drawn on the same axes:

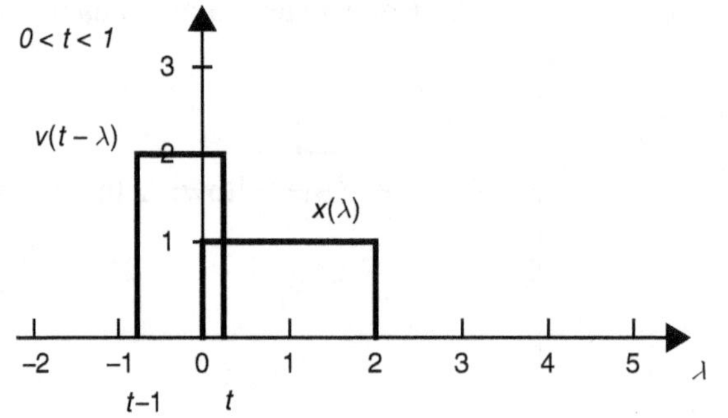

Figure 11.11

The function $v(t-\lambda)$ slides over the function $x(\lambda)$. The second region of overlap and function to be integrated is $0 \leq t < 1$ with the lower limit of the overlapping area determined by $x(\lambda)$ and the upper limit t of the area is determined by $v(t-\lambda)$.

Table 11.8

Time shift, t Region of Overlap	λ lower limit of integration	λ upper limit of integration	Area of Overlap (Integral)
$t < 0$	---	---	0
$0 \leq t < 1$	0	t	$\int_{\lambda\,lower}^{\lambda\,upper} (2)(1)d\lambda$

The third region of overlap is $1 \leq t < 2$ as shown in Table 11.9. There is complete overlap of the two areas. Therefore, the integration limit of the overlap area are from $t-1$ to t defined by $v(t-\lambda)$ in the region $1 \leq t < 2$.

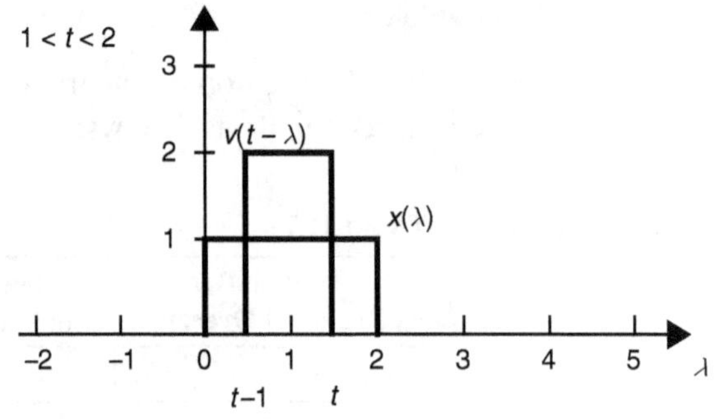

Figure 11.12

Table 11.9

Time shift, t Region of Overlap	λ lower limit of integration	λ upper limit of integration	Area of Overlap (Integral)
$t < 0$	---	---	0
$0 \le t < 1$	0	t	$\int_{\lambda lower}^{\lambda upper} (2)(1)d\lambda$
$1 \le t < 2$	$t-1$	t	$\int_{\lambda lower}^{\lambda upper} (2)(1)d\lambda$

The fourth region of overlap is $2 \le t < 3$ over which the upper limit of integration is 2 as defined by $x(\lambda)$ and the lower limit is $t-1$ as defined by $v(t-\lambda)$.

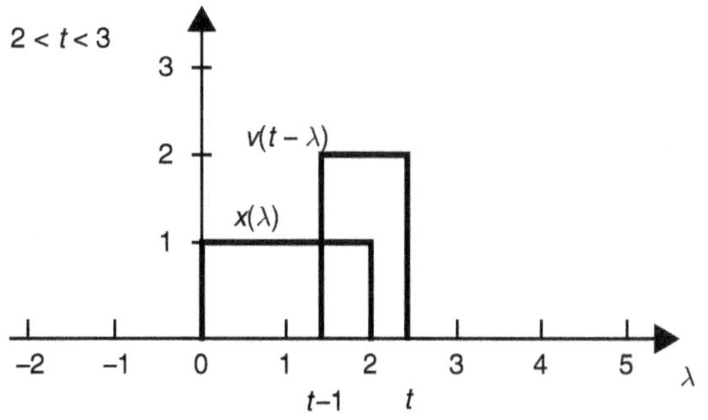

Figure 11.13

Table 11.10

Time shift, t Region of Overlap	λ lower limit of integration	λ upper limit of integration	Area of Overlap (Integral)
$t < 0$	---	---	0
$0 \le t < 1$	0	t	$\int_{\lambda lower}^{\lambda upper} (2)(1)d\lambda$
$1 \le t < 2$	$t-1$	t	$\int_{\lambda lower}^{\lambda upper} (2)(1)d\lambda$
$2 \le t < 3$	$t-1$	2	$\int_{\lambda lower}^{\lambda upper} (2)(1)d\lambda$

The last region is trivial in that there is no overlap between the two functions. The resultant area of overlap is 0.

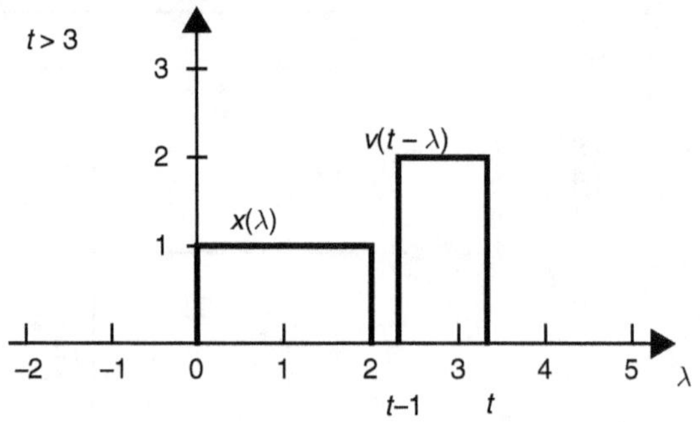

Figure 11.14

Table 11.11

Time shift, t Region of Overlap	λ lower limit of integration	λ upper limit of integration	Area of Overlap (Integral)
$t<0$	---	---	0
$0\le t<1$	0	t	$\int_{\lambda lower}^{\lambda upper} (2)(1)d\lambda$
$1\le t<2$	$t-1$	t	$\int_{\lambda lower}^{\lambda upper} (2)(1)d\lambda$
$2\le t<3$	$t-1$	2	$\int_{\lambda lower}^{\lambda upper} (2)(1)d\lambda$
$t\ge 3$	---	---	0

The result of the convolution is:

$$x(t)*v(t)=\begin{cases}0 & ,t<0\\ 2t & ,0\le t<1\\ 2 & ,1\le t<2\\ -2t+6 & ,2\le t<3\\ 0 & ,t\ge 3\end{cases}$$

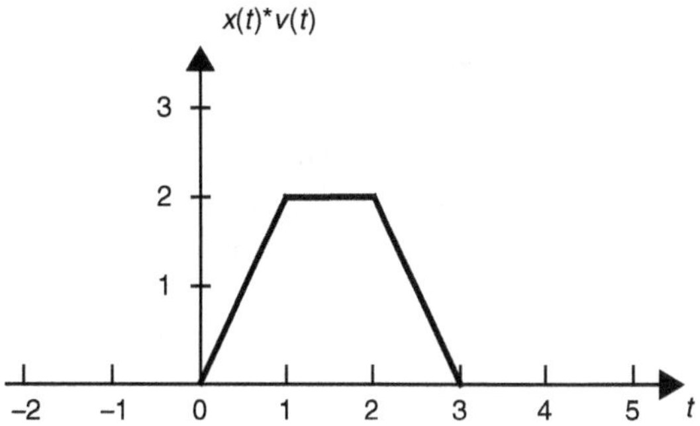

Figure 11.15 Result of the convolution.

Example 11.2

Convolve the following functions:

$$x(t) = \Lambda\left(\frac{t-1}{2}\right)$$

$$v(t) = \Lambda\left(\frac{t-1}{2}\right).$$

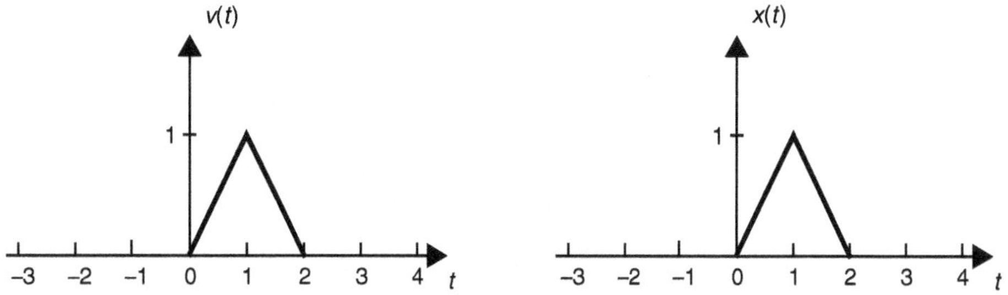

Exhibit 3

Choose to flip $v(t)$ about the y-axis. This will then be the convolution at $t = 0$.

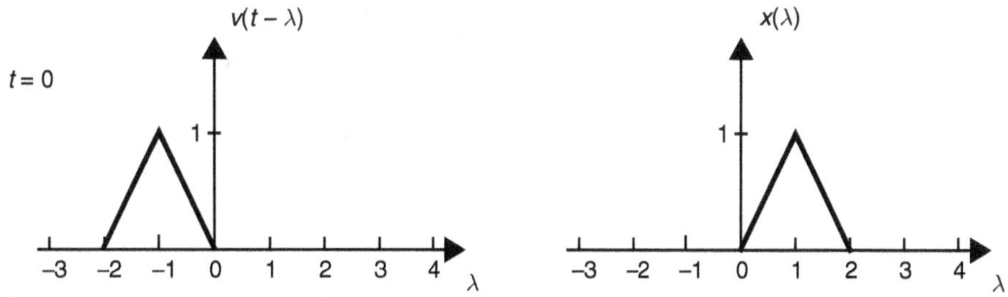

Exhibit 4

The first region of integration is $t < 0$ for which no overlapping area exists. We construct a table as follows:

Table 11.12

Time shift, t Region of Overlap	λ lower limit of integration	λ upper limit of integration	Area of Overlap (Integral)
$t < 0$	---	---	0

For ease of viewing the "overlap" intervals, the two functions are drawn on the same axes:

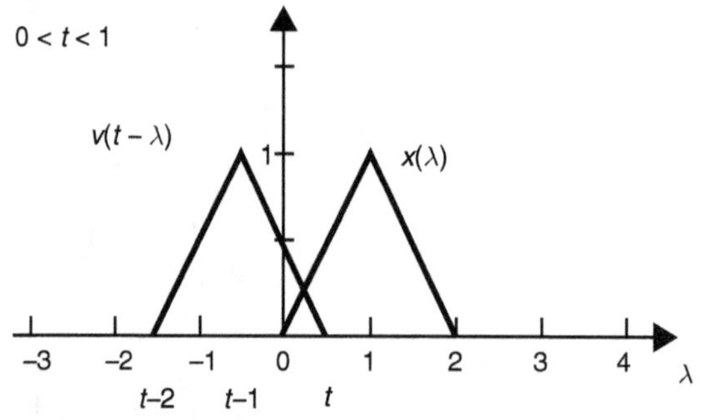

Figure 11.16

The function $v(t-\lambda)$ slides over the function $x(\lambda)$. The second region of overlap and function to be integrated is $0 \le t < 1$ with the lower limit of the overlapping area determined by $x(\lambda)$ and the upper limit t of the area is determined by $v(t-\lambda)$.

Table 11.13

Time shift, t Region of Overlap	λ lower limit of integration	λ upper limit of integration	Area of Overlap (Integral)
$t < 0$	---	---	0
$0 \le t < 1$	0	t	$\int_{\lambda\, lower}^{\lambda\, upper} (t-\lambda)\lambda d\lambda$

The third region of overlap is $1 \le t < 2$ as shown in the following figure. There is complete overlap of the two areas. Three different integrals must be added to yield the overlap area defined by $v(t-\lambda)$ in the region $1 \le t < 2$.

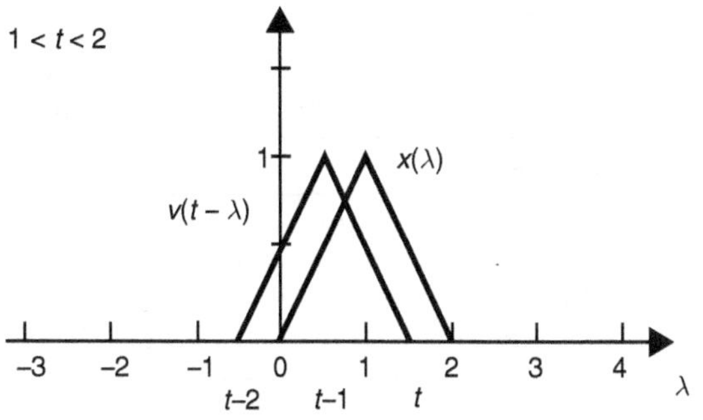

Figure 11.17

Table 11.14

Time shift, t Region of Overlap	λ lower limit of integration	λ upper limit of integration	Area of Overlap (Integral)
$t < 0$	---	---	0
$0 \le t < 1$	0	t	$\int_{\lambda lower}^{\lambda upper} (t-\lambda)\lambda d\lambda$
$1 \le t < 2$	0	$t-1$	$\int_{\lambda lower}^{\lambda upper} [(\lambda-t)+2]\lambda d\lambda$
	$t-1$	1	$+\int_{\lambda lower}^{\lambda upper} (t-\lambda)\lambda d\lambda$
	1	t	$+\int_{\lambda lower}^{\lambda upper} (t-\lambda)(2-\lambda) d\lambda$

The fourth region of overlap is $2 \le t < 3$. There are three limits of integration defined by the three integrals that need to be summed to yield the overlap area.

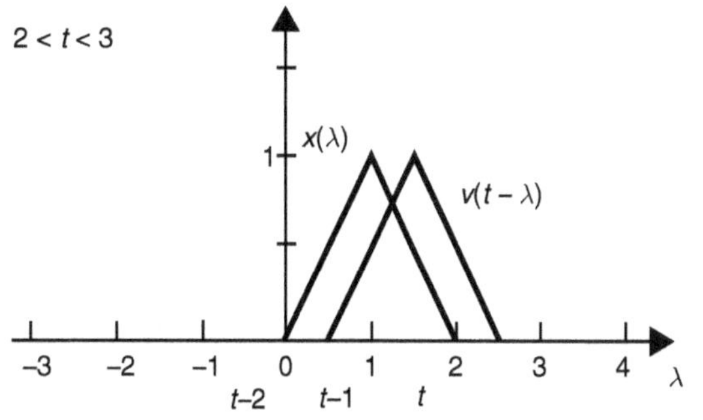

Figure 11.18

Table 11.15

Time shift, t Region of Overlap	λ lower limit of integration	λ upper limit of integration	Area of Overlap (Integral)
$t<0$	---	---	0
$0 \le t < 1$	0	t	$\int_{\lambda lower}^{\lambda upper} (t-\lambda)\lambda d\lambda$
$1 \le t < 2$	0	$t-1$	$\int_{\lambda lower}^{\lambda upper} [(\lambda-t)+2]\lambda d\lambda$
	$t-1$	1	$+\int_{\lambda lower}^{\lambda upper} (t-\lambda)\lambda d\lambda$
	1	t	$+\int_{\lambda lower}^{\lambda upper} (t-\lambda)(2-\lambda) d\lambda$
$2 \le t < 3$	$t-2$	1	$\int_{\lambda lower}^{\lambda upper} [(\lambda-t)+2]\lambda d\lambda$
	1	$t-1$	$+\int_{\lambda lower}^{\lambda upper} [(\lambda-t)+2](2-\lambda) d\lambda$
	$t-1$	2	$+\int_{\lambda lower}^{\lambda upper} (t-\lambda)(2-\lambda) d\lambda$

The next region is $3 \le t < 4$ with the lower and upper limits of $t-2$ and 2, respectively, with the integral of the area shown in the following table. For the region $t > 4$, there is no overlap, so the integral is zero.

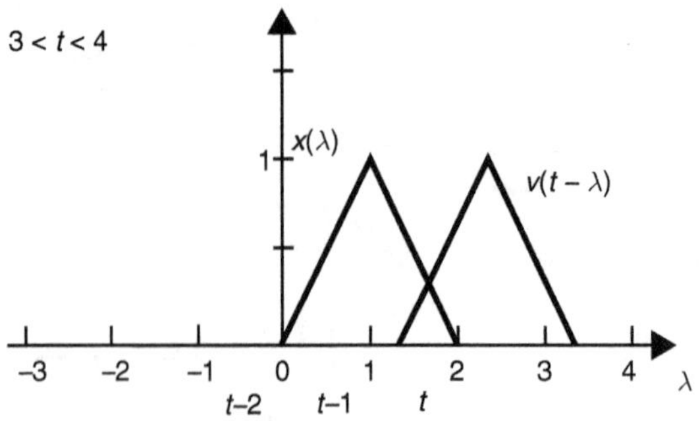

Figure 11.19

Table 11.16

Time shift, t Region of Overlap	λ lower limit of integration	λ upper limit of integration	Area of Overlap (Integral)
$t<0$	---	---	0
$0 \le t < 1$	0	t	$\int_{\lambda\,lower}^{\lambda\,upper} (t-\lambda)\lambda d\lambda$
$1 \le t < 2$	0	$t-1$	$\int_{\lambda\,lower}^{\lambda\,upper} [(\lambda-t)+2]\lambda d\lambda$
	$t-1$	1	$+\int_{\lambda\,lower}^{\lambda\,upper} (t-\lambda)\lambda d\lambda$
	1	t	$+\int_{\lambda\,lower}^{\lambda\,upper} (t-\lambda)(2-\lambda) d\lambda$
$2 \le t < 3$	$t-2$	1	$\int_{\lambda\,lower}^{\lambda\,upper} [(\lambda-t)+2]\lambda d\lambda$
	1	$t-1$	$+\int_{\lambda\,lower}^{\lambda\,upper} [(\lambda-t)+2](2-\lambda) d\lambda$
	$t-1$	2	$+\int_{\lambda\,lower}^{\lambda\,upper} (t-\lambda)(2-\lambda) d\lambda$
$3 \le t < 4$	$t-2$	2	$\int_{\lambda\,lower}^{\lambda\,upper} [(\lambda-t)+2](2-\lambda) d\lambda$
$t>4$	---	---	0

PROPERTIES OF CONVOLUTION

Associativity

For any signals $x(t)$, $v(t)$, and $w(t)$,

$$(x(t) * v(t)) * w(t) = x(t) * (v(t) * w(t)).$$

Commutativity

$$x(t) * v(t) = v(t) * x(t)$$

Distributivity with Addition

$$x(t) * (v(t) + w(t)) = x(t) * v(t) + x(t) * w(t)$$

Shift Property

$$x(t-c) * v(t-c) = x(t-c) * v(t) = x(t) * v(t-c)$$

Derivative Property

If the signal $x(t)$ has an ordinary first derivative $\dot{x}(t)$, the convolution $x(t) * v(t)$ has an ordinary first derivative,

$$\frac{d}{dt}\left[x(t) * v(t)\right] = \dot{x}(t) * v(t) = x(t) * \dot{v}(t).$$

If both $x(t)$ and $v(t)$ are differentiable then,

$$\frac{d^2}{dt^2}\left[x(t) * v(t)\right] = \dot{x}(t) * \dot{v}(t).$$

Integration Property

Let $x(-1)(t)$ and $v(-1)(t)$ denote integrals of $x(t)$ and $v(t)$,

$$x^{(-1)}(t) = \int_{-\infty}^{t} x(\lambda)d\lambda \quad \text{and} \quad v^{(-1)}(t) = \int_{-\infty}^{t} v(\lambda)d\lambda.$$

Then,

$$[x(t) * v(t)]\,(-1) = x(-1)(t) * v(t) = x(t) * v(-1)(t).$$

Convolution with the Unit Impulse

$$x(t) * \delta(t) = \delta(t) * x(t) = x(t).$$

Convolution with the Shifted Unit Impulse

$$x(t) * \delta(t-c) = x(t-c).$$

z-Transforms and Difference Equations

z-transform is one of the mathematical tools used for the analysis and design of discrete-time control systems. The role of the *z*-transform in digital control systems is analogous to that of the Laplace transform in the continuous-time control systems.

Just like a linear ordinary differential equation characterizes the dynamics of a linear time invariant system, a constant coefficient difference equation characterizes the dynamics of a linear discrete-time system. In order to determine the response of a discrete-time system to a given input, a difference equation must be solved. Just as the Laplace transformation transforms linear time invariant differential equations into algebraic equations of the Laplace variable s, the *z*-transformation transforms the constant coefficient difference equations into algebraic equations of the *z*-transform variable z. By using the *z*-transformation, a linear discrete-time system may be represented by a transfer function called the *pulse transfer function*.

The z-transform of the output signal can then be expressed as the product between the system's pulse transfer function and the z-transform of the input signal.

$x(k)$ or x_k will be used to represent $x(kT)$. In addition, the signal (sequence) is assumed as zero values for $k < 0$ (i.e., $x(k) = 0$ for $k < 0$).

Difference Equations

Difference equations are used to represent discrete time signal generation of a sequence of inputs $u(k)$ given a sampled sequence of the system output $y(k)$. In general, control effort at sample instance k base on the sampled system output at sample instance k and a finite number of previous sampled outputs and control efforts is determined mathematically. Mathematically this can be written as

$$u(k) = f\,[y(k), y(k-1), y(k-2), \ldots, y(k-m), u(k-1), u(k-2), \ldots, u(k-n)].$$

There are an infinite number of ways the $n + m - 1$ values on the right-hand side of the previous equation can be combined to form $u(k)$. In this course, we shall only focus on the cases where the right-hand side of the previous equation involves a linear combination of the past samples of the measurements and controls, in other words

$$u(k) = a_m \cdot y(k) + a_{m-1} \cdot y(k-1) + a_{m-2} \cdot y(k-2) + \cdots a_0 \cdot y(k-m)$$

$$+ b_{n-1} \cdot u(k-1) + b_{n-2} \cdot u(k-2) + \cdots b_0 \cdot u(k-n) \quad \textbf{(11.1)}$$

Equation (11.1) is a linear difference equation. If the coefficients a_i and b_j are constants (independent of sample instance k), it is a constant coefficient difference equation.

Example **11.3**

In numerical analysis, there are many methods to approximate the integral of a function

$$x(t) = \int_0^t y(\tau) \cdot d\tau$$

The backward rectangular rule is one of the simplest. It uses a rectangular approximation to approximate the area under the function $y(t)$, as shown in Exhibit 5.

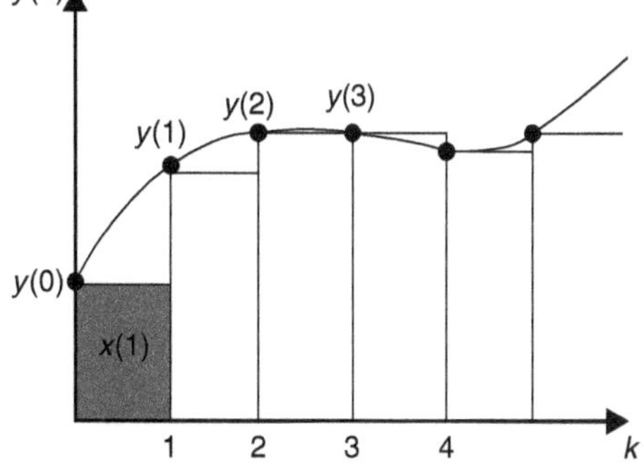

Exhibit 5 Approximate Numerical Integration

Let $x(k)$ be the value of the integral at sample instance k, while $x(k-1)$ is the value of the integral at the previous sample instance. Then, $x(k)$ can be calculated using

$$x(k) = x(k-1) + T \cdot y(k-1). \qquad \textbf{(11.2)}$$

Equation (11.2) provided an algorithm to successively approximate the integral of the function $y(t)$. This algorithm takes the form of a constant coefficient difference equation.

Example 11.4

Solving a constant coefficient difference equation often involves tedious algebraic manipulations. To find the solution for Equation (11.2) [i.e., find an expression for solving $x(k)$ given current and previous values of $y(k)$], first write out Equation (11.2) for $k = 1, 2, \ldots$

$$\begin{aligned} x(k) &= x(k-1) + T \cdot y(k-1) \\ x(k-1) &= x(k-2) + T \cdot y(k-2) \\ x(k-2) &= x(k-3) + T \cdot y(k-3) \\ &\vdots \\ x(2) &= x(1) + T \cdot y(1) \\ x(1) &= x(0) + T \cdot y(0) \end{aligned}$$

Adding the above k equations and noting that many $x(k)$'s can be cancelled, we can obtain

$$x(k) = x(0) + T \cdot \sum_{j=0}^{k-1} y(j) \qquad \textbf{(11.3)}$$

Equation (11.3) represented the solution to the difference equation (11.2). The solution for a constant coefficient difference equation requires the initial value of the solution as well as all the past values of the input, in this case, $y(k)$.

The first order difference equation is

$$y[k] + a_1 y[k-1] = x[k].$$

A second-order difference equation is

$$y[k] + a_1 y[k-1] + a_2 y[k-2] = x[k]$$

Example **11.5**

Sequence {1, 1, 2, 3, 5, 8, 13, 21, . . .} is called Fibonacci sequence, generated with rule $y(k + 2) = y(k + 1) + y(k)$ for $k = 0, 1, 2, 3, \ldots$ and initial value $y(0) = 1$ and $y(1) = 1$.

To solve for the sequence using the Fibonacci equation, a table of values is created:

k	$y(k)$	$y(k+1)$	$y(k+2)$
0	$y(0) = 1$	$y(1) = 1$	$y(0+2) = y(2) = 1 + 1 = 2$
1	$y(1) = 1$	$y(2) = 2$	$y(1+2) = y(3) = 1 + 2 = 3$
2	$y(2) = 2$	$y(3) = 3$	$y(2+2) = y(4) = 2 + 3 = 5$
3	$y(3) = 3$	$y(4) = 5$	$y(3+2) = y(5) = 3 + 5 = 8$
4	$y(4) = 5$	$y(5) = 8$	$y(4+2) = y(6) = 5 + 8 = 13$
5	$y(5) = 8$	$y(6) = 13$	$y(5+2) = y(7) = 8 + 13 = 21$

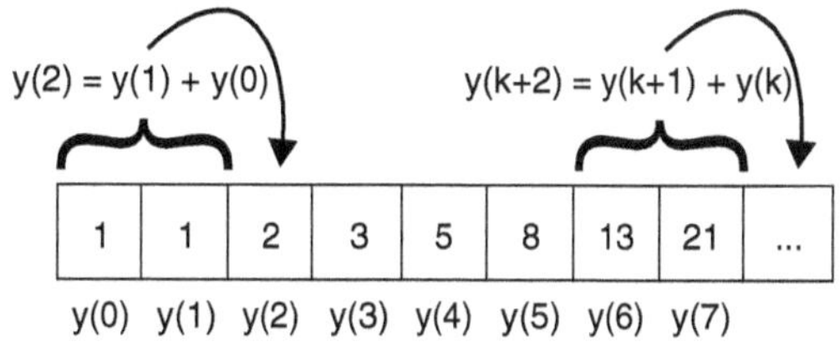

Exhibit 6

Not all constant coefficient difference equations can be solved using the manipulation illustrated in Example 11.3. A more general, systematic approach is needed.

THE *Z*-TRANSFORM

The Laplace transform is used as an analysis tools for continuous-time linear time invariant systems. The reasons are two-folds: (1) the input/output relationship for continuous-time systems, a convolution operation in the time domain, is simplified to an algebraic relationship in the s-domain, and (2) the Laplace transform relates the time domain and frequency domain characteristic of the system. The discrete-time analogy of the Laplace transform is the z-transform, which transforms a discrete sequence of time domain signal into a function of the z-transform variable z.

Definition: *z*-Transform

The z-transform of a sampled sequence $x(kT)$ or $x(k)$, where k represents non-negative integers and T is the sampling period, is defined by

$$X(z) = Z[x^*(t)] = Z[x(kT)] = Z[x(k)] = \sum_{k=0}^{\infty} x(kT)z^{-k} = \sum_{k=0}^{\infty} x(k)z^{-k} \quad \textbf{(11.4)}$$

where the complex variable z must be selected so that the summation converges.

This z-transform is called the *one-sided z-transform*. The symbol Z[•] is used as "the z-transform of." In the one-sided z-transform, we assume $x^*(t) = 0$ for $t < 0$ or $x(kT) = x(k) = 0$ for $k < 0$. For most engineering applications, the one-sided z-transform will have a convenient closed form representation in its region of convergence. From Equation (11.3), $X(z)$ is an infinite series of $z - 1$ that converges outside the circle $z = R$, where R is called the *radius of convergence*.

- This transformation produces a new representation of $x[n]$ denoted $X(z)$.
- Returning to the original sequence (*inverse z-transform*) $x[n]$ requires finding the coefficient associated with the nth power of z^{-1}.
- Formally transforming from the time/sequence/n-domain to the z-domain is represented as

$$n\text{-Domain} \leftrightarrow z\text{-Domain}$$

$$x[n] = \sum_{k=0}^{N} x[k]\,\delta[n-k] \xleftrightarrow{z} X(z) = \sum_{k=0}^{N} x[k]\,z^{-k}$$

- A sequence and its z-transform are said to form a *z-transform pair* and are denoted

$$x[n] \xleftrightarrow{z} X(z)$$

— In the sequence or n-domain, the independent variable is n.
— In the z-domain, the independent variable is z.

Example 11.6

Find the z-transform of

$$x[n] = \delta[n - n_0]$$

Using the definition

$$X(z) = \sum_{k=0}^{N} x[k]\,z^{-k} = \sum_{k=0}^{N} \delta[k - n_0]\,z^{-k} = z^{-n_0}$$

So,

$$\delta[n - n_0] \xleftrightarrow{z} z^{-n_0}$$

Example 11.7

Find the z-transform of the difference equation,

$$x[n] = 2\delta[n] + 3\delta[n-1] + 5\delta[n-2] + 2\delta[n-3]$$

By inspection we find that

$$X(z) = 2 + 3z^{-1} + 5z^{-2} + 2z^{-3}$$

Example 11.8

Unit Step Function (Sequence)

Consider the unit step function defined by

$$u(k) = \begin{cases} 1 & k \geq 0 \\ 0 & k < 0 \end{cases}.$$

The z-transform of $u(k)$ is

$$U(z) = Z[u(k)] = \sum_{k=0}^{\infty} 1 \cdot z^{-k} = 1 + z^{-1} + z^{-2} + \ldots = \frac{1}{1 - z^{-1}}$$

$$= \frac{z}{z-1} \text{ for } |z^{-1}| < 1 (\text{or} |z| > 1)$$

Example 11.9

Polynomial Function

Consider a polynomial function defined by

$$x(k) = \begin{cases} a^k & k \geq 0 \\ 0 & k < 0 \end{cases}.$$

The z-transform of $x(k)$ is

$$X(z) = Z[x(k)] = \sum_{k=0}^{\infty} a^k \cdot z^{-k} = \sum_{k=0}^{\infty} (a^{-1} z)^{-k}$$

$$= \frac{1}{1 - (a^{-1} z)^{-1}} = \frac{z}{z - a} \text{ for } |z| > a.$$

Example 11.10

Exponential Function

Consider the exponential function defined by

$$x(k) = \begin{cases} e^{-akT} & k \geq 0 \\ 0 & k < 0 \end{cases}.$$

The z-transform of $x(k)$ is

$$X(z) = Z[x(k)] = \sum_{k=0}^{\infty} e^{-akT} \cdot z^{-k} = \sum_{k=0}^{\infty} (e^{aT} z)^{-k}$$

$$= \frac{1}{1 - (e^{aT} z)^{-1}} = \frac{z}{z - e^{=aT}} \text{ for } |z| > e^{-akT}.$$

Example 11.11

Sinusoidal Function

Consider the sinusoidal function defined by

$$x(k) = \begin{cases} \sin(\omega kT) & k \geq 0 \\ 0 & k < 0 \end{cases}.$$

The z-transform of $x(k)$ is

$$X(z) = Z\left[x(k)\right] = \sum_{k=0}^{\infty} \sin(\omega kT) \cdot z^{-k} = \sum_{k=0}^{\infty} \frac{e^{j\omega kT} - e^{-j\omega kT}}{2j} \cdot z^{-k}$$

$$= \frac{1}{2j}\left(\frac{1}{1-e^{j\omega T}z^{-1}} - \frac{1}{1-e^{-j\omega T}z^{-1}}\right) = \frac{1}{2j}\frac{\left(e^{j\omega T} - e^{-j\omega T}\right)z^{-1}}{1-\left(e^{j\omega T} + e^{-j\omega T}\right)z^{-1} + z^{-2}}$$

$$= \frac{z^{-1}\sin(\omega T)}{1-2z^{-1}\cos(\omega T) + z^{-2}} = \frac{z \cdot \sin(\omega T)}{z^2 - 2z \cdot \cos(\omega T) + 1} \text{ for } |z| > 1.$$

The expansion of the right-hand side of Equation (11.4) yields

$$X(z) = x(0) + x(T)z^{-1} + x(2T)z^{-2} + \ldots + x(kT)z^{-k} + \ldots$$

The previous equation implies that the z-transform of any discrete sequence can be written in the infinite series form by inspection. The z^{-k} in this series indicates the position in time at which the amplitude $x(kT)$ occurs. Conversely, if $X(z)$ is given in the series form as above, the inverse z-transform can be obtained by inspection as a sequence of values $x(kT)$ that correspond to the values of $x(t)$ at the sampling instances.

Just as in working with Laplace and Fourier transformations, extensive use of a table of z-transforms is recommended for commonly encountered functions, rather than calculating the z-transform directly from its definition.

$f[k]$	$F(z)$
$\delta[k]$, Impulse at $k = 0$	1
$u[k]$, Step at $k = 0$	$1/(1 - z^{-1})$
β^k	$1/(1 - \beta z^{-1})$
$y[k - 1]$	$z^{-1}Y(z) + y(-1)$
$y[k - 2]$	$z^{-2}Y(z) + y(-2) + y(-1)z^{-1}$
$y[k + 1]$	$zY(z) - zy(0)$
$y[k + 2]$	$z^2Y(z) - z^2y(0) - zy(1)$
$\sum_{m=0}^{\infty} X[k-m]h[m]$	$H(z)X(z)$
$\lim_{k\to 0} f[k]$	$\lim_{z\to\infty} F(z)$
$\lim_{k\to\infty} f[k]$	$\lim_{z\to 1}(1 - z^{-1})F(z)$

[Note: The last two transform pairs represent the Initial Value Theorem (I.V.T.) and the Final Value Theorem (F.V.T.) respectively.]

Source: NCEES, *FE Reference Handbook: 9.1 Version for Computer-Based Testing*, (Clemson, SC, 2013) 201.

Exhibit 7 *z*-Transform Table

Properties of the *z*-Transform

The *z*-transform has a few very useful properties, and its definition extends to infinite signals/impulse responses.

The Superposition (Linearity) Property

$$ax_1[n] + bx_2[n] \overset{z}{\longleftrightarrow} aX_1(z) + bX_2(z)$$

proof

$$X(z) = \sum_{n=0} (ax_1[n] + bx_2[n]) z^{-1}$$

$$= a\sum_{n=0}^{N} x_1[n]z^{-1} + b\sum_{n=0}^{N} x_2[n]z^{-1}$$

$$= aX_1(z) + bX_2(z)$$

The Time-Delay Property

$$x[n-1] \overset{z}{\longleftrightarrow} z^{-1}X(z)$$

and

$$x[n-n_0] \overset{z}{\longleftrightarrow} z^{-n_0}X(z)$$

The *z*-Transform as an Operator

The *z*-transform can be considered as an operator.

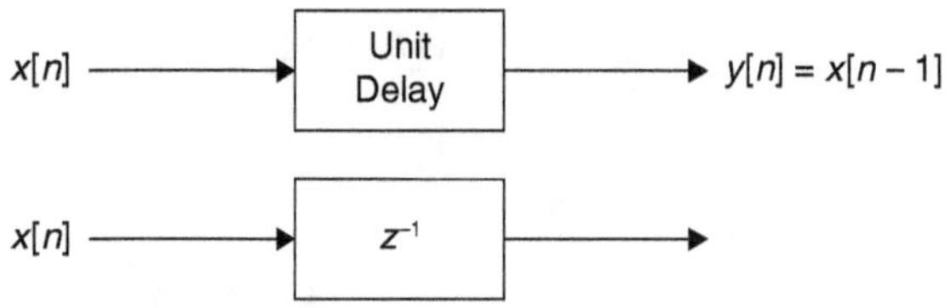

Figure 11.20 Unit-Delay Operator

In the case of the unit delay, we observe that

$$y[n] - \underset{\uparrow}{z^{-1}}\{x[n]\} = x[n-1]$$

unit delay operator

which is motivated by the fact that $Y(z)z^{-1} = X(z)$.

Similarly, the filter can be viewed as the operator since

$$y[n] = x[n] - x[n-1]$$

can be viewed as the operator

$$y[n] = z^{-1} = \{x[n]\} = x[n] - x[n-1]$$

since

$$Y(z) = X(z) - z^{-1}X(z) = (1 - z^{-1})X(z)$$

Example **11.12**

Two-Tap FIR (Finite Impulse Response)

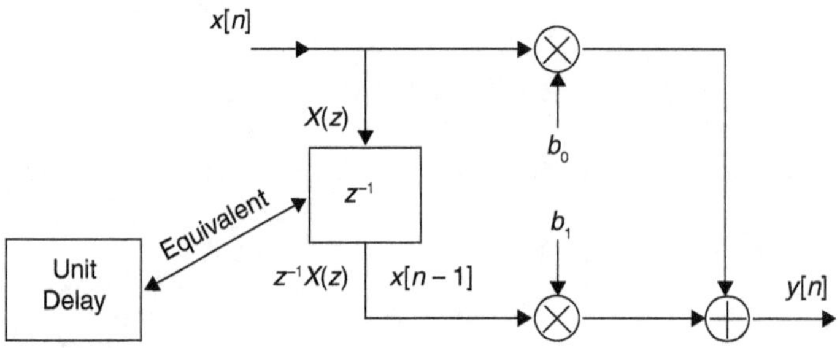

Exhibit 8

Using the operator convention, we can write by inspection that

$$Y(z) = b_0X(z) + b_1z^{-1}X(z)$$
$$y[n] = b_0x[n] + b_1x[n-1]$$

Convolution and the z-Transform

The impulse response of the unity delay system is

$$h[n] = \delta[n-1],$$

and the system output written in terms of a convolution is

$$y[n] = x[n]*\delta[n-1] = x[n-1].$$

The system function (z-transform of $h(n)$) is

$$H(z) = z^{-1},$$

and by the previous unit delay analysis,

$$Y(z)z^{-1} = X(z).$$

We observe that

$$Y(z) = H(z)X(z).$$

Example 11.13

Convolving Finite Duration Sequences

Suppose that

$$x[n] = 2\delta[n] - 3\delta[n-2] + 4\delta[n-3]$$
$$h[n] = \delta[n] + 2\delta[n-1] + \delta[n-2].$$

We wish to find $y[n]$ by first finding $Y(z)$.
We begin by z-transforming each of the sequences

$$X(z) = 2 - 3z^{-2} - 4z^{-3}$$
$$H(z) = 1 + 2z^{-1} + z^{-2}.$$

We find by direct multiplication

$$Y(z) = H(z)X(z) = (1 + 2z^{-1} + z^{-2})\,(2 - 3z^{-2} - 4z^{-3}).$$

We find $y[n]$ using the delay property on each of the terms of $Y(z)$

$$y[n] = 2\delta[n] + 4\delta[n-1] - \delta[n-2] - 2\delta[n-3] + 5\delta[n-4] + 4\delta[n-5].$$

Polynomial multiplication can be used to replace sequence convolution, when we work in the z-domain, or the z-Transform Convolution Theorem.

$$y[n] = h[n]*x[n] \stackrel{z}{\longleftrightarrow} H(z)X(z) = Y(z)$$

Cascading Systems

We have seen cascading of systems in the time-domain and the frequency domain; we now consider the z-domain:

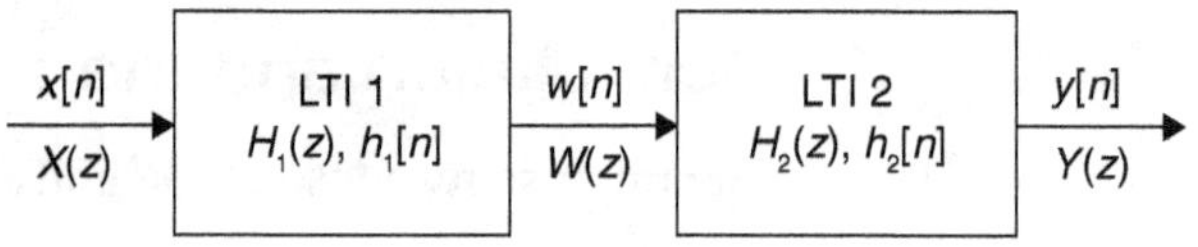

Figure 11.21

We know from the convolution theorem that

$$W(z) = H_1(z)X(z).$$

It also follows that

$$Y(z) = H_2(z)W(z),$$

so by substitution

$$Y(z) = [H_2(z)H_1(z)]\, X(z) = [H_1(z)H_2(z)]\, X(z).$$

In summary, when we cascade two LTI systems, the cascade impulse response is a cascade of impulse responses in the time-domain and a product of the z-transforms in the z-domain,

$$h[n] = h_1[n]*h_2[n] \overset{z}{\longleftrightarrow} H_1(z)H_2(z) = H(z)$$

Factoring z-Polynomials

Multiplying z-transforms creates a cascade system, so factoring must create subsystems.

Example 11.14

Factor $H(z) = 1 + 3z^{-1} - 2z^{-2} + z^{-3}$

Since this is a third-order polynomial, we should be able to factor it into a first-degree and second-degree polynomial. Let $H(z) = 0$, and multiply the equation by z^3 yields a third-order polynomial by equation $z^3 + 3z^2 - 2z + 1 = 0$. The coefficients can be best found by using a calculator:

$$z = -3.627,\ 0.314 + j0.421, \text{ and } 0.314 - j0.421.$$

Since the factored form of the transfer function is $(1 - az^{-1} - az^{-2} - \ldots)$, the polynomial coefficients are entered as –1, –3, +2, –1.

So,

$$H_1(z) = (1 - 3.6274z^{-1})$$
$$H_2(z) = (0.3137 + j0.4211)z^{-1}\ (0.3137 + j0.4211)z^{-1} = 1 - 0.6274z^{-1} - 0.2757z^{-2}.$$

The cascade system is:

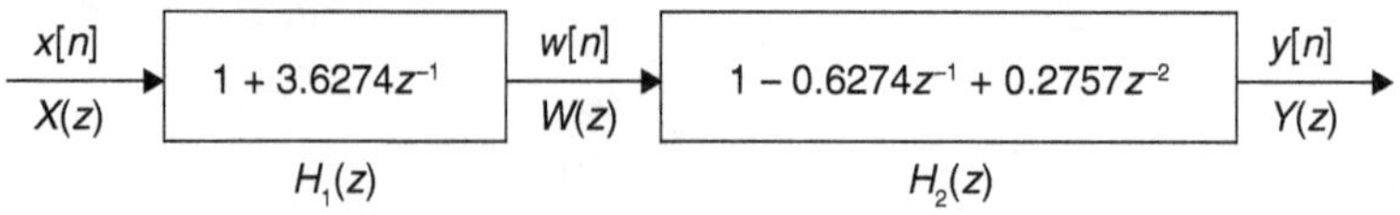

Exhibit 9

The difference equations for each subsystem are

$$w[n] = x[n] + 3.6274x[n-1]$$
$$y[n] = w[n] - 0.6274w[n-1] + 0.2757w[n-2].$$

Poles and Zeros

The z-transform of a signal often takes the form of a rational function of z

$$X(z) = \frac{b_0 z^m + b_1 z^{m-1} + \cdots + b_m}{z^n + a_1 z^{n-1} + \cdots + a_n} = \frac{b_0 (z - z_1)(z - z_2)\cdots(z - z_m)}{(z - p_1)(z - p_2)\cdots(z - p_n)}$$

where the p_is are the *poles* of $X(z)$, and the z_is are the *zeros* of $X(z)$. The location of the poles and zeros of $X(z)$ determines the characteristics of $x(k)$, a sequence of values or numbers. A graphical representation on the z plane of the location of the poles and zeros of $X(z)$ can be used.

Note in signal processing and control engineering, $X(z)$ is often represented as a ratio of polynomials in z^{-1}.

$$X(z) = X(z^{-1}) = \frac{b_0 z^{-(n-m)} + b_1 z^{-(n-m+1)} + \cdots + b_m z^{-n}}{1 + a_1 z^{-1} + a_2 z^{-2} + \cdots + a_n z^{-n}}$$

In determining the poles and zeros of $X(z)$, it is more convenient to express $X(z)$ as a ratio of polynomials in z. For example,

$$X(z) = \frac{z^2 + 0.5z}{z^2 + 3z + 2} = \frac{z(z + 0.5)}{(z+1)(z+2)}.$$

$X(z)$ has poles at $z = -1$ and $z = -2$ (denominator equal to zero) and zeros at $z = 0$ and $z = -0.5$ (numerator equal to zero). If $X(z)$ is written as a ratio of polynomials in $z - 1$, the proceeding $X(z)$ can be written as

$$X(z) = X(z^{-1}) = \frac{1 + 0.5z^{-1}}{1 + 3z^{-1} + 2z^{-2}} = \frac{(1 + 0.5z^{-1})}{(1 + z^{-1})(1 + 2z^{-1})}$$

From the above representation, although the poles at $z = -1$ and $z = -2$ and the zero $z = -0.5$ are clearly seen, the zero at $z = 0$ is not explicitly shown and will often be overlooked. Therefore, when determining the poles and zeros of z-transforms, it is preferable to express the z-transform as ratios of polynomials in z rather than in z^{-1}.

Inverse z-transform Using Partial Fraction Expansion

The procedure of using partial fraction expansion to calculate the inverse z-transform is identical to the one used in solving the inverse Laplace transform.

Distinct Real Poles Example

Find the time sequence that corresponds to the following z-transform:

$$X(z) = \frac{0.5(1 - e^{-T})^2 (z^2 + e^{-T} z)}{(z-1)(z - e^{-T})(z - e^{-2T})}$$

Solution

The denominator of the z-transform is already in the factored form so $X(z)$ can be written using partial fraction expansion

$$X(z)=\frac{0.5\left(1-e^{-T}\right)^2\left(z^2+e^{-T}z\right)}{(z-1)\left(z-e^{-T}\right)\left(z-e^{-2T}\right)}=A_1\frac{z}{z-1}+A_2\frac{z}{z-e^{-T}}+A_3\frac{z}{z-e^{-2T}}.$$

Solving for the constant coefficients A_1, A_2, and A_3,

$$A_1=\frac{z-1}{z}X(z)\Bigg|_{z=1}=\frac{0.5\left(1-e^{-T}\right)^2\left(1+e^{-T}\right)}{\left(1-e^{-T}\right)\left(1-e^{-2T}\right)}=0.5\frac{\left(1-e^{-T}\right)\left(1+e^{-T}\right)}{\left(1-e^{-2T}\right)}=0.5$$

$$A_2=\frac{z-e^{-T}}{z}X(z)\Bigg|_{z=e^{-T}}=\frac{0.5\left(1-e^{-T}\right)\left(e^{-2T}+e^{-2T}\right)}{e^{-T}\left(e^{-T}+e^{-2T}\right)}=-1$$

$$A_3=\frac{z-e^{-2T}}{z}X(z)\Bigg|_{z=e^{-2T}}=\frac{0.5\left(1-e^{-T}\right)^2\left(e^{-4T}+e^{-3T}\right)}{e^{-2T}\left(e^{-2T}-1\right)\left(e^{-2T}-e^{-T}\right)}=0.5.$$

The inverse z-transform of $X(z)$ is therefore,

$$x(k)=Z^{-1}[X(z)]=0.5-\left(e^{-T}\right)^k+0.5\left(e^{-2T}\right)^k=0.5-e^{-kT}+0.5-e^{-2kT},$$

for $k = 0, 1, 2, \ldots$

Example 11.15

Solving Difference Equation Using the z-Transform

Find the solution to the following difference equation:

$$x(k+2)+3x(k+1)+2x(k)=0,\ x(0)=0,\ x(1)=1$$

Take the z-transform of both sides of the equation,

$$z^2X(z)-z^2x(0)-z\cdot x(1)+3z\cdot X(z)-3z\cdot x(0)+2X(z)=0.$$

Substituting in the initial conditions and simplifying gives

$$X(z)=\frac{z}{z^2+3z+2}=\frac{z}{(z+1)(z+2)}=\frac{z}{z+1}-\frac{z}{z+2}$$

Take the inverse z-transform of the above equation,

$$x(k)=Z^{-1}[X(z)]=Z^{-1}\left[\frac{z}{z-(-1)}\right]-Z^{-1}\left[\frac{z}{z-(-2)}\right]=(-1)^k-(-2)^k,$$

for $k = 0, 1, 2, \ldots$

Example 11.16

Using the z-transform to solve the following difference equation

$$x(k+2) + 0.4 \cdot x(k+1) - 0.32 \cdot x(k) = u(k)$$

where $x(0) = 0$ and $x(1) = 1$. The input $u(k)$ is a unit step input (i.e., $u(k) = 1$) for $k \geq 0$.

Take the z-transform of the difference equation,

$$z^2 X(z) - z^2 x(0) - z \cdot x(1) + 0.4 \cdot z \cdot X(z) - 0.4 \cdot z \cdot x(0) - 0.32 \cdot X(z) = \frac{z}{z-1}$$

Substituting the initial conditions and simplifying,

$$X(z) = \frac{z^2}{(z-1)(z^2+0.4z-0.32)} = \frac{z^2}{(z-1)(z^2+0.8)(z-0.4)}$$

The partial fraction expansion of the solution $X(z)$ is

$$X(z) = 0.926\frac{z}{z-1} - 0.3704\frac{z}{z+0.8} - 0.5556\frac{z}{z-0.4}$$

Taking the inverse z-transform yields,

$$x(k) = 0.926 - 0.3704 \cdot (-0.8)^k - 0.5556 \cdot (0.4)^k, \text{ for } k = 0, 1, 2, \ldots$$

Note $x(k)$ will exhibit oscillatory response caused by the $(-0.8)^k$ component.

Example 11.17

Impulse Response Function

Assuming that the system is initially at rest, find the impulse response of the following discrete time system:

$$y(k+3) = 2u(k+3) - u(k+2) + 4u(k+1) + u(k)$$

The pulse transfer function of the system can be written as

$$G(z) = \frac{2z^3 - z^2 + 4z + 1}{z^3} = 2 - z^{-1} + 4z^{-2} + z^{-3}.$$

The impulse response of the system with zero initial condition is then the inverse z-transform of the pulse transfer function,

$$g(k) = Z^{-1}[G(z)] = Z^{-1}[2 - z^{-1} + 4z^{-2} + z^{-3}]$$

$$= 2 \cdot \delta_0(k) - \delta_0(k-1) + 4 \cdot \delta_0(k-2) + \delta_0(k-3).$$

Hence,

$$g(0) = 2,\ g(1) = -1,\ g(2) = 4,\ g(3) = 1,\ g(k) = 0, \text{ for } k > 3$$

The impulse response of a system with all of its poles at the origin will have finite non-zero terms. Impulse response of this type is often called finite impulse response, and the system (digital filter) that has all its poles at the origin is called a *finite impulse response (FIR) filter.*

ANALOG FILTERS

Filter Characteristics

Filters are classified according to the function that they perform. Ideal frequency selective filters have three fundamental design goals:

- To have no attenuation of input signals over a range of frequencies, called the *passband*
- Over another, distinct range of frequencies, called the *stopband*, to have complete attenuation of input signals
- To have no distortion of signals whose frequency content lies within the passband

The relative frequency location of the passband and the stopband give rise to the four most common types of filters: low-pass, high-pass, band-pass, and band-stop. The magnitude of the ideal frequency response characteristics of these four filter types is depicted in Figure 11.22.

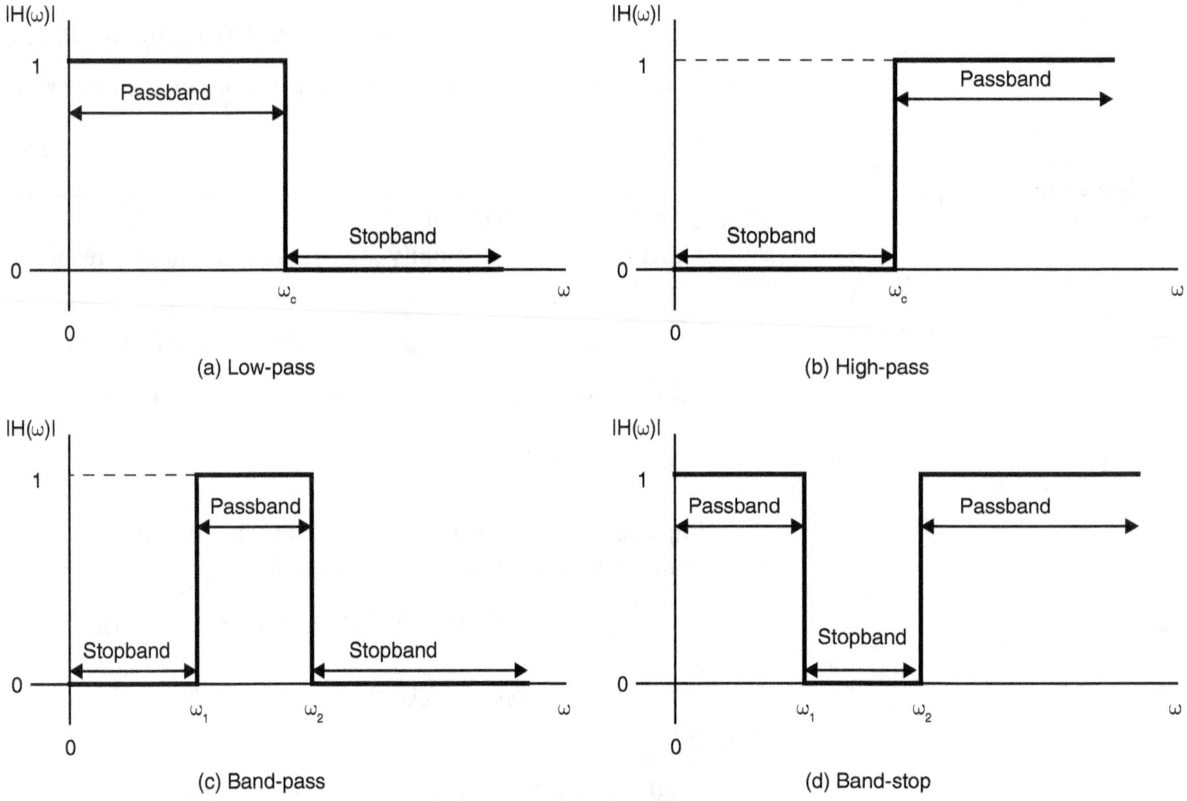

Figure 11.22 Filter Idealized Characteristics

An ideal low-pass transfer characteristic is shown in Figure 11.22 with the passband extending from zero frequency to a cutoff frequency, $\omega = \omega_c$, and the stopband extending from ω_c to infinite frequency. The filter gain in the passband is unity and zero in the stopband. The ideal high-pass filter is the inverse of the low-pass filter: the stopband extends from zero frequency to $\omega = \omega_c$, and the passband from ωc to infinite frequency. A band-pass filter has a single passband extending in the frequency range, $\omega_1 < \omega < \omega_2$, while all other frequencies are stopped. Band-stop filters have a single stopband extending in the frequency range, $\omega_1 < \omega < \omega_2$, while all other frequencies are passed. Band-stop filters are often called band-elimination filters or notch filters.

The requirement for constant magnitude of the frequency response in the pass-band is a consequence of the need to pass signals whose frequency content lies within the passband without distortion. In order that a signal pass through a filter without distortion, the output of the filter must be an amplified duplicate of the input signal possibly delayed by a time lag, *td*:[1]

$$x_0(t) = K_0\, x_i(t - td)$$

The frequency domain equivalent of $x_0(t)$ is obtained through the use of the Fourier Transform:

$$X_0(\omega) = \Im\left[x_0(t)\right] = \int_{-\infty}^{\infty} x_0(t)\, e^{-j\omega t}\, dt\ .$$

Here $X_0(\omega)$ is the spectrum of $x_0(t)$. Replacing $x_0(t)$ by its definition yields the frequency domain relationship between the input signal spectrum and the undistorted output signal spectrum:

$$X_o(\omega) = K_o e e^{-jt_d} X_i(\omega).$$

The transfer characteristic of the nondistorting filter, $H(\omega)$, is interpreted to be the multiplier of the input signal spectrum:

$$H(\omega) = K_o e e^{-jt_d}.$$

The properties of a nondistorting filter are apparent. It is necessary that, over the range of frequencies contained in the input signal, the magnitude of the filter transfer function be constant with respect to frequency, and the phase shift induced by the filter be linear with respect to frequency:

$$| H(\omega) | = K_0 \quad \& \quad \angle H(\omega) = -t_d.$$

Notice that for zero time delay, $t_d = 0$, the phase shift induced by the filter is also zero.[2]

Real filters can only approximate the ideal transfer relationships. The abrupt transition between the passband and the stopband of the various types of ideal filters is, unfortunately, impossible to achieve with a finite number of real circuit elements. In addition, zero gain in the stopband and no variation in gain in the passband are, at best, difficult to achieve. It is necessary to relax the design goals for these filters in order to be able to design and fabricate practical, real filters. A

---

1 The time lag for many low-frequency filters can be approximated as $t_d \approx 0$. As frequencies become large, the physical size of an electronic filter and the internal capacitance of its elements can make time lag a significant property of the filter.

2 Often a constant phase shift of 180 (radians) is also acceptable: constant 180 phase shift is a simple inversion of the signal when passing through the filter.

realistic set of *practical* design goals for frequency-selective filters includes the following:

- In the *passband*, to have relatively small attenuation (or a gain) of input signals over a range of frequencies. The variation in gain over the passband is specified by a maximum variation value, γ_{max}.
- Over the *stopband*, to have relatively large attenuation of input signals specified by a minimum attenuation value, γ_{min}.
- To have a *transition region* lying between passband and stopband specified by a passband cutoff frequency, ω_c and a stopband edge, ω_s.
- To have minimal distortion of signals whose frequency content lies within the passband.

A graphical representation of these design goals applied to a low-pass filter is shown in Figure 11.23. Here the separation of the passband and the stopband by a transition band is apparent. The ratio of the frequencies that specify the transition band, ω_c/ω_s, is called the selectivity factor and indicates the "sharpness" of the filter. The shaded areas represent tolerances in the passband and stopband gains: one of many possible filter responses that meet the design goals is presented as an arbitrary example.

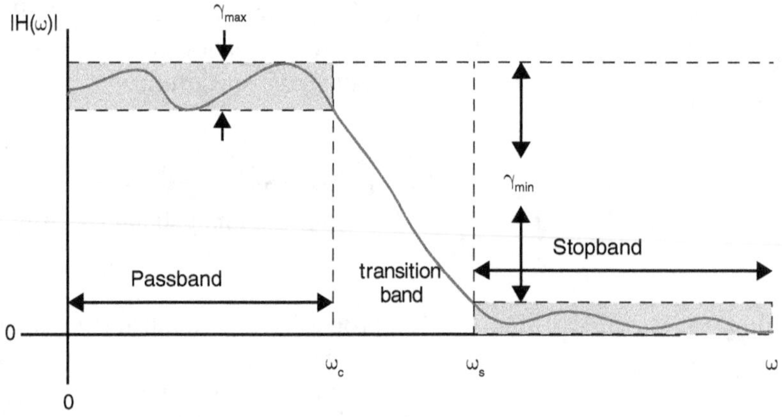

Figure 11.23 Realistic Low-Pass Filter Design Goals and One Possible Solution

As the tolerances for a filter are reduced, (γ_{max} reduced, γ_{min} increased, and ω_c/ω_s increased), the filter approaches ideal characteristics. While this goal may seem worthwhile in all cases, reducing tolerances increases the complexity of the circuitry involved to accomplish the more stringent design goals. Good design involves a balance between constraints and complexity.

There are several families of filters that meet the practical design goals of realistic filters in an efficient manner. Each family meets the goals in a unique manner. Three of the common families include the following:

- Butterworth Filters
- Chebyshev Filters
- Elliptic Filters

Butterworth Filters are smooth filters. There is no ripple in the response in either the passband or the stopband, and the transition between bands is monotonic. The edge of the passband is the frequency at which the magnitude of the fil-

ter transfer function. | $H(\omega)$ | drops by γ_{max}. The edge of the stopband occurs at the frequency at which | $H(\omega)$ | drops by γ_{min} below the nominal passband gain. Chebyshev Filters have a ripple in either the passband or in the stopband; once out of the region of ripple they are monotonic. Chebyshev filters can achieve a smaller transition region as compared to an equivalent-complexity Butterworth Filter. Elliptic Filters achieve an even smaller transition region by allowing an equal amount of ripple in both the passband and in the stopband.

All real filters introduce some phase shift. In good filters, this shift is reasonably linear with frequency throughout most of the passband; it can be interpreted as a time delay between the input and the output. As the order of the filter increases, the delay typically increases as well. Near the junction between the passband and the transition region, the phase shifts become increasingly nonlinear; frequencies near the edge of the passband suffer from phase distortion as well as magnitude distortion.

The following analog filters are commonly used in communication systems and signal processing.

First-Order Low-Pass Filters

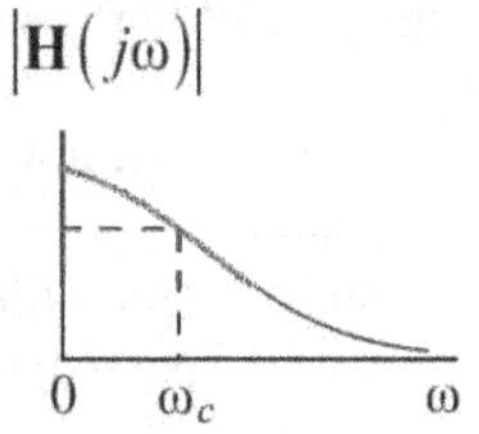

$$|\mathbf{H}(j\omega_c)| = \frac{1}{\sqrt{2}}|\mathbf{H}(0)|$$

Frequency Response

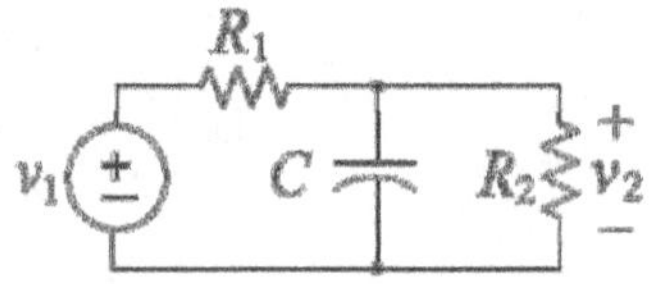

$$\mathbf{H}(s) = \frac{\mathbf{V}_2}{\mathbf{V}_1} = \frac{R_P}{R_1} \bullet \frac{1}{1 + sR_PC}$$

$$R_P = \frac{R_1R_2}{R_1 + R_2} \qquad \omega_c = \frac{1}{R_PC}$$

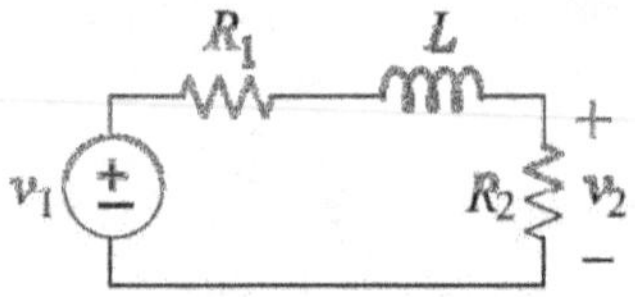

$$\mathbf{H}(s) = \frac{\mathbf{V}_2}{\mathbf{V}_1} = \frac{R_2}{R_S} \bullet \frac{1}{1 + s\,L/R_S}$$

$$R_S = R_1 + R_2 \qquad \omega_c = \frac{R_S}{L}$$

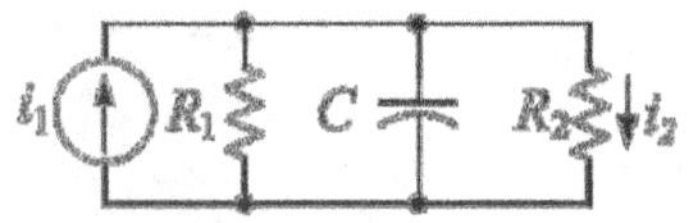

$$\mathbf{H}(s) = \frac{\mathbf{I}_2}{\mathbf{I}_1} = \frac{R_P}{R_2} \bullet \frac{1}{1 + sR_PC}$$

$$R_P = \frac{R_1R_2}{R_1 + R_2} \qquad \omega_c = \frac{1}{R_PC}$$

First-Order High-Pass Filters

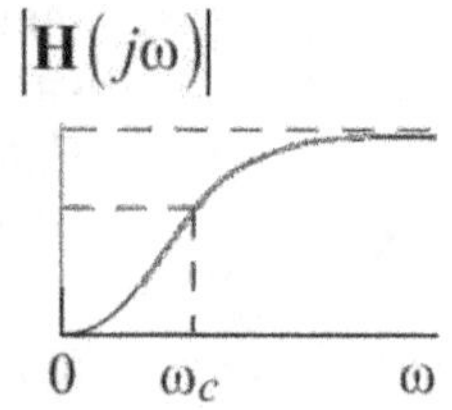

$$|\mathbf{H}(j\omega_c)| = \frac{1}{\sqrt{2}}|\mathbf{H}(j\infty)|$$

Frequency Response

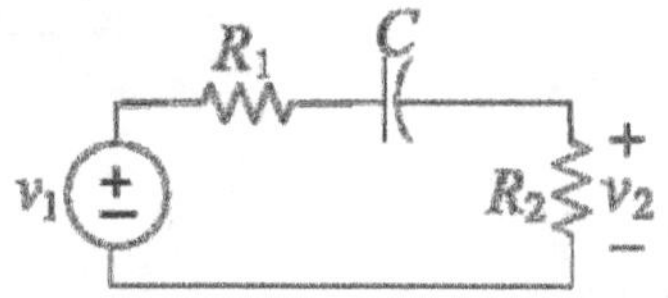

$$\mathbf{H}(s) = \frac{\mathbf{V}_2}{\mathbf{V}_1} = \frac{R_2}{R_S} \bullet \frac{sR_SC}{1 + sR_SC}$$

$$R_S = R_1 + R_2 \qquad \omega_c = \frac{1}{R_SC}$$

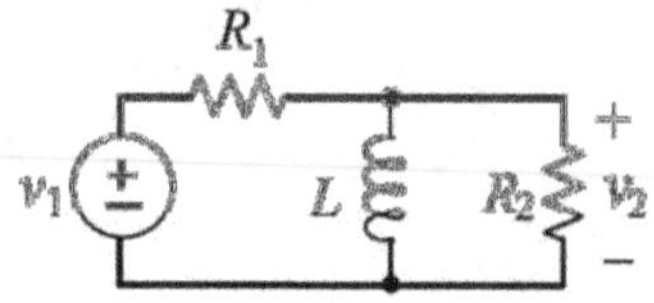

$$\mathbf{H}(s) = \frac{\mathbf{V}_2}{\mathbf{V}_1} = \frac{R_P}{R_1} \bullet \frac{s\,L/R_P}{1 + s\,L/R_P}$$

$$R_P = \frac{R_1R_2}{R_1 + R_2} \qquad \omega_c = \frac{R_P}{L}$$

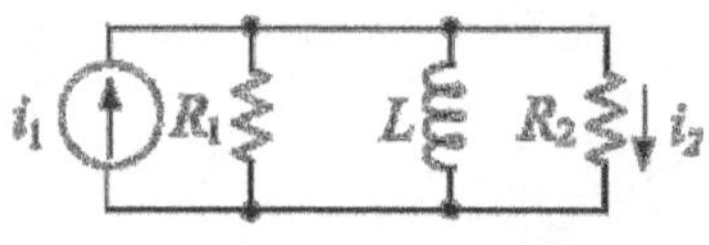

$$\mathbf{H}(s) = \frac{\mathbf{I}_2}{\mathbf{I}_1} = \frac{R_P}{R_2} \bullet \frac{s\,L/R_P}{1 + s\,L/R_P}$$

$$R_P = \frac{R_1R_2}{R_1 + R_2} \qquad \omega_c = \frac{R_P}{L}$$

Source: NCEES, *FE Supplied-Reference Handbook, 8th edition, 2nd revision* (NCEES, 2010)

Figure 11.24

Band-Pass Filters

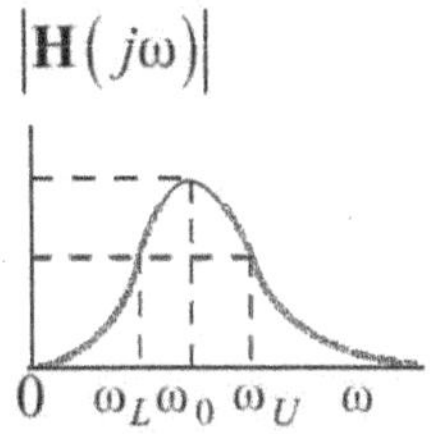

$$|\mathbf{H}(j\omega_L)| = |\mathbf{H}(j\omega_U)| = \frac{1}{\sqrt{2}}|\mathbf{H}(j\omega_0)|$$

3-dB Bandwidth = $BW = \omega_U - \omega_L$

Frequency Response

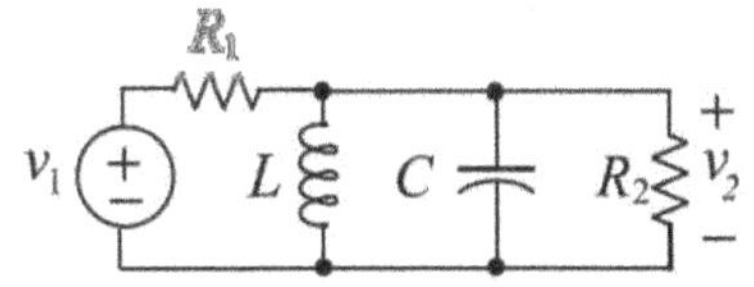

$$\mathbf{H}(s) = \frac{\mathbf{V}_2}{\mathbf{V}_1} = \frac{1}{R_1C} \bullet \frac{s}{s^2 + s/R_PC + 1/LC}$$

$$R_P = \frac{R_1R_2}{R_1 + R_2} \qquad \omega_0 = \frac{1}{\sqrt{LC}}$$

$$|\mathbf{H}(j\omega_0)| = \frac{R_2}{R_1 + R_2} = \frac{R_P}{R_1} \qquad BW = \frac{1}{R_PC}$$

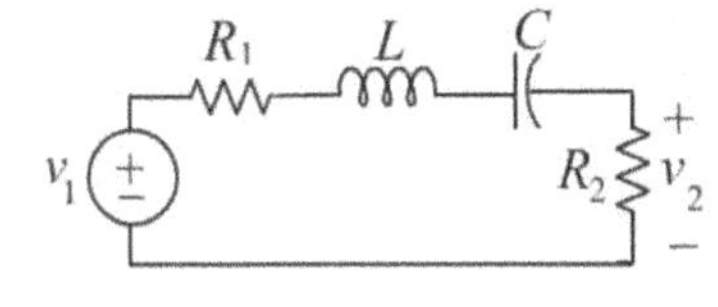

$$\mathbf{H}(s) = \frac{\mathbf{V}_2}{\mathbf{V}_1} = \frac{R_2}{L} \bullet \frac{s}{s^2 + sR_S/L + 1/LC}$$

$$R_S = R_1 + R_2 \qquad \omega_0 = \frac{1}{\sqrt{LC}}$$

$$|\mathbf{H}(j\omega_0)| = \frac{R_2}{R_1 + R_2} = \frac{R_2}{R_S} \qquad BW = \frac{R_S}{L}$$

Band-Reject Filters

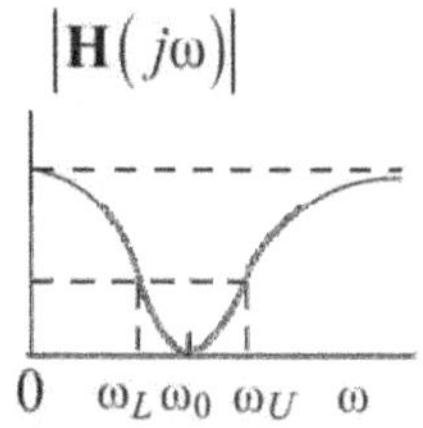

$$|\mathbf{H}(j\omega_L)| = |\mathbf{H}(j\omega_U)| = \left[1 - \frac{1}{\sqrt{2}}\right]|\mathbf{H}(0)|$$

3-dB Bandwidth = $BW = \omega_U - \omega_L$

Frequency Response

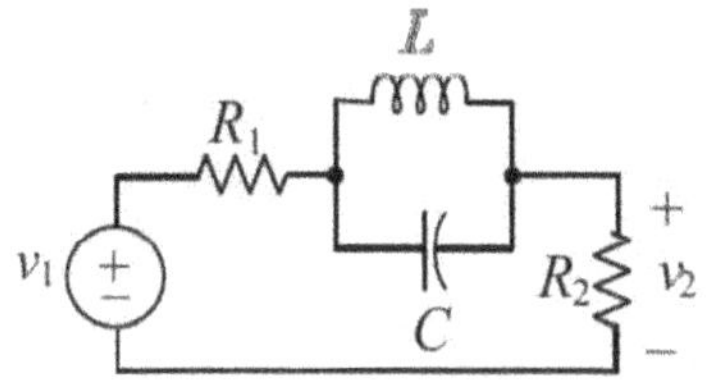

$$\mathbf{H}(s) = \frac{\mathbf{V}_2}{\mathbf{V}_1} = \frac{R_2}{R_S} \bullet \frac{s^2 + 1/LC}{s^2 + s/R_SC + 1/LC}$$

$$R_S = R_1 + R_2 \qquad \omega_0 = \frac{1}{\sqrt{LC}}$$

$$|\mathbf{H}(0)| = \frac{R_2}{R_1 + R_2} = \frac{R_2}{R_S} \qquad BW = \frac{1}{R_SC}$$

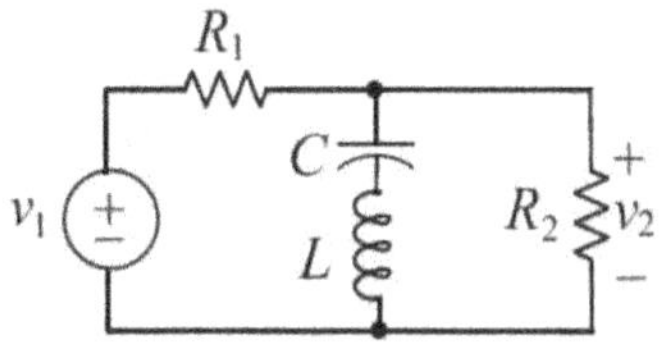

$$\mathbf{H}(s) = \frac{\mathbf{V}_2}{\mathbf{V}_1} = \frac{R_P}{R_1} \bullet \frac{s^2 + 1/LC}{s^2 + sR_P/L + 1/LC}$$

$$R_P = \frac{R_1R_2}{R_1 + R_2} \qquad \omega_0 = \frac{1}{\sqrt{LC}}$$

$$|\mathbf{H}(0)| = \frac{R_2}{R_1 + R_2} = \frac{R_P}{R_1} \qquad BW = \frac{R_P}{L}$$

Source: NCEES, *FE Supplied-Reference Handbook, 8th edition, 2nd revision* (NCEES, 2010)

Figure 11.25

Phase-Lead Filter	Phase-Lag Filter

Phase-Lead Filter

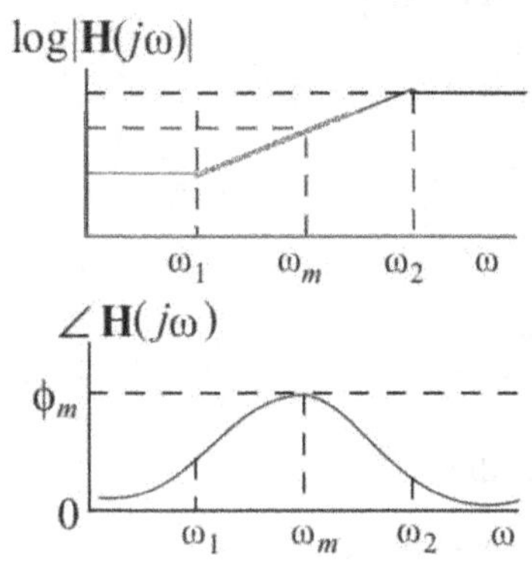

Frequency Response

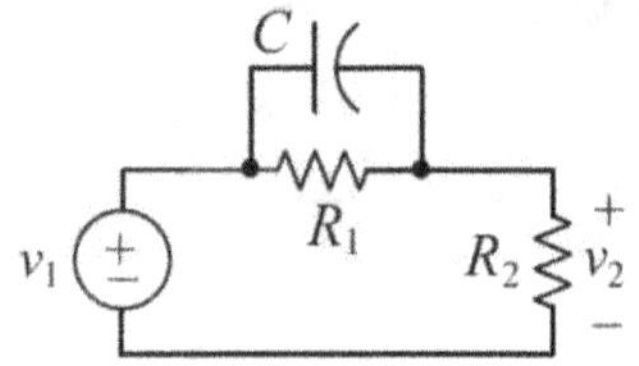

$$\mathbf{H}(s)=\frac{\mathbf{V}_2}{\mathbf{V}_1}=\frac{R_P}{R_1}\bullet\frac{1+sR_1C}{1+sR_PC}$$

$$=\frac{\omega_1}{\omega_2}\bullet\frac{1+s/\omega_1}{1+s/\omega_2}$$

$$R_P=\frac{R_1R_2}{R_1+R_2}\qquad \omega_1=\frac{1}{R_1C}\qquad \omega_2=\frac{1}{R_PC}$$

$$\omega_m=\sqrt{\omega_1\omega_2}\qquad \max\{\angle\mathbf{H}(j\omega_m)\}=\phi_m$$

$$\phi_m=\arctan\sqrt{\frac{\omega_2}{\omega_1}}-\arctan\sqrt{\frac{\omega_1}{\omega_2}}$$

$$=\arctan\frac{\omega_2-\omega_1}{2\omega_m}$$

$$\mathbf{H}(0)=\frac{R_P}{R_1}=\frac{\omega_1}{\omega_2}$$

$$|\mathbf{H}(j\omega_m)|=\sqrt{\frac{\omega_1}{\omega_2}}$$

$$\mathbf{H}(j\infty)=1$$

Phase-Lag Filter

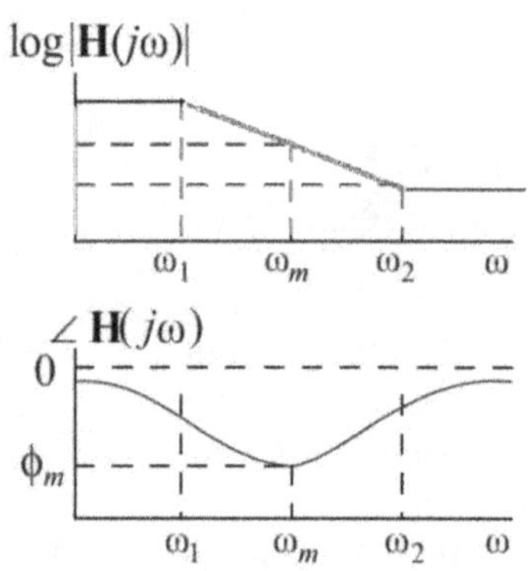

Frequency Response

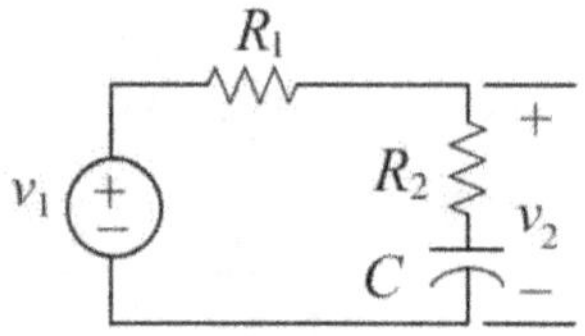

$$\mathbf{H}(s)=\frac{\mathbf{V}_2}{\mathbf{V}_1}=\frac{1+sR_2C}{1+sR_SC}$$

$$=\frac{1+s/\omega_2}{1+s/\omega_1}$$

$$R_S=R_1+R_2\qquad \omega_1=\frac{1}{R_SC}\qquad \omega_2=\frac{1}{R_2C}$$

$$\omega_m=\sqrt{\omega_1\omega_2}\qquad \min\{\angle\mathbf{H}(j\omega_m)\}=\phi_m$$

$$\phi_m=\arctan\sqrt{\frac{\omega_1}{\omega_2}}-\arctan\sqrt{\frac{\omega_2}{\omega_1}}$$

$$=\arctan\frac{\omega_1-\omega_2}{2\omega_m}$$

$$\mathbf{H}(0)=1$$

$$|\mathbf{H}(j\omega_m)|=\sqrt{\frac{\omega_1}{\omega_2}}$$

$$\mathbf{H}(j\infty)=\frac{R_2}{R_S}=\frac{\omega_1}{\omega_2}$$

Source: NCEES, *FE Supplied-Reference Handbook, 8th edition, 2nd revision* (NCEES, 2010)

Figure 11.26

SAMPLING

The lowpass sampling theorem states that we must sample at a rate, f_s, at least twice that of the highest frequency of interest in analog signal. Specifically, for having spectral content extending up to B Hz, we choose $f_s = 1/T_s \cdot 2B$ in forming the sequence of samples

$$x[n] = x(nT_s), -\infty < n < \infty.$$

Recall from the course introduction that a discrete-time signal can be obtained by uniformly sampling a continuous-time signal at $t_n = nT_s$ (i.e., $x[n] = x[nT_s]$).

- The values $x[n]$ are *samples* of $x(t)$.
- The time interval between samples is T_s.
- The *sampling rate* is $f_s = 1/T_s$.
- An alternate expression for $x[n] = x[n/f_s]$.

A system that performs the sampling operation is called a *continuous-to-discrete* (C-to-D) converter.

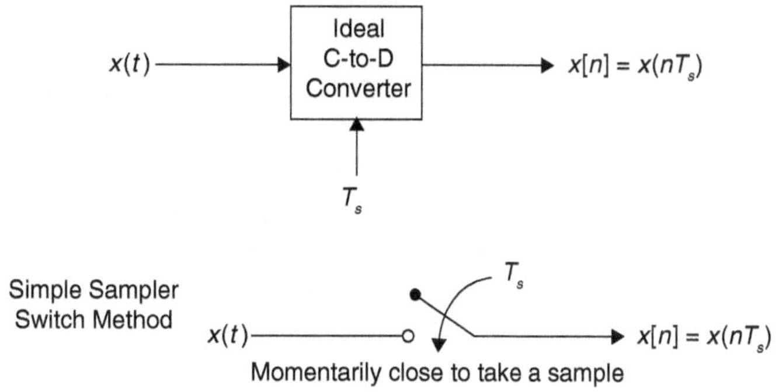

Figure 11.27

Sampling Sinusoidal Signals

When we sample $x(t) = A\cos(\omega t + \phi)$, the sinusoidal sequence obtained is

$$\begin{aligned} x[n] &= x(nT_s) \\ &= A\cos(\omega nT_s + \phi) \\ &= A\cos(\omega n + \phi) \end{aligned}$$

A new frequency variable known as the *discrete-time frequency*, or normalized continuous-time frequency, is introduced where

$$\hat{\omega} \equiv \omega T_s = \frac{\omega}{f_s} \text{ rad.}$$

- Note that ω has units of radians, but could also be called radians/sample, to emphasize the fact that sampling is involved.
- Since $\omega = 2\pi f$, discrete-time frequency in cycles/sample can be defined as

$$\hat{f} = fT_s$$

Example **11.18**

Sampling Rate Comparisons

Consider $x(t) = \cos(2\pi 60t)$ at sampling rates of 240 and 1000 samples per second.

The corresponding sample spacing values are

$$T_s = \frac{1}{240} = 4.166 \text{ ms}, \; T_s = \frac{1}{1000} = 1.0 \text{ ms}$$

The analog frequency is $2\pi(60)$ rad/s or 60 Hz.

When sampling $f_s = 240$ and 1000 Hz, respectively.

$$\hat{\omega}_{240} = 2\pi \cdot 60/240 = 2\pi(0.25) \text{ rad}$$

$$\hat{\omega}_{1000} = 2\pi \cdot 60/1000 = 2\pi(0.06) \text{ rad}$$

The sinusoidal sequences are respectively

$$x_{240}[n] = \cos(0.5\pi n)$$

$$x_{1000}[n] = \cos(0.12\pi n)$$

The Concept of Aliasing

Definition

Each of a set of signal frequencies that, when sampled at a given uniform rate, would give the same set of sampled values, and thus might be incorrectly substituted for one another when reconstructing the original signal.

To process analog signals in computers, the signals are converted to "digital" form. While an analog signal is continuous in both time and amplitude, a digital signal is discrete in both time and amplitude. To convert a signal from continuous time to discrete time, a process called sampling is used. The value of the signal is measured at certain intervals in time. Each measurement is referred to as a sample. (The analog signal is also quantized in amplitude, but that process is not discussed in this chapter.)

When the continuous analog signal is sampled at a frequency f, the resulting discrete signal has more frequency components than did the analog signal. To be precise, the frequency components of the analog signal are repeated at the sample rate. That is, in the discrete frequency response, they are seen at their original position and are also seen centered around $+/- f$, and around $+/- 2f$, and so forth.

The problem is to determine the number necessary to ensure that the informaton in the signal is preserved when digitized. If the signal contains high frequency components, a higher sampling rate is required to avoid losing information in the signal. In general, to preserve the full information in the signal, it is necessary to sample at twice the maximum frequency of the signal. This is known as the Nyquist rate. The Sampling Theorem states that a signal can be exactly reproduced if it is sampled at a frequency f, where f is greater than twice the maximum frequency in the signal.

If the signal is sampled at a frequency that is lower than the Nyquist rate, the signal that converted back into a continuous time signal will exhibit a phenomenon called ***aliasing***. Aliasing is the presence of unwanted frequency components in the reconstructed signal. These components were not present when the original signal was sampled. In addition, some of the frequencies in the original signal may be

lost in the reconstructed signal. Aliasing occurs because signal frequencies can overlap if the sampling frequency is too low. Frequencies "fold" around half the sampling frequency, which is why this frequency is often referred to as the folding frequency.

Sometimes the highest frequency components of a signal are simply noise or do not contain useful information. To prevent aliasing of these frequencies, we can filter out these components before sampling the signal. Because we are filtering out high frequency components and letting lower frequency components through, this is known as low-pass filtering.

Nyquist Sampling Theorem

A continuous-time signal $x(t)$ is called *band limited* if its Fourier transform is zero outside a certain frequency range.

Suppose we sample a band-limited signal and choose the sampling frequency such that $f_s \geq 2f_m$. The spectra of the continuous-time signal and of the sampled signal are exemplified in the figure below. Notice that in this case, the replicas in the sampled signal do not overlap. This is the principle of the Nyquist rate of sampling.

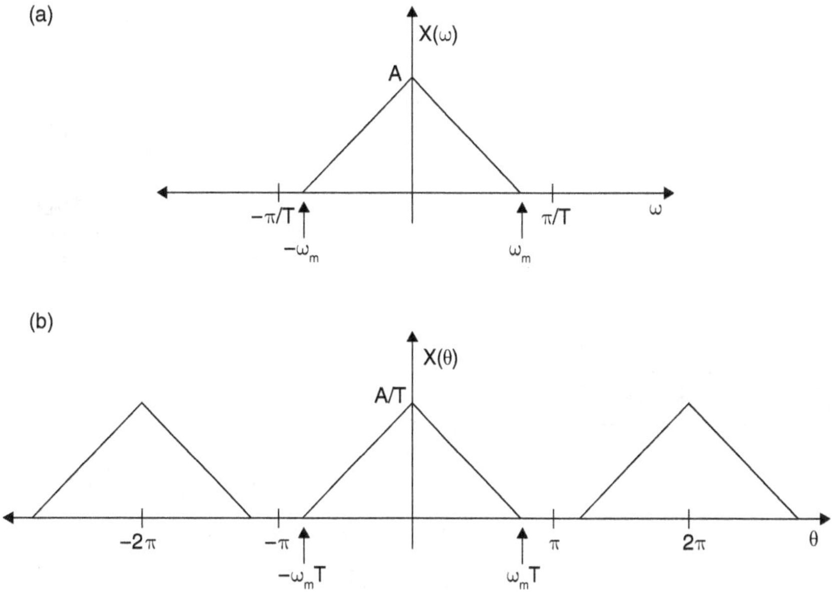

Figure 11.28 Sampling of a band-limited signal above the Nyquist rate
(a) Fourier transform of the continuous-time signal
(b) Fourier transform of the sampled signal

The *Nyquist sampling rate*, or the critical sampling rate for a band limited signal, is mathematically defined by

$$f_s = \frac{1}{T} = 2f_m$$

where f_m is the frequency of the signal.

By definition, if a band limited signal is sampled at a rate equal to or greater than the Nyquist sampling frequency $2f_m$, the shape of the Fourier transform of the sampled signal in the range $[-\pi, \pi]$ is identical to the shape of the Fourier transform of the given signal, except for multiplication of the frequency axis by a factor T, and multiplication of the amplitude axis by a factor $1/T$, as shown.

Aliasing is caused by sampling at a rate lower than that of the Nyquist frequency for a given signal. Now let us consider the case of a band limited signal when it is sampled at a lower rate than the Nyquist frequency. Figure 11.29 illustrates the case of sampling at $f_{sam} = 3f_m/2$. The shape of the Fourier transform of the sampled signal in the range $[-\pi, \pi]$ becomes distorted. Distortion occurs in this frequency range because two adjacent replicas overlap and their superposition give rise to the shape illustrated.

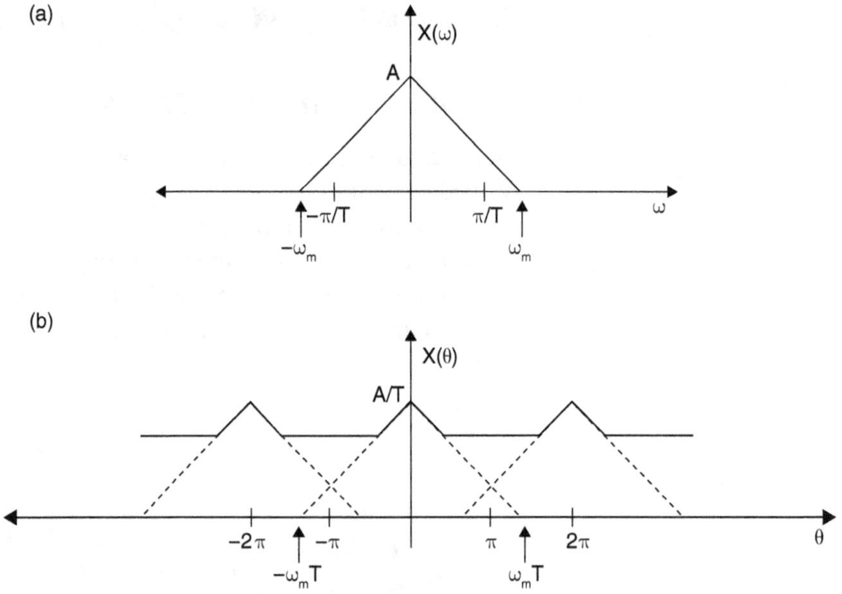

Figure 11.29 Sampling of a band-limited signal below the Nyquist rate
(a) Fourier transform of the continuous-time signal
(b) Fourier transform of the sampled signal

Example 11.19

Consider the signal

$$x(t) = 25\cos(2\pi(1000)t + \theta) + 10\cos(6000\pi t + \phi)$$

which is sampled at $f_s = 2500$ Hz to obtain $x[n] = x(n/f_s)$.

- Is there aliasing present?

Note that the frequencies present in $x(t)$ are 1000 Hz and 3000 Hz, and since $f_s = 2500$ Hz, we see that 2500 is not greater than 3000.

The 3000 Hz sinusoid will be aliased down to 3000 – 2500 = 500 Hz.

- What are the principle alias frequencies, in Hz, present in $x(t)$ relative to the given sampling frequency?

The principle alias band, in terms of positive frequencies, lies on the interval $[0, f_s/2)$ or [0, 1250) Hz

Since $f_1 = 1000 < 1250$, aliasing will be present.

Since $f_2 = 3000 >< 1250$, to find the principle alias $f_{p2} = \ell f_s - f_2$ or $f_{p2} = \ell f_2 - f_s$ for ℓ and integer such that f_{p2} is in the range [0, 1250].

The result is that for $\ell = 1, f_{p2} = 3000 - 2500 = 500$ Hz.

- Find the corresponding $\hat{\omega}$ for each of the principle alias frequencies of $x(t)$.

  Convert from f in Hz to $\hat{\omega}$ in rad/sample using $\hat{\omega} = {}^{2\pi f}\!/\!_{f_s}$.

  The frequencies of interest are

$$\hat{\omega} = 2\pi\frac{1000}{2500} = 0.8\pi \quad \text{and} \quad \hat{\omega} = 2\pi\frac{500}{2500} = 0.4\pi.$$

A sketch of the amplitude line spectra plot of along with the principle alias spectral lines is shown in Exhibit 10.

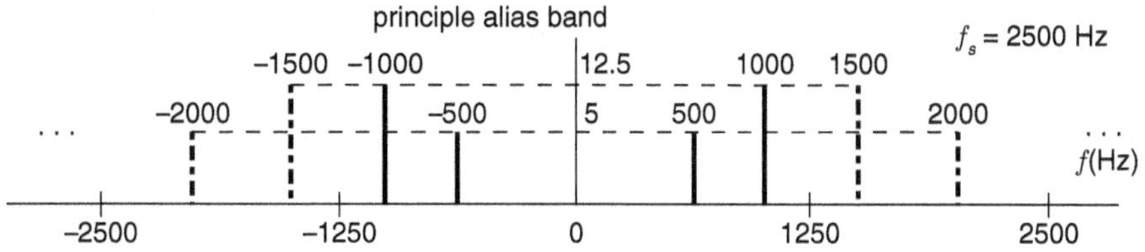

Exhibit 10 Sampling of a band-limited signal below the Nyquist rate

PROBLEMS

11.1 Find the energies of the signals. What is the effect on energy of sign change, time shifting, or doubling of the signal? What is the effect on the energy if the signal is multiplied by k?

a. $f(t) = \sin(t)$ on the interval $0, 2\pi$
b. $f_b(t) = -f(t)$
c. $f_c(t) = f(t - 2p)$
d. $f_d(t) = 2\,f(t)$

11.2 Find the power of the periodic signal $f(t)$ shown. Also find the powers and rms values of $-f(t)$, $2f(t)$, $cf(t)$.

$$f(t) = t^3 \qquad \forall -2 \le t < 2,$$

then repeats this pattern $\forall t$

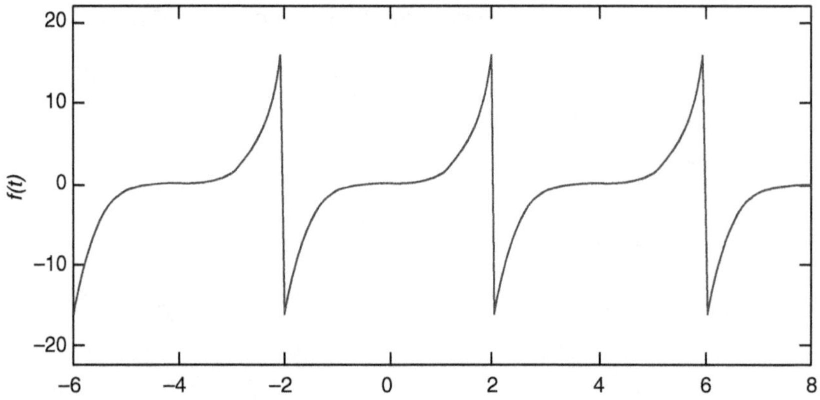

11.3 Find $\exp(-at)u(t)[\exp(-at)u(t)]$.

11.4 Find $u(t)*u(t)$.

11.5 Find the unit impulse response for the given $h(t)$ and $f(t)$.

a. $h(t) = \left(2 \cdot e^{-3t} - e^{-2t}\right)u(t)$

$f(t) = u(t)$

b. $h(t) = \left(2 \cdot e^{-3t} - e^{-2t}\right)u(t)$

$f(t) = e^{-t}u(t)$

11.6 For the given $h(t)$, find the system response to the given $f(t)$.

$$h(t) = e^{-t} \cdot u(t)$$

$y(t)$ will be the convolution of the input, $f(t)$, with $h(t)$, for each of the different $f(t)$s in parts a, b, c, and d.

a. $f(t) = u(t)$
b. $f(t) = e^{-t} \cdot u(t)$
c. $f(t) = e^{-2t} \cdot u(t)$
d. $f(t) = \sin(3t) \cdot u(t)$

11.7 Sketch the signal $f(t) = t^2$ and find the trigonometric Fourier series, $\phi(t)$, that represents $f(t)$ over the interval from –1 to +1.

11.8 Find the trigonometric series for the triangle wave shown.

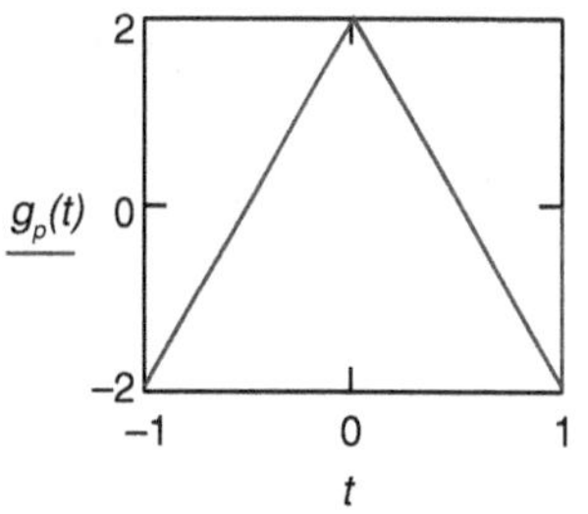

11.9 Using the frequency shifting property, find the inverse Fourier Transform of the spectra in Exhibits 11.9a and b.

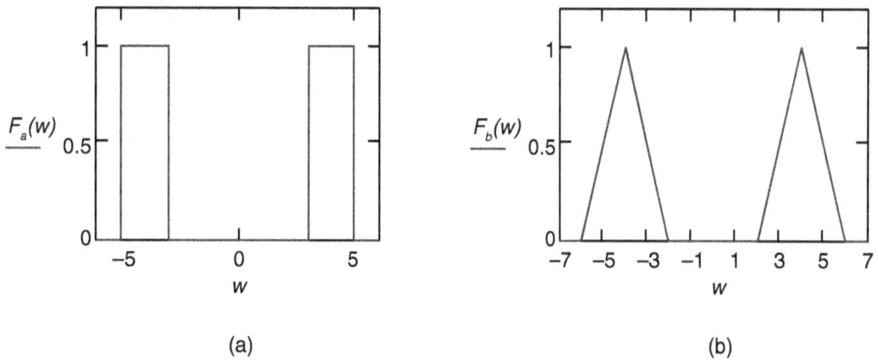

Exhibit 11.9

11.10 Sketch the functions

a. $f_a(t) = \Pi(t/2)$
b. $f_b(t) = \Lambda(3\omega/100)$
c. $f_c(t) = \Pi[(t - 10)/8]$
d. $f_f(t) = \text{sinc}(t/5)\ \Pi(t/10\pi)$

11.11 Show the Bode Plot of

$$H_a(s) = \frac{s \cdot (s+100)}{(s+2) \cdot (s+20)}$$

11.12 Find the Bode Plot of

$$H_b(s) = \frac{(s+10) \cdot (s+20)}{s^2 \cdot (s+100)}$$

SOLUTIONS

11.1 Time shifting and/or multiplying by negative 1 has no effect on the energy. The area under the curve of the square of the function will still be the same. Multiplying the signal by k will change the energy because the square of the function is now multiplied by k^2. Thus, the energy will change by a factor of k^2.

Finding the energy of the original $f(t)$: $f(t) = \sin(t)$ on the interval $0,2\pi$

$$\int_{-\infty}^{\infty} |f(t)|^2 dt = \int_0^{2\pi} \sin^2(t)dt = \int_0^{2\pi} \frac{1}{2}(1-\cos(2t))dt$$

$$= \frac{1}{2}\left[\int_0^{2\pi} 1dt - \int_0^{2\pi} \cos(2t)dt\right]$$

$$= \frac{1}{2}\left[2\pi - \frac{1}{2}\sin(2t)\Big|_0^{2\pi}\right] = \pi$$

a. $f(t) = \sin(t)$ on the interval $0,2\pi$ — $E_a = \pi$.
b. $f_b(t) = -f(t)$ — $E_b = \pi$.
c. $f_c(t) = f(t - 2p)$ — $E_c = \pi$.
d. $f_d(t) = 2f(t)$ — $E_d = 4\pi$.

11.2 The power is the average of the square:

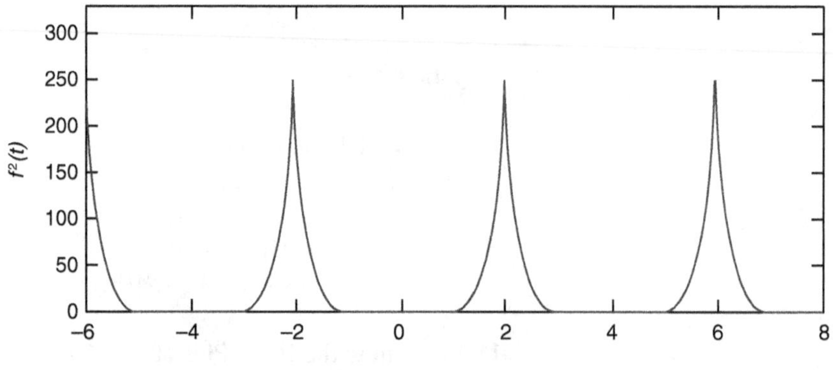

By symmetry, the area under the curve from 0 to 2 is the same as from 0 to −2, so just integrate over that region:

$$\frac{1}{2}\int_0^2 t^6 dt = \frac{1}{2}\left[\frac{1}{7}t^7\right]\Bigg|_0^2 = \frac{1}{7}[64-0] = \frac{64}{7} = P_f \quad \text{rms value: } f_{rms} = \sqrt{(64/7)}$$

a. $-f(t) \rightarrow P = P_f$ — $f_{arms} = f_{rms}$
b. $2f(t) \rightarrow P = 4P_f$ — $f_{brms} = 2f_{rms}$
c. $cf(t) \rightarrow P = c^2 P_f$ — $f_{crms} = cf_{rms}$

11.3

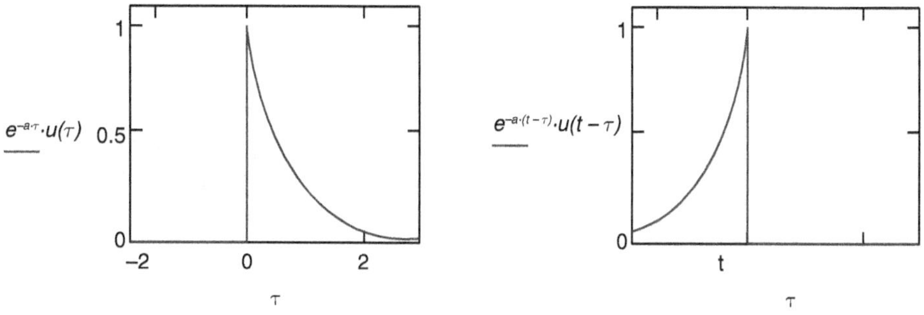

$$\int_0^t e^{-a\cdot\tau}\cdot e^{-a\cdot(t-\tau)}d\tau = e^{-a\cdot t}\cdot\int_0^t e^{-a\cdot\tau}\cdot e^{-a\cdot(-\tau)}d\tau = e^{-a\cdot t}\cdot\int_0^t 1d\tau = e^{-a\cdot t}\cdot t$$

$$c(t) = t\cdot e^{-a\cdot t}\cdot u(t)$$

11.4

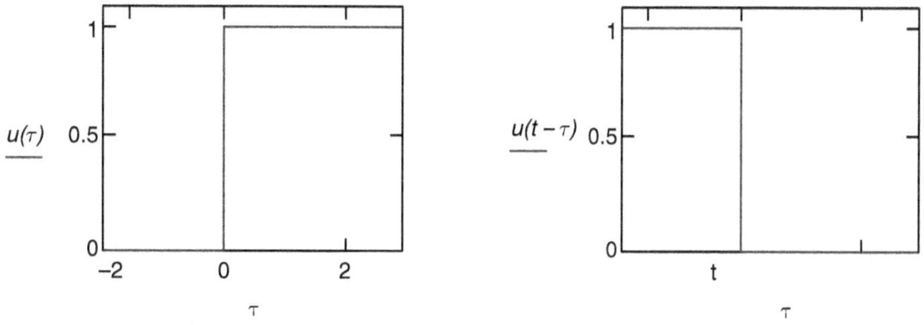

For $t < 0$, product of two will be 0. For $t < 0$, product will be 1 from 0 up to t.

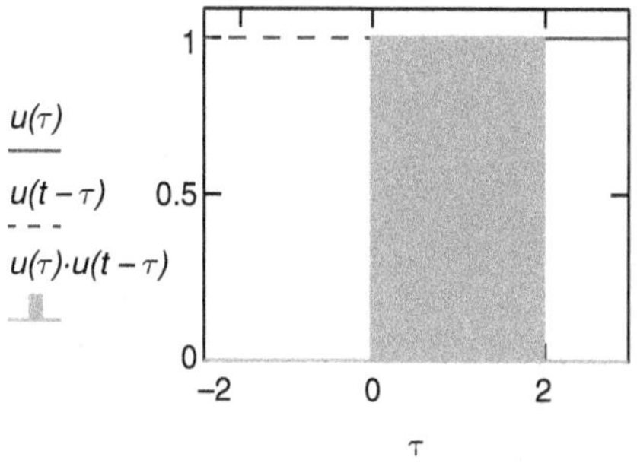

$$\int_0^t 1d\tau$$

$$c(t) = t\cdot u(t)$$

11.5 a.

$$h_1(t)=2\cdot e^{-3t}\cdot u(t) \qquad h_2(t)=-e^{-2t}\cdot u(t)$$

$$c_1(t)=2\frac{1-e^{-3t}}{3}u(t) \quad c_2(t)=-1\frac{1-e^{-2t}}{2}u(t)$$

$$y(t)=\left(2\cdot\frac{1-e^{-3\cdot t}}{3}-\frac{1-e^{-2t}}{2}\right)\cdot u(t)$$

b.

$$h(t)=\left(2\cdot e^{-3t}-e^{-2t}\right)u(t)$$

$$f(t)=e^{-t}u(t)$$

$y(t) = h(t)*f(t)$ . . . we can break this up into the sum of smaller convolutions and use the table to get the answer

$$h_1(t)=2\cdot e^{-3t}\cdot u(t) \qquad h_2(t)=-e^{-2t}\cdot u(t)$$

$$c_1(t)=2\frac{e^{-t}-e^{-3t}}{3-1}u(t) \quad c_2(t)=-1\frac{e^{-t}-e^{-2t}}{2-1}u(t)$$

$$y(t)=\left[\left(e^{-t}-e^{-3\cdot t}\right)-\left(e^{-t}-e^{-2t}\right)\right]\cdot u(t)$$

$$y(t)=\left(-e^{-3\cdot t}+e^{-2t}\right)\cdot u(t)$$

11.6

a. $y_a(t)=\dfrac{1-e^{-t}}{--1}\cdot u(t)$

b. $y_b(t)=t\cdot e^{-t}\cdot u(t)$

c. $y_c(t)=\left(\dfrac{e^{-t}-e^{-2t}}{-1--2}\right)\cdot u(t)$

d. $\alpha=0 \quad \beta=3 \quad \theta=\dfrac{-\pi}{2} \quad \lambda=-1$

$$\phi=a\tan\left(\frac{-\beta}{\alpha+\lambda}\right) \qquad \phi=1.249$$

$$y_d(t)=\left[\frac{\cos\left(-\frac{\pi}{2}\right)\cdot e^{-t}-\cos\left(3t-\frac{\pi}{2}-\phi\right)}{\sqrt{0+(-1)^2+(3)^2}}\right]\cdot u(t)$$

$$y_d(t)=\left[\frac{-\cos\left(3t-\frac{\pi}{2}-\phi\right)}{\sqrt{1+(3)^2}}\right]\cdot u(t)$$

$f(t)=\cos\left(3t-\dfrac{\pi}{2}\right)\cdot u(t)$ based on trig identity

11.7 $f(t) = t^2$

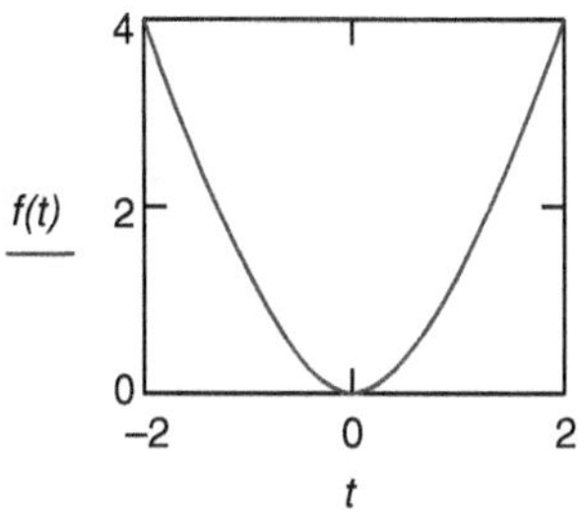

$$u(t) = \Phi(t)$$
$$f_p(t) = t^2 \cdot (u(t+1) - u(t-1))$$

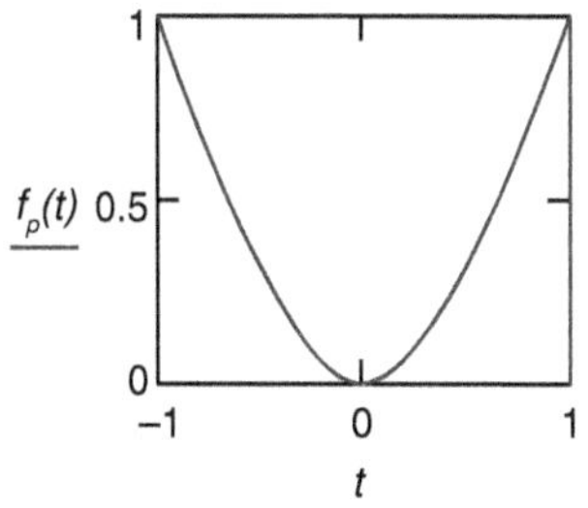

$$T_0 = 2$$

$$f_0 = \frac{1}{T_0}$$

$$\omega_0 = 2 \cdot \pi \cdot f_0 \qquad \omega_0 = \pi$$

Finding the Fourier series for the function that is $fp(t)$ repeated over and over . . .

$$a_0 = \frac{1}{2}\left(\int_{-1}^{1} t^2 dt\right) \qquad a_0 = \frac{1}{2}\left[\frac{1}{3}\cdot 1^3 - \frac{1}{3}\cdot(-1)^3\right] \qquad a_0 = \frac{1}{3}$$

$$a_n = \frac{2}{2}\cdot\int_{-1}^{1} t^2 \cdot \cos(n\cdot\pi\cdot t)\,dt$$

From integral table:

$$\int t^2 \cdot \cos(a\cdot t)\,dt = \frac{1}{a^3}\cdot\left(2a\cdot t\cdot\cos(a\cdot t) - 2\cdot\sin(a\cdot t) + a^2\cdot t^2\cdot\sin(a\cdot t)\right)$$

$$a_n = \frac{1}{(n\cdot\pi)^3}\left[\begin{array}{l}\left[2n\cdot\pi\cdot\cos(n\cdot\pi) - 2\cdot\sin(n\cdot\pi) + (n\cdot\pi)^2\cdot\sin(n\cdot\pi)\right]\ldots \\ + -\left[-2n\cdot\pi\cdot\cos(n\cdot\pi) + 2\cdot\sin(n\cdot\pi) - (n\cdot\pi)^2\cdot\sin(n\cdot\pi)\right]\end{array}\right]$$

This uses $\cos(-x) = \cos(x)$ and $\sin(-x) = -\sin(x)$

$$a_n = \frac{1}{(n\cdot\pi)^3}\left[\begin{array}{l}\left[2n\cdot\pi\cdot\cos(n\cdot\pi) - 2\cdot\sin(n\cdot\pi) + (n\cdot\pi)^2\cdot\sin(n\cdot\pi)\right]\ldots \\ + \left[2n\cdot\pi\cdot\cos(n\cdot\pi) - 2\cdot\sin(n\cdot\pi) + (n\cdot\pi)^2\cdot\sin(n\cdot\pi)\right]\end{array}\right]$$

Now, we can use $\cos(n_\pi)$ and $\sin(n_\pi)$ identities.

$$\cos(n\cdot\pi)=(-1)^n \qquad \sin(n\cdot\pi)=0$$

$$a_n=\frac{1}{(n\cdot\pi)^3}\left[2\cdot n\cdot\pi\cdot(-1)^n+2\cdot n\cdot\pi\cdot(-1)^n\right]$$

$$a_n=\frac{4}{(n\cdot\pi)^2}\cdot(-1)^n \qquad b_n=0 \qquad \text{since the function is odd.}$$

$$n=1\,..\,100$$

$$\phi_{FS}(t)=\frac{1}{3}+\sum_{n=1}^{100}\left[\frac{4}{(n\cdot\pi)^2}\cdot(-1)^n\cdot\cos(n\cdot\pi\cdot t)\right]+0$$

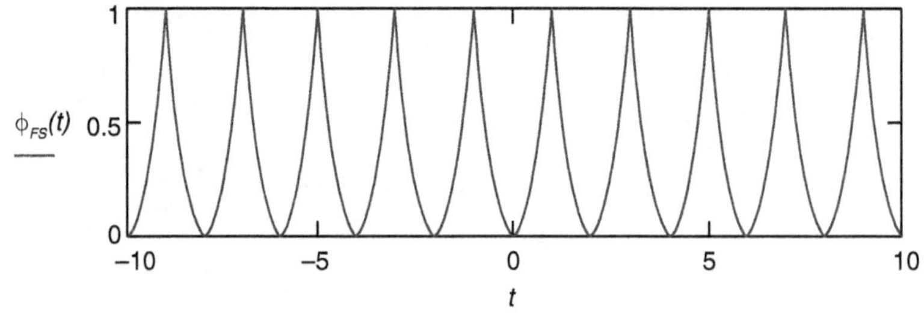

11.8 $A=2$

$g_p(t)=A\cdot(2t+1)\cdot(u(t+1)-u(t))+A\cdot(1-2t)(u(t)-u(t-1))$

$a_0=0$ Since the average value is zero, by inspection.

$b_n=0$ Since the function is even.

$$a_n=\frac{2}{2}\cdot\int_{-1}^{1}g_p(t)\cdot\cos(n\cdot\pi\cdot t)\,dt$$

$$=\int_{-1}^{0}A\cdot(2t+1)\cdot\cos(n\cdot\pi\cdot t)\,dt$$

$$+\int_{0}^{1}A\cdot(1-2t)\cdot\cos(n\cdot\pi\cdot t)\,dt$$

Since function is even, we can just integrate over half interval and double:

$$a_n = \int_0^1 2\cdot A\cdot(1-2t)\cdot\cos(n\cdot\pi\cdot t)dt$$

$$\int \cos(n\cdot\pi\cdot t)dt = \frac{1}{n\cdot\pi}\sin(n\cdot\pi\cdot t)$$

$$\int t\cdot\cos(n\cdot\pi\cdot t)dt = \frac{1}{(n\cdot\pi)^2}\left(\cos(n\cdot\pi\cdot t)+n\cdot\pi\cdot t\cdot\sin(n\cdot\pi\cdot t)\right)$$

$$a_n = \frac{2\cdot A}{n\cdot\pi}\cdot\left(\sin(n\cdot\pi)-\sin(n\cdot\pi\cdot 0)\right)$$

$$-\frac{4\cdot A}{(n\cdot\pi)^2}\cdot\begin{bmatrix} \left(\cos(n\cdot\pi)+n\cdot\pi\cdot\sin(n\cdot\pi)\ldots\right) \\ +-\left(\left(\cos(n\cdot\pi\cdot 0)+n\cdot\pi\cdot 0\cdot\sin(n\cdot\pi\cdot 0)\right)\right)\end{bmatrix}$$

Now, we can get rid of many terms—sin(0) = 0, sin(n_π) = 0, cos(0) = 1

$$a_n = \frac{-4\cdot A}{(n\cdot\pi)^2}\cdot\left(\cos(n\cdot\pi)-1\right)$$

Now, we can use cos(n_π) = $(-1)^n$

$$a_n = \frac{4\cdot A}{(n\cdot\pi)^2}\cdot\left[1-(-1)^n\right]$$

for n odd, $1-(-1)^n = 2$

for n even, $1-(-1)^n = 0$

$$a_n = \frac{8\cdot A}{(n\cdot\pi)^2} \quad \text{for } n = 1,3,5,\ldots \quad a_n = 0 \quad \text{for all other } n$$

$$g(t) = 0 + \sum_{m=0}^{100}\left[\frac{8\cdot A}{\left[(2\cdot m+1)\cdot\pi\right]^2}\cdot\cos\left[(2\cdot m+1)\cdot\pi\cdot t\right]\right]+0$$

$2m + 1$ is used to make it just odd integers.

11.9

a. $F_1(w) = rect\left(\frac{w}{2}\right)$

$$F_a(w) = F_1(w+4)+F_1(w-4)$$

By the frequency shifting property,

$$f_a(t) = f_1(t)\cdot\left(e^{j\cdot 4t} + e^{-j\cdot 4\cdot t}\right)$$

$$f_a(t) = f_1(t)\cdot\left(2\cdot\cos(4\cdot t)\right)$$

$$f_1(t) = \frac{1}{2\pi}\cdot\operatorname{sin}c(t)$$

$$f_a(t) = \frac{2}{\pi}\cdot\operatorname{sin}c(t)\cdot\cos(4\cdot t)$$

b. $f_b(t) = f_2(t)\cdot\left(e^{j\cdot 4t} + e^{-j\cdot 4\cdot t}\right)$

$$f_b(t) = f_2(t)\cdot 2\cdot\cos(4t)$$

$$f_2(t) = \frac{1}{\pi}\cdot\operatorname{sin}c(t)^2$$

$$f_b(t) = \frac{2}{\pi}\cdot\operatorname{sin}c(t)^2\cdot\cos(4\cdot t)$$

11.10

a.

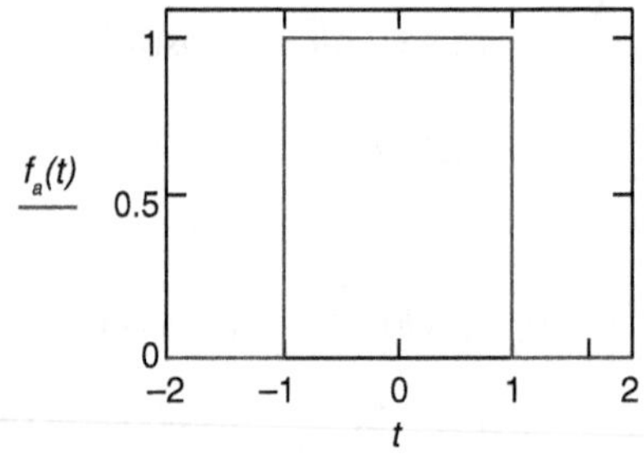

b.

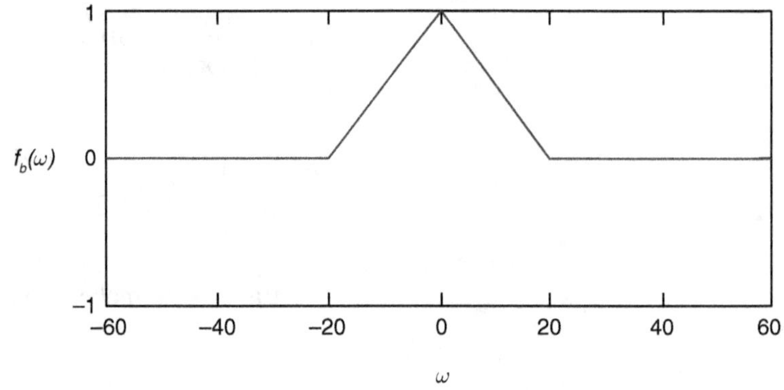

c.

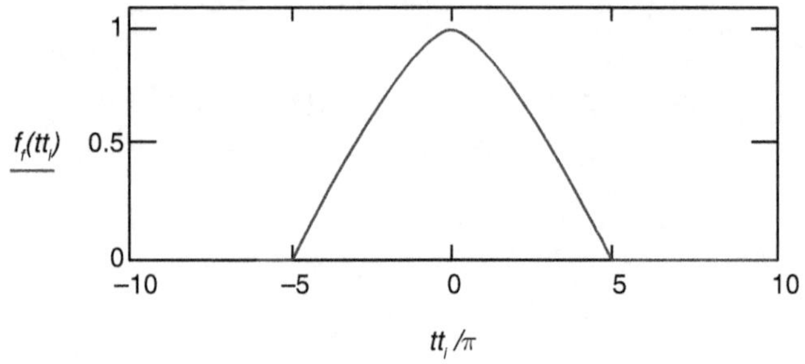

d.

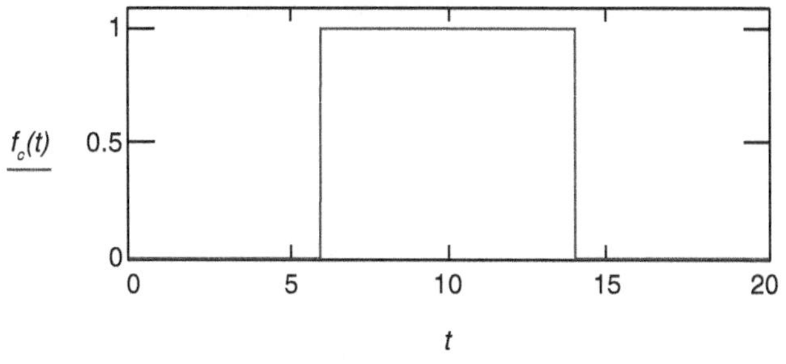

11.11

$$H_a(s) = \frac{100 \cdot s \cdot \left(1 + \frac{s}{100}\right)}{40 \cdot \left(1 + \frac{s}{2}\right) \cdot \left(1 + \frac{s}{20}\right)}$$

The phase plot is formed by adding the numerator phase terms and subtracting the denominator phase terms.

$$\theta_{Ha}(w) = \theta_0 - \theta_1(w,2) - \theta_1(w,20) + \theta_1(w,100)$$

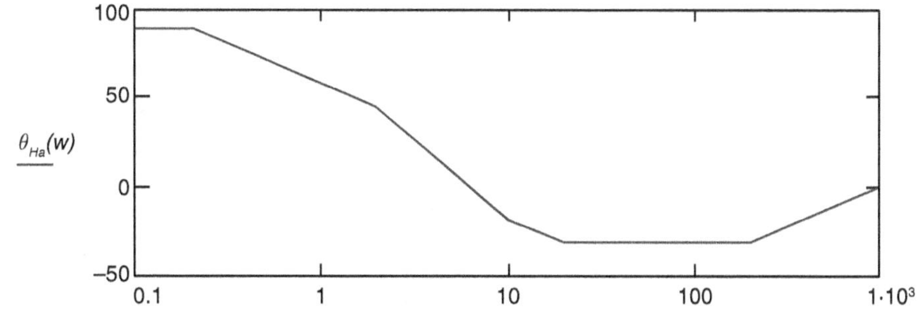

This transfer function has factors:

$$K = \frac{100}{40} \qquad H_{dB0}(K) = 7.959$$

simple zero at 0, so slop of 20 dB/dec, this factor contributes 0 dB at w = 1.

simple pole at 2, so slope of –0 dB/dec at w = 2.

simple pole at 20, so slope of –20 dB/dec at w = 20.

simple zero at 100, so slope of 0 dB/dec at w = 100.

The magnitude plot is formed by adding the numerator dB terms and subtracting the denominator dB terms.

$$H_{adB}(w) = H_{dB0}\left(\frac{100}{40}\right) + H_{dBz}(w) - H_{dB1}(w,2) - H_{dB1}(w,20) + H_{dB1}(w,100)$$

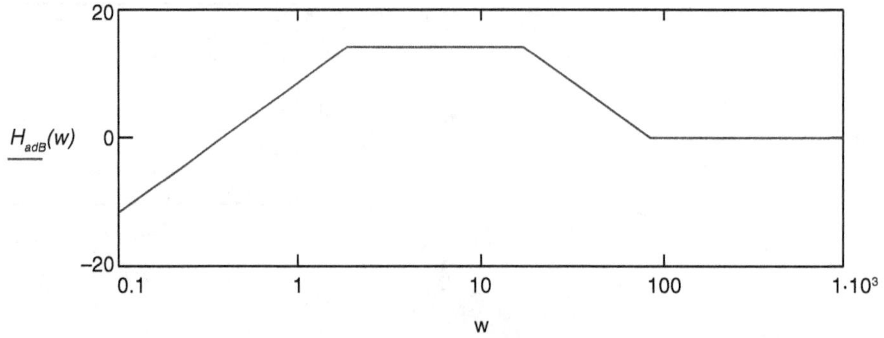

11.12 $$H_b(s) = \frac{20 \cdot 10 \cdot \left(1 + \frac{s}{10}\right) \cdot \left(1 + \frac{s}{20}\right)}{100 \cdot s^2 \cdot \left(1 + \frac{s}{100}\right)}$$

$$H_{bdB}(w) = H_{dB0}(2) - 2\,H_{dBz}(w) + H_{dB1}(w,10) + H_{dB1}(w,20) - H_{dB1}(w,100)$$

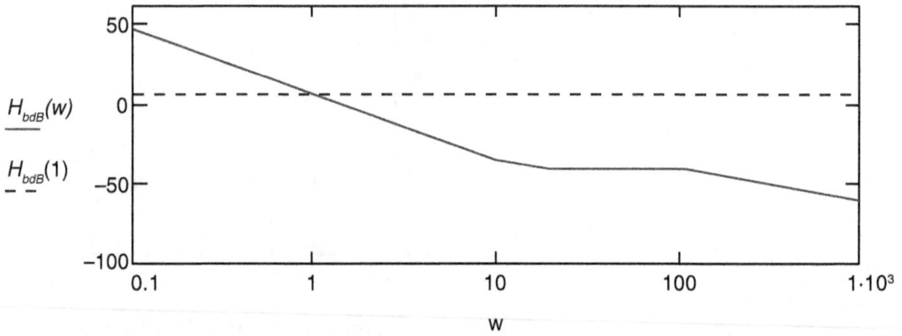

The phase plot is formed by adding the numerator phase terms and subtracting the denominator phase terms.

$$\theta_{Hb}(w) = (-2\theta_0 + \theta_1(w,10)) + \theta_1(w,20) - \theta_1(w,100)$$

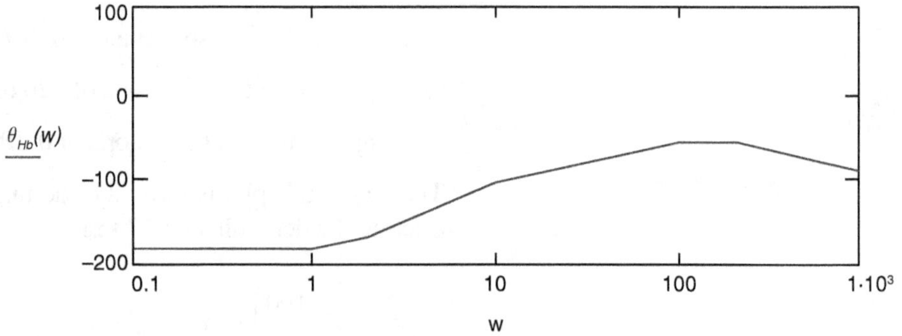

CHAPTER 12

Electronics

OUTLINE

A large number of topics are included under this heading, so each subject will be presented only briefly. Some of the important topics are conductivity of semiconductors, diode equations, characteristic equations for JFETS and MOSFETS, and bipolar junction transistor small-signal device models. In modern electronics, MOSFETS are predominant.

Paying attention to subscript notation is especially important in the field of electronics. If the *symbol* is uppercase it implies a dc or average value if the *subscript* is also uppercase; if, on the other hand, the subscript is lowercase, it may imply an rms value or a function of frequency (either in the s-domain or the $j\omega$-domain). If the symbol is lowercase, and the subscript is uppercase, a time-varying function with a dc value is implied; whereas if the subscript is also lowercase, the implication is a small-signal, time-varying quantity without a dc value. When working examination problems, consider carefully what seems reasonable, as different notations exist and notational mistakes, which could contradict the problem, may inadvertently appear in a text or on an examination problem.

It appears that the FE exam does not always keep pace with this rapidly changing field. Therefore, do not be surprised if some of the electronics problems on the exam address technologies that are not cutting-edge.

CONDUCTIVITY WITHIN SEMICONDUCTOR MATERIALS

By far the most used semiconductor materials are silicon and germanium. Conduction in these materials is caused by negatively and positively charged particles drifting in opposite directions when an electric field is present. It may be shown that the current density J is given by

$$J = (n\mu_n + p\mu_p)qE = \sigma E \text{ A/m}^2 \quad \textbf{(12.1a)}$$

and the conductivity σ is

$$\sigma = (n\mu_n + p\mu_p)q \quad \textbf{(12.1b)}$$

where q is the charge on an electron (1.6×10^{-19} coulombs), μ_n and μ_p are electron and hole mobilities, and n and p are the electron and hole concentrations (volume densities).

At equilibrium conditions, the generation rate must be just equal to the recombination rate; thus, in doped semiconductor situations, the product of n and p should be constant. Thus, if either n or p is increased, the other must be decreased. The carrier concentration is given as

$$pn = (n_i)^2 \quad \textbf{(12.1c)}$$

where n_i is the intrinsic concentration. For doped semiconductors, mobile charge carrier concentration (n_n or p_p) is almost equal to doping atom concentrations (N_d or N_a). (Here, N_a and N_d are acceptor and donor concentrations, respectively.) These doping concentrations essentially determine the conductivity since the carrier concentration of the opposite sign (p_n or n_p) is obviously reduced.

DIODES AND P-N JUNCTIONS

In order to have diode action in a semiconductor, a p–n junction must exist. The potential (or contact potential) of this junction is given by

$$V_o = kT/q \ln\left(N_a N_d / n_i^2\right) \quad \textbf{(12.2)}$$

where k is Boltzmann's constant and T is temperature (K).

The equation for diode operation may be given as

$$i = I_s(e^{v_D/\eta V_T} - 1) \quad \textbf{(12.3a)}$$

where I_s is the reverse saturation current, v_D is the voltage applied across the diode, η is a material variable ($\eta \approx 1$) for germanium and silicon (except for certain discrete silicon ones, where $\eta = 2$), and V_T is the thermal voltage. For most diodes at room temperature (20 °C or 293 K), $1/\eta V_T$ is approximately 40 units/volt (with $\eta = 1$). Then Equation (12.3a) may be written as

$$I \approx I_o(e^{40V} - 1) \quad \text{for germanium and many silicon diodes,} \qquad \textbf{(12.3b)}$$

$$I \approx I_o(e^{20V} - 1) \quad \text{for certain discrete silicon diodes.} \qquad \textbf{(12.3c)}$$

Recall that I_s is in the order of a few μA for Germanium and a few nA (or less) for Silicon. I_s is fairly constant with reverse voltage, but not so for temperature. I_s approximately doubles for every 10 °C rise in temperature.

As an example, consider a germanium diode whose reverse current at −1 V is −50 μA at 20 °C. It is desired to find the current at 0.2 and −0.2 V. The reverse current is given as −50 μA, which is effectively equal to $-I_s$. At a reverse bias voltage of – 0.2, $e^{40(-0.2)}$ is almost zero; thus $I = -I_0 = -50\ \mu$A. And, at 0.2 volts, $e^{40(0.2)} = 3000$; thus $I = 50(3000 - 1) \times 10^{-6} = 150$ mA.

P-N JUNCTION CAPACITANCE

The variable junction capacitance (sometimes referred to as Varactor capacitance) may be significant (with a range of 1 to 500 pF) if the *p-n* junction is reversed biased. This value of capacitance is given by Eq. 12.4 as

$$C = C_o/(1 - V/V_o)^{1/n} \qquad \textbf{(12.4)}$$

where C_o is the actual junction capacitance at zero voltage, V_o is the built-in potential, V is the applied voltage, and n $\Uparrow$ 2 for abrupt junctions and $n \approx 3$ for graded junctions. For larger negative bias (V more negative) the depletion width increases and the capacitance decreases.

Example 12.1

P-N Junction Capacitance

If the zero-bias capacitance of a *p-n* junction is 5 pF and the built-in potential, φ_o, is 640 mV, determine the junction capacitance at junction voltages

$$V_d = -20\text{ V}, -10\text{ V}, -5\text{ V}, -1\text{ V}, 0.3\text{ V and } 0.6\text{ V}.$$

Assume the junction grading coefficient has value, $m = 0.40$.

Solution

Equation 12.4 yields:

$$C_j \approx \frac{5\text{ pF}}{\left(1 - \frac{V_d}{0.64}\right)^{0.40}}$$

The tabulated results are:

V_d =	−20 V	C_j =	1.25 pF
	−10 V		1.62 pF
	−5 V		2.09 pF

–1 V	3.43 pF
0.3 V	6.44 pF
0.6 V	15.2 pF

The small variation in the junction capacitance for a wide range of negative bias is evident.

One of the fundamental characteristics of an amplifier is its gain. Gain is defined as the factor that relates the output to the input signal intensities. Referring to Figure 12.1, a time dependent input signal, $x(t)$, is introduced to the "black box" which represents an amplifier and another time dependent signal, $y(t)$, appears at the output.

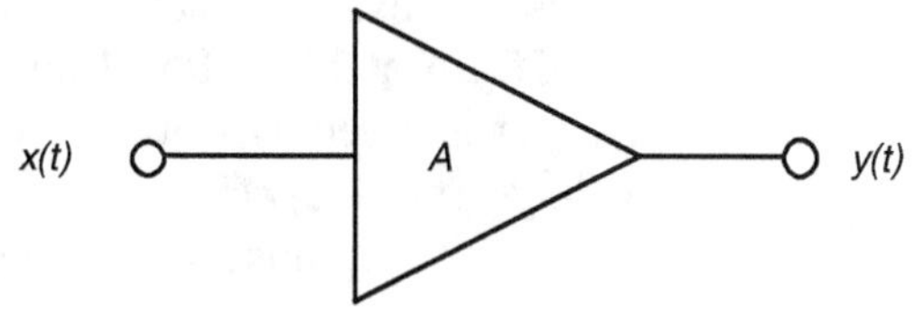

Figure 12.1 "Black Box" Representation of an Amplifier with Input $x(t)$ and Output $y(t)$

In actuality, $x(t)$ can represent either a time dependent or time independent signal. The output of a good amplifier, $y(t)$, is of the same functional form as the input with two significant differences; the magnitude of the output is scaled by a constant factor, A, and the output is delayed by a time, t_d. This input-output relationship can be expressed as:

$$y(t) = A_x(t - t_d) + \alpha \quad \mathbf{(12.5)}$$

where
A = the gain of the amplifier
α = the output DC offset
t_d = the time delay between the input and output signals

The signal is "amplified" by a factor of A. Amplification is a ratio of output signal level to the input signal level. The output signal is amplified when $|A|$ is greater than 1. For $|A|$ less than 1, the output signal is said to be attenuated. If A is a negative value, the amplifier is said to invert the input. Should $x(t)$ be sinusoidal, inversion of a signal is equivalent to a phase shift of 180°; negative A implies the output signal is ±180° out of phase with the input signal.

For time-varying signals, it may be convenient to find the amplification (ratio) by comparing either the root-mean-squared (RMS) values or the peak values of the input and output signals. Good measurement technique dictates that amplification is found by measuring the input and output RMS values because peak values may, in many instances, be ambiguous and difficult to quantify. Unfortunately, in many practical instances, RMS or power meters are not available dictating the measurement of peak amplitudes. The delay time is an important quantity often overlooked in electronic circuit analysis and design. The signal encounters delay between the input and output of an amplifier simply because it must propagate through a number of the internal components of the amplifying block.

In Figure 12.1, $x(t)$ and $y(t)$ are time dependent signals. Depending on the amplifier, $x(t)$ and $y(t)$ can be either current or voltage signals. Every amplifier draws power from a power supply, typically in the form of current from a DC voltage source. As will be shown in later sections of this text, the maximum possible output signal level is determined largely by the power supply voltage and current

limitations. For instance, assume that the amplifier in Figure 12.1 is powered by a DC voltage source with output equal to V_{cc}. If the output signal, *y(t),* is a voltage signal, the maximum output voltage attainable under ideal conditions for the gain block is V_{cc}. The phenomenon of limiting output voltage levels to lie within the limits set by the power supplies is called *saturation*. Should the power supply be unable to provide sufficient current to the gain block, the output will also be limited, although in a manner that is not as simple as in saturation.

The terminals of interest are:

- the inverting input,
- the noninverting input,
- the output,
- the positive power supply (designated $+V_{cc}$), and
- the negative power supply (designated $-V_c$).

The offset null pins (1 and 5) are used to compensate for minor fabrication imperfections as well as degradation due to aging. Although commonly left disconnected by the circuit designer, these pins are sometimes utilized in applications that require the amplification of very small level signals. The many OpAmps are a compensated amplifier. The performance implications of compensated and uncompensated amplifiers is related to frequency response and stability.

A conventional simplified OpAmp schematic representation is shown in Figure 12.2. This representation shows two input terminals designated (–) and (+) corresponding to the inverting and noninverting inputs, respectively, the output terminal, and the positive and negative power supply terminals labeled *V*+ and *V*–, respectively. Not shown are the offset null pins. Unless used, these pins are usually not included in schematic representations.

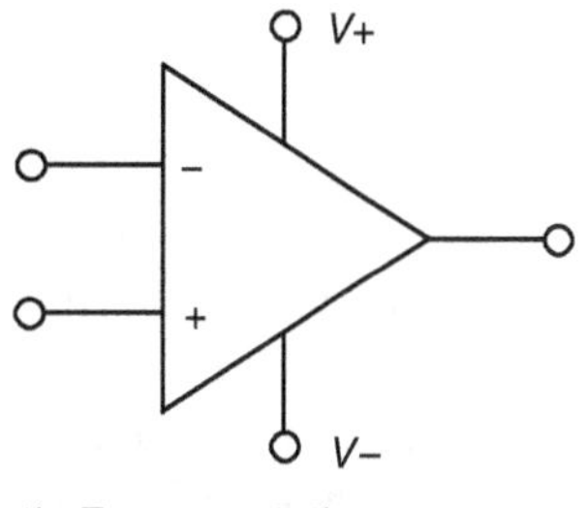

Figure 12.2 OpAmp Schematic Representation

Notice that the schematic symbol of the OpAmp does not have a ground pin. In many ways, the lack of a ground pin on the OpAmp is the key to its operation. Ideally, only the differential voltage between the two input pins affect the output voltage of an OpAmp. A ground reference is provided external to the chip package.

Modeling the OpAmp

Terminal voltages and currents are used to characterize OpAmp behavior. In order to unify all discussions of OpAmp circuitry, it is necessary to define appropriate descriptive conventions. All voltages are measured relative to a common reference node (or ground), which is external to the chip as is shown in Figure 12.3. The voltage between the inverting pin and ground is denoted as v_1; the voltage between the noninverting pin and ground is v_2. The output voltage referenced to ground is

denoted as v_O. Power is typically applied to an OpAmp in the form of two equal-magnitude supplies, denoted V_{CC} and $-V_{CC}$, which are connected to the $V+$ and $V-$ terminals of the OpAmp, respectively.

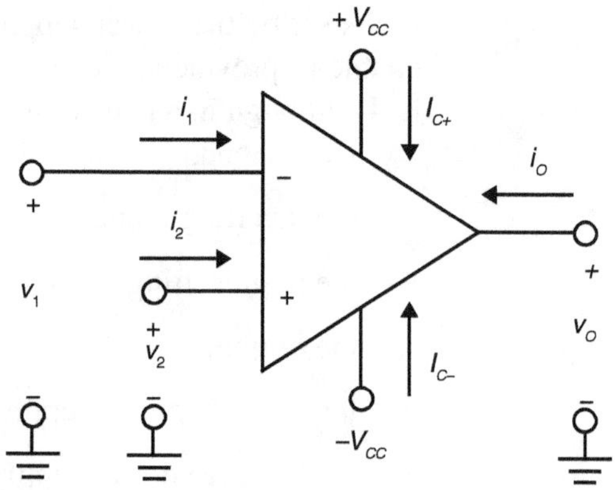

Figure 12.3 Terminal Voltages and Currents

The reference current directions are shown in Figure 12.3. The direction of current flow is always into the nodes of the OpAmp. The current into the inverting input terminal is i_1; current into the noninverting input terminal is i_2; current into the output terminal is i_O; and the currents into the positive and negative power supply terminals are I_{C-} and I_{C+}, respectively.

The voltage and current constraints inherent to the input and output terminals of an OpAmp must be understood prior to connecting external circuit elements. The OpAmp is considered as a building block element with specific rules of operation. A short discussion of these rules of operation follows.

The terminal voltages are constrained by the following relationships:

$$v_O = A(v_2 - v_1) \tag{12.6}$$

and

$$-V_{CC} \le v_O \le V_{CC}. \tag{12.7}$$

The first of the two voltage constraints states that the output voltage is proportional to the difference between the noninverting and inverting terminal inputs, v_2 and v_1, respectively. The proportionality constant A is the called the *open loop gain*, whose significance will be detailed later. The second voltage constraint states that the output voltage is limited to the power supply rails. That is, v_O must lie between $\pm V_{CC}$. If the output reaches the limiting values, the amplifier is said to be saturated. In reality, the amplifier saturates at voltages slightly shy of $\pm V_{CC}$ due to device characteristics within the OpAmp. So long as $|v_O| < V_{CC}$, the amplifier is operating in the linear region. Between the limiting values lies the "linear region" where the output voltage is related to the input voltage by the proportionality constant A. Figure 12.4a shows an idealized voltage transfer characteristic of an OpAmp. A more realistic voltage transfer characteristic is shown in Figure 12.4b where the amplifier response gradually tapers toward saturation at higher input voltages due to the characteristics of the circuit design internal to the chip.

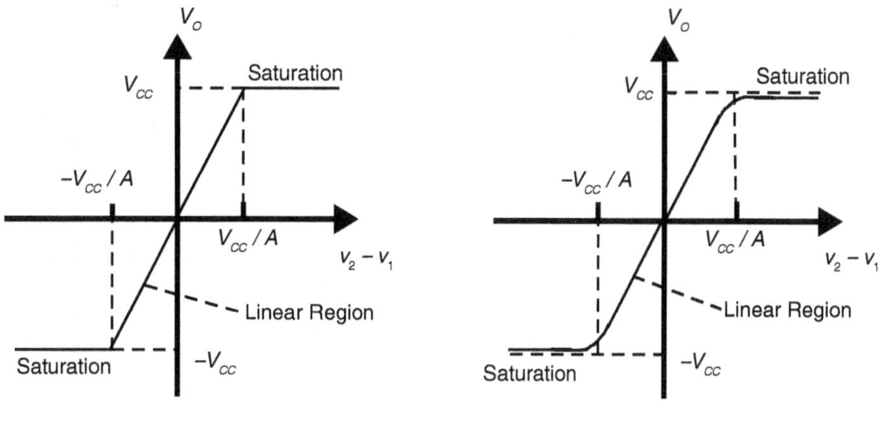

(a) (b)

Figure 12.4 Transfer Characteristics of (a) an Ideal OpAmp and (b) More Realistic "Soft-Limiting" OpAmp Transfer Characteristic

Table 12.1 OpAmp Characteristic Property Values

Property	Typical OpAmp Value	Ideal OpAmp Value
Gain, A	> 200,000	∞
Input resistance, R_i	> 2 MΩ	∞
Output resistance, R_o	< 75 Ω	0
Input voltage difference, $(v_2 - v_1)$	< 0.1 mV	0 (virtual short)
Input current, i_1 or i_2	< 50 pA	0 (virtual short)
Output voltage limits	$\lvert v_o \rvert < VCC$	$\lvert v_o \rvert < V_{CC}$

The voltage and current constraints given are the parameters used to describe an *ideal* OpAmp model. By attaching external components to an OpAmp, a functional circuit can be designed. The significance of this exercise is to demonstrate the power of modeling active elements (in this case an OpAmp) in terms of its current and voltage characteristics at the input and output ports. Although an understanding of the internal operation of the active device is desirable, circuits can be designed using the device's input and output port parameters. The terminal characteristics of the active device in conjunction with the Kirchhoff's current and voltage laws are used to analyze the circuit.

A simple application of an OpAmp is the unity gain buffer, which is primarily used to isolate electronic signals. A unity gain buffer or voltage follower is shown in Figure 12.5. The circuit can be analyzed using the voltage and current constraints given by the following equations,

$$v_1 \approx v_2$$

and

$$i_1 = i_2 \approx 0.$$

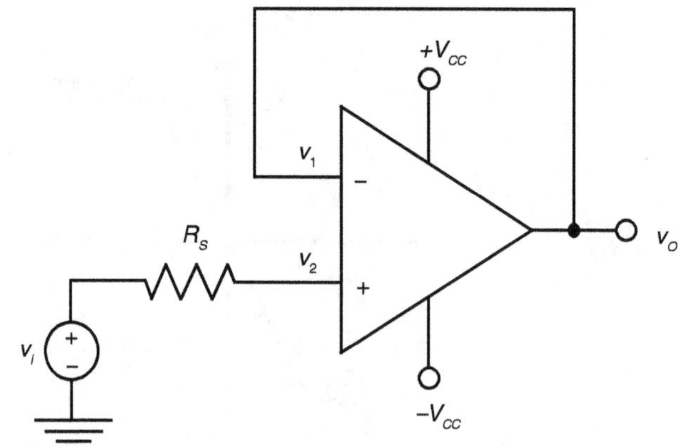

Figure 12.5 Unity Gain Buffer

The input signal voltage v_i is equal to v_2 since negligible current flows into the positive input terminal of the OpAmp ($i_2 = 0$); there is no voltage drop across R_s. Owing to the virtual short between the inverting and noninverting terminals, the noninverting terminal voltage is also at the same voltage level, v_i, that is,

$$v_i = v_2 = v_1.$$

Since the inverting terminal is directly connected to the output of the OpAmp,

$$v_o = v_1 = v_i,$$

or

$$\frac{v_o}{v_1} = 1. \tag{12.8}$$

The voltage follower is called a unity gain *buffer* since it is an ideal impedance transformer. The input impedance of the voltage follower is very high, and its out impedance is, for all practical purposes, zero. Verification of these impedance characteristics provides a useful exercise in the study of OpAmp properties.

The input and output resistances of the voltage follower can be found by using the simplified equivalent circuit for the OpAmp. The simplified equivalent circuit, shown in Figure 12.6, differs from the ideal OpAmp model in that the equivalent circuit is a lumped parameter (resistors and sources) model of the OpAmp in the linear region of operation. It is a functional equivalent of the OpAmp, which is not the actual circuitry in the OpAmp chip but behaves functionally as an OpAmp to external circuitry (the principle is much the same as Thévenin or Norton equivalent circuits). The simplified OpAmp equivalent model shown in Figure 12.6 assumes frequency independent behavior; that is, the response of the amplifier is independent of signal frequency.

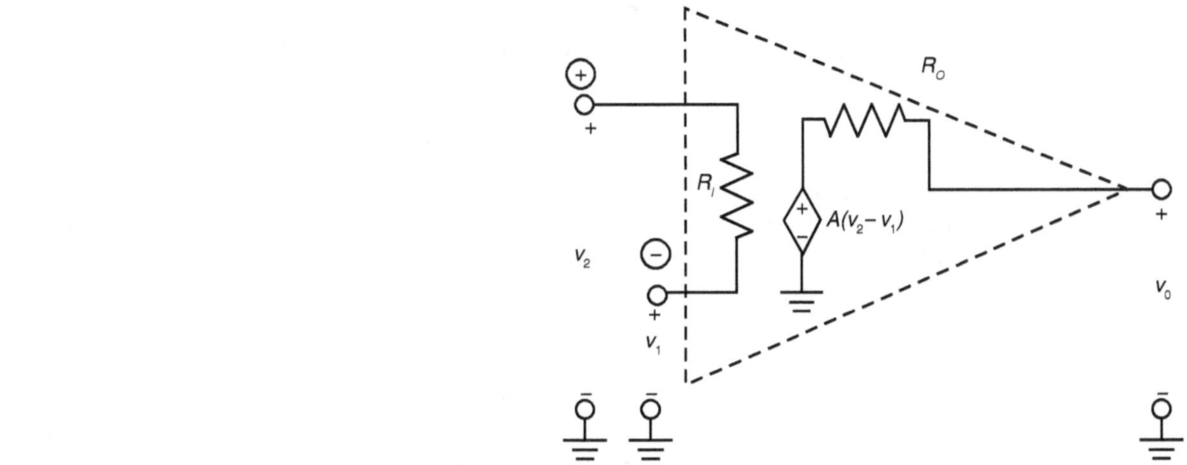

Figure 12.6 Simplified Equivalent Circuit Model of the OpAmp

The current and voltage constraints used for Figure 12.5 assumed in the ideal OpAmp model must be discarded when using the simplified equivalent model. Equation (12.6) is no longer valid due to the non-zero output resistance, R_O.

The voltage follower circuit is analyzed using the simplified equivalent circuit as shown in Figure 12.7. In the model, $R_i = 2\ \text{M}\Omega$, $R_O = 75\Omega$, and $A = 200\text{k}$. Let $R_S = 1\ \text{k}\Omega$.

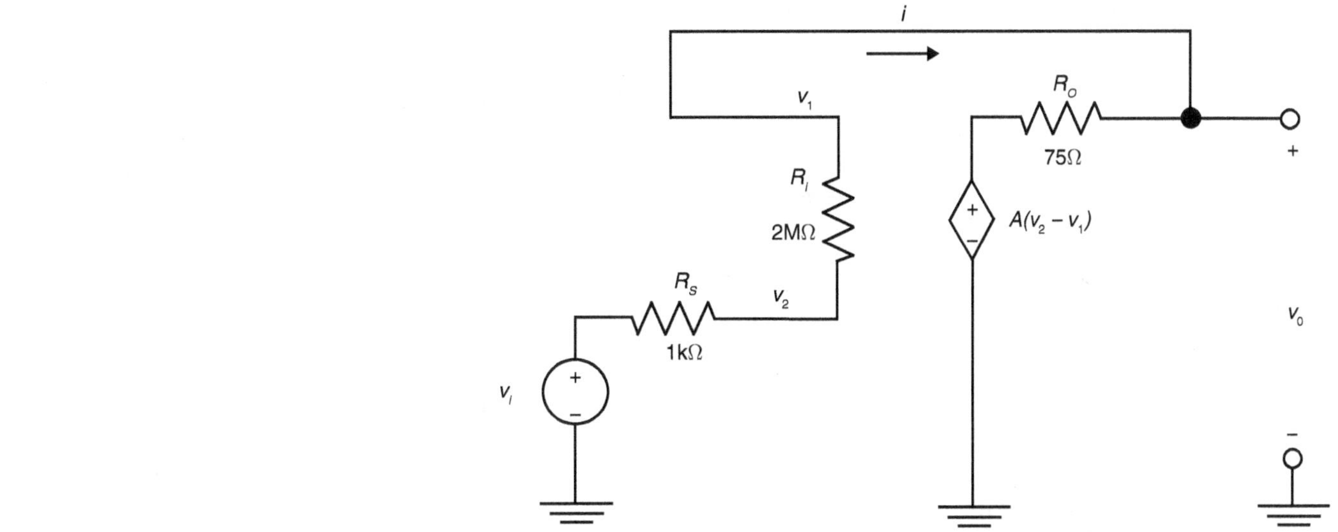

Figure 12.7 Voltage Follower Analysis with Simplified Equivalent OpAmp Model

The current i is found by Kirchhoff's Voltage Law (KVL),

$$i = \frac{v_i - A\left(v_2 - v_1\right)}{R_i + R_O + R_S}, \qquad \textbf{(12.9)}$$

but i is also given by:

$$i = \frac{v_2 - v_1}{R_i} \qquad \textbf{(12.10)}$$

Since the output terminal of a voltage follower is connected to the negative input terminal of the OpAmp,

$$v_O = v_1 \qquad \textbf{(12.11)}$$

Equating Equations (12.9) and (12.10), substituting v_i for v_2, and solving for $\frac{v_o}{v_i}$ yields the expression for voltage gain for the voltage follower:

$$\frac{v_o}{v_i} = 1 - \frac{R_i}{R_S + R_o + R_i(1+A)}, \tag{12.12}$$

It can easily be seen that large values of the OpAmp gain, A, will lead to a voltage gain closely approximating unity. The parameter values for this example, R_i = 2 MΩ, R_O = 75 Ω, R_S = 1 kΩ, and A = 200k, result in:

$$\frac{v_o}{v_i} = 1 - 2.6875 \times 10 - 9 \approx 1. \tag{12.13}$$

The input and output resistances of the voltage follower can be calculated using the simplified equivalent model. Thévenin equivalent resistances are found using the standard "test source" method. To calculate the input resistance, a test source, v_t is used to excite the circuit shown in Figure 12.8. Note that v_t is applied directly to v_2. The input resistance directly from the voltage source v_i in Figure 12.7 is found by adding R_S to the Thévenin resistance found at v_2. The Thévenin equivalent input resistance, R_{in}, is the ratio of the test voltage over the current delivered by the test source,

$$R_{in} = \frac{v_t}{i_t}. \tag{12.14}$$

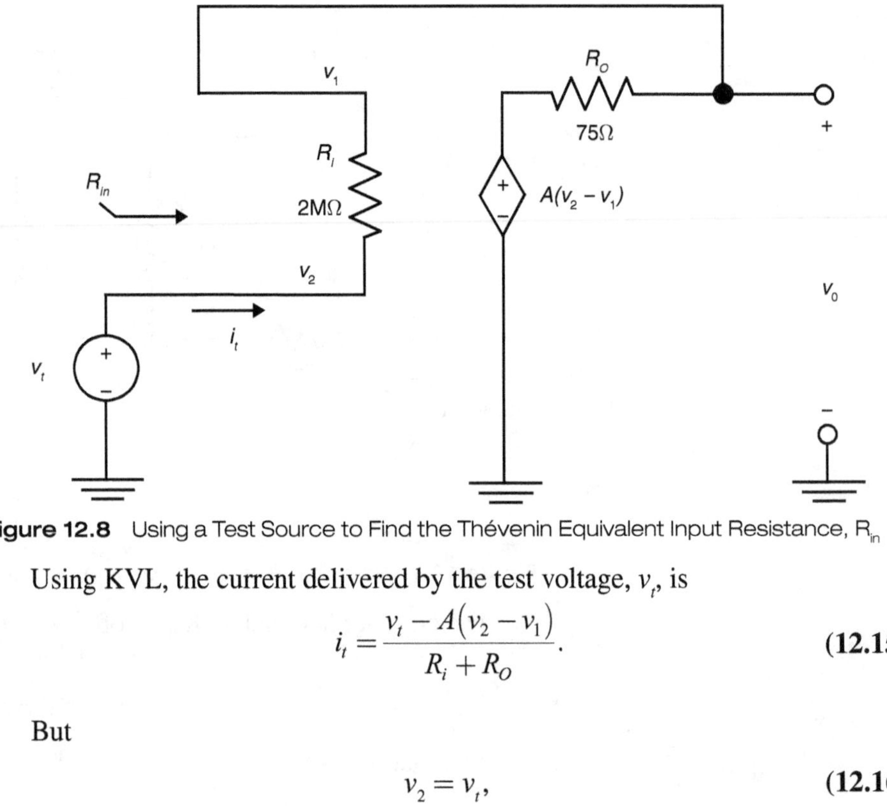

Figure 12.8 Using a Test Source to Find the Thévenin Equivalent Input Resistance, R_{in}

Using KVL, the current delivered by the test voltage, v_t, is

$$i_t = \frac{v_t - A(v_2 - v_1)}{R_i + R_O}. \tag{12.15}$$

But

$$v_2 = v_t, \tag{12.16}$$

and knowing the voltage drop across R_i,

$$v_1 = v_t - i_t R_i \tag{12.17}$$

Substituting Equations (12.16) and (12.17) into Equation (12.15) yields

$$i_t = \frac{v_t - A i_t R_i}{R_i + R_O}. \tag{12.18}$$

The Thévenin input resistance, R_{in}, is found by rearranging Equation (12.18),

$$R_{in} = \frac{v_t}{i_t} = R_i(1+A) + R_O. \qquad \textbf{(12.19)}$$

For the given typical parameter values ($R_i = 2$ MΩ, $A = 200$K, and $R_O = 75\Omega$), the input resistance can be calculated to be the very large value $R_{in} = 400 \times 109\ \Omega$. It is reasonable to assume that the input resistance of a unity gain buffer, R_{in}, is, for all practical purposes, infinite.

Example 12.2

Determine the output resistance of an OpAmp voltage follower.

Solution

To find the output resistance, R_{out}, a test voltage source is connected to the output of the voltage follower to find the Thévenin equivalent resistance at the output. Note also that all independent sources must be zeroed. That is, all independent voltage sources are short circuited, and all independent currents are open circuited. The circuit used to find R_{out} is shown in Exhibit 1.

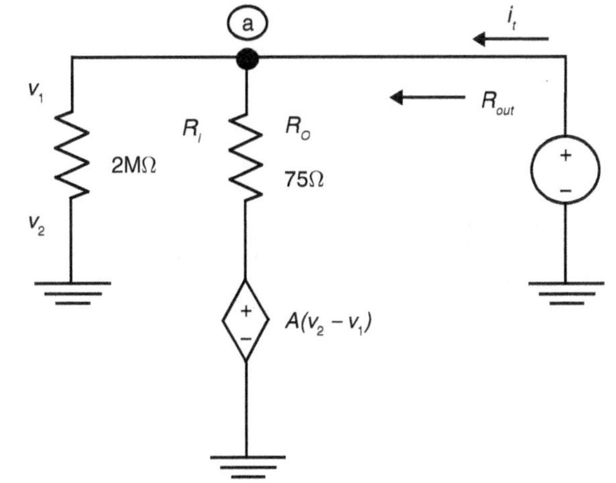

Exhibit 1 Simplified Equivalent Circuit for Finding R_{out} of an OpAmp Voltage Follower

To find the Thévenin equivalent output resistance, a test voltage source, v_t is connected at the output. The circuit draws i_t source current. The input at v_2 has been short circuited to ground to set independent sources to zero.

Using the node voltage method of analysis by summing all currents flowing into node a yields:

$$i_t + \frac{v_2 - v_1}{R_i} + \frac{A(v_2 - v_1) - v_t}{R_O} = 0. \qquad \textbf{(12.20)}$$

But

$$v_2 = 0 \text{ and } v_1 = v_t. \qquad \textbf{(12.21)}$$

Then Equation (12.20) is simplified to,

$$i_t = \frac{R_o + (A+1)R_i}{R_o R_i} v_t \qquad \textbf{(12.22)}$$

and R_{out} is,

$$R_{out} = \frac{v_t}{i_t} = \frac{R_o R_i}{R_o + (A+1)R_i}. \tag{12.23}$$

A typical value for the output resistance of the unity gain buffer, R_{out}, can be calculated using the given typical OpAmp values of $R_i = 2\ \text{M}\Omega$, $R_O = 75\ \Omega$, and $A = 200\text{k}$. R_{out} is found to be 375 $\mu\Omega$, which, in most circuit applications, can be considered essentially zero.

Basic Applications of the OpAmp

Although the OpAmp can be used in infinite circuit configurations, several configurations have become basic electronic building blocks. These commonly found OpAmp circuit configurations are the inverting amplifier, summing amplifier, non-inverting amplifier, difference amplifier, integrator, and differentiator.

Table 12.2 Common Op Amp Topologies

<table>
<tr><th>OpAmp Topology</th><th>Circuit</th><th>Relevant Equations</th></tr>
<tr><td>Inverting amplifier</td><td>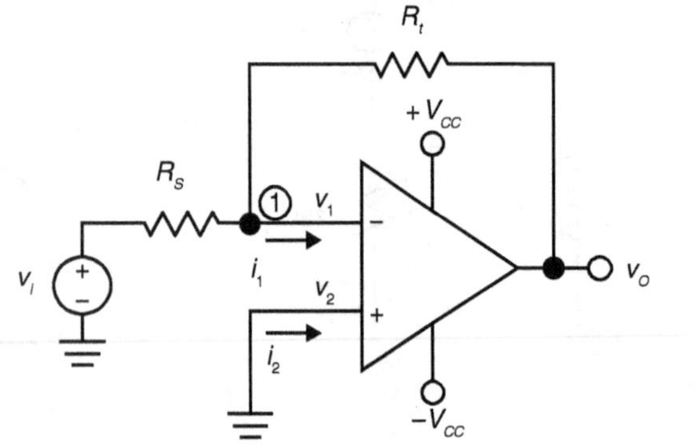
</td><td>$\frac{v_O}{v_i} = -\frac{R_f}{R_S}$
In linear region, $\frac{R_f}{R_S} < \left|\frac{V_{CC}}{v_i}\right|$</td></tr>
<tr><td>Summing amplifier</td><td>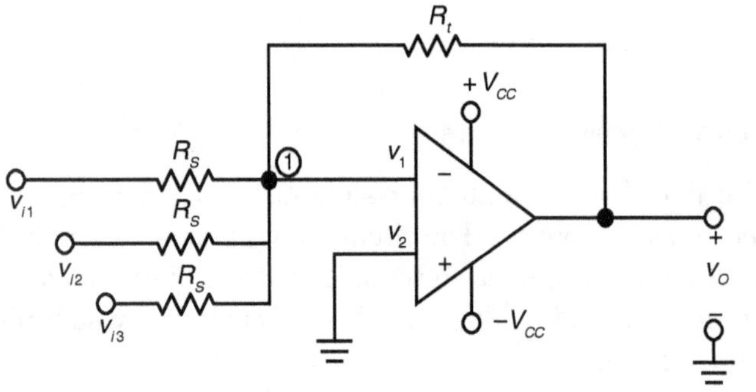
</td><td>$v_O = -\left[\frac{R_f}{R_1} v_{i1} + \frac{R_f}{R_2} v_{i2} + \frac{R_f}{R_3} v_{i3}\right]$
$v_O = -\frac{R_f}{R_S}(v_{i1} + v_{i2} + v_{i3})$
when $R_1 = R_2 = R_3 = R_S$.
Generally, $v_O = -\frac{R_f}{R_S}\sum_{j=1}^{n}(v_i)_j$</td></tr>
</table>

Table 12.2 Common Op Amp Topologies

OpAmp Topology	Circuit	Relevant Equations
Noninverting amplifier	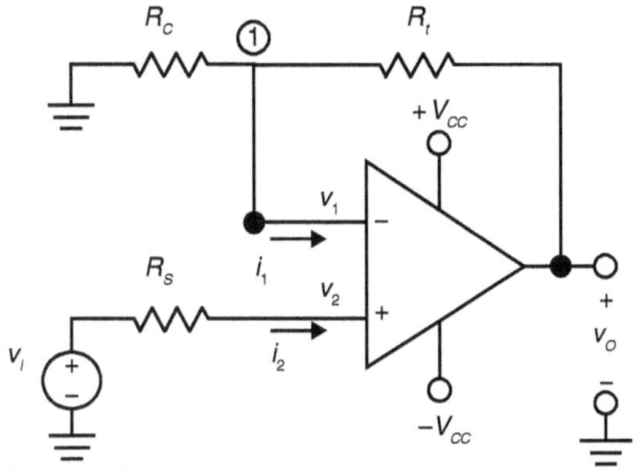	$\frac{v_O}{v_i} = 1 + \frac{R_f}{R_G}$ In linear region, $1 + \frac{R_f}{R_G} < \left\|\frac{V_{CC}}{v_s}\right\|$
Difference amplifier	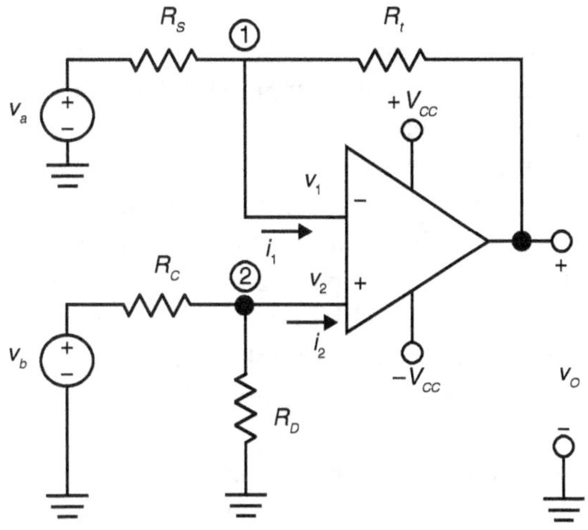	$v_O = \frac{R_D}{R_C + R_D}\left(\frac{R_B}{R_A} + 1\right)v_b - \frac{R_B}{R_A}v_a;$ $v_O = \frac{R_B}{R_A}(v_b - v_a)$ when $\frac{R_A}{R_B} = \frac{R_C}{R_D}$
Integrator	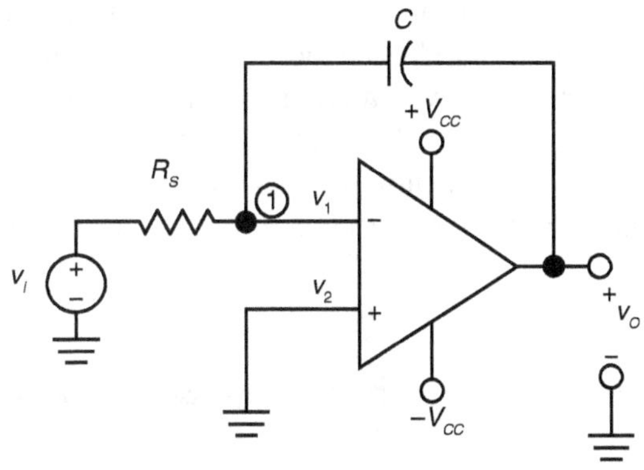	$v_O = -\frac{1}{RC}\int v_i dt$

Table 12.2 Common Op Amp Topologies

OpAmp Topology	Circuit	Relevant Equations
Differentiator	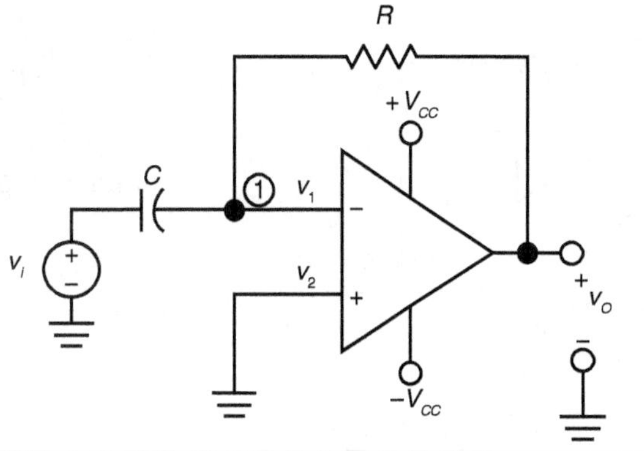	$v_O = -RC\frac{dv_i}{dt}$

Differential amplifiers are not restricted to circuits with single OpAmps. It is possible to construct a differential amplifier without any OpAmps, while many differential amplifiers have three or more OpAmps as essential elements. Figure 12.9 shows the basic schematic representation of an instrumentation amplifier using two OpAmps. Instrumentation amplifiers are high performance voltage amplifiers primarily used for the initial amplification of signals from a variety of types of transducers. They are available packaged as a single item in a dual in-line package (DIP) or can be realized with discreet components. Packaged instrumentation amplifiers usually have greater control on the factors contributing to common-mode rejection ratio (CMRR) and are often the advantageous choice for the circuit designer.

The basic topology of this particular instrumentation amplifier is that of an inverting amplifier connected in series with a summing amplifier. The extra resistors at the positive terminals of each OpAmp, R_2 and R_2', serve no obvious function if the OpAmps are considered to be ideal. Their function is to reduce the effects of input parameter variations, which are nonideal properties of OpAmps. The inversion of v_{i1} prior to summation allows for the output of the amplifier to be a multiple of the difference of the two inputs. This particular circuit topology also allows, with appropriate external resistor choices, for large (on the order of 100V) input voltages.

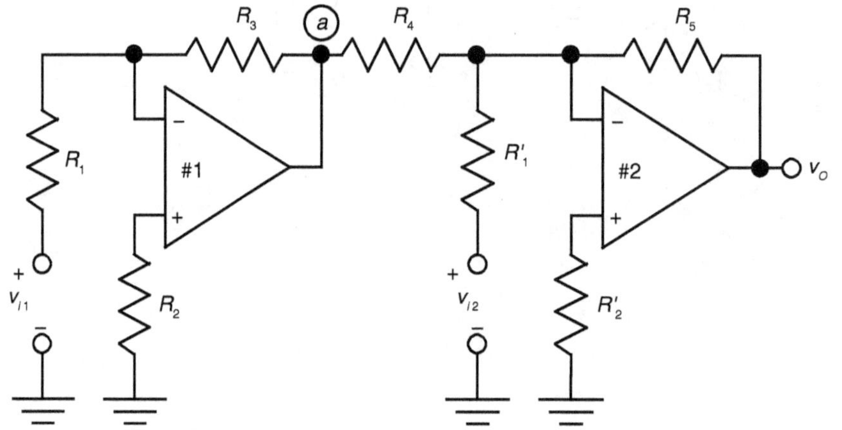

Figure 12.9 Instrumentation Amplifier with High Input Voltage Capability

Analysis of this amplifier begins, as usual, with the assumption that each OpAmp is near-ideal. The input are virtually shorted, the gain is infinite, the input resistance is infinite, and the output resistance is zero. Since no current flows into the inputs of either OpAmp, there is no voltage drop across the resistors, R_2 and $R_2{}'$. The OpAmp positive input terminals are, therefore, at ground potential; each OpAmp circuit acts in the same manner as if its positive terminal were directly connected to ground. The zero output resistance of the first OpAmp implies that the remainder of the circuit does not affect its output, and the voltage at node *a* is obtained from the gain equation for an inverting amplifier:

$$v_a = -\frac{R_3}{R_1} v_{i1}. \tag{12.24}$$

The zero output resistance of the first OpAmp circuit also implies that it acts as a perfect voltage source input to the summing amplifier of the second OpAmp. The output of the summing amplifier is then given by:

$$v_o = -\frac{R_5}{R_4} v_a - \frac{R_5}{R_1'} v_{i2} \tag{12.25}$$

or, with the results of Equation (12.24),

$$v_o = \frac{R_5 R_3}{R_4 R_1} v_{i1} - \frac{R_5}{R_1'} v_{i2}. \tag{12.26}$$

If proper resistor value choices are made, this instrumentation amplifier becomes a true differential amplifier. The necessary restriction on the resistor values to create a differential amplifier is:

$$\frac{R_1 R_4}{R_3} = R_1'. \tag{12.27}$$

Additional decisions are made for good design. It is often important to load the input sources equally. The input resistance at each input to the instrumentation amplifier is therefore set to the same value: $R'_1 = R_1$. The restriction of Equation (12.27) then requires that $R_4 = R_3$. With these restrictions, the final idealized output relationship for this instrumentation amplifier is:

$$v_o = \frac{R_5}{R_1}\left(v_{i1} - v_{i2}\right), \tag{12.28}$$

which is of the general form for a differential amplifier.

NONIDEAL CHARACTERISTICS OF OPAMPS

In this section, the most significant limitations of the nonideal Operational Amplifier are discussed. A fundamental understanding of these nonideal properties allows the electronics designer to choose circuit topologies and parameter values so that the performance of real, practical circuitry closely approximates the ideal case. The concept of an *ideal* OpAmp has allowed the use of simplified circuit analysis techniques to determine the performance of OpAmp circuits and concentration

on the design philosophy behind the various OpAmp circuit topologies. The ideal OpAmp was defined with the following properties:

- Infinite voltage gain
- Infinite input resistance
- Zero output resistance
- Output independent of power source characteristics
- Properties independent of input frequency

A number of nonideal characteristics have been considered briefly in prior sections of this chapter:

- Output saturation
- Finite input resistance
- Finite voltage gain
- Non-zero output resistance

These characteristics will be further discussed along with the following additional nonideal characteristics:

- Input parameter variations
- Output parameter limitations
- Supply and package related parameters

In addition, the performance of an OpAmp is dependent on the frequency of the input signals. In many low-frequency applications, this frequency dependence is not significant. OpAmps are commonly used in the audio frequency range and beyond without significant distortion. A discussion of frequency-dependent behavior and its close relative, slew rate, is beyond the scope of this section. A discussion of the frequency dependence of OpAmp circuit performance can be found in Section 9.9 of this text.

Finite Gain, Finite Input Resistance, and Non-Zero Output Resistance

The properties of finite gain, finite input resistance, and non-zero output resistance were observed in previous discussions concerning using an OpAmp to create a unity gain buffer in Section 1.2. The effect of these nonideal properties was approached through a simple equivalent model of the OpAmp as shown in Figure 12.6; that approach will be continued here. While the effects due to these properties may vary slightly with OpAmp application, a demonstration of their typical effects on circuit performance will be illustrated using the basic inverting amplifier configuration.

An inverting amplifier can be constructed using an OpAmp as shown in Figure 12.10. While the power supply, $\pm V_{CC}$, is not shown in this figure, its presence is assumed.

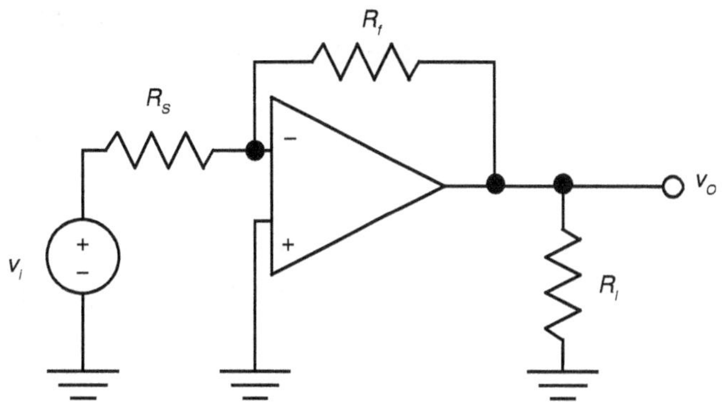

Figure 12.10 Simple Inverting Amplifier

Analysis of this circuit begins with replacing the OpAmp with its simple equivalent circuit as shown in Figure 12.11. Here the OpAmp model is enclosed within the dashed box with an input voltage, $v+ = v_2 - v_1$.

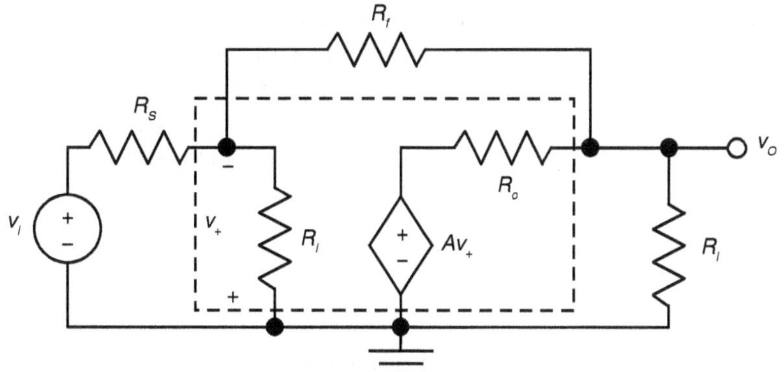

Figure 12.11 Inverting Amplifier Equivalent Circuit

Equations expressing Kirchhoff's Current Law at the input and output terminals of the OpAmp are the first step to obtaining an expression for the voltage gain:

$$\frac{v_i - (-v_+)}{R_S} + \frac{v_+}{R_i} + \frac{v_o - (-v_+)}{R_f} = 0 \qquad \textbf{(12.29)}$$

and

$$\frac{Av_+ - v_o}{R_o} - \frac{v_o}{R_l} + \frac{(-v_+) - v_o}{R_f} = 0. \qquad \textbf{(12.30)}$$

Solving for v_+ in Equation (12.30) yields:

$$v_+ = v_o\left(\frac{G_o + G_l + G_f}{AG_o - G_f}\right). \qquad \textbf{(12.31)}$$

Where the subscripted quantities $|Gx|$ are conductances corresponding to the resistances with the same subscript $|Rx|$. For example:

$$G_f = \frac{1}{R_f} \quad \text{and} \quad G_o = \frac{1}{R_o}.$$

Equations (12.31) and (12.29) can now be combined to obtain an expression for the voltage gain:

$$\frac{v_o}{v_i} = -\frac{G_S}{G_f + \dfrac{(G_o + G_l + G_f)(G_S + G_i + G_f)}{(AG_o - G_f)}}. \tag{12.32}$$

The expression for voltage gain using the ideal OpAmp model in Section 1.3 was:

$$\frac{v_o}{v_i} = -\frac{R_f}{R_S} = -\frac{G_S}{G_f}. \tag{12.33}$$

Consideration of the nonideal characteristics of an OpAmp has added complexity to the gain function and increases the magnitude of the denominator of the expression; the overall gain is reduced. Good circuit design practices imply that near-ideal performance is the desired goal. With *appropriate* external element choices, the gain function can approach the ideal. A first obvious design choice to decrease the size of the additional term in the denominator of Equation (12.32) is to make the parallel combination of R_l and R_f large with respect to the output impedance of the OpAmp, R_o. This choice of resistors is equivalent to making $G_o >> (G_l + G_f)$, which allows for the simplification of the gain expression to:

$$\frac{v_o}{v_i} \approx -\frac{G_S}{G_f + \dfrac{1}{A}(G_S + G_i + G_f)} = -\frac{R_f \| \{A \bullet (R_S \| R_i \| R_f)\}}{R_S}. \tag{12.34}$$

If A is large, the parallel combination of R_f and $A \bullet (R_S // R_i // R_f)$ will be very close to R_f in value, and the gain of the circuit will be near that of the idealized case.

Example 12.3

Given the following circuit parameters for an inverting amplifier,

$R_f = 47\ \text{k}\Omega$
$R_S = 10\ \text{k}\Omega$
$R_l = 22\ \text{k}\Omega$

and nonideal OpAmp parameters,

$R_i = 2\ \text{M}\Omega$
$R_o = 75\ \Omega$
$A = 200{,}000$

determine the voltage gain of the amplifier and compare to the ideal gain.

Solution

The admittances are first calculated:

$G_f = 21.28\ \mu\text{S}$	$G_i = 0.500\ \mu\text{S}$
$G_S = 100.0\ \mu\text{S}$	$G_o = 13.33\ \text{mS}$
$G_l = 45.46\ \mu\text{S}$	

Equation (12.32) becomes:

$$\frac{v_o}{v_i} = -\frac{100\mu}{21.28\mu + \dfrac{(13.33\text{m} + 45.46\mu + 21.28\mu)(100\mu + 0.5\mu + 21.28\mu)}{(200{,}000 \bullet 13.33\text{m} - 21.28\mu)}}$$

$$= -\frac{100\mu}{21.28\mu + 611.96\text{p}} = -4.699865.$$

This result corresponds to a –0.0029% change in value from the ideal case (–4.7). Obviously, proper choices lead to near-ideal performance. Equation (12.34) could have also been used with the given set of circuit parameter values (the resistor values fit the necessary restriction). It yields similar results (4.699865).

The input resistance of an inverting amplifier using a nonideal OpAmp can be obtained using many of the results from the gain calculations previously derived. In order to simplify the process, R_S is removed from the circuit, as shown in Figure 12.12, and the Thévenin input resistance of the remaining circuit is calculated. The input resistance of the total amplifier will be:

$$R_{in} = R_S + R_{th} \quad \textbf{(12.35)}$$

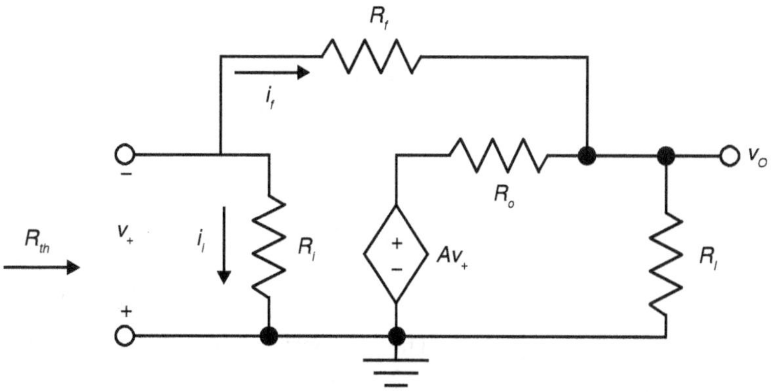

Figure 12.12 Inverting Amplifier Equivalent Circuit with R_S Removed

Calculation of the Thévenin input resistance begins with determination of the two currents, i_i and i_f:

$$i_i = \frac{-v_+}{R_i} \quad \textbf{(12.36a)}$$

and

$$i_f = \frac{-v_+ - v_o}{R_f}. \quad \textbf{(12.36b)}$$

Equation (12.31) can be combined with Equation (12.36b) to eliminate v_o:

$$i_f = -v_+\left[G_f\left\{1 + \frac{AG_o - G_f}{G_0 + G_l + G_f}\right\}\right]. \quad \textbf{(12.37)}$$

Which leads to the Thévenin resistance:

$$R_{th} = \frac{-v_+}{i_i + i_f} = \frac{1}{G_i + G_f\left\{1 + \dfrac{AG_o - G_f}{G_o + G_l + G_f}\right\}} \quad \textbf{(12.38)}$$

and the total input resistance, R_{in}:

$$R_{in} = R_S + R_{th} = R_S + \frac{1}{G_i + G_f\left\{1 + \frac{AG_o - G_f}{G_o + G_l + G_f}\right\}}. \quad (12.39)$$

The input resistance has been increased by the quantity R_{th}. In order to make the nonideal performance mirror the ideal approximations, *appropriate* external element choices can be made. Once again, if the resistors are chosen so that $R_l \parallel R_f >> R_o$, the expression for the input resistance reduces to:

$$R_{in} \approx R_S + \frac{1}{G_i + G_f(1+A)} = R_S + \left\{R_i // \frac{R_f}{1+A}\right\}. \quad (12.40)$$

If Equation (12.40) is to be a reasonable approximation to the idealized expressions ($R_{in} = R_S$), it is necessary that R_f be limited in magnitude. If R_{in} is not to vary by more than a few ohms from the ideal value, a reasonable choice for the maximum value of R_f is:

$$R_f < 1 + A\ \Omega \quad (12.41)$$

Example 12.4

Given the circuit in Example 12.2, determine the input resistance of the inverting amplifier and compare to the ideal case.

Solution

Equation (12.39) yields:

$$R_{in} = 10\ \text{k}\Omega + 0.2362\ \Omega.$$

The appropriate choices for external resistor values have been made for Equation (12.40) to be valid. It yields a value for the input resistance of:

$$R_{in} = 10\ \text{k}\Omega + 0.2350\ \Omega.$$

The results are deviations of less than 0.0024% from the ideal value of 10 kΩ.

Calculation of the output resistance of an inverting amplifier using a nonideal OpAmp is accomplished using Thévenin techniques. The input source is set to zero, the load is removed (output resistance calculations rarely include the load), and the output is driven by a voltage source as shown in Figure 12.13. The ratio of the driving voltage, v_t, to the driving current, i_t, gives the output resistance, R_{out}.

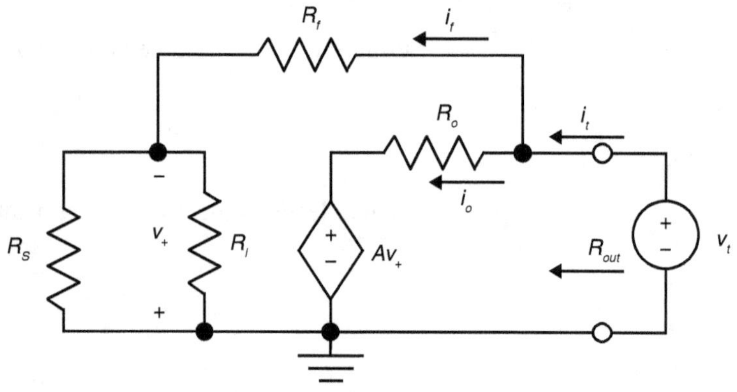

Figure 12.13 Inverting Amplifier Adjustments for R_{out} Calculations

The driving current is the sum of the currents through R_f and R_o:

$$i_t = i_o + i_f. \tag{12.42}$$

The current through R_f is given by:

$$i_f = \frac{v_t}{R_f + R'} \tag{12.43}$$

where

$$R' = R_S \parallel R_i.$$

The current through R_o is given by:

$$i_o = \frac{v_t - Av_+}{R_o} \tag{12.44}$$

where v_+ can be obtained through a simple voltage division:

$$v_+ = -\frac{R'}{R' + R_f} v_t. \tag{12.45}$$

Combining Equations (12.44) and (12.45) with Equations (12.43) and (12.41) gives the total driven current:

$$i_t = \frac{R_o + R_f + (1 + A)R'}{R_o(R_f + R')} v_t \tag{12.46}$$

and finally the output resistance:

$$R_{out} = \frac{v_t}{i_t} = \frac{R_o(R_f + R')}{R_o + R_f + (1 + A)R'} \tag{12.47}$$

$$= \frac{R_o(R_f + R_S // R_i)}{R_o + R_f + (1 + A)(R_S // R_i)}.$$

Reasonable assumptions (such as have been previously described) on the choice of external resistor values lead to an approximation of the output resistance expression:

$$R_{out} \approx \frac{R_o(R_f + R_S)}{(1 + A)R_S}. \tag{12.48}$$

Example 12.5

Given the circuit of Example 12.2, determine the output resistance of the inverting amplifier and compare to the ideal case.

Solution

Equation (12.47) yields

$$R_{out} = 0.00215\ \Omega.$$

The external resistor simplification parameters leading to the use of Equation (12.48) have been met, therefore,

$$R_{out} \approx 0.00214\ \Omega.$$

The idealized value of $R_{out} = 0$ seems justified for practical circuitry given appropriate choices of external components.

It has been shown that finite input impedance, finite gain, and non-zero output resistance do have an effect on the performance of an inverting amplifier. Still, it is possible to have near-ideal performance if appropriate choices on the external circuitry are imposed. A reasonable set of restrictions on the external components has been shown to be:

- $R_l \parallel R_f >> R_o$
- $R_f < (1 + A)\Omega$

If resistances connected to the inputs and output of an OpAmp circuit obey these general restrictions, the OpAmp circuit performance will be near-ideal. Any nonideal variations can be detected with a computer simulation; good circuit design practice always includes simulation.

The Diode as a Circuit Element

Due to the nonlinear nature of the *V-I* relationship for a semiconductor diode, analysis techniques for circuits containing diodes are complex. Simplified piecewise linear modeling techniques that allow for the use of linear analysis techniques are discussed.

One of the most simple circuits involving a diode is shown in Figure 12.14. This circuit consists of an independent voltage source, a resistor, and a diode in series. Simple Thévenin extensions of this circuit show that the discussion presented here can be extended to any linear circuit connected in series with a single diode.

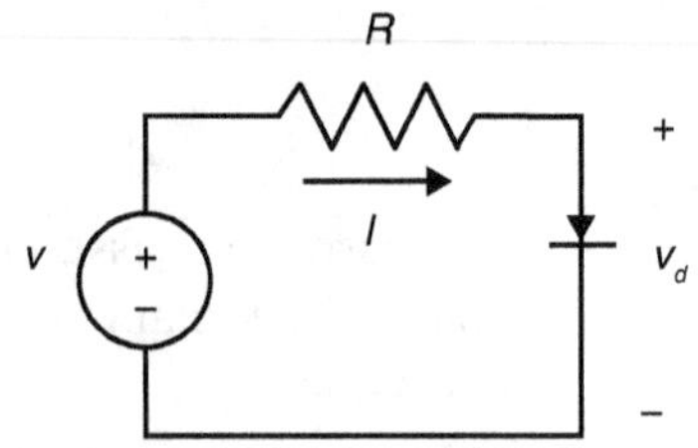

Figure 12.14 Simple Diode Circuit

Kirchhoff's Voltage Law taken around the closed loop yields:

$$V - I_R - V_d = 0 \tag{12.49}$$

where

$$V_d = \eta V_t \ln\left(\frac{I}{I_s} + 1\right), \tag{12.50}$$

which leads to the nonlinear equation,

$$V - IR - \eta V_t \ln\left(\frac{I}{I_s} + 1\right) = 0 \tag{12.51}$$

that must be solved for *I*. Equation (12.50) is the diode *V-I* relationship expressed as the voltage across the diode as a function of the diode current.

Numerical Solutions

A simple closed-form solution for Equation (12.51) does not exist. The best technique for solution is usually a structured numerical search. Structured searches can be easily performed using mathematical software packages or a similar calculator with equation solver capabilities. The common technique uses programmable calculators with a built-in numerical equation solver (root-finder).

Example 12.6

For the circuit of Figure 12.14, assume the following values:

$$V = 5\text{ V}$$
$$R = 1\text{k}\Omega$$

and diode parameters:

$$IS = 2\text{ nA}$$
$$\eta = 2$$

Find, at room temperature, the diode current, the voltage across the diode, and the power dissipated by the diode.

Solution

Given

$$V_d = \eta \cdot V_t \cdot \ln\left(\frac{I}{I_s} + 1\right)$$
$$V - I \bullet R - V_d = 0$$

The solution is:

$$I = 4.242\text{ mA}$$
$$V_d = 0.758\text{ V.}$$

Simplified Piecewise Linear Models of the Diode

The previous sections of this chapter have treated a diode as either an extremely simple device (the ideal diode) or as a complex nonlinear device represented by nonlinear equations or curves. While each of these treatments has its place in the analysis of electronic circuits, it is often useful to find a technique in the middle ground between these two extremes. One such technique involves the regional linearization of circuit element *V-I* characteristics.

When this technique is applied to a diode there are two basic regions:

- The region when the diode is basically conducting (forward bias)
- The region when the diode is basically nonconducting (reverse bias)

In Example 12.6, the groundwork for the two-region linearization was laid with the boundary between the two regions being at the origin of the ideal diode *V-I* transfer relationship. With real diodes the transition between the two regions lies at a positive diode voltage, hereafter called the *threshold voltage*, V_t.

Forward Bias Modeling

In the region where the diode is conducting, a good linear model of the diode is a straight line tangent to the diode *V-I* relationship at a Q-point. The slope of this line is the dynamic resistance of the diode at the Q-point:

$$r_d = \frac{\partial V}{\partial I} = \frac{\eta V_t}{I_s + I} = \frac{\eta V_t}{I_s} e^{-\frac{V}{\eta V_t}}. \qquad \textbf{(12.52)}$$

The value of the threshold voltage can be derived by finding the intersection of this tangent line with the diode voltage axis:

$$V_\gamma = V - Ir_d = V - \eta V_t \left(1 - e^{\frac{V}{\eta V_t}}\right). \qquad \textbf{(12.53)}$$

Figure 12.15 demonstrates this principle showing a line tangent to a diode curve at the Q-point of:

$$I = 3\text{ mA}$$
$$V = 0.776\text{ V}.$$

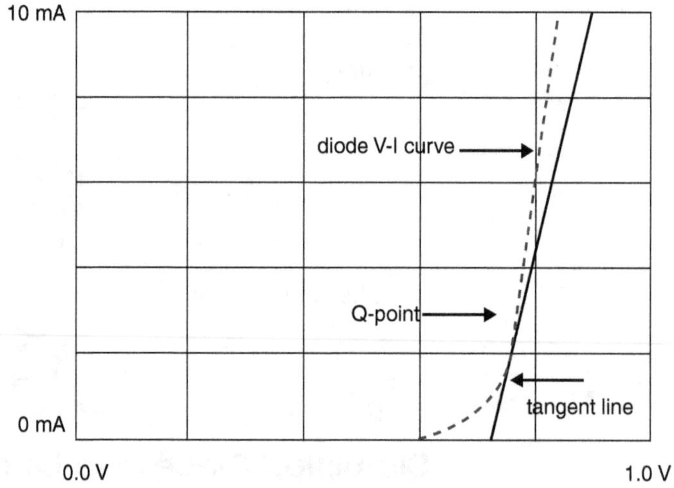

Figure 12.15 Modeling a Diode with a Tangent Line at the Q-point

Example **12.7**

Determine a linear forward-bias model for a diode with the following parameters:

$$I_s = 1\text{ nA}, \eta = 2$$

near the region where the diode current is 3 mA.

Solution:

The diode voltage at this Q-point is given by:

$$V_d = \eta V_t \ln\left(\frac{I}{I_s} + 1\right)$$

$$V = 2(0.026)\ln\left(\frac{3\text{mA}}{\ln A} + 1\right) = 0.776V$$

The diode dynamic resistance can then be calculated as:

$$r_d = \frac{\eta V_t}{I + I_S}$$

$$r_d = \frac{2(0.026)}{1nA + 3\text{mA}} = 17.33\Omega$$

And finally the threshold voltage is calculated as:

$$V_\gamma = V - I_{rd}$$
$$V_\gamma = 0.776 - (3\text{ mA})(17.33\Omega) = 0.724\text{ V}$$

The linear forward-bias model of the diode therefore has a *V-I* relationship:

$$V = V_\gamma + I_{rd} = 0.724 + 17.33\, I$$

as is shown in Figure 12.15.

The linear model of a forward-biased diode can simply be modeled with linear circuit elements as a voltage source (typically shown as a battery) in series with a resistor. The voltage source takes the value V_γ and the resistor becomes r_d. The approximate model is shown in Figure 12.16. Care should be taken as to the polarity of the voltage source. Forward biased diodes experience a voltage drop as is shown in Figure 12.16.

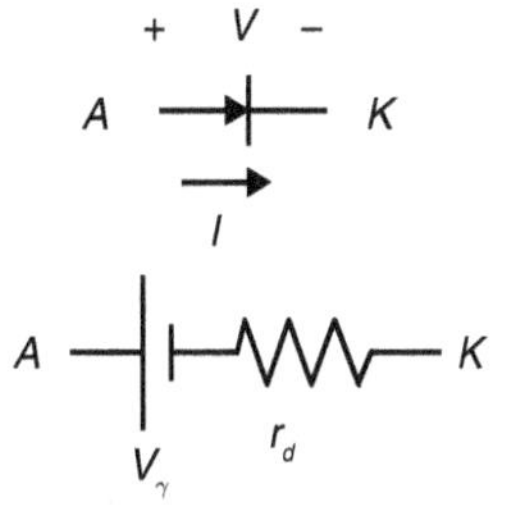

Figure 12.16 Linear Modeling of a Forward-Biased Diode

While this technique gives an accurate approximation of the diode *V-I* characteristic about a Q-point, it is not always clear what Q-point should be chosen. In practice, one usually chooses a Q-point by:

- using an ideal diode model to get an approximate Q-point for static cases, or
- choosing a Q-point that approximately bisects the expected range of diode currents within the application of interest.

If ideal diode modeling is excessively difficult or if the range of diode currents is not easily determined, then less accurate approximations must be made. Figure 12.17 is a plot of the threshold voltage as a function of diode quiescent current for a typical Silicon diode with reverse saturation current of 1 nA. The threshold voltage increases sharply for small diode quiescent currents and then becomes relatively constant at a value between 0.7V and 0.8V; approximate values should lie in that range for this Silicon diode. The dynamic resistance of this diode as a function of threshold voltage is given in Figure 12.18. This resistance, while not constant, has value of only a few Ohms (here seen to be $27 > r_d > 4$). A reasonable guess at the dynamic resistance, without prior knowledge of the diode state might be $r_d \approx 15\ \Omega$ for this diode. (Obviously, diodes with different defining parameters will have other dynamic resistance values.) Approximate models create an error in

the calculation of solutions but allow for the use of simple linear algebraic solution techniques.

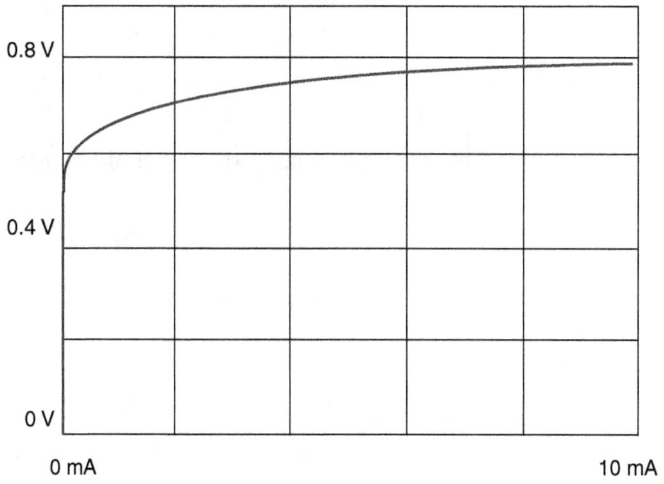

Figure 12.17 Threshold Voltage, V_γ, as a Function of Diode Current

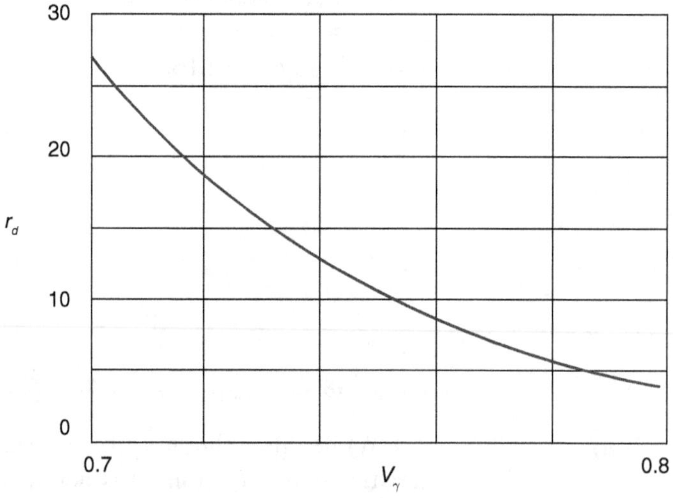

Figure 12.18 Diode Resistance, r_d, as a Function of Threshold Voltage

Example **12.8**

Assume the diode of Example 12.7 is connected in series with a 4V source and a resistance of 820Ω so that the diode is forward biased.

a). Calculate the diode current and voltage with an approximate diode model.

b). Calculate the diode current and voltage using the model derived previously.

Solution

a). Using an ideal model for the diode, one would expect the diode current to be somewhat less than 5 mA. Since curves for the diode threshold voltage as a function of diode current exist, choose $V_\gamma = 0.74$ V. Again, since these curves exist, Figure 12.18 implies a diode resistance, $r_d = 13\Omega$ for that threshold voltage.

The diode V-I relationship can now be approximated by:

$$V = V_\gamma + r_d I$$
$$V = 0.74 + 13\, I.$$

The load line derived from the other circuit elements is given by:

$$V = V_s - RI$$
$$V = 4 - 820\, I.$$

Simple linear algebraic techniques applied to two equations with two unknowns lead to a solution of:

$$V = 0.791\text{V} \qquad I = 3.91 \text{ mA}.$$

If the diode curves for threshold voltage and resistance didn't exist, other approximate values could be chosen. For example $V_t = 0.7$, $r_d = 15\Omega$ lead to:

$$V = 0.759\text{V} \qquad I = 3.95 \text{ mA}.$$

b). With the model derived in the previous example, the diode V-I relationship is given by:

$$V = 0.724 + 17.33\, I.$$

The load line is the same as in part a). Similar linear algebraic techniques give the solution:

$$V = 0.792\text{V} \qquad I = 3.91 \text{ mA}.$$

Notice that all the approximate models give solutions that are within 1% in the diode current and ≈5% in the diode voltage. Numerical solution of this problem as outlined in the previous example (using the theoretical nonlinear diode V-I relationship) give the exact solution to be:

$$V = 0.789\text{V} \qquad I = 3.92 \text{ mA}.$$

The models have all given results within 0.8% in current and 4% in voltage of the exact theoretical values.

When accuracy of the order seen in the previous example is not necessary, a diode can be represented as simply a voltage drop of approximately V_γ. This model assumes that the small series resistance is assumed to be negligible with respect to the circuit Thévenin resistance as seen by the diode, and it forms an intermediate linear model between the ideal diode model and the two-element linear model. Use of this model leads to inaccuracies much larger than seen in previous linear models. It does, however, simplify circuit analysis greatly.

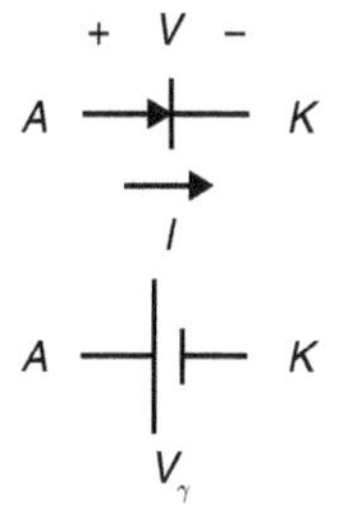

Figure 12.19 Simplified Forward Bias Diode Model

Example 12.9

Assume the diode of Example 12.8 is connected in series with a 4V source and a resistance of 820Ω so that the diode is forward biased.

Calculate the diode current and voltage using a simplified forward bias diode model.

Solution

The diode voltage for this simple model is just a voltage source, V_γ. For this simple model, choose the approximate value:

$$V_\gamma = 0.7.$$

Kirchhoff's voltage law applied to the loop yields:

$$V_\gamma = V_s - RI.$$

Thus

$$0.7 = 4 - 820\, I$$

and

$$I = 4.02 \text{ mA}.$$

This approximate solution has an error of approximately 2.7%. The diode voltage (which was just guessed at) is in error by approximately 11.3%.

Reverse Bias Modeling

In the region where the diode is basically not conducting, there are several possible linear models from which to choose. Each of these is based on the principle that the diode has a small leakage current that is fairly constant in the reverse bias region. That is, when the diode voltage is between a few negative multiples of V_γ and the Zener breakdown voltage, the diode current is constant at $-I_S$. The two common models are a current source of value $-I_S$ or a large resistor. These models are shown in Figure 12.20.

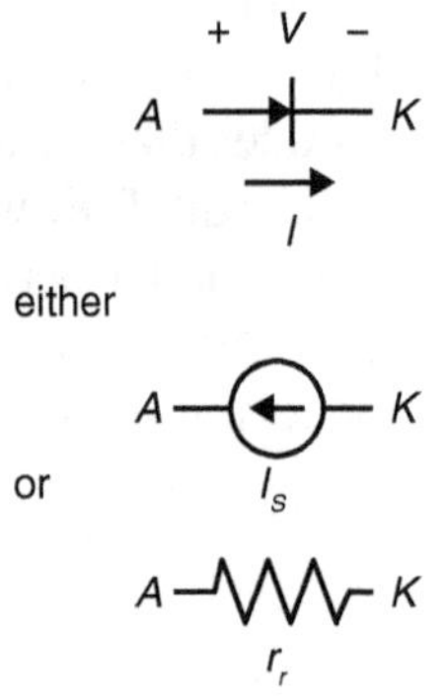

Figure 12.20 Linear Reverse Bias Diode Models

The value of the reverse resistance, r_r, for the second model can be approximated using one of two techniques: (a) using Equation 12.52 to determine the dynamic resistance about some Q-point, or (b) assuming that the diode achieves its true reverse saturation current at the Zener breakdown voltage. While method (a) allows for an exact dynamic resistance a some point, it is often difficult to choose the proper Q-point for a particular application. Method (b) is easier to calculate but

is less accurate at any point and underestimates the dynamic resistance for large reverse voltages.

A summary table of diode characteristics is shown in Figure 12.21.

DIODES			
Device and Schematic Symbol	**Ideal $I - V$ Relationship**	**Piecewise-Linear Approximation of the $I - V$ Relationship**	**Mathematical $I - V$ Relationship**
(Junction Diode) 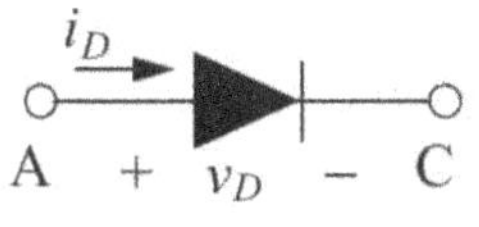	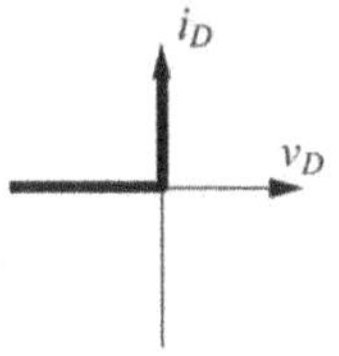	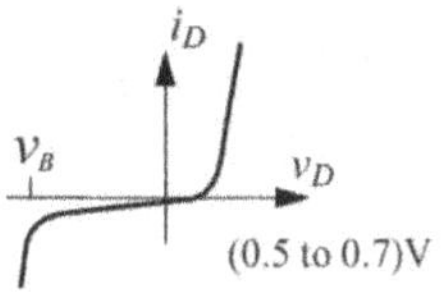 V_B = breakdown voltage	Shockley Equation $i_D \approx I_s\left[e^{(v_D/\eta V_T)} - 1\right]$ where I_s = saturation current η = emission coefficient, typically 1 for Si V_T = thermal voltage $= \frac{kT}{q}$
(Zener Diode) 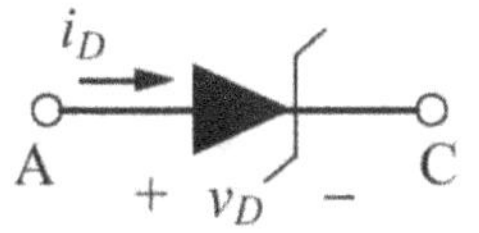	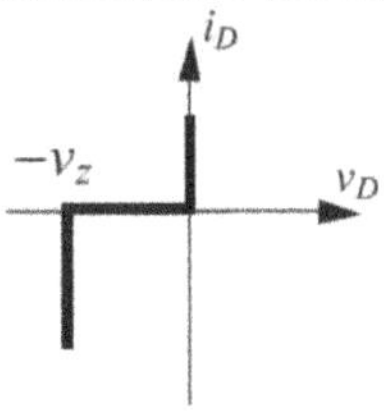	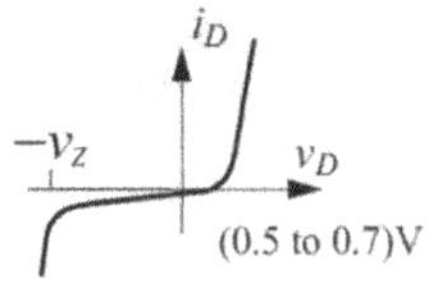 V_Z = Zener voltage	Same as above.

Figure 12.21 Diode Characteristics
Source: NCEES Fundamentals of Engineering Handbook of Equations 8th Edition, 2nd Printing

Diode Applications

Typical applications of diodes are considered in this section. The diode circuits studied are:

- Limiter or clipping circuit
- Full- and half-wave rectifiers
- Peak detector
- Clamping or DC restoring circuit
- Voltage multiplier
- Diode logic gates
- "Superdiode"

All of the circuits analyzed in this section perform some form of wave shaping operation on the input signal to yield a desired output. The clipping circuit "truncates" the input to some desired value beyond which the signal is not to exceed. Full- and half-wave rectifiers pass only the signals of the desired polarity (positive or negative amplitude) and are commonly used in dc power supply designs. The peak detector follows only the maximum amplitudes of an incoming signal and is commonly used in amplitude modulation (AM) radio receivers in communications applications. Clamping circuits perform a level shifting operation on the input waveform, and are used to measure the duty cycle of a pulse waveform. Clamping circuits are commonly used to detect information carried on pulse-width

modulated signals (i.e., the information of interest is represented by increasing or decreasing the pulse-width of a pulse waveform) by retrieving the dc component of the modulated signal. Voltage multipliers perform an integer multiplication on the input signal to yield a higher output voltage. Diode logic gates are simple circuits for performing Boolean operations. The "Superdiode" is a combination of an OpAmp and diode, which eliminates the undesirable diode threshold voltage and dynamic resistance characteristics. Diodes in a circuit can, in most instances, be replaced by Superdiodes to design precision circuits.

Limiter or Clipping Circuit

Diodes are often used in waveshaping applications. In particular, when used with a dc voltage in series with the diode, the output signal can be limited to the reference voltage level of the dc voltage source. Examples of clipping circuits are shown in Figure 12.22.

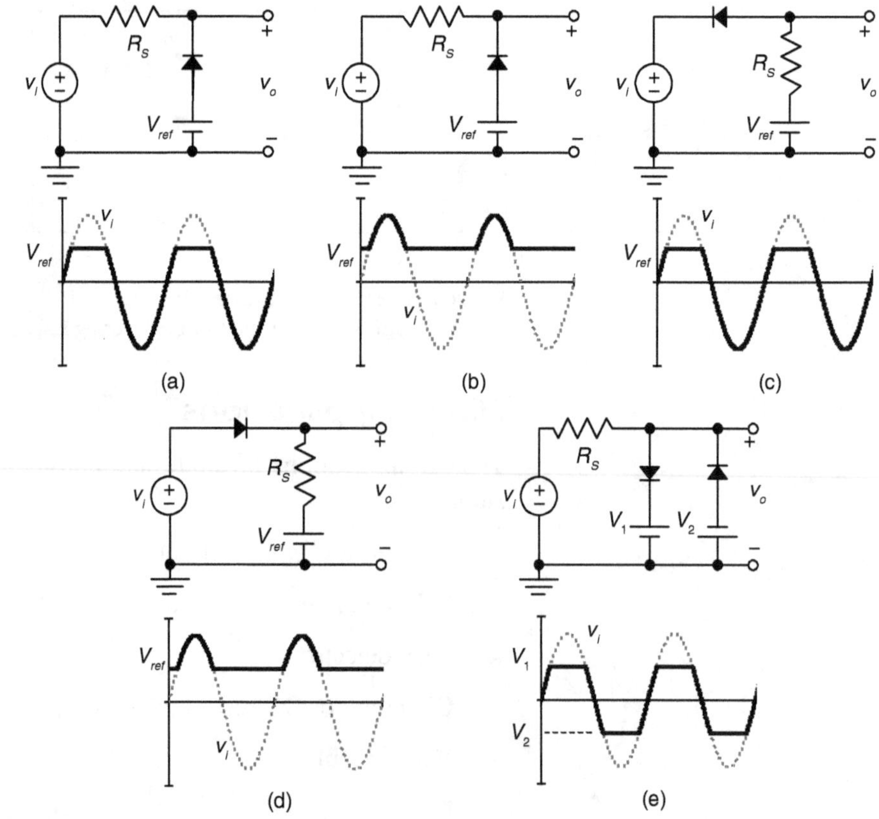

Figure 12.22 Diode Circuits

The simplified forward bias diode model can be used to analyze clipping circuits.

The circuit of Figure 12.22a will be used as an example of this analysis. When the input voltage $v_i \leq V_\gamma + V_{REF}$, the diode is reverse biased (or OFF). Therefore, the diode can be thought of as an open circuit. The output voltage in this case follows the input voltage,

$$v_o = v_i.$$

When the voltage $v_i > V_\gamma + V_{REF}$, the diode is forward biased (or ON). Using the piecewise linear model of the forward biased diode, a simplified equivalent circuit of the clipping circuit of is developed in Figure 12.23.

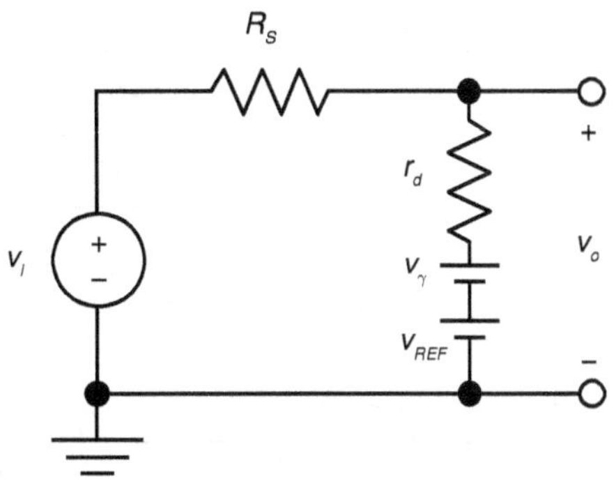

Figure 12.23 Simplified Equivalent Circuit of the Clipping Circuit for $v_i > V_\gamma + V_{REF}$

The output voltage v_o of the clipping circuit when the diode is forward biased is found by analyzing the circuit in Figure 12.23 using superposition and voltage division,

$$v_0 = \frac{r_d}{R_s + r_d} v_i + \frac{R_s}{R_s + r_d}\left(v_\gamma + V_{REF}\right)$$

If $r_d << R_S$, then the output voltage is held at a constant value

$$v_o = V_\gamma + V_{REF}.$$

The input/output voltage relationships for the five diode clippers circuits are given in Table 12.3.

Table 12.3 Input/Output Voltage Relationships for Diode Clipping Circuits

Clipping Circuits of Figure 12.22	Output Voltage, v_o	Simplified Output Voltage, v_o
(a)	$v_o = \frac{r_d}{R_s + r_d} v_i + \frac{R_s}{R_s + r_d}(V_\gamma + V_{REF}), v_i > V_\gamma + V_{REF}$ $v_o = v_i, v_i \le V_\gamma + V_{REF}$	$v_o \approx V_\gamma + V_{REF}, v_i > V_\gamma + V_{REF}$ $v_o = v_i, v_i \le V_\gamma + V_{REF}$
(b)	$v_o = \frac{r_d}{R_s + r_d} v_i + \frac{R_s}{R_s + r_d}(V_{REF} - V_\gamma), v_i < V_{REF} - V_\gamma$ $v_o = v_i, v_i \ge V_{REF} - V_\gamma$	$v_o \approx V_{REF} - V_\gamma, v_i < V_{REF} - V_\gamma$ $v_o = v_i, v_i \ge V_{REF} - V_\gamma$
(c)	$v_o = V_{REF}, v_i + V_\gamma > V_{REF}$ $v_o = \frac{r_d}{R_s + r_d} V_{REF} + \frac{R_s}{R_s + r_d}(v_i + V_\gamma), v_i + V_\gamma \le V_{REF}$	$v_o = V_{REF}, v_i + V_\gamma > V_{REF}$ $v_o \approx v_i + V_\gamma, v_i + V_\gamma \le V_{REF}$
(d)	$v_o = V_{REF}, v_i - V_\gamma < V_{REF}$ $v_o = \frac{r_d}{R_s + r_d} V_{REF} + \frac{R_s}{R_s + r_d}(v_i - V_\gamma), v_i - V_\gamma \ge V_{REF}$	$v_o = V_{REF}, v_i - V_\gamma < V_{REF}$ $v_o \approx v_i - V_\gamma, v_i - V_\gamma \ge V_{REF}$
(e)	$v_o = \frac{r_d}{R_s + r_d} v_i + \frac{R_s}{R_s + r_d}(V_1 + V_\gamma), v_i > V_\gamma + V_1$ $v_o = \frac{r_d}{R_s + r_d} v_i - \frac{R_s}{R_s + r_d}(V_2 + V_\gamma), v_i < -V_2 - V_\gamma$ $v_o = v_i, -V_\gamma - V_2 \le V_\gamma + V_1$	$v_o \approx V_\gamma + V_1, v_i > V_\gamma + V_1$ $v_o \approx -V_2 - V_\gamma, v_i < -V_2 - V_\gamma$ $v_o = v_i, -V_\gamma - V_2 \le v_i \le V_\gamma + V_1$

Example 12.10

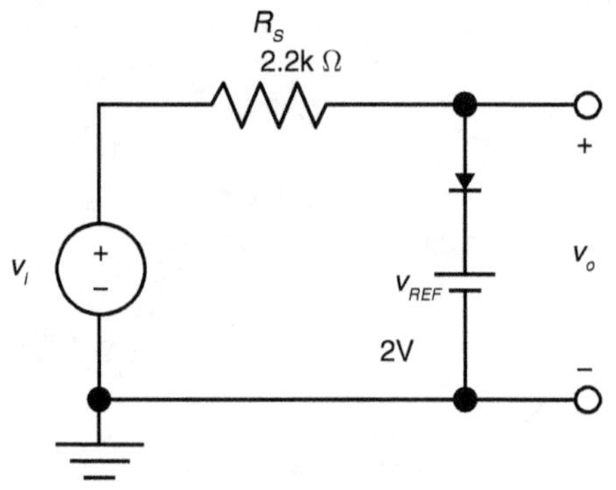

Exhibit 2

For the clipping circuit shown, find the output waveform v_o for the input voltage,

$$v_i = 5\sin\omega_o t.$$

The diode has the following characteristics:

$$r_d = 15\ \Omega, V_\gamma = 0.7\text{ V, and } r_r \rightarrow \infty.$$

Solution

Since $R_s >> r_d$, the simplified output voltage result from Table 12.3 can be constructed. That is,

$$v_o = V_\gamma + V_{REF}, \quad v_i > V_\gamma + V_{REF}$$
$$v_o = v_i, \quad v_i \leq V_\gamma + V_{REF}.$$

So, when $v_i > 2.7\ V$, $v_o = 2.7\ V$.
When $v_i < 2.7\ V$, $v_o = 5\sin\omega_o t$.

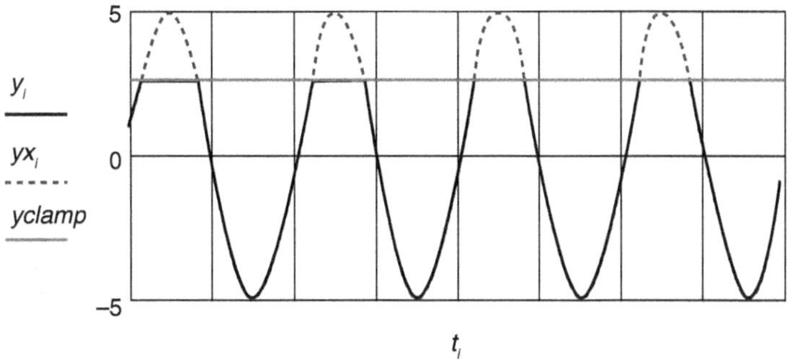

Exhibit 3

Half-Wave Rectifiers

One of the most common diode application is the conversion of power from ac to dc for use as power supplies. Today's power supplies involve sophisticated design. The basic principles of converting from ac to dc power can be explored in this section.

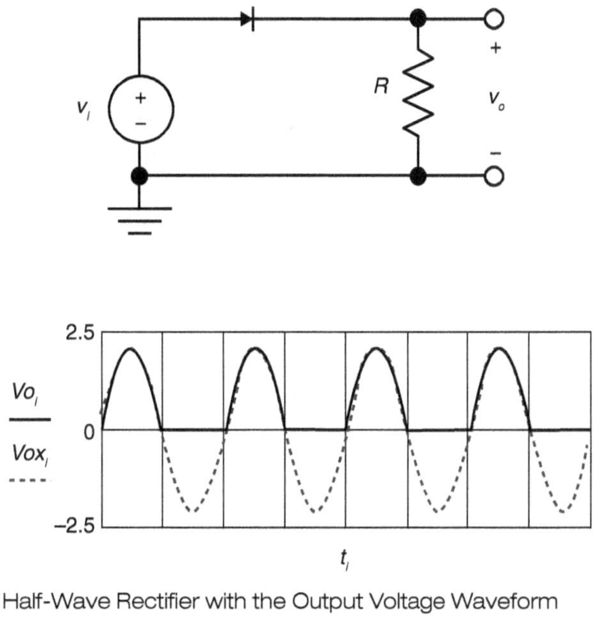

Figure 12.24 Half-Wave Rectifier with the Output Voltage Waveform

Figure 12.24 shows a half-wave rectifier circuit. The circuit is so named because it only allows current from the positive half cycle of the input to flow through the load resistor, R. This is identical to the clipping circuit with zero reference voltage.

If v_i is a sinusoidal voltage with peak voltage, V_m, and radian frequency, ω,

$$v_i(t) = V_m \sin \omega t$$

the average voltage V_{dc} across the load, R, is

$$V_{dc} = \frac{1}{T}\int_0^T v_o(t)dt$$

where T is the period of the sinusoid.

Since the diode is OFF in the interval $\frac{T}{2} \leq t \leq T$, output voltage is

$$v_o(t) = V_m \sin \omega\ t - V_\gamma, 0 \leq t < \frac{T}{2}$$

$$= 0, \frac{T}{2} \leq t \leq T.$$

V_{dc} is

$$V_{dc} = \frac{1}{T}\int_0^{\frac{T}{2}} \left(V_m \sin \omega\ t - V_\gamma\right)dt$$

$$= \frac{V_m}{\omega\ t}\left(-\cos \omega\ t\right)\Big|_0^{\frac{T}{2}} - \frac{V_\gamma}{T}(t)\Big|_0^{\frac{T}{2}}$$

$$= \frac{-V_m}{\omega\ t}\left(\cos \omega\ t - 1\right) - \frac{V_\gamma}{2}.$$

But $\omega = \frac{2\pi}{T}$, so the equation simplifies to

$$V_{dc} = \frac{V_m}{\pi} - \frac{V_\gamma}{2}. \quad \textbf{(12.54)}$$

Recall that the "effective" or root-mean-squared (rms) voltage quantifies the amount of energy delivered to a resistor in T seconds. The use of rms comes from the desire to compare the ability of a sinusoid to deliver energy to a resistor with the ability of a dc source.

The rms value of any periodic waveform vo(t) is defined as,

$$V_{rms} = \left[\frac{1}{T}\int_0^T v_o^2(t)dt\right]^{\frac{1}{2}}. \quad \textbf{(12.55)}$$

Diode Output Characteristics and Circuits

The output *rms* voltage for the half-wave rectifier with an output waveform defined by Equation (2.6.2-2) is

$$V_{rms} = \left[\frac{1}{T}\int_0^{\frac{T}{2}} \left(V_m \sin\omega t - V_\gamma\right)^2 dt\right]^{\frac{1}{2}} \tag{12.56}$$

$$= \left[\frac{1}{T}\int_0^{\frac{T}{2}} \left(V_m^{\,2} \sin^2\omega t - 2V_\gamma V_m \sin\omega t + V_\gamma^{\,2}\right) dt\right]^{\frac{1}{2}}$$

$$= \left[\frac{V_m^{\,2}}{4} - \frac{2V_\gamma V_m}{2\pi} + \frac{V_\gamma^{\,2}}{2}\right]^{\frac{1}{2}}.$$

If $V_\gamma << V_m$, then Equation (12.56) reduces to

$$V_{rms} = \left[\frac{1}{T}\int_0^{\frac{T}{2}} \left(V_m \sin\omega\ t\right)^2 dt\right]^{\frac{1}{2}} \tag{12.57}$$

$$= \frac{1}{\sqrt{2}}\frac{V_m}{\sqrt{2}} - \frac{V_m}{2}.$$

The efficiency of rectification is defined as

$$\eta = \frac{P_{dc}}{P_{ac}}, \tag{12.58}$$

where P_{ac} and P_{dc} are ac and dc powers, respectively. For the half-wave rectifier, the efficiency is

$$\eta = \frac{P_{dc}}{P_{ac}} = \frac{\frac{\left(V_m/\pi\right)^2}{R}}{\frac{\left(V_m/2\right)^2}{R}} = \frac{4}{\pi^2} \Rightarrow 40.6\% \tag{12.59}$$

The result of Equation (12.59) is for an ideal half-wave rectifier and represents the maximum efficiency attainable. In real systems, the efficiency will be lower due to power losses in the resistor and diode.

In order to produce a dc voltage from a half-wave rectifier, a large capacitor is placed in parallel to the load resistor. The capacitor must be large enough so that the RC time constant of the capacitor and load resistor is large compared to the period of the output waveform. This has the effect of "smoothing" the output waveform. Clearly, an efficient filter is required to eliminate any ripple in the output waveform.

In many rectifier applications, it is desirable to transformer couple the input voltage source to the rectifier circuit. This method is commonly used in the design of power supplies where there is a requirement to "step-down" the ac input voltage to a lower dc voltage. For example, a 15V peak half-wave rectified voltage can be

derived from a 120 VAC (household power is defined in *rms* volts) source through the use of a transformer. Transformers also provide isolation of the circuit from the household power line, providing protection from the possibility of shock from those lines.

The turns ratio N_p/N_s (primary winding over the secondary windings) determines the "step-down" ratio. For example, if the voltage input at the primary is 120 VAC (*rms*), which is approximately 170 V_{peak}, a transformer turns ratio of 11:1 (actually 11.3:1) is required to yield a 15V peak half-wave rectified signal. If the coefficient of coupling is nearly 1.0, implying no loss occurs in the transformer, the inductance ratio of the primary coil L_p and the secondary coil L_s is,

$$\frac{L_p}{L_s} = \left(\frac{N_p}{N_s}\right)^2. \tag{12.60}$$

Example 12.11

For the circuit in Exhibit 4, determine the inductance of the secondary coil for a transformer turns ratio of 11:1. What is the peak output voltage? Assume that the coefficient of coupling is $k = 1$ and that the diode threshold voltage V_γ of the 1N4148 is 0.76 V.

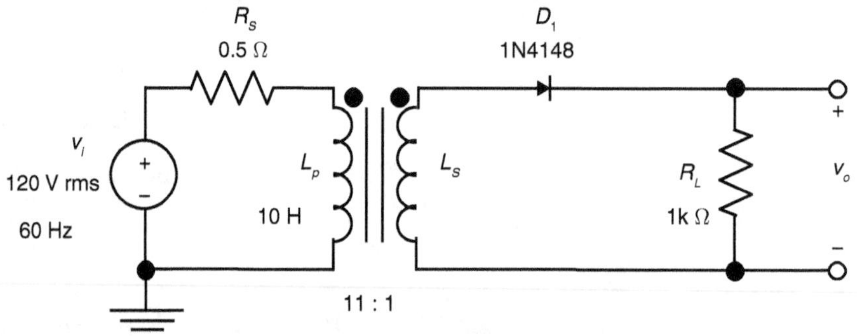

Exhibit 4 Transformer-Coupled Input to a Half-Wave Rectifier

Solution

Apply Equation (12.60) to find the secondary inductance:

$$L_s = \frac{L_p N_s^2}{N_p^2} = \frac{(10)(1^2)}{11^2} = 82.6mH.$$

The peak output voltage is,

$$v_o = \frac{(v_{i\ peak})}{N_p/N_s} - V_d = \frac{120\sqrt{2}}{11} - 0.76 = 14.64Vpeak.$$

If the transformer is assumed to have a coupling coefficient of nearly 1.0, then it may be replaced by one of the equivalent circuits of the ideal transformer shown in Figure 12.25.

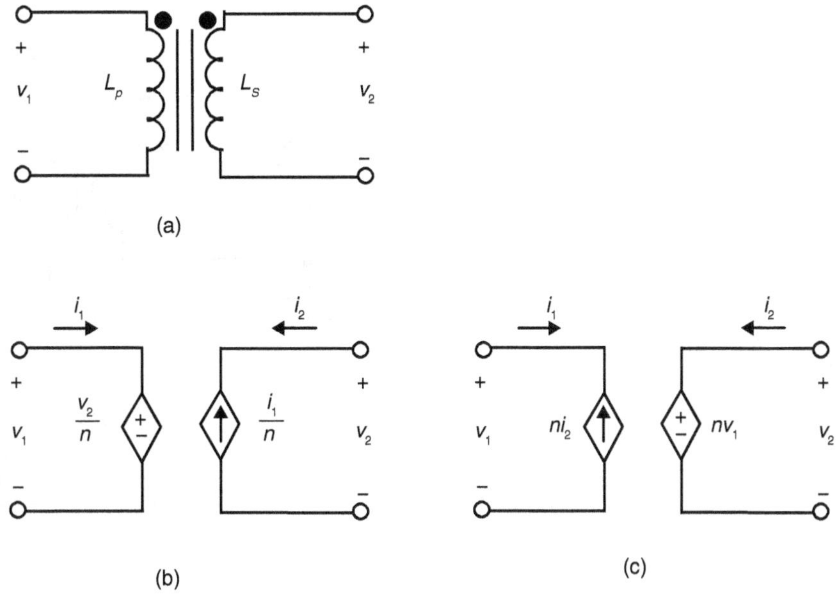

Figure 12.25 (a) Ideal Transformer; (b) and (c) Equivalent Circuits

Full-Wave Rectifiers

To remove the ripple from the output of a half-wave rectifier may require a very large capacitance. In many instances, the capacitor required to reduce the ripple on the half-wave rectified output voltage to the desired design specification may be prohibitively large.

A full-wave rectifier circuit can be used as a more efficient way to reduce ripple on the output voltage. A center-tapped input transformer-coupled full-wave rectifier is shown in Figure 12.26. Each half of the transformer with the associated diode acts as a half-wave rectifier. The diode D_1 conducts when the input $v_i > V_{D1}$ and D_2 conducts when the input $v_i < V_{D2}$. Note that the secondary winding is capable of providing twice the voltage drop across the load resistor. Additionally, the input to the diodes and the output share a common ground between the load resistor and the center-tap.

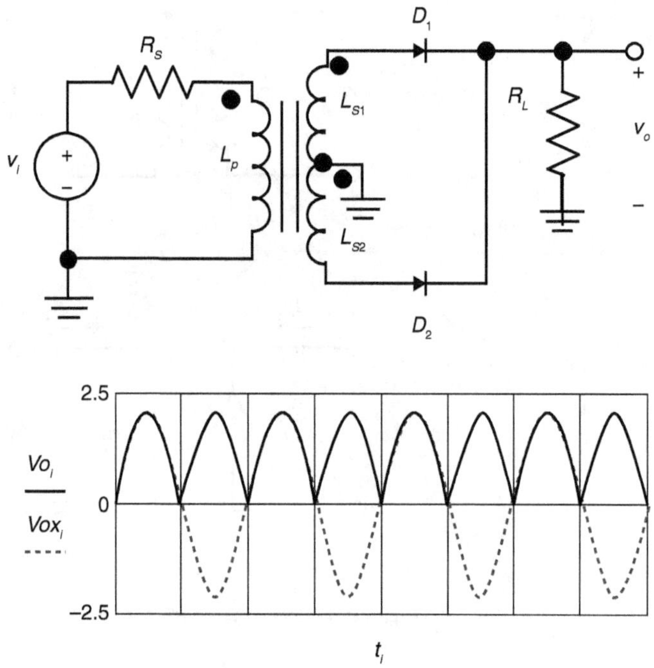

Figure 12.26 Full-Wave Rectifier with Center-Tapped Transformer

An isolation transformer is not required to design a full-wave rectifier. If ground isolation is not required, only a center-tapped, well-coupled coil is required as shown in Figure 12.27.

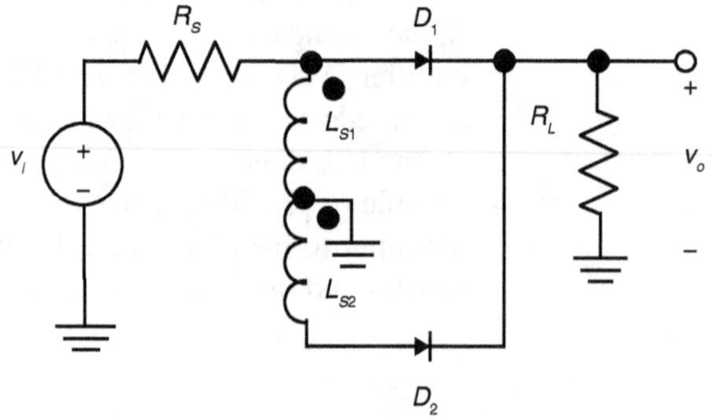

Figure 12.27 Full-Wave Rectifier Without an Isolation Transformer

An alternate configuration for a full-wave rectifier exists with an addition of two diodes. In the alternate configuration, called the *bridge rectifier* shown in Figure 12.28, the source and load do not share an essential common terminal. Additionally, the secondary transformer does not require a center tap and provides a voltage only slightly greater than half that of the secondary in Figure 12.26.

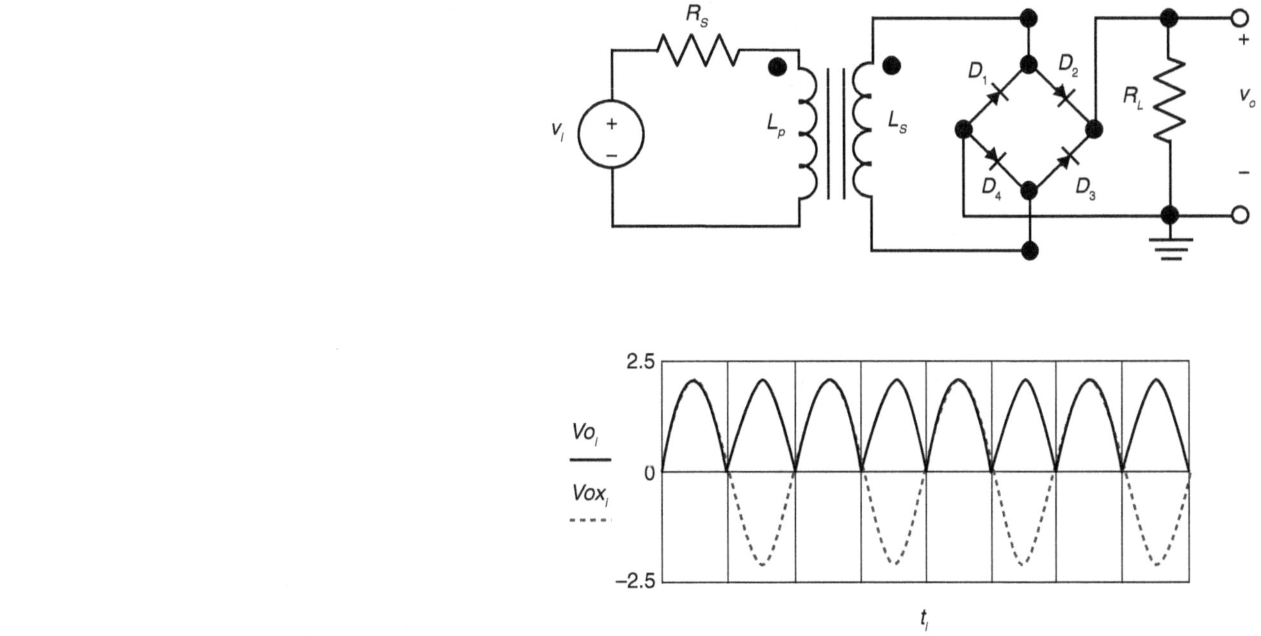

Figure 12.28 Bridge Rectifier with Input Transformer

In the bridge rectifier circuit, diodes D_2 and D_4 are ON for the positive half cycle of the voltage across the secondary of the transformer. Diodes D_3 and D_1 are OFF in the positive half cycle since their anode voltages are less than the cathode voltages. This is due to the voltage drop across the ON diodes and the load resistor. In the negative half cycle of the voltage across the secondary of the transformer, diodes D_3 and D_1 are ON, with D_2 and D_4 OFF. In both half cycles, the current through the load resistor is in the same direction. Therefore, each half cycle, the output voltage appears in the same polarity.

The output dc voltage of a full-wave rectifier circuit is twice that of the half-wave rectifier since its period is half that of the half-wave rectifier circuit,

$$\left[V_{dc}\right]_{full\text{-}wave} = \frac{1}{T}\int_0^T v_o(t)\,dt \qquad (12.61)$$

$$= 2\left[V_{dc}\right]_{half\text{-}wave}$$

$$= \frac{2V_m}{\pi}\ .$$

Similarly, the *rms* output voltage of a full-wave rectifier is found,

$$V_{rms} = \left[\frac{1}{T}\int_0^T v_o^2(t)\,dt\right]^{\frac{1}{2}} \qquad (12.62)$$

$$= \frac{V_m}{\sqrt{2}}\ .$$

The maximum possible efficiency of the full-wave rectifier is significantly greater than that of the half-wave rectifier since power from both positive and negative cycles are available to produce a dc voltage,

$$\eta_{full\text{-}wave} = \frac{P_{dc}}{P_{ac}} = \frac{\dfrac{\left(2V_m/\pi\right)^2}{R_L}}{\dfrac{\left(V_m/\sqrt{2}\right)^2}{R_L}} = \frac{8}{\pi^2} = 2\eta_{half\text{-}wave} \Rightarrow 81.2\% \qquad \textbf{(12.63)}$$

In order to produce a dc source from the output of a full-wave rectifier, a capacitor is placed in parallel to the load resistor as shown in Figure 12.29. The RC time constant must be long with respect to $\frac{T}{2}$ to "smooth out" the output waveform.

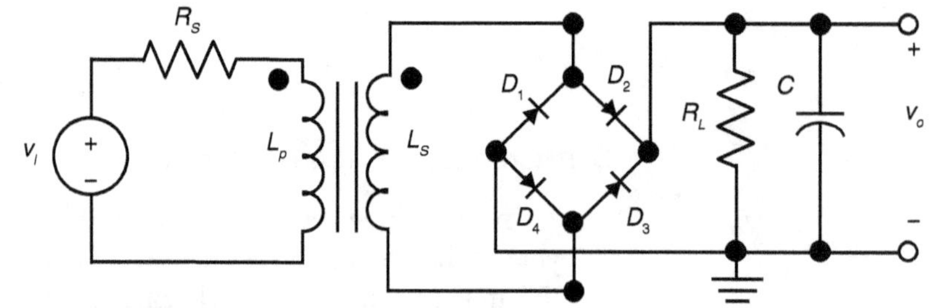

Figure 12.29 Filtered Full-Wave Rectifier Circuit

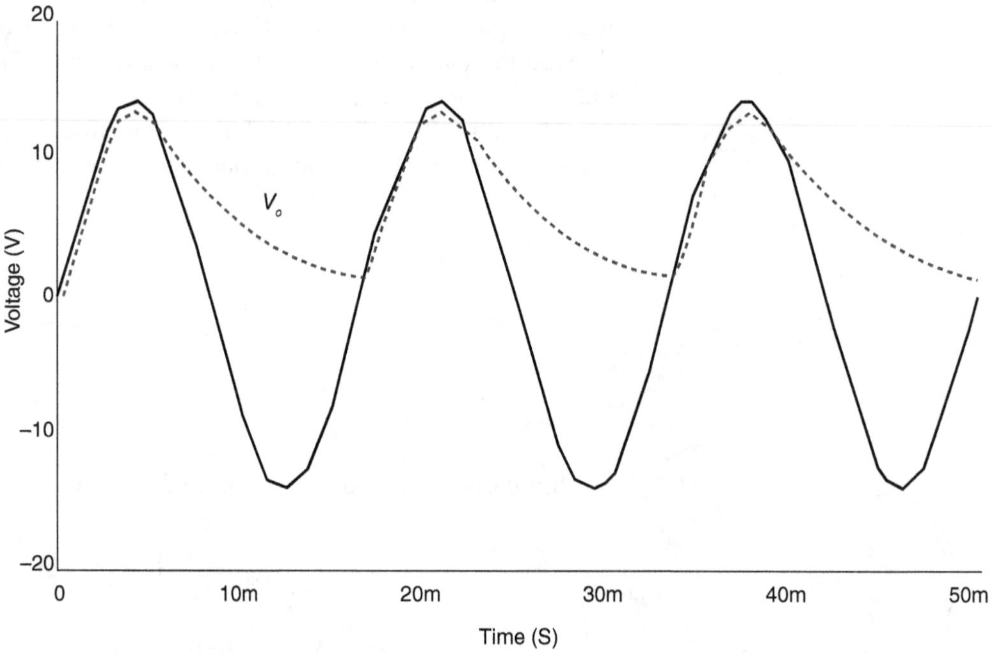

Figure 12.30 Full-Wave Rectified Voltage with Ripple

Let t_1 and t_2 be the time between two adjacent peaks of the filtered rectified voltage as shown in Figure 12.30 Then the output voltage between t_1 and t_2 is,

$$v_o = V_m e^{-(t-t_1)/R_L C}, t_1 \le t \le t_2. \qquad \textbf{(12.64)}$$

The peak-to-peak ripple is defined as,

$$v_r = v_o(t_1) - v_o(t_2) \qquad \textbf{(12.65)}$$

$$= V_m\left(1 - e^{-\left(t_2 - t_1\right)/R_L C}\right).$$

If $R_L C >> (t_2 - t_1)$, then the exponential approximation can be used,

$$e^{-x} \approx 1 - x, \quad \text{for } |x| << 1. \qquad \textbf{(12.66)}$$

A good approximation for the peak-to-peak ripple voltage can be derived,

$$v_r(\textit{peak-to-peak}) \approx V_m \frac{t_2 - t_1}{R_L C}. \qquad \textbf{(12.67)}$$

Since $t_2 - t_1 \approx \frac{T}{2} = \frac{1}{2f_0}$, where f_o is the frequency of the input signal and T is the period of that signal, the peak-to-peak ripple voltage for a full-wave rectifier circuit is

$$v_r(\textit{peak-to-peak})_{\textit{full-wave}} \approx \frac{V_m}{2f_o R_L C}. \qquad \textbf{(12.68)}$$

The dc component of the output signal is

$$V_{O,dc} = V_{dc} = V_m - \frac{1}{2}v_r \qquad \textbf{(12.69)}$$

$$= V_m\left(1 - \frac{1}{4f_o R_L C}\right).$$

For a half-wave rectifier, $t_2 - t_1 \approx T = \frac{1}{f_0}$, since only half the cycle of the input signal is passed. Therefore, the peak-to-peak ripple voltage of a half-wave rectifier is

$$v_r(\textit{peak-to-peak})_{\textit{half-wave}} \approx \frac{V_m}{f_o R_L C}. \qquad \textbf{(12.70)}$$

In both the half- and full-wave rectifiers, the dc voltage is less than the peak rectified voltage.

Example 12.12

Consider the full-wave rectifier circuit of Figure 12.29 with $C = 47\mu F$ and transformer winding ratio of 14:1. If the input voltage is 120 VAC (rms) at 60 Hz, what is the load resistor value for a peak-to-peak ripple less than 0.5 V? What is the output dc voltage?

Solution

Since the transformer turns ratio is 14:1, the voltage across the secondary is,

$$V_m = \frac{120\sqrt{2}}{14} = 12.1V$$

From Equation (2.6.3-8) for peak-to-peak ripple,

$$R \le \frac{V_m}{2 f_o C v_r} = \frac{12.1}{2(60)(47\times10^{-6})(0.5)}$$

$$\le 4.29 k\Omega .$$

The dc voltage at the output is found as

$$V_{dc} \le V_m - \frac{1}{2} v_r$$

$$\le 12.1 - \frac{1}{2}(0.5)$$

$$\le 11.9\,V.$$

Peak Detector

One of the first applications of the diode was a "detector" in radio receivers that retrieved information from "amplitude modulated" (AM) radio signals. The AM signal consists of a radio-frequency "carrier" wave, which is at a high frequency and varies in amplitude at an audible frequency. The detector circuit, shown in Figure 12.31, is similar to a half-wave rectifier. The RC time constant is approximately the same as the period of the carrier so that the output voltage can follow the variation in amplitude of the input.

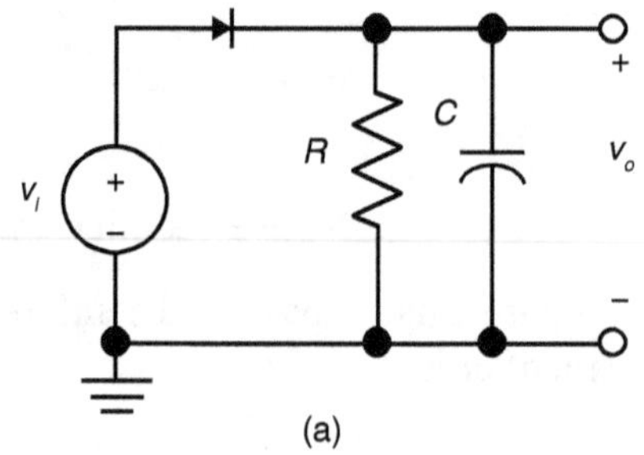

(a)

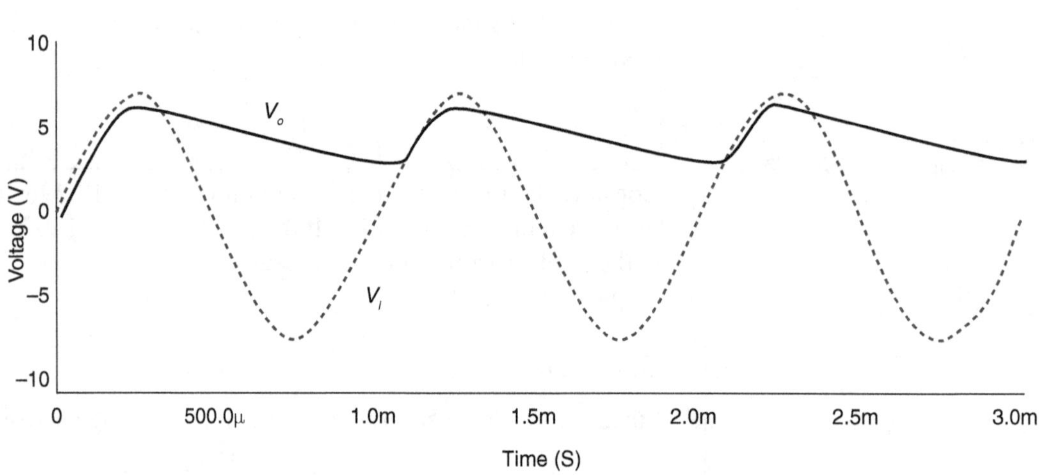

Figure 12.31 Peak Detector and Associated Waveforms

Diode Logic Gates

Diodes together with resistors can be used to perform logic functions. Figure 12.32 shows diode AND and OR gates.

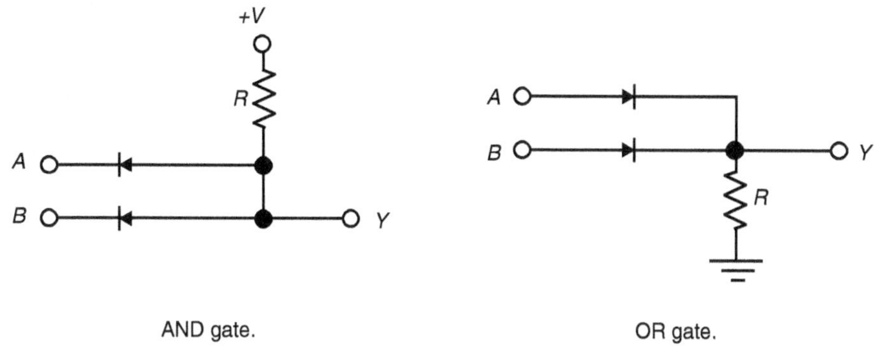

Figure 12.32 Diode Logic AND and OR Gates

In the AND gate, when either input is connected to ground, the diode in series with that input is forward biased. The output is then equal to one forward biased diode voltage drop above ground, which is interpreted as logic "0". When both inputs are connected to $+V$, both diodes are zero biased, yielding an output voltage of $+V$, which is interpreted as logic "1". The Boolean notation for the circuit is,

$$Y = A \bullet B.$$

In the OR gate, if one or both of the diodes is connected to $+V$, that (those) diode(s) will conduct, clamping the output voltage to a value equal to $+V - V_\gamma$, or logic "1". Therefore, the Boolean notation for the circuit is,

$$Y = A + B.$$

The Superdiode

Figure 12.33 shows a precision half-wave rectifier using a "Superdiode." The Superdiode consists of an OpAmp and diode. The operation of the circuit is as follows: For positive v_i, the output of the OpAmp is will go positive causing the diode to conduct. This in turn closes the negative feedback path creating an OpAmp voltage follower. Therefore,

$$v_o = v_i, \quad v_i \geq 0. \qquad \textbf{(12.71)}$$

The slope of the voltage follower transfer function is unity.

For $v_i < 0$, the output voltage of the OpAmp follows the input and goes negative. The diode will not conduct since it is reverse biased. Therefore, no current flows through the resistor R, and

$$v_o = 0, \quad v_i < 0. \qquad \textbf{(12.72)}$$

The advantage of the Superdiode is the very small turn-on voltage exhibited and ideal transfer function for positive v_i.

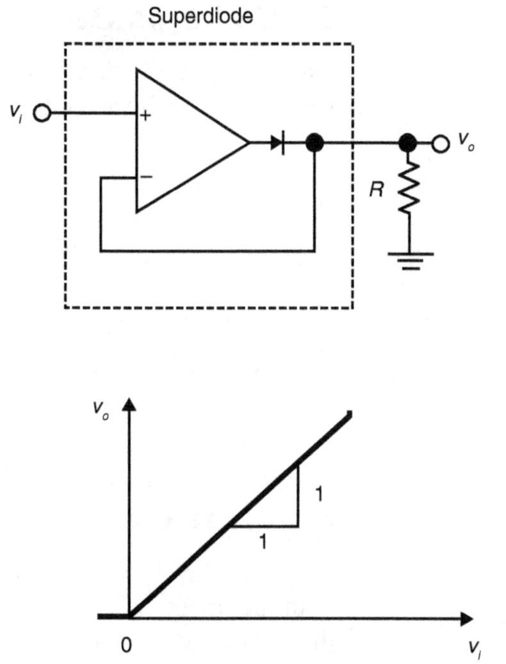

Figure 12.33 Precision Rectifier Using a Superdiode

Precision circuits (clamper, peak detector, etc.) can be designed using the Superdiode in place of regular diodes to eliminate dynamic resistance and diode threshold voltage effects. The Superdiode is commonly used in small-signal applications and is not used in power circuits.

Other Common Diodes and Applications

In the previous sections of this chapter, the conventional *p-n* junction diode and the Zener diode and their applications were introduced. Although the conventional *p-n* junction diode and the Zener diode are the most common diode types used in electronic design, other types of diodes are designed into certain electronic applications. Some of the different types of diode include the tunnel diode, backward diode, Schottky barrier diode, Varactor Diode, p-i-n diode, IMPATT diode, TRAPATT diode, BARRITT diode, solar cell, photodiode, light-emitting diode, and semiconductor laser diode.

Unfortunately, it is far beyond the scope of this book to discuss all of the different types listed above. However, four common types of diodes from the above list are presented in this section for discussion. They include the following:

- Tunnel diode
- Schottky barrier diode
- Photodiode
- Light-emitting diode

Tunnel Diode

The tunnel diode (also called the Esaki diode after the L. Esaki who announced the new diode in 1958) voltage-current characteristic is shown in Figure 12.34. The figure shows that the tunnel diode is an excellent conductor in the reverse direction. Figure 12.35 is the circuit symbol for the tunnel diode.

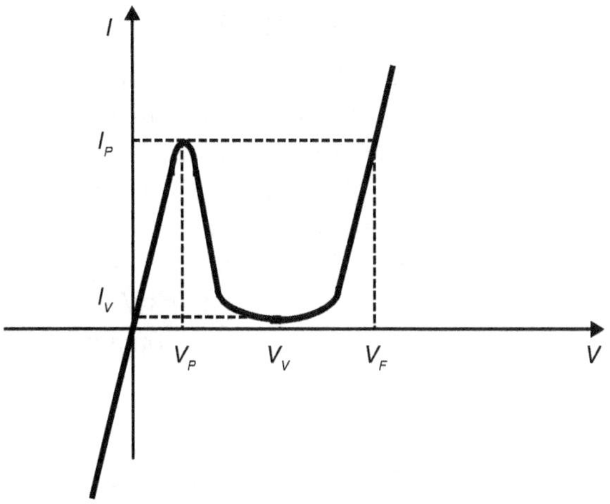

Figure 12.34 Voltage-current Characteristic of a Tunnel Diode

Figure 12.35 Tunnel Diode Symbol

For small forward voltages (in the order of 50 mV in Ge), the resistance is in the order of 5 Ω. At the peak current I_P corresponding to the voltage V_P, the slope of the characteristic curve is zero. As the voltage increases beyond V_P, the current also decreases. The tunnel diode characteristic curve in this region exhibits a *negative dynamic resistance* between the peak current I_P and the minimum or valley current I_P. At the valley voltage V_V corresponding to the valley current I_V, the slope of the characteristic curve is again zero. Beyond V_V, the curve remains positive. At the peak forward voltage, V_F, the current again reaches the value of I_P.

Since it is difficult to manufacture silicon tunnel diodes with a high ratio of peak-to-valley current I_P / I_V, most commercially available tunnel diodes are made from germanium (Ge) or gallium arsenide (GaAs). Table 12.4 summarizes some of the static characteristics of these devices.

Table 12.4 Typical Tunnel Diode Parameters

Parameters	Ge	GaAs	Si
$\frac{I_P}{I_V}$	8	15	3.5
V_P, in Volts	0.055	0.15	0.065
V_V, in Volts	0.35	0.5	0.42
V_F, in Volts	0.5	1.1	0.7

The operating characteristics of the tunnel diode are highly dependent on the load line of the circuit in which the diode is operating. Some load lines may intersect the tunnel diode characteristic curve in three places: the region between 0 and V_P, between V_P and V_V, and beyond V_V. This multivalued feature makes the tunnel diode useful in high speed pulse circuit design. High frequency (microwave) oscillators are often designed so that the tunnel diode is biased in its negative dynamic resistance region.

Schottky Barrier Diode

The Schottky barrier diode (or simply Schottky diode) is a metal-semiconductor diode. The circuit symbol of the Schottky diode is shown in Figure 12.36. Metal-semiconductor diodes are formed by bonding a metal (usually aluminum or platinum) to *n*- or *p*-type silicon. Metal-semiconductor diode voltage-current characteristics are very similar to conventional *p-n* junction diodes and can be described by the diode equation with the exception that the threshold voltage V_γ is in the range from 0.3 V to 0.6 V. The physical mechanisms of operation of the conventional *p-n* junction diode and the metal-semiconductor diode are not the same.

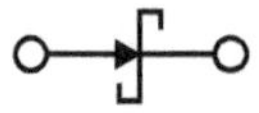

Figure 12.36 Schottky Diode Symbol

The primary difference between metal-semiconductor and *p-n* junction diodes is in the charge storage mechanism. In the Schottky diode, the current through the diode is the result of the drift of majority carriers. The Schottky diode switching time from forward to reverse bias is very short compared to the *p-n* junction diode.

Therefore, Schottky diodes are often used in integrated circuits for high speed switching applications. The Schottky diode is easy to fabricate on integrated circuits because of its construction. The low noise characteristics of the Schottky diode is ideal for the detection of low-level signals like those encountered in radio frequency electronics and radar detection applications.

Zener Diodes and Applications

Diodes that are designed with adequate power dissipation capabilities to operate in breakdown are called Zener diodes and are commonly used as voltage reference or constant voltage devices.

The two mechanisms responsible for the breakdown characteristics of a diode are avalanche breakdown and Zener breakdown. Avalanche breakdown occurs at high voltages (≥10 V) where the charge carriers acquire enough energy to create secondary hole-electron pairs, which act as secondary carriers. This chain reaction causes an avalanche breakdown of the diode junction and a rapid increase in current at the breakdown voltage. Zener breakdown occurs in the heavily doped *p*- and *n*-regions on both sides of the diode junction and occurs when the externally applied potential is large enough to create a large electric field across the junction to force bound electrons from the *p*-type material to *tunnel* across to the *n*-type region. A sudden increase in current is observed when sufficient external potential is applied to produce the required ionization energy for tunneling.

Regardless of the mechanism for breakdown, the breakdown diodes are usually called Zener diodes. The symbol and characteristic curve of a low voltage (referring to the breakdown voltage) Zener diode are shown in Figure 12.37. The forward bias characteristic is similar to conventional *p-n* junction diodes. The reverse bias region depicts the breakdown occurring at V_Z, which is nearly independent of diode current. A wide range of Zener diodes are commercially available over a wide range of breakdown voltages and power ratings to 100W.

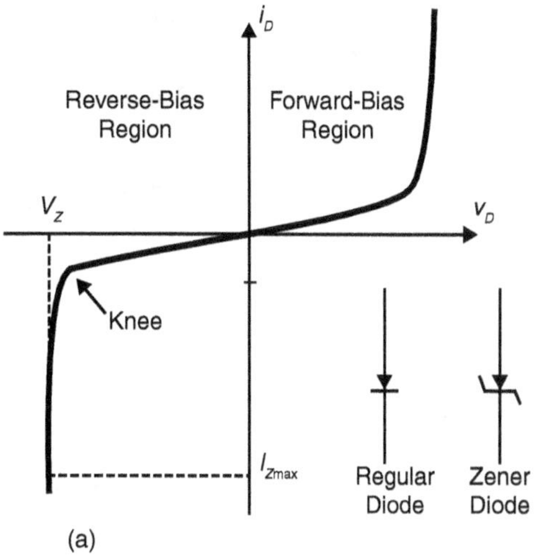

Figure 12.37 (a) Characteristic Curve of a Zener Diode, (b) Zener Diode Symbol

Changes in temperature generally cause a shift in the breakdown voltage. The temperature coefficient is approximately +2 mV/°C for Zener breakdown. For avalanche breakdown, the temperature coefficient is negative.

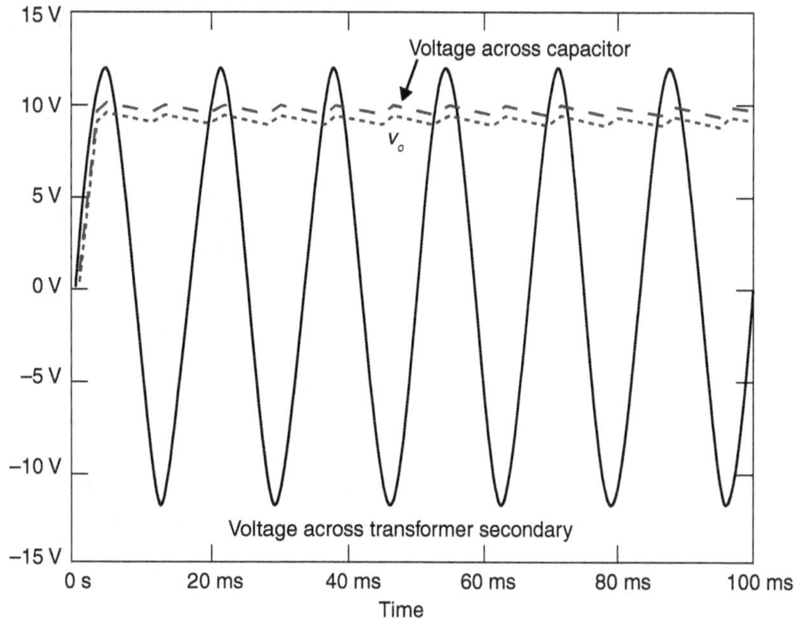

Figure 12.38 Reverse Breakdown "Knee" Voltage B_v and the Corresponding Current I_{bv}

Both B_v and I_{bv} are positive quantities. If I_{bv} is large, the reverse breakdown curve is steeper.

The dynamic resistance of the Zener diode in the reverse breakdown region, r_Z, is the slope of the diode curve at the operating reverse bias current. Since the

reverse current increases rapidly with small changes in the diode voltage drop, r_Z is small (typically 1 to 15 Ω). The Zener diode piecewise linear model and its simplified version are shown in Figure 12.39.

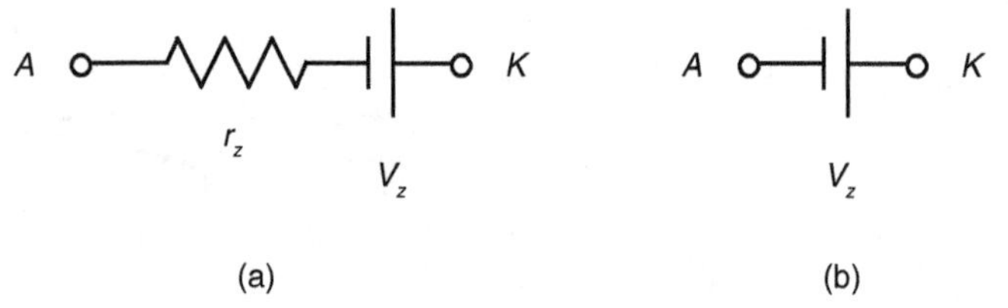

Figure 12.39 (a) Zener Diode Piecewise Linear Model, (b) Simplified Zener Diode Model

A typical application of Zener diodes is in the design of the voltage reference circuit shown in Figure 12.40.

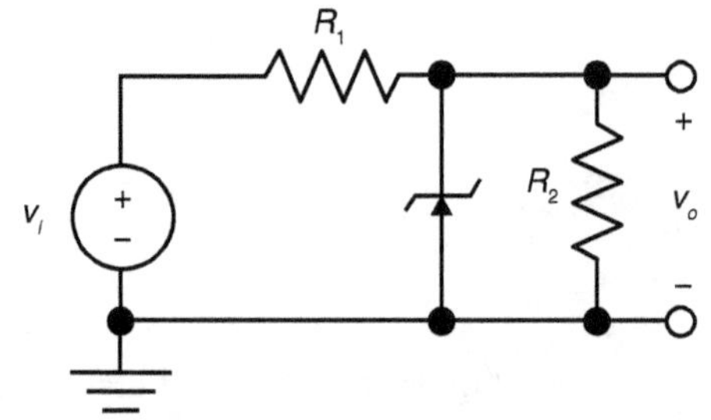

Figure 12.40 Zener Diode Voltage Reference Circuit

To simplify the analysis, first consider the circuit without the Zener diode. The output voltage is simply that of a voltage divider,

$$v_{O,\,no\ diode} = \frac{R_2}{R_1 + R_2} v_I \tag{12.73}$$

where the input voltage v_I and output voltage v_O have both ac and dc components. Replace the Zener diode in the circuit. If the breakdown voltage V_Z is greater than $v_{O,\,no\ diode}$, then the Zener diode is operating in the reverse-bias region between the Zener knee and 0 V or in the forward-bias region. Therefore, the Zener diode operates as a conventional diode and,

$$v_O = \begin{cases} -V_\gamma, v_I \leq \dfrac{R_1 + R_2}{R_2}\left(-V_\gamma\right) \\ v_{O,\,no\,diode}, v_I > \dfrac{R_1 + R_2}{R_2}\left(-V_\gamma\right) \end{cases}. \tag{12.74}$$

If the breakdown voltage V_Z is less than $v_{O,\,no\,diode}$, then the Zener diode operates in the breakdown region beyond V_Z and forces

$$v_O = V_Z, \text{when } v_I \geq \frac{R_1 + R_2}{R_2}\left(V_Z\right). \tag{12.75}$$

Figure 12.41 shows the input, output, and transfer characteristics of a Zener voltage reference circuit.

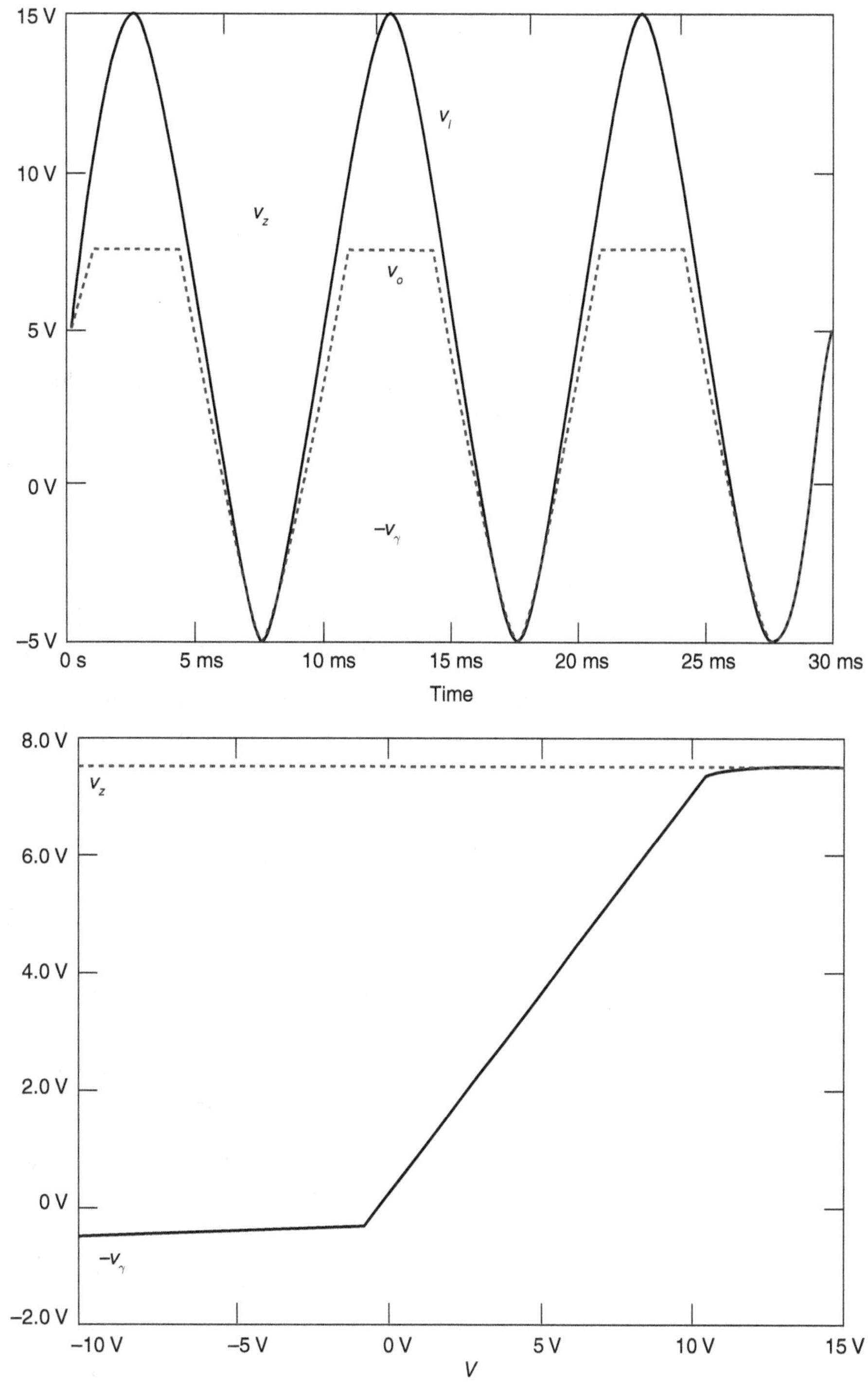

Figure 12.41 (a) Input and Output Waveforms, (b) Transfer Characteristic of the Zener Voltage Reference

The Zener voltage reference circuit clamps the output voltage to the Zener breakdown voltage. The current through the Zener diode forces the voltage drop across resistor R_1 to $v_O - v_I$ since V_Z is invariant over a wide range of currents I_Z and the dynamic resistance in the breakdown region is negligible compared to R_2. R_1 must be chosen to limit I_Z to safe operating values as specified by the diode manufacturer.

Example 12.13

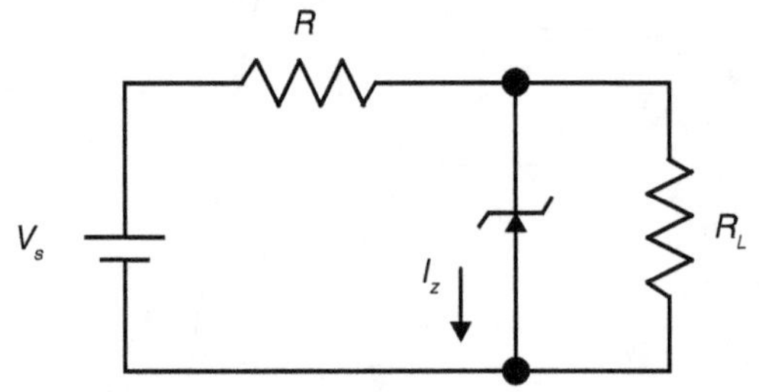

Exhibit 5

The Zener diode in the circuit shown has a working range of current for proper regulation:

$$5 \text{ mA} \leq I_z \leq 50 \text{ mA}$$

and a Zener voltage

$$V_z = 50 \text{ V}.$$

a). If the input voltage, V_s, varies from 150 and 250 V and $R_L = 2.2 \text{ k}\Omega$, determine the range of values for the resistor, R, to maintain regulation.

b). If R is chosen as the midpoint of the range determined in part a)., how much variation in the load resistance, R_L, is now possible without losing regulation?

Solution

a). The current through the load is given by:

$$I_L = \frac{50\text{V}}{2.2\text{k}\Omega} = 22.74\text{mA}.$$

The current through the resistor R must lie in the range of the load current plus the diode current:

$$5 \text{ mA} + 22.74 \text{ mA} \leq I \leq 50 \text{ mA} + 22.74 \text{ mA}$$
$$27.74 \text{ mA} \leq I \leq 74.74 \text{ mA}$$

but this current is also dependent on the source voltage, the Zener voltage, and the resistance R:

$$I = \frac{V_S - V_Z}{R} = \frac{V_S - 50}{R}$$

or

$$R = \frac{V_S - 50}{I}.$$

Since regulation must occur for both extremes of the source voltage, R must be the intersection of the limits determined by the previous equation:

$$\frac{V_{s(\min)} - 50}{I_{(\max)}} \leq R \leq \frac{V_{s(\min)} - 50}{I_{(\min)}} \quad \& \quad \frac{V_{s(\max)} - 50}{I_{(\max)}} \leq R \leq \frac{V_{s(\max)} - 50}{I_{(\min)}}$$

or, after applying the intersection of the ranges:

$$\frac{V_{s(\max)} - 50}{I_{(\max)}} \le R \le \frac{V_{s(\min)} - 50}{I_{(\min)}}$$

$$\frac{250 - 50}{72.74} \le R \le \frac{150 - 50}{27.74} \Rightarrow 2.75\,k \le R \le 3.60\,k.$$

b). The midpoint of the above range is $R = 3.175$ kΩ.

The resistor current is given by:

$$I = \frac{V_s - 50}{R} \quad \Rightarrow \quad 31.5 \text{ mA } \le I \le 63 \text{ mA}.$$

Since regulation must hold for all values of R, the load current must lie in the intersection of the possible ranges of the resistor current minus the diode current:

$$31.5 - 50 \text{ mA} \le I_L \le 31.5 - 5 \text{ mA} \quad \text{and} \quad 63 - 50 \text{ mA} \le I_L \le 63 - 5 \text{ mA}$$

thus,

$$13 \text{ mA} \le I_L \le 26.5 \text{ mA}.$$

Since

$$R_L = \frac{V_Z}{I_L}$$

the range of R_L is found to be

$$3.85 \text{ k}\Omega \ge R_L \ge 1.93 \text{ k}\Omega.$$

Another typical application of Zener diodes occurs in ac-dc conversion. Recall that the output of a filtered rectifier has residual voltage ripple. By adding a Zener diode voltage reference circuit at the output of a rectifier and filter circuit, as shown in Figure 12.42, the residual voltage ripple at the output can be eliminated. The resistors R_1 and R_L must be carefully selected to yield the desired voltage output. If R_1 is chosen to be much less than R_L, and if the voltage across the capacitor is greater than V_Z, then the output voltage will be clamped at V_Z.

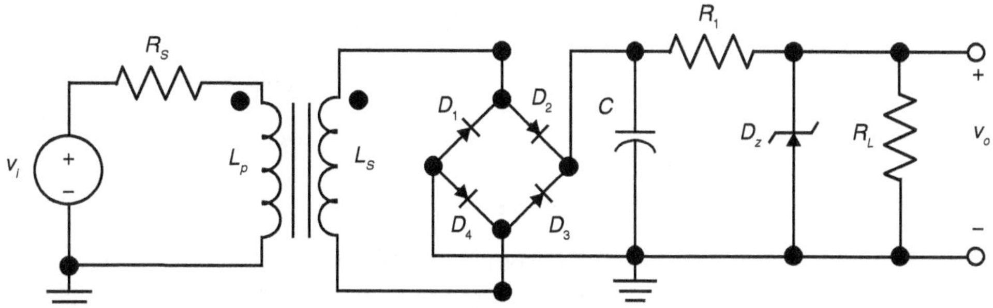

Figure 12.42 Full-Wave Rectifier Circuit with Output Voltage Reference

Example 12.14

Consider the full-wave rectifier circuit with a Zener clamp shown in Exhibit 6. If the input voltage is 120 VAC (*rms*) at 60 Hz, transformer winding ratio is 14:1, $C = 47\ \mu F$, $R_L = 3.8\ k\Omega$, $R_1 = 220\ \Omega$, show that the output is clamped to 5 V if a Zener diode with $V_Z = 5$ V is used.

Solution:

This is the same problem as in the previous example. The resistance for the circuit without R_1 and the Zener diode was found to be less than 4.29 kΩ. The dc output voltage was determined to be less than or equal to 11.9 V. Since $V_Z < 11.9$ V, the resulting output voltage is clamped to 5 V.

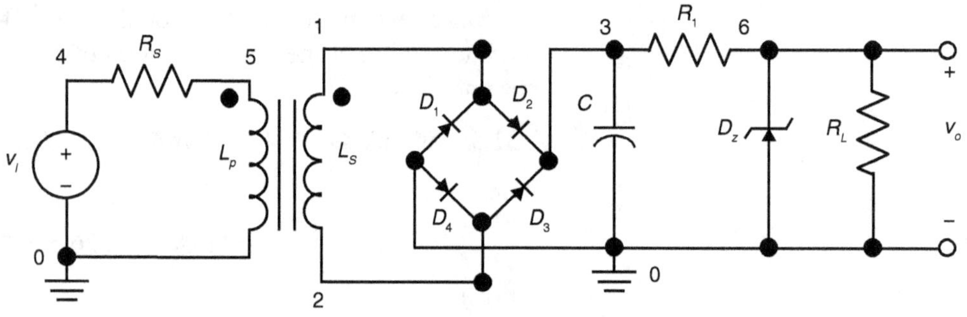

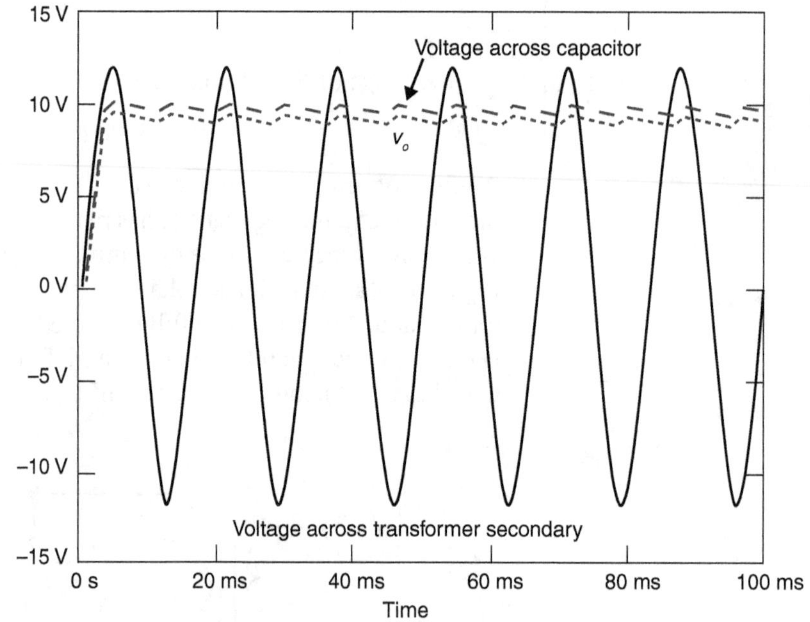

Exhibit 6

A design trade-off exists between using a large capacitor filter to remove the output voltage ripple or a smaller capacitor and a Zener diode clamp. Large capacitors have require large "real-estate" or space on a printed circuit board and height above the circuit board. However, capacitor filters only dissipate energy when in the charging or discharging cycles.

Although the Zener diode is small in size and requires substantially less circuit volume than large capacitors, the diode must be able to dissipate from zero to the maximum current delivered to the load. If the Zener diode is to carry large cur-

rents over much of the operating cycle, the power dissipation is high and a large capacitor filter may be preferred. The Zener diode may be preferred if the power dissipation in the diode can be limited.

FIELD-EFFECT TRANSISTORS

Junction Field-Effect Transistors

Junction field-effect transistors (JFETs) are either *n*-channel or *p*-channel devices. The terminal voltage and current relationships of *n*-channel JFETs are developed in this section. The *p*-channel JFET terminal voltage and current relationships are identical to that of the *n*-channel JFET with the exception that the polarities of the voltages and currents are reversed. A brief description of the *p*-channel JFET characteristics will be presented at the end of this section.

The circuit symbol for the *n*-channel JFET is shown in Figure 12.43a. The terminal connection to the gate has an arrow whose direction indicates the channel type of device depicted. For *n*-channel JFETs the arrow points to the source on the gate terminal. For *p*-channel JFETs, the arrow points away from the source as shown in Figure 12.43b.

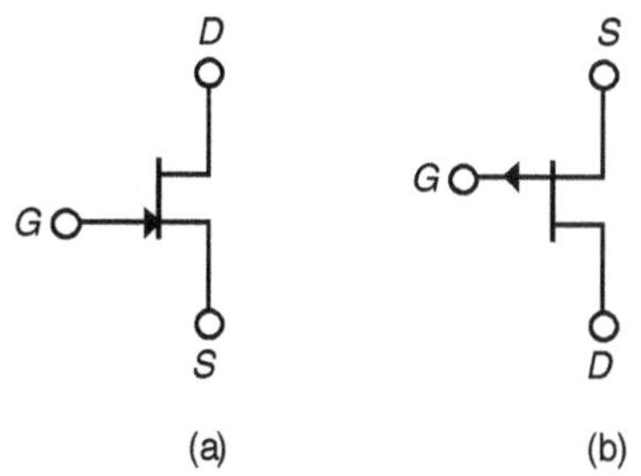

Figure 12.43 Circuit Symbol for (a) *n*-channel JFET and (b) *p*-channel JFET

All FETs are three-terminal devices with the gate acting as the current regulating terminal between the drain and the source. The voltage and current sign conventions for *n*-channel JFETs are shown in Figure 12.44.

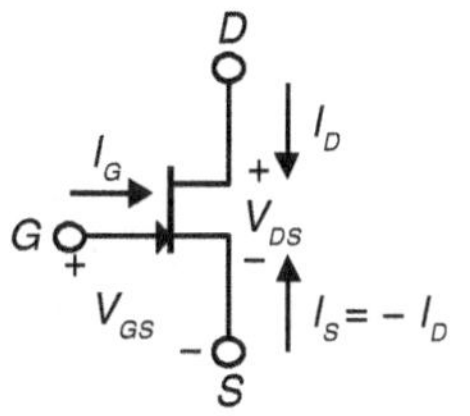

Figure 12.44 Voltage and Current Directions for the *n*-channel JFET

When the gate-source junction is reverse-biased in *n*-channel JFETs, the conductivity of the drain-source channel is reduced with decreasing gate to source voltage, V_{GS}. The current through the drain-source channel is I_D. The source current is equal to $-I_D$

$$I_S = -I_D. \tag{12.76}$$

n-channel JFET

Since JFETs normally operate with the gate junction reverse-biased, the gate current is essentially zero

$$I_G = 0 \tag{12.77}$$

The gate-to-source voltage that "pinches off" the drain-source channel is called the pinch-off voltage, V_{PO},

$$V_{PO} = V_{GS}\Big|_{I_D=0,\, V_{DS}\ small} \tag{12.78}$$

For *n*-channel devices, V_{PO} is a negative voltage and is specific to the particular FET. If V_{GS} is positive (for *n*-channel JFETs), the gate junction is forward biased and the equations developed in this section do not apply.

The drain (common source) *n*-channel JFET characteristics are shown in Figure 12.45. The transfer characteristic is presented in Figure 12.46. The current and voltage reference directions were shown in Figure 12.44.

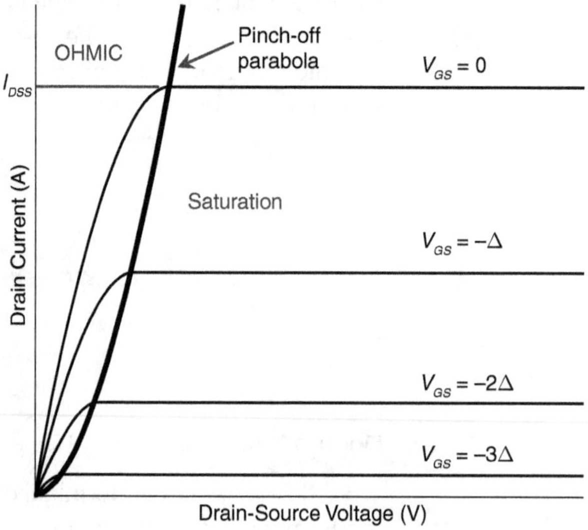

Figure 12.45 Output Characteristics of *n*-channel JFET

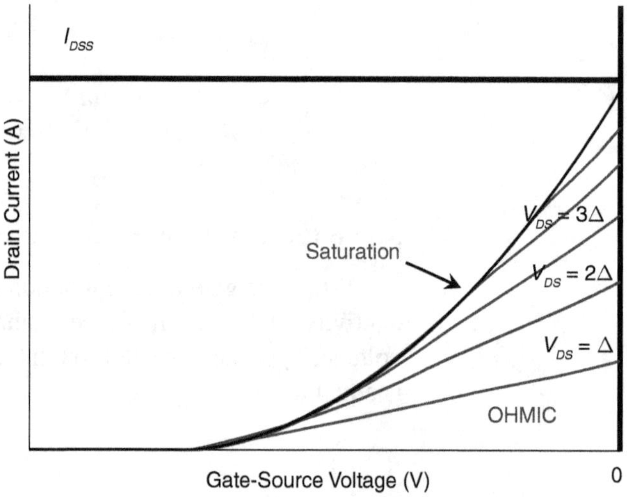

Figure 12.46 Transfer Characteristic *n*-channel JFET

The different regions of operation of the *n*-channel JFET can be illustrated by selecting one curve from the output characteristics (for example, the curve cor-

responding to $V_{GS} = 0$). For small values of V_{DS}, the channel allows current to readily flow with an initial resistance, R_{DS}. The output curve in this region can be approximated by a straight line of slope $R_{DS} - 1$. This approximate linear relationship of I_D versus V_{DS} leads to the descriptive name for this region of operation, the *Ohmic Region*. In the ohmic region, the JFET acts as a voltage variable resistor; the gate-source voltage, V_{GS}, controls the value of the equivalent resistance. As V_{GS} increases, the channel narrows, causing an increase in resistance. The result is a decrease in the slope of the characteristic curve.

With increasing V_{DS}, when V_{GS} is held constant, the channel resistance increases as evidenced by the leveling of I_D. At pinch-off, the drain current, I_D, remains almost constant due to low conductivity through the channel. The resistance of the device in this region is very high. The drain-to-source voltage at pinch-off is

$$V_{DS}\ (\text{at pinch-off}) = V_{GS} - V_{PO}. \qquad \textbf{(12.79)}$$

The boundary between the *Ohmic* and *Saturation* region is the so-called pinch-off parabola (refer to Figure 12.45) defined by the relationship in Equation (12.79). The JFET is said to be in Saturation when

$$V_{DS} > V_{GS} - V_{PO}. \qquad \textbf{(12.80)}$$

Saturation in FETs differs from saturation in BJTs. FETs operating in the saturation region are analogous to BJTs in the forward-active region. As can be seen in the FET output characteristic of Figure 12.45, operation in saturation allows the drain current to be adjusted by a varying a control voltage at the gate, in this case V_{GS}, independent of V_{DS}. Amplifiers designed using JFETs takes advantage of the small voltage variations in V_{GS} controlling the current flow through the device. JFETs can also be used as switches since large and abrupt changes in V_{GS} causes the current I_D to change from zero to a relatively large value.

The JFET does not require significant input gate current. Therefore, the input characteristic of the device provides limited and nearly useless information for circuit design. The transfer characteristic shown in Figure 12.46 is far more useful. Since the gate channel diode in JFETs must be reverse biased, only negative values of *VGS* allow for operation in the ohmic and saturation regions.

From the transfer function, the current at $V_{GS} = 0$ is defined as I_{DSS}. I_{DSS} is the drain current at $V_{GS} = 0$ at pinch-off ($V_{DS} = V_{PO}$). I_{DSS} is temperature dependent and decreases with increasing temperature.

The voltage and current relationships of *n*-channel JFETs can be described for the three most common regions of operation: Ohmic, Saturation, and Cut-Off. For *n*-channel JFETs operating in the ohmic or saturation regions, the following voltage and current conditions must hold:

$$I_D > 0 \qquad V_{PO} < V_{GS} \leq 0 \qquad V_{DS} > 0.$$

The *n*-channel JFETs have the following characteristic parameters:

$$V_{PO} < 0 \qquad I_{DSS} > 0.$$

In the negative quadrant, where $I_D < 0$ and $V_{DS} < 0$, the drain-gate junction becomes forward biased causing the drain current to increase rapidly. The characteristics in this region are similar to diode characteristics (except that $I_D < 0$ and $V_{DS} < 0$) with the turn-on voltage determined by V_{GS}.

Ohmic Region

The ohmic region is that portion of the curve between $V_{DS} = 0$ and pinch-off on the output characteristic curve in Figure 12.45. The mathematical expression defining this region is

$$0 < V_{DS} \leq V_{GS} - V. \tag{12.81}$$

The *V-I* relationship in this region is,

$$I_D = I_{DSS}\left[2\left(\frac{V_{GS}}{V_{PO}} - 1\right)\frac{V_{DS}}{V_{PO}} - \left(\frac{V_{DS}}{V_{PO}}\right)^2\right] \tag{12.82}$$

For small values of V_{DS}, the drain current in Equation (12.82) is approximately,

$$I_D \approx 2I_{DSS}\left(\frac{V_{GS}}{V_{PO}} - 1\right)\frac{V_{DS}}{V_{PO}} \tag{12.83}$$

If V_{GS} is held constant, Equation (12.83) is a linearly varying function of I_D and V_{DS}.

Therefore the output resistance in this region is found by taking the derivative of Equation (12.83) with respect to V_{DS}:

$$R_{DS}^{-1} = \frac{\partial I_D}{\partial V_{DS}} = \frac{2I_{DSS}}{V_{PO}}\left(\frac{V_{GS}}{V_{PO}} - 1\right) \tag{12.84}$$

Saturation Region

The saturation region occupies the portion of the output characteristic curve of Figure 12.45 where $I_D > 0$ and to the right of the pinch-off parabola. That is,

$$V_{DS} \geq V_{GS} - V_{PO}. \tag{12.85}$$

The drain current is virtually independent of V_{DS} in this region,

$$I_D = I_{DSS}\left(1 - \frac{V_{GS}}{V_{PO}}\right)^2 \tag{12.86}$$

Equation (12.86) is called the transfer characteristic and is shown in Figure 12.46. The values of V_{PO} and I_{DSS} are specified by the manufacturers.

The expression for the pinch-off parabola can be derived from Equation (12.86) by substituting $V_{GS} = V_{DS} + V_{PO}$,

$$I_D = I_{DSS}\left(\frac{V_{DS}}{V_{PO}}\right)^2 \tag{12.87}$$

Cut-Off Region

The JFET is said to be in the cut-off region when,

$$V_{GS} < V_{PO}. \tag{12.88}$$

The drain current is zero when the JFET is cut-off,

$$ID = 0. \tag{12.89}$$

The p-channel JFET

The voltage and current sign conventions for *p*-channel JFETs is illustrated in Figure 12.47.

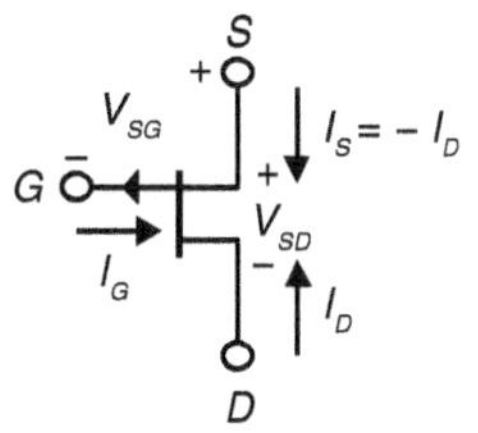

Figure 12.47 Voltage and Current Directions of *p*-channel JFETs

The arrow on the gate is leaving the device. Also note that the direction of the drain current is opposite that for the *n*-channel JFET. In essence, all terminal voltages and currents have been reversed. The *p*-channel operating voltages and currents are given as follows:

$$V_{PO} > 0 \qquad V_{SD} > 0 \qquad -V_{PO} < V_{SG} \leq 0$$
$$I_{DS}S < 0 \qquad I_D < 0.$$

The conditions that identify the regions of operation are,

Ohmic Region:	$0 < V_{SD} < V_{PO} + V_{SG}$	
Saturation Region:	$V_{SD} \geq V_{PO} + V_{SG}$	**(12.90)**
Pinch-off Parabola:	$V_{SD} = V_{PO} + V_{SG}.$	

The output characteristic curve and the transfer characteristic for a *p*-channel JFET are shown in Figures 12.48 and 12.49.

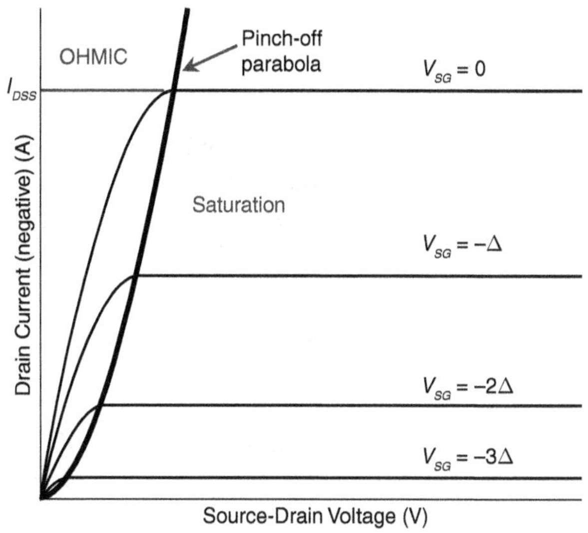

Figure 12.48 *p*-channel JFET Output Characteristic Curve

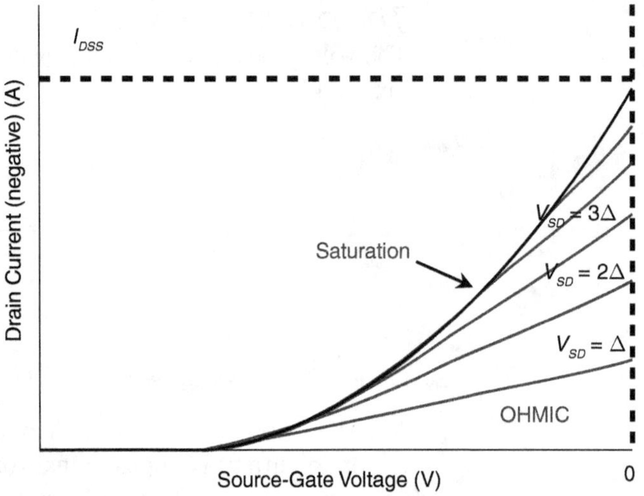

Figure 12.49 Transfer Characteristic for *p*-channel JFET

The *V-I* relationship in the three regions can be found by using the mathematical expressions for *n*-channel JFETs in Equations (12.81) to (12.89). In the *p*-channel JFET in the Ohmic and Saturation regions, the gate-to-source and drain-to-source voltages are of the opposite polarity to the *n*-channel JFET voltage. That is, in the *p*-channel JFET, the gate-to-source voltage is positive ($V_{GS} > 0$ or $V_{SG} < 0$), and the drain-to-source voltage is negative ($V_{DS} < 0$ or $V_{SG} > 0$).

In both *p*- and *n*-channel JFETs, V_{PO} and I_D have opposite polarities.

Example 12.15

An *n*-channel JFET has the following characteristics:

$$V_{PO} = -3.5 \text{ V}$$

and

$$I_{DSS} = 10 \text{ mA}.$$

Find the minimum drain-to-source voltage, V_{DS}, for the JFET to operate at in saturation for a gate-to-source voltage, $V_{GS} = -2$V. What is its resistance in the ohmic region?

Solution

The condition for saturation is,

$$V_{DS} \geq V_{GS} - V_{PO}.$$

Substituting yields,

$$V_{DS} \geq -2 - (-3.5) = 1.5 \text{ V}.$$

In the ohmic region the resistance is,

$$R_{DS}^{-1} = \frac{\partial I_D}{\partial V_{DS}} = \frac{2I_{DSS}}{V_{PO}}\left(\frac{V_{GS}}{V_{PO}} - 1\right).$$

Substituting $V_{GS} = -2$ V, $V_{PO} = -3.5$V, and $_{IDSS} = 10$ mA yields an output resistance of

$$R_{DS} = 408\ \Omega.$$

Example 12.16

Given a *p*-channel JFET with the following parameters:

$$V_{PO} = 4\ \text{V}$$

and

$$I_{DSS} = -\ 8\ \text{mA},$$

What is the drain current I_D for $V_{SG} = -\ 3$ V and $V_{SD} = 2$ V?

Solution

Determine the operating region of the FET.

$$V_{PO} + V_{SG} = 4 - 3 = 1\ \text{V}.$$

But $V_{SD} = 2$ V so,

$$V_{SD} \geq V_{PO} + V_{SG},$$

which indicates that the transistor is in saturation. Therefore, the drain current is,

$$I_D = I_{DSS}\left(1 - \frac{V_{GS}}{V_{PO}}\right)^2.$$

Substituting and solving for *ID* yields,

$$I_D = -\ 8\times10^{-3}\left(1 - \frac{-(-\ 3)}{4}\right)^2 = -0.5\ \text{mA}.$$

Metal-Oxide-Semiconductor Field-Effect Transistors

Metal-oxide-semiconductor field-effect transistors (MOSFETs) are widely used in integrated circuits. Because metal-oxide-semiconductor (MOS) devices can be fabricated in very small geometries and are relatively simple to manufacture, most very-large-scale integrated (VLSI) circuits are fabricated from MOS devices.

MOSFETs come in either of two types:

- Depletion type
- Enhancement type

Both types of MOSFETs are either *n*- or *p*-channel devices, commonly abbreviated NMOSFET and PMOSFET, respectively. The depletion MOSFET can operate in either the depletion or enhancement modes. The enhancement MOSFET operates in the enhancement mode only.

This section considers the depletion- and enhancement-type MOSFETs separately.

Depletion-Type MOSFET

In this section, the terminal voltage and current relationships of depletion-type *n*-channel MOSFETs (NMOSFETs) will be developed. The depletion-type *p*-channel MOSFET (PMOSFET) terminal voltage and current relationships are identical to the NMOSFET with the exception that the polarities of the voltages and currents are reversed. The depletion MOSFET regions of operation are identical to those of the JFET. In fact, the *V-I* relationships of the depletion MOSFET are identical in form to those of the JFET. Both types of transistors are depletion mode devices; that is, with the application of the appropriate polarity potential between the gate and the source (a negative potential for NMOSFETs), the carriers in the channel are depleted which squeezes off the channel through which charge carriers flow. Therefore, the same types of transistor parameters are used to describe the *V-I* characteristics of the depletion MOSFET as for the JFET. The operational characteristics of the depletion MOSFET does differ from the JFET by one important attribute: the depletion MOSFET can additionally operate in the enhancement mode by applying a positive gate-source potential, thus "enhancing" the channel through which the charge carriers flow.

The circuit symbol for the depletion NMOSFET is shown in Figure 12.50a. In addition to the three FET terminals of gate, drain, and source, the symbol depicts a terminal representing the substrate of the semiconductor ("B" for body) with an arrow pointing into the junction. It is common for the substrate to be electrically connected to the source; this connection does not affect the characteristics of the MOSFET. However, in integrated circuits using NMOSFETs, the substrate is commonly connected to the most negative supply voltage. With NMOSFETs connected in this fashion, it is guaranteed that the substrate is at signal ground. Unfortunately, there is some possibility that circuit performance may be compromised.

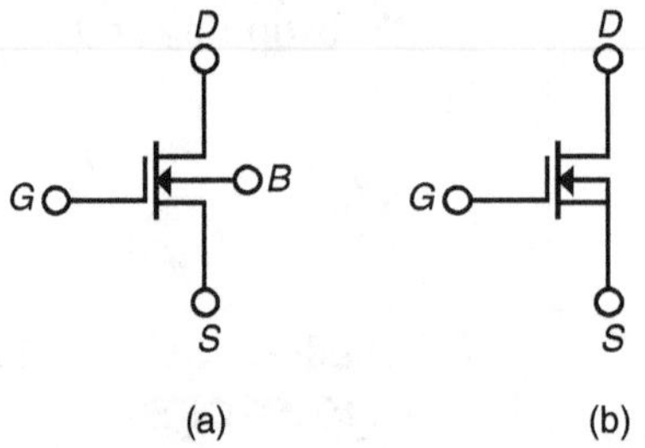

Figure 12.50 (a) Circuit Symbol for the Depletion-Type NMOSFET, (b) Depletion-Type NMOSFET with the Substrate Connected to the Source

A simplified circuit symbol for the depletion-type NMOSFET is shown in Figure 12.51 with the standard voltage and current directions indicated. For NMOSFETs, the arrow points toward the source from the junction. The direction of the arrow corresponds to the direction of standard current flow toward the source terminal.

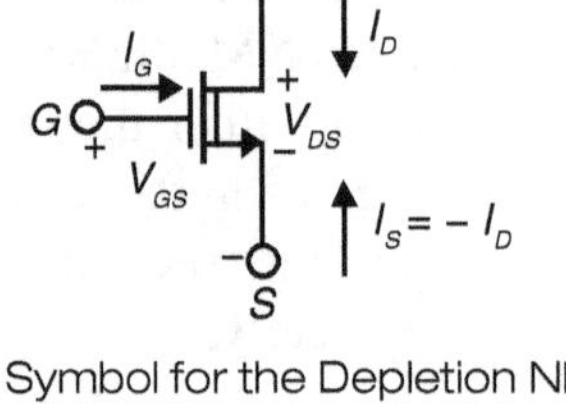

Figure 12.51 Simplified Circuit Symbol for the Depletion NMOSFET

As in the n-channel JFET, the source current is equal to the negative of the drain current when the gate-source junction is reverse biased,

$$I_S = -I_D. \tag{12.91}$$

The depletion-type MOSFET operates similarly to the JFET. Like the JFET, the MOSFET gate current is essentially zero,

$$I_G = 0. \tag{12.92}$$

As in the JFET, the pinch-off voltage is the gate-to-source voltage that depletes, or "squeezes off," the drain-source channel. For NMOSFETs, V_{PO} is negative and is transistor specific.

Unlike the n-channel JFET, the depletion-type NMOSFET allows for enhancement mode operation with the application of a positive V_{GS}. Application of a positive gate-to-source potential "opens up" the drain-source channel by increasing the channel conductivity, allowing more current to flow. Enhancement mode operation of the depletion-type NMOSFET allows for drain currents in excess of I_{DSS}.

Typical depletion-type NMOSFET drain characteristics are shown in Figure 12.52. The transfer characteristic of the depletion NMOSFET is shown in Figure 12.53.

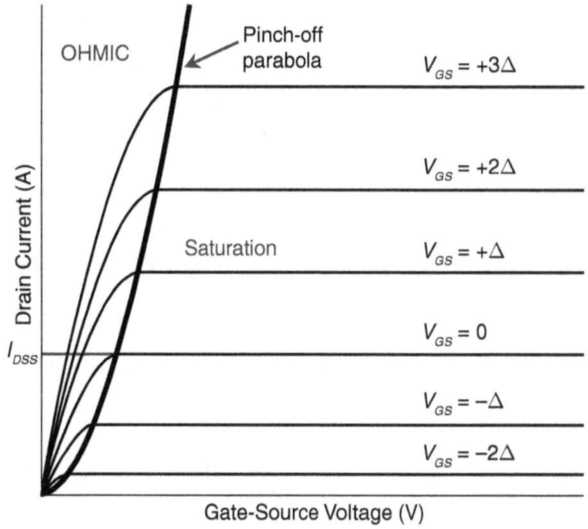

Figure 12.52 Depletion-Type NMOSFET Drain Characteristics

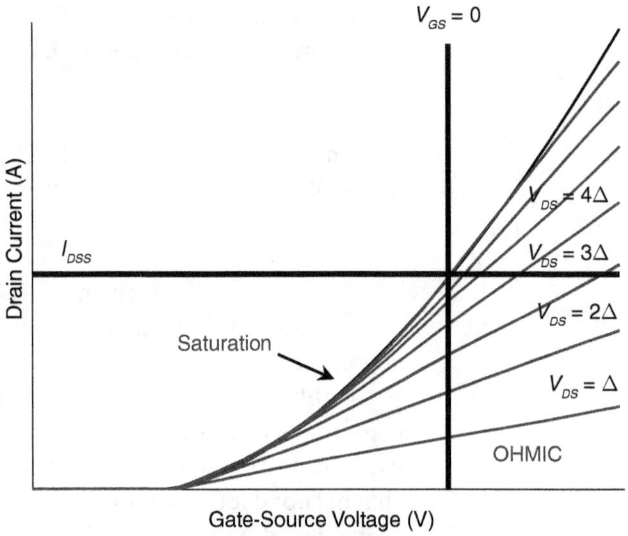

Figure 12.53 Depletion-Type NMOSFET Transfer Characteristic

The depletion NMOSFET characteristic curves of Figures 12.52 and 12.53 are very similar to those of the n-channel JFET curves of Figures 12.45 and 12.46. The equations describing the curves for the depletion NMOSFET and the n-channel JFET are identical. As in the JFET, there are three common regions of operation: the Ohmic, Saturation, and Cut-Off regions.

For the depletion-type NMOSFET operating in the depletion-mode ohmic or saturation regions, the following voltage and current conditions must hold:

$$I_D > 0 \qquad V_{PO} < V_{GS} \le 0 \qquad V_{DS} > 0.$$

For the depletion-type NMOSFET operating in the enhancement mode, V_{GS} changes sign. The voltage and current conditions become:

$$I_D > 0 \qquad V_{GS} > 0 \qquad V_{DS} > 0.$$

Depletion-type NMOSFETs have the following characteristic parameters:

$$V_{PO} < 0 \qquad I_{DSS} > 0.$$

As in the JFET operating in the negative quadrant, where $I_D < 0$ and $V_{DS} < 0$, the drain-gate junction becomes forward biased causing the drain current to increase rapidly. The characteristics in this region are similar to a diode (except that $I_D < 0$ and $V_{DS} < 0$) with the turn-on voltage determined by V_{GS}.

Ohmic Region

The ohmic region lies between $V_{DS} = 0$ and the pinch-off parabola in the drain characteristic curve. The mathematical expression defining this region is,

$$0 < V_{DS} \le V_{GS} - V_{PO}. \tag{12.93}$$

The V-I relationship in this region is,

$$I_D = I_{DSS}\left[2\left(\frac{V_{GS}}{V_{PO}} - 1\right)\frac{V_{DS}}{V_{PO}} - \left(\frac{V_{DS}}{V_{PO}}\right)^2\right] \tag{12.94}$$

For small values of I_D, the drain current in Equation (12.94) is approximately,

$$I_D \approx 2I_{DSS}\left(\frac{V_{GS}}{V_{PO}} - 1\right)\frac{V_{DS}}{V_{PO}} \tag{12.95}$$

Saturation Region

The saturation region occupies the portion of the output characteristic curve of Figure 12.52 where $I_D > 0$ and to the right of the pinch-off parabola. That is,

$$V_{DS} \geq V_{GS} - V_{PO}. \tag{12.96}$$

The drain current is virtually independent of V_{DS} in this region and is described by the transfer characteristic (shown in Figure 12.53),

$$I_D = I_{DSS}\left(1 - \frac{V_{GS}}{V_{PO}}\right)^2 \tag{12.97}$$

The values of V_{PO} and I_{DSS} are specified by the manufacturers.

The expression for the pinch-off parabola can be derived from Equation (12.97) by substituting $V_{GS} = V_{DS} + V_{PO}$,

$$I_D = I_{DSS}\left(\frac{V_{DS}}{V_{PO}}\right)^2 \tag{12.98}$$

Cut-off Region

The depletion-type NMOSFET is said to be in the cut-off region when,

$$V_{GS} < V_{PO}. \tag{12.99}$$

When the depletion-type NMOSFET is cut-off,

$$I_D = 0. \tag{12.100}$$

Example 12.17

For a depletion-type NMOSFET with $V_{PO} = -3$ V and $I_{DSS} = 8$ mA what is the drain to source voltage required to saturate the transistor at $V_{GS} = +2$ V? What is the drain current?

Solution

The pinch-off condition is,

$$V_{DS} = V_{GS} - V_{PO}.$$

Substituting the values of the pinch-off voltage and the gate-source voltage,

$$V_{DS} = 2 - (-3) = 5 \text{ V}.$$

To find the drain current at pinch-off, the expression for the current in the saturation region is used,

$$I_D = I_{DSS}\left(1 - \frac{V_{GS}}{V_{PO}}\right)^2.$$

Substituting in the values for I_{DSS}, V_{GS}, and V_{PO} yields the drain current,

$$I_D = 8\times10^{-3}\left(1-\frac{2}{-(-3)}\right)^2 = 22.2\text{ mA}.$$

Since $I_D > I_{DSS}$, the MOSFET is in the enhancement mode of operation.

Depletion-type PMOSFET

The circuit symbol of the depletion-type PMOSFET is shown in Figure 12.54. All of the voltages and currents of the depletion-type PMOSFET are the opposite polarity to those of the NMOSFET. The pinch-off voltage of the depletion-type PMOSFET is greater than zero,

$$V_{PO} > 0. \qquad \textbf{(12.101)}$$

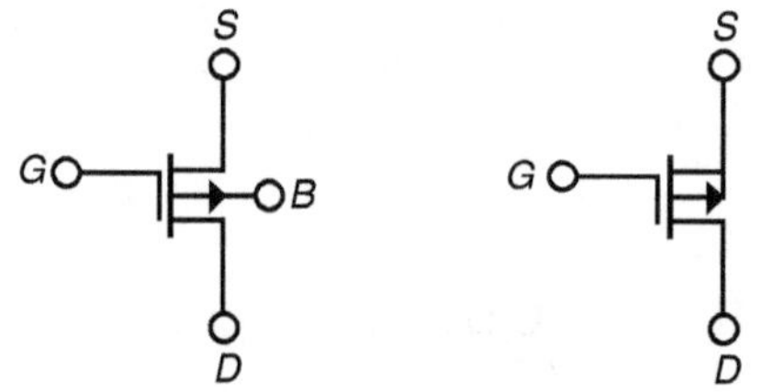

Figure 12.54 (a) Circuit Symbol of the Depletion-Type PMOSFET, (b) Symbol for Depletion-Type PMOSFET with the Substrate Electrically Connected to the Source

The simplified circuit symbol of the depletion-type PMOSFET is shown in Figure 12.55. The current and voltage sign conventions are also shown.

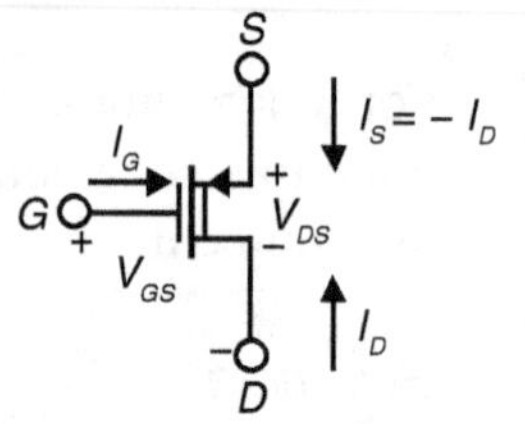

Figure 12.55 Simplified Circuit Symbol of the Depletion-Type PMOSFET. Current Directions and Voltage Polarities are also Indicated.

The *V*-*I* relationship in the three regions of the depletion PMOSFET can be found by using the mathematical expressions for depletion NMOSFET in Equations (12.93) to (12.100). In both *p*- and *n*-channel depletion MOSFETs, the polarity of V_{PO} is always opposite from I_D.

For the depletion-type PMOSFET operating in the depletion mode ohmic or saturation regions, the following voltage and current relationships must hold:

$$I_D < 0 \qquad -V_{PO} < V_{SG} \leq 0 \qquad V_{SD} > 0.$$

For the depletion-type PMOSFET operating in the enhancement mode, V_{SG} change sign and the conditions become:

$$I_D < 0 \qquad V_{SG} > 0 \qquad V_{SD} > 0.$$

Note that

$$V_{SG} = -V_{GS}$$

and

$$V_{SD} = -V_{DS}.$$

Enhancement-Type MOSFETs

The enhancement-type MOSFET is commonly used in integrated circuit design because of its ease of fabrication, small geometry, and low power dissipation. Without an applied voltage between the gate source terminals, the drain-source channel is closed. With the application of a gate-to-source potential, the channel becomes "enhanced" to conduct carriers. The enhancement-type carrier conduction mechanism can be thought of as the antithesis of that of the depletion MOSFET.

An *n*-type channel layer (for the enhancement NMOSFET) is formed to conduct carriers from the drain to the source with the application of a positive V_{GS}. A *p*-type channel layer conducts carriers from the drain to the source with the application of a positive V_{SG} (negative V_{GS}) in enhancement PMOSFETs. The gate-to-source voltage that starts to form the drain-source channel is called the *threshold voltage,* V_T. When V_{GS} is less than V_T (in NMOSFETs), I_D is zero since the drain-source channel does not exist. The value of V_T is dependent on the specific MOSFET device and commonly ranges in value from 1 to 5 volts for enhancement NMOSFETs. Since $I_D = 0$ for $V_{GS} = 0$, the quantity I_{DSS} found in the depletion MOSFET and JFET is not pertinent to the enhancement-type MOSFET.

Unlike the depletion MOSFETs that operate in both enhancement and depletion modes, enhancement MOSFETs can only operate in the enhancement mode.

Enhancement-Type NMOSFET

The circuit symbol for the enhancement-type NMOSFET is shown in Figure 12.56. The symbol is similar to that of the depletion NMOSFET with the exception of the three short lines representing the junction area. As with the depletion-type NMOSFET, the symbol depicts a terminal representing the substrate with an arrow pointing into the junction.

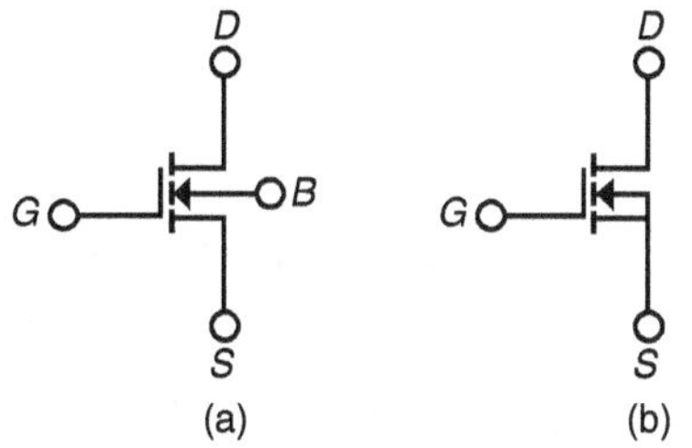

Figure 12.56 (a) Circuit Symbol for the Enhancement-Type NMOSFET, (b) Enhancement-Type NMOSFET with the Substrate Connected to the Source

A simplified circuit symbol for the enhancement-type NMOSFET is shown in Figure 12.57 with the applicable voltage and current sign conventions. The arrow on the circuit symbol points away from the junction to the source. The direction of the arrow corresponds to the direction of the current flow relative to the source terminal.

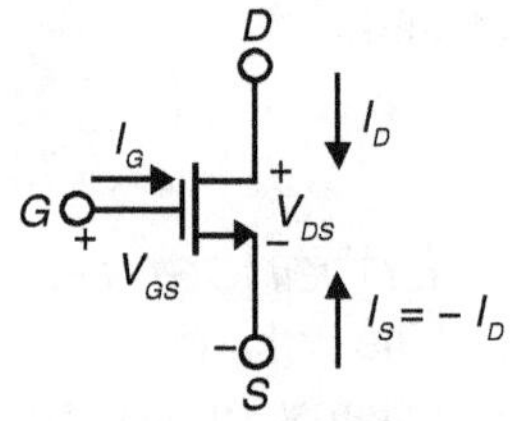

Figure 12.57 Simplified Circuit Symbol for the Enhancement NMOSFET

In the enhancement NMOSFET, the FET channel allows charge flow only when the gate-source potential, V_{GS}, is greater than some threshold voltage V_T. When $V_{GS} > V_T$,

$$I_S = -I_D,$$

and

$$I_G = 0.$$

The enhancement NMOSFET characteristics are shown in Figure 12.58. The transfer characteristic of the enhancement NMOSFET is shown in Figure 12.59.

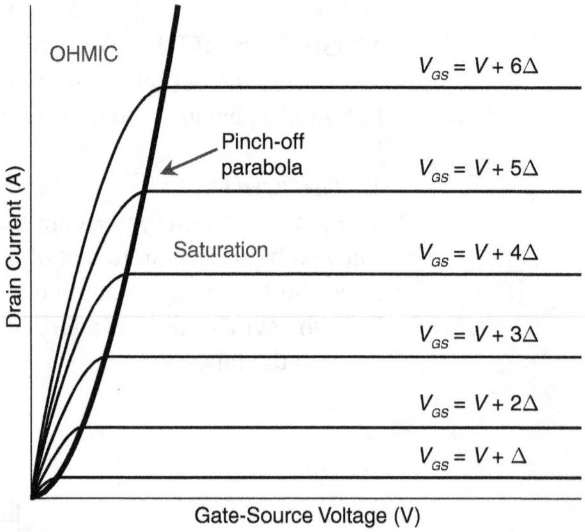

Figure 12.58 Enhancement-Type NMOSFET Drain Characteristics

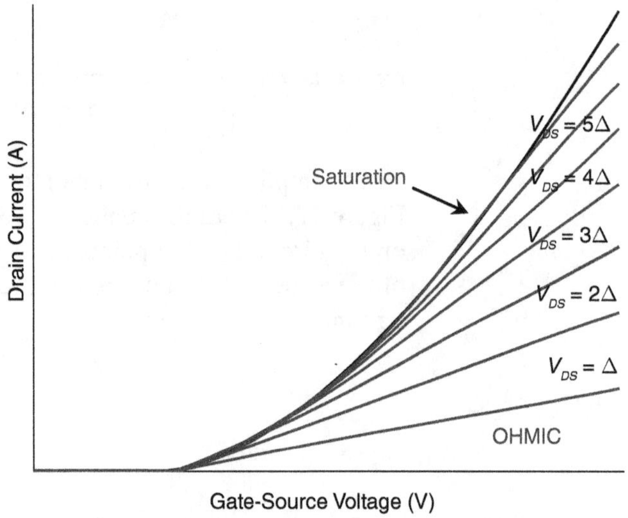

Figure 12.59 Enhancement-Type NMOSFET Transfer Characteristic

The threshold voltage, V_T, for the enhancement-type NMOSFET is a positive value. A positive V_{GS} greater than V_T allows current to flow through the FET by the formation of the drain-source channel. The NMOSFET is in the ohmic region when,

$$0 < V_{DS} \leq V_{GS} - V_T. \qquad \textbf{(12.102)}$$

The pinch-off parabola, which delineated the boundary between the ohmic and saturation regions, is defined by:

$$V_{DS} = V_{GS} - V_T. \qquad \textbf{(12.103)}$$

The saturation region lies beyond the pinch-off parabola:

$$V_{DS} \geq V_{GS} - V_T. \qquad \textbf{(12.104)}$$

For the enhancement-type NMOSFET operating in the ohmic or saturation regions,

$$I_D > 0 \qquad V_{GS} > V_T \qquad V_{DS} > 0.$$

Enhancement-type NMOSFETs have a positive valued threshold voltage,

$$V_T > 0.$$

Ohmic Region

The ohmic region is that portion of the output characteristic curve between $V_{DS} = 0$ and the pinch-off parabola. The mathematical expression defining this region is,

$$0 < V_{DS} \leq V_{GS} - V_T. \qquad \textbf{(12.105)}$$

The V-I relationship in this region is,

$$I_D = K\left[2\left(V_{GS} - V_T\right)V_{DS} - V_{DS}^2\right] \qquad \textbf{(12.106)}$$

The constant K is the transconductance factor in units of amperes/volt^2. This transconductance factor is determined by the geometry of the FET, gate capacitance per unit area, and the surface mobility of the electrons in the n channel.

For small values of V_{DS}, the drain current in Equation (12.106) is approximately,

$$I_D = K\,[\,2\,(V_{GS} - V_T)\,V_{DS}]. \qquad \textbf{(12.107)}$$

Equation (12.107) is a linearly varying function of I_D and V_{DS} for constant V_{GS}. The output resistance in this region is the derivative of Equation (12.107) with respect to V_{DS} for constant V_{GS},

$$R_{DS}^{-1} = \frac{\partial I_D}{\partial V_{DS}} = 2K\left(V_{GS} - V_T\right) \qquad \textbf{(12.108)}$$

By substituting Equation (12.103) into (12.106) the pinch-off parabolas is given by,

$$I_D = K\,V_{DS}2. \qquad \textbf{(12.109)}$$

Saturation Region

The saturation region occupies the region of the output characteristic curve of Figure 12.58 where $I_D > 0$ and to the right of the pinch-off parabola. That is,

$$V_{DS} \geq V_{GS} - V_T. \quad \textbf{(12.110)}$$

The drain current is virtually constant with respect to V_{DS} for a given V_{GS} in this region due to high conductivity in the drain-source channel. The transfer characteristic is obtained by substituting $V_{GS} - V_T$ for V_{DS} in Equation (12.109),

$$I_D = K\,(V_{GS} - V_T)^2. \quad \textbf{(12.111)}$$

The transfer characteristic [Equation (12.110)] is shown in Figure 12.59.

Cut-Off Region

The cut-off region is defined as

$$V_{GS} < V_T. \quad \textbf{(12.112)}$$

In cut-off, the drain current is zero,

$$I_D = 0. \quad \textbf{(12.113)}$$

The FET is OFF in this region and does not conduct current. The region is used to implement the OFF state of a switch.

The substrate potential affects the threshold current. In particular, for increasing negative substrate potential with respect to the source, the threshold voltage of the enhancement NMOSFET increases.

Example 12.18

An enhancement-type NMOSFET with $V_T = 2$ V that conducts a current $I_D = 5$ mA for $V_{GS} = 4$ V and $V_{DS} = 5$ V. What is the value of I_D for $V_{GS} = 3$ V and $V_{DS} = 6$ V?

Solution

First determine the region of operation at $V_{GS} = 4$ V and $V_{DS} = 5$ V.

$$V_{GS} - V_T = 4\text{ V} - 2\text{ V} = 2\text{ V}.$$

But $V_{DS} = 5$ V so,

$$V_{DS} > V_{GS} - V_T,$$

implying that the FET is in the saturation region.

The unknown quantity is the transconductance factor, K, of Equation (12.111),

$$I_D = K\,(V_{GS} - V_T)2.$$

Solving for K,

$$K = \frac{I_D}{(V_{GS} - V_T)^2} = \frac{5\times 10^{-3}}{(4-2)^2}$$

$$= 1.25\times 10^{-3}\, A/V2.$$

With this information, the value of I_D for $V_{GS} = 3$ V and $V_{DS} = 6$ V can be determined.

Again, the region of operation must be determined for the new operating parameters,

$$V_{GS} - V_T = 3\text{ V} - 2\text{ V} = 1\text{ V}.$$

But $V_{DS} = 6$ V so,

$$V_{DS} > V_{GS} - V_T,$$

implying that the FET is again in the saturation region.

The current at I_D for $V_{GS} = 3$ V and $V_{DS} = 6$ V is

$$I_D = K(V_{GS} - V_T)2$$
$$= 1.25 \times 10^{-3}(3 - 2)^2$$
$$I_D = 1.25\text{ mA}.$$

Enhancement-Type PMOSFET

The circuit symbol for the enhancement-type PMOSFET is shown in Figure 12.60. The symbol is similar to that of the enhancement NMOSFET with the exception of the direction of the arrow on the body (substrate) terminal. As with the depletion-type PMOSFET, the symbol depicts a terminal representing the substrate with an arrow pointing into the junction.

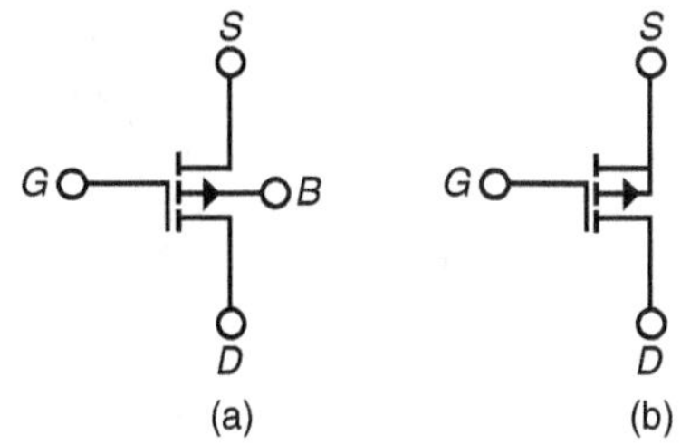

Figure 12.60 (a) Circuit Symbol for the Enhancement-Type PMOSFET, (b) Enhancement-Type PMOSFET with the Substrate Connected to the Source

A simplified circuit symbol for the enhancement-type PMOSFET is shown in Figure 12.61 with the voltage and current sign conventions. The arrow on the circuit symbol points toward the junction to the source. The direction of the arrow corresponds to the direction of the current flow relative to the source terminal.

Figure 12.61 Simplified Circuit Symbol for the Enhancement PMOSFET

All terminal voltages are of opposite polarity from that of the enhancement NMOSFET. The polarity of the threshold voltage is opposite that of the enhancement NMOSFET. The enhancement-type *p*-channel MOSFET voltages and currents have the following characteristics:

$$V_T < 0 \qquad K > 0 \qquad V_{SD} > 0$$
$$V_{SG} > 0 \qquad I_D < 0.$$

The conditions that identify the regions of operation are,

$$
\begin{aligned}
&\text{Ohmic Region:} && 0 < V_{SD} < V_{SG} + V_T \\
&\text{Saturation Region:} && V_{SD} \geq V_{SG} + V_T \qquad \textbf{(12.114)} \\
&\text{Pinch-Off Parabola:} && V_{SD} = V_{SG} + V_T.
\end{aligned}
$$

The enhancement PMOSFET characteristics are shown in Figure 12.62. The transfer characteristic of the enhancement PMOSFET is shown in Figure 12.63.

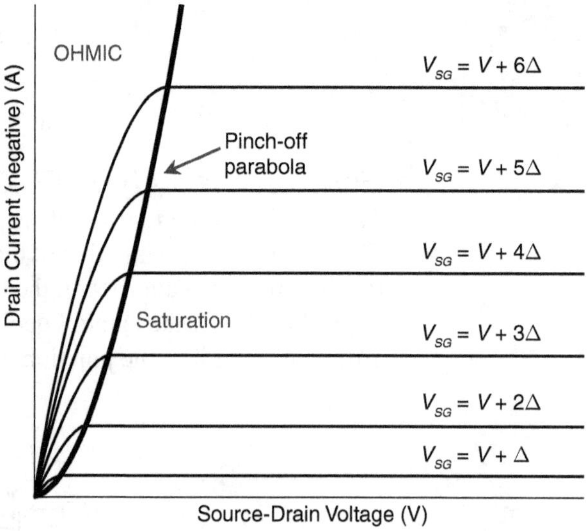

Figure 12.62 Enhancement-Type PMOSFET Drain Characteristics

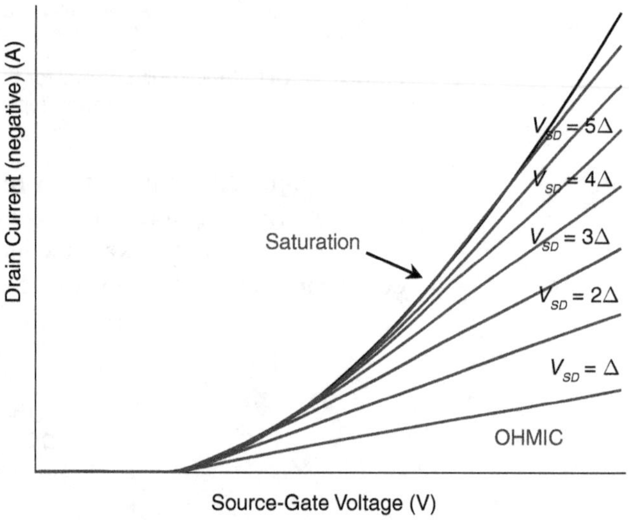

Figure 12.63 Enhancement-Type PMOSFET Transfer Characteristic

The threshold voltage, V_T, for the enhancement-type PMOSFET is a negative value. A positive V_{SG} greater than $|V_T|$ allows current to flow through the FET by the formation of the drain-source channel.

The FET as a Circuit Element

Using the terminal behavior of JFETs and MOSFETs, simple circuits using FETs can be developed. FETs are used in circuits as constant current devices, active loads, and voltage variable resistors, to name a few. MOSFETs are used extensively in digital circuits and have certain advantages over BJT designs. The SPICE model for the JFET and MOSFET are also developed in this section.

FET as a Voltage Variable Resistor

A voltage variable resistor (VVR) is a three terminal device where the resistance between two of the terminals is controlled by a voltage on the third. In the ohmic region, FETs demonstrate a variation in resistance, R_{DS}, described by Equations (12.84) and (12.108),

$$R_{DS}^{-1} = \frac{\partial I_D}{\partial V_{DS}} = \frac{2I_{DSS}}{V_{PO}}\left(\frac{V_{GS}}{V_{PO}} - 1\right)$$

$$R_{DS}^{-1} = \frac{\partial I_D}{\partial V_{DS}} = 2K\left(V_{GS} - V_T\right).$$

Written more conveniently as resistances, the drain-source resistances in the ohmic region of the n-JFET and of the depletion mode NMOSFET are:

$$R_{DS} = \frac{V_{PO}^{\ 2}}{2I_{DSS}\left(V_{GS} - V_{PO}\right)}. \qquad \textbf{(12.115)}$$

For the enhancement mode NMOSFET, the drain-source resistance is,

$$R_{DS} = \frac{1}{2K\left(V_{GS} - V_T\right)} \qquad \textbf{(12.116)}$$

The n-channel JFET is used as an example in this section. Operation of n-JFETs in the ohmic region implies that the drain-source voltage is held small. Figure 12.64 illustrates typical n-JFET and resistor characteristics. The slope of V_{DS}/I_D is a function of V_{GS}, and the drain-source resistance R_{DS} is controlled by V_{GS}.

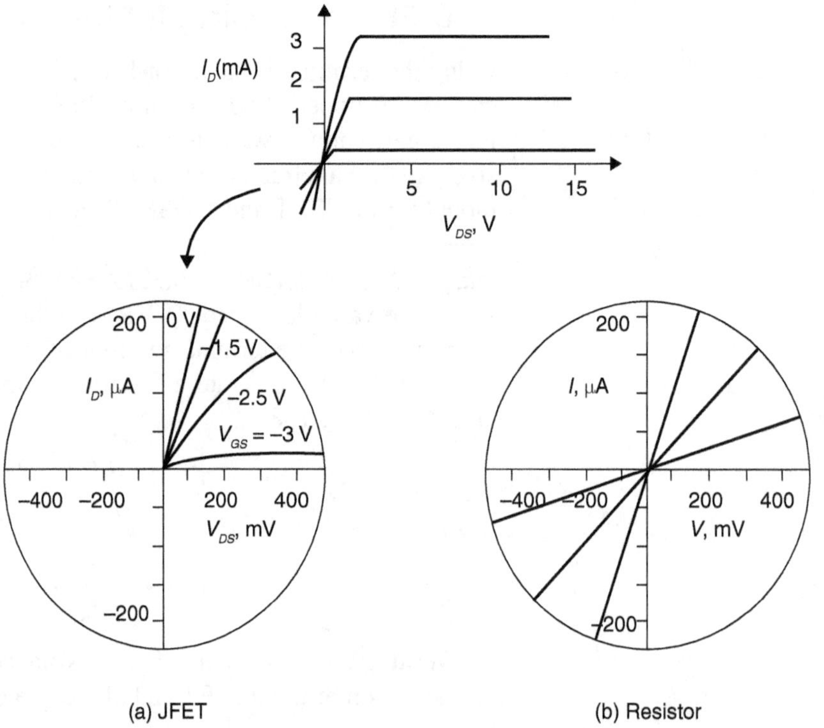

Figure 12.64 Comparison of *n*-JFET and Resistor Characteristics

Figure 12.65 is the circuit diagram for a simple voltage-controlled voltage divider using an *n*-JFET VVR to provide a means of voltage-controlling the divider ratio. As V_{GS} is changed from zero to V_{PO}, R_{DS} is changed.

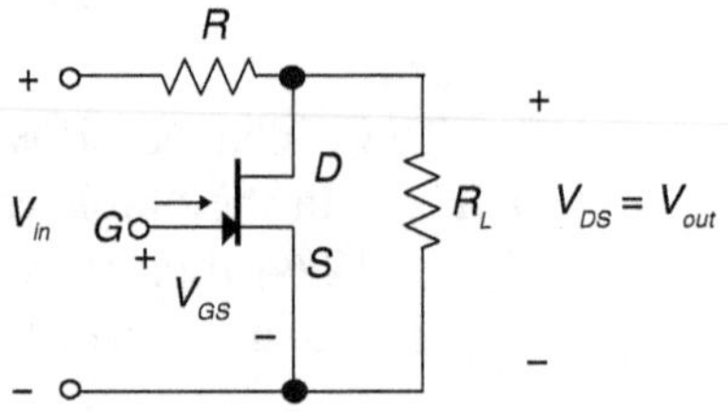

Figure 12.65 Simple Voltage-Controlled Voltage Divider

The output voltage is,

$$V_{OUT} = V_{IN} \frac{R_L \left(1 + R_{DS}{}^{-1} R_L\right)^{-1}}{R + R_L \left(1 + R_{DS}{}^{-1} R_L\right)^{-1}}. \tag{12.117}$$

When V_{GS} approaches V_{PO}, R_{DS} approaches zero and the FET causes no signal attenuation. If $R_L >> R_{DS}$, Equation (12.115) can be simplified to,

$$V_{OUT} = V_{IN} \frac{1}{1 + RR_{DS}}. \tag{12.118}$$

Using Equation (12.84), The output voltage is expressed as a function of V_{GS},

$$V_{OUT} = \frac{1}{1 + RR_{DSO}^{-1}\left[\left(\frac{V_{PO} - V_{GS}}{V_{PO}}\right)\right]}. \qquad \textbf{(12.119)}$$

where

$$R_{DSO} = \frac{\partial V_{GS}}{\partial I_D} \text{ at } V_{GS} = 0 \text{ and } V_{DS} = 0.$$

n-JFET as a Constant-Current Source

The ideal constant-current source would supply a given current to a load independent of the voltage across the load. In such a case, the output resistance of the source is infinite. The drain current of the JFET approaches saturation when operated with the gate-drain voltage greater than V_{PO}. Under this condition, the FET can be used as a constant current source.

One way to force V_{GD} to be greater than V_{PO} is to tie the gate of the *n*-JFET directly to the source as shown in Figure 12.66.

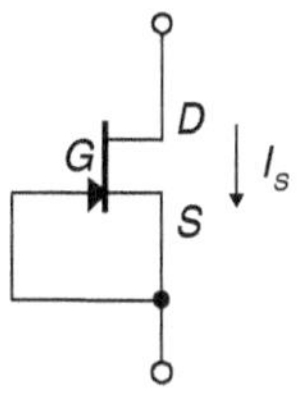

Figure 12.66 *n*-JFET constant Current Source

In Figure 12.66, $V_{GS} = 0$, therefore in saturation, $V_{DS} = -V_{PO}$ and the drain current $I_D = I_{DSS}$. As long as the FET remains in saturation, it will provide a constant current flowing through the drain-source channel.

FET Inverter

The methods used to analyze FET circuits are similar to that used to solve BJT circuits in Chapter 3. Three choices are available to analyze FET circuits. They are:

- Use the set of FET equations in Sections 4-1 and 4-2 along with additional circuit-dependent equations to obtain a numerical solution.
- Use empirical V-I curves and obtain a graphical solution.
- Use SPICE to obtain the solution.

As in BJT circuit analysis, the choice of technique used to analyze the circuit is strongly dependent on the complexity of the FET circuit.

Example 12.19

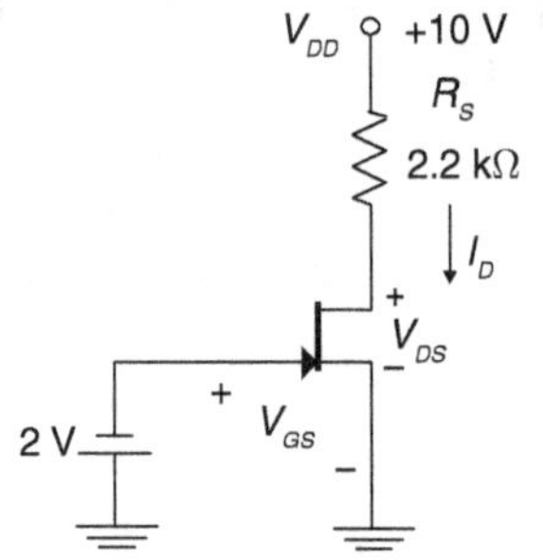

Exhibit 7 *n*-JFET Inverter

Consider an *n*-JFET inverter shown in Exhibit 7. The JFET characteristics are:

$$I_{DSS} = 8 \text{ mA and } V_{PO} = -4\text{V}.$$

Find the drain current I_D and the drain-source voltage V_{DS} when $V_{GS} = -2\text{V}$.

Solution #1 (Using characteristic equations for the n-JFET)

In order to find V_{DS}, an additional equation dependent on circuit topology is required. The loop equation needed is,

$$V_{DD} = I_D R_D + V_D.$$

Assume that the JFET is operating in saturation. The drain current can then be calculated from Equation (12.86):

$$I_D = I_{DSS}\left(1 - \frac{V_{GS}}{V_{PO}}\right)^2 = 8\times10^{-3}\left(1 - \frac{-2}{-4}\right)^2 = 2 \text{ mA}.$$

The drain-source voltage can then be obtained:

$$V_{DS} = V_{DD} - I_D R_D = 10 - \left(2\times10^{-3}\right)\left(2200\right) = 5.6 \text{ V}.$$

To confirm that the *n*-JFET is operating in saturation, the condition for saturation is checked:

$$V_{DS} \geq V_{GS} - V_{PO}$$

$$5.6 \geq -2 - (-4)$$

$$5.6 \geq 2.$$

The saturation region assumption is verified and the calculations are valid.

FET as an Active Load

In some applications, a FET active load to replace the passive resistor used as a load in an inverting FET amplifier may be desirable. For instance in integrated circuit fabrication, passive resistors consume large areas of the chip compared to transistors. Both enhancement and depletion NMOSFET active loads are commonly used. However, the load-line characteristics are quite different between the two types of NMOSFETs.

An enhancement NMOSFET inverting amplifier with an enhancement NMOSFET load is shown in Figure 12.67. In this circuit, Q_1 acts as the load and Q_2 is the driver.

Figure 12.67 Enhancement NMOSFET Inverting Amplifier with Enhancement NMOSFET Active Load

By studying the circuit, several interesting relationships can be found. The output voltage V_O is

$$V_O = V_{DS2}.$$

Since the gate of Q_1 is connected to its own drain,

$$V_{GS1} = V_{DS1}.$$

Because the Q_2 gate-source and drain-source voltages are equal, Q_2 is in saturation since the difference between the gate-source and threshold voltages will always be greater than the drain-source voltage,

$$V_{DS} \geq V_{GS} - V_T.$$

The relationship between the two NMOSFETs is readily apparent using elementary circuit analysis. The sum of the voltages V_{DS1} and V_{DS2} must always equal the source voltage V_{DD},

$$V_{DS1} + V_{DS2} = V_{DD}.$$

The load-line created by Q_1 can be found by replacing V_{DS1} with $V_{DD} - V_{DS2}$,

$$I_{D1} = K\left(V_{GS1} - V_T\right)^2 \qquad \textbf{(12.120)}$$

$$= K\left[\left(V_{DD} - V_{DS2}\right) - 2\right]^2.$$

The Q_1 load-line superimposed on the Q_2 characteristic equation is shown in Figure 12.68. The curves were created using

$$K = ½\text{KP} = 625 \times 10^{-6} \qquad V_T = 2\text{V} \qquad V_{DD} = 10\text{V}$$

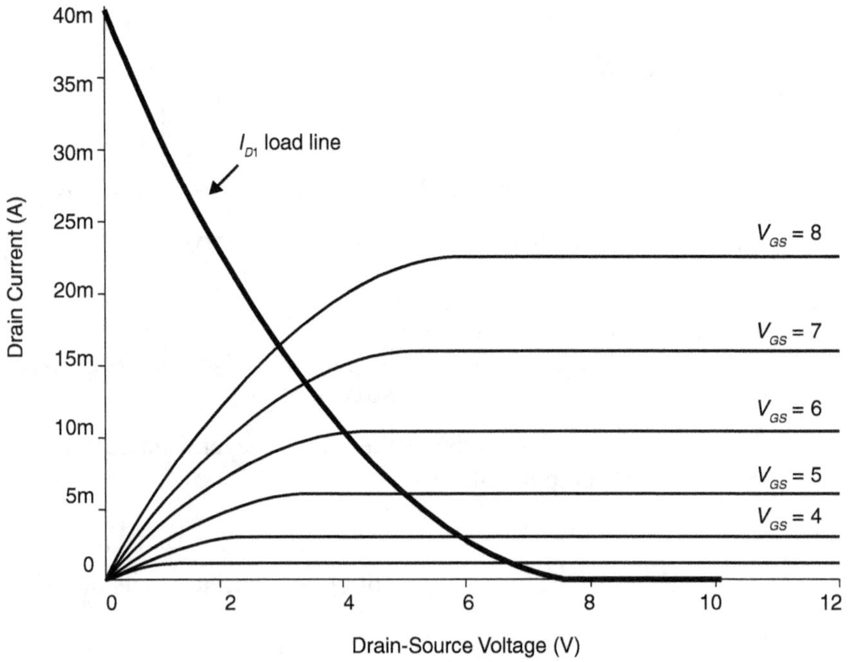

Figure 12.68 Enhancement NMOSFET Inverting Amplifier with Enhancement NMOSFET Load

The load-line ends at

$$V_{DD} - V_{T1} = 8\text{V} \qquad I_D = K(V_{DD} - V_T)^2 = 40 \text{ mA}.$$

If the load line is plotted using Equation (12.120), the load-lines curves back up at $V_{DS} > V_{DD} - V_T$. In real circuits, the line ends at $V_{DS} = V_{DD} - V_T$.

Another common configuration is the enhancement NMOSFET driver with a depletion NMOSFET active load shown in Figure 12.69.

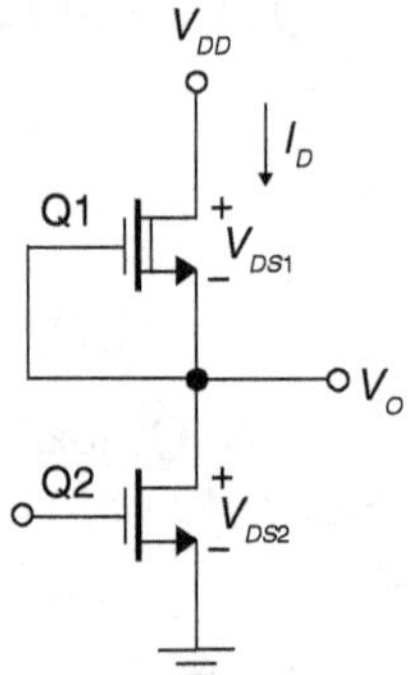

Figure 12.69 Enhancement NMOSFET Inverting Amplifier with Depletion NMOSFET Active Load

Several circuit relationships are evident from studying the circuit in Figure 12.69,

$$V_O = V_{DS2} \qquad V_{GS1} = 0 \qquad V_{DS1} + V_{DS2} = V_{DD}.$$

The depletion NMOSFET Q_1 is in saturation only when

$$V_{DS1} = V_{DD} - V_{DS2} \geq V_{GS1} - V_{PO} \geq -V_{PO}.$$

Since $V_{GS} = 0$, the current through Q_1 is I_{DSS} in the saturation region.

As V_{DS2} increases toward V_{DD}, V_{DS1} eventually becomes less than $-V_{PO}$ causing Q_1 to operate in the ohmic region. As Q_1 enters its ohmic region, the load-line curves down toward V_{DD} following the characteristic equation of the ohmic region,

$$I_D = I_{DSS}\left[2\left(\frac{V_{GS1}}{V_{PO}} - 1\right)\frac{V_{DS1}}{V_{PO}} - \left(\frac{V_{DS1}}{V_{PO}}\right)^2\right] \tag{12.121}$$

$$= I_{DSS}\left[-2\frac{V_{DS1}}{V_{PO}} - \left(\frac{V_{DS1}}{V_{PO}}\right)^2\right]$$

$$= I_{DSS}\left[-2\frac{V_{DD} - V_{DS2}}{V_{PO}} - \left(\frac{V_{DD} - V_{DS2}}{V_{PO}}\right)^2\right].$$

The resulting graphical solution is shown in Figure 12.70.

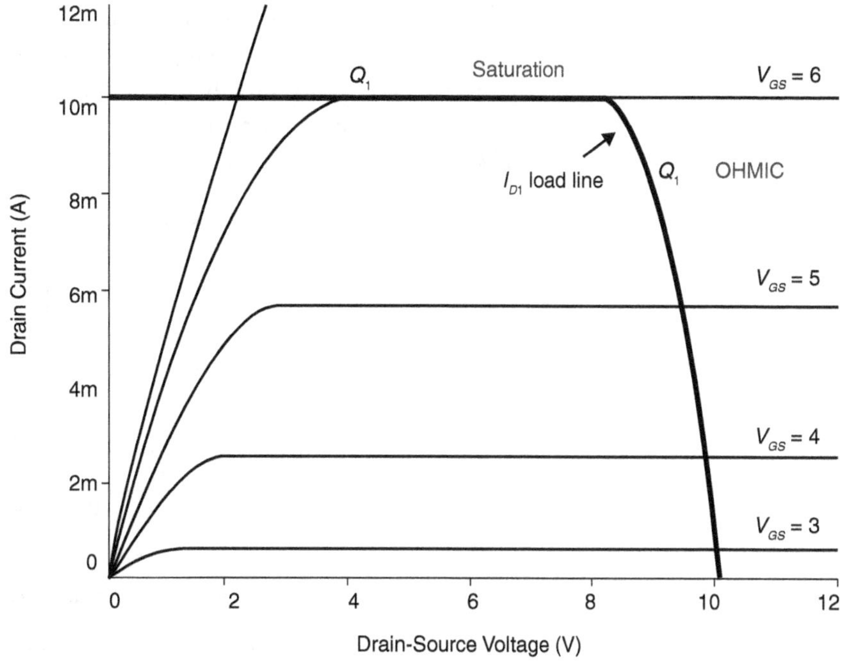

Figure 12.70 Enhancement NMOSFET Inverting Amplifier

CMOS Inverter

Complementary symmetry MOS (CMOS) circuits are fabricated with both enhancement NMOSFETs and enhancement PMOSFETs on the same chip. The main advantage of CMOS technology is the ability to design circuits with essentially zero DC power dissipation. Power is dissipated only during switching transitions. The CMOS inverter is shown in Figure 12.71. In Figure 12.71 Q_1, the enhancement PMOSFET, is the load, and Q_2, the enhancement NMOSFET, is the driver.

Figure 12.71 CMOS Inverter

Qualitatively, the operation of the CMOS inverter is simple. When $V_I = 0$, $V_{SG1} = V_{DD}$, and $V_{GS2} = 0$. When the gate-source voltage of the enhancement NMOSFET is zero, Q_2 is cut off. Therefore, $V_O = V_{DD}$.

When $V_I = V_{DD}$, $V_{GS2} = V_{DD}$ and $V_{SG1} = 0$. Since the source-gate voltage of the Q_1 the enhancement PMOSFET is zero, Q_1 is cut off. Therefore, $V_O = 0$.

Note that at logic zero and logic one outputs ($V_O = 0$ and V_{DD}), there is no current flowing though the circuit. Therefore, the CMOS inverter only dissipates power when transitioning between the two logic levels.

A SPICE simulation clearly shows the transfer function of the CMOS inverter. The transfer function is shown in Figure 12.72.

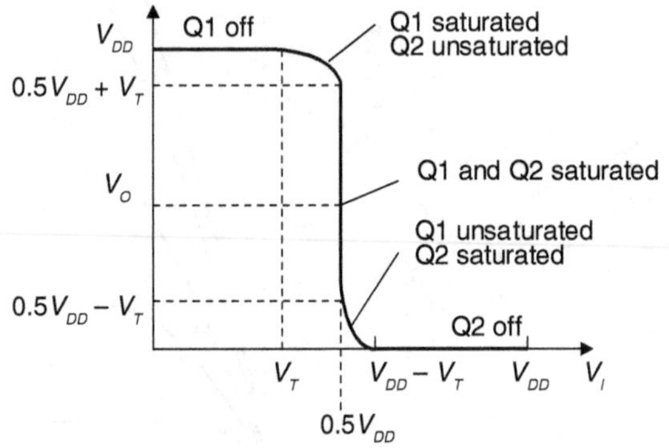

Figure 12.72 Transfer Characteristics of a CMOS Inverter

Load-line analysis of the CMOS circuit is similar to other active load analysis. The circuit yields the following relationships,

$$V_O = V_{DS2} \qquad V_1 = V_{GS1} = V_{GS2}.$$

Using the condition for saturation, a graphical solution of the CMOS inverter can be found. The load-lines are shown in Figure 12.73.

$$V_{DS} \geq V_{GS} - V_T.$$

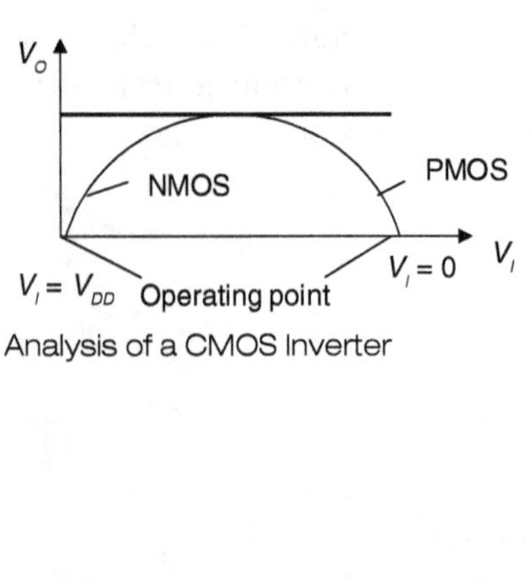

Figure 12.73 Load-Line Analysis of a CMOS Inverter

Regions of Operation in FETs

FET operation has been seen to fall into three regions of useful operation. The regions are described by the state of the drain-source channel controlled by the gate voltage. The three regions of interest are shown in Figure 12.74. Briefly, the following explains the three regions of operation:

- The cut-off region is defined as that region where the gate voltage disallows charge flow in the drain-source channel. The FET essentially looks like an open circuit. Applications for this region are primarily in switching and digital logic circuits.
- The ohmic region is defined by a gradual increase in charge flow in the drain-source channel, the rate of which is controlled by the gate voltage. Applications for this region include the use of FETs as voltage variable resistors.
- The saturation region. This region is defined by constant charge flow in the drain-source channel without regard to the drain-source voltage. The amount of constant current flow is regulated by the gate voltage. The region is commonly used for amplification with the modulation of the gate voltage and for constant current source applications.

In addition to these three regions, there is an additional region of severe consequences: the breakdown region. FETs are not manufactured to withstand extended use in the breakdown region and will exhibit catastrophic thermal runaway and destruction. To insure proper operation of the devices, manufacturers' specifications on maximum voltages must be heeded.

Due to the JFET fabrication process, the drain and source can, in most cases, be interchanged when the JFET is used as a circuit element without affecting the desired operating characteristics. This property (drain-source reciprocity) is not common to all types of FETs.

The characteristics of the FETs in the different regions are shown in Table 12.5.

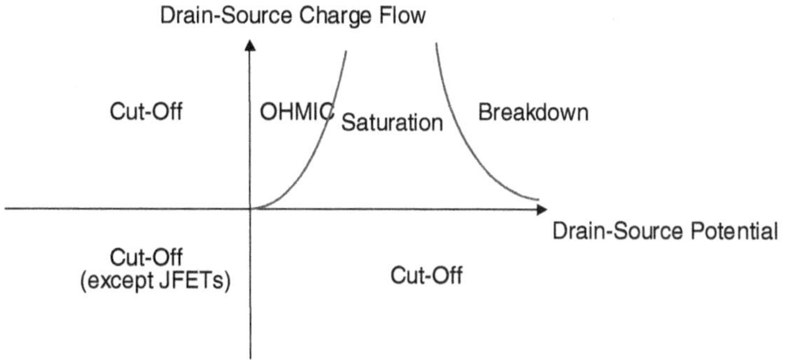

Figure 12.74 FET Regions of Operation

The FET as an Analog Switch

Both BJTs and FETs can be used as switches in a wide variety of analog electronic applications. Each type provides a great advantage over mechanical switches in both speed, reliability, and resistance to deterioration. FETs are the more common choice due to the inherent symmetry of FETs and the undesirable offset voltage (V_{CE} at $I_C = 0$) that is present in BJTs. The offset voltage of BJTs, typically on

the order of a few millivolts, can produce significant errors in the transmission of low-level analog signals. Another advantage of FET switches is the high gate input impedance and the consequent low load that the voltage control port presents to control electronics.

Table 12.5 FET Characteristics

Regions / **FET type**	**Ohmic**	**Saturation**	**Cut-Off**
n-JFET	$0 < V_{DS} \le V_{GS} - V_{PO}$ $I_D = I_{DSS}\left[2\left(\frac{V_{GS}}{V_{PO}} - 1\right)\frac{V_{DS}}{V_{PO}} - \left(\frac{V_{DS}}{V_{PO}}\right)^2\right]$	$V_{DS} \ge V_{GS} - V_{PO}$ $I_D = I_{DSS}\left(1 - \frac{V_{GS}}{V_{PO}}\right)^2$	$V_{GS} < V_{PO}$ $I_D = 0$
p-JFET	$0 < V_{SD} \le V_{SG} + V_{PO}$ $I_D = I_{DSS}\left[2\left(\frac{V_{GS}}{V_{PO}} - 1\right)\frac{V_{DS}}{V_{PO}} - \left(\frac{V_{DS}}{V_{PO}}\right)^2\right]$	$V_{SD} \ge V_{SG} + V_{PO}$ $I_D = I_{DSS}\left(1 - \frac{V_{GS}}{V_{PO}}\right)^2$	$V_{SG} < -V_{PO}$ $I_D = 0$
Enhancement NMOSFET	$0 < V_{DS} \le V_{GS} - V_T$ $I_D = K[2(V_{GS} - V_T)V_{DS} - V_{DS}^2]$	$V_{DS} \ge V_{GS} - V_T$ $I_D = K(V_{GS} - V_T)^2$	$V_{GS} < V_T$ $I_D = 0$
Depletion NMOSFET In depletion mode: $I_D > 0;\ V_{PO} < V_{GS} \le 0;\ V_{DS} > 0$ In enhancement mode: $I_D > 0;\ V_{GS} > 0;\ V_{SD} > 0$	$0 < V_{SD} \le V_{SG} - V_{PO}$ $I_D = I_{DSS}\left[2\left(\frac{V_{GS}}{V_{PO}} - 1\right)\frac{V_{DS}}{V_{PO}} - \left(\frac{V_{DS}}{V_{PO}}\right)^2\right]$	$V_{DS} \ge V_{GS} - V_{PO}$ $I_D = I_{DSS}\left(1 - \frac{V_{GS}}{V_{PO}}\right)^2$	$V_{GS} < V_{PO}$ $I_D = 0$
Enhancement PMOSFET	$0 < V_{SD} \le V_{SG} + V_T$ $I_D = K[2(V_{GS} - V_T)V_{DS} - V_{DS}^2]$	$V_{SD} \ge V_{SG} + V_T$ $I_D = K(V_{GS} - V_T)^2$	$V_{SG} < -V_T$ $I_D = 0$
Depletion PMOSFET In depletion mode: $I_D < 0;\ -V_{PO} < V_{SG} \le 0;\ V_{SD} > 0$ In enhancement mode: $I_D < 0;\ V_{SG} > 0;\ V_{SD} > 0$	$0 < V_{SD} \le V_{SG} + V_{PO}$ $I_D = I_{DSS}\left[2\left(\frac{V_{GS}}{V_{PO}} - 1\right)\frac{V_{DS}}{V_{PO}} - \left(\frac{V_{DS}}{V_{PO}}\right)^2\right]$	$V_{SD} \ge V_{SG} + V_{PO}$ $I_D = I_{DSS}\left(1 - \frac{V_{GS}}{V_{PO}}\right)^2$	$V_{SG} < -V_{PO}$ $I_D = 0$

Among the many possible electronic applications of solid-state analog switches are the following:

- Sample-and-hold circuits
- Switchable gain amplifiers
- Switched-capacitor filters
- Digital-to-analog conversion
- Signal gating and squelch control
- Chopper stabilization of amplifiers

In addition, multiple switches connected to share a common output form a multiplexer: a common building block for analog and digital systems.

The basic function of a switch is to electrically isolate or connect two sections of a circuit. In order to accomplish that functionality, an ideal analog switch has the following design goals:

- In the ON state, it passes signals without attenuation or distortion.
- In the OFF state, signals are not passed.
- The transitions between the ON and OFF states are instantaneous.

In order to accomplish the previous design goals, real switches have the more realistic specifications:

- Very low ON resistance compared to other circuit resistances
- Very high OFF resistance compared to other circuit resistances
- Low leakage currents in the OFF state
- Low capacitive and/or inductive effects

FETs satisfy these specifications satisfactorily for many applications. Control signals applied to the gate-source port of a FET will vary the drain-source port between ON and OFF switch positions. Reasonably low ON resistance combined with extremely high OFF resistance make the FET ideal as a voltage controlled analog switch element. In Section 4.3.2 it was seen that the drain-source resistance, R_{DS}, for a FET is highly dependent on the gate-source voltage. The drain-source resistance expression for depletion-type FETs is

$$R_{DS} = \frac{V_{PO}^2}{2I_{DSS}\left(V_{GS} - V_{PO}\right)},\ V_{GS} \geq V_{PO}. \tag{12.122}$$

For enhancement-type FETs,

$$R_{DS} = \frac{1}{2K\left(V_{GS} - V_T\right)},\ V_{GS} \geq V_T. \tag{12.123}$$

Variation in the control signal, V_{GS}, can change this resistance from the range of a few ohms to many megohms. A simple application of an analog switch using a single FET is shown in Figure 12.75. Such simple analog switches typically use enhancement mode FETs, although it is possible to form a switch with depletion mode FETs. In order to keep the switch in the OFF state for all values of the input voltage, v_s, the control voltage, v_c, must be less than the minimum input signal value plus the threshold voltage of the FET:

$$v_{c\,(\mathrm{OFF})} < v_{s\,(\mathrm{min})} + V_T. \tag{12.124}$$

Similarly, to keep the switch in the ON state for all values of the input voltage, the control voltage must be greater than the maximum input signal value plus the threshold voltage of the FET:

$$v_{c\,(\mathrm{ON})} > v_{s\,(\mathrm{max})} + V_T. \tag{12.125}$$

Equations (12.124) and (12.125) provide expressions for the absolute limits of ON and OFF control voltages. In order to ensure good switch performance, it is necessary to provide a design margin beyond these absolute limits.

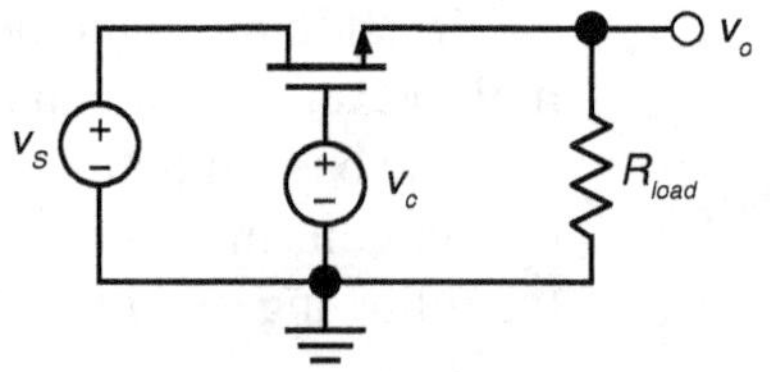

Figure 12.75 A Simple FET Analog Switch Application

Example 12.20

The FET analog switch of Equation (12.124) is used on the output of an OpAmp whose power supplies are set at ±15 V_{DC}. These voltages are chosen as the control voltages for the switch. If the threshold voltage for the FET is 2V, what range of output voltages will be properly controlled by the switch?

Solution

The minimum signal voltage is given by Equation (12.124):

$$v_{s\,(\mathrm{min})} > v_{c\,(\mathrm{OFF})} - V_T$$

or

$$v_{s\,(\mathrm{min})} > -15\mathrm{V} - 2\mathrm{V} = -17\ \mathrm{V}.$$

But, for this case, the signal voltage is limited by the output of the OpAmp to −15 V.

The maximum signal voltage is given by Equation (12.125):

$$v_{s\,(\mathrm{max})} < v_{c\,(\mathrm{ON})} - V_T$$

or

$$v_{s\,(\mathrm{max})} < 15\ \mathrm{V} - 2\mathrm{V} = +13\ \mathrm{V}.$$

Thus the absolute maximum signal range is limited to:

$$-15\ \mathrm{V} < v_s < +13\ \mathrm{V}.$$

Good design practice would place tighter limits on the signal. These limits are functions of whatever additional design specifications may apply to the particular application of this switch.

One of the problems associated with the simple FET analog switch of Figure 12.75 is that the ON resistance of the switch is not constant as the input signal varies. Variation in ON resistance can be a serious limitation in some circuit applications as it can cause distortion of the analog signal. Variation in the input signal will cause the voltage at the source of the FET to vary. If the gate terminal of the FET is set at a specific control voltage level, the input signal variation, therefore, produces a variation in V_{GS} for the FET and consequently a variation in the drain-source resistance of the switch. Determination of the switch resistance as a function of input signal level requires the solution of two nonlinear equations. For this particular circuit the equations reduce to:

$$R_{DS} = \frac{v_s}{i} - R_{load}, \qquad \textbf{(12.126)}$$

and

$$R_{DS} = \frac{1}{v_{c(ON)} - i\,R_{load} - V_T}. \qquad \textbf{(12.127)}$$

Computer simulation or the application of load line techniques are perhaps the two best methods to calculate the variation of switch resistance with input. A typical graph of the switch resistance as a function of input signal is given in Figure 12.76. Notice that while the switch resistance is fairly small throughout most of the input signal range (24 Ω < R_{DS} < 100 Ω as –15 V < v_s < 6.6 V), it increases dramatically as the level of the input signal approaches the positive control voltage. This drastic increase in switch resistance can greatly diminish the utility of such a simple switch. The OFF resistance of this switch is typically very high (≥ 20 MΩ), and the OFF performance of such a switch is limited only by a very small leakage current in the FET.

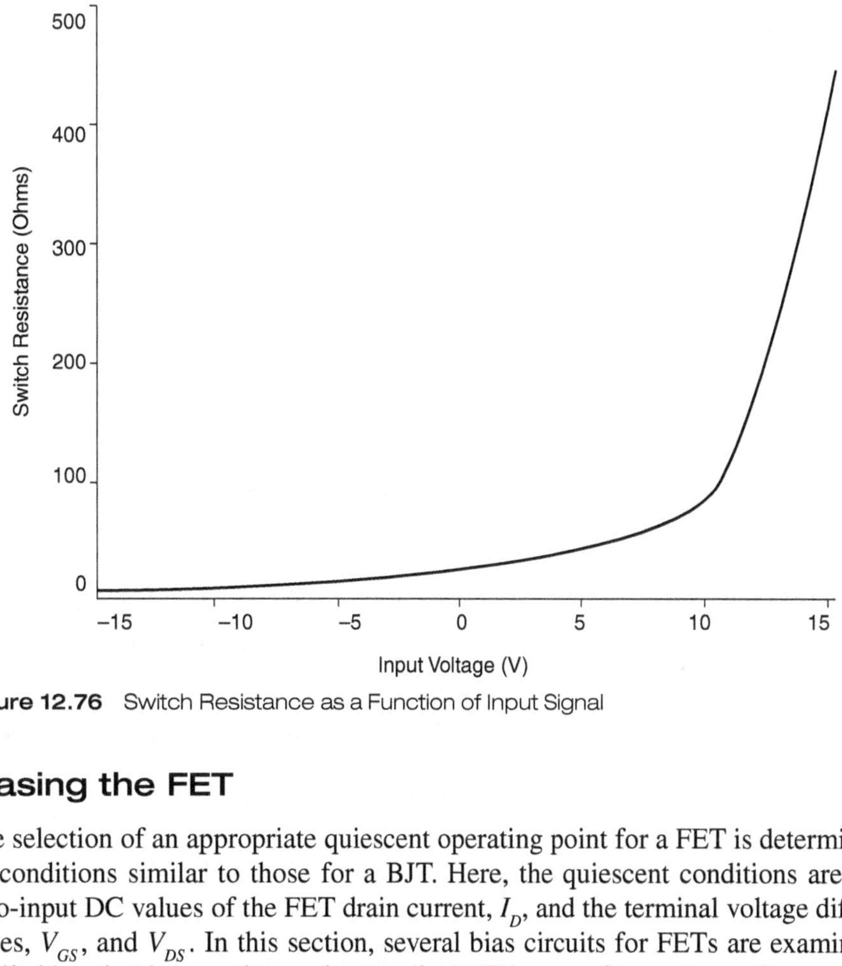

Figure 12.76 Switch Resistance as a Function of Input Signal

Biasing the FET

The selection of an appropriate quiescent operating point for a FET is determined by conditions similar to those for a BJT. Here, the quiescent conditions are the zero-input DC values of the FET drain current, I_D, and the terminal voltage differences, V_{GS}, and V_{DS}. In this section, several bias circuits for FETs are examined. While bias circuitry can be used to put the FET in any of its regions of operation, the focus of this section is the saturation region. The saturation region is, of course, significant as the region where FET amplification occurs. While the examples in this section use *n*-channel FETs, *p*-channel FETs are biased in a similar manner except for a change in polarity of the voltage supplies.

The emphasis in this section is on biasing using voltage supplies and resistors. It is also common to bias transistors using current sources. Biasing FETs for amplifier applications using current sources is discussed extensively in Chapter 6.

The Source Self-Bias Circuit

The source self-bias circuit shown in Figure 12.77 is particularly useful in biasing JFETs and depletion mode FETs of other types. In this application, the external gate resistor, R_g serves to tie the voltage at the gate of the FET to ground (the gate current is essentially zero). This resistor is typically chosen to be a very large value (often on the order of a few megohms). For a specified drain current, I_D, the gate-source voltage, V_{GS}, can be determined from the FET transfer characteristic in either analytic or graphical form. R_s is then determined from V_{GS} and I_D:

$$R_s = -\frac{V_{GS}}{I_D} \qquad \textbf{(12.128)}$$

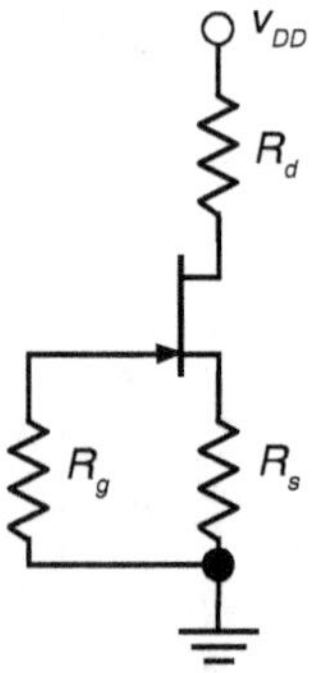

Figure 12.77 A Source Self-Bias Circuit

Example 12.21

An n-channel JFET with the following characteristics:

$$V_{PO} = -3.5 \text{ V} \quad \text{and} \quad I_{DSS} = 10 \text{ mA}$$

is placed in the source self-bias circuit of Figure 12.77. Quiescent conditions of

$$I_D = 5 \text{ mA} \quad \text{and} \quad V_{DS} = 5 \text{ V}$$

are desired. Determine the bias resistors necessary to establish the quiescent conditions if the power supply voltage is $V_{DD} = 15$ V.

Solution

The quiescent conditions for the JFET distinctly imply that it is in saturation:

$$V_{DS} \geq V_{GS} - V_{PO}.$$

Therefore, the Equation (12.86) is the determining factor in finding V_{GS}:

$$I_D = I_{DSS}\left[1 - \frac{V_{GS}}{V_{PO}}\right]^2.$$

Substitution of values yields:

$$\frac{5}{10} = \left[1 - \frac{V_{GS}}{-3.5}\right]^2 \text{ or } V_{GS} = 3.5\left(\pm\frac{1}{\sqrt{2}} - 1\right) = -1.025\text{V}, -5.975\text{V}.$$

The value between 0 V and V_{PO} is the only valid solution to Equation (12.86); the other is a spurious result caused by taking the square root. Thus, $V_{GS} = -1.025$ V. The resistor R_S can now be determined:

$$R_S = -\frac{-1.025\,\text{V}}{5\,\text{mA}} = 205\,\Omega.$$

The resistor R_D is determined by writing a loop equation around the drain-source loop:

$$I_D R_S + V_{DS} + I_D R_D - V_{DD} = 0$$

or

$$R_d = \frac{V_{DD} - V_{DS}}{I_D} - R_s = \frac{15 - 5}{5m} - 205 = 1.795\,k\Omega.$$

The Resistor R_g is typically chosen arbitrarily large:

$$R_g = 1\,\text{M}\Omega.$$

One drawback of the source self-bias circuit is that the quiescent conditions are sensitive to variation in the FET parameters V_{PO} and I_{DSS}. The restriction of Equation (12.128),

$$V_{GS} = -I_D R_d,$$

coupled with the FET characteristic equations potentially leads to wide variation in quiescent condition. This variation is best described graphically as in Figure 12.78. In the circuit of Example 12.21, a FET with the following parameter variations is used.

$$8\text{ mA} < I_{DSS} < 12\text{ mA} \qquad -4\text{ V} < V_{PO} < -3\text{ V}$$

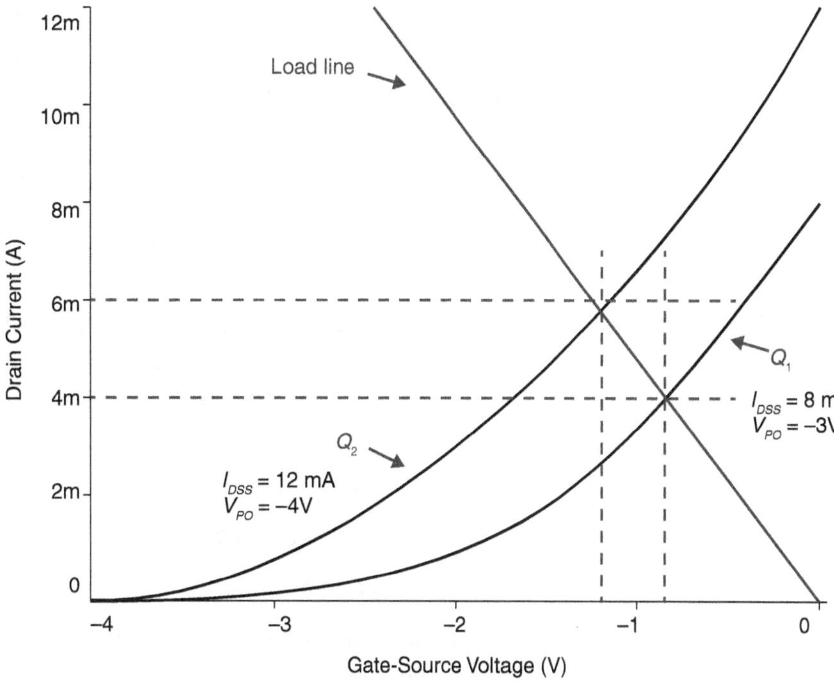

Figure 12.78 Change in Quiescent Point Due to FET Parameter Variation

If the design procedure results of Example 12.21 are used, the resultant ranges in quiescent conditions due to FET parameter variation can be read off Figure 12.78. They are:

$$-1.20\text{ V} < V_{GS} < -0.85\text{ V} \qquad \text{and} \qquad 4.13\text{ mA} < I_D < 5.87\text{ mA}.$$

The variation in FET parameters has caused a change in the two quiescent quantities of more than ±17% from the nominal quiescent conditions calculated in Example 12.21. In many cases it is necessary to control the quiescent point to a greater degree than is possible with the source self-bias circuit.

The Fixed-Bias Circuit

In addition to sensitivity to FET parameter variation, the source self-bias circuit mandates overly restrictive constraints on the external bias resistors in many applications. The resistors, R_d and R_s, play important roles in determining amplifier gain and output impedance. It is a rare occurrence when quiescent conditions are more significant than these two amplifier performance factors. The restrictive nature of the source self-bias circuit is centered at the holding of the FET gate terminal at ground potential. Removing that restriction greatly improves the versatility of a bias scheme. The fixed-bias circuit of Figure 12.79 is a simple depletion-mode FET bias circuit that allows the gate to be at voltages other than ground.

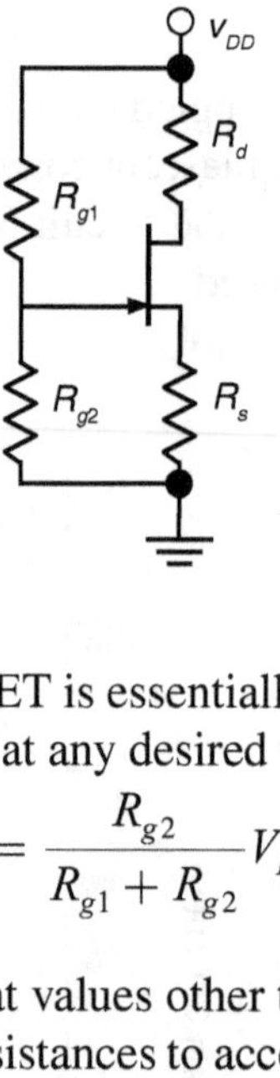

Figure 12.79 Fixed-Bias Circuit

Since the gate current in the FET is essentially zero, the two gate resistors, R_{g1} and R_{g2}, set the voltage at the gate at any desired value between ground and V_{DD}:

$$V_G = \frac{R_{g2}}{R_{g1} + R_{g2}} V_{DD} \tag{12.129}$$

Setting the FET gate voltage at values other than zero allows for a wider possible choice of source and drain resistances to accomplish specific quiescent conditions. Design choices for these resistors are based primarily on one or more of the following specific criteria:

- Amplification specifications
- Output resistance specifications
- Quiescent point stability

The first two of these design criteria will be discussed later in this book, quiescent point stability involves reducing the variation in drain current due to FET

parameter variation. The relationship of drain current to the external resistors in a fixed-bias circuit is determined by the voltage across the drain resistor:

$$I_D = \frac{V_S}{R_s} = \frac{V_G - (V_G - V_S)}{R_s} = \frac{V_G - V_{GS}}{R_s} \tag{12.130}$$

where V_G is given by Equation (12.129). The variation of I_D due to variation of the FET parameter, V_{GS}, is inversely proportional to the value of the source resistor, R_s. While other design criteria may put upper limits on R_s, quiescent point stability indicates that a large value for R_s is desirable. The basic load line interpretation of this stability principle is described in Figure 12.80.

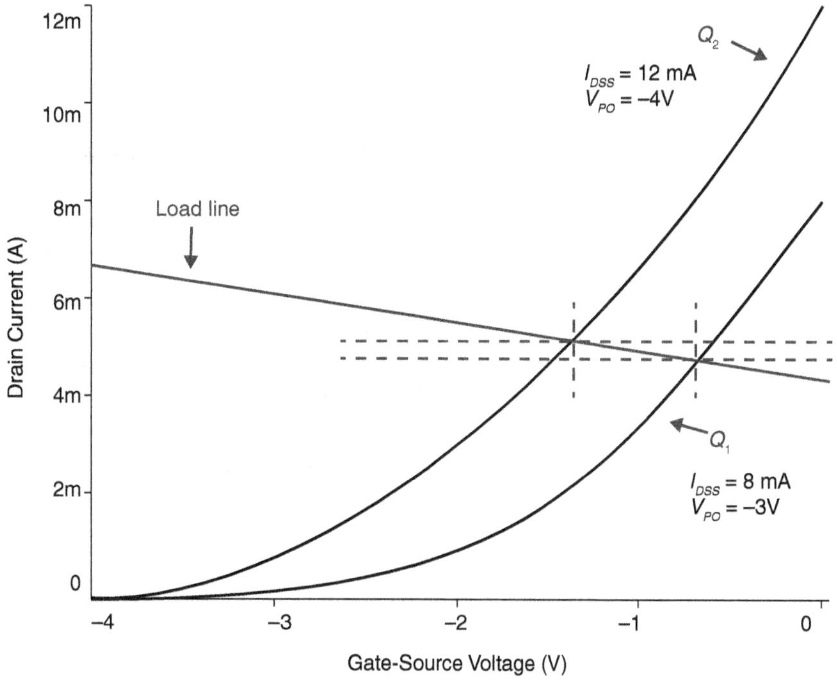

Figure 12.80 Change in Quiescent Point Due to FET Parameter Variation, Fixed-Bias Circuit

Example 12.22

An n-channel JFET with the following nominal characteristic parameters:

$$V_{PO} = -3.5 \text{ V} \qquad \text{and} \qquad I_{DSS} = 10 \text{ mA}$$

is to be biased with quiescent conditions of

$$I_D = 5 \text{ mA} \qquad \text{and} \qquad V_{DS} = 5 \text{ V}.$$

The FET is subject to parameter variation:

$$-4 \text{ V} < V_{PO} < -3 \text{ V} \qquad \text{and} \qquad 8 \text{ mA} < I_{DSS} < 12 \text{ mA}$$

Determine the bias resistors necessary to establish the quiescent conditions so that the drain current will not vary more than ±4% due to the FET parameter variation. The power supply is given to be: $V_{DD} = 20$ V.

Solution

The nominal quiescent conditions for the FET are identical to those of Example 12.21. Thus, the value of V_{GS} is obtained in the same manner and is:

$$V_{GS(\text{nominal})} = -1.025 \text{ V}.$$

The extreme values of V_{GS} can be obtained either graphically, as in Figure 12.80, or analytically using Equation (12.86):

$$I_D = I_{DSS}\left[1 - \frac{V_{GS}}{V_{PO}}\right]^2$$

These extreme values are found to be:

$$V_{GS(\min)} = -1.37 \text{ V } \{I_{D(\max)} = 5.2 \text{ mA}\}$$
$$V_{GS(\max)} = -0.676 \text{ V } \{I_{D(\min)} = 4.8 \text{ mA}\}$$

The minimum value of R_s that will satisfy the stability requirements can be calculated as the *maximum* value of

$$R_{s(\min)} = \max\left\{\frac{\Delta V_{GS}}{\Delta I_D}\right\}.$$

For this particular case,

$$R_{s(\min)} = \max\left\{\frac{-1.025 + 1.367}{0.0002} \quad \text{or} \quad \frac{-1.025 + 0.676}{-0.0002}\right\} = 1.75\,k\Omega.$$

If R_s is chosen to be this minimum value, the nominal voltage at the source and gate of the FET are:

$$V_s = I_{D(\text{nominal})}R_s = 8.75 \text{ V} \qquad V_G = V_S + V_{GS(\text{nominal})} = 7.725 \text{ V}.$$

The gate voltage can be obtained with a combination of a large variety of resistors. One pair that will satisfy the minimal design goals for this case is:

$$R_{g1} = 1.62 \text{ M}\Omega \qquad \text{and} \qquad R_{g2} = 1.02 \text{ M}\Omega.$$

The remaining resistor, R_d, can be determined from the drain-source voltage requirement as:

$$R_d = \frac{V_{DD} - V_{DS}}{I_D} - R_s = \frac{20 - 5}{5m} - 1750 = 1.25\,k\Omega$$

Biasing Enhancement Mode FETs

The fixed-bias circuit presented in the preceding section is also useful in biasing enhancement mode FETs. The only significant difference in the procedure necessary to determining resistance values to properly bias the FET is in the initial determination of the quiescent conditions. V_{GS} in enhancement FETs carries the opposite sign as for depletion FETs and a different relationship between V_{GS} and I_D exists. The proper expression for the FET gate-source voltage in the saturation region is given by Equation (4.2-21):

$$I_D = K(V_{GS} - V_T)^2.$$

Bias stability can be achieved by following the procedure outlined in Example 12.22.

The source self-bias circuit of Figure 12.77 is not useful for enhancement FETs. However, several other possibilities for biasing of this type of FET exist. In

addition to the fixed-bias circuit of Figure 12.79, two other common bias circuits for enhancement-mode FETs are given in Figure 12.81. Both circuits offer some bias stabilization with the circuit of Figure 12.81b, offering superior stability and flexibility in resistor value choice. The connection in these two circuits between the gate and drain through resistor R_f provides a signal path between input and output when the FET is used in amplifier applications.

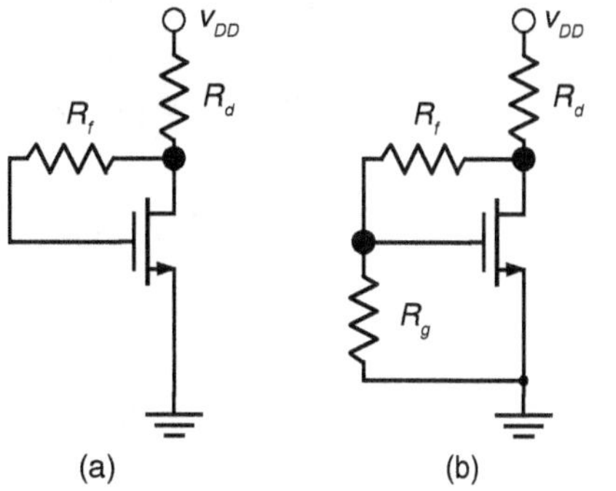

Figure 12.81 Additional Bias Circuits for Enhancement-Mode FETs

FET AMPLIFIERS

The FET saturation region with small-signal input variations about the DC quiescent operating point (Q-point) is considered approximately linear in nature. Therefore, like the BJT, small-signal approximations in the form of approximate circuit networks are commonly used to model FET operation in the saturation region. The model is used to approximate all FET types.

Figure 12.82 shows a "generic" FET biased in the saturation region by a gate-source voltage V_{GSQ}, with a drain-source voltage V_{DSQ} and drain current I_{DQ}. The effect of small changes of the bias voltages on I_D can be found by independently varying V_{GSQ} and V_{DSQ} as shown in Figure 12.82.

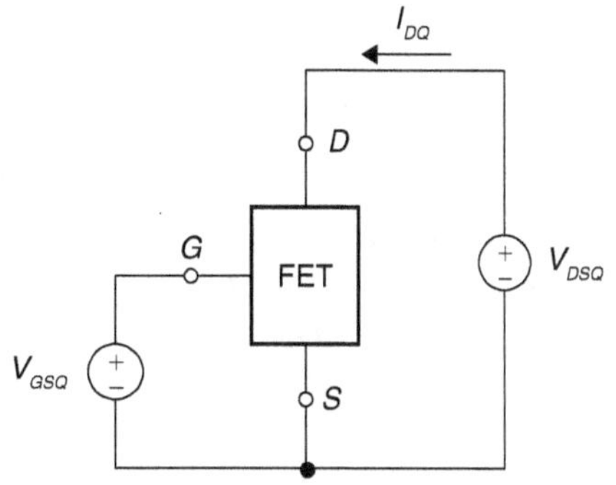

Figure 12.82 Generic FET biased in the Saturation Region by a Gate-Source Voltage V_{GSQ}, with a Drain-Source Voltage V_{DSQ}, and Drain Current I_{DQ}.

The change in I_D with respect to small variations in V_{GS} and V_{DS} are expressed as conductance parameters. These parameters include the following:

1. *Small-signal transconductance or mutual conductance,* g_m, often referred to simply as "transconductance." The mathematical relation for determining transconductance is

$$g_m = \left.\frac{\partial I_D}{\partial V_{GS}}\right|_{V_{DS}=\text{constant}} \approx \left.\frac{\Delta I_D}{\Delta V_{GS}}\right|_{V_{DS}=\text{constant}} . \tag{12.131}$$

2. *Small-signal drain conductance* or *output conductance*, g_d. The output conductance is defined as

$$g_d = r_d^{-1} = \left.\frac{\partial I_D}{\partial V_{DS}}\right|_{V_{GS}=\text{constant}} \approx \left.\frac{\Delta I_D}{\Delta V_{DS}}\right|_{V_{GS}=\text{constant}} \quad \textbf{(12.132)}$$

where $r_d - 1$ is the drain resistance or output resistance in Ohms.
Both g_m and g_d have units of conductance and are expressed in Siemens [S].

Consider the general case where both V_{DS} and V_{GS} changed simultaneously. The corresponding total change in the drain current is

$$\Delta I_D = \left(\left.\frac{\partial I_D}{\partial V_{GS}}\right|_{V_{DS}=\text{constant}}\right)\Delta V_{GS} + \left(\left.\frac{\partial I_D}{\partial V_{DS}}\right|_{V_{GS}=\text{constant}}\right)\Delta V_{DS}. \quad \textbf{(12.133)}$$

If ΔI_D, ΔV_{DS}, and ΔV_{GS} are time-varying quantities about the Q-point, they are AC signals. Equation (12.133) can then be rewritten as:

$$i_d = \left(\left.\frac{\partial i_D}{\partial v_{GS}}\right|_Q\right)v_{gs} + \left(\left.\frac{\partial i_D}{\partial v_{DS}}\right|_Q\right)v_{ds}. \quad \textbf{(12.134)}$$

Substituting the small-signal conductances into Equation (12.134) yields

$$i_d = g_m v_{gs} + g_d v_{ds}. \quad \textbf{(12.135)}$$

Recall from Chapter 4 that the gate current is assumed to be zero. Therefore,

$$\Delta I_G = 0. \quad \textbf{(12.136)}$$

Equations (12.135) and (12.136) relate small-signal quantities that can are represented by the small-signal equivalent circuit of Figure 12.83.

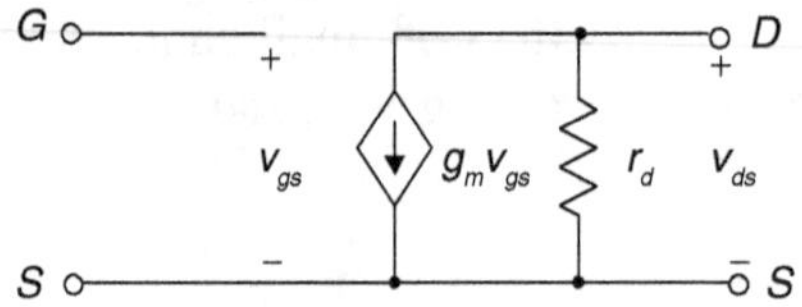

Figure 12.83 Low Frequency Small-Signal Model of an FET

The voltage-controlled current source in the low frequency small-signal FET model in Figure 12.83 may be changed to a voltage-controlled voltage source by source transformation. The source transformed FET model is shown in Figure 12.84. The gain or amplification factor μ is defined as

$$\mu = \frac{g_m}{g_d} = g_m r_d \quad \textbf{(12.137)}$$

The FET models shown in Figures 12.83 and 12.84 are valid for all types of FETs biased in the saturation region. The actual values of the elements in the model vary for different FETs.

Figure 12.84 Equivalent Low Frequency Model of an FET with a Voltage-Controlled Voltage Source

The value of $r_d = g_{d-1}$ can be obtained from the output characteristic curve of the FET at the desired Q-point. From Equation (12.132), g_d is the slope of the line defined by I_D and V_{DS} at the desired Q-point defined by a constant V_{GSQ},

$$g_d = \left.\frac{\Delta i_D}{\Delta v_{DS}}\right|_{V_{GSQ}} = r_d^{-1}. \tag{12.138}$$

Typical values for $r_d = g_{d-1}$ range from 10kΩ to 100kΩ. r_d can also be determined from I_D and the early voltage, V_A, using the following relationship:

$$r_d = \frac{V_A}{I_D}. \tag{12.139}$$

The small-signal value for g_m for the JFET and depletion MOSFET is found by taking the derivative of I_D from Table 12.5 with respect to V_{GS},

$$g_m = \frac{\partial I_D}{\partial V_{GS}} = \frac{\partial\left[I_{DSS}\left(1-\frac{V_{GS}}{V_{PO}}\right)^2\right]}{\partial V_{GS}} \tag{12.140}$$

$$= \frac{-2I_{DSS}\left(1-\frac{V_{GS}}{V_{PO}}\right)}{V_{PO}} = 2\left(\frac{I_{DSS}}{V_{PO}^{\ 2}}\right)\left(V_{GS}-V_{PO}\right).$$

But, by definition,

$$I_D = I_{DSS}\left(1-\frac{V_{GS}}{V_{PO}}\right)^2 \quad \text{or} \quad I_{DSS} = \frac{I_D}{\left(1-\frac{V_{GS}}{V_{PO}}\right)^2}. \tag{12.141}$$

Substituting Equation (12.141) into (12.140) and simplifying yields an alternate expression for the small-signal transconductance of depletion-type FETs:

$$g_m = \frac{2I_D}{\left(V_{GS}-V_{PO}\right)} = 2\sqrt{I_D\left(\frac{I_{DSS}}{V_{PO}^{\ 2}}\right)}. \tag{12.142}$$

For the enhancement MOSFET, g_m is found by taking the derivative of I_D from Table 12.5 with respect to V_{GS},

$$g_m = \frac{\partial I_D}{\partial V_{GS}} = \frac{\partial\left[K\left(V_{GS}-V_T\right)^2\right]}{\partial V_{GS}} \tag{12.143}$$

$$= \frac{2I_D}{\left(V_{GS}-V_T\right)} = 2K\left(V_{GS}-V_T\right) = 2\sqrt{I_D K}.$$

Typical values for g_m range from 10^{-4} to 10^{-2} S.

An alternate method for arriving at the small-signal FET model is through the use of two-port analysis. The y-parameter two-port parameters are used since the independent variables are port voltages (V_{GS} and V_{DS}), and the dependent variable is the drain current I_D. As in the BJT, one terminal of the FET is assigned as a common terminal to both ports. In practice, the FET source is assigned as the common terminal.

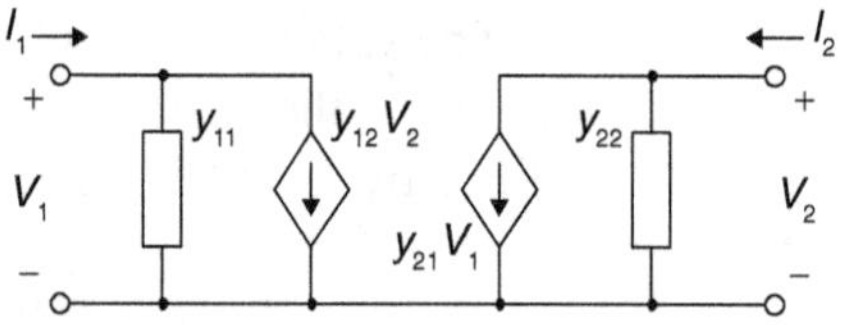

Figure 12.85 Generic y-parameter Two Port Network

The generic y-parameter two port network is shown in Figure 12.85. The y-parameter equations are:

$$\begin{bmatrix} I_1 \\ I_2 \end{bmatrix} = \begin{bmatrix} y_{11} & y_{12} \\ y_{21} & y_{22} \end{bmatrix} \begin{bmatrix} V_1 \\ V_2 \end{bmatrix},$$

and

$$y_{ij} = \left.\frac{\partial I_i}{\partial V_j}\right|_{V_{k \neq j} = \text{constant}}.$$

For the FET, v_{gs} and v_{ds} are represented as V_1 and V_2 in the two-port network, respectively. The currents I_1 and I_2 are I_G and I_D, respectively. However, the gate current in the FET is approximately zero. Therefore, $I_1 = 0$, which implies that the dependent current source $y_{12}V_2 = 0$, and the two-port network exhibits an infinite input impedance ($y_{11} = 0$). The remaining two parameters of the y-parameter two-port network are the transadmittance, y_{21}, and the output admittance, y_{22}. The real components of the transadmittance and output admittance were found in Equations (12.131) and (12.132):

$$|y_{21}| = g_m \tag{12.144}$$

and

$$|y_{22}| = g_d. \tag{12.145}$$

y-parameters with descriptive subscripts are often used to specify parameters in manufacturers' data sheets. The second subscript defines which terminal is chosen as common (the source), and the first subscript identifies the function of the parameter:

$$yfs = y_{21} = g_m$$
$$= \text{input admittance – source as common terminal} \tag{12.146}$$

$$yos = y_{22} = g_d$$
$$= \text{output admittance – source as common terminal} \tag{12.147}$$

The small-signal parameters for the FET are summarized in Table 12.6. The FET parameters are dependent on quiescent conditions.

Table 12.6 FET Small-Signal Parameters

Small-Signal Parameter	Value
JFET and Depletion MOSFET: g_m	$2\left(\frac{I_{DSS}}{V_{PO}^2}\right)(V_{GS}-V_{PO})=\frac{2I_D}{(V_{GS}-V_{PO})}=2\sqrt{I_D\left(\frac{I_{DSS}}{V_{PO}^2}\right)}$
Enhancement MOSFET: g_m	$2K(V_{GS}-V_T)=\frac{2I_D}{(V_{GS}-V_T)}=2\sqrt{I_D K}$
All FETs r_d	$\left\lvert\frac{V_A}{I_D}\right\rvert$

Example 12.23

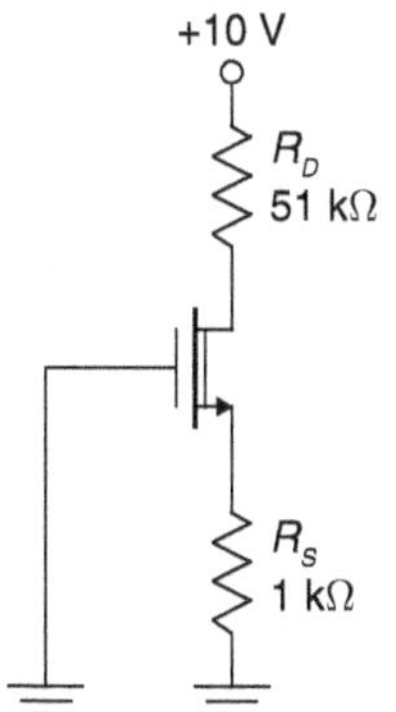

Exhibit 8

Given a depletion NMOSFET with parameters:

$$I_{DSS} = 5 \text{ mA} \qquad V_{PO} = -2 \text{ V}$$

operating in the circuit shown in Exhibit 8, determine the small-signal transconductance for the FET.

Solution

The quiescent conditions must first be obtained.

Note that $V_G = 0$. Therefore,

$$V_{GS} = V_G - V_S = -V_S = -I_D(1000)$$

Solving for V_{DS},

$$V_{DS} = 10 - I_D(1000 + 5100)$$
$$= 10 - I_D(6100)$$

Assume that the FET is in saturation. That is,

$$V_{DS} > V_{GS} - V_{PO}$$

Then,

$$I_D = I_{DSS}\left(1 - \frac{V_{GS}}{V_{PO}}\right)^2$$

Use the quadratic equation to solve for I_D. The two roots of the second order equation are:

$$I_D = 1.07 \text{ mA or } 3.725 \text{ mA}.$$

For $I_D = 1.07$ mA,

$$V_{GS} = -I_D(1\text{ K}) = -1.07 \times 10^{-3}(1000) = -1.07 \text{ V}$$

and

$$V_{DS} = 10 - I_D(6.1\text{k})$$
$$= 10 - 1.07 \times 10^{-3}(6100)$$
$$= 3.47 \text{ V}.$$

Similarly, for $I_D = 3.725$ mA,

$$V_{GS} = -I_D(1\text{k}) = -3.725 \times 10^{-3}\,(1000) = -3.725\text{ V}$$

and

$$\begin{aligned} V_{DS} &= 10 - I_D(6100) \\ &= 10 \times 10^{-3}(6100) \\ &= -2.7\text{ V.} \Leftarrow \text{This solution is clearly not valid.} \end{aligned}$$

Therefore, the drain current is $I_D = 1.07$ mA.
Confirm that the FET is in saturation:

$$V_{DS} > V_{GS} - V_{PO} = -1.07 + 2 = 0.93\text{ V}$$

and

$$3.47\text{ V} > 0.93\text{ V.} \Leftarrow \text{The FET is in saturation.}$$

The transconductance of the FET is

$$g_m = \frac{-2I_D}{\left(V_{PO} - V_{GS}\right)} = \frac{-2\left(1.07 \times 10^{-3}\right)}{-2 - (-1.07)} = 2.3\text{mS.}$$

Common-Drain and Common-Source Amplifier High-Frequency Characteristics

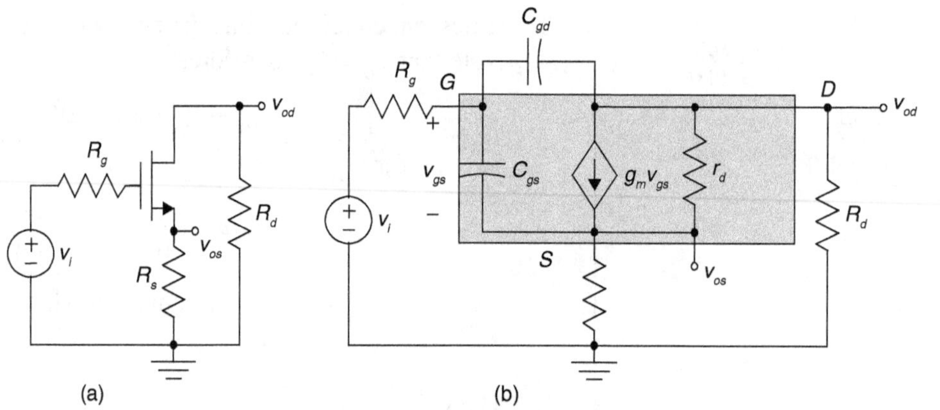

Figure 12.86 Common Source or Common Drain Equivalent Circuits
(a) Midband AC Equivalent, (b) High-Frequency Equivalent

The low frequency voltage gain of the common source FET amplifier is

$$A = \frac{v_{ds}}{v_{gs}} \approx -g_m\left[r_d/\left(R_d R_c\right)\right] \tag{12.148}$$

where the internal device capacitances are considered open circuits.

A summary of FET equations and models relationships is given in Figure 12.87:

N-Channel Junction Field Effect Transistors (JFETs) and Depletion MOSFETs (Low and Medium Frequency)		
Schematic Symbol	**Mathematical Relationships**	**Small-Signal (AC) Equivalent Circuit**
N-CHANNEL JFET 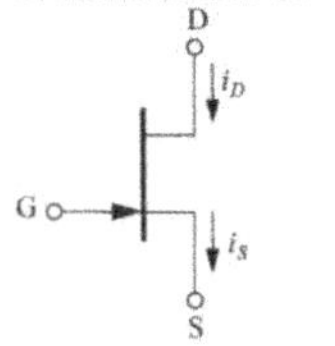 P-CHANNEL JFET 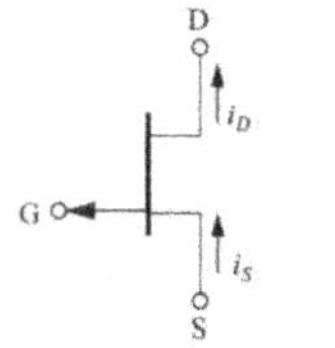 N-CHANNEL DEPLETION MOSFET (NMOS) 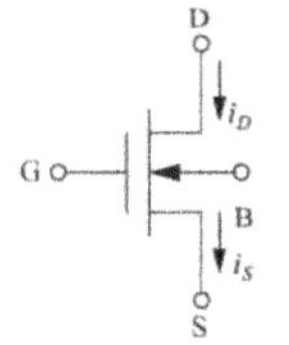 SIMPLIFIED SYMBOL 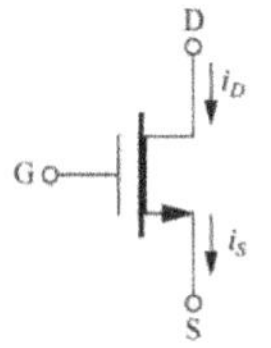	Cutoff Region: $v_{GS} < V_p$ $i_D = 0$ Triode Region: $v_{GS} > V_p$ and $v_{GD} > V_p$ $i_D = (I_{DSS}/V_p^2)[2v_{DS}(v_{GS} - V_p) - v_{DS}^2]$ Saturation Region: $v_{GS} > V_p$ and $v_{GD} < V_p$ $i_D = I_{DSS}(1 - v_{GS}/V_p)^2$ where I_{DSS} = drain current with $v_{GS} = 0$ (in the saturation region) $= KV_p^2$, K = conductivity factor, and V_p = pinch-off voltage.	$g_m = \dfrac{2\sqrt{I_{DSS} I_D}}{\lvert V_p \rvert}$ in saturation region 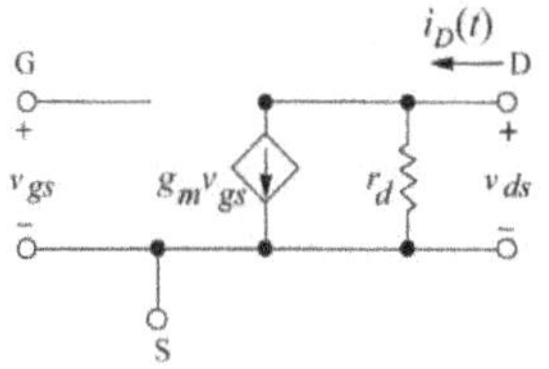 where $r_d = \left\lvert \dfrac{\partial v_{ds}}{\partial i_d} \right\rvert_{Q_{point}}$
P-CHANNEL DEPLETION MOSFET (PMOS) 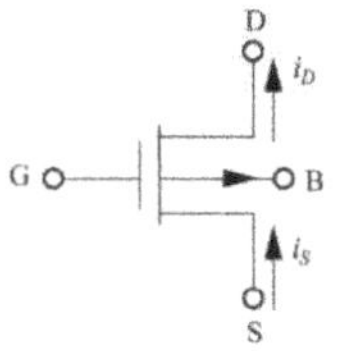 SIMPLIFIED SYMBOL 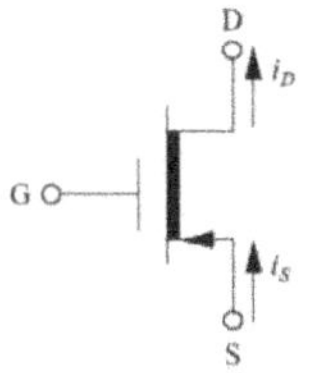	Same as for N-Channel with current directions and voltage polarities reversed.	Same as for N-Channel.

Source: NCEES, *FE Reference Handbook: 9.0 Version for Computer-Based Testing*, (Clemson, SC, 2013) 211.

Figure 12.87

Enhancement MOSFET (Low and Medium Frequency)		
Schematic Symbol	**Mathematical Relationships**	**Small-Signal (AC) Equivalent Circuit**
N-CHANNEL ENHANCEMENT MOSFET (NMOS) 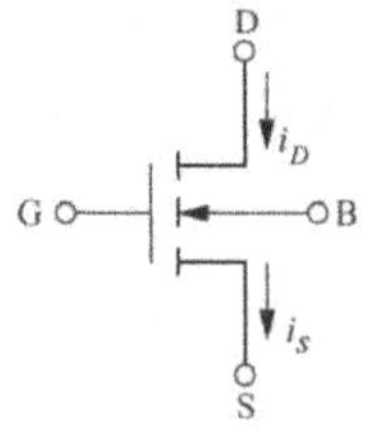 SIMPLIFIED SYMBOL 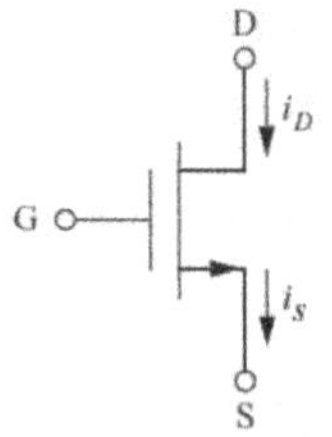	Cutoff Region: $v_{GS} < V_t$ $i_D = 0$ Triode Region: $v_{GS} > V_t$ and $v_{GD} > V_t$ $i_D = K\,[2v_{DS}(v_{GS} - V_t) - v_{DS}^2]$ Saturation Region: $v_{GS} > V_t$ and $v_{GD} < V_t$ $i_D = K\,(v_{GS} - V_t)^2$ where $K =$ conductivity factor $V_t =$ threshold voltage	$g_m = 2K(v_{GS} - V_t)$ in saturation region 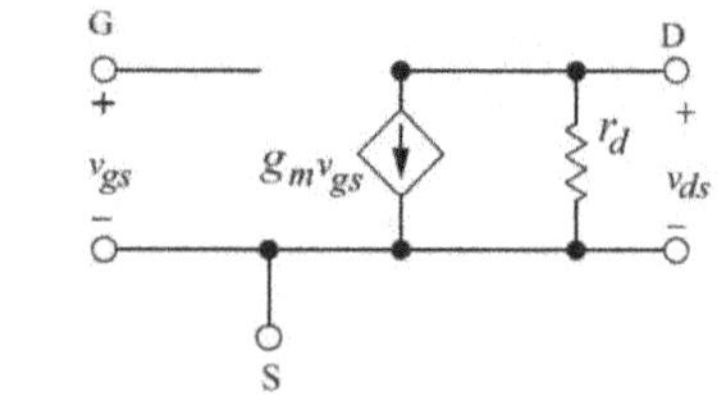 where $r_d = \left\| \frac{\partial v_{ds}}{\partial i_d} \right\|_{Q_{\text{point}}}$
P-CHANNEL ENHANCEMENT MOSFET (PMOS) 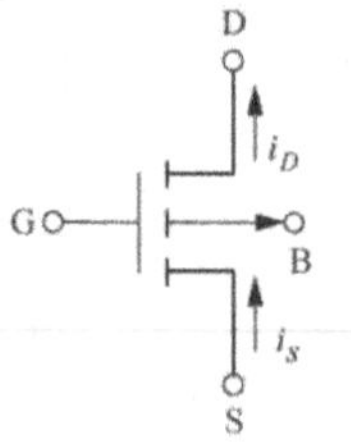 SIMPLIFIED SYMBOL 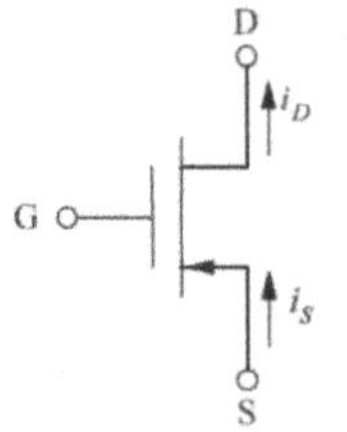	Same as for N-channel with current directions and voltage polarities reversed.	Same as for N-channel.

Figure 12.87 (continued)

BIPOLAR JUNCTION TRANSISTOR (BJT) AMPLIFIERS

BJT Low-Frequency Models

In previous sections it has been shown that the Ebers-Moll model is an effective model in all regions of a BJT operation. It has also been shown that for large-signal behavior, a simplified set of models can bring additional insight into the operation of an electronic circuit. These models are first-order approximations to

BJT operation and exhibit some degree of error. When a BJT is operating in the forward-active region, it is appropriate to improve the modeling of its operation with a second-order approximation. As in most series approximations to behavior, second-order effects are a linearization, about the first-order (in this case, the quiescent) behavior, and are therefore added to the first-order behavior.

In the case of BJT operation, small-signal (often called AC) variations are linearized approximates to the operation of a transistor about its large-signal (often called DC or quiescent) behavior. Previous discussions of BJTs have shown that the forward-active region (and, similarly, the inverse-active region) of BJT operation are approximately linear in nature. Therefore, it is quite reasonable to assume that small-signal approximations have great validity in the modeling of BJT operation. The small-signal approximations are made in the form of approximate models that take the form of two-port networks. Two-port network characterizations are valid for nonlinear systems that have regions of linearity; the BJT operating in either of its active regions is such a system.

The first obvious problem in modeling a BJT as a two-port is that there are only three terminals rather than the four that seem to be necessary. This obstacle is overcome by assigning one BJT terminal *common* to both ports. Practice has made two possibilities for this common terminal standard: either the emitter or the base are chosen to be the common terminal. In Figure 12.88, an npn BJT is shown as a two-port network with the emitter terminal chosen as common. In Chapter 3, it was shown that the major controlling port of a BJT is the base-emitter junction. Thus, the port containing the base-emitter junction is considered the input port, and the remaining port (which contains the collector terminal and the common terminal), is the output port. Since the terminal voltages and currents for BJTs have previously been identified with subscripts that are descriptive rather than the general numerical form of Section 12.1, the descriptive subscripts will be continued in the BJT two-port representation.

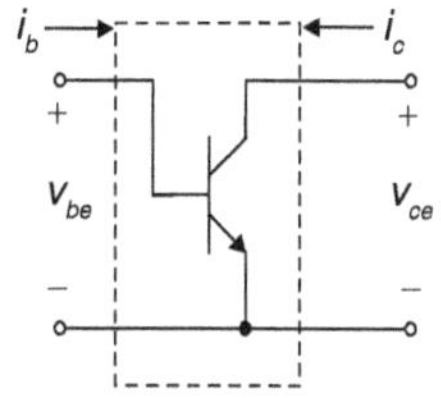

Figure 12.88 A Bipolar Junction Transistor as a Two-Port Network (Emitter as Common Terminal)

Here is the modeling process for transistor circuit performance:

1. Model the BJT with an appropriate DC model.
2. Determine the circuit quiescent (DC) conditions – verify BJT active region.
3. Determine the BJT AC model parameters from the quiescent conditions.
4. Create an AC equivalent circuit.
5. Determine the circuit AC performance by:
   - replacing the BJT by its AC model, or
   - using previously derived results for the circuit topology.
6. Add the results of the DC and AC analysis to obtain total circuit performance.

Techniques for the DC modeling of BJTs and the determination of quiescent conditions have been discussed thoroughly in Chapter 3; discussions of AC modeling follow. The steps relating to circuit performance are discussed in later sections of this chapter.

The choice of which set of two-port parameters will be most helpful in the modeling of a BJT is important. One good starting point is the Ebers-Moll model. The Ebers-Moll model for an *npn* BJT is shown in Figure 12.89.

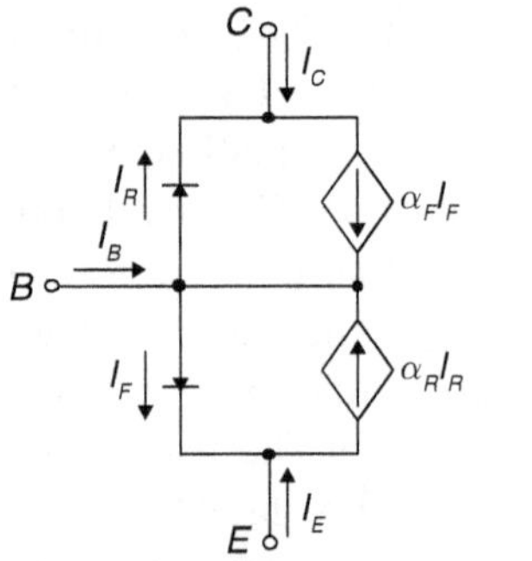

Figure 12.89 Ebers-Moll Model of an *npn* BJT

In the forward-active region of operation, the base-emitter junction is forward-biased, and the base-collector junction is reverse biased. Approximate models for forward-biased and reverse-biased diodes lead to the base-collector junction diode taking on the appearance of a very large resistance, while the base-emitter junction diode can be linearized about the quiescent point to a much smaller resistance. The forward current source (described by α_F) remains significant while the reverse current source supplies very little current. This small-signal model is shown in Figure 12.90, with the two junction dynamic resistances defined as:

r_{df} = base-emitter diode forward dynamic resistance,
r_{dr} = base-collector diode dynamic reverse resistance.

The dynamic resistance of a junction was derived in Chapter 2 to be:

$$r_d = \frac{\partial V}{\partial I} = \frac{\eta V_t}{I_s + I} = \frac{\eta V_t}{I_s} e^{-\frac{V}{\eta V_t}} \qquad \textbf{(12.149)}$$

The forward-biased value of this dynamic resistance is strongly dependent on the quiescent conditions, while the reverse-biased value is, in an active-region BJT, not. Thus r_{df} is strongly dependent on the quiescent conditions, while r_{dr}, a much larger value, is not. While the derivation of this small-signal model was based on the Ebers-Moll model of an *npn* BJT, the small-signal model itself is valid for ***both*** *npn* and *pnp* BJTs. Reversing the direction of the junctions only changes quiescent conditions; it does not change the expressions for dynamic resistance.

The analysis of electronic systems could be implemented using the model of Figure 12.90; however, two-port techniques simplify many aspects of analysis. The two-port realization of such a system would most effectively be accomplished by an *h*-parameter representation. This *h*-parameter realization is a common representation for small-signal, low-frequency BJT operation. Figure 12.91 shows the *h*-parameter realization of a small-signal model of a BJT.

Figure 12.90 Forward-Active Small-Signal Model of a BJT

The governing equations for the h-parameter model are:

$$v_{be} = h_{ie} i_b + h_{re} v_{ce} \tag{12.150a}$$

and

$$i_c = h_{fe} i_b + h_{oe} v_{ce} \tag{12.150b}$$

Figure 12.91 Common-Emitter h-parameter Model for a BJT

where descriptive subscripts have been chosen for the subscripts of the h-parameters. The second subscript defines which terminal is chosen as common (either the base or the emitter), and the first subscript identifies the function of the parameter:

h_{ie} = input impedance — emitter as common terminal
h_{re} = reverse voltage gain — emitter as common terminal
h_{fe} = forward current gain — emitter as common terminal
h_{oe} = output admittance — emitter as common terminal

The parameters can be found as:

$$h_{ie} = \left.\frac{\partial V_{BE}}{\partial I_b}\right|_{V_{CE}=V_{CE_q}} \qquad h_{re} = \left.\frac{\partial V_{BE}}{\partial V_{CE}}\right|_{I_B=I_{B_q}} \tag{12.151}$$

$$h_{fe} = \left.\frac{\partial I_C}{\partial I_B}\right|_{V_{CE}=V_{CE_q}} \qquad h_{oe} = \left.\frac{\partial I_C}{\partial V_{CE}}\right|_{I_B=I_{B_q}}.$$

Equation (12.151) can be revised using AC voltages and currents. Realizing that AC signals are variations about the quiescent point and that constant values have zero AC component, the h-parameters can also be defined as:

$$h_{ie} = \left.\frac{v_{be}}{i_b}\right|_{v_{ce}=0} \qquad h_{re} = \left.\frac{v_{be}}{v_{ce}}\right|_{i_b=0} \tag{12.152}$$

$$h_{fe} = \left.\frac{i_c}{i_b}\right|_{v_{ve}=0} \qquad h_{oe} = \left.\frac{i_c}{v_{ce}}\right|_{i_b=0}.$$

All the signals in Equation (12.152) are AC signals. Setting an AC signal (i.e., i_b or v_{ce}) to zero holds the AC variation of that signal to zero; it does not change the quiescent conditions of the BJT.

Determination of the small-signal BJT h-parameters is accomplished by applying Equation (12.152) to the circuit of Figure 12.90.

High-Frequency Models of the BJT

Analysis of the response of BJT circuits at high frequencies is based on accurate modeling of the frequency dependent performance of transistors. The dominant model used for small-signal analysis of a BJT in the forward-active region, the h-parameter model as presented in Chapter 3, does not contain frequency sensitive elements and is therefore invariant with respect to changes in frequency. As a result, it is necessary to introduce a new BJT model or to reinterpret an old model to include frequency-dependent terms. Once again, the Ebers-Moll model provides an excellent basis for creation of a more simple model in the forward-active region. In this modeling process, it is necessary to begin with a slight variation of the Ebers-Moll model that was presented in Chapter 3. As is shown in Figure 12.92, this presentation has added an additional base resistance of small value, r_b, to model the parasitic bulk resistance between the physical base terminal contact and the active base region and a large output resistance, r_o, to model reduced output resistance due to early voltage (V_A) effects.

In the forward-active region and at low frequencies, the Ebers-Moll Model of Figure 12.92 can be replaced by the linear two-port model shown in Figure 12.93. This model is known as the hybrid-π model. It is similar to the h-parameter model used previously in this text but has particular utility when frequency-dependent terms are included. Also of particular interest is the direct correlation between the individual hybrid-π impedances and the corresponding circuit elements in the Ebers-Moll model.

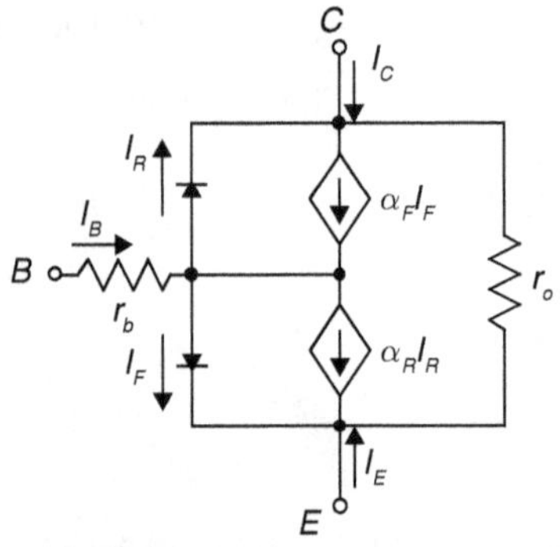

Figure 12.92 Ebers-Moll Model of a BJT

The resistances r_b and r_o are directly carried from one model to the other, while r_π and r_μ are the forward resistance of the base-emitter junction and the reverse resistance of the base-collector junction, respectively.

Figure 12.93 Low-Frequency Hybrid-π BJT Model

The relationships between h-parameter and hybrid-π models can be obtained by application of the two-port parameter tests as was performed (albeit on the Ebers-Moll model) in Section 5.2.

The base-collector junction reverse resistance is extremely large ($r_\mu > 20$ MΩ) and is typically ignored (left as an open circuit) the model. The simplified hybrid-π parameters are related to the h-parameter model parameters by:

$$g_m = \frac{h_{fe}}{r_\pi} = \frac{|I_c|}{\eta V_t} \qquad r_\pi = \beta_F \frac{\eta V_t}{|I_c|} = \frac{\beta_F}{g_m}, \tag{12.153}$$

$$r_o \approx \frac{1}{h_{oe}} = \frac{|V_A|}{|I_c|} \qquad r_b = h_{ie} - r_\pi.$$

Common Emitter Amplifier High-Frequency Characteristics

The midband AC model of a typical common emitter amplifier and its high-frequency equivalent, which uses the hybrid-π BJT model, are shown in Figure 12.94.

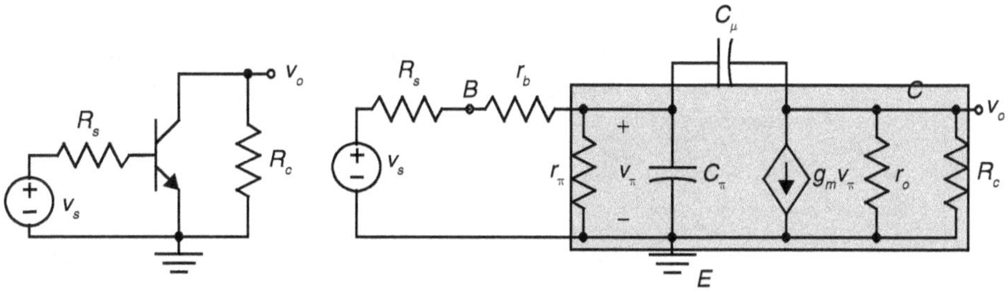

(a) (b)

Figure 12.94 Common Emitter Equivalent Circuits
(a) Midband AC Equivalent. (b) High-Frequency Equivalent

The use of the analysis techniques previously developed in this text for this circuit is made difficult by the presence of the capacitor C_μ, which interconnects the input and output sections of the amplifier. Miller's Theorem is particularly useful in reducing the analysis complexity for this case. In Figure 12.94b, the shaded two-port network has two terminals for which the voltage gain is well-known:

$$A = \frac{v_o}{v_\pi} = -g_m \left(r_o \| R_C\right) = -g_m R_C{}' \tag{12.154}$$

where $R_C{}'$ is the equivalent load resistance including the output impedance of the BJT:

$$R_C{}' = r_b \,||\, R_C \tag{12.155}$$

For low frequency analysis of BJT amplifiers, the device capacitances C_μ and C_π are open circuits.

Common Collector Amplifier High-Frequency Characteristics

The midband AC model of a typical common collector amplifier and its high-frequency equivalent are shown in Figure 12.95. While common collector amplifiers are often constructed without a collector resistor, it is included here for generality. Common emitter amplifiers with an emitter resistor have the same general topology as the common collector amplifier and, therefore, have virtually the same pole locations.

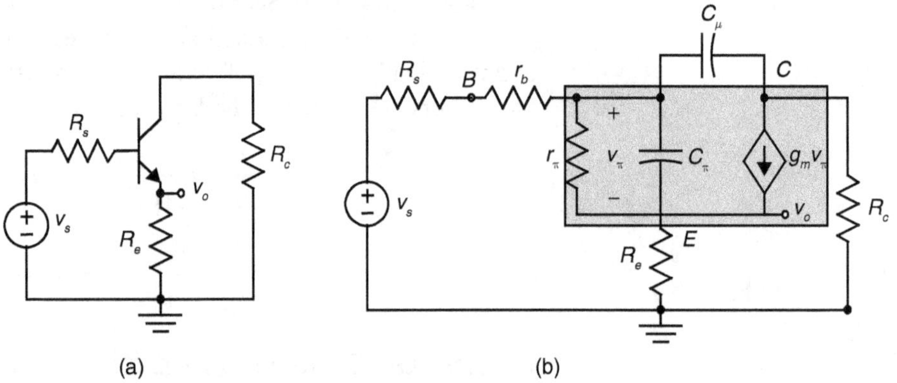

Figure 12.95 Common Collector Equivalent Circuits
(a) Midband AC Equivalent, (b) High-Frequency Equivalent

The analysis procedure for this circuit is once again complicated by the presence of the capacitor, C_μ. Miller's Theorem is one of many possible techniques that can be applied to reduce the analysis complexity for this case. In Figure 12.95b, the shaded two-port network has two terminals for which the voltage gain, with respect to the collector, can be approximated as:

$$A = \frac{v_{ec}}{v_\pi} = -g_m\left(R_C + R_E\right) \qquad \textbf{(12.156)}$$

where v_{ec} is the small-signal emitter-collector voltage.

A summary of BJT equations and models are given in Figure 12.96:

NPN Bipolar Junction Transistor (BJT)			
Schematic Symbol	**Mathematical Relationships**	**Large-Signal (DC) Equivalent Circuit**	**Low-Frequency Small-Signal (AC) Equivalent Circuit**
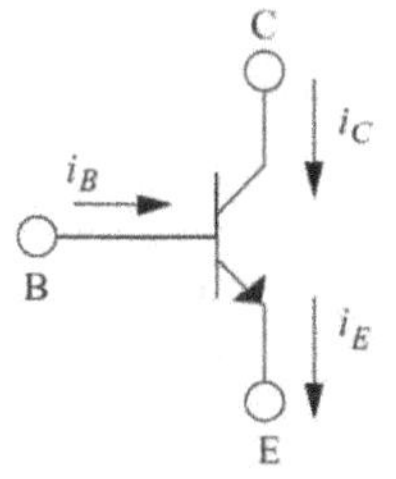 NPN – Transistor	$i_E = i_B + i_C$ $i_C = \beta i_B$ $i_C = \alpha i_E$ $\alpha = \beta/(\beta + 1)$ $i_C \approx I_S e^{(V_{BE}/V_T)}$ I_S = emitter saturation current V_T = thermal voltage Note: These relationships are valid in the active mode of operation.	Active Region: base emitter junction forward biased; base collector juction reverse biased 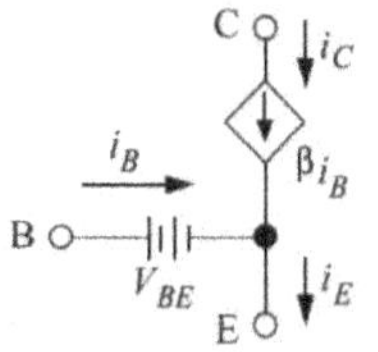 Saturation Region: both junctions forward biased 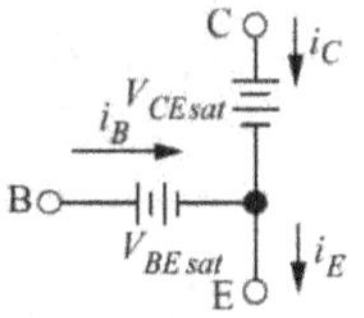	Low Frequency: $g_m \approx I_{CQ}/V_T$ $r_\pi \approx \beta/g_m$, $r_o = \left[\frac{\partial v_{CE}}{\partial i_c}\right]_{Q_{point}} \approx \frac{V_A}{I_{CQ}}$ where I_{CQ} = dc collector current at the Q_{point} V_A = Early voltage 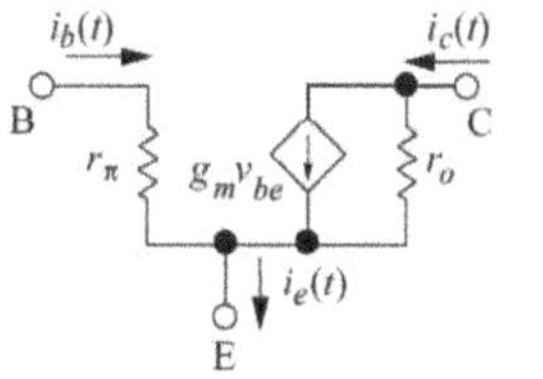
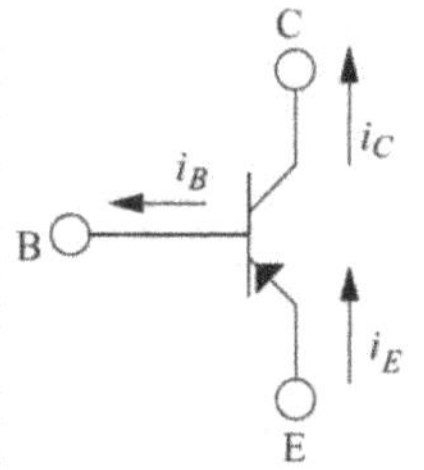 PNP – Transistor	Same as for NPN with current directions and voltage polarities reversed.	Cutoff Region: both junctions reverse biased 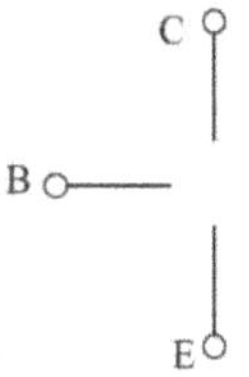 Same as NPN with current directions and voltage polarities reversed	Same as for NPN.

Source: NCEES, *FE Reference Handbook: 9.0 Version for Computer-Based Testing*, (Clemson, SC, 2013) 210.

Figure 12.96

PROBLEMS

12.1 At room temperature the reverse germanium diode current is measured to be 2 μA in a certain circuit. If the source voltage polarity is changed so the current flow is in the forward direction and the voltage directly across the diode is measured to be 0.3 V, determine the current flow.

12.2 For a variable junction capacitance that is known to have a graded junction, a known zero-voltage capacitance of 4 pF and a "built in" potential of 0.5 V, determine the capacitance if the bias voltage is –2 V.

12.3 A MOSFET in the *n*-channel enhanced mode operates in the saturation region. It is known that the conductivity factor K is 0.2 mA/V2 and the threshold voltage is 5 V and VGS is unknown but ID is 4 mA. Determine VGS.

12.4 A simplified bipolar common emitter amplifier has been designed for a small-signal, low-frequency sinusoidal input. The following parameters have been established

$$\text{Quiescent Load Current } I_C = 10 \text{ mA}, \quad \beta = 100, \quad R_L = 25 \text{ k}\Omega.$$

Using the small-signal simplified model (see Exhibit 12.4), determine the approximate voltage gain.

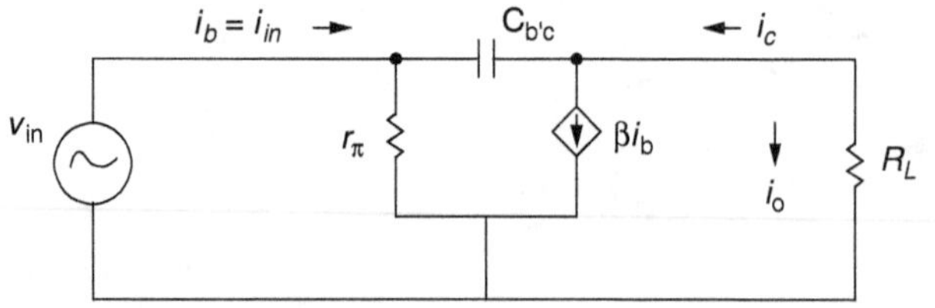

Exhibit 12.4 An approximate small signal BJT amplifier circuit

12.5 A simple one-stage BJT amplifier circuit model is shown with coupling capacitors (see Exhibit 12.5). Determine the output of the amplifier at mid-frequency.

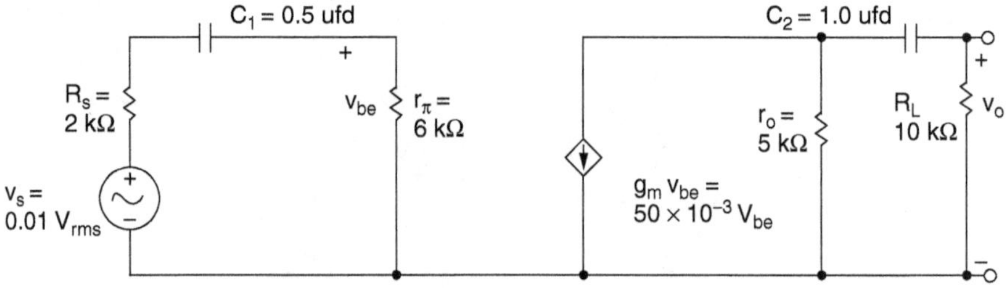

Exhibit 12.5 A one-stage BJT amplifier small signal model

12.6 Design a noninverting amplifier with a voltage gain of approximately 12 with an input resistance of 12 kΩ.

12.7 Determine the current through the load resistor, *RL*, as a function of the input voltage, *vi*, for the given circuit. Know that $v_2 = v_1$ and that $i_{RL} = v_2 / R_L$.

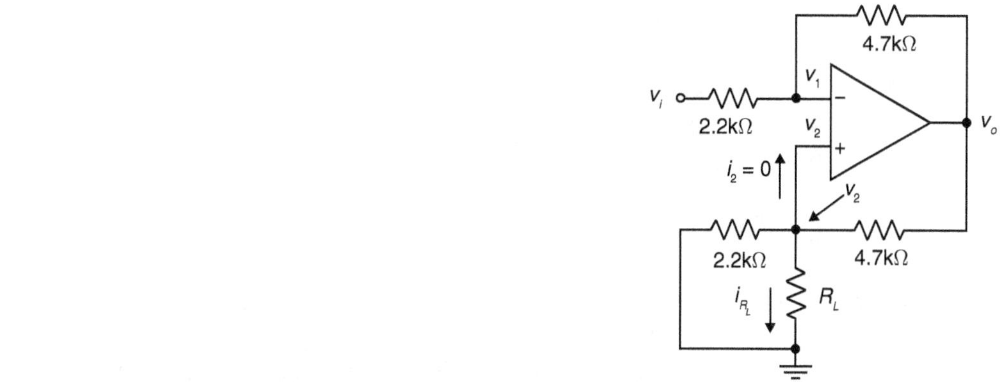

12.8 What is the expression of the output voltage for the circuit shown for $v_{i1} = \cos(w_0 t)$ and $v_{i2} = 1.5\cos(w_0 t + 30°)$?

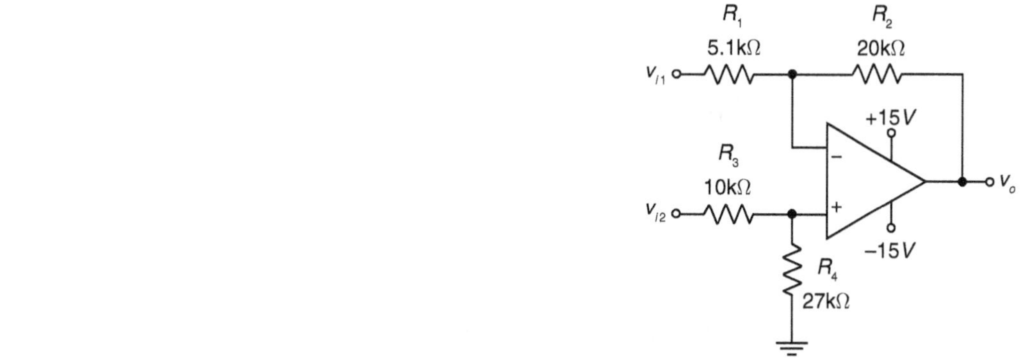

Use SPICE to confirm the result.

12.9 A silicon diode has a reverse saturation current of 0.1 nA and an empirical scaling constant, $\eta = 2$. Assume operation at room temperature.

a. At what diode voltage will the reverse current attain 99% of the saturation value?
b. At what diode voltage will the forward current attain the same magnitude?
c. Calculate the forward currents at diode voltages of 0.5V to 0.8V in 0.1V increments.

12.10 Let the reverse saturation current of a diode equal 15 nA and $\eta V_t =$ 25.6 mV.

If $I_D = 5$ mA, find

a. V_d
b. V_d / I_D
c. r_d

If I_D varies over the range 4.8 mA $\leq I_D \leq$ 5.2 mA, what is the range of

d. V_d
e. r_d

12.11 Experimental data at 25° C indicates that the forward biased current, I_D, flowing through a diode is 2.5 μA with $\eta = 2$, a voltage drop across the diode, V_D, of 0.53 V and $I_D = 1.5$ mA at $V_D = 0.65$ V. Determine:
a. I_S
b. I_D at $V_D = 0.60$ V

12.12 For the diode in 12.11, what is the diode voltage drop, V_D, at
a. $I_D = 1.0$ mA at 50° C
b. $I_D = 1.0$ mA at 0° C

12.13 Given $V_t = 0.026\ V$, $V_d = 0.7V$, and $I_d = 2.3$ mA, find n and I_s.

12.14 The four-diode circuits in Exhibit 12.14 use identical diodes described by $\eta = 2$ and $I_S = 1.5$ pA.
a. For the circuit shown in Exhibit 12.14 (a), determine the value of the current source to obtain an output voltage $V_O = 2.6$ V.
b. Find the change in output voltage for the circuit in Exhibit 12.14 (b). How much current is drawn away by the load?

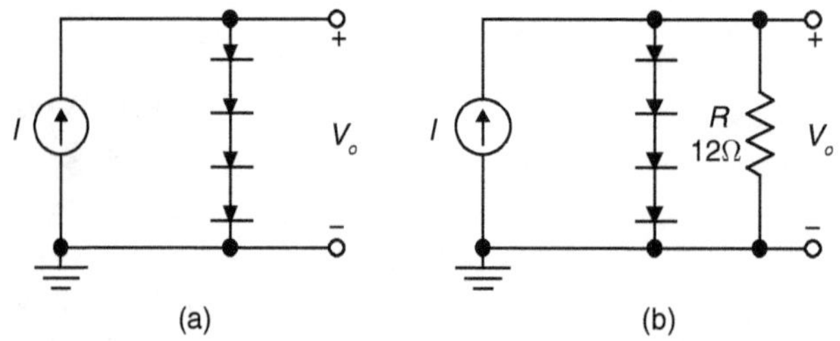

Exhibit 12.14

12.15 An n-channel JFET is described by the following parameters:

$$IDSS = 4.5 \text{ mA}$$
$$VPO = -3.6 \text{ V}$$

a. If the JFET is in saturation, what gate-to-source voltage, VGS, is necessary to achieve a drain current of 2.6 mA?
b. What is the minimum VDS that will satisfy the conditions stated in part a?
c. If VDS = 2 V, what gate-to-source voltage is necessary to achieve the same drain current?

12.16 A p-channel JFET is described by the following parameters:

$$IDSS = 4.0 \text{ mA}$$
$$VPO = -2.8 \text{ V}$$

a. If the JFET is in saturation, what source-to-gate voltage, VSG, is necessary to achieve a drain current of 1.8 mA?
b. What is the minimum VSD that will satisfy the conditions stated in part a?
c. If VSD = 1.5 V, what gate-to-source voltage is necessary to achieve the same drain current?

12.17 The parameters for a given JFET are:

$$IDSS = 7.5 \text{ mA}$$
$$VPO = -4 \text{ V}$$

The JFET is to be biased at

$$\text{ID} = 2 \text{ mA}$$
$$\text{VDS} = 6 \text{ V}$$

with the circuit topology as shown.

Determine the values of RD and RS to complete this design if VDD = 20 V.

12.18 Use the n-channel JFET circuit shown. If the JFET is described by

$$VPO = -2.5\text{V and } IDSS = 4 \text{ mA},$$

find *ID* and *VDS*.

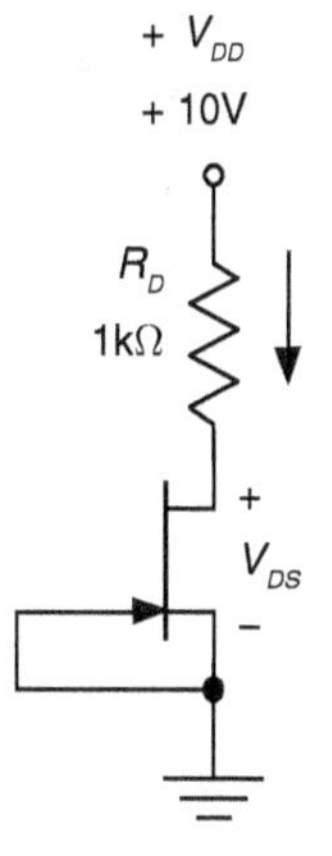

12.19 Find the values of *I* and *V* for the circuits shown in Exhibit 12.19. Assume that the diodes are ideal.

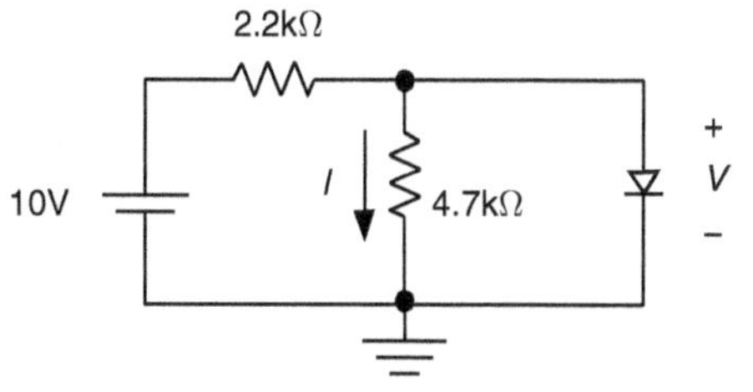

Exhibit 12.19

12.20 For the logarithmic amplifier shown in Exhibit 12.20, let $v_D >> \eta V_t$ (assume ideal OpAmps):

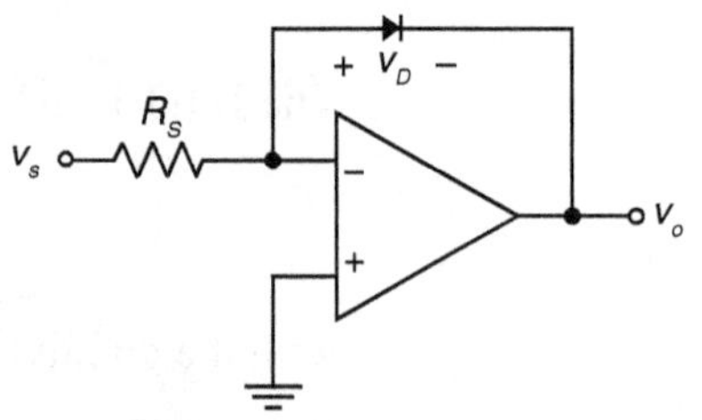

Exhibit 12.20

a. Find the expression for the output voltage in terms of the input voltage.
b. Find the expression for the output voltage in terms of the input voltage for the antilogarithmic amplifier.

12.21 A silicon **npn** BJT is described by the following parameters (remember $\eta = 1$ for silicon BJTs):

$$I_S = 1 \text{ fA}$$
$$a_F = 0.992$$
$$a_R = 0.94$$

The BJT is operating at room temperature, and its junctions are biased so that:

$$V_{BC} = -1.2\text{V}$$
$$V_{BE} = 0.6 \text{ V}$$

a. Determine the base, collector, and emitter currents.
b. The junction biasing is changed so that:

$$V_{BC} = 0.6 \text{ V}$$
$$V_{BE} = -1.2\text{V}$$

Repeat part a.

12.22 For the given circuit, determine the following transistor currents and voltages using load line analysis:

- The collector current
- The base current
- The base-emitter voltage
- The collector-emitter voltage

Assume $\beta_F = 170$.

12.23 An n-channel MOSFET has the following characteristics:

$$VPO = -3 \text{ V},\ VA = 170 \text{ V, and } IDSS = 8 \text{ mA}.$$

a. Determine the minimum drain-source voltage, *VDS*, for the MOSFET to be in saturation.

b. Determine the output resistance of the MOSFET in the ohmic region when $VGS = -1.5$ V

c. Determine the output resistance of the MOSFET in the saturation region when $ID = 2$ mA.

12.24 Find the drain current, drain-source voltage, and gate-drain voltage for the given circuit. Assume $K = 0.25$ mA/V2 and $VT = 2.5$ V.

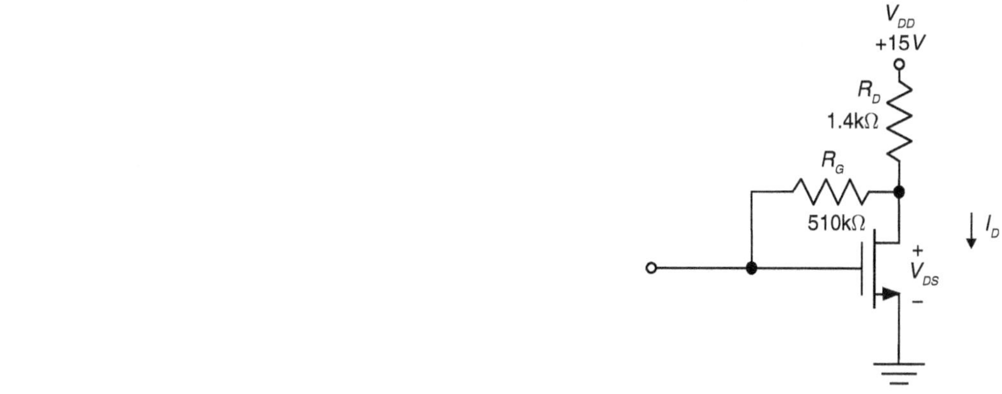

12.25 Determine the differential voltage gain for the given circuit. Assume identical BJTs with

$$\beta_F = 120$$

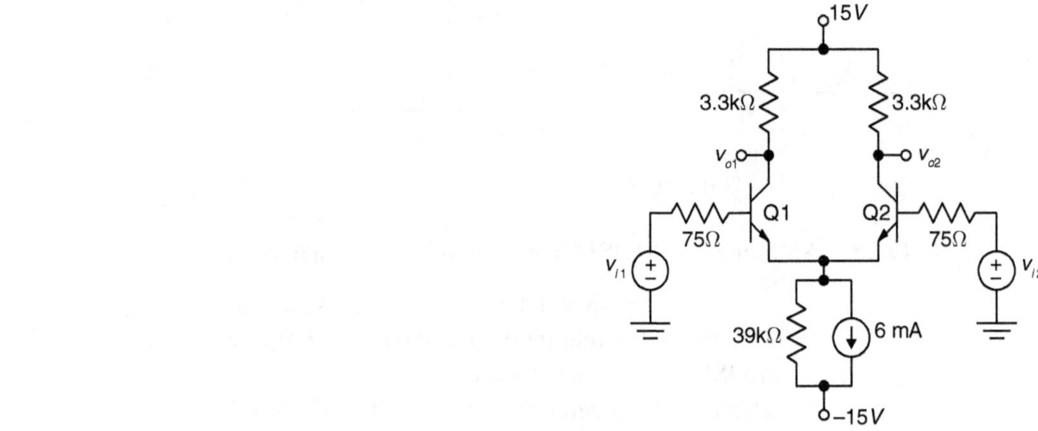

12.26 Use exact expressions for currents, resistances, and gains in the circuit of Example 12.25 to determine the single and differential voltage gains and the CMRR for the circuit.

12.27 For the Widlar current source shown in Exhibit 12.27, the required load current is I_{C2} = 5 μA, I_{C1} = 1 mA, V_{CC} = 5 V, V_{BE} = 0.7 V, V_T = 0.026 V, β_F = 200, and η = 1. Find the two resistance values and the reference current.

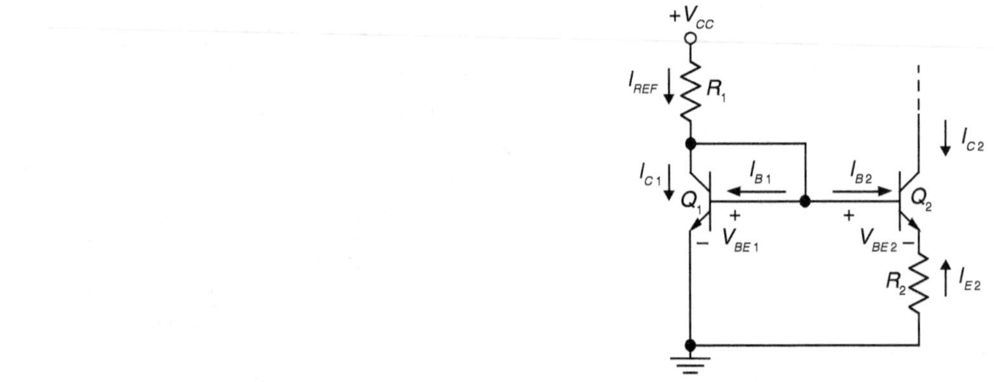

Exhibit 12.27

12.28 Given a silicon npn BJT with parameters:

$$\beta_F = 150$$
$$V_A = 350 \text{ V}$$

operating in the given circuit at room temperature.
Determine the amplifier small-signal performance characteristics.

12.29 Given a silicon npn BJT with parameters:

$$\beta_F = 150$$
$$V_A = 350 \text{ V}$$

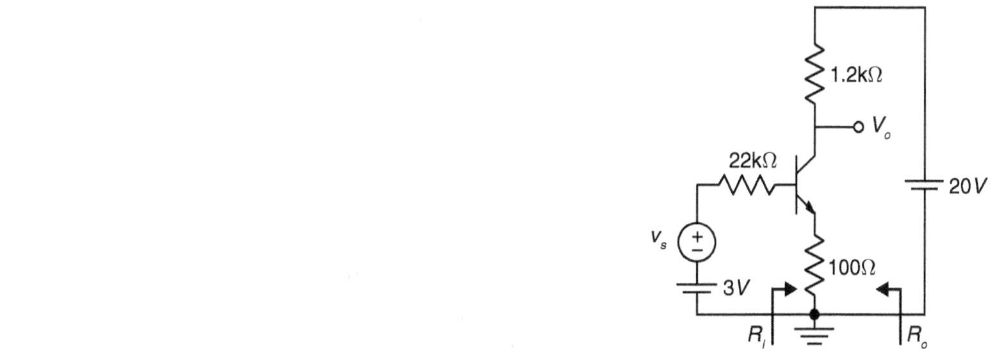

operating in the given circuit at room temperature.
Determine the following small-signal characteristics:

Voltage gain, v_o/v_s

Input resistance, R_i
Output resistance, R_o

12.30 A Silicon BJT with parameters:

$$\beta_F = 150$$
and
$$V_A = 350$$

is placed in the amplifier shown in Exhibit 12.30.

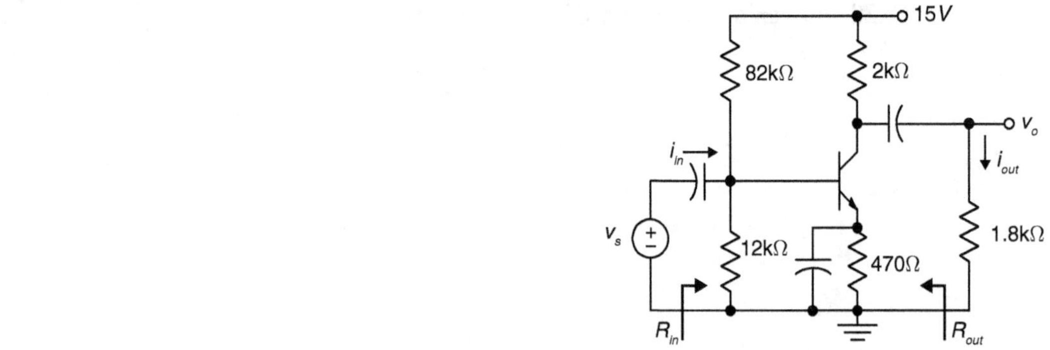

Exhibit 12.30

Assume the amplifier is operating in its midband frequency range, determine the following circuit performance parameters:

$$A_V = \frac{v_o}{v_s}, A_I = \frac{i_{out}}{i_{in}},$$

$$R_{in}, \text{ and } R_{out}.$$

12.31 A silicon BJT with parameters:

$$\beta_F = 100$$
and
$$V_A = 250\text{ V}$$

is placed in the amplifier shown in Exhibit 12.31.

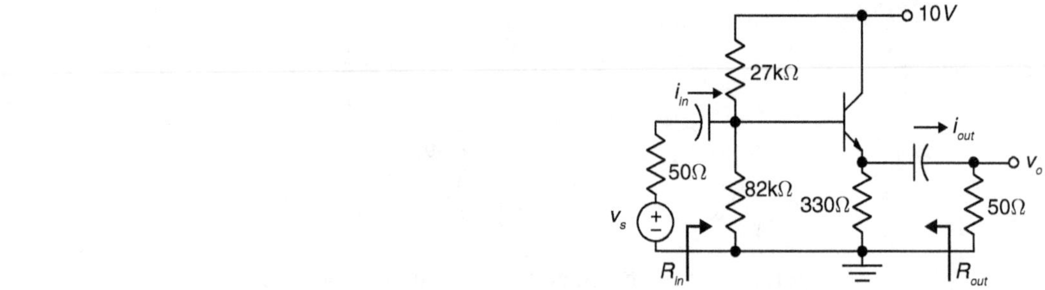

Exhibit 12.31

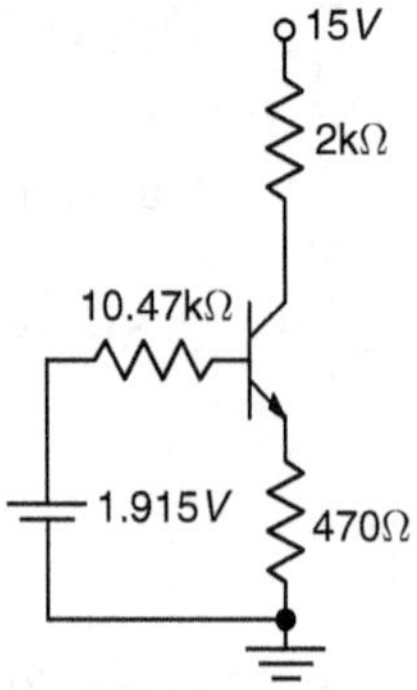

Exhibit 12.31

Assuming the amplifier is operating in its midband frequency range, determine the following circuit performance parameters:

$$A_V = \frac{v_o}{v_s}, A_I = \frac{i_{out}}{i_{in}}, R_{in}, \text{ and } R_{out}.$$

12.32 Given an n-JFET with parameters:

$$V_{PO} = -5\text{V}$$
$$I_{DSS} = 6 \text{ mA}$$
$$I_S = 1 \text{ pA}$$
$$\text{Early voltage} = V_A = 100 \text{ V}$$

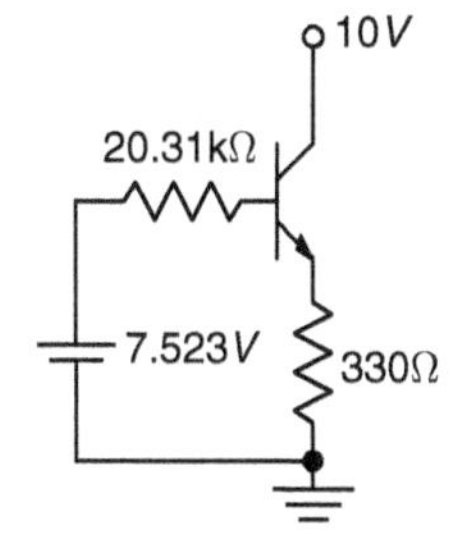

operating in the circuit below at room temperature, determine the amplifier small signal performance characteristics in its midband frequency range.

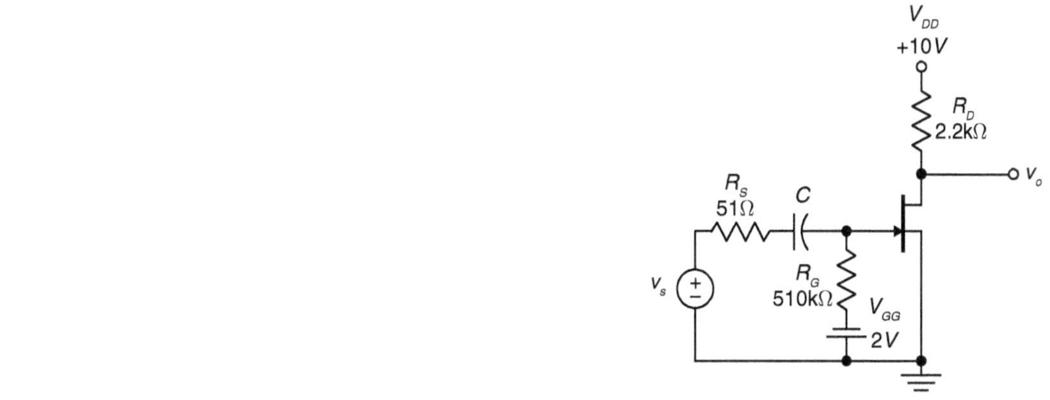

12.33 An enhancement NMOSFET with parameters:

$$K = 2.96 \times 10^{-3} \text{ A/V}^2$$
$$V_T = 2 \text{ V}$$
$$r_d = 30\text{k}\Omega$$
$$I_D = 5 \text{ mA}$$

is placed in the amplifier shown in Exhibit 12.33.

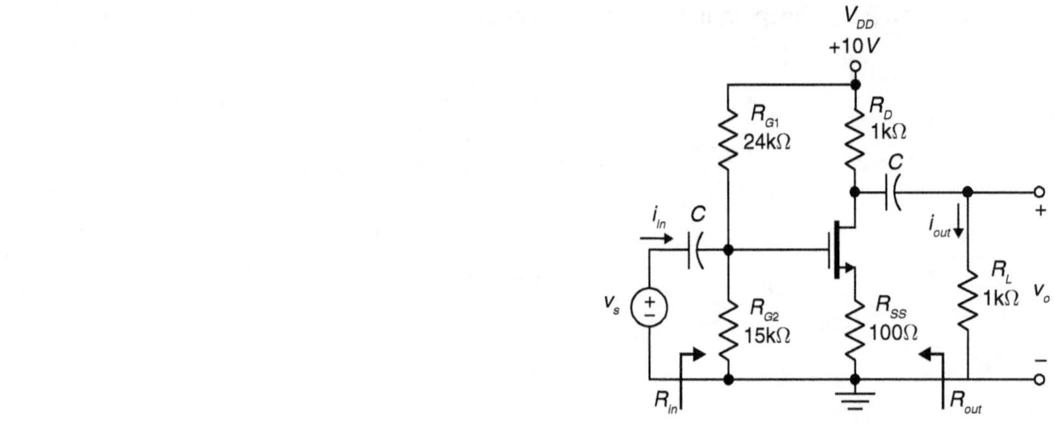

Exhibit 12.33

Assume that the amplifier is operating in its midband frequency range, determine the following circuit parameters:

$$A_{VS} = \frac{v_o}{v_s}, R_{in}, \text{ and } R_{out}.$$

SOLUTIONS

12.1 The solution is:

$$I = 2 \times 10^{-6} (e^{40 \times 0.3} - 1) = 2 \times 10^{-6}(0.163 \times 10^{6} - 1) = 326 \text{ mA}$$

12.2 This is an application and yields a solution of

$$C = C_o/(1 - V/V_o)^{1/3} = 4/[1 - (-2/0.5)]^{1/3} = 4/(5)^{1/3} = 2.34 \text{ pF}$$

12.3 The solution is:

$$i_D = K(v_{GS} - V_T)^2 = 4 \times 10^{-3} = 0.0002(v_{GS} - 5)^2, \quad v_{GS} = 9.47 \text{ V}$$

12.4 Since this circuit will be operating at a low frequency, $C_{b\otimes c}$ is negligible and is thus neglected.

$$r_\pi = \beta/g_m$$

where $g_m \Uparrow I_C/0.026$ at room temperature, where I_C is in A. Thus,

$$r_\pi = (100)(0.026/I_C)$$
$$= (100)(0.026/10^{-3}) = 2600\ \Omega.$$

Also,

$$V_{in} = I_b r_\pi$$

and,

$$V_o = I_o R_L = -\beta I_b R_L$$

Therefore,

$$A = V_o/V_{in} = -100 I_b(25{,}000)/(2600 I_b) = -962 \text{ V/V}$$

(Note that gain is actually negative here, but is often expressed only in terms of its absolute value.)

12.5 Although the coupling capacitors are given, they may be considered to have negligible reactance of mid-frequencies. Then the voltage output may be found directly from the given circuit parameters. To obtain the current $g_m V_{be}$, it is only necessary to calculate V_{be} as

$$V_{be} = [r_\pi/(R_s + r_\pi)]V_s = [6\text{k}/(2\text{k} + 6\text{k})](0.01) = (6/8)(0.01) = 0.0075 \text{ V}$$

and,

$$V_o = -g_m V_{be}[R_o R_L/(R_o + R_L)]$$
$$= -50 \times 10^{-3} \times 7.5 \times 10^{-3} [10\text{K} \times 5\text{K}/(10\text{K} + 5\text{K})]$$
$$= -375 \times 10^{-6} [50 \times 10^{+6}/15 \times 10^{3}] = -1.25 \text{ V}$$

Note: An interesting additional question might have been to ask for the lower cutoff frequency.

For C_1

$$C_1 = 1/[C_1(R_S + r_\pi)] = 1/[0.5 \times 10^{-6}(2 + 6) \times 10^3] = 250 \text{ r/s}$$

For C_2

$$C_2 = 1/[C_2(R_o + R_L)] = 1/[1 \times 10^{-6}(5 + 10) \times 10^3] = 67 \text{ r/s}$$

Therefore the lower cutoff frequency is 250 r/s or 40 Hz.

12.6 The noninverting amplifier has an input resistance of infinity. Therefore, one alternative is to place a 12k resistor from the positive input terminal of the OpAmp to ground. This yields an input resistance of 12k || (Large OpAmp R_i) ≈ 12k.

To yield a gain of 12, choose resistor ratio in the branched from the negative terminal of the OpAmp to have a ratio of 11:1 because the noninverting gain is:

$$A_v = \left(1 + \frac{R_f}{R_G}\right)$$

where R_f is the feedback resistor connecting the output to the negative OpAmp input terminal and R_G is the resistor connecting the negative OpAmp input terminal to ground. Using standard value resistors, choose $R_G = 2k$ and $R_f = 22k$.

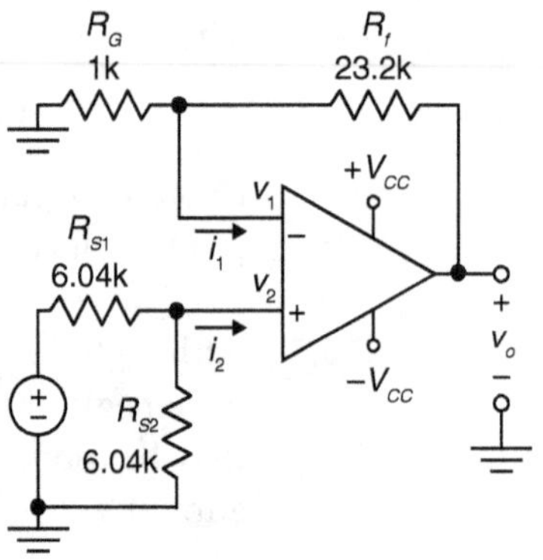

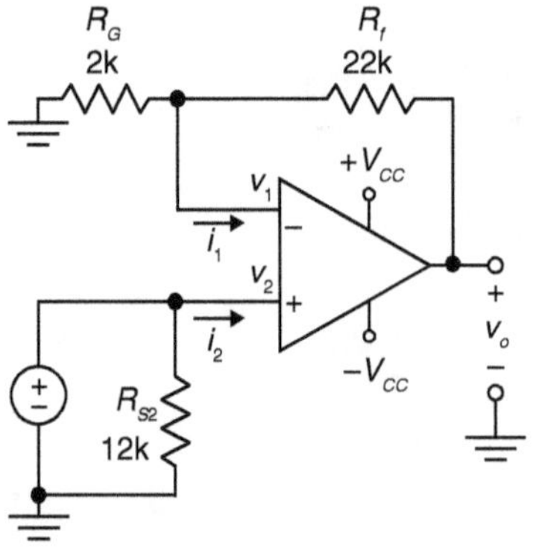

12.7 Write node voltage equations at v_2 and v_1:
At v_1:

$$0=\frac{v_1-v_i}{2.2k}+\frac{v_1-v_o}{4.7k}$$

At v_2:

$$0=\frac{v_2-0}{2.2k\|R_L}+\frac{v_2-v_o}{4.7k}=\frac{v_1}{2.2k\|R_L}+\frac{v_1-v_o}{4.7k},\ \text{since } v_2=v_1$$

but $(v_1-v_o)/4.7\text{k}=(v_i-v_1)/2.2k=(v_i-v_2)/2.2k$ so:

$$0=\frac{v_2}{2.2k\|R_L}+\frac{v_i-v_2}{2.2k}.$$

Note also that $i_{RL}=v_2/R_L$.
Simplifying yields the solution:

$$i_{RL}=\frac{v_2}{R_L}+-\frac{v_i}{2.2k}.$$

12.8 By superposition: $v_o=v_{i2}\left(\frac{R_4}{R_3+R_4}\right)\left(1+\frac{R_2}{R_1}\right)-v_{i1}\left(\frac{R_2}{R_1}\right)$. Plugging in the resistor values yields:

$$v_o=3.59\,v_{i2}-3.92\,v_{i1}.$$

Now substitute v_{i1} and v_{i2} into the previous expression:

$$v_o=3.59\,[1.5\cos(\omega_o t+30°)]-3.92\cos(\omega_o t).$$

You can do this by using Euler's equation:

$$v_o=3.59\cdot 1.5\cdot 0.5[\exp(j(\omega_o t+30°))+\exp(-j(\omega_o t+30°))]$$
$$-3.92\cdot 0.5[\exp(j\omega_o t)+\exp(-j\omega_o t)]$$

or use a calculator for the phasor notation to get the result:

$$v_o=2.79\angle 74.56°=2.79\cos(\omega_o t+74.56°)$$

12.9 $I_s=0.1\cdot 10^{-9}$ $\quad\eta=2\quad$ $V_t=0.026$

a. $I=-0.99\cdot I_s$
Solve for the diode voltage, V, for I using solve block.
Guess $V=0.1$

Given $I=I_s\cdot\left(e^{\frac{V}{\eta\cdot V_t}}-1\right)$

Find $(V)=-0.239$
The diode voltage required for $I=-0.99\,L$ is $V=-0.239$ V.

b. $I=0.99\cdot I_s$
Solve for the diode voltage, V, for I using solve block.
Guess $V=0.05$

Given $I=I_s\cdot\left(e^{\frac{V}{\eta\cdot V_t}}-1\right)$

Find $(V)=0.036$
The diode voltage required for $I=0.99\,A$ is $V=0.036$ V.

c. $i = 0..3$

$$V_i = 0.5 + 0.1 \cdot i$$

$$I_i = I_s \cdot \left(e^{\frac{V_i}{\eta \cdot V_t}} - 1 \right)$$

I_i
$1.499 \cdot 10^{-6}$
$1.026 \cdot 10^{-5}$
$7.019 \cdot 10^{-5}$
$4.802 \cdot 10^{-4}$

The diode currents are:

V	I
0.5 V	1.5 μA
0.6 V	10.3 μA
0.7 V	70.2 μA
0.8 V	480.2 μA

12.10 $I_s = 15 \cdot 10^{-9}$ $\eta V_t = 0.0256$

Let ID = 0.005

a. $V_d = \eta V_t \cdot \ln\left[\left(\frac{I_D}{I_s}\right) + 1\right]$ So the diode voltage is $V_d = 0.326$.

b. $\frac{V_d}{I_D} = 65.111$ $V_d/I_D = 65.111\ \Omega$.

c. The dynamic resistance is 65.111 Ω.

I_D varies between 4.8 mA =< I_D =< 5.2 mA.

d. $I_D = 0.0048, 0.005 \ldots 0.0052$

$$V_d(I_D) = \eta V_t \cdot \ln\left[\left(\frac{I_D}{I_s}\right) + 1\right]$$

$V_d(I_D)$
0.325
0.326
0.3127

Therefore, the range is 0.325V =< V_d =< 0.327V.

e.

$\frac{V_d(I_D)}{I_D}$
67.606
65.111
62.799

The dynamic resistance r_d varies from 62.80 Ω =< r_d =< 67.61 Ω.

12.11

a. $I = 10^{-3}$

$V_d = 0.6$

$n = 2$

$V_t = 0.026$

$$I_s = \frac{I}{\left[\exp\left[\frac{V_d}{(n \cdot V_t)}\right] - 1\right]}$$

$I_s = 9.748 \times 10^{-9}$

$I_s = 9.75nA$

b. $V_d = 0.7$

$$I = I_s \cdot \left[\exp\left[\frac{V_d}{(n \cdot V_t)}\right] - 1\right]$$

$I = 6.842 \times 10^{-3}$

$I = 6.8mA$

12.12

a. $V_t = 0.026$

Guess

$n = 2$

$I_s = 10^{-9}$

Given

$$2.3 \cdot 10^{-3} = I_s \cdot \left[\exp\left[\frac{V_d}{(n \cdot V_t)}\right] - 1\right]$$

$$\text{Find}(I_s, n) = \begin{pmatrix} 4.096 \times 10^{-10} \\ 2 \end{pmatrix}$$

$I_s = 0.41nA$

$= 2$

b. $I_d = I_s \cdot \left[\exp\left[\frac{V_d}{(n \cdot V_t)}\right] - 1\right]$

$I_d = 7.019 \times 10^{-4}$

A

$I_d = 10^{-3}$

12.13 $k = 13.8 \cdot 10^{-24}$

$q = 1.6 \cdot 10^{-19}$

$n = 2$

$I_s = 4.096 \times 10^{-10}$

$T = 50 + 273$

$V_t = \frac{k \cdot T}{q}$

a. $V_t = 0.028$

$I_d = 10^{-3}$

Guess

$V_d = 0.7$

Given

$I_d = I_s \cdot \left[\exp\left[\frac{V_d}{(n \cdot V_t)}\right] - 1\right]$

$\text{Find}(V_d) = 0.819$

$V_d = 0.819V$

$T = 0 + 273$

$V_t = \frac{k \cdot T}{q}$

b. $V_t = 0.024$

$I_d = 10^{-3}$

Guess

$V_d = 0.7$

Given

$$I_d = I_s \cdot \left[\exp\left[\frac{V_d}{(n \cdot V_t)}\right] - 1\right]$$

$\text{Find}(V_d) = 0.693$

$V_d = 0.693V$

12.14 $n = 2$

$I_s = 1.5 \cdot 10^{-12}$

$V_t = 0.026$

$V_o = 2.6$

a. Assuming identical diodes:

$$V_d = \frac{V_o}{4}$$

$V_d = 0.65$

$V_d = 0.65V$

$$I_d = I_s \cdot \left[\exp\left[\frac{V_d}{(n \cdot V_t)}\right] - 1\right]$$

$I_d = 4.025 \times 10^{-7}$

$I_d = 0.403A$

b. Guess

$V_d = 1$

$I = 10^{-4}$

$I_d = 10^{-6}$

Given

$$0 = -I + I_d + \frac{V_d \cdot 4}{12}$$

$$I_d = I_s \cdot \left[\exp\left[\frac{V_d}{(n \cdot V_t)}\right] - 1\right]$$

$I = 0.334mA$

$$\text{Find}(I, I_d) = \begin{pmatrix} 0.334 \\ 3.372 \times 10^{-4} \end{pmatrix}$$

$I_d = 0.337mA$

$I = 0.334$

$I_d = 3.372 \times 10^{-4}$

$V_d = 12 \cdot (I - I_d)$

$V_d = 4.004$

$V_o = 4V$

12.15

$IDSS = 0.0045$
$VPO = -3.6$

a. $I_D = 0.0026$

Guess

$VGS = -1$

Given

$$I_D = IDSS \cdot \left[1 - \left(\frac{VGS}{VPO}\right)\right]^2$$

$\text{Find}(VGS) = -0.864$

So,

$VGS = -0.864$

V

b. Minimum

$VDS = VGS - VPC$

$VDS = 2.736$

V

c. $VDS = 2.736$

$VGS = VDS - VPC$

$VGS = 6.336$

12.16

$IDSS = -0.004$
$VPO = 2.8$

a. $I_D = -0.0026$

Guess

$VGS = 1$

Given

$$I_D = IDSS \cdot \left[1 - \left(\frac{VGS}{VPO}\right)\right]^2$$

$\text{Find}(VGS) = 0.543$

$VGS = 0.543$

So,

$VGS = -0.543$

b. Minimum

$VSD = VSG + VPC$

$VSD = 2.257$

c. $VSD = 1.5$

$VSG = VSD - VPC$

$VSG = -1.3$

$VGS = 1.3$

12.17 $IDSS = 0.0075$

$VPO = -4$

$I_D = 0.002$

$VDS = 6$

$VDD = 20$

Guess

$VGS = -1$

Given

$$I_D = IDSS \cdot \left[1 - \left(\frac{VGS}{VPO}\right)\right]^2$$

$\text{Find}(VGS) = -1.934$

$VGS = -1.934$

V

Know that ID = 2 mA, so $VGS = VG - VS = 0 - VS = 0 - ID*RS$

$$RS = \frac{-VGS}{ID}$$

$RS = 967$

Ohms

and the drain-source loop is $0 = VDD - ID*RS - VDS - ID*RS$

$$RS = \frac{(20 - VDS - ID \cdot RS)}{ID}$$

$RS = 6.033 \times 10^3$

Ohms

12.18 $IDSS = 0.004$

$VPO = -2.5$

$VDD = 10$

$RDD = 1000$

Circuit shows that $VG = VS$ so that

$VGS = 0$

$$ID = IDSS \cdot \left[1 - \left(\frac{VGS}{VPO}\right)\right]^2$$

$ID = 4 \times 10^{-3}$

A

Now do drain-source loop 0 = $VDD - ID*RD - VDS$ to find VDS
$VDS = VDD - ID \cdot RD$
$VDS = 6$
V

12.19 Because the diodes are ideal, the characteristics are short ckt when $V_d = 0$ and open circuit when $V_d < 0$.

The anode of the diode will not be negative because a positive voltage source is used. Therefore, the ideal diode acts as a short circuit causing the diode voltage $V = 0$V and $I = 0$A.

Similarly, the voltage of the anodes of diodes D_1 and D_2 are never negative. Therefore, they can be treated as short circuits. By circuit theory,

$$V = 5\frac{1.2k \| 4.7k}{1.2k \| 4.7k + 2.2k} = 1.52\text{V and } I = 1.52/1200 = 1.26\text{mA}$$

12.20

a. Perform node voltage (KCL) at the negative OpAmp terminal:

$$0 = -v_S/R_S + I_D, \text{ and } v_o = -v_D.$$

Using the diode equation, we know that

$$I_D = I_S\left(e^{\frac{v_D}{\eta V_t}} - 1\right) = I_s\left(e^{\frac{-v_o}{\eta V_t}} - 1\right).$$

$$v_s = R_s I_s\left(e^{\frac{-v_o}{\eta V_t}} - 1\right).$$

Therefore, the output voltage is then $v_o = -\eta V_t \ln\left(1 + \frac{v_S}{R_s I_s}\right)$.

b. Perform node voltage (KCL) at the negative OpAmp terminal:

$$0 = -v_o/R_F + I_D,\text{ and } v_S = -v_D.$$

Using the diode equation, we know that

$$I_D = I_S\left(e^{\frac{v_D}{\eta V_t}} - 1\right) = I_s\left(e^{\frac{-v_s}{\eta V_t}} - 1\right).$$

But $v_o = R_F I_D$.

Therefore, the circuit is an antilog amplifier.

12.21 $I_s = 10^{-15}$ $\alpha_f = 0.992$ $\alpha_r = 0.94$ $V_t = 0.026$

$$I_{cs} = \frac{I_s}{\alpha_r} \qquad I_{es} = \frac{I_s}{\alpha_f}$$

a. $V_{bc} = -1.2$ $V_{be} = 0.6$

$$I_e = -I_{es}\cdot\left(e^{\frac{V_{be}}{V_t}} - 1\right) + \alpha_r\cdot I_{cs}\cdot\left(e^{\frac{V_{bc}}{V_t}} - 1\right)$$

$$I_e = -1.061\cdot 10^{-5}$$

$$I_c = -I_{cs}\cdot\left(e^{\frac{V_{bc}}{V_t}} - 1\right) + \alpha_f\cdot I_{es}\cdot\left(e^{\frac{V_{be}}{V_t}} - 1\right)$$

$$I_c = 1.052\cdot 10^{-5}$$

b. $V_{bc} = 0.6$ $V_{be} = -1.2$

$$I_e = -I_{es}\cdot\left(e^{\frac{V_{be}}{V_t}} - 1\right) + \alpha_r\cdot I_{cs}\cdot\left(e^{\frac{V_{bc}}{V_t}} - 1\right)$$

$$I_e = 1.052\cdot 10^{-5}$$

$$I_c = -I_{cs}\cdot\left(e^{\frac{V_{bc}}{V_t}} - 1\right) + \alpha_f\cdot I_{es}\cdot\left(e^{\frac{V_{be}}{V_t}} - 1\right)$$

$$I_c = -1.12\cdot 10^{-5}$$

12.22 Assume forward active operation. Then B-E KVL loop: $0 = 2 - I_B 22k - V_{BE}$, where $V_{BE} = 0.7$V.

Solving for I_B = 59m A. From the 2N2222 characteristic curve, $\beta_F = 170$. This implies that $I_C = \beta_F I_B$ = 10mA.

The C-E KVL loop: $0 = 10 - 680\, I_C - V_{CE}$. Solving for V_{CE} = 3.2V.

12.23

$$VPO = -3$$
$$VA = 170$$
$$IDSS = 0.008$$

a. $VDS >= VGS - VPO$

b. $VGS = -1.5$

RDS is the same as that for n-JFET

$$RDS = \left(\frac{VPO}{2 \cdot IDSS}\right) \cdot \left[\frac{1}{\left[\left(\frac{VGS}{VPO}\right) - 1\right]}\right]$$

$$RDS = 375$$

c. In saturation with $ID = 2$ mA, basically it is the slope for the line from $ID = 2$ mA to $VA = 170$ V. The pinch-off parabola for $ID =$ 2 mA must be found using $0 < VDS <= VGS - VPO$, so we must find VGS just at saturation on the pinch-off parabola.

Guess

$$VGS = -1$$

Given

$$I_D = IDSS \cdot \left[1 - \left(\frac{VGS}{VPO}\right)\right]^2$$

$$\text{Find}(VGS) = -1.163$$

$$VGS = -1.163$$

$$VDS = VGS - VPC$$

$$VDS = 1.837$$

$$RDS = \frac{(170 + VDS)}{0.002}$$

$$RDS = 8.592 \times 10^4$$

12.24 $VDD = 15$

$K = 0.25 \cdot 10^{-3}$

$VT = 2.5$

$VDD = 15$

$RD = 1400$

$RG = 510 \cdot 10^3$

Note: $VGS = VDS$

$ID = \mathrm{K} \cdot (\mathrm{VGS} - \mathrm{VT})^2$

$ID = 4.524 \times 10^{-3}$

A

$VDS = VDD - ID \cdot RD$

$VDS = 8.666$

V

$VGS = VDS$

$VGS = 8.666$

V

12.25 The output resistance of the current source is much large than either of the output resistances of the sources, thus

$$I_C \approx \frac{\alpha_F}{2}\left(I_{EE} + \frac{V_{EE} - V_{BE(\mathrm{on})}}{R_{EE}}\right)$$

$$I_C \approx 0.4959\left(6m + \frac{14.3}{39k}\right) = 3.157\mathrm{mA}$$

A check of V_{CE} must be made:

$$V_{CE} = V_C - V_E = (15 - I_C R_c) - (0 - I_B R_i - V_{BE(\mathrm{on})}) = 4.58 - (-0.702) = 5.28\ \mathrm{V}$$

The BJT is in the forward-active region. The significant BJT parameters are then:

$$h_{fe} = 120 \quad \text{and} \quad h_{ie} = 996.5\ \Omega$$

The differential gain is given by:

$$A_{VD} = \frac{v_{o1} - v_{o2}}{v_{i1} - v_{i2}} = \frac{-h_{fe} R_c}{h_{ie} + \frac{1}{2}\{R_{i1} + R_{i2}\}} = \frac{-120(3.3k)}{996.5 + 75} = -370$$

12.26 The exact collector current expression is:

$$I_C = \beta_F\left(\frac{V_{EE} + I_{EE}R_{EE} - V_{BE(\mathrm{on})}}{2(\beta_F + 1)R_{EE} + R_i}\right) = 120\left(\frac{15 + 234 - 0.7}{2(121)39k + 75}\right) = 3.157\mathrm{mA}$$

There is no significant change from the approximate value of the previous example: the BJTs are in the forward-active region. The BJT *h*-parameters are:

$$h_{fe} = 120 \quad \text{and} \quad h_{ie} = 996.5\ \Omega$$

The resistance R_2 is given by:

$$R_2 = \frac{h_{ie} + R_{i2}}{h_{fe} + 1} = \frac{996.5 + 75}{121} = 8.86\Omega$$

and the resistance R_1 is

$R_1 = h_{ie} + (h_{fe} + 1)(R_{EE}// R_2) = 996.5 + (121)(39k//8.86) = 2.068\ k\Omega$

The load resistance for the common-collector stage is given by:

$$R_E = R_{EE}//R_2 = 8.8535\ \Omega$$

Which leads to the gain expressions:

$$A_{V1} = \frac{-120(3.3k)}{2.068k}\left(\frac{2.068k}{2.068k+75}\right) = -184.807$$

$$A_{V2} = -A_{V1}\left(\frac{2.068k-996.5}{996.5+75}\right) = 184.768$$

The total transfer relationships can then be written as:

$v_{o1} = -184.807\ v_{i1} + 184.768\ v_{i2}$ and $v_{o2} = 184.768\ v_{i1} - 184.807\ v_{i2}$

The differential gain is given by:

$$v_{od} = v_{o1} - v_{o2} = -369.575\ (v_{i1} - v_{i2})$$

and the common-mode gain is

$$v_{oc} = \frac{v_{o1}+v_{o2}}{2} = -0.039234\left(\frac{v_{i1}+v_{i2}}{2}\right)$$

Which yields a common-mode rejection ratio

$$CMRR = 20\log_{10}\left|\frac{-369.575}{-0.039234}\right| = 79.5\text{dB}$$

12.27 From

$$\eta V_t\left(\frac{I_{C1}}{I_{C2}}\right) = \frac{\beta_F+1}{\beta_F} I_{C2}R_2,$$

$$(0.026)\ln\left(\frac{10^{-3}}{5\times10^{-6}}\right) = \frac{201}{200}\left(5\times10^{-6}\right)R_2,$$

yielding the value

$$R_2 = 27.5\ k\Omega \approx 27\ k\Omega.$$

Using Kirchhoff's Current Law at the collector node of Q_1,

$$I_{REF} = I_{C1} + I_{B1} + I_{B2}$$

$$= I_{C1}\left(1+\frac{1}{\beta_F}\right) + \frac{I_{C2}}{\beta_F}$$

$$= 10^{-3}\left(1+\frac{1}{200}\right) + \frac{5\times10^{-6}}{200} = 1.005\text{mA}$$

The reference resistor is found by applying Kirchhoff's Voltage Law to the collector-base-emitter loop of Q_1,

$$R_1 = \frac{V_{CC} - V_{BE}}{I_{REF}} = \frac{5 - 0.7}{1.005 \times 10^{-3}} = 4.28k\Omega \approx 4.3k\Omega.$$

12.28 The modeling process for transistor circuit performance was:

1. Model the BJT with an appropriate DC model.
2. Determine the circuit quiescent (DC) conditions—verify BJT active region.
3. Determine the BJT AC model parameters from the quiescent conditions.
4. Create an AC equivalent circuit.
5. Determine the circuit AC performance by:
   a). replacing the BJT by its AC model, or
   b). using previously derived results for the circuit topology.
6. Add the results of the DC and AC analysis to obtain total circuit performance.

Step #1: Model the BJT with an appropriate DC model. Hopefully, the BJT will be found to be in the forward-active region so the circuit can operate as an amplifier. The DC forward-active model of the BJT is derived and shown in Exhibit 12.28a. The appropriate transistor quantities that must be used in this case are $\beta_F = 150$ and $V_\gamma = 0.7$ (Silicon BJT).

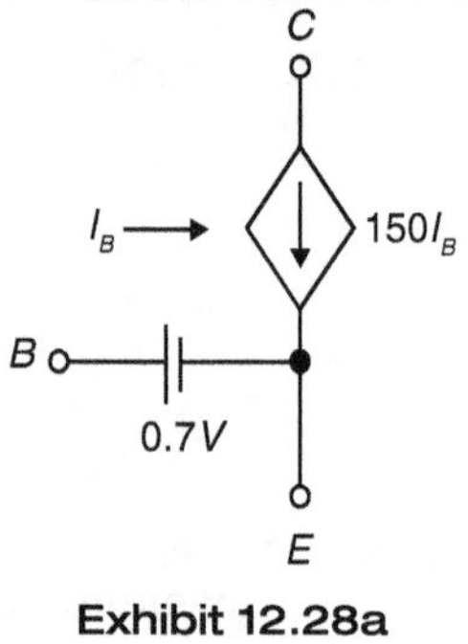

Exhibit 12.28a

Step #2: Determine the circuit quiescent (DC) conditions: verify BJT active region. The BJT model of Step #1 replaces the BJT as shown in Exhibit 12.28b.

Exhibit 12.28b

Quiescent conditions are then calculated. Around the base-emitter loop, Kirchhoff's Current Law yields:

$$1.5 - 22k\,(I_B) - 0.7 = 0.$$

So that

$$I_B = 36.36\ \mu\text{A},$$

and

$$I_C = 150\,I_B = 5.45\ \text{mA}.$$

Both currents are positive: only V_{CE} must be checked to see if it is larger than $V_{CE(\text{sat})} = 0.2$ V. Kirchhoff's Current Law applied to the collector-emitter loop yields:

$$V_{CE} = 22 - 1.2k\,(I_C) = 15.46\ \text{V}.$$

The transistor is in the forward-active region; the circuit will operate as an amplifier.

Step #3: Determine the BJT AC model parameters from the quiescent conditions. The relevant *h*-parameters are:

$$h_{fe} \approx \beta_F = 150$$

$$h_{ie} \approx (\beta_F + 1)\frac{\eta V_t}{|I_C|} = (151)\frac{26\text{mV}}{|5.45\text{mA}|} = 720\Omega$$

$$h_{oe} - \left|\frac{I_C}{V_A}\right| = \left|\frac{|5.45\text{mA}|}{350V}\right| = 15.6\mu S \approx 0$$

$$h_{re} = 0$$

Step #4: Create an AC equivalent circuit.

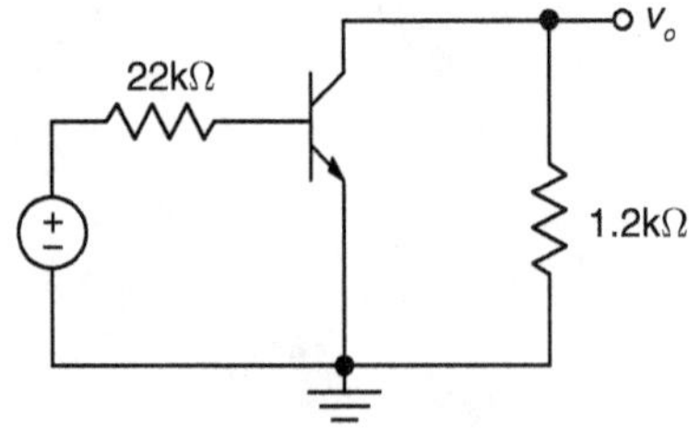

The DC sources are set to zero, and the output voltage becomes a small-signal quantity.

Step #5: Determine the circuit AC performance by:
a) replacing the BJT by its AC model, or
b) using previously derived results for the circuit topology.

In this case it appears easiest to use previously derived results. The input resistance at the base of the BJT is given by:

$$R_i = h_{ie} = 720\ \Omega$$

If the input resistance is measured to the left of the 22 $k\Omega$ resistor then:

$$R_i' = 22\ k\Omega + 720\ \Omega = 22.7\ k\Omega.$$

The current gain is given by:

$$A_I = -h_{fe} = -150.$$

The voltage gain from the base of the BJT is given by:

$$A_V = \frac{-h_{fe}R_c}{h_{ie}} = \frac{-150(1.2k)}{720} = -250.$$

The voltage gain from the source is given by:

$$A_{VS} = \frac{-h_{fe}R_c}{h_{ie} + R_s} = \frac{-150(1.2k)}{720 + 22k} = -7.92.$$

The output resistance is given by:

$$R_o = \frac{1}{h_{oe}} = 64.17k\Omega.$$

If the collector resistance is included in the output resistance,

$$R_{ol} = R_o\ //\ R_c = \frac{(64.17)(1.2k)}{64.17k + 1.2k} = 1.18k\Omega.$$

12.29 The modeling process begins with solving for the quiescent circuit conditions. I There is no need to repeat identical operations to find the small-signal model of the BJT. The results of process steps 1 through 3 were:

$I_B = 62.0\ \mu A$ $\quad I_C = 9.30\ mA$
$h_{fe} = 150$ $\quad h_{ie} = 422\ \Omega$ $\quad r_o = 37.6\ k\Omega$

The next step is to create an AC equivalent circuit and insert the BJT h-parameter model into the AC equivalent circuit or use previously derived results. The general topology of a common-emitter amplifier with an emitter resistor has previous results. The AC equivalent circuit is shown in Exhibit 12.29.

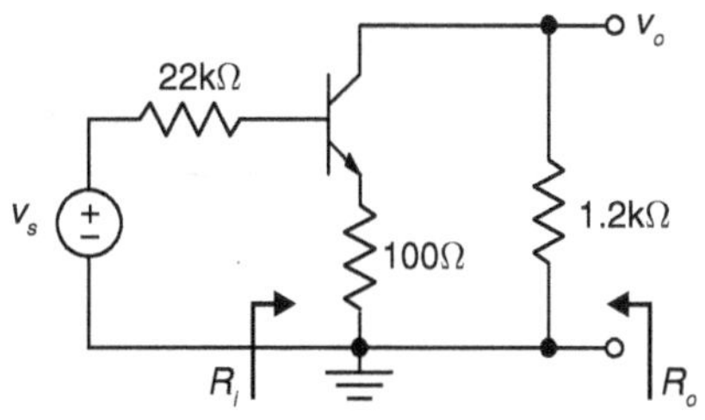

Exhibit 12.29

The voltage gain, as defined, is:

$$A_{VS} = \frac{-(150)(1200)}{422+(151)(100)+22{,}000} = -4.7972 \approx -4.80.$$

R_i, as shown, is:

$$R_i = 422+(151)(100) = 15{,}522 \approx 15.5k\Omega.$$

The output resistance, R_o, is given by the parallel combination of the output resistance of the amplifier and the collector resistor, R_c:

$$R_o \approx \infty / / 1.2k\Omega = 1.2k\Omega.$$

12.30 The quiescent point of the BJT must be found first to ensure that it is in the forward-active region and to find its h-parameters. For DC operation, all capacitors appear as open circuits.

The base and collector currents are:

$$I_B = \frac{1.915-0.7}{10.47k+151(470)} = 14.92\mu A$$

and

$$I_C = 150 I_B = 2.238 \text{ mA}.$$

V_{CE} must be checked to verify that the BJT is in the forward-active region.

$$V_{CE} = 15 - I_C(2k) - \frac{151}{150} I_C(470) = 9.47V \geq 0.2V.$$

The BJT h-parameters can now be determined:

$$h_{fe} = 150, \qquad h_{ie} = 151\frac{\eta V_t}{|I_C|} = 1.755k\Omega, \text{ and} \qquad \frac{1}{h_{oe}} = \left|\frac{V_A}{I_C}\right| = 156.4k\Omega.$$

An AC equivalent circuit can now be determined. All DC sources are set to zero and, since the circuit is in its midband frequency range, all capacitors are replaced by short circuits. The 470 Ω resistor is totally eliminated from the circuit. The AC equivalent circuit leads to the determination of amplifier performance characteristics.

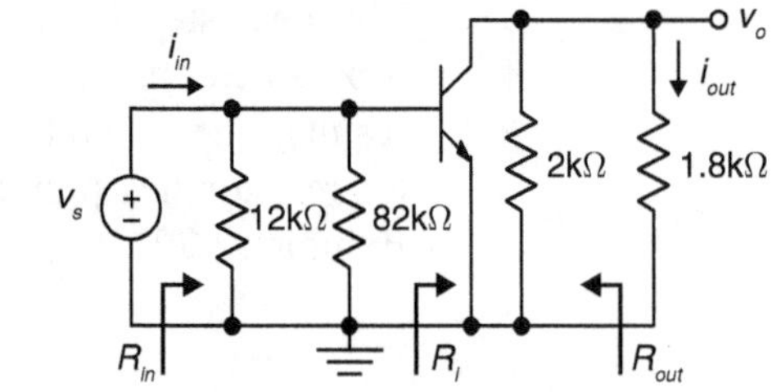

$$A_V = -\frac{h_{fe}R_c}{h_{ie}} = -\frac{150(2k//1.8k)}{1.755k} = -81.0$$

$$R_{in} = 82k//12k//R_i = 10.47k//h_{ie} = 1.50k\Omega$$

$$R_{out} = 2k//r_o = 1.98k \approx 2.0k\Omega$$

$$A_I = \frac{i_{out}}{i_{in}} = \left(\frac{i_{out}}{v_o}\right)\left(\frac{v_o}{v_s}\right)\left(\frac{v_s}{i_{in}}\right) = \left(\frac{1}{1.8k}\right)(-81.0)(1.50k) = -67.5$$

12.31 The quiescent point of the BJT must be found first to ensure that it is in the forward-active region and to find its h-parameters. For DC operation, all capacitors appear as open circuits.

The base and collector currents are:

$$I_B = \frac{7.523 - 0.7}{20.31k + 101(330)} = 127.2\mu A$$

and

$$I_C = 100 I_B = 12.72 \text{ mA}.$$

V_{CE} must be checked to verify that the BJT is in the forward-active region.

$$V_{CE} = 10 - \frac{151}{150} I_C(330) = 5.76V \geq 0.2V.$$

The BJT h-parameters can now be determined:

$$h_{fe} = 100, \qquad h_{ie} = 101\frac{\eta V_t}{|I_C|} \approx 210\Omega, \text{ and} \qquad \frac{1}{h_{oe}} = \left|\frac{V_A}{I_C}\right| = 19.65k\Omega$$

An AC equivalent circuit can now be determined. All DC sources are set to zero and, since the circuit is in its midband frequency range, all capacitors are replaced by short circuits. The AC equivalent circuit leads to the determination of amplifier performance characteristics. Care must be taken concerning parameter definitions.

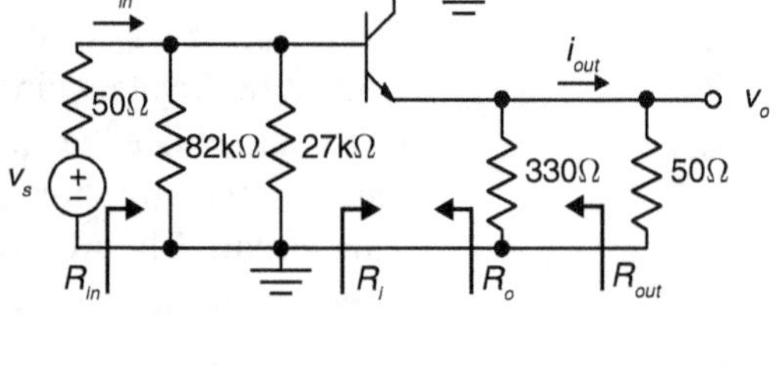

$$R_i = h_{ie} + (h_{fe} + 1) R_e$$

$$= 210 + (101)(330 // 50) = 4.596k\Omega$$

$$R_{in} = 82k\Omega // 27k\Omega // R_i = 3.75k\Omega$$

$$A_v = \frac{v_o}{v_s} = \left(\frac{v_o}{v_b}\right)\left(\frac{v_b}{v_s}\right) = \left(1 - \frac{h_{ie}}{R_i}\right)\left(\frac{R_{in}}{R_{in} + 50}\right) = \left(1 - \frac{210}{4596}\right)\left(\frac{3750}{2800}\right) = 0.942$$

$$R_o = \frac{R_s + h_{ie}}{h_{fe} + 1} = \frac{50 // 82k // 27k + 210}{101} = 2.573\Omega$$

$$R_{out} = R_o // 330 = 2.55\Omega$$

$$A_I = \frac{i_{out}}{i_{in}} = \left(\frac{i_b}{i_{in}}\right)\left(\frac{i_o}{i_b}\right)\left(\frac{i_{out}}{i_o}\right) = \left(\frac{82k // 27k}{82k // 27k + 3.75k}\right)(101)\left(\frac{330}{330 + 50}\right) = 74.0$$

12.32 The modeling process for FET circuit performance contain the following steps:

1. Determine the quiescent (DC) conditions—verify FET in saturation region.
2. Determine the FET AC model parameters from the quiescent conditions.
3. Create the AC equivalent circuit.
4. Determine the AC performance by replacing the FET by its AC model.
5. Add the results of the DC and AC analysis to obtain total circuit performance.

Step #1: Determine the circuit quiescent (DC) conditions; verify that the FET is in the saturation region. Using the equations for the n-JFET,

$$V_{GS} = V_G - V_S = -2 - 0 = -2\text{V}$$

and $$I_D = I_{DSS}\left(1 - \frac{V_{GS}}{V_{PO}}\right)^2 = 6 \times 10^{-3}\left(1 - \frac{-2}{-5}\right)^2 = 2.16\,mA.$$

So the drain-source voltage is,

$$V_{DS} = V_{DD} - I_D R_D = 10 - (2.16 \times 10^{-3})(2200) = 5.25\text{V}.$$

The condition for saturation is,

$$V_{DS} \geq V_{GS} - V_{PO} = -2 - (-5) = 3\text{V}$$
$$5.25\text{ V} > 3\text{ V}.$$

The circuit is confirmed to be in saturation.

Step #2: Determine the FET AC model parameters from the quiescent conditions. The relevant parameters are:

$$r_d = \frac{V_A}{I_D} = \frac{100}{2.16\times10^{-3}} = 46.3k\Omega$$

$$g_m = \frac{-2I_{DSS}\left(1-\frac{V_{GS}}{V_{PO}}\right)}{V_{PO}} = \frac{-2\left(6\times10^{-3}\right)\left(1-\frac{-2}{-5}\right)}{-5} = 1.44mS.$$

Step #3: Create an AC equivalent circuit. The DC sources are set to zero, and the output voltage becomes a small-signal quantity.

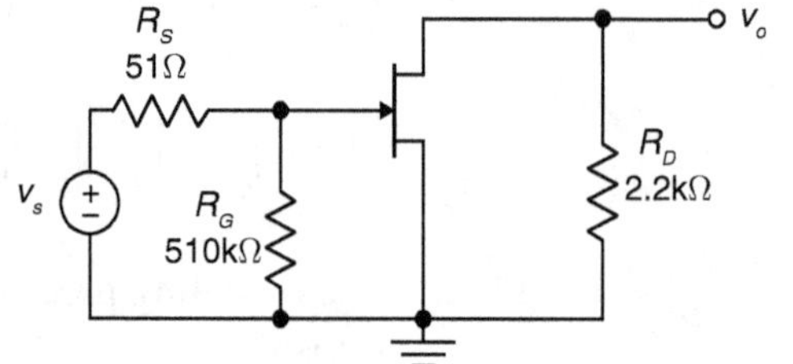

Exhibit 12.27a

Step #4: Determine the AC performance by replacing the FET by its AC model. The small-signal circuit model of the amplifier is shown in Exhibit 12.27b.

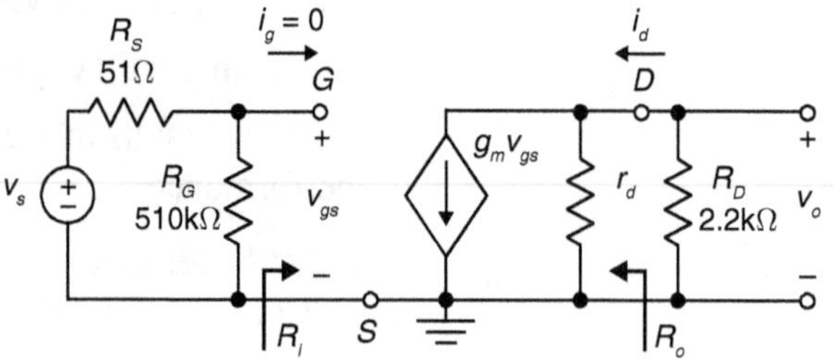

Exhibit 12.27b

The input resistance to the gate of the FET is,

$$R_i = \infty.$$

If the input resistance is measured to the left of R_S, then

$$R_{iS} = R_S + (R_G||R_i) = 51 + 510k = 510k\Omega.$$

The voltage gain from the gate of the FET is

$$A_V = -g_m(r_d||R_D) = -1.44 \times 10^{-3}\,(46.3k||2200) = -3.$$

The voltage gain from the source is given by,

$$A_{VS} = -g_m\left(r_d \| R_D\right)\left(\frac{R_G}{R_G + R_S}\right)$$

$$= -1.44\times10^{-3}\left(46.3k \| 2.2k\right)\left(\frac{510k}{510k+51}\right) \approx A_V = -3$$

The output resistance is

$$R_o = r_d \| \infty = r_d = \left|\frac{V_A}{I_D}\right| = \left|\frac{100}{2.16\times10^{-3}}\right| = 46.3k\Omega.$$

If the drain resistance is included in the output resistance,

$$R_{o1} = R_o || R_D = r_d || R_D = 46.3k || 2.2k = 2.1k\Omega.$$

Step #6 is beyond the requirements of this problem, but all the data is present to add the quiescent solution to the small-signal solution for total circuit response.

12.33 The quiescent point of the FET must be found first to ensure that it is in the saturation region. For DC operation, all capacitors appear as open circuits. By voltage division, the gate voltage is

$$V_G = \frac{V_{DD}R_{G2}}{R_{G1}+R_{G2}} = \frac{10(15k)}{24k+15k} \approx 3.8V.$$

The voltage at the source terminal of the FET is,

$$V_S = I_D R_{SS} = \left(5\times10^{-3}\right)(100) = 0.5V.$$

Therefore, the gate-source voltage is

$$V_{GS} = V_G - V_S = 3.8 - 0.5 = 3.3\text{V}.$$

The drain-source voltage is,

$$V_{DS} = V_{DD} - I_D\left(R_D + R_{SS}\right) = 10 - 5\times10^{-3}(1100) = 4.5V$$

For the FET to be in saturation, $V_{DS} \geq V_{GS} - V_T$. For the circuit in this example,

4.5V > 3.3V
> 1.3V ⇒ the FET is in saturation.

The small-signal transconductance is

$$g_m = 2\sqrt{I_D K} = 2\sqrt{\left(5\times10^{-3}\right)\left(2.96\times10^{-3}\right)} \approx 7.7mS$$

The AC equivalent circuit can be found by setting all DC sources to zero and, since the circuit is in its midband frequency range, all capacitors are replaced by short circuits.

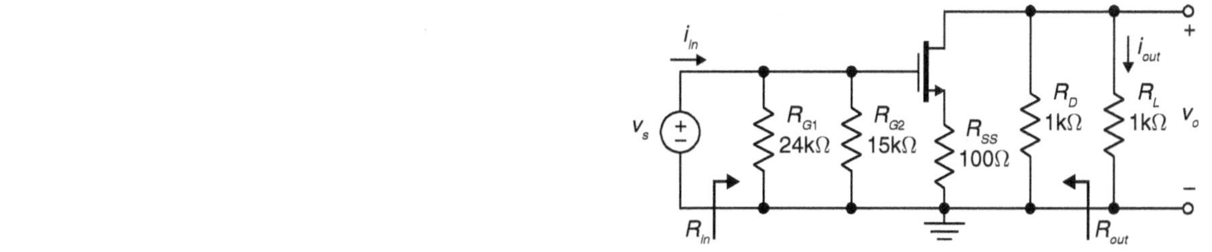

The AC equivalent circuit leads to the small-signal equivalent circuit for the amplifier:

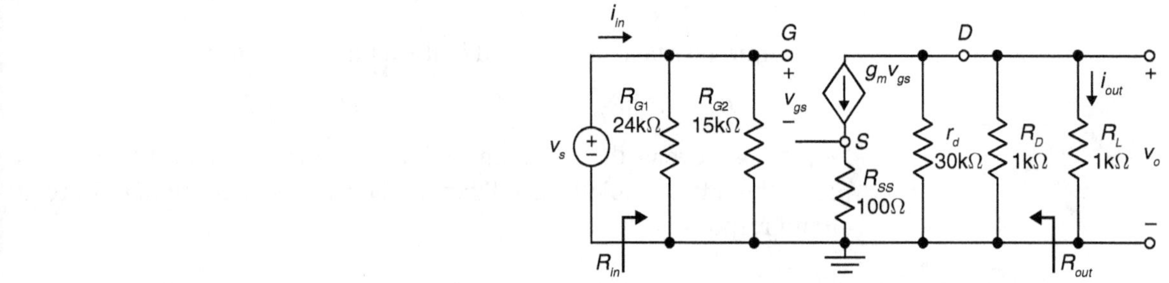

$$A_{VS} = A_V = -\frac{g_m r_d R_D}{R_{SS} + r_d + R_D + g_m r_d R_{SS}}$$

$$= -\frac{7.7\times10^{-3}(30k)(1k)}{100 + 30k + 1k + 7.7\times10^{-3}(30k)(100)} \approx -4.3$$

$$R_{in} = 24k \| 15k = 9.23k\Omega$$

$$R_{out} = R_D \| R_o = R_D \| (r_d + R_{SS} + g_m r_d R_{SS})$$

$$= 1k \| [30k + 100 + 7.7\times10^{-3}(30k)(100)] \approx 980\Omega$$

CHAPTER 13

Power

OUTLINE

Our review of three-phase theory begins with the typical *balanced three-phase source*: a simplified *synchronous generator* (*alternator*) modeled by an ideal set of synchronized sinusoidal sources in series with impedances. For balanced applications, this leads to a *per-phase equivalent* of the generator, involving a single-phase

ideal voltage source in series with a *synchronous reactance*, which can then be interconnected with per-phase models of transformers, lines, loads, etc.

More likely, an *ideal* three-phase source (having no internal impedance) will be found adequate, or will be expressly stated in the problem; its use simplifies the problem even more.

The three-phase equations given in the *Fundamentals of Engineering Supplied-Reference Handbook* address only the simplest issues. The presentation in this chapter will illustrate the use of these equations, as well as introducing other concepts that will help you work balanced three-phase problems (and, in fact, will help you with single-phase, steady-state problems as well).

In using equations concerned with steady-state ac analysis, it is important to know whether only the magnitudes or the actual phasor quantities are needed. In fact, it is important to note which quantities might be complex-number phasors (**V**, **I**, magnetic fluxes), which may be complex numbers (**Z**, **Y**, **S**) but are not usually considered phasors, and which, by definition, are scalars (R, L, C, X, B, P, Q, angles, etc.). Usually, complex quantities will be shown in **boldface** in this and other exam materials, as well as in the general literature. We will adhere to this practice to some extent in this book, but since some actual past exam problems are used as examples, slight differences in notation will sometimes appear. Careful attention to the problem statement will usually clear up what is given and what is required.

Just to emphasize the difference in vector and scalar quantities, we ask you to remember, in particular, that real (average) power P and reactive power Q are scalars and therefore not complex numbers (this is a very common mistake). Thus P and Q may be found from magnitudes (as in $P = VI\cos\theta$) or as the real and imaginary parts, respectively, of an equation involving complex numbers ($P + jQ = \mathbf{VI}^*$). Also recall that resistance, conductance, inductance, capacitance, reactance, and susceptance are always real numbers; susceptance and reactance may be positive or negative. Steady-state voltages and currents may be phasors. Complex power **S** is always a complex number although its magnitude, called *apparent power*, is of course real.

If you feel that you need another review text in this area, a good one is Glover and Sarma, *Power Systems Analysis and Design* published by Brooks/Cole (now in the 3rd edition, 2002). Texts on electric circuits and electric machinery often have a chapter or appendix addressing balanced three-phase circuits as well. As mentioned above, it's probably not necessary, for the exam, to cover symmetrical components, per unit values, unbalances, and other more advanced power-system topics in great detail.

THREE-PHASE GENERATOR

We will begin with an actual three-phase source, the three-phase synchronous generator (alternator). A simplified alternator, with stator windings and controllable rotor field winding, is shown in Figure 13.1.

The *stator* (stationary part of the machine), shown in Figure 13.1a, carries the *armature coils*, which deliver the three-phase voltages. In an actual machine, these are usually much heavier than the rotor winding.

The *rotor* (the rotating part of the generator) is assumed to be driven at a fixed speed ω by some mechanical source. The rotor consists of a ferromagnetic pole set carrying a field winding, as shown in Figure 13.1b. Direct current is con-

veyed to the field winding by means of *slip rings*, making the rotor a controllable electromagnet.

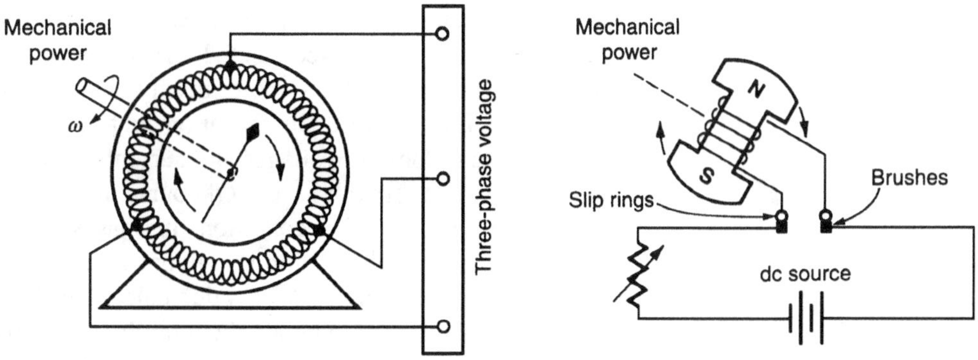

(a) Synchronous generator stator

(b) Controllable rotor

Figure 13.1 Synchronous alternator in generator mode

Note that the polarity of the rotor magnetic poles in Figure 13.1b conforms to the *right-hand rule* in terms of the current setting up that field, which is out of the positive terminal of the dc source.

The effect of the rotating field pole set is to produce a rotating magnetic vector (we call this the *revolving field*) rotating at angular velocity ω that, in turn, produces a set of three-phase voltages in the stator windings. The magnitude of each of these phase voltages is a function of the dc field current and machine inductances. (Conversely, a set of three-phase currents applied to such a device would result in a revolving field, dragging the rotor with it in what is called *motor* operation. A generator and a motor are the same device; the terms just distinguish how the machine is used.)

Since the moving rotor of the generator gives rise to a stator revolving field that also rotates at the same speed, the angle between the revolving field induced by the rotor and that associated with the stator is constant for constant load. Since electromagnetic torque is a function of this angle, the angle is called the *torque angle* (usually denoted δ) This angle plays an important role in synchronous-machine operation, as indicated in the next chapter. Note that this torque angle is distinct from the *power-factor angle* (also called *phase angle*), which is the angle (usually designated by φ or θ) between the respective terminal currents and voltages.

THREE-PHASE CONNECTIONS

Balanced three-phase sources or loads may be connected in one of two *configurations: wye (Y) or delta* (Δ). *A wye may or* may not be grounded; for a balanced system it theoretically makes no difference since neutral current is zero in a balanced system operated at fundamental frequency. Note that the generator shown above happens to have a delta-connected armature. Most generators (at least smaller machines) are connected in wye (actually *grounded wye*), primarily to provide a firmly grounded output. For simplicity, a wye source connection is normally assumed if the emphasis is not on the actual generator connection. Three-phase *motors* are often connected in ungrounded wye but may be connected in grounded wye or delta.

The phase angle θ_p referred to in three-phase relationships is the angle between a given phase voltage and its corresponding current. Phases are usually labeled with the letters a, b, and c; the angle θ_p (often called simply φ or θ) can therefore

be considered the angle by which the phase-a voltage leads the phase-a current (i.e., the angle by which $\mathbf{V}_p$ leads $\mathbf{I}_p$).

Balanced three-phase problems are almost always solved on a per-phase, line-to-neutral basis. This per-phase equivalent lends itself especially well to wye-connected devices, so delta-connected transformers, loads, etc. are often converted to an equivalent wye (for some primarily delta-connected circuits, this step is not necessary). It is usually a great solution aid to draw the per-phase equivalent circuit for any given problem. Voltages and currents in this per-phase equivalent are usually taken to be those of phase a. Of course, if we know what is happening in phase a, then the corresponding conditions in phases b and c may be readily evaluated. Furthermore, each phase supplies or consumes one third of the total real, reactive, or complex power, so any such value calculated for the per-phase equivalent can be multiplied by three to obtain the total. In simple problems on the exam, such as those involving one source and one load (with perhaps a connecting line of given impedance), it may not be necessary to draw or solve a per-phase equivalent in order to obtain what is requested. However, we reiterate that sketching the per-phase equivalent is usually helpful, at least to help you avoid errors.

In connection with this we should also point out that *three-phase device ratings are usually specified in terms of line-to-line voltage and total three-phase apparent power.* Thus, a load rated 208 V, 5 kVA will imply a line-to-line voltage of 208 V and will consume a total of 5 kVA when this voltage is applied. We will discuss the somewhat self-evident concepts of line-to-line and line-to-neutral voltage below.

The per-phase representation of a three-phase generator is simply a Thevenin equivalent, with an ideal sinusoidal source in series with an impedance. As mentioned above, it can be expected that some FE problems might specify a generator and that some may simply specify an ideal source (perhaps called a constant-voltage source or just a source).

Wye Connections

A simple system consisting of an ideal, balanced three-phase source and resistive load is shown in Figure 13.2 where, to start with, we have connected each of the phases as separate single-phase circuits (we will see shortly how they are actually interconnected in practice). The voltage source in each phase (which gives rise to a *phase voltage*) is connected to each load resistance in the diagram by lines representing zero impedance. The presence of the three separate single-phase circuits in this illustration emphasizes the somewhat independent aspect of each of these phases.

The bundle of return lines will shortly be called the *neutral*. As is typical, we have let phase a be the reference by setting its source voltage to zero degrees.

As an example, suppose that each phase voltage in Figure 13.2a is 100 V and that each resistor is of value 5 Ω. Then, in phase a the current is $\mathbf{I}_a = \mathbf{V}_a/R$, or 20 A (at an angle identical to that of the voltage $\mathbf{V}_a$) and the power dissipated in the resistor is $P = I^2R$ or 2 kW. This is clearly seen in the single-phase equivalent of Figure 13.2b, which typifies conditions in phase a. In the complete, balanced three-phase circuit, of course, the total power dissipated in all of the loads is merely the sum of the individual powers, or 6 kW. Also, since this is a wye connection, the phase currents (denoted I_p in the *Handbook*) are the same as the line currents (denoted I_L in the *Handbook*).

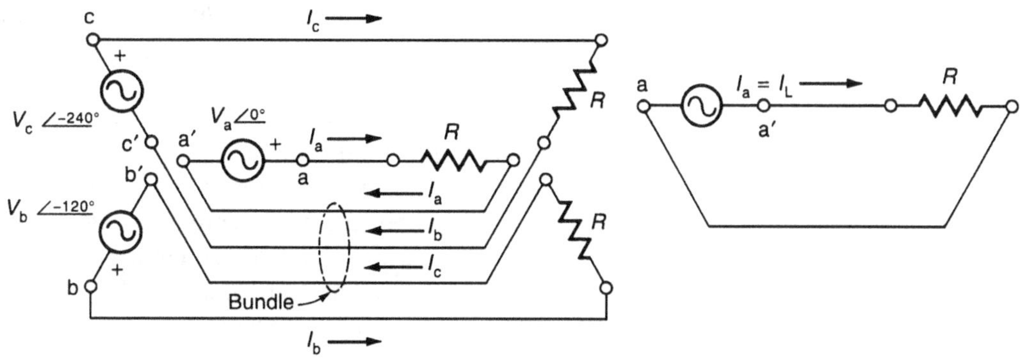

(a) Three individual circuits (b) Single-phase equivalent circuit

Figure 13.2 A conceptual "three-source" system

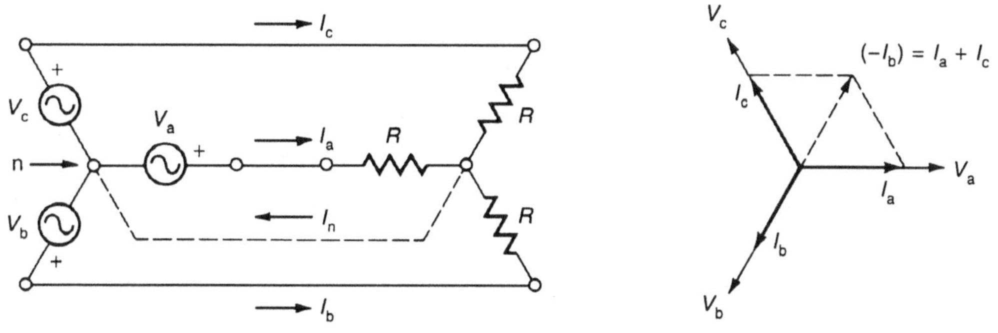

(a) Circuit (b) Phasor diagram

Figure 13.3 A wye-wye three-phase circuit with ideal source and resistive load

All three currents represented by the bundle of return lines are, of course, the same as their corresponding phase currents. Since the return currents are independent, the wires in the return bundle could be connected together as one single conductor, called the *neutral*. This is, in fact, done in practice, as shown in Figure 13.3a. The current in the neutral wire is, by Kirchhoff's current law,

$$\mathbf{I}_n = \mathbf{I}_a + \mathbf{I}_b + \mathbf{I}_c$$

which, for this balanced case becomes

$$\begin{aligned}\mathbf{I}_n &= I_a\angle 0° + I_b\angle{-120°} + I_c\angle{+120°}\\ &= I_a\,(1\angle 0° + 1\angle{-120°} + 1\angle{+120°}) = 0\end{aligned}$$

Since it carries zero current, there is no theoretical need for the (dashed) neutral conductor in a perfectly balanced system. Usually, the neutral conductor is, in fact, present; its purpose is to carry any unbalanced currents and to keep the potential of the neutral point close to zero.

A phasor diagram showing the voltages and currents in the simple wye-connected circuit is shown in Figure 13.3b. Note that the *phase sequence* is *abc*; we call this *positive sequence* or *abc sequence*. Most three-phase problems will involve positive sequence only. (The other sequence, *acb*, is called *negative sequence*. There is also a *zero sequence*, associated with the method of symmetrical components, but it represents vectors of identical magnitude and phase in each of the phases, and is, thus, not really a rotating sequence.)

As with single-phase circuits, the voltage from any point to neutral is sometimes expressed in *single-subscript* notation (where a reference is implied), and sometimes in *double-subscript* notation (which emphasizes, correctly, the point-

function nature of an electric potential difference). The two notations carry the same meaning; thus,

$$\mathbf{V}_{an} = \mathbf{V}_a$$

Both notations will be found in practice.

Note that in a three-phase system there are two kinds of voltages, *line-to-line* and *line-to-neutral*, the former sometimes being known simply as *line voltages* and, in the case of the wye, the latter sometimes being called *phase voltages*. The voltage between any two lines can, of course, be found in terms of the two respective line-to-neutral voltages; for example,

$$\mathbf{V}_{ab} = \mathbf{V}_{an} - \mathbf{V}_{bn}$$

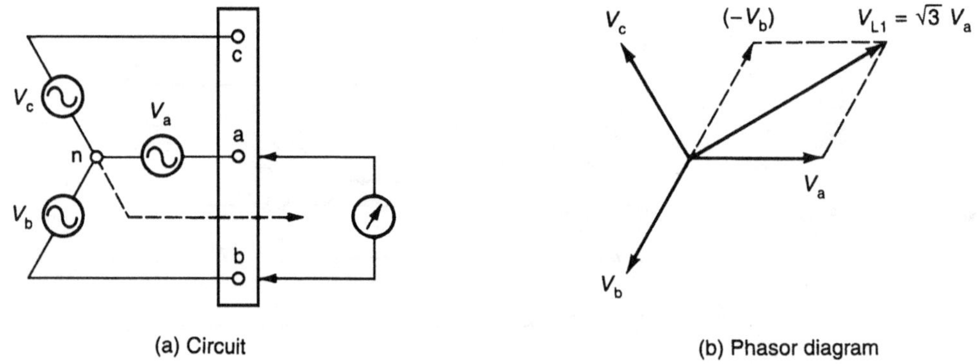

Figure 13.4 The phase- and line-voltage relationship for a wye connection

This line-to-line voltage is shown as a measurement in Figure 13.4a. From the phasor diagram of Figure 13.4b, we see that the resulting line voltage, $\mathbf{V}_{L1}$, (or $\mathbf{V}_{ab}$) is $\sqrt{3}$ times as large as $\mathbf{V}_{an}$ and leads $\mathbf{V}_{an}$ by 30°. Of course, the other two line-to-line voltages may be found in the same manner. It should be emphasized that, for balanced loads, only the one leg need actually be solved, and the required values in the other two are found by similarity. Note that, for a wye circuit and using the notation of the *FE Handbook*,

$$\mathrm{I}_L = \mathrm{I}_p \quad \text{and} \quad \mathrm{V}_{L1} = \sqrt{3}\,\mathrm{V}_p \angle 30° \qquad \textbf{(13.1a,b)}$$

part b of which is often written more expressively as

$$\mathbf{V}_{ab} = \sqrt{3}\mathbf{V}_a \angle 30°$$

The total power taken from the source or dissipated by the full load (assuming no power line loss) is given for balanced conditions by the following easily derived three-phase formula (which is, in fact, valid for both delta and wye connections)

$$P_{\mathrm{tot}} = \sqrt{3}V_L I_L \cos\theta_P \qquad \textbf{(13.2a)}$$

where V_L is the magnitude of a line-to-line voltage and I_L is the magnitude of a line current.

Be careful to note that *the power-factor angle θ_P is the angle between the voltage and current in the reference phase* (i.e., the angle between $\mathbf{V}_a$ and $\mathbf{I}_a$); it is said that the angle is *lagging* if the current is behind the voltage phasor and *leading* if ahead. The power factor is defined as $\cos\theta_P$. Note that these definitions follow single-phase practice exactly. Another way of writing Equation 13.2a is given in Equation 13.2b:

$$P_{\mathrm{tot}} = \sqrt{3}V_L I_L(\mathrm{PF}) \qquad \textbf{(13.2b)}$$

Of course, since the load is balanced, and since line and phase currents are the same in the wye load, the total load power is also $P_{tot} = 3(I_p)^2R$ for load resistance R.

Delta Connections

In a delta connection, the three load (or source) elements are connected line-to-line as shown in Figure 13.5a, rather than line-to-neutral. It is obvious that there is no neutral return and that the phase voltage across each leg of the delta is equal to the line voltage (one of these is usually made the reference in solving delta-connection problems that are not converted into an equivalent wye). These line voltages are, of course, 120° out of phase with each other in the balanced case. The phase currents are merely the respective line voltages divided by the phase impedances; these three currents, of course, are also 120° out of phase with each other (see Figure 13.5b which, as an example, gives conditions for a unity power-factor load). The subscript p on the currents in the figure emphasizes that these are phase currents; i.e., the currents in the actual phase components (the resistors in this case), as distinct from line currents.

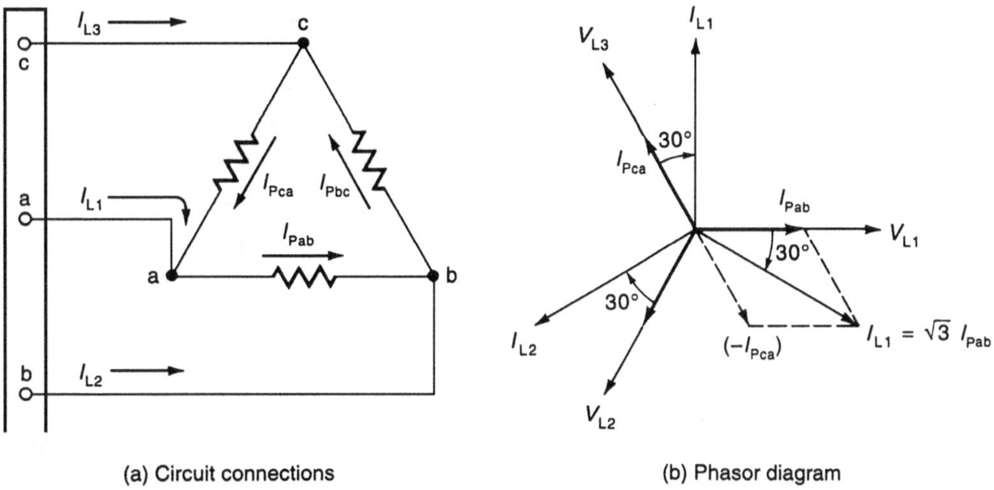

Figure 13.5 The delta relationship

In the balanced delta the phase current is the same in magnitude for each leg. The line currents are the phasor sums at each junction of the respective phase currents, and it is easily shown that each line current is equal to $\sqrt{3}$ times the phase current in magnitude, with the two sets of currents separated by respective angles of 30°. For a delta circuit, then, we could say that, using the notation of Figure 13.5 and of the *FE Handbook*,

$$\mathbf{V}_L = \mathbf{V}_p$$

and

$$\mathbf{I}_{L1} = \sqrt{3}\mathbf{I}_p\angle{-30°} \qquad \textbf{(13.3a,b)}$$

With reference to Figure 13.5, the second of these equations can be written more specifically as

$$\mathbf{I}_a = \mathbf{I}_{L1} = \sqrt{3}\mathbf{I}_{pab}\angle{-30°}$$

As an example of a balanced delta connection, consider a load having three phase impedances of 5 + j5 Ω each, to be connected as a delta, with the applied

line (line-to-line) voltage equal to 173 V. Here, the reference phase current within the delta is

$$\mathbf{I}_p = (\mathbf{V}_p)/\mathbf{Z} = (173\angle 0°)/(5 + j5) = 24.5\angle -45° \text{ A}$$

The power per phase is found as

$$P = (I_p)^2 R = (24.5)^2 5 = 3 \text{ kW}$$

and, thus, the total power is 9 kW. Again, using the general power formula as a check, the power taken from the source is given by

$$\begin{aligned} P_{tot} &= \sqrt{3}\, V_L I_L (\text{PF}) \\ &= \sqrt{3} \times 173 \times (\sqrt{3} \times 24.5) \times 0.707 = 9\text{kW} \end{aligned} \quad \textbf{(13.4)}$$

COMPLEX POWER

Complex power, designated **S** or VA, is defined as

$$\mathbf{S} = P + jQ \quad \textbf{(13.5a)}$$

where P is the real power (in watts) and Q is the reactive power (in VAR's). This equation is valid for a single-phase device, for any leg of a three-phase circuit (if the values are interpreted as per-phase), or for total values of a three-phase device (if so interpreted). Total P and Q in a balanced three-phase circuit, as scalars, are three times their respective per-phase quantities. In addition, for the three-phase case, we could show that the total complex power is given by

$$\mathbf{S} = \sqrt{3} V_L I_L (\cos \theta_p + j \sin \theta_p) \quad \textbf{(13.5b)}$$

where θ_p is the power-factor angle associated with one phase (i.e., the angle between a line-to-line voltage and its corresponding phase current in a delta connection, or a line-to-neutral voltage and its corresponding line or phase current in a wye connection).

Be sure to remember that, just as in single-phase circuits, *real (or average) power P can only be dissipated in a pure resistance, and reactive power Q is produced by capacitors and consumed by inductors.* As a scalar, real power dissipation can always be found by summing all the I^2R values in the circuit, the only caution being that in ac machinery analysis there may be a fictitious resistance that represents mechanical power. Reactive power can be found similarly by summing all of the I^2X terms.

TRANSFORMERS

Since transformers transfer energy through a time-changing magnetic field, they are often considered to be in the machinery category even though they are not designed to involve relative mechanical motion. Steady-state energy transfer in magnetic systems functions only with time-changing signals. We will restrict our attention to transformers in the sinusoidal steady state here.

Transformers are also considered with electric machines since they have been, for more than a century, important components of electric power systems. Furthermore, the electromagnetic fundamentals underlying transformer analysis are the same as for machines (with the added potential for relative motion in the latter case). Thus, an understanding of transformers should help you work problems in the machines area.

The fundamental mathematical relations between voltage, current, complex power, and impedance are easy to establish for the ideal transformer in the steady state. For the ideal transformer presented in Chapter 1 and shown in the circuit of Figure 13.6, a relation for the rms phasor primary and secondary voltages may be found by means of Faraday's law ($v = N\, d\phi/dt$) in terms of the number of turns of each winding as

$$\mathbf{V}_1/\mathbf{V}_2 = \mathrm{N}_1/\mathrm{N}_2 \tag{13.6}$$

Similarly, using Ampere's circuital law we find that the currents are related by

$$\mathbf{I}_1/\mathbf{I}_2 = \mathrm{N}_2/\mathrm{N}_1 \tag{13.7}$$

These two equations hold for rms (or even peak) magnitudes as well as phasors.

From these relations, it is easy to show that a load impedance $\mathbf{Z}_L$ on the secondary side is seen, when looking into the primary side, as

$$\mathbf{Z}_{\mathrm{pri}} = \mathrm{a}^2\mathbf{Z}_L \tag{13.8}$$

where, as shown earlier, the turns ratio a is

$$a = N_1/N_2 = |V_p/V_s| = |V_1/V_2| = |I_s/I_p| = |I_2/I_1| \tag{13.9}$$

Thus, we see that the ideal transformer refers impedances according to the square of the turns ratio. Here the subscripts p and s (signifying primary and secondary) are introduced since transformer problems are sometimes expressed in those terms (see below).

Just as important as the idea of impedance referral is the complex-power relationship for the ideal transformer, which can be obtained from the Faraday and Ampere relationships cited above, in complex form as

$$\mathbf{V}_1\mathbf{I}_1 = \mathbf{V}_2\mathbf{I}_2$$

Since it is then true that

$$\mathbf{V}_1\mathbf{I}_1{}^* = \mathbf{V}_2\mathbf{I}_2{}^*, \tag{13.10}$$

we can see that the complex power on each side of the ideal transformer must be the same; that is,

$$\mathbf{S}_1 = \mathbf{S}_2$$

and, thus, the real and reactive power on each side (which are scalars) are related as

$$P_1 = P_2$$
$$Q_1 = Q_2$$

This tells us that the ideal transformer does not consume real or reactive power.

Actual transformers (especially large ones) approach this ideal fairly closely, but do not attain it in practice. They are addressed below.

The foregoing equations should enable the solution of many simple transfer problems, certainly all of those in which the transformer is stated to be "ideal." It only remains to account for the non-ideal behavior of real transformers (at low frequencies).

Note that we have used the terms *primary* and *secondary* in discussing windings, as is often done in industry. Do not let this become a point of confusion. Usually this terminology simply implies that the primary is the energized side and the secondary is the load side of the transformer. Energy flow can be in either direction through the transformer, so the primary might be either the high- or the low-volt-

age side. It is more specific to use the subscripts 1 and 2 (or the terms *high voltage* and *low voltage*) to designate the particular windings specifically. Note, though, that a transformer might have more than two windings; in such cases it is usually assumed in practice that one winding is the primary and that the others are secondary windings, or more usually, *secondary* and *tertiary* for a 3-winding transformer.

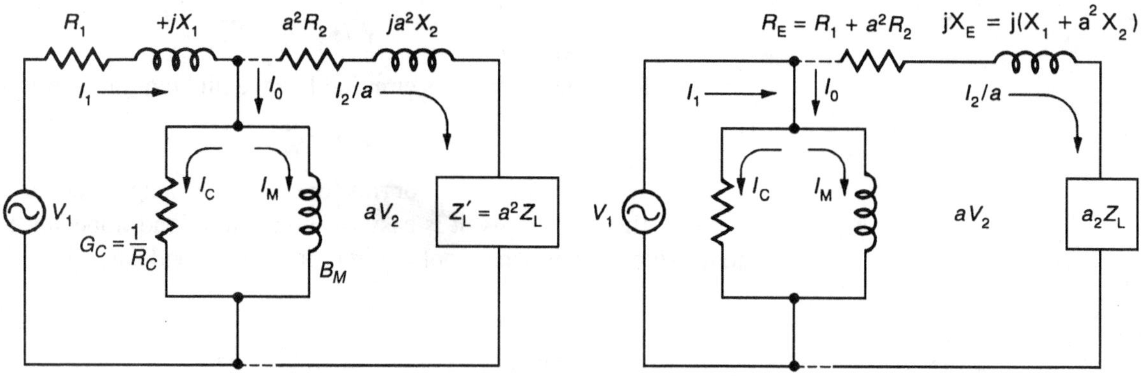

(a) Transformer model

(b) Simplified model

Figure 13.6 A two-winding transformer model

Actual (as opposed to ideal) transformers, of course, do consume real and reactive power when energized by a source, whether they are supplying a load or not. This behavior can be modeled in a straightforward way. The most frequently used, general circuit model (called the *T-model* because of its resemblance to the letter *T*) that takes into account the non-ideal behavior of the transformer is shown in Figure 13.6a. A source and load are shown connected, as well. This transformer-equivalent circuit includes the resistance and inductive reactance of the primary windings (as R_1 and X_1, respectively) in series with the referred secondary values a^2R_2 and a^2X_2 (all of this together is called the *series*, or *leakage*, branch of the model). The model also includes the shunt-branch parameters (which will be discussed below). The choice of referring all quantities to primary (as in Figure 13.6a), or all to secondary, is dependent upon the particular problem. Note that the process of referring quantities from one winding to another, as in Figure 13.6a, moves or does away with the ideal transformer, at least as far as turns ratio is concerned (more on this later).

The resistances in the series branch, of course, model the resistances of the respective windings, and thus allow calculation of power loss in the windings (sometimes called *winding loss*). The series reactances (*leakage reactances*) model the flux leakage (flux that links one winding but not the other). Of course, the most desirable transformer would have extremely low leakage flux and winding resistance, making these four series parameters very low (zero for the ideal transformer). The equivalent leakage reactance (X_E in Fig. 13.6b) is usually the most important parameter in the analysis of a large transformer, especially at high values of load current.

Now consider the *shunt branch* in the transformer model of Figure 13.6a, which consists of a resistance and a reactance. The changing magnetic field in the core causes power loss within the transformer core by *eddy-current* and *hysteresis* mechanisms; these core losses are represented by the current $\mathbf{I}_C$. The current parameter $\mathbf{I}_M$ represents core *magnetization* (i.e., $\mathbf{I}_M$ is the component of primary current that must flow just to set up the magnetic field in the core). In an ideal transformer, of course, both of these shunt current components would be zero; in a good

practical power transformer they are much smaller than (perhaps on the order of a few percent of) rated full-load current. For this reason, the shunt branch is sometimes neglected, although it must be included when performing efficiency studies (recall that efficiency = P_{out}/P_{in}, and, thus, its evaluation is based upon loss). *Core loss* can be calculated if the core-loss current and equivalent shunt resistance or conductance G_C are known. G_C can be measured approximately by performing an *open-circuit test* in which one winding is energized and instrumented for voltage, current, and power, with the other winding open-circuited. All of the impedance parameters shown in the model of Figure 13.6a may be easily obtained through simple laboratory tests (the series parameters are obtained by means of the *short circuit* test). The significant (several orders of magnitude) difference between the shunt and series impedances of the model allows the tests for the series and shunt parameter to be *decoupled* from each other for most practical purposes.

It is this decoupling that allows the simplification of Figure 13.6b, in which the shunt branch has been moved to the source terminals and the resulting series impedances combined. These series impedances can be added directly in the circuit of Figure 13.6b because the secondary leakage parameters have been referred to the primary. When you work such a problem, *make sure that all parameters appear on a common base*, as shown here (i.e., all referred to the primary in this case). A telltale sign of this, of course, is that the ideal transformer does not appear between any groups of impedance.

The phasor sum of the two shunt current components $\mathbf{I}_C$ and $\mathbf{I}_M$ a small fraction of full-load current and is the total shunt current $\mathbf{I}_O$ (this current, sometimes called *exciting current*, is essentially constant at constant applied voltage, whether a load current is present or not). We can view the simplification of Figure 13.6b in terms of this shunt branch to get a different perspective. Because either $\mathbf{I}_1$ or $\mathbf{I}_2$ is usually much greater in magnitude than $\mathbf{I}_O$, it is possible to move the shunt branch to one end or the other of the model. (If the shunt branch is moved to the left side, as shown in Figure 13.6b, the result is said to be an equivalent circuit as referred to the primary side). Given this type of equivalent circuit, one may easily compute the primary current, the power input, the efficiency, the secondary voltage with and without a load, the resulting voltage regulation and other performance characteristics for a given particular load. For example, the efficiency *Eff* may be obtained as

$$Eff = (P_{out}/P_{in}) = P_{out}/(P_{out} + \text{copper loss} + \text{winding loss})$$
$$= P_{out} / [P_{out} + I_1^2(R_1 + a^2R_2) + I_C^2R_C] \qquad \textbf{(13.11)}$$

where R_C is the equivalent core-loss resistance, as given in Fig. 13.6a.

Voltage regulation, an important parameter in the analysis of devices such as transmission lines and transformers, is usually defined, in terms of no-load and full-load voltage at the specified load point, as

$$VREG = (V_{R,NL} - V_{R,FL})/V_{R,FL} \qquad \textbf{(13.12)}$$

where $V_{R,NL}$ is the no-load voltage at the receiving point R and $V_{R,FL}$ is the full-load voltage at the receiving point R.

The parameter *VREG* is a measure of the effect that a load will have when switched on to a system. For instance, if you switch on a reading lamp and the light in another room dims as a result, we say that this part of the power system has poor voltage regulation (which translates to a high numerical value of *VREG*). Ideally, we would usually prefer a voltage regulation of zero (in which the outlet voltage will not change as load is added, in the example above). Many power transmission

systems tolerate a voltage regulation of no more than 10% since values in this range can be compensated by transformer taps.

The voltage regulation of a typical power transformer is determined primarily by the leakage impedances. We find it by looking at both the open-circuit and loaded cases, referring all appropriate quantities from one side to the other in each case so as to be able to work on a common base.

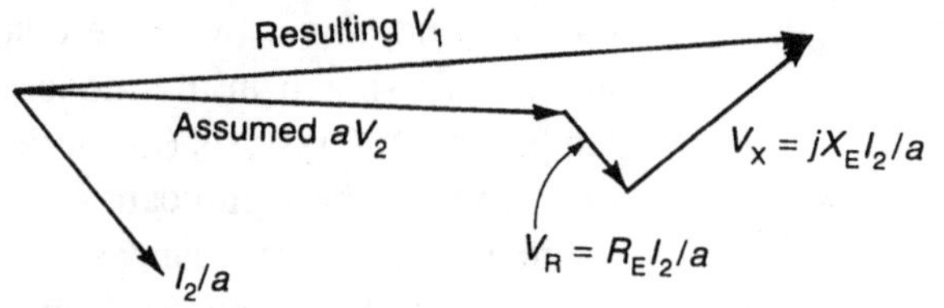

Figure 13.7 Transformer phasor diagram for lagging load

Consider the phasor diagram of Figure 13.7, in which secondary (winding 2) quantities have been referred to the primary (winding 1). This typical example assumes a load $\mathbf{V}_2$ at rated secondary voltage (which, when referred, becomes aV_2) with a lagging power factor (and, thus, a lagging load current of I_2/a). Equivalent leakage impedance $R_E + jX_E$, expressed on the base of the primary side, causes a voltage drop between the source and the load. Note that it takes a much greater value of V_1 in order to achieve this value of V_2 in a lagging circuit. The magnitudes of these voltages may be calculated and the resulting voltage regulation evaluated. You can rearrange the phasor diagram easily to show that a highly capacitive load (for example, a large bank of power-factor-correction capacitors) might actually force the sending end voltage to be lower than that at the receiving end.

In problems like these, the phasor diagram can serve as a check on your understanding and your calculations. *It is highly recommended that you sketch appropriate phasor and circuit diagrams.*

SYNCHRONOUS ROTATING MACHINES

We will assume that you have read the introductory material on the three-phase synchronous generator at the beginning of Chapter 3 (and, in fact, the entire three-phase review of that chapter), so most of that material is not repeated here.

Except for small single-phase synchronous motors used in clocks, timers, and other applications where constant speed is important, most synchronous machines are normally large, three-phase units (which are, in fact, easier to analyze than single-phase machines). In fact, synchronous generators have been built as large as about 1500 MVA. We will center on three-phase machines and, for ease of analysis, will consider them to be wye-connected (see Chapter 3).

The synchronous machine may be either a *generator* (sometimes called an *alternator*), in which current is assumed directed out of the positive terminal of the model or a *motor* (where the reverse is assumed). Of course, the machine is defined as a motor or a generator depending on whether the mechanical power is the input or output. The same synchronous machine can operate in either mode (although we should mention that some other motor types do not make good generators).

By definition, a *synchronous machine* is one in which, under steady state conditions, the mechanical speed of rotation (called the synchro*nous speed* n_s) is

directly proportional to the frequency of the armature currents. The synchronous speed n_s is related to the number of poles as

$$n_s = 120f/p \text{ rpm} \tag{13.13}$$

where f is the electrical frequency of the armature currents in Hz and p is the number of poles. It is important to recall that magnetic poles occur in pairs, so p is always an even number. The highest speed (corresponding to the minimum number of poles $p = 2$) for 60Hz operation is therefore 3600 rpm. Note, also, that, for a given frequency, it is practical to have only a few possible values of synchronous speed. And since there is no slip for a synchronous machine (unlike an induction machine), *a synchronous machine delivers uniform torque only at synchronous speed.*

From Equation 13.13, you can see that, in order to reduce the speed of a synchronous machine with respect to its line frequency, you need to increase the number of poles. For a 60Hz machine of four poles, for instance, $n_s = 1800$ rpm; for a machine of six poles, $n_s = 1200$, and so forth. Some very slow hydroelectric generators have approximately 50 poles.

In order to convert energy uniformly, a synchronous machine must be designed with the same number of rotor poles as it has stator poles per phase. A machine having p stator pole projections per phase is designated a p-pole machine. Of course, that machine must have p poles on its rotor, so it is usually easier to count the rotor poles.

A polyphase machine in operation is characterized by a *revolving field* that rotates at some integer multiple of its synchronous mechanical speed. This revolving field is analogous to the field of a bar magnet when the magnet is spun at constant speed on an axis through its center, halfway between the poles. Constructing a machine with a greater number of poles means that this magnetic field must make more revolutions for a single mechanical revolution, since an electrical cycle is completed for each movement of a rotor pole from a stator a-phase pole to the next a-phase pole of like polarity. For example, a 4-pole machine contains twice as many stator pole projections as a 2-pole machine wound for the same number of phases, and two electrical (or magnetic) cycles will be completed in moving the rotor through a complete mechanical revolution. Thus, we define *electrical synchronous speed n_e* in terms of the mechanical speed given above as

$$n_e = n_s p/2 \text{ rpm}$$

Thus, for a 2-pole machine, $n_s = n_e$, while for $p > 2$, $n_s < n_e$. Electrical speed is sometimes expressed as a frequency, and is called *electrical frequency*. It is, of course, identical to frequency f above. The main reason that electrical frequency, or electrical speed, is discussed frequently is that machines are normally connected electrically to the same system, and, thus, have their electrical frequency in common.

Although the polyphase synchronous machine is probably the simplest machine in concept (that of a dc magnetic field rotating in the presence of a set of stator conductors in the usual configuration) it is not the most frequently used large machine. That distinction goes to the *induction motor*, which is discussed later in this chapter.

Just as with the transformer, we would like to find a simple circuit model that adequately represents the synchronous machine over the range of operation of interest while preserving information on all of the effects with which we are concerned. A synchronous generator is usually modeled by an ideal voltage source

(the *internal voltage*) in series with an impedance (which for large machines is very highly inductive). The typical per-phase model of a synchronous generator, attached to the equally typical RL load, is shown in Figure 13.8a. Often, one considers the terminal voltage $\mathbf{V}_t$ constant and, if necessary, finds the internal voltage $\mathbf{E}_f$ required to support V_t for a given load, usually assuming a wye connection. The magnitude E_f of this internal, fictitious source is a function of the dc field current. The parameter X_s is the *synchronous reactance* of the machine (with the internal resistance being assumed negligible here).

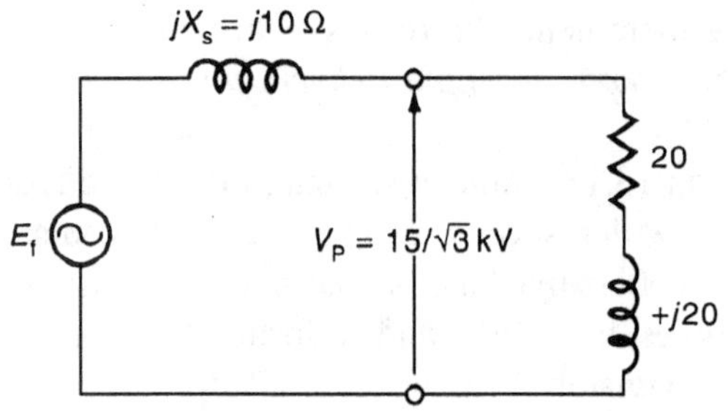

(a) Per-phase model

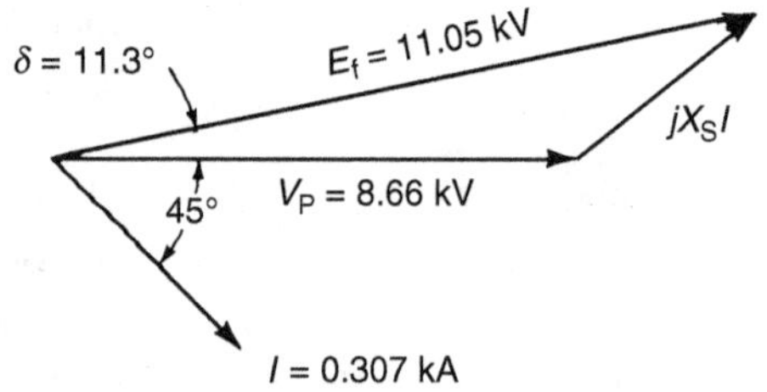

(b) Phasor diagram

Figure 13.8 Synchronous generator problem

As an example, assume that the rated line voltage in a three-phase circuit is 15 kV, the synchronous reactance of a given synchronous generator is 10 Ω/phase, and a load of 20 + j20 Ω/phase is present in a wye configuration. Compute the line currents and the power output of the machine.

The per-phase circuit is shown in Figure 13.8a, with the terminal voltage $\mathbf{V}_p$ labeled. It is evident in this RL circuit, even before calculations are made, that the internal voltage E_f will lead the terminal voltage, and the current into the load will lag it. Since it is customary to specify voltages in line-to-line form, the 15 kV will be understood as a line-to-line value and must be converted into a line-to-neutral voltage for the per-phase model by dividing by the square root of 3.

The line current $\mathbf{I}$ is

$$\mathbf{I} = \mathbf{V}_p/(20 + j20) = (15/\sqrt{3}\angle 0°)/(20\sqrt{2}\angle 45°) = 0.307\angle{-45°}\text{ kA}.$$

Then the per-phase value of $\mathbf{E}_f$ is

$$\mathbf{E}_f = jX_s\mathbf{I} + \mathbf{V}_p = (j10)(0.307\angle{-45°}) + 8.67\angle 0° = 11.04\angle 11.3°\text{ kV}$$

and the output power in the per-phase model is

$$P_o = V_pI\cos\Phi = (8.67\times 10^3)(0.307\times 10^3)\cos 45° = 1.88\times 10^6\text{ W} = 1.88\text{ MW}$$

The total output power is three times the per-phase power

$$P_o(\text{Total}) = 3P_o = 3\times 1.88 = 5.63\text{ MW}.$$

The phasor diagram corresponding to this condition is shown in Figure 13.8b. Study this phasor diagram and note how it would change if the load had been RC (i.e., leading power factor). Also note the similarity between the calculations above and those for the transformer. To emphasize an important point, recall that calculations for balanced three-phase circuits are almost always made on a per-phase basis, assuming a wye connection.

For the synchronous motor, the calculations are essentially the same as for the generator except that current is usually assumed into the positive terminal of the machine.

Most large ac generators are synchronous machines. This includes those found in utility steam power plants, hydroelectric facilities, and backup generation units. Another example of the three-phase synchronous generator, on a smaller scale, is the *alternator* found in most automobiles. Driven by the engine, it provides dc power (through a group of diodes and a regulator) to charge the battery and power auxiliary devices such as headlights and ignition system.

Just in case you may be required to make calculations involving *torque*, we might point out that speed ω, torque T, and power P are related by the equation

$$P = T\omega$$

Conversions are necessary if non-MKS units are used.

POLYPHASE INDUCTION MOTORS

Like other machines, an *induction motor* operates because of the interaction of two magnetic fields: a stator magnetic field and the magnetic field of the rotor. As the name implies, the rotor field is induced magnetically from the stator, and there need be no external rotor connections in the usual form of the device. Induction motors are of two types, distinguished by the form of the rotor: *cage* (or *squirrel cage*) *rotor* and *wound rotor*. We will concentrate on only the simpler and more frequently encountered cage-rotor machine, although most of the theory holds for either type.

The stator of an induction motor is essentially the same as for a synchronous machine. However, the rotor is drastically different. A cage rotor essentially consists of a number of conducting bars, short-circuited at the ends, on a laminated core. A wound rotor contains a winding similar to that of the stator; the windings are either shorted directly or through resistance. There are no external rotor connections for a cage rotor. In either device, voltage is applied only to the stator winding, and currents induced by transformer-like action flow in the short-circuited rotor.

The vast majority of single- and three-phase motors (especially above about 1/8 hp) in use in ac systems are induction motors since they are simple and reliable. Most of these machines are cage-rotor machines, for the same reason. Examples (both single-phase and polyphase) include most fan motors, appliance and shop-tool motors (having speeds below 3600 rpm at 60 Hz), barbecue-spit motors, etc.

The synchronous speed n_s of the motor (i.e., the speed of the revolving magnetic field) is the same as for a synchronous machine (see Equation 13.13). However, the actual speed of the induction machine's rotor (*shaft speed*, designated by n when given in rpm) must be slightly less than n_s in order to have the speed difference allowing for a voltage to be induced in the rotor windings. It is this induced voltage in the short-circuited rotor winding that causes a current to flow to produce torque. Shaft speed n is related to synchronous speed n_s by a quantity called the *slip*, denoted s, and is given by

$$n = (1 - s)n_s \quad \textbf{(13.14a)}$$

Thus, the slip can be expressed as

$$s = (n_s - n)/n_s \quad \textbf{(13.14b)}$$

The slip s is obviously dimensionless but is usually expressed in percent. It is typically on the order of 0.02 to 0.05 (i.e., 2% to 5%) under load, or less than 0.01

for very light or no-load conditions in a typical motor. Obviously, at starting (zero speed) $s = 1$, and at synchronous speed (which the motor cannot attain) s would be zero. It is easy to see why induction motors cannot operate at synchronous speed, since at that speed there would be no relative motion (i.e., no slip) between the stator field and the rotor windings.

It may be helpful to think of the two kinds of motors discussed so far as complementary to each other: the synchronous motor can deliver uniform power at only one speed (synchronous speed) for a given electrical frequency, while the induction motor can deliver power at any practical speed *except* synchronous speed. In fact, an induction motor whose shaft is driven faster than synchronous speed becomes a generator, and the slip is negative. Such generators are sometimes used in wind-power systems and other variable-speed applications since, as *asynchronous* machines, their output electrical frequency is that of the power system to which they are connected (in such applications, synchronous machines would require a frequency converter).

As an example, assume that a 60 Hz induction motor has 4 poles and operates at a slip of 0.03 (3%) at rated load. For this machine, the speed of the revolving magnetic field (n_s) would be

$$n_s = 120 \times 60/4 = 1800 \text{ rpm}$$

and the actual shaft speed would be

$$n = (1 - 0.03) \times 1800 = 1746 \text{ rpm}$$

The electrical behavior of the induction motor (particularly as seen from the terminals), of course, changes in response to mechanical load. For determining starting current, efficiency, current characteristics, speed-torque characteristics, etc., the per-phase circuit model equivalent of Figure 13.9 is often used (its derivation appears in machines books). Note that the load is represented as a slip-dependent, fictitious variable resistance of value

$$R_L = r_2(1 - s)/s \qquad \textbf{(13.15)}$$

As with the transformer, all of the parameters in Figure 13.9 may be determined for an actual motor by test. By knowing these parameters, one can compute output power and the various losses, as well as real and reactive power consumption, power factor, efficiency, input current, etc. at any given value of slip (or speed). Questions based upon this equivalent circuit may be slightly beyond the scope of the examination. However, the use of this model represents a good steady state circuit review.

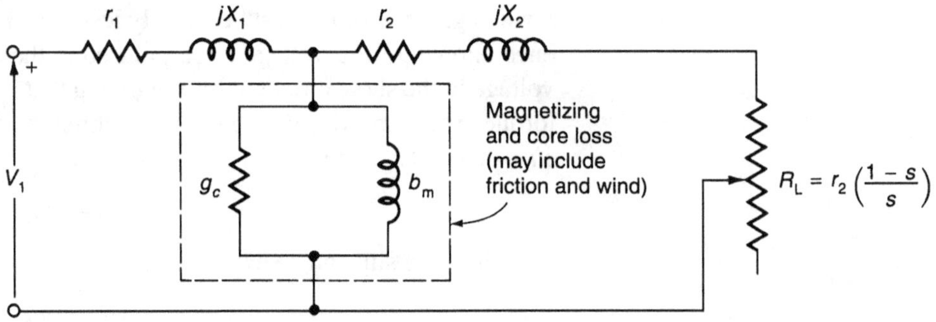

Figure 13.9 Induction motor per-phase equivalent circuit

SINGLE-PHASE SYNCHRONOUS AND INDUCTION MOTORS

Synchronous and induction motors can be made in single-phase and two-phase configurations as well. Two-phase applications, widely used in positioning systems, are not often found in large ac power contexts (although it is noteworthy that the early induction machines built by the device's inventor, Nikola Tesla, were two-phase). Single-phase induction motors, of course, are very popular especially in the smaller sizes. The main differences between polyphase (higher phase order than 1) machines and single-phase ones are the methods of getting the single-phase machines to start and to develop a rotating flux phasor.

In general, two- and three-phase machines behave very much alike from the standpoint of starting: Two- and three-phase induction motors are inherently self-starting and directional, while two- and three-phase synchronous machines are not self-starting (they are usually fitted with a short-circuited *damper* or *amortisseur* winding on the rotor to emulate an induction machine under starting conditions). Single-phase synchronous and induction machines are neither inherently self-starting nor directional; something artificial must be done to shape the magnetic field in order to make the motor accelerate a load from rest. Popular single-phase motor types (named for the way in which they modify the air-gap field) include shaded-pole and split-phase. Regardless of which technique is used for starting, they essentially have one thing in common (except for shaded-pole and a few other types of specialized machines): they have two revolving flux phasors rotating in opposite directions until started. Then as they accelerate, one or the other flux phasor predominates in the rotational direction of starting. From then on, the machine acts much like the corresponding three-phase machine. As in the case of two- or three-phase machines, whether the single-phase machine is synchronous or induction depends upon the rotor structure.

The same equations relating to synchronous speed apply regardless of the number of phases. For single-phase induction machines, the previous equations involving slip still apply also. Questions involving slip for single-phase machines might be expected on the examination.

SOME OTHER MACHINE TYPES

Several other types of machines are found in common practice, especially in the smaller sizes. *DC machines* may be of the permanent-magnet type, in which the stator field is provided by a permanent magnet and the wound rotor is supplied power through a mechanical switching device consisting of a split-segment *commutator* and *slip rings*. Such machines are often found in electric toys, inexpensive tape recorders, videocassette rewinders, and so forth. Larger dc machines usually have windings on both rotor and stator. They may have two or more field windings (on the stator) as well as the armature (rotor) winding. These windings may be interconnected in *series* or *shunt*, or in *compound* (where both series and shunt field windings are used). By controlling the relative values of the currents and voltages in these field windings, a wide variety of speed-torque characteristics may be obtained.

Many applications require the use of a high-speed motor with a high value of *speed regulation* (i.e., a significant drop of speed with increasing load); speed regulation is analogous to voltage regulation given in Equation 13.7. Some examples of such applications are hand-held drill motors, electric mixers, blenders, and other small high-speed appliances. The motor used here is essentially a series-connected

dc motor, commonly called a *universal motor* since it can be used with dc or ac. Sometimes this device is simply called a *commutator motor* because, unlike other ac machines, it contains a commutator. Another application of the series-connected commutator machine, for many decades, has been for engine cranking in internal-combustion engines, since this type of device has a very high power-to-weight ratio. We should point out one unique characteristic of this machine: its speed will continue to increase to a theoretically high value as load is reduced or removed. Thus, this type of motor is never operated without mechanical load.

Stepper motors, which are usually driven by synchronized, electronically generated pulses, have found wide application in recent years in positioning devices such as electric typewriter carriages, computer printers, and robotics. You can often distinguish a de-energized stepper motor by the *cogging*; i.e., as the rotor is turned it seems to seek specific rest positions because of the interaction of an internal rotor magnet and the salient stator poles.

Probably the most fertile field for unique design has been the area of small (fractional-horsepower), single-phase induction and synchronous machines. From about the 1920s onward, many different designs, often widely different in appearance, have been marketed, culminating in, for example, today's very inexpensive, simple, and reliable ac clock and timer motors.

As with transformers, it is generally true that electric machines of a given horsepower rating have become successively smaller, lighter, and more reliable over the years, as better shaping of the magnetic field and better insulating, conductor, and core materials are used. Some modern designs for high-speed, low-inertia motors actually dispense with the ferromagnetic rotor core.

A device related to motors is the linear actuator called the *solenoid*, which consists essentially of a ferromagnetic plunger free to move within a coil. Solenoids are typically used where straight-line mechanical motion is required; for example, to move the clutch mechanism in a washing machine. *Rotary solenoids* operate similarly, but produce rotary motion but not continuous rotation. In order to make solenoids efficient for operation with sinusoidal ac currents, *shading coils* (heavy short-circuited turns) are often placed on the stator as is done with the shaded-pole induction or synchronous motor.

It is probably not likely that these machine types will be included on the test. If they are, it is often sufficient to develop a simple circuit model and solve for the unknowns, or to use standard equations relating torque, power, and so forth.

POWER FACTOR CORRECTION

Consider a circuit for a single-phase AC power system, where a 120 V, 60 Hz AC voltage source is delivering power to a resistive load.

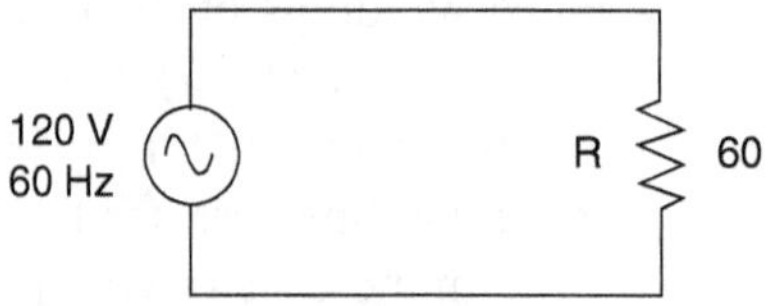

Figure 13.10

AC source drives a purely resistive load.

$$Z_R = 60 + j0\Omega = 60\angle 0°\Omega$$

$$I = \frac{V}{Z} = \frac{120V}{60\Omega} = 2A$$

In this example, the current to the load would be 2 Arms. The power dissipated at the load would be 240 W. Because this load is purely resistive (no reactance), the current is in phase with the voltage, and calculations look similar to that in an equivalent DC circuit. If we were to plot the voltage, current, and power waveforms for this circuit, it would look like Figure 13.11.

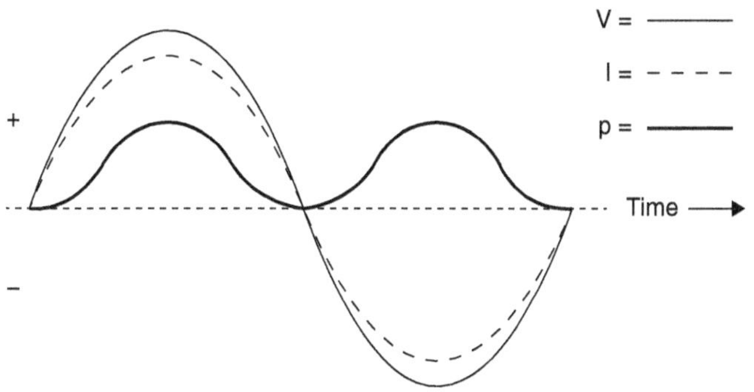

Figure 13.11

Current is in phase with voltage in a resistive circuit.

Note that the waveform for power is always positive, never negative for this resistive circuit. This means that power is always being dissipated by the resistive load and never returned to the source as it is with reactive loads. If the source were a mechanical generator, it would take 240W worth of mechanical energy (about 1/3 horsepower) to turn the shaft.

Also note that the waveform for power is not at the same frequency as the voltage or current. Rather, its frequency is *double* that of either the voltage or current waveforms. This different frequency prohibits our expression of power in an AC circuit using the same complex (rectangular or polar) notation as used for voltage, current, and impedance because this form of mathematical symbolism implies unchanging phase relationships. When frequencies are not the same, phase relationships constantly change.

Consider now a simple AC circuit with a purely reactive load in Figure 13.12.

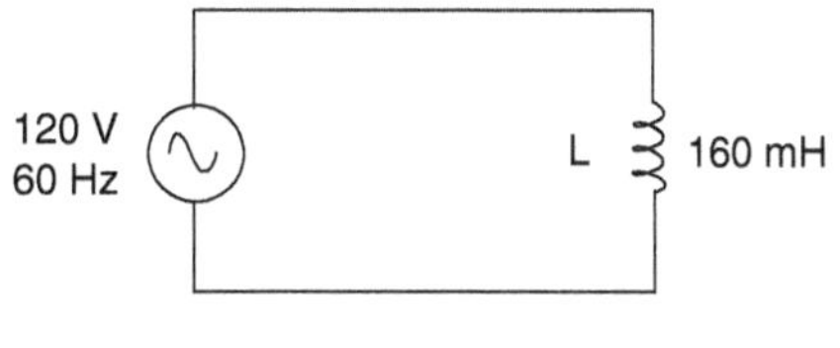

Figure 13.12

AC circuit with a purely reactive (inductive) load.

$$X_L = 60.319\Omega$$

$$Z_L = 0 + j60.319\Omega \quad \text{or} \quad 60.319\Omega\angle 90^\circ$$

$$I = \frac{E}{Z}$$

$$I = \frac{120V}{60.319\Omega}$$

$$I = 1.989A$$

$$X_L = \omega L = 2\pi(60Hz)(0.160H) = 60.319\Omega$$

so

$$Z_L = 0 + j60.319\Omega = 60.319\angle 90°$$

and

$$I = \frac{V}{Z} = \frac{120V}{60.319\Omega} = 1.989A$$

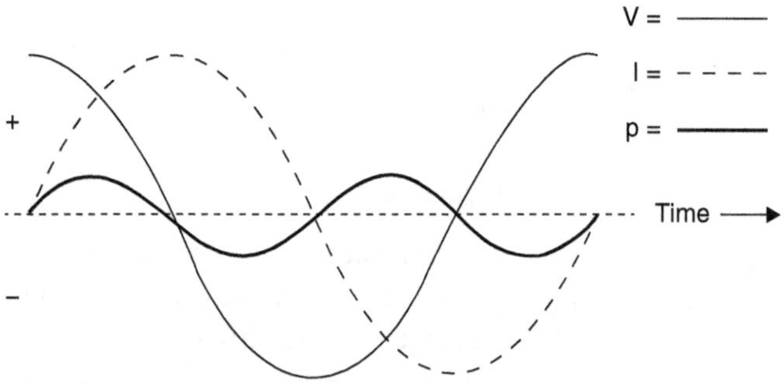

Figure 13.13

Power is not dissipated in a purely reactive load, though it is alternately absorbed from and returned to the source.

Note that the power alternates equally between cycles of positive and negative in Figure 13.13. This means that power is being alternately absorbed from and returned to the source. If the source were a mechanical generator, it would take (practically) no net mechanical energy to turn the shaft because no power would be used by the load. The generator shaft would be easy to spin, and the inductor would not become warm as a resistor would.

Consider an AC circuit with a load consisting of both inductance and resistance in Figure 13.14.

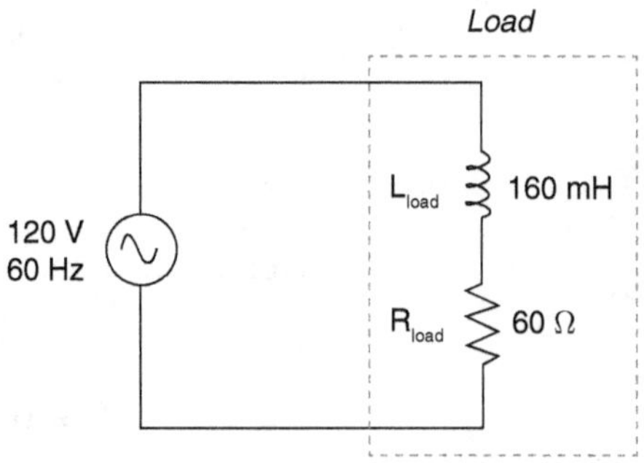

Figure 13.14

AC circuit with both reactance and resistance.

$$X_L = \omega L = 2\pi(60Hz)(0.160H) = 60.319\Omega$$

so

$$Z_L = 0 + j60.319\Omega = 60.319\angle 90°$$

and

$$Z_R = 60 + j0\Omega = 60\angle 0°$$

for a total impedance of

$$Z_{total} = 60 + j60.319\Omega = 85.078\angle 45.152°$$

The current is therefore,

$$I = \frac{V}{Z} = \frac{120V}{|85.078\angle 45.152°|\Omega} = \frac{120V}{85.078\Omega} = 1.410A$$

At a frequency of 60 Hz, the 160 mH of inductance yields 60.319 Ω of inductive reactance. This reactance combines with the 60 Ω of resistance to form a total load impedance of 60 + j60.319 Ω, or 85.078 Ω ∠ 45.152°. Not taking into account phase angles at this point, the current in the circuit can be calculated by taking the polar magnitude of the voltage source (120 V) and dividing it by the polar magnitude of the impedance (85.078 Ω). With a power supply voltage of 120 Vrms, the load current is 1.410 A. This is the figure an RMS ammeter would indicate if connected in series with the resistor and inductor.

The reactive components dissipate zero power, as they equally absorb power from, and return power to, the rest of the circuit. Therefore, any inductive reactance in this load will likewise dissipate zero real power. The only thing left to dissipate real power here is the resistive portion of the load impedance. The waveform plot of voltage, current, and total power for this circuit, is shown in Figure 13.15.

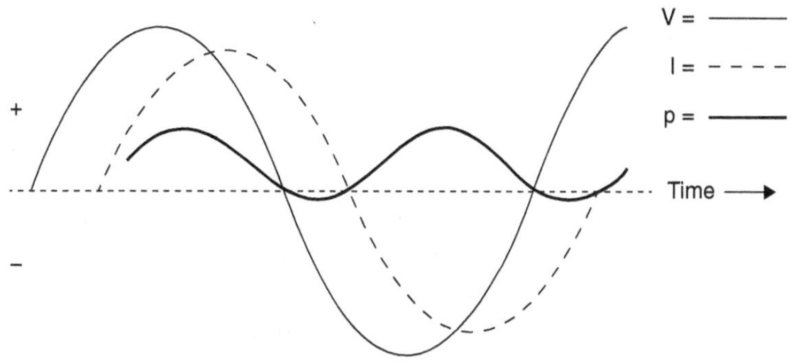

Figure 13.15

A combined resistive/reactive circuit dissipates more power than it returns to the source. The reactance dissipates no power; though, the resistor does.

As with any reactive circuit, the power alternates between positive and negative instantaneous values over time. In a purely reactive circuit that alternation between positive and negative power is equally divided, resulting in a net power dissipation of zero. However, in circuits with mixed resistance and reactance like this one, the power waveform will still alternate between positive and negative, but the amount of positive power will exceed the amount of negative power. In other words, the combined inductive/resistive load will consume more power than it returns back to the source.

Looking at the waveform plot for power, the wave spends more time on the positive side of the center line than on the negative, indicating that there is more power absorbed by the load than there is returned to the circuit. What little returning of power that occurs is due to the reactance; the imbalance of positive versus negative power is due to the resistance as it dissipates energy outside of the circuit (usually in the form of heat). If the source were a mechanical generator, the amount of mechanical energy needed to turn the shaft would be the amount of power averaged between the positive and negative power cycles.

Mathematically representing power in an AC circuit is a challenge because the power wave isn't at the same frequency as voltage or current. Furthermore, the phase angle for power means something quite different from the phase angle for either voltage or current. Whereas the angle for voltage or current represents a relative *shift in timing* between two waves, the phase angle for power represents a *ratio* between power dissipated and power returned. Because of this way in which AC power differs from AC voltage or current, it is actually easier to arrive at figures for power by calculating with *scalar* quantities of voltage, current, resistance, and reactance than it is to try to derive it from *vector*, or *complex* quantities of voltage, current, and impedance.

Points to remember:

- In a purely resistive circuit, all circuit power is dissipated by the resistor(s). Voltage and current are in phase with each other.
- In a purely reactive circuit, no circuit power is dissipated by the load(s). Rather, power is alternately absorbed from and returned to the AC source. Voltage and current are 90° out of phase with each other.
- In a circuit consisting of resistance and reactance mixed, there will be more power dissipated by the load(s) than returned, but some power will definitely be dissipated and some will merely be absorbed and returned. Voltage and current in such a circuit will be out of phase by a value somewhere between 0° and 90°.

Since reactive loads such as inductors and capacitors dissipate zero power, the fact that they drop voltage and draw current gives the deceptive impression that they actually *do* dissipate power. This "phantom power" is called *reactive power*, and it is measured in a unit called *Volt-Amps-Reactive* (VAR) rather than Watts. The mathematical symbol for reactive power is Q. The actual amount of power being used, or dissipated, in a circuit is called *real power*, and is denoted P in Watts (W).

The combination of reactive power and real power is called *apparent power*, S, and it is the product of a circuit's voltage and current, without reference to phase angle. Apparent power is measured in the unit of *Volt-Amps* (VA).

As a rule, real power is a function of a circuit's dissipative elements, usually resistances (R). Reactive power is a function of a circuit's reactance (X). Apparent power is a function of a circuit's total impedance (Z). When working with scalar quantities for power calculation, any complex starting quantities such as voltage, current, and impedance must be represented by their *polar magnitudes*, not by real or imaginary rectangular components. For instance, to calculate real power from current and resistance, use the polar magnitude for current and not merely the "real" or "imaginary" portion of the current. If calculating the apparent power from voltage and impedance, both of these formerly complex quantities must be reduced to their polar magnitudes for the scalar arithmetic.

There are several power equations relating the three types of power to resistance, reactance, and impedance (all using scalar quantities):

P is real power in units of Watts:

$$P = I^2 R = \frac{V^2}{R}$$

Q is the reactive power in units of VAR:

$$Q = I^2 X = \frac{V^2}{X}$$

S is the apparent power in units of VA:

$$S = I^2 Z = \frac{V^2}{Z} = VI^*$$

There are two equations each for the calculation of true and reactive power. There are three equations available for the calculation of apparent power, $P = IV$ being useful *only* for that purpose. The following circuits show how these three types of power interrelate for a purely resistive load, a purely reactive load, and a resistive/reactive load, all shown in Figure 13.16.

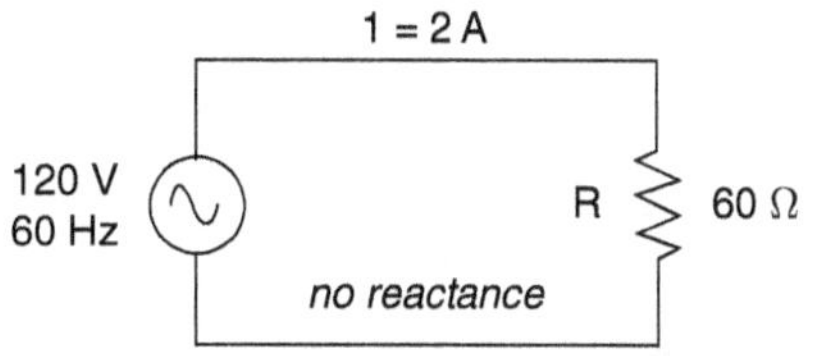

Figure 13.16

True power, reactive power, and apparent power for a purely resistive load.

Real power: $P = I^2R = 240$ W

Reactive power: $Q = I^2X = 0$ VAR

Apparent power: $S = I^2Z = 240\ VA$

For a reactive load only:

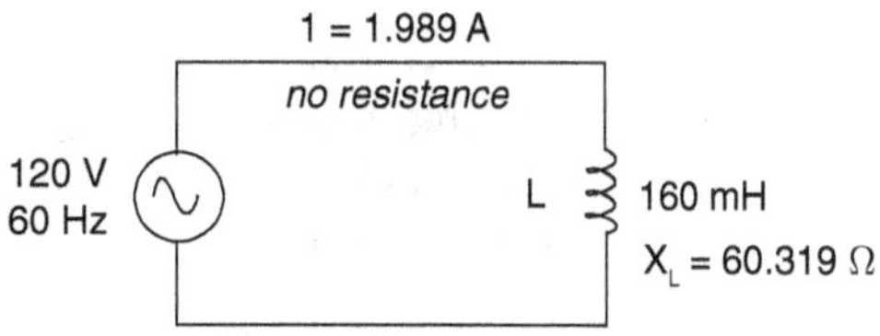

Figure 13.17

True power, reactive power, and apparent power for a purely reactive load.

Real power: $P = I^2R = 0$ W

Reactive power: $Q = I^2X = 238.73$ VAR

Apparent power: $S = I^2Z = 238.73\ VA$

Resistive/reactive load:

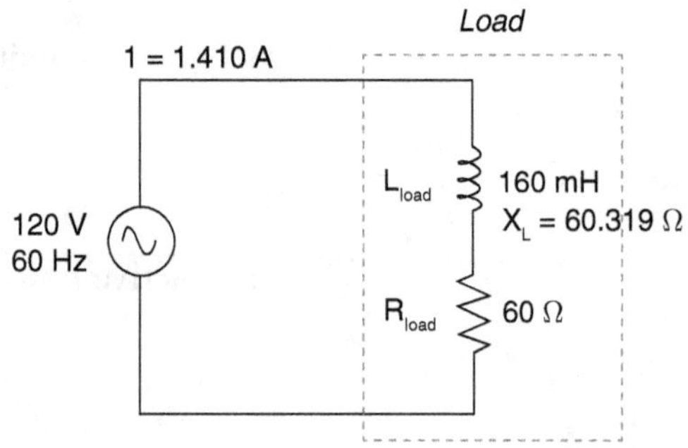

Figure 13.18

True power, reactive power, and apparent power for a resistive/reactive load.

Real power: $P = I^2R = 119.365$ W

Reactive power: $Q = I^2X = 119.998$ VAR

Apparent power: $S = I^2Z = 169.256$ *VA*

These three types of power—real, reactive, and apparent—relate to one another in trigonometric form called the *power triangle* (as seen in Figure 13.19).

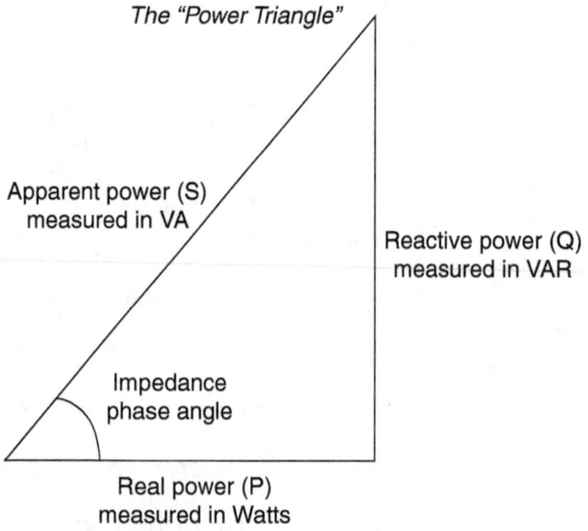

Figure 13.19

Power triangle relating apparent power to real power and reactive power.

Using the laws of trigonometry, the length of any side (amount of any type of power) can be calculated given the lengths of the other two sides or the length of one side and an angle.

Points to remember:

- Power dissipated by a load is referred to as *ral power*. Real power is symbolized by the letter *P* and is in units of Watts (W).
- Power merely absorbed and returned in load due to its reactive properties is referred to as *reactive power*. Reactive power is symbolized by the letter *Q* and is measured in the units of Volt-Amps-Reactive (VAR).

- Total complex power in an AC circuit, both dissipated and absorbed/returned, is referred to as *apparent power*. Apparent power is symbolized by the letter S and is measured in the unit of Volt-Amps (VA).
- These three types of power are trigonometrically related to one another. In a right triangle, $P =$ adjacent length, $Q =$ opposite length, and $S =$ hypotenuse length. The opposite angle is equal to the circuit's impedance (Z) phase angle.

CALCULATING POWER FACTOR

The angle of the "power triangle" graphically indicates the ratio between the amount of dissipated (or *consumed*) power and the amount of absorbed/returned power. It is also the angle of the circuit's impedance in polar form. When expressed as a fraction, this ratio between ral power and apparent power is called the *power factor* for this circuit. Because real power and apparent power form the adjacent and hypotenuse sides of a right triangle, respectively, the power factor ratio is also equal to the cosine of that phase angle. Using values from the previous example circuit:

Power factor:

$$pf = \frac{\text{real power}}{\text{apparent power}} = \frac{119.365W}{169.263VA} = 0.705$$

So the angle between the real power and apparent power is:

$$\theta = \cos^{-1}0.705 = 45.152°$$

The power factor, like all ratio measurements, is a *unitless* quantity.

For the purely resistive circuit, the power factor is 1.0 (perfect) because the reactive power equals zero. For a purely resistive load, the power triangle will be a horizontal line because the opposite (reactive power) side would have zero length.

For the purely inductive circuit, the power factor is zero because real power equals zero. For the purely inductive load, the power triangle will be a vertical line because the adjacent (real power) side would have zero length.

The same could be said for a purely capacitive circuit. If there are no dissipative (resistive) components in the circuit, then the real power must be equal to zero, making any power in the circuit purely reactive. The power triangle for a purely capacitive circuit would again be a vertical line (pointing down instead of up as it was for the purely inductive circuit).

Power factor can be an important aspect to consider in an AC circuit because any power factor less than 1.0 means that the circuit's wiring has to carry more current than what would be necessary with zero reactance in the circuit to deliver the same amount of (real) power to the resistive load. If the last example circuit had been purely resistive, the circuit will be capable of delivering a full 169.256 W to the load with the same 1.410 amps of current rather than the mere 119.365 W that it is presently dissipating with that same current quantity. The poor power factor makes for an inefficient power delivery system.

Power factors less than 1.0 can be corrected by adding another load to the circuit drawing an equal and opposite amount of reactive power to cancel out the effects of the load's inductive reactance. Inductive reactance can only be canceled by capacitive reactance, so a *capacitor* is added in parallel to the example circuit as the additional load. The effect of these two opposing reactances in parallel is to

bring the circuit's total impedance equal to its total resistance (to make the impedance phase angle equal, or at least closer, to zero).

Since the (uncorrected) reactive power is 119.998 VAR (inductive), the correct capacitor value must be calculated to produce the same quantity of (capacitive) reactive power. Since this capacitor will be directly in parallel with the source (of known voltage), the power formula is used:

$$Q = \frac{V^2}{X}$$

Solving for the reactance X,

$$X = \frac{V^2}{Q} = \frac{(120V)^2}{119.998VAR} = 120.002\Omega$$

Since capacitive reactance is

$$X_c = \frac{1}{\omega C}$$

The required capacitance can be solved,

$$C = \frac{1}{2\pi(60Hz)(120.002\Omega)} \approx 22\mu F$$

The power correction capacitor is then placed in parallel to the original load as shown in Figure 13.20.

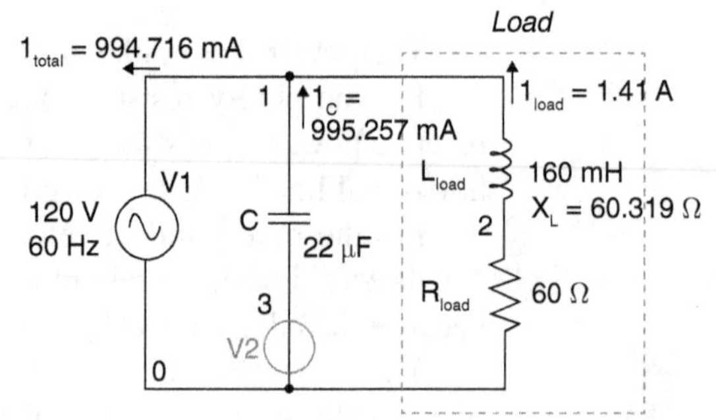

Figure 13.20

The total impedance is now Z_C in parallel with the sum of the impedances of the inductor and resistor load $Z_L + Z_R$,

$$Z_{total} = Z_C \,||\, (Z_L + Z_R)$$

Substituting the impedances into the total impedance equation,

$$Z_{total} = (120.57\angle -90°\ \Omega)\,||\,(60.319\angle\ 90°\ \Omega + 60\angle\ 0°\ \Omega)$$
$$Z_{total} = 120.64 - j0.574\ \Omega = 120.64\angle 0.274°\ \Omega$$

Real power: $P = I^2R = 119.365$ W

Apparent power: $S = I^2Z = 119.366\ VA$

The power factor for the circuit has been substantially improved. The source current has been decreased from 1.41 A to 994.7 mA, while the power dissipated at the load resistor remains unchanged at 119.365 W. The power factor is much closer to being 1.

Power factor:

$$pf = \frac{\text{real power}}{\text{apparent power}} = \frac{119.365W}{119.366VA} = 0.9999887$$

So the angle between the real power and apparent power is:

$$\theta = \cos^{-1} 0.999887 = 0.272°$$

Since the impedance angle is still a positive number, the circuit is slightly more inductive than it is capacitive. If the power factor correction design had been perfect, the calculated impedance angle of exactly zero, or purely resistive, would have been achieved. If a larger power correction capacitor had been used and installed in parallel to the original load, a negative impedance angle would have been derived, indicating that the circuit was more capacitive than inductive.

If a circuit is predominantly inductive, its power factor is said to be *lagging* (because the current wave for the circuit lags behind the applied voltage wave). Conversely, if a circuit is predominantly capacitive, its power factor is said to be *leading*. In the previous example, the original load had a power factor of 0.705 lagging and was corrected to a power factor of 0.999 lagging.

Points to remember:

- Poor power factor in an AC circuit may be "corrected," or re-established at a value close to 1, by adding a parallel reactance opposite the effect of the load's reactance. If the load's reactance is inductive in nature (which it almost always will be), parallel *capacitance* is what is needed to correct poor power factor.

PRACTICAL POWER FACTOR CORRECTION

When the need arises to correct for poor power factor in an AC power system, the exact load inductance will probably be unknown. In that case, a *power factor meter* may be used to arrive at the power factor (a number between 0 and 1), and the apparent power (which can be found by taking a voltmeter reading in volts and multiplying by an ammeter reading in amps). In less favorable circumstances, an oscilloscope may be used to compare voltage and current waveforms, measuring phase shift in *degrees* and calculating power factor by the cosine of that phase shift.

Most likely, a wattmeter will be used for measuring real power, whose reading can then be compared against a calculation of apparent power (from multiplying total voltage and total current measurements). From the values of real and apparent powers, the reactive power and power factor can be determined. Figure 13.21 shows how a wattmeter might be used.

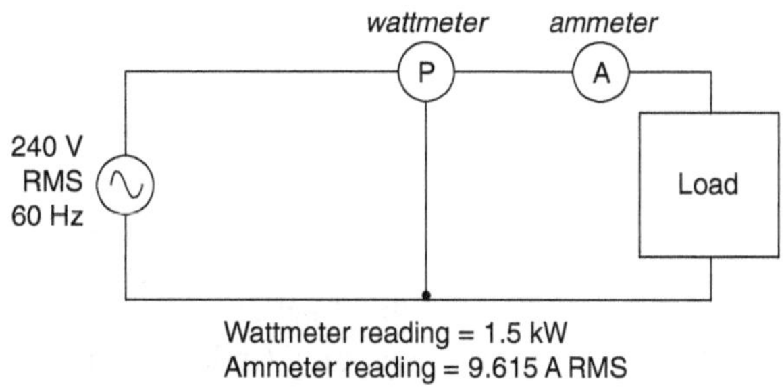

Figure 13.21

Wattmeter reads true power; product of voltmeter and ammeter readings yields apparent power.

First, calculate the apparent power in kVA. This is accomplished by multiplying load voltage by load current:

$$S = VI^* = (240\text{V})(9.615\text{A}) = 2.308\ \text{kVA}$$

Since only the magnitudes are indicated by the wattmeter, the magnitude of the current $I = 9.615\text{A}$ is also the magnitude of its complex conjugate, I^*.

The apparent power of 2.308 kVA is larger than 1.5 kW, indicating that the power factor in this circuit is rather poor (substantially less than 1). The power factor of this load can be calculated by dividing the real power by the apparent power:

$$\text{Power factor} = \frac{P}{S}$$

$$\text{Power factor} = \frac{1.5kW}{2.308kVA}$$

$$\text{Power factor} = 0.65$$

$$\text{Power factor: } pf = \frac{P}{S} = \frac{1.5kW}{2.308kVA} = 0.65$$

Using this value for power factor, the power triangle can be drawn and the reactive power of this load can be calculated as shown in Figure 13.22.

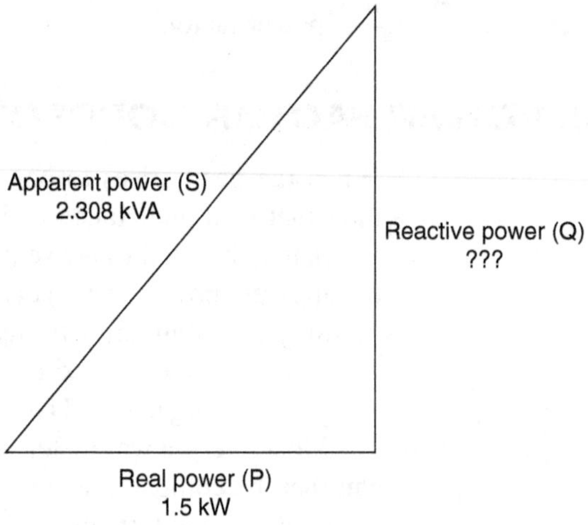

Figure 13.22

Reactive power may be calculated from true power and apparent power.

To determine the unknown (reactive power) triangle quantity, the Pythagorean Theorem can be used where,

$$S^2 = P^2 + Q^2$$

so,

$$Q = \sqrt{S^2 - P^2} = 1.754kVAR$$

If this load is an electric motor, or most any other industrial AC load, it will have a lagging (inductive) power factor that will be corrected with a *capacitor* of appropriate size, wired in parallel to the load.

The power factor correction capacitor now can be calculated,

$$Q = \frac{V^2}{X}$$

Solving for the reactance X,

$$X = \frac{V^2}{Q} = \frac{(240V)^2}{1.754kVAR} = 32.845\Omega$$

Since capacitive reactance is

$$X_c = \frac{1}{\omega C}$$

The required capacitance can be solved,

$$C = \frac{1}{2\pi(60Hz)(32.845\Omega)} \approx 80\mu F$$

The power factor correction capacitor of 80 μF is placed in parallel with the original load in the circuit as shown in Figure 13.23.

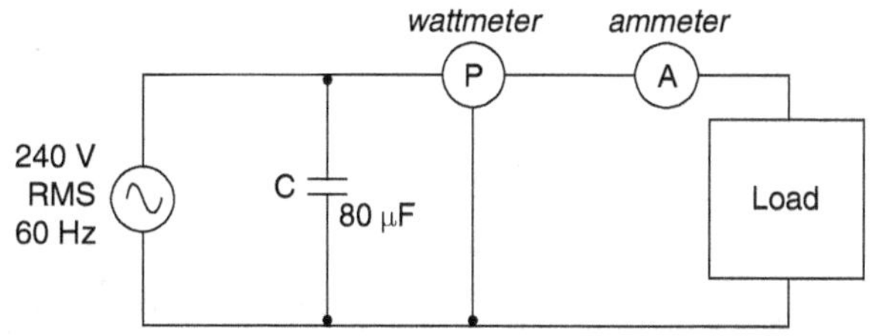

Figure 13.23

Parallel capacitor corrects lagging (inductive) load.

An 80 μF capacitor will have a capacitive reactance of 33.157 Ω, giving a current of 7.238 amps and a corresponding reactive power of 1.737 kVAR (for the capacitor *only*). Since the capacitor's current is 180° out of phase from the load's inductive contribution to current draw, the capacitor's reactive power will directly subtract from the load's reactive power, resulting in:

$$\text{Total kVAR} = \text{Inductive kVAR} - \text{Capacitive kVAR}$$
$$= 1.754 \text{ kVAR} - 1.737 \text{ kVAR} = 16.519 \text{ kVAR}$$

This correction, of course, will not change the amount of real power consumed by the load, but it will result in a substantial reduction of apparent power and of the total current drawn from the 240 volt source as shown in Figure 13.24.

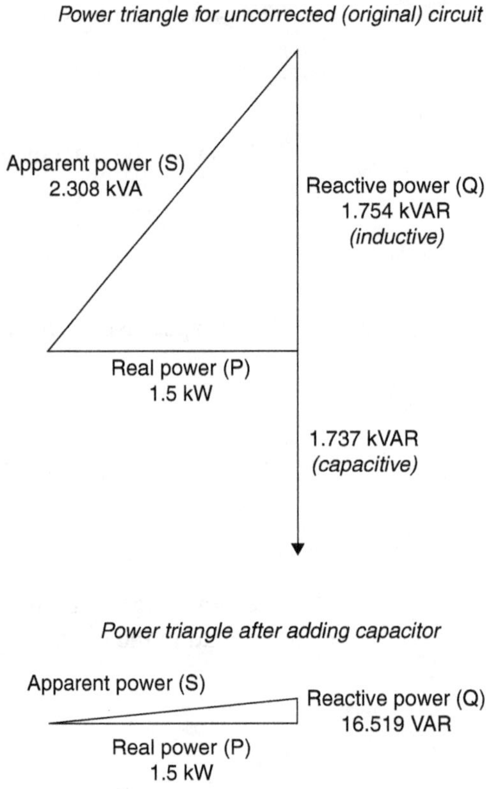

Figure 13.24

Power triangle before and after capacitor correction.

The new apparent power can be found from the real and new reactive power values,

$$S = \sqrt{P^2 + Q^2} = 1.50kVA\,.$$

This gives a corrected power factor of (1.5kW / 1.50 kVA), or 0.99994, and a new total current of (1.50 kVA / 240 volts), or 6.25 A, which is a substantial improvement over the uncorrected value of 9.615 A. This lower total current will translate to less heat losses in the circuit wiring, meaning greater system efficiency (less wasted power).

LUMPED PARAMETER MODEL OF LINE

At a frequency of 60 Hz, and for lines of realistic length (perhaps 150 miles at the most), we can use a relatively straightforward procedure to concentrate on how the line behaves when viewed from the ends. The calculations are relatively simple but involve complex numbers. When line length exceeds one-fourth wavelength, some interesting reversals in parameter trends appear. Wavelength at 60 Hz is about 3100 miles though, so these effects are only of academic interest in most cases. No matter the length of the line, its parameters can always be accurately found, at least for balanced operating conditions, and a simple equivalent model, as far as terminal behavior is concerned, can always be obtained. Acceptable modeling of longer lines, and, therefore, accurate modeling of most lines, requires evaluation of hyperbolic trigonometric functions with complex arguments or, equivalently, complex exponentials. These are presented later in the chapter.

However, let's start at the beginning. Using common sense, we can postulate the per-phase, lumped-parameter circuit model for a line. The elements of this model are

R = ac resistance of conductor
X_L = inductive reactance of conductor
B_C = shunt susceptance corresponding to capacitance between conductors

Note that we have broken the shunt capacitance into two equal parts and placed one at each end of the line. This model is called a **pi (π) model** because it looks like the Greek letter pi. It is a **lumped-parameter** model because parameters of the line can be represented as lumped parameters. We will discuss these ideas and another lumped-parameter structure later in this chapter.

We will assume balanced conditions for all of the work in this chapter, and thus the models will provide positive- and negative-sequence parameters only, but not zero-sequence. However, the presentation here will apply to most cases of interest. If desired, zero-sequence impedance of an open-wire line can be estimated as approximately three times the positive-sequence impedance value calculated in this chapter, while negative-sequence impedance is equal to positive-sequence impedance for a line. More detailed treatments of this can be found in the recommended references.

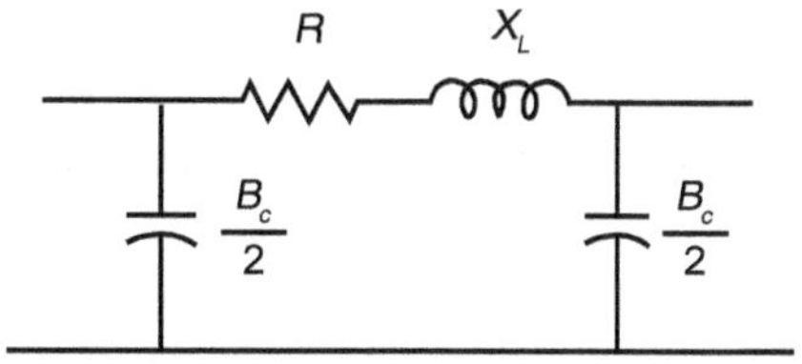

Figure 13.25 Transmission line model

The model of Figure 13.25 can be made to include factors such as the capacitances between phase conductors in the three-phase system as well as capacitances to ground and the inductive couplings between all conductors. Furthermore, although the reference bus in the figure is shown as an equipotential surface, the resistive and inductive effects of the earth can be accounted for as well.

With proper parameter values, the model of Figure 13.25 gives good results for lines up to about 150 miles in length. For longer lines, or in general for better accuracy, the parameters in the model must be modified by the *long-line equations* cited in the section "Long-Line Equations" later in this chapter.

CONDUCTOR TYPES AND CONFIGURATIONS

Most three-phase lines are open-wire, supported by porcelain, fiberglass, or (more frequently in new work) polymer insulators; only about 1% of transmission in the United States is underground. Thus, we concentrate on open-wire structures. Many of the principles here apply to cables as well, however.

A three-phase line should have, of course, three phase-conductors. There may also be one or more **ground wires (static wires)** whose purpose is not only to carry return currents (which should be small in balanced, fundamental-frequency situations) but, more importantly, to provide shielding against lightning strikes. Typically, the angle from vertical between the shield or ground wire and the outermost phase conductor should not exceed 30° for good lightning protection. Ground

wires may be stranded steel because they bear mechanical load but are not designed primarily to carry current. (Steel has lower conductivity than copper or aluminum.) There may be more than one conductor per phase. **Bundling** refers to the practice of using more than one conductor per phase, both electrically and physically in parallel. In practice, a bundle of two conductors, usually 1.5 feet apart, is typically used in lines of voltage greater than about 220 kV. This not only increases the current-handling capacity (by doubling the conductor cross-sectional area) but has important advantages such as reducing the inductive reactance and the radio-frequency interference given off by the circuit. Three, and even four, conductors in symmetrical configurations (equilateral triangle or square) are sometimes used in bundles for high-voltage lines. We will examine this below.

The conductors discussed so far are typically not single, solid wires but instead are **composite conductors**; that is, they are each composed of a number of smaller solid wires, spiraled in alternate layers, and are typically bare (see Chapter # for related safety concerns of bare wires). Thus, they are somewhat like large versions of the stranded conductors in extension cords. The largest conventionally-used composite conductors may be nearly two inches in diameter.

Although copper wire, in various forms, was traditionally used in early power lines, most modern power conductors are made of aluminum or one of its alloys, which is lighter in weight and less expensive than copper. Another advantage of aluminum is that a larger-diameter conductor than a copper equivalent is necessary to obtain the same current-carrying capacity (**ampacity**). The electrical advantage of a larger conductor will become evident in the equations below, and one could show that the larger-diameter conductor leads to less radio frequency interference and reduced power loss due to corona as well. Research continues both in exploring possible new conductor types (especially for cables) and, more particularly, in structures for supporting these wires.

Besides **all-aluminum-alloy conductors (AAAC)**, one important and frequently-used type of composite conductor is the **aluminum conductor steel-reinforced (ACSR)** type, which has few center strands of steel surrounded by more strands of aluminum. The purpose of the steel strands is for structural strength—conductors must often cover spans of many feet—while the aluminum strands provide most of the current-carrying capacity. Conductors used in high-voltage transmission lines are typically ACSR; distribution lines with their shorter spans often use all-aluminum-alloy conductors.

UNITS, MEASUREMENTS, AND CONVERSION FACTORS

In the United States, it is still common practice to specify line dimensions in English units. Thus, length is usually given in miles (mi), conductor dimensions in inches (in), and conductor spacing in feet (ft). Accordingly, the equations for line parameters are often expressed in terms of these units. Some useful conversions involving metric and English units are as follows:

$$1 \text{ m} = 39.37 \text{ in} \tag{13.16}$$

$$1 \text{ mi} = 1.609 \text{ km} \tag{13.17}$$

$$1 \text{ km} = 0.6214 \text{ mi} \tag{13.18}$$

$$1 \text{ in} = 2.54 \text{ cm} \quad \textbf{(13.19)}$$

$$1 \text{ ft} = 12 \text{ in} \quad \textbf{(13.20)}$$

$$1 \text{ mi} = 5280 \text{ ft} \quad \textbf{(13.21)}$$

OBTAINING THE PARAMETER VALUES FOR THE PER-PHASE MODEL

Following are some useful ideas and equations for finding the parameters of the per-phase line model. *We will assume that the currents and voltages in the line are balanced and, thus, that only positive-sequence values are required*. Furthermore, we will assume the line to be **transposed**, which means that the phases are geometrically "rolled" at intervals of one-third of the line length. Therefore, each of the three phase conductors or composites occupies each conductor position for one-third of the line length. (Although typically assumed, transposition is not always needed or implemented in practice.)

Resistance

Conductor resistance is found from tables provided by manufacturers; on the PE exam, it probably will be given to you. (You can find tables for the characteristics, including the resistance of several conductor types, in most undergraduate power-systems texts, such as the two listed as references at the end of the chapter.) There may be very slight differences between the values of the line parameters given by different manufacturers or textbook authors. Especially in the case of resistance, this may be due to the calculation of the values at different temperatures. If a table is supplied with an exam problem, be sure to use the correct column with regard to temperature as stated in the problem.

If conductors are bundled, the per-phase resistance is found by dividing the per-phase resistance of one such conductor by the number of conductors in the bundle (usually 2, 3, or 4). The ac resistance of the conductor (which is of interest here) is greater than its dc resistance, because a phenomenon known as **skin effect** tends to force the current density to be greater near the outside of the conductor, in contrast to the uniform current density typical of dc currents. In fact, for large-diameter conductors, skin effect has a pronounced oscillatory behavior in terms of a *Bessel function* from the center to the outside of the conductor.

Values of resistance are typically given in Ω/mile in tables, but occasionally in Ω/meter.

Inductance

Because it is a more useful property, line inductance is usually expressed in reactance at fundamental frequency (60 Hz).

Shunt Capacitance

Being a shunt parameter, line capacitance is instead expressed as capacitive susceptance in siemens (S).

Equations will be given for inductive reactance and capacitive susceptance once some important prerequisites have been introduced, such as geometric mean radius, geometric mean distance, and bundling. Before doing this, though, the

entries for a typical conductor in a table of conductor characteristics provided by a manufacturer will be examined to see what information is typically given, and identification of what is needed in particular from the table to calculate the line parameters will follow.

The Circular Mil and the Conductor Tables

Manufacturers provide tables of ACSR conductors' characteristics. We will look at some of the more important information given in such tables, including the three critical items needed for electrical parameter calculation. You can find such tables in the recommended references.

ACSR conductors were long ago given bird names, which are used conventionally in the United States. Thus, when a utility engineer speaks of a CARDINAL or FALCON conductor, for example, it is well known which specific conductor is meant.

Consider the frequently-used ACSRconductor denoted DRAKE. According to published tables, this conductor has a designation 795,000 because the cross-sectional area of the aluminum material in this conductor is 795,000 circular mils (cmil).

The **circular mil** is a unit of cross-sectional area that was very useful in pre-calculator times because it removed the irrational factor π (= 3.1416) from the calculations. One circular mil is simply the area of a circle of diameter one mil (= 0.001 in), so one circular mil is equal to π/4 square mils, or

$$1 \text{ cmil} = \pi / 4 \text{ mil}^2. \quad \textbf{(13.22)}$$

This may be useful to know in case you have to perform this conversion.

Returning to the DRAKE conductor entry in the table, we would see other geometric information about the conductor, such as is having 26 aluminum strands, each of diameter 0.1749 inches, and 7 steel strands, each of diameter 0.1360 inches. Its overall outside diameter, Dia, is 1.108 inches, and it weighs 5770 pounds/mile. Its ac resistance, *R*, for "75% capacity" is 0.1288 Ω/mile, and its geometric mean radius (GMR, explained below) at 60 Hz is 0.0375 feet. The current-carrying capacity of this conductor is stated in the table to be approximately 900 A.

The previous items are interesting and useful, but the three pieces of information we need most from the table for this DRAKE conductor for calculation of the parameters are

- per-phase resistance r = 0.1288 Ω/mi,
- conductor diameter Dia = 1.108 in (so conductor radius r_C = Dia / 2 = 0.5540 in), and
- D_S = GMR = 0.0375 ft.

D_S or GMR, called the *geometric mean radius* of the conductor, is a property of the conductor that allows calculation of inductive reactance, whereas conductor radius r_C is used in the calculation of capacitive susceptance.

Example 13.1 illustrates the use of these characteristics.

Conductor Bundling

As mentioned earlier, conductors on EHV (extra high voltage) lines are often bundled by placing several identical composite conductors close to each other, usually no farther apart than two feet.

For a two-conductor bundle, we define a term

$$D_{SL} = (D_S\ d)^{0.5}, \tag{13.23a}$$

which replaces D_S, the conductor GMR, in inductance calculations where bundling is present. Here, *d* is the bundle spacing, the center-to-center distances between composite conductors in the phase bundle. Often, d = 1.5 feet in practice.

Similarly, for capacitive calculations, we will need the term

$$D_{SC} = (r_C\ d)^{0.5}. \tag{13.23b}$$

For a three-conductor bundle, in an equilateral triangle formation,

$$D_{SL} = (D_S\ d^2)^{0.333} \tag{13.24a}$$

and

$$D_{SC} = (r_C\ d^2)^{0.333} \tag{13.24b}$$

where, again, *d* is the center-to-center spacing of the composite conductors.

For the occasionally encountered, four-conductor bundle, in a square formation with the sides of the square equal to *d*,

$$D_{SL} = 1.091\ (D_S\ d^3)^{0.25} \tag{13.24c}$$

and

$$D_{SC} = 1.091\ (r_C\ d^3)^{0.25} \tag{13.24d}$$

where, again, *d* is the center-to-center spacing of the composite conductors.

Although the symmetrical bundle configurations given above are the ones encountered in practice, it is in fact a simple matter to find expressions for D_{SL} and D_{SC} in a bundle spacing of any arbitrary geometry, as given in the recommended references.

In the absence of bundling, D_{SL} is replaced by conductor GMR from the table and D_{SC} is replaced by conductor radius r_C.

Geometric Mean Distance (GMD)

Useful in the calculation of both X_L and B_C is the idea of **geometric mean distance** (**GMD**, not to be confused with **GMR**). For a transposed three-phase line,

$$GMD = (D_{ab}\ D_{bc}\ D_{ca})^{0.333} \tag{13.25}$$

where D_{ab}, D_{bc}, and D_{ca} are the respective center-to-center phase spacings of the phase conductors. Note that while GMR is a function of only one (usually composite) phase conductor, GMD has to do with the spacings *between the phases*. Also, you should observe that in the case of bundled conductors, these centers may not lie within conductors at all but in the air space between conductors in a bundle.

Calculation of Inductive Reactance and Capacitive Susceptance

We now find the *per-mile* parameters (shown as lower-case letters) as

$$x_L = [0.1213 \ln (GMD / D_{SL})]\ \Omega/mi \tag{13.26}$$

$$b_C = (3.3727 \times 10^{-5} / [\ln (GMD / D_{SC})])\ S/mi \tag{13.27}$$

and finally we can express the total parameters as

$$X_L = [0.1213 \ln (GMD / D_{SL})]\ l\ \Omega \tag{13.28}$$

$$B_C = (3.3727 \times 10^{-5} / [\ln (GMD / D_{SC})])\ l\ S \tag{13.29}$$

where l is the line length in miles.

Often we introduce the complex per-mile impedance and admittance

$$\mathbf{z} = r + j\, x_L\ \Omega/mi \tag{13.30}$$

$$\mathbf{y} = jb_C\ S/mi. \tag{13.31}$$

These complex numbers are used in Example 13.1.

Example 13.1

Six DRAKE conductors are used to make a three-phase line. There are two conductors per phase with a center-to-center spacing of d = 1.5 feet in each phase. The line is 80 miles in length. The conductors are in a horizontal configuration (as in the well-known H-frame structure) with center-to-center spacings between the three phases of 10, 10, and 20 feet. Find the parameters for this line.

Solution

Because there are two conductors per phase, the resistance per phase is half the resistance of one conductor:

$$R = (0.5)\,(0.1288\ \Omega/mi)\,(80\ mi) = 5.152\Omega.$$

Geometric mean distance, needed for inductance and capacitance calculations, is

$$GMD = (D_{ab}\, D_{bc}\, D_{ca})^{0.333} = [(10)(10)(20)]^{0.333} = 12.60\ ft.$$

Because of the bundling, the modified GMR(called D_{SL}) and the modified radius D_{SC} must be calculated:

$$D_{SL} = (D_S\, d)^{0.5} = [(0.0375)(1.5)]^{0.5} = 0.2372\ ft.$$
$$D_{SC} = (r_C\, d)^{0.5} = [(0.5540/12)(1.5)]^{0.5} = 0.2631\ ft.$$

At this point, the line parameters can be calculated as

$$X_L = [0.1213 \ln (12.60 / 0.2372)](80) = 38.55\ \Omega$$
$$B_C = (3.3727 \times 10^{-5} / [\ln (12.60 / 0.2631)])(80) = 697.4 \times 10^{-6}\ S.$$

SHORT AND MEDIUM-LENGTH MODELS

The calculations of Example 13.1 gave the parameters of what is often called the **medium-length line model**, which is generally considered valid for line lengths up to 150 miles. *Note that, to find each parameter for the medium-length model, the per-mile value is simply multiplied by line length.*

A simplification can often be made for open-wire lines with lengths below about 50 miles. Called the **short-line model**, it simply neglects the shunt capacitive susceptance and employs series resistance and inductive reactance as in the medium-length model. Such simplifications were used more frequently before the advent of digital calculators but may at times be useful in hand calculations if they apply.

For lines above about 150 miles in length, the **long-line model** is necessary. It is discussed in the section "Long Line Equations" later in this chapter.

RECOMMENDED REFERENCE

Glover and Sarma, Power system analysis and design, Third Ed., Brooks/Cole.

For additional review reference material, almost any electric machinery text (even though a decade or more old) will be suitable. Two texts that are widely available and have appeared in a number of editions, including recent issues, are as follows:

Fitzgerald, Kingsley, and Kusko. *Electrical Machinery* various editions. McGraw-Hill.

Stephen J. Chapman. *Electric Machinery Fundamentals*, various editions. McGraw-Hill.

See also the power-systems reference for chapter 3.

Machinery and power-systems texts often contain useful reviews of steady state ac problems as well, usually in an early chapter or an appendix.

PROBLEMS

13.1 For a balanced, three-phase wye circuit, the voltage-current relationship in one leg of the wye, consisting of a resistor in series with an inductance, yields the following rms measurements: the current is 5 A, the voltage across R is 70.7 V, and the voltage across L is, likewise, 70.7 V. Determine the magnitude of the reactive power Q taken by the total three-phase configuration.

13.2 A balanced delta load is connected to a three-phase source of 200 V. If each leg of the load has an impedance of $10 + j10\ \Omega$, determine the magnitude of the line currents and the total power dissipated in the load.

13.3 Two balanced three-phase loads are connected to the same voltage source of 173 V (line-to-line). Each load has an impedance of $10 + j10\ \Omega$ in each leg, but one load is connected in wye while the other is connected in delta. What is the magnitude of the line current as measured at the source?

13.4 The real power input to a 240 V, three-phase motor is 10 kW. The motor's efficiency is 80%, and the power factor of the device is also 80%, lagging. Determine the hp output of the motor and the magnitude of the input line current.

13.5 If the motor in Problem 13.4 is connected to a terminal board as shown in Exhibit 13.5 and the meter connected between terminals a and b reads 240 V, determine both (a) the phase voltage and (b) the angle between the line voltage and the current.

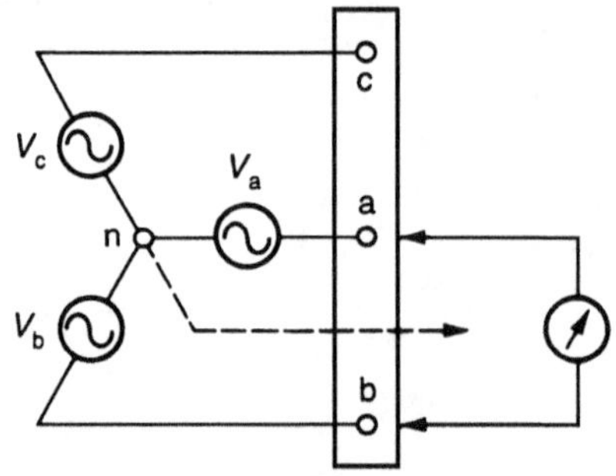

Exhibit 13.5 A three-phase voltage source connected internally as a wye

13.6 A step-down transformer (with turns ratio of 4:1) has an input current I1 of 10 A when the load is a pure resistance of 10 ¾. It is known that the transformer-equivalent circuit parameters (see Figure 13.6 in text) are $R1 = X1 = 1\ \Omega$, $R2 = X2 = 1/16$. It is also known from tests that the core loss of the transformer is 125 W; but for this problem, you may ignore the exciting current IO when considering I1. Determine the transformer efficiency when operating under the above assumptions.

13.7 Consider the synchronous alternator whose per-phase equivalent circuit is shown in Figure 4.3 in the text. The circuit is altered by replacing the 20 + j20 Ω load by one of impedance 20 – j20 Ω. Taking the per-phase terminal voltage as reference, determine the magnitude and phase of the internal voltage Ef, with respect to the reference.

13.8 A 60Hz, three-phase induction motor operating at full load has a slip of 0.04. With the load removed, the slip reduces to 0.002 and the speed is measured to be slightly under 1200 rpm. Determine the full-load speed in rpm.

13.9 The efficiency of a typical induction motor may be expressed as

$$P_{out}/P_{in} = P_{out}/(P_{out} + \text{all losses})$$

The losses usually considered are the electrical winding losses (I^2R), the magnetic core losses (P_{core}), and the friction & windage loss ($P_{F\&W}$).

A particular 60Hz, cage-rotor induction motor is known to produce a shaft output power of 5 hp at a speed of 1750 rpm. Determine (a) the slip when producing 5 hp, and (b) the power input if the winding loss is 200 W, the core loss is 100 W, and the friction and windage loss is 150 W.

13.10 Two wye-connected, three-phase synchronous machines are connected in parallel at their armature terminals. The per-phase equivalent circuit, with additional information, is shown in Exhibit 13.10. One machine is acting as a source (generator) and the other as a load (motor). The terminal voltage VT (which, of course, is the same for the two machines) is 400 V (phase-to-neutral) and the synchronous reactances are XGen = 0.5XMot = 0.4. Furthermore, the dc field currents of the machines are adjusted such that the system is operating at unity power factor. Determine the internal motor voltage EMot if it is known that the current I is 100 A. The internal resistances are all negligible.

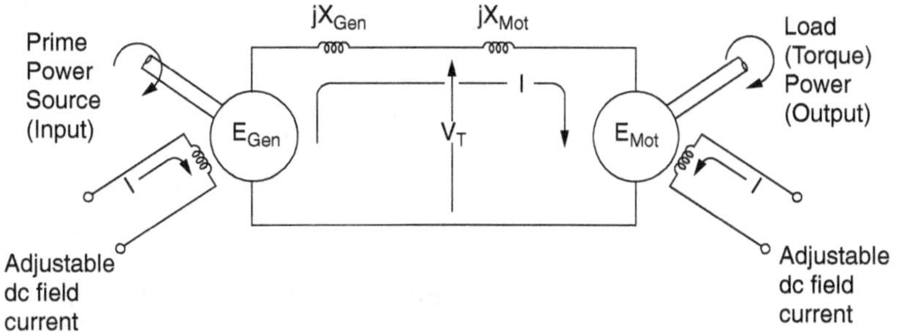

Exhibit 13.10 Equivalent circuit for a synchronous generator connected to a synchronous motor

SOLUTIONS

13.1 The phase (line-to-neutral) voltage must be

$$\mathbf{V}_P = 70.7 + j70.7 = 100\angle 45°$$

Then,

$$V_L = \sqrt{3}V_p = 173 \text{ V}$$

so,

$$Q_{tot} = \sqrt{3}V_L I_L \sin_P = \sqrt{3} \times 173 \times 5 \times \sin 45° = 1061 \text{ VARS}$$

Another method of solution is the following

$$Q_{tot} = 3I^2 X_L = 3 \times 25(70.7/5) = 1061 \text{ VARS}$$

13.2 $IL = \sqrt{3}IP = \sqrt{3}[200/|(10 + j10)|] = 24.5 \text{ A}$

so,

$$P_{tot} = \sqrt{3}V_L I_L \cos\theta_P = \sqrt{3} \times 200 \times 24.5 \cos 45° = 6 \text{ kW}$$

13.3 Although the problem does not state it, a parallel connection of loads is logical to assume. For instructional purposes, we will solve this problem in three ways.
First, let us assume that the line voltage is reference. Then, for the wye, the reference phase voltage is

$$V_P = 100\angle{-30°} \text{ V}$$

and, also for the wye-connected load,

$$\mathbf{I}_L = \mathbf{I}_P = \mathbf{V}_P/\mathbf{Z} = (100\angle{-30°})/(10 + j10) = 7.07\angle{-75°} \text{ A}$$

For the delta load, $\mathbf{V}_L = \mathbf{V}_P$, so,

$$\mathbf{I}_P = \mathbf{V}_P/\mathbf{Z} = 173\angle 0°/(10 + j10) = 12.23\angle{-45°} \text{ A}$$

and,

$$\mathbf{I}_L = \sqrt{3}\mathbf{I}_P\angle{-30°} = \sqrt{3}(12.23\angle(-45° - 30°) = 21.2\angle{-75°} \text{ A}$$

The line current is the phasor sum of the total load current

$$\mathbf{I}_{L,\text{ total}} = \mathbf{I}_{L,\text{ wye}} + \mathbf{I}_{L,\text{ delta}} = 7.07\angle{-75} + 21.2\angle{-75°} = 28.27\angle{-75°}$$

and, thus, the magnitude of the total current is

$$I_{L,\text{ total}} = 28.3 \text{ A}$$

This method of solution is correct, but requires careful consideration of the reference angle. Thus, it is not the way in which this kind of balanced problem is usually solved.
Another method of solution is to first find the values of power using the current *magnitudes* in the separate loads (we will use the values shown before)

$$P(\text{wye}) = 3(I_P)^2R = 3(7.07)^2 10 = 1500 \text{ W}$$
$$P(\text{delta}) = 3(I_P)^2R = 3(12.23)^2 10 = 4500 \text{ W}$$

Since real power values are scalars,

$$P(\text{total}) = P(\text{wye}) + P(\text{delta}) = 6000 \text{ W}$$

But we know, since both loads have the same power factor, that the source sees a power-factor angle $\theta_P = 45°$ and that

$$P(\text{total}) = \sqrt{3}V_L I_L \cos \theta_P = \sqrt{3} \times 173 \times I_L \cos 45°$$

Solving for I_L,

$$I_L = 6000/(1.73 \times 173 \times 0.707) = 28.3 \text{ A}$$

Probably the *simplest and least error-prone way* to solve this kind of problem, however, is to convert the delta load to a wye and build the per-phase equivalent (as suggested in the text).

The per-phase equivalent of the delta-connected load is then (10 + j10)/3 = 3.33 + j3.33 Ω, and paralleling this with the original wye-conneted load of 10 + j10 Ω yields an equivalent impedance (by the product-over-sum rule for parallel impedances) of

$$\mathbf{Z}_{eq} = (10 + j10)(3.33 + j3.33)/(10 + j10 + 3.33 + j3.33) = 3.54\angle 45° \ \Omega$$

Letting the phase-to-neutral voltage be the reference this time (which is what is most frequently done in practice),

$$\boldsymbol{I}_{L,\text{total}} = (173/\sqrt{3})/3.54\angle 45° = 28.3\angle -45° \text{ A}$$

13.4 Since the efficiency is 80%, the power output is equivalent to 8000 W. In horsepower, this is

$$hp_{\text{out}} = 8000 \text{ W}/746 \text{ W/hp} = 10.7 \text{ hp}$$

The equation for power input is

$$P = \sqrt{3}V_L I_L(\text{PF})$$

thus,

$$I_L = P/[\sqrt{3}V_L(\text{PF})] = 10{,}000/[\sqrt{3} \times 240(0.8)] = 30.1 \text{ A.}$$

Note that this is the same *magnitude* of current as would be obtained if the power factor had been 80% leading.

13.5 **(a)** Since, for a wye-connected source, the line voltage is

$$\mathbf{V}_L = \sqrt{3}\mathbf{V}_P\angle 30°$$

and the line current is $\mathbf{I}_L = \mathbf{I}_P$ (see Equation 3.1),

$$\mathbf{V}_P = [\mathbf{V}_L\angle -30°]/\sqrt{3} = [240/\sqrt{3}]\angle -30° = 138\angle -30° \text{ V}$$

(assuming line current is reference)

(b) Since the power factor is given in terms of the angle from the phase voltage to the phase current, it is clear (from PF = cos θ = 0.8, then θ = 36.9°) the angle between the line voltage and the line (or phase) current is 30 + 36.9 = 66.9° lagging the line voltage.

13.6 It is probably easier here to solve this problem by referring secondary quantities to the primary. Since the current is already given and only the series portion of the circuit need be considered (as the core-loss power is already given), one only has to add all of the I2R losses to get the efficiency.

Ignoring I_0 means, of course, that the referred secondary current is equal to the primary current (10 A). Referring the load resistance to the primary yields a value of referred resistance of $(4)^2(10) = 160\ \Omega$, which consumes a power of $(10^2)(160) = 16{,}000$ W. The referred secondary winding resistance is 1 ohm, making a total $R_{eq} = 2\ \Omega$. *Thus*, the power loss in the windings will be $(10^2)(2) = 200$ W. Then,

$$Eff = P_O/(P_O + \text{all losses})$$
$$= 16{,}000/(16{,}000 + 200 + 125) = 0.98 \text{ or } 98\%$$

13.7 $\text{IP} = \text{VP}/\text{ZL} = (15{,}000/\sqrt{3})\angle 0°/(20 - \text{j}20) = 0.3062\angle 45°\ \text{kA}$

$\mathbf{E}_f = \text{jX}_s\mathbf{I} + \mathbf{V}_P = (\text{j}10)(0.306\angle 45°) + (15/\sqrt{3})\angle 0° = 6.85\angle 18.4°\ \text{kV}$

13.8 Here, since synchronous speeds for a 60 Hz machine are 3600 rpm (for 2-poles), 1800 rpm (for 4-poles), 1200 rpm (for 6-poles), and so forth, it is obvious that this is a 6-pole machine. For a slip of 0.002, this machine would have a speed of

$n = (1 - 0.002)1200 = 1197.6$ rpm (this checks for the no-load condition)

At full-load (for a slip of 0.04), the speed would be

$$n = (1 - 0.04)1200 = 1152 \text{ rpm}$$

which, as you would expect, is lower than that at a smaller value of load.

13.9 (a) Since the machine is rated for 60Hz service, the synchronous speed must be 3600 rpm, 1800 rpm, 1200 rpm, or some other speed corresponding to an even value of p in Equation 4.8. The actual speed (under load) is slightly less than ns. It should be obvious that ns is 1800 rpm (i.e., it is a 4-pole machine). The slip is given as follows (see Equation 4.9b)

$s = (n_s - n)/n_s = 1800 - 1750)/1800 = 0.028$ or 2.8% (a typical value, incidentally)

(b) The output power must be converted from hp to W. The power input is given by

$$P_{\text{in}} = P_{\text{out}} + \text{all losses} = 5 \times 746 + 200 + 100 + 150 = 4180 \text{ W}$$

Incidentally, the efficiency would be 3730/4180 = 0.892 = 89.2%, which, again, is a typical value for an induction machine.

13.10 This is a typical problem in steady state synchronous operation, and emphasizes that a synchronous machine may act as either a motor or a generator. By looking at the equivalent circuit, you can see that it reduces to a simple ac circuit problem containing two ideal sources and impedances. A simple application of Kirchhoff's voltage law yields

$$\mathbf{E}_{\mathrm{Gen}} = \mathrm{j}X_{\mathrm{Gen}}\mathbf{I} + \mathrm{j}X_{\mathrm{Mot}}\mathbf{I} + \mathbf{E}_{\mathrm{Mot}}$$

Similarly,

$$\mathbf{V}_{\mathrm{T}} = \mathrm{j}X_{\mathrm{Mot}}\mathbf{I} + \mathbf{E}_{\mathrm{mot}}, \quad \text{or} \quad \mathbf{E}_{\mathrm{mot}} = \mathbf{V}_{\mathrm{T}} - \mathrm{j}X_{\mathrm{Mot}}\mathbf{I}$$

Since unity power factor at the machine terminals is specified, we know that $\mathbf{V}_T$ and $\mathbf{I}$ are in phase. Letting the terminal voltage (and, also in this case, the armature current) be the angular reference,

$$\mathbf{E}_{\mathrm{Mot}} = 400\angle 0° - \mathrm{j}(0.4/0.5)(100\angle 0°) = 400 - \mathrm{j}80 = 408\angle -11.3° \ \mathrm{V}$$

Note that many problems like these, relating to power and machinery, can be solved as straightforward, steady state ac circuit problems. In the case of three-phase devices, be careful to distinguish between line-to-neutral and line-to-line voltages, and between three-phase and single-phase P and Q (see Chapter 3).

CHAPTER 14

Electromagnetics

OUTLINE

ELECTRIC FIELDS

In reviewing this topic we will look at scalar potential, charge density, gradient, divergence, and curl.

Scalar Potential as a Line Integral

The difference in potential between two points in a static electric field due to a single charge source is the same whether the path is the shortest distance between the points or any other path; thus this potential is single-valued. If the path between two points a and b is located in a uniform electric field of electric field intensity **E** (rather than simply being near a point charge), and if a test charge is moved from point a to point b against the field, the potential difference is obviously

$$V_{ba} = (x_b - x_a)E\cos\theta$$

where θ is the angle between the uniform field direction and the path direction, and x_a, x_b are the coordinates of the points. For an infinitesimal distance dl, the relationship is

$$dV = -E\cos\theta\, dl$$

and the potential difference is

$$V_{ba} = \int_a^b dv = v_b - v_a = -\int_a^b E\cos\theta\, dl = -\int_a^b \mathbf{E}\cdot d\mathbf{l} \qquad \textbf{(14.1a)}$$

It is easily shown that for a point charge, or any number of charges contained in a closed path where the path is in a static electric field, the line integral is given as

$$V_{aa} = -\int_a^a \mathbf{E}\cdot d\mathbf{l} = -\oint \mathbf{E}\cdot d\mathbf{l} = 0 \qquad \textbf{(14.1b)}$$

Here the $\oint$ (closed-path integral) symbol implies that one starts and ends at the same point. And, as usual, the direction of **E** is the direction that a positive charge would take if released. Also, recall that, in a uniform field, the greater the potential difference between two equipotential lines or surfaces, the greater the field.

Another relationship worth recalling is that of electric flux density **D**

$$\mathbf{D} = \mathbf{e}_o\,\mathbf{E} = \mathbf{a}_r[\mathbf{Q}/(4\pi r^2)], \qquad \textbf{(14.1c)}$$

where, $\mathbf{e}_o$ is the electric permittivity of free space and $\mathbf{a}_r$ is a unit vector in the outward radial direction.

Charge Density

The charge density ρ is usually expressed as the ratio of the total charge within a volume to the volume. Similar expressions exist for surface density ρ_s and line density ρ_L.

This charge density may also be thought of as a charge density *at a point.* Assuming a homogeneous charge throughout a region, consider an amount of charge ΔQ within a volume element Δv. The volume charge density $\rho = \Delta Q/\Delta v$ is the limit as $\Delta v \to 0$.

The potentials for the three kinds of charge densities mentioned above are given as follows. (Please be aware that many texts do not show the double or triple integration sign; instead, they indicate a subscript on the integral, such as *S* for surface area and *V* for volume.)

$$V_L = \frac{1}{4\pi\varepsilon}\int \frac{\rho_L}{r}\,dl = \text{potential due to a linear charge density} \qquad \textbf{(14.2a)}$$

$$V_S = \frac{1}{4\pi\varepsilon}\iint \frac{\rho_S}{r}\,ds = \text{potential due to a surface charge density} \qquad \textbf{(14.2b)}$$

$$V_V = \frac{1}{4\pi\varepsilon}\iiint \frac{\rho_V}{r}\,dv = \text{potential due a volume charge density} \qquad \textbf{(14.2c)}$$

If these various charge densities are present near a point *P*, then the total potential at point *P* is the algebraic sum of the potentials

$$V = V_L + V_S + V_V \qquad \textbf{(14.2d)}$$

Gradient

As previously stated, when equipotential lines or surfaces become closer together, the field becomes stronger; one defines the *gradient* of the potential at a point as the potential rise ΔV along a length Δl (in the direction of the field) divided by Δl. It is easily shown that the gradient of electric potential V (a scalar) is a vector quantity that is the negative of **E**

$$\text{grad } V = \nabla V = -\text{E} \tag{14.3a}$$

It will be of interest to define the vector that represents the magnitude and direction for the maximum rate of increase of a scalar (maximum rate will be a normal vector $\mathbf{a}_n$) as the gradient of the scalar; here, the maximum rate will be the shortest distance between two equipotential lines or surfaces

$$\text{grad } V = \nabla V = \mathbf{a}_n(dV/dn) \tag{14.3b}$$

The gradient of V may also be expressed in Cartesian coordinates as

$$\text{grad } V = \nabla V = \left(\mathbf{a}_x \frac{\partial V}{\partial x} + \mathbf{a}_y \frac{\partial V}{\partial y} + \mathbf{a}_z \frac{\partial V}{\partial z}\right), \tag{14.3c}$$

where the $\mathbf{a}_x$, $\mathbf{a}_y$, and $\mathbf{a}_z$ represent unit vectors along the respective axes.

For an application of Equation (14.3c), see Problem 14.1.

Divergence

To understand divergence, it will help to recall the definition of flux lines: lines representing the directions and magnitudes of vector fields. For a two- or three-dimensional field, the number of lines (designated by the density of lines—or sometimes by the length of lines—passing through a unit surface normal to the vector) is a measure of the vector field strength. Consider a specific volume with a closed surface; if inside the volume there is a positive source, then a net positive divergence exists. The divergence is a measure of the strength of the enclosed source.

The divergence for any vector field (e.g., some field A) at a particular point is the net outward flux per unit volume as the volume about this point tends toward zero, or

$$\text{div}\mathbf{A} = \nabla \cdot \mathbf{A} = \lim_{V \to 0} \frac{\oint_S \mathbf{A} \cdot d\mathbf{s}}{V} \tag{14.4a}$$

The divergence operation here is read in words as "del dot A." As with Equation (14.3c), this relationship may be expressed in Cartesian coordinates as

$$\text{div}\mathbf{A} = \frac{\partial A_x}{\partial x} + \frac{\partial A_y}{\partial y} + \frac{\partial A_z}{\partial z}. \tag{14.4b}$$

From Equation (14.4a), we see that the volume integral of the divergence of a vector field is the same as the total outgoing flux of the vector through the surface enclosing the volume, where the direction of $d\mathbf{s}$ is outward and perpendicular to the surface element. This relationship may be expressed as

$$\int_V \nabla \cdot \mathbf{A}\, dv = \oint_S \mathbf{A} \cdot d\mathbf{s} \tag{14.4c}$$

Equation (14.4c) clearly shows a conversion between the volume integral of the divergence and that of a closed surface integral of the vector, suggesting the relationship between the "point form" and "integral form" expressions of field equations.

Curl

The divergence is a measure of the strength of the flow source (that is, a surface integral taken around an infinitesimal surface divided by the volume enclosed). There is another kind of operation similar to this called the *curl*, which is defined in terms of a line integral taken around an infinitesimal path divided by the area enclosed by this path. The curl of a vector field **A** is a vector quantity whose magnitude is the net (maximum) circulation of **A** per unit infinitesimal area; the direction is normal to the surface area when the area orientation is adjusted for maximum circulation. The curl of a function is described in words as "del cross **A**" and is given as

$$\nabla \times \mathbf{A} = \lim_{\Delta S \to 0} \frac{1}{\Delta s}\left[\mathbf{a}_n \int_C \mathbf{A} \cdot dl\right]_{\max}, \qquad \textbf{(14.5a,b)}$$

and for non-time-varying electric fields we can see that

$$\nabla \times \mathrm{E} = 0$$

The curl of **A** (a vector result) is an expression of the "vorticity" of the field; it represents the maximum circulation (for a per-unit infinitesimal surface area) and is maximum when the area *ds* is oriented such that it is normal to the direction of curl **A**.

MAGNETIC FIELDS

For static magnetic fields there are no magnetic sources; it is thus clear that the magnetic flux lines always close on themselves. Recall that, for an electric field, the electrostatic force on the charge is proportional to the charge and to the electric field intensity

$$\mathbf{F}_{\mathrm{e}} = q\mathbf{E}$$

However, the same electrical charge, if in motion in a *magnetic* field, experiences a force $\mathbf{F}_{\mathrm{m}}$ that is proportional to q and whose direction is normal to the velocity vector **u**. This magnetic force leads directly to the definition of magnetic flux density **B**, and is given as

$$\mathbf{F}_m = q\mathbf{u} \times \mathbf{B} \qquad \textbf{(14.6a)}$$

and thus the total force on the charge can be written as

$$\mathbf{F}_{\text{total}} = q\mathbf{E} + q\mathbf{u} \times \mathbf{B} = q(\mathbf{E} + \mathbf{u} \times \mathbf{B}) \qquad \textbf{(14.6b)}$$

Note that a charge has to be *in motion* to experience a force due to a *magnetic* field.

For steady magnetic fields in free space, Equations (14.6a) and (14.6b) lead to the following postulates

$$\nabla \cdot \mathbf{B} = 0 \tag{14.7a}$$

$$\nabla \times \mathbf{B} = \mu_0 \mathbf{J} \tag{14.7b}$$

$$\nabla \times \mathbf{H} = \mathbf{J} \tag{14.7c}$$

where μ_0 is the *magnetic permeability* of free space.

The integral forms of these equations (again in free space) may be given as

$$\oint_S \mathbf{B} \cdot d\mathbf{s} = 0 \tag{14.7d}$$

$$\oint_C \mathbf{B} \cdot dl = \mu_0 \mathbf{I}. \tag{14.7e}$$

For Equation (14.7e), one may visualize a circular path around a current-carrying conductor; the line integral around this closed path is equal to $\mu_0 I$. The variable **B** is referred to as the *magnetic flux density*, and another quantity, the *magnetic field intensity* **H**, is defined as being proportional to **B** and in the same direction

$$\mathbf{H} = (1/\mu)\mathbf{B} \tag{14.8a}$$

and thus

$$\int_C \mathbf{H} \cdot d\mathbf{l} = \mathbf{N}I \tag{14.8b}$$

where N is the number of turns of the conductor and I is the current enclosed by these turns. The units of each side of Equation (14.8b) are frequently referred to as AT (amp-turns).

DYNAMIC FIELDS

For the static electric fields, the electrical quantities **E** and **D** are not related to the static magnetic quantities **B** and **H**, but there is a definite relationship if the fields are changing. For example, when working with static fields, the curl of **E** is zero; see Equation (14.5b). Early in the nineteenth century, however, Michael Faraday discovered that a current was induced in a loop (due to an induced voltage) when the enclosed magnetic field was changing. This discovery led to a number of postulates for time-changing fields including

$$\nabla \times \mathbf{E} = -\frac{\partial \mathbf{B}}{\partial t} \tag{14.9a}$$

$$\nabla \times \mathbf{H} = \mathbf{J} + \frac{\partial \mathbf{D}}{\partial t} = \sigma \mathbf{E} + \mathbf{e}\frac{\partial \mathbf{E}}{\partial t} \tag{14.9b}$$

$$\nabla \cdot \mathbf{D} = \rho \tag{14.9c}$$

$$\nabla \cdot \mathbf{B} = 0 \tag{14.9d}$$

These equations should be compared to those of Equations (14.7a) through (14.7e) above. Their integral forms (again, valid for time-varying as well as static fields) are

$$\oint \mathbf{E}\cdot d\mathbf{l} = -\int_S \frac{\partial \mathbf{B}}{\partial t}\cdot d\mathbf{s} = -\iint \frac{\partial \mathbf{B}}{\partial t}\cdot d\mathbf{s} \qquad \textbf{(14.10a)}$$

$$\oint \mathbf{H}\cdot d\mathbf{l} = I + \int_S \frac{\partial \mathbf{D}}{\partial t}\cdot d\mathbf{s} = I + \iint \frac{\partial \mathbf{D}}{\partial t}\cdot d\mathbf{s} \qquad \textbf{(14.10b)}$$

$$\oint_{SV} \mathbf{D}\cdot d\mathbf{s} = Q = \int_V \rho dv = \iiint \rho dv \qquad \textbf{(14.10c)}$$

$$\oint_{SV} \mathbf{B}\cdot d\mathbf{s} = \iint \mathbf{B}\cdot d\mathbf{s} = 0 \qquad \textbf{(14.10d)}$$

Note, for example, that Equation (14.10a) does not equal zero in the presence of a time-varying magnetic field, although for non–time-varying fields it does, as shown in Equation (14.1b).

Wave Equation and Poynting's Theorem

Another important quantity that may appear on the examination is the uniform plane wave, or the "wave equation." Here, assume a sinusoidal steady-state quantity far from the source (a distance such that a small area on a sphere of the radius of the distance from the source may be considered a plane) and in an isotropic medium. Then

$$\nabla^2 \mathbf{E} = \frac{1}{c^2}\frac{\partial^2 \mathbf{E}}{\partial t^2} = -\omega^2 \mu\varepsilon \mathbf{E} \qquad \textbf{(14.11)}$$

where

$c = 1/(\mu\varepsilon)^{1/2}$

$=$ speed of light $= 3 \times 10^8$ m/s

For free space, $\mu\varepsilon \rightarrow \mu_0\varepsilon_0$

The rate of energy transfer to distant points by electric and magnetic field intensities can be related by Poynting's theorem as

$$\oint_S (\mathbf{E}\times\mathbf{H})\cdot d\mathbf{s} = -\left[\int_V \mathbf{J}\cdot \mathbf{E} dv + \frac{\partial}{\partial t}\int_V \frac{1}{2}(\varepsilon E^2 + \mu H^2) dv\right] \qquad \textbf{(14.12)}$$

The vector quantity inside the first integral, **E** × **H**, is known as the *Poynting vector* **P** (some books use **S**), and is the power flow per unit area (**P** = **S** = **E** × **H**). Note that the direction of this Poynting vector is normal to both **E** and **H**. Referring to Equation (14.12), it is also worth noting that the integral on the left side is the closed surface integral of the power density; i.e., the power flow into the volume V_S. The first term on the right side of the equation is the ohmic power dissipated due to conduction current in the presence of an electric field **E**, and the last two terms represent the time rate of change of the energy stored by the two fields.

Because most calculations involving time-changing electric and magnetic fields can be quite tedious, the questions given in the examination will probably be in the nature of recognizing the appropriate equations and will likely involve only simple manipulations and/or partial solutions. Any calculations should be mini-

mal. When preparing for the examination, all of the major equations given in this chapter should be studied for their physical meanings, along with those given for the morning session. Other equations involving field theory may be needed but they should be ones that you already know.

TRANSMISSION LINE THEORY

A transmission line has propagating electromagnetic fields down its length described by a propagating electric field

$$E_X = E_{0,X}\cos(\omega t - kz)$$

where ωt is the time factor, and kz is the space factor.

The phase velocity of the propagating electric field is

$$v_p \lambda\ f = \frac{1}{\sqrt{\varepsilon\mu}} = \frac{c}{\sqrt{\varepsilon_r}}.$$

Voltage, current, or power emanating from a source impedance Z_s and delivered to a load Z_L can be considered to be in the form of incident and reflected waves traveling in opposite directions along a transmission line of characteristic impedance Z_o.

A transmission line is typically shown diagrammatically as shown in Figure 14.1.

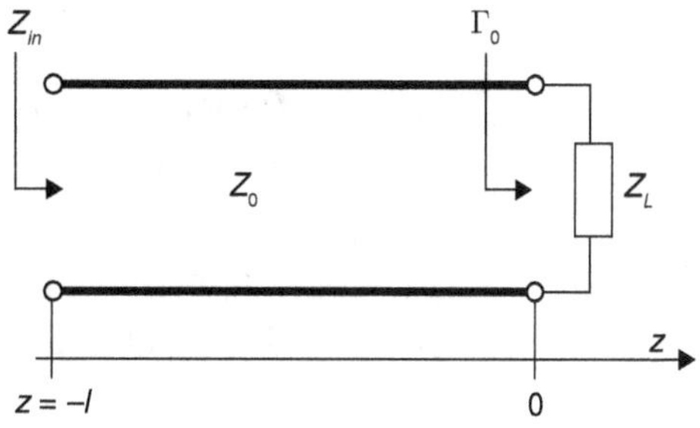

Figure 14.1 Transmission Line Diagram

The impedance of a lossless transmission line at a distance $z = -l$ from the load toward the source is

$$Z(-l) = Z_0 \frac{Z_L + jZ_0 \tan\beta l}{Z_0 + jZ_L \tan\beta l}$$

where the characteristic impedance of the transmission line is

$$Z_o = \sqrt{\frac{L}{C}}.$$

If Z_L is a short circuit or $Z_L = 0$, then

$$Z(-l) = jZ_o\tan(\beta l) = jX$$

If Z_L is an open circuit $Z_L = \infty$, then

$$Z(-l) = -jZ_o\cot(\beta l) = -jX$$

- If $Z_1 = Z_o$, the incident wave is totally absorbed in the load.
- If Z_1 is not equal to Z_o, some of the incident wave is not absorbed in the load but is reflected back toward the source.

- If $Z_s = Z_o$, the reflected wave would be absorbed by the source entirely.
- For Z_s not equal to Z_o, the reflected-from-the-load wave is re-reflected from the source back toward the load, and the entire process repeats itself.

The degree of mismatch between Z_o and Z_L, or Z_s determines the amount of incident wave that is reflected. The ratio of the reflected wave to the incident wave is known as the **reflection coefficient.**

The **reflection coefficient,** Γ is a complex number often expressed as a magnitude and an angle in a polar form.

The reflection coefficient at the load is

$$\Gamma_0 = \frac{Z_L - Z_0}{Z_L + Z_0}$$

where:

$\Gamma_0 = 1$ for $Z_L \to \infty$
$\Gamma_0 = 1$ for $Z_L \to 0$

The Standing Wave Ratio (SWR) is a measure of mismatch of the load to the transmission line.

$$SWR = \frac{1+|\Gamma_0|}{1-|\Gamma_0|}.$$

where

$SWR = 1$ for a matched load Z_L to the transmission line characteristic impedance Z_o

$SWR = 0$ for a total mismatch between the load impedance Z_L to the transmission line characteristic impedance Z_o.

A special case is the quarter-wave transformer. A quarter-wave transmission line is shown in Figure 14.2 where the length of the transmission line to the input impedance (Z_{in}) point is a quarter wavelength from the load.

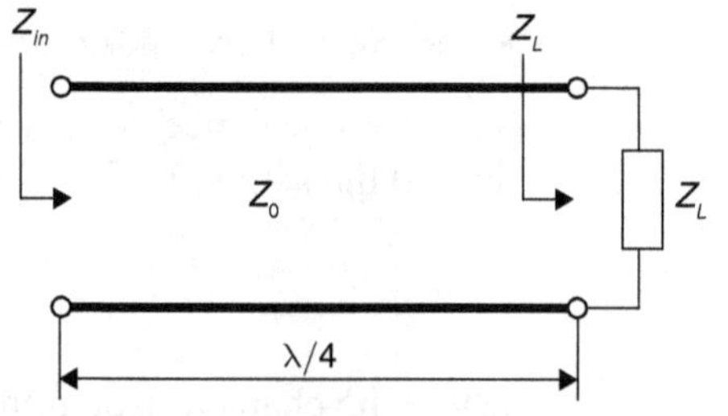

Figure 14.2 Quarter-Wave Transmission Line

$$Z_{in}(\lambda/4) = Z_0 \frac{Z_L + jZ_0 \tan(\beta\lambda/4)}{Z_0 + jZ_L \tan(\beta\lambda/4)} = \frac{Z_0^{\ 2}}{Z_L}$$

In the quarter-wave transformer case,

$$Z_0 = \sqrt{Z_L Z_{in}}.$$

For sourced and loaded transmission lines, the voltage at the beginning of the transmission line is composed of an incident and reflected component.

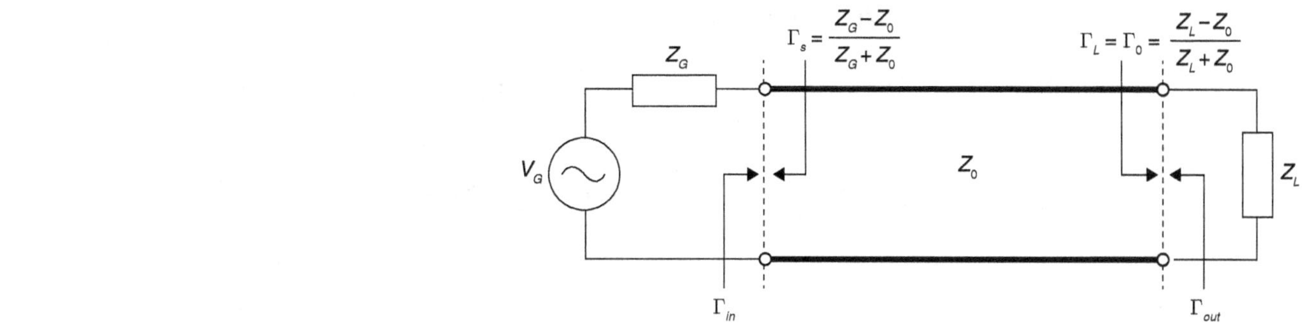

Figure 14.3

$$V_{in} = V_{in}^{+}\left(1+\Gamma_{in}\right) = V_G\left(\frac{Z_{in}}{Z_{in}+Z_G}\right)$$

where V_{in} is the voltage at the interface Γ_{in}, and V_{in}^{+} is the positive going voltage (wave) from the source to the load.

In determining the power input P_{in} at the Γ_{in} interface where the source meets the transmission line

$$I = \frac{V_{in}^{+}}{Z_0}\left(1-\Gamma_{in}\right)$$

so $P_{in} = \frac{1}{2}\text{Re}\left\{V_{in}I_{in}^{*}\right\}$

where I_{in}^{*} is the complex conjugate of I_{in}.

$$P_{in} = \frac{1}{2}\frac{\left|V_{in}^{+}\right|^2}{Z_o}\left(1-\left|\Gamma_{in}\right|^2\right)$$

so

$$P_{in} = \frac{1}{8}\frac{\left|V_G\right|^2}{Z_o}\frac{\left|1-\Gamma_S\right|^2}{\left|1-\Gamma_S\Gamma_{in}\right|^2}\left(1-\left|\Gamma_{in}\right|^2\right)$$

There are two special cases:
For load and source matched line $\Gamma_o = \Gamma_s = 0$, $P_{in} = \frac{1}{8}\frac{\left|V_G\right|^2}{Z_o}$,

and for mismatch at source but match at load $\Gamma_o = 0$, $P_{in} = \frac{1}{8}\frac{\left|V_G\right|^2}{Z_o}\left|1-\Gamma_S\right|^2$.

Power is measured as $P[\text{dBm}] = 10\log\frac{P(\text{in Watts})}{1\text{ mW}}$.

Return loss is defined as,

$$RL = -10\log\left(\frac{P_r}{P_i}\right) = -10\log\left|\Gamma_{in}\right|^2 = -20\log\left|\Gamma_{in}\right| \text{ in dB.}$$

Insertion loss is defined as,

$$IL = -10\log\left(\frac{P_t}{P_i}\right) = -10\log\left(\frac{P_i - P_r}{P_i}\right) = -10\log\left(1 - |\Gamma_{in}|^2\right) \text{ in dB}$$

where P_t is the transmitted power, P_r is the reflected power, and P_i is the input power.

Example 14.1

Commercial coaxial line is 50 Ohms; flat antenna line is 300 Ohms.

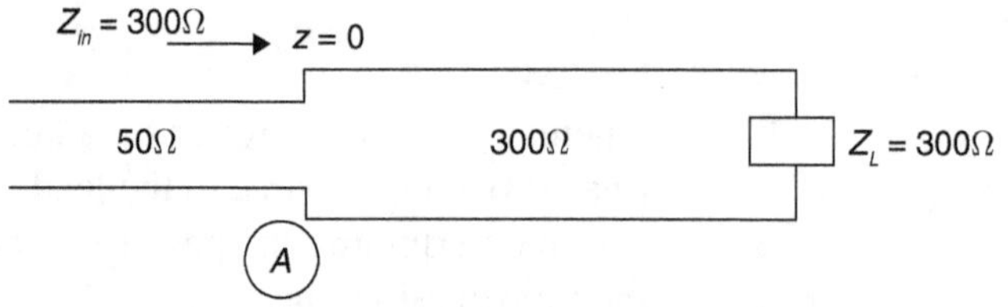

Exhibit 1

What is the reflection coefficient at A?

$$\Gamma = \frac{Z_{in} - Z_o}{Z_{in} + Z_o} = \frac{300 - 50}{300 + 50} = 0.714$$

The transmission coefficient

$$\tau = 1 + \Gamma = 1.714$$

The fraction of power reflected is $\Gamma^2 = 0.51$.

The fraction of power transmitted to the 300 Ω line and on to the load is $1 - 0.51 = 0.49$.

Example 14.2

An RF signal is sent on a parallel wire 300 Ohm transmission line, which has $\varepsilon_r = 5$, to a receiver (which can be represented as a load Z_L). A VSWR of SWR = 3 is measured on the line.

The distance between two minima is 0.67 m, and the nearest minimum to the load minimum is 0.45 m away. Find the frequency of the signal and the impedance of the load (receiver input).

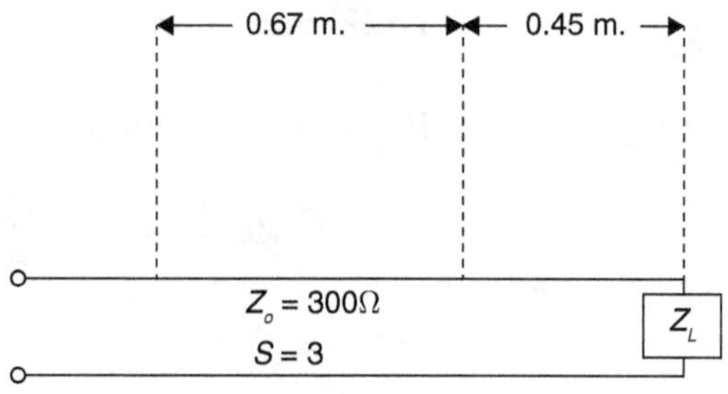

Exhibit 2

$$\lambda_m / 2 = 0.67 \qquad \lambda_m = 1.34$$

$$\lambda = \lambda_m \sqrt{\varepsilon_r} = 1.34 \cdot \sqrt{5} = 3m$$

$$f = \frac{c}{\lambda} = \frac{3 \times 10^8}{3} = 10^8 = 100 MHz$$

$$\beta = \frac{2\pi}{\lambda_m} = \frac{2\pi}{1.34} = 1.49\pi m^{-1}$$

$$-2\beta 1_{\min} + \theta_r = \pi \qquad \therefore 2.98\pi l_m + \pi = \theta_r$$

$$2.34\pi = \theta_r = 0.34\pi = 61.2°$$

$$SWR = \frac{1 + |\Gamma|}{1 - |\Gamma|}$$

$$\text{so } \Gamma = \frac{SWR - 1}{SWR + 1} = \frac{2}{4} = 0.5$$

$$\Gamma = 0.5 \angle 61.2° = 0.24 + j0.44$$

$$\Gamma = \frac{Z_L - Z_o}{Z_L + Z_o} = \frac{Z_L - 300}{Z_L + 300}$$

so

$$Z_L(1 - \Gamma) = Z_L(1 + \Gamma)$$

$$Z_L = (0.76 - j0.44) = 300(1.24 + j0.44)$$

Then

$$Z_L = 300 \frac{(1.24 + j0.44)}{(0.76 + j0.44)} = 450\angle 49.5°$$

PRINCIPLES OF EMC

Electromagnetic compatibility refers to the capability of two or more electrical devices to operate simultaneously without interference. A system that is electromagnetically compatible, therefore, satisfies the following criteria:

1. It does not cause interference with other systems.
2. It is not susceptible to emissions from other systems.
3. It does not cause interference with itself.

Additionally, the system must meet regulatory requirements. The interference that EMC refers to is known as electromagnetic interference (EMI). A common name for EMI is "noise." Noise can be natural (e.g., lightning, solar disturbances) or human (e.g., relays, radio, radar) in origin.

One class of EMI is called radio frequency interference (RFI). RFI is propagated as an electromagnetic wave at radio frequencies (e.g., ignition coils, switch arcs).

There are always three elements involved in a noise problem: a *noise source* (line transients, relays, magnetic field, etc.) a *coupling medium* (capacitance, inductance, wire, air) and a *receiver* (a circuit that is susceptible to the noise).

Figure 14.4 Diagram of Basic EMC Problem

To solve a noise problem (make something electromagnetically compatible), one or more of these elements must be removed, reduced, or diverted. Their role in the problem must be understood before the problem can be solved.

Types of Sources

Noise in any electronic system can originate at a large number of sources including digital circuits, power supplies, adjacent equipment. Noise sources can even include improperly connected shields and ground wires that were intended to combat noise.

Supply Line Transients

Anything that is switched will cause a transient on the supply lines. This can range from a digital circuit switching between a high and low state or an appliance connected to a GPO.

The basic mechanism behind supply line transients is shown in Figure 14.5:

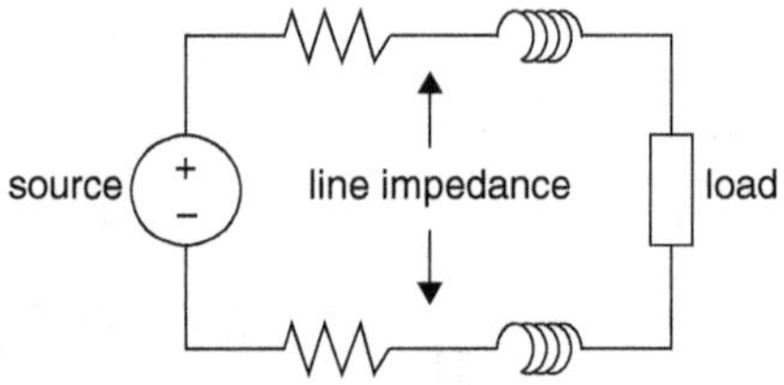

Figure 14.5 Supply Line Transients

Any change in the load causes a transient due to the line inductance. Supply line voltage dips can cause reset conditions in microprocessors, cause distortion in analog outputs, and at the very worst, even destroy components.

EMP and RFI

Anything that produces arcs or sparks will radiate electromagnetic pulses (EMP) or radio frequency interference (RFI). Arcs and sparks occur in automotive ignition systems, electric motors, switches, static discharges, and so forth. In switches, the transients on the supply line will cause an opening switch to throw a spark.

ESD

Electrostatic discharge (ESD) is the spark that occurs when a person picks up a static charge (e.g., from walking on carpet) and then discharges it onto a metallic (door handle) or electronic device (CMOS chip). ESD can be very damaging to an electronic system; it can blow craters in silicon.

Intentional Sources

The power supply is an intentional signal transmitted to most electronic devices. Although it is intended to supply power, it can also couple into other signal paths.

Digital circuits are by their very nature switching circuits. They also operate at high frequencies. Therefore, they have supply line transient problems and emit RFI.

Coupling

There are four main ways that noise is coupled into a system. Different noise problems require different solutions. Adding a capacitor or shield will not solve every problem.

Common Impedance ("Ground") Coupling

One of the most common methods of coupling noise is through poor design. Consider the following digital and analog system:

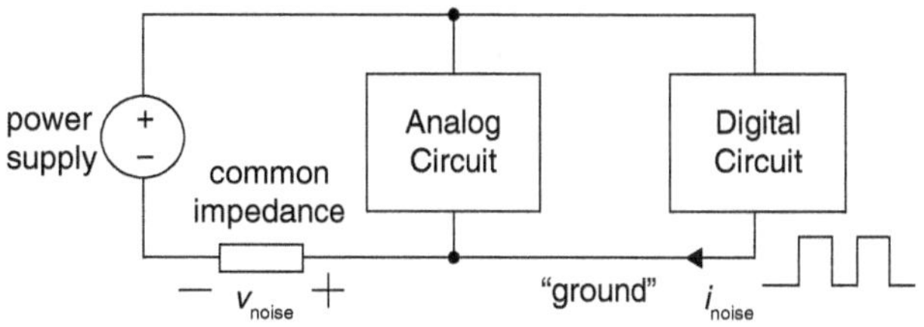

Figure 14.6 Development of noise by a common impedance

The "ground" point in this arrangement could be connected to op-amp non-inverting terminals inverting terminals (for example) and output transistors of digital logic (when they are driving low). The "ground" point has a tangible impedance to the power supply common. The noise current causes a noise voltage across the common impedance, which will present itself as a noise voltage to the analog circuit.

Capacitive Coupling

Capacitive coupling involves the passage of interfering signals through mutual (or "stray") capacitances that are never shown on the circuit diagram but we know are there. This type of noise is often associated with fast rise and fall times or high frequencies (a capacitor is like a short circuit to high frequencies).

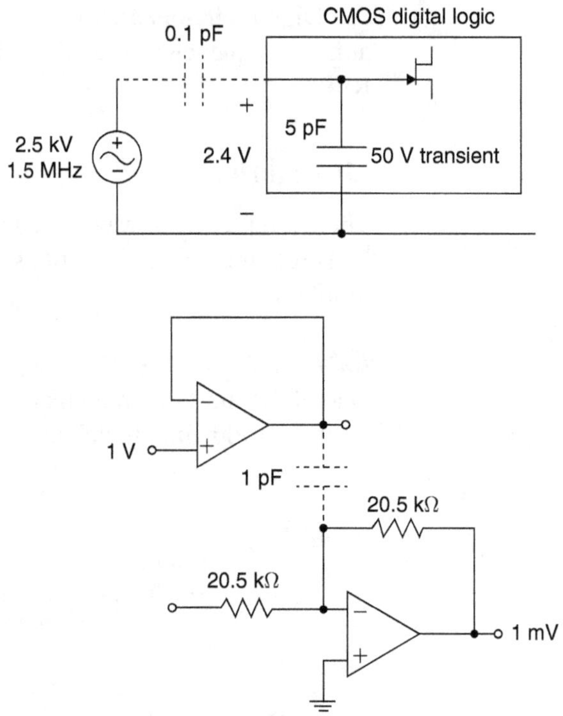

Figure 14.7 Stray capacitance couples "noise" into other circuits

Inductive Coupling

Inductive coupling is where a magnetic field from some external source links with a current loop in the victim circuit.

A current exists only in a loop. Sometimes it is difficult to determine where the current is (e.g., a ground plane), and we often ignore its path on a schematic due to the "common" and op-amp symbols. The physical geometry of the loop formed by the current is the key to understanding inductive coupling.

Any current creates a magnetic field. We know from Ampère's Law that the field strength is dependent on the current enclosed by our path of integration in circling the current. A current loop therefore creates a magnetic field.

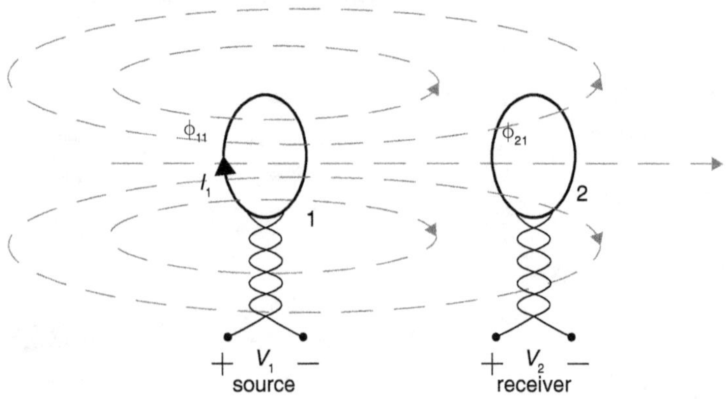

Figure 14.8 Inductive coupling caused by current loops

If a time varying magnetic field links with a conductive loop, then Faraday's Law applies and a voltage will be induced in the loop.

Minimizing inductive coupling does not necessarily involve magnetic materials. If two conductors, each carrying a current *I* in opposite directions, are in close proximity then the external magnetic field tends to cancel.

Radiated Coupling

A time-varying electric field generates a time-varying magnetic field and vice versa. Far from the source of a time-varying EM field, the ratio of the amplitudes of the electric and magnetic fields is always 377 Ω (the characteristic impedance of free space or air). Close to the source of the fields, however, this ratio can be quite different and dependent on the nature of the source. The region in space where the ratio is near 377 Ω is called the far field, and the region where the ratio is significantly different from 377 Ω is called the near field.

The near field goes out about 1/6 of a wavelength from the source. At 1 MHz this is about 50 m, and at 10 MHz it's about 5 m. This means that if an EMI source is in the same room with the victim circuit, then it's most likely to be a near field problem. The reason this matters is that in the near field an RF interference problem could be almost entirely due to *E*-field coupling or *H*-field coupling, and this influences the way in which we combat this type of noise.

In the near field of a whip antenna, the *E H* ratio is higher than 377 Ω, which means it's mainly an *E*-field generator. A wire-wrap post or a test point terminal can be a whip antenna. Interference from a whip antenna would be by electric field coupling, which is basically capacitive coupling. In the near field of a loop antenna, the *E H* ratio is lower than 377 Ω, which means it's mainly an *H*-field generator. Any current loop is a loop antenna. Interference from a loop antenna would be by magnetic field coupling, which is basically the same as inductive coupling.

Even so, in the near field and far field, the fact that the EMI is being radiated means treatment of this type of coupling must be handled differently.

Combating EMI

There is a whole range of techniques that help combat EMI. They range from minimizing the generation of noise voltages, reducing the coupling, and making a graceful recovery after being subjected to an electromagnetic disturbance.

Some techniques, like grounding and shielding, attack the EMI problem from many sides. *Consideration of EMC at the design stage, such as PCB layout, can prevent many noise problems from ever occurring.*

Combating Capacitive Coupling

Reducing Mutual (Stray) Capacitance on a PCB

- Lay tracks as far apart as possible on a PCB (separate high- and low-level signals).

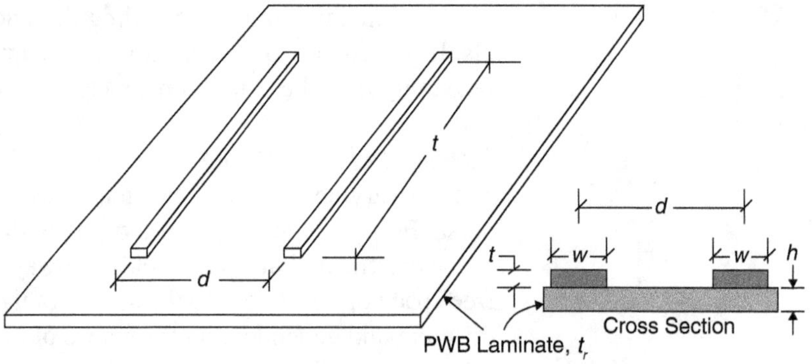

Figure 14.9 Separate tracks to reduce capacitance

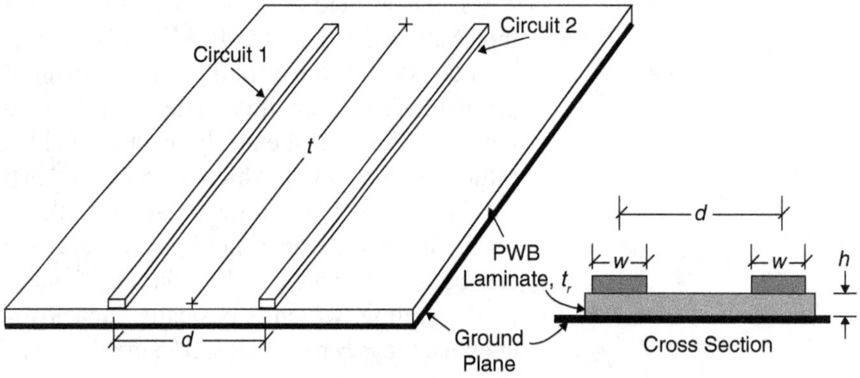

Figure 14.10 Use a ground plane to minimize mutual capacitance

Some example figures of properly implemented shields include:

- Connect shields to the common at the source.

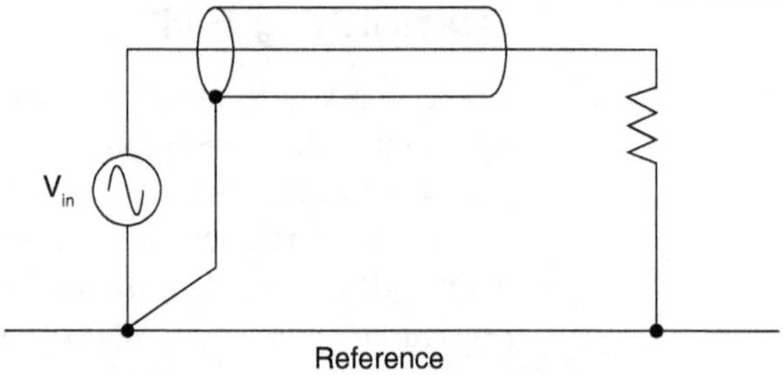

Figure 14.11 Connect shields to the common (reference) at the source

- Don't connect both ends of the shield to "ground."

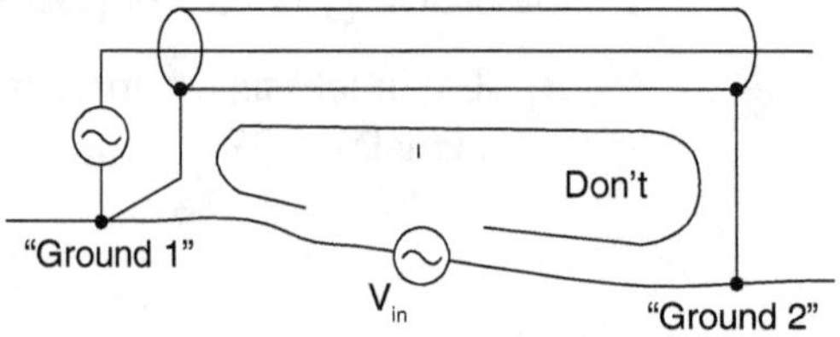

Figure 14.12 Don't connect the shield to ground at more than one point

- Don't allow shield current to exist (conflicts with combating inductive coupling).

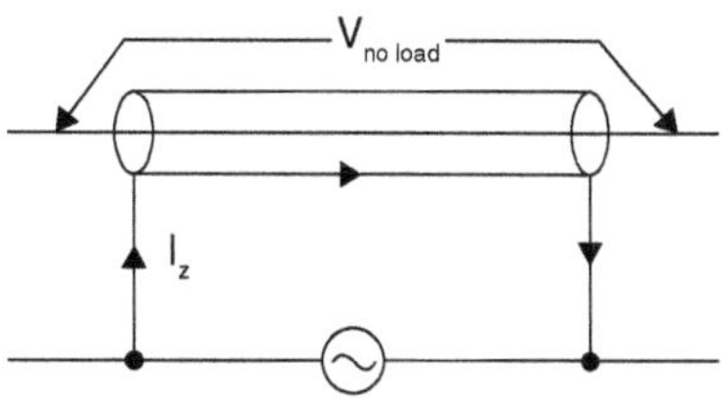

Figure 14.13 Magnetic pickup from current through a cable shield

- Don't allow the shield to be at a voltage with respect to the reference potential.

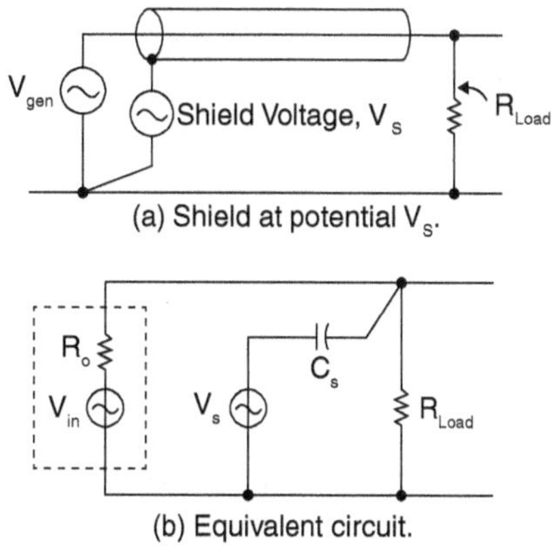

Figure 14.14

- Don't allow the shield to be at a voltage with respect to the reference potential.
- Know by careful study how the noise current that has been captured by the shield returns to "ground."

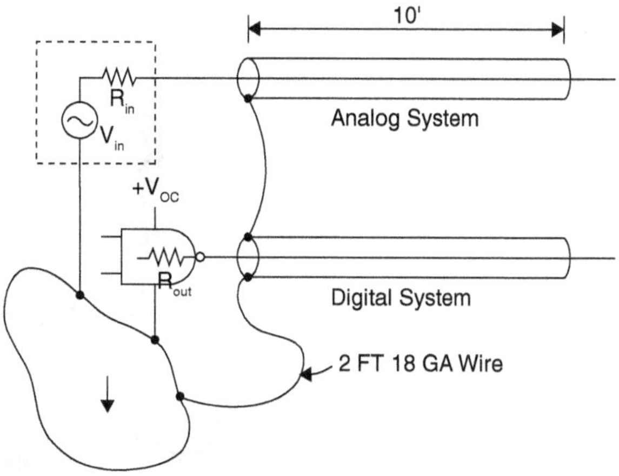

Figure 14.15 The figure shows a situation that generates transient shield voltages.

- Use a Faraday shield to isolate whole circuits

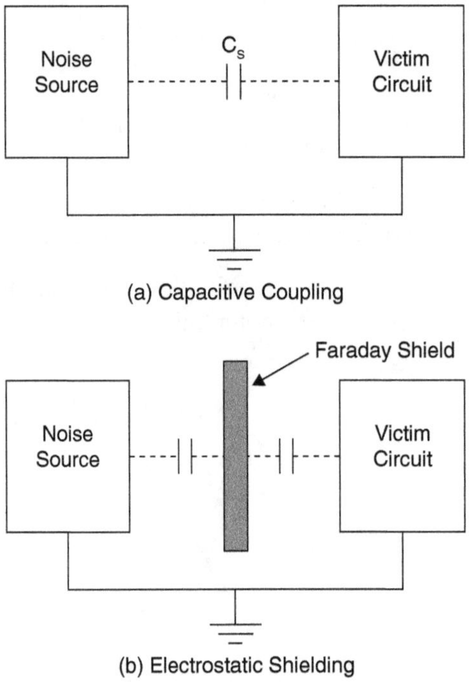

Figure 14.16 Faraday shield in use

Combating Inductive Coupling

Reducing Mutual Inductance on a PCB

- Minimize current loop areas.
- Use a ground plane (or gridded-ground).

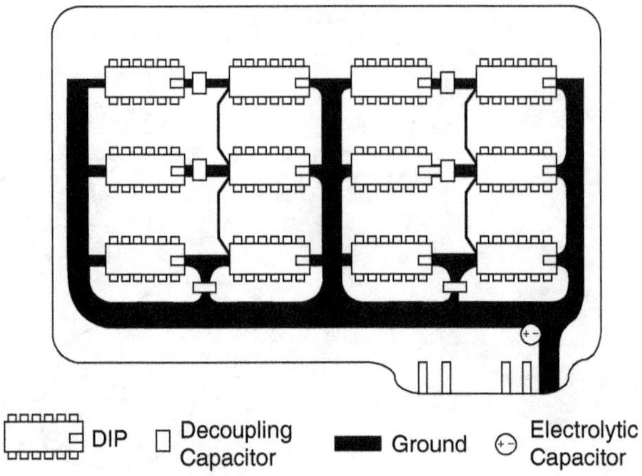

Figure 14.17 PCB with gridded ground

- Orient susceptible loops at right angles to the magnetic field, if possible.

Shields

- Use coaxial cable.

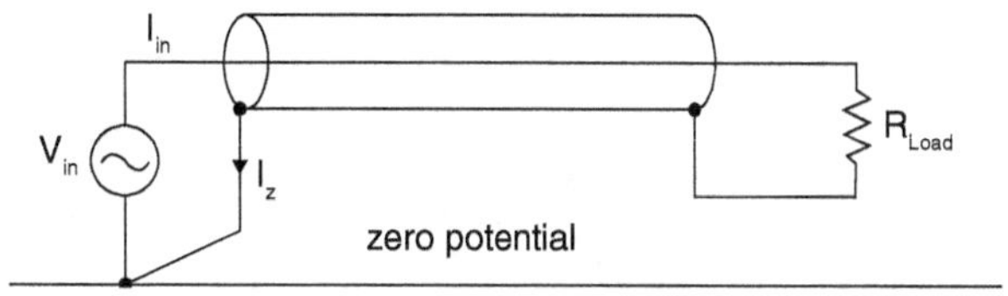

Figure 14.18

Use a shield for return current to a noisy source

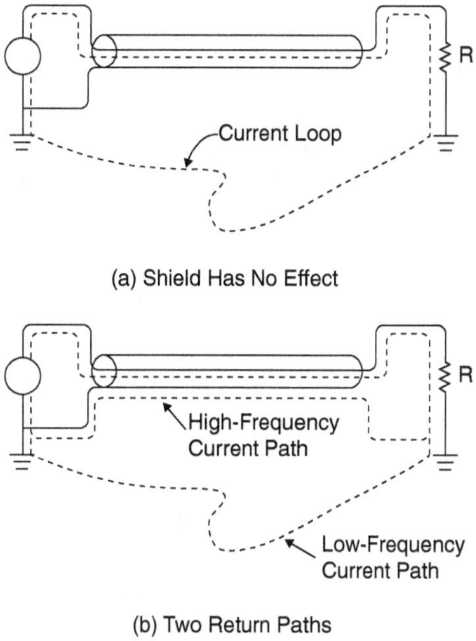

Figure 14.19

When using coaxial cables, be aware of current loops

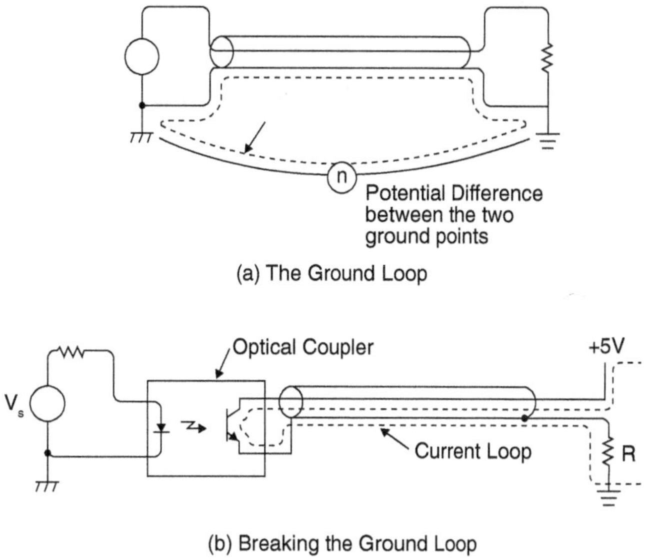

Figure 14.20

Increasing isolation by using an optical coupler

- Use twisted pair cables

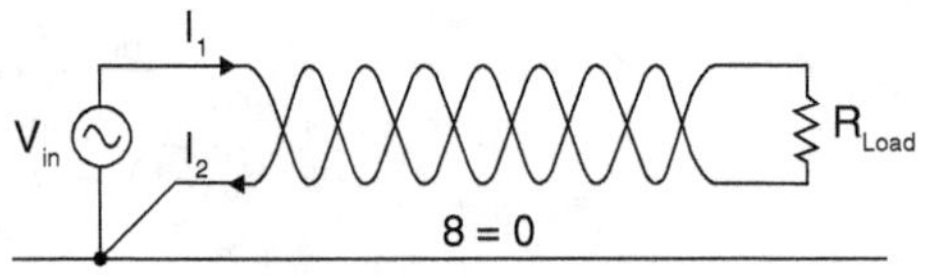

a. Correct connection with balanced currents.

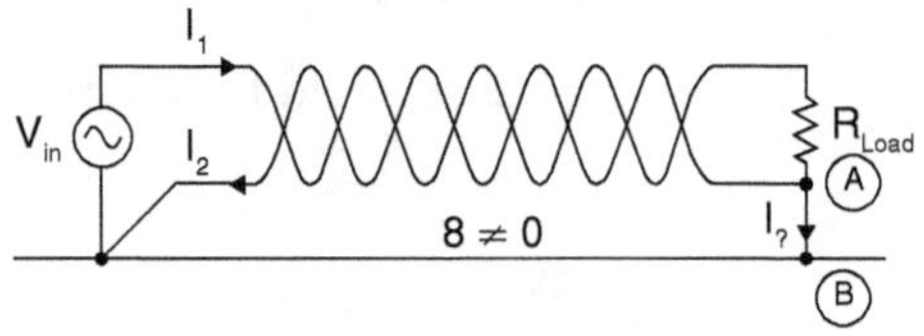

b. Incorrect connection forming ground loop.

Figure 14.21

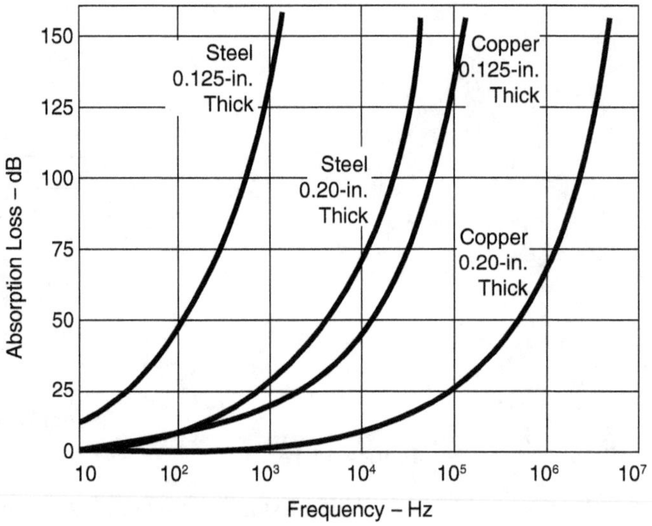

Figure 14.22

Absorption loss vs. frequency for two thicknesses of copper and steel

- Use steel or mumetal at power frequencies.

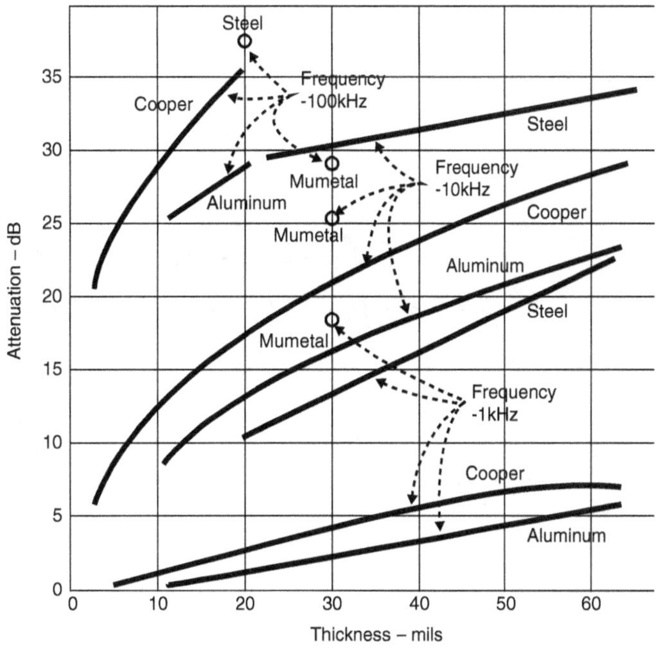

Figure 14.23 Absorption loss vs. frequency for two thicknesses of copper

RF Shielding

- Use copper or aluminum for *E*-field shielding (rare).

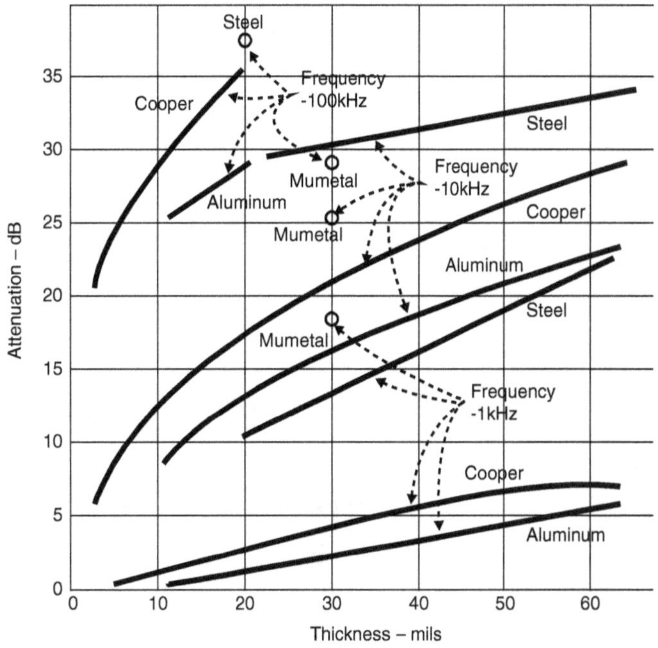

Figure 14.24 Absorption loss vs. frequency for two thicknesses of copper

- Use copper or aluminum for *E*-field shielding (rare).

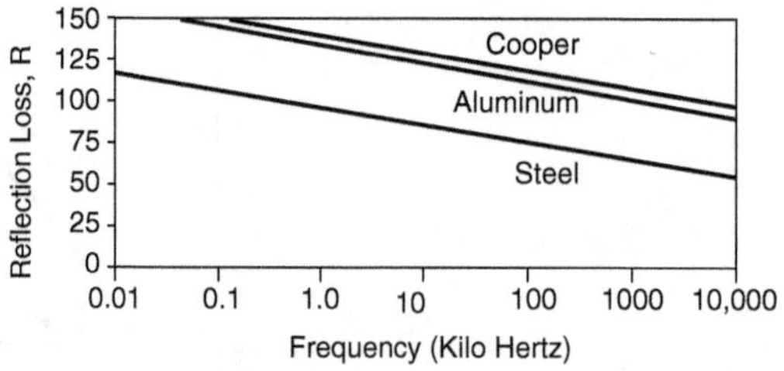

Figure 14.25 E-field shielding

- Use steel for *H*-field and far field shielding (common).

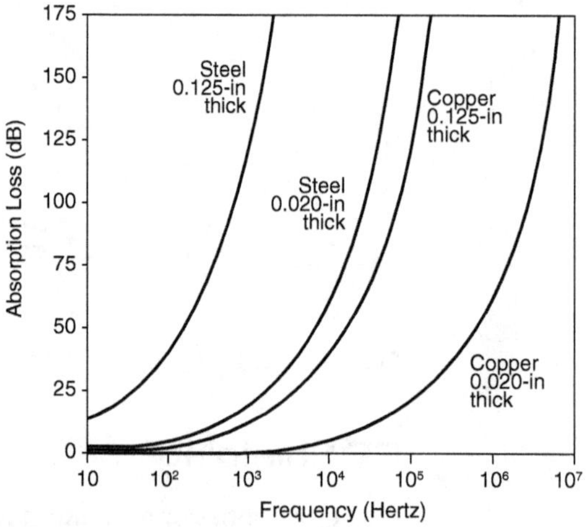

Figure 14.26 H-field shielding

- Use steel if in doubt.

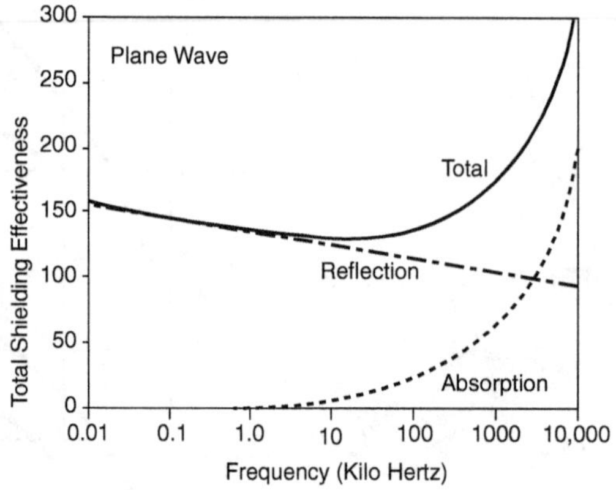

Figure 14.27 E- and H-field shielding

- Avoid seams, joints, and large holes in the shield.

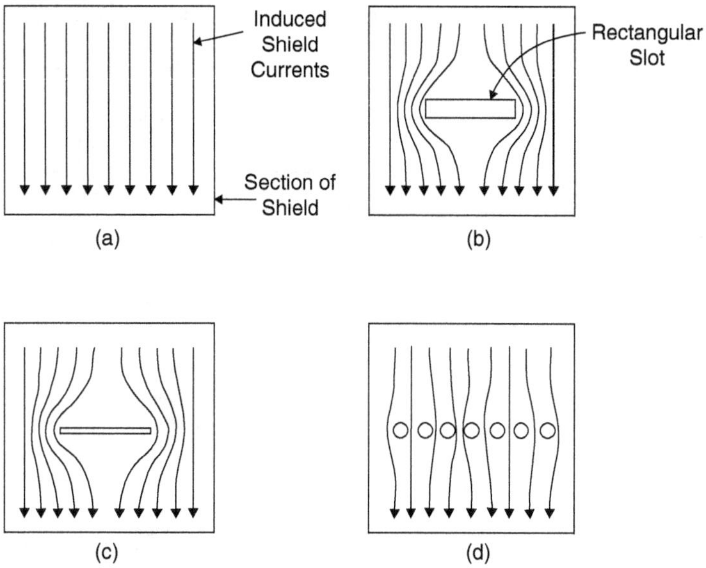

Figure 14.28 Effect of shield discontinuity on magnetically induced shield current

Grounds

- Use a combination of serial and parallel ground-wiring.

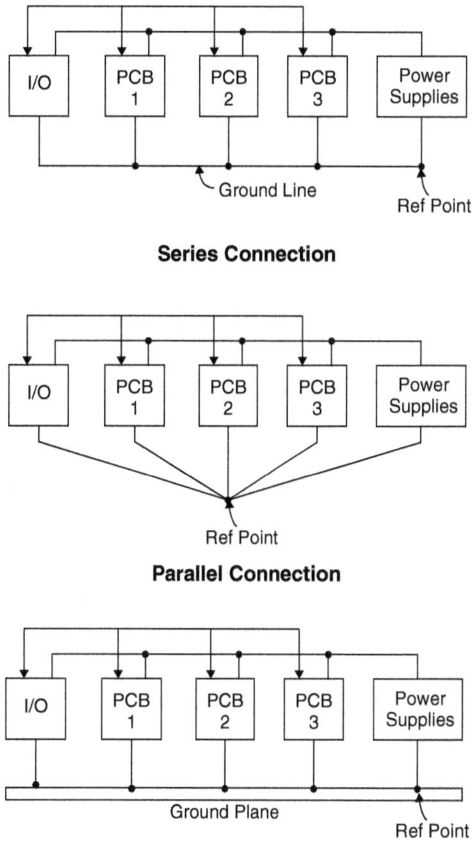

Figure 14.29 Three ways to wire the grounds

- Separate digital grounds and analog grounds.

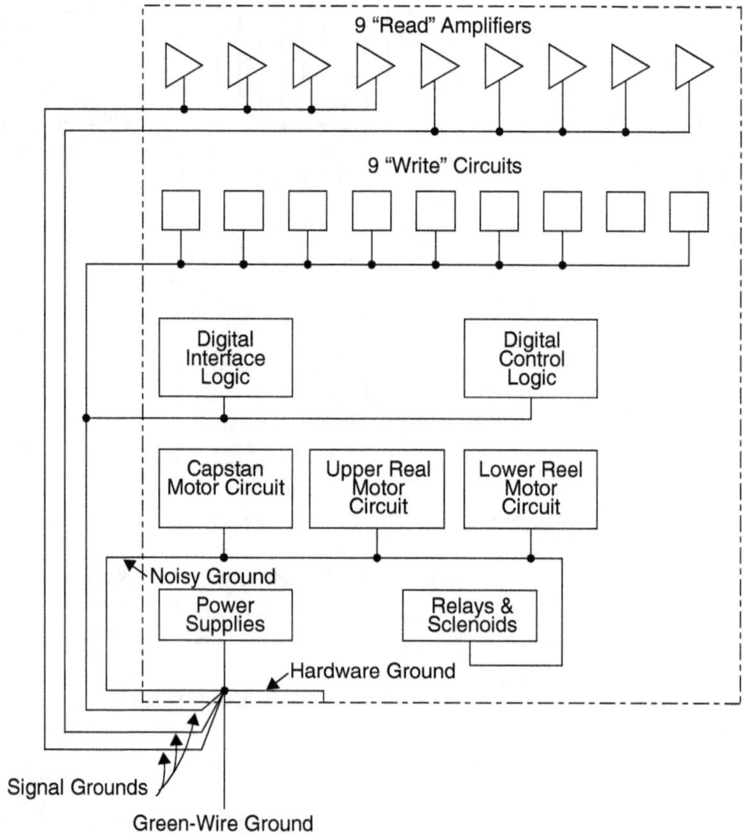

Figure 14.30 Ground systems for digital and analog grounds

- Separate power grounds and signal grounds.

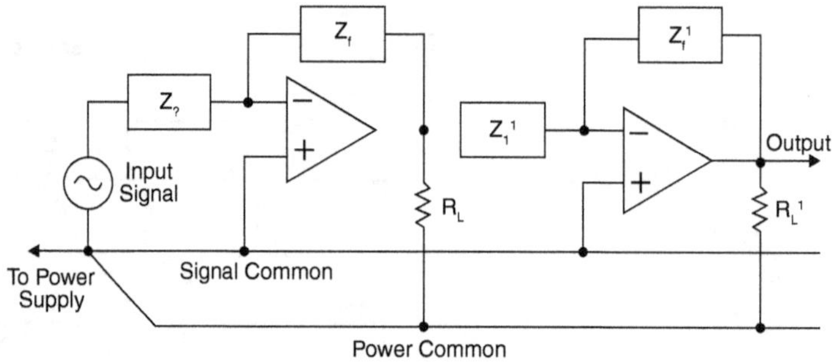

Figure 14.31 Minimizing common impedance coupling

- Use a ground plane.

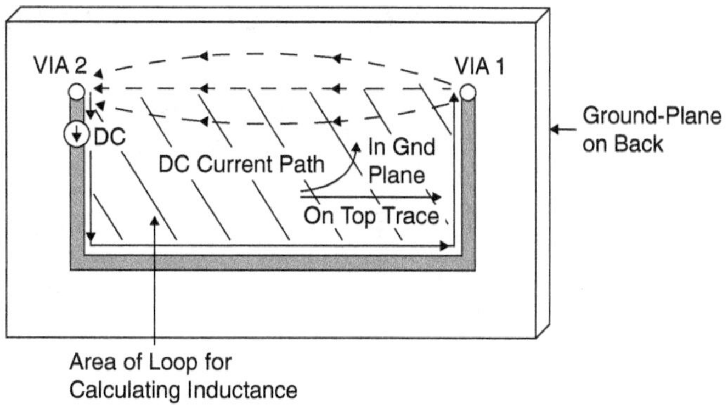

Figure 14.32 DC Current Path

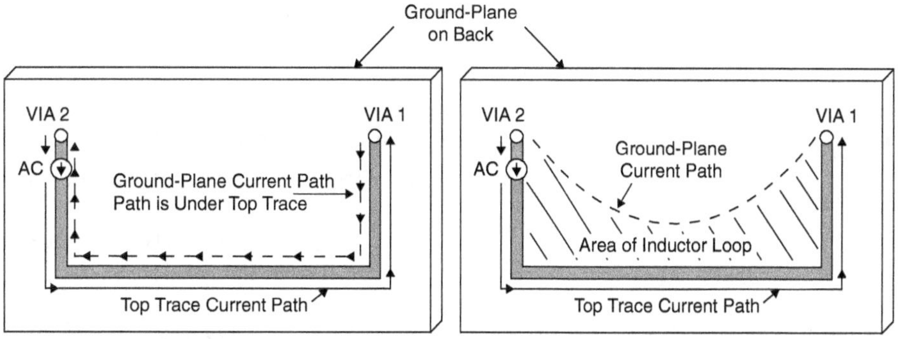

Figure 14.33 AC current path without (left) and with (right) resistance in ground plane

- Connect signal grounds to AC power ground for safety.

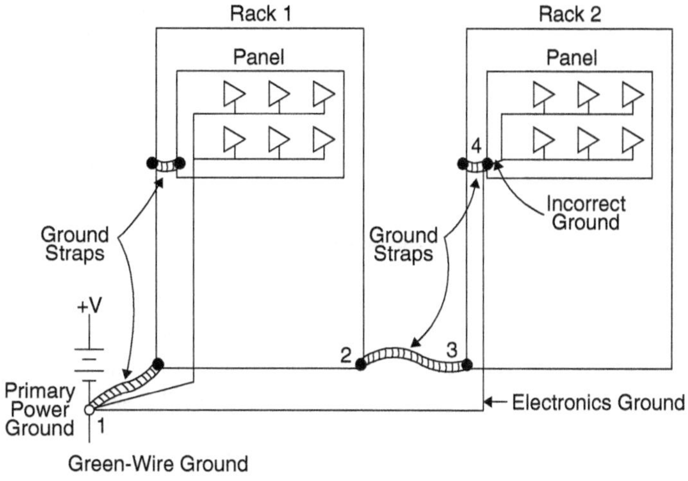

Figure 14.34 Electronic circuits mounted in equipment racks should have separate ground connections. Rack 1 shows correct grounding; Rack 2 shows incorrect grounding.

Power Supply Distribution and Decoupling

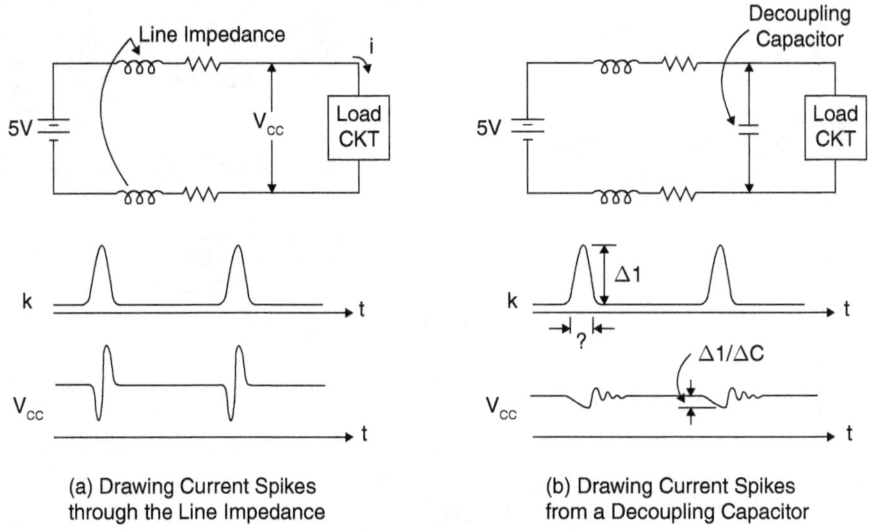

(a) Drawing Current Spikes through the Line Impedance

(b) Drawing Current Spikes from a Decoupling Capacitor

Figure 14.35 Decoupling capacitor reduces current spikes

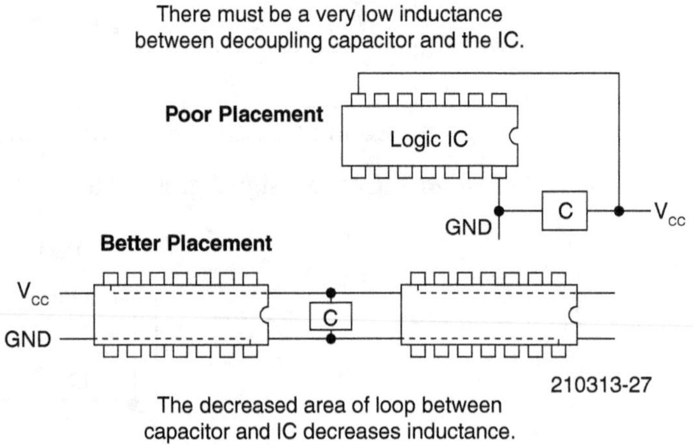

Figure 14.36 Placement of decoupling capacitors

- Use a large decoupling capacitor (usually electrolytic) for the whole PCB.
- Use regulators.
- Use transient suppressors.

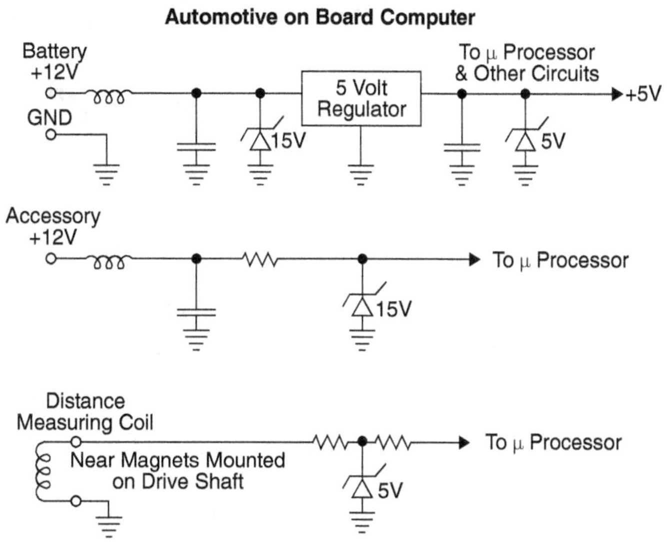

Figure 14.37 Use transient suppressors

- Minimize loop areas to decoupling capacitors.

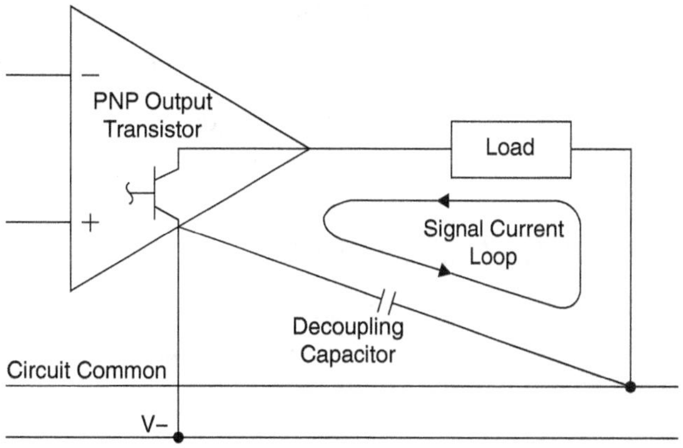

Figure 14.38 Decoupling of negative supply for a grounded load

- Use large tracks for power distribution on PCBs (minimize impedance).

REGULATORY STANDARDS

In the early 1990s, countries in Europe started taking the issue of electromagnetic compatibility seriously as the number of interfering and susceptible devices increased, especially in the automotive and medical environments. The European Union (EU) established numerous standards in the late 1990s that were later adopted by the International Electrotechnical Commission (IEC). These IEC standards form the basis of standards worldwide. The EU enforced EMC-compatibility in 1997 by passing laws barring products from the marketplace that were not compliant with the standards. Products that are compliant are labeled with a "CE marking."

In the United States, EMC compliance is handled by the Federal Communications Commission's "Part 15 – Radio Frequency Devices." Products that conform to the guidelines receive an FCC marking.

EMC compliance markings for Western markets are shown here:

CE marking
EU

FCC marking
USA

Figure 14.39 EMC compliance markings

- EN 55024:1998 *Information technology equipment – Immunity characteristics* – Limits and methods of measurement
- EN 61000-3-2:2000 *Electromagnetic compatibility (EMC) – Part 3-2: Limits* – Limits for harmonic current emissions (equipment input current up to and including 16 A per phase)
- EN 61000-3-3:1995 *Electromagnetic compatibility (EMC) – Part 3-3: Limits* – Limitation of voltage changes, voltage fluctuations and flicker in public low-voltage supply systems, for equipment with rated current ≤16 A per phase and not subject to conditional connection
- FCC Part 15 – *Radio Frequency Devices*

Products that do not comply with local regulations are *illegal* and cannot be placed in that market.

RECOMMENDED REFERENCE

David Cheng, *Fields and Wave Electromagnetics*, Addison-Wesley, 2nd ed. (1989), 4th printing, 1991.

PROBLEMS

14.1 Assuming a two-dimensional potential distribution (at 45°) as shown in Exhibit 14.1, determine the gradient of V at point P with respect to the x-axis.

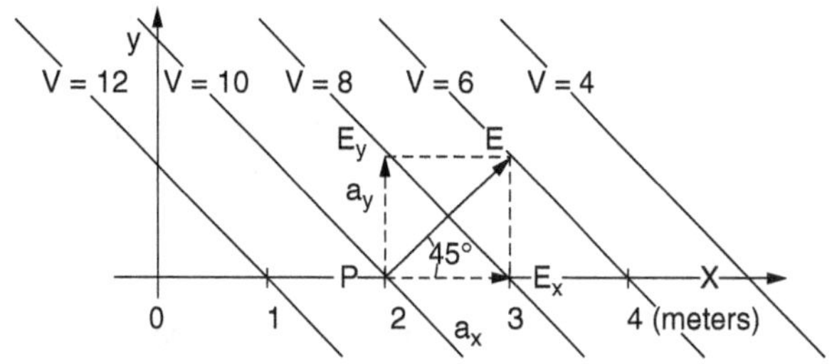

Exhibit 14.1 A plot of the potential distribution in a two-dimension plane

14.2 The potential difference between two points in a static electric field due to a single charge is the same whether the path is the shortest distance between the two points or not, and a test charge moved around a fixed charge in a uniform field and then back to its starting point (i.e., along a closed path) yields a line integral of zero volts. If this same situation exists in a time time-varying magnetic field, what does this line integral equal?

14.3 In the following equation, what does the first integral on the right side of the equation represent?

$$\oint_S (\mathbf{E}\times\mathbf{H})\cdot d\mathbf{s}\times\mathbf{H} = -\left[\int_V \mathbf{J}\cdot\mathbf{E}dv + \frac{\partial}{\partial t}\int_V \frac{1}{2}(\varepsilon E^2 + \mu H^2)dv\right]$$

14.4 An existing transmission line is to be used to connect a voltage source to a resistive load, as shown in Exhibit 14.4. The problem is that the characteristic impedance of the line does not match either the source or the load. Assume the source voltage Vg is 100 V (rms) *with an internal impedance of* 75 Ω, the load RL *is* 100 Ω, and the line is lossless and had a characteristic impedance Z0 = 50 Ω and is 25.0 cm long. The frequency of the source is 300 MHz and the phase velocity U is 300 × 108 m/s. Determine (a) the capacitance and inductance per unit length of line, and (b) the input impedance of the line looking toward the load.

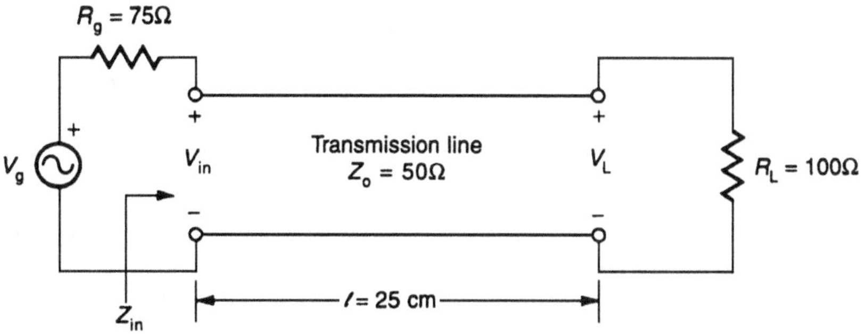

Exhibit 14.4 An unbalanced transmission line with given parameters

14.5 Refer to Problem 14.4 and Exhibit 14.4. Determine (a) the reflection coefficient Γ and (b) the standing-wave ratio (SWR).

SOLUTIONS

14.1 E_x and E_y are both 2 V/m (since the x and y scale are same), with the potential in the decreasing direction. Thus, with reference to Equation (14.3c),

$$\mathrm{E} = -\text{grad } V = -[-\mathbf{a}_x(2) - \mathbf{a}_y(2)] = \sqrt{8}\angle 45° \text{ V/m}$$

14.2 The line integral in the presence of a time varying magnetic field is

$$\oint \mathbf{E}\cdot d\mathbf{l} = -\int_S \frac{\partial \mathbf{B}}{\partial t}\cdot d\mathbf{s}$$

Thus the electromotive force induced in the closed circuit (whether the path is a physical wire or not) is equal to the negative rate of increase of the magnetic flux linkages.

14.3 This equation relates to the Poynting vector. The full right side of the equation relates to the total power flow into a closed surface, whereas only the first integral is the ohmic power dissipated in heat in the volume enclosed by the surface area.

14.4 Formulas for the characteristic impedance, wavelength, reflection coefficient, SWR, and propagation constant of an ideal (lossless) transmission line are given in the *FE Handbook*, and make this kind of problem easy to solve on the test. These concepts are also covered in electromagnetics texts (and even in power-systems texts such as the Glover and Sarma book referred to in Chapter 4, which discusses transmission-line equations).
In general, for complex **Z** and **Y** as per-length quantities,

$$Z_0 = \sqrt{(Z/Y)}$$

which becomes

$$Z_0 = \sqrt{(L/C)}$$

if the line is lossless.
The velocity of propagation $U = \lambda f$ where U is usually taken as the velocity of light, 3×10^8 m/s. Since

$$\beta = 2\pi/\lambda \quad \text{and} \quad \omega = 2\pi f$$

we could show that

$$U = \lambda f = 1/[\sqrt{(LC)}]$$

(a) The capacitance and inductance are easily found from the previous equations, by rearranging and substituting

$$C = 1/(Z_0 U) = 1/[50 \times (3 \times 10^8)] = 66.7 \text{ pF}$$

$$L = Z_0^2\, C = (50)^2 \times (66.7 \times 10^{-12}) = 167 \text{ nH}$$

(b) Since $\lambda = U/f = (3 \times 10^8)/(300 \times 10^6) = 1$ m and $l = 25$ cm $= \lambda/4$ (i.e., a quarter wavelength), this calculation is simplified. For this special quarter-wavelength case,

$$Z_{in} = Z_0^2/R_L = 50^2/100 = 25\,\Omega$$

14.5 The reflection coefficient and the SWR are given as follows

(a) $\Gamma = (R_L - Z_0)/(R_L + Z_0) = (100 - 50)/(100 + 50) = 1/3$

(b) $\text{SWR} = (1 + |\Gamma|)/(1 - |\Gamma|) = [1 + (1/3)]/[1 - (1/3)] = 2$

CHAPTER 15

Control Systems

OUTLINE

This chapter reviews classical control systems theory and provides an introduction to modern control systems (i.e., state variable analysis). In the past, the examination typically included only the former; now, however, questions on state variables may appear as well. In recent years many undergraduate control systems courses have included an introduction to z-transforms, but it is probably unlikely that the examination will include questions on this subject.

CLASSICAL CONTROL SYSTEMS

More than likely, the bulk of the exam questions in the controls area will involve classical control theory, which may include the following topics: block diagram formulation and reduction, linear system stability, system error, second-order system specifications (with higher-ordered systems being approximated by second-order ones), frequency response methods, and system compensation. The background for this material includes a good understanding of Laplace transforms, complex variables, pole-zero maps, and transient response analysis.

Control Systems Design Methodology

The design of control systems follows a step-by-step methodology. The first step involves *obtaining a mathematical model* of the system to be considered. This may involve writing equations based on the laws of physics (e.g., Kirchoff's voltage and current laws, Newton's equations of motion, etc.). It may involve manipulation of subsystems in an overall block diagram. The overall objective of this modeling is to obtain a mathematical representation in either a transfer function or state variable form.

The second step usually involves *system analysis*. This includes time-domain analysis for performance (figures of merit) and frequency-domain analysis (Bode, Nyquist) for stability robustness.

The third step involves *applying the analysis methods* in a way that provides a controller design to meet the desired system specifications. Techniques used for this design process might include Root Locus, Lead/Lag, PID, and model reference designs.

The fourth and final step usually involves *testing* at various levels. Simulation or prototype testing is usually included in this step.

Block Diagrams

The general form of the block diagrams will usually be some variation of Fig. 15.1, where $R(s)$ is the reference (tracking) input, $Y(s)$ is the controlled (plant) output, $U(s)$ is the control (manipulation) signal, and $L(s)$ may be a disturbance (or loading) signal. (The names or labels for these signals may vary.) For a simple, single loop system, the closed loop transfer function equation is easily found by realizing that the numerator(s) are nothing more than the products of the transfer functions in the forward path(s) of the signals from source to output and that the denominator(s) are merely one plus the loop gains (the product of the transfer functions in the loop). If more than one loop exists, then somewhat more formal definitions and techniques are used; the equations are derived from Mason's rules and signal flow graph methods. The equation relating the input(s) to the output relies on the Laplace transforms (rather than time domain relationships), since a *convolution* in the time-domain (calculus) can be replaced with a *product* in the frequency domain (algebra). This simplifies the effort.

The relationship between the inputs R and L and the output Y in Fig. 15.1 is given (dropping the notation involving explicit dependence on (s)) by

$$Y = \frac{G_C G_p}{1 + G_C G_p H} G_F R + \frac{G_p}{1 + G_C G_p H} L \tag{15.1}$$

The denominator $1 + G_c G_p H$, when set equal to zero, defines the poles of the system (i.e., values of s that make the denominator zero) and, of course, is the *characteristic polynomial* of the system. It is clear that if these poles could easily be found, then system stability would be known and further tests, such as the Routh-Hurwitz test or root-locus paths, would be unnecessary. Also note that this characteristic equation is not a function of either R or L, which means that stability for linear systems is independent of the inputs.

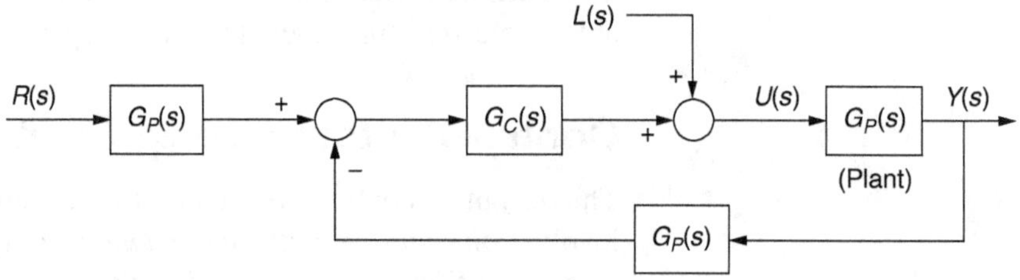

Figure 15.1 A system block diagram with negative feedback

Routh-Hurwitz Criterion for Stability

It is important to have a simple, straightforward test for stability. The *Routh-Hurwitz Criterion* is such a test. It gives information as to whether any poles lie in the right half-plane (RHP) (although it does not give their actual locations). Another technique, the *root locus method*, will give the root location in both planes but is more involved. In each test, we consider an nth order polynomial (usually the characteristic polynomial) of the form

$$a_0 s^n + a_1 s^{n-1} + a_2 s^{n-2} + \dots a_n = 0 \qquad \textbf{(15.2a)}$$

The simplest test, the Routh test, is easy to apply, but does not cover all systems. This test states that all the coefficients a_i must have the same sign (i.e., either all positive or all negative) for the system to be stable. If this is not the case, or if any coefficients are zero, the polynomial definitely has roots outside the left half-plane (LHP). In the event that all the coefficients are the same sign, this test actually has nothing to say. For example, the polynomial $s^3 + 9s^2 + 10s + 200$ has all positive coefficients but actually has a pair of complex poles in the RHP. The Routh test is simple and is often a good screening tool, but generally a stronger test is needed.

For the *Routh-Hurwitz* criterion, one needs only to set up an array from the characteristic polynomial and examine the first column of this array to determine stability. This test can be used for any polynomial, such as the characteristic polynomial. The test involves making an array out of the coefficients a_i, with additionally created new coefficients b_i, as follows.

The first two rows, starting with the highest coefficient a_0, are formed by making the first row of all even values of the a_i (every other value); the second row is made up of the odd coefficients. The next row of b_i is created as shown in Equation (15.2b). The following row of coefficients c_i is also created as shown in Equation (15.2b). The tabulation continues such that the overall number of rows is equal to $n + 1$. Each coefficient is computed from the preceding two rows and involves a determinant of the first column alongside the column immediately to the right of the desired coefficient. At the left of the table, we will run out of coefficients, in which case we may use a 0. The resulting array will taper down to a single coefficient in the s^0 row.

$$\begin{array}{c|cccccc} s^n & a_0 & a_2 & a_4 & a_6 & \cdots & \cdots \\ s^{n-1} & a_1 & a_3 & a_5 & a_7 & \cdots & \\ s^{n-2} & b_1 & b_2 & b_3 & \cdots & & \\ \vdots & \vdots & & & & & \\ s^0 & z_1 & & & & & \end{array} \qquad \textbf{(15.2b)}$$

where

$$b_1 = \frac{-1}{a_1}\begin{vmatrix} a_0 & a_2 \\ a_1 & a_3 \end{vmatrix}, \quad b_2 = \frac{-1}{a_1}\begin{vmatrix} a_0 & a_4 \\ a_1 & a_5 \end{vmatrix}, \dots$$

$$c_1 = \frac{-1}{b_1}\begin{vmatrix} a_1 & a_3 \\ b_1 & b_2 \end{vmatrix}, \quad c_2 = \frac{-1}{b_1}\begin{vmatrix} a_1 & a_5 \\ b_1 & b_3 \end{vmatrix}, \dots$$

$$\vdots \qquad\qquad \vdots$$

$$z_1 = \frac{-1}{y_1}\begin{vmatrix} x_1 & x_2 \\ y_1 & 0 \end{vmatrix}$$

Once this Routh array has been computed, the Routh-Hurwitz criterion may be applied. This states that if all of the coefficients in the first column of the Routh array are the same sign (and nonzero), then all of the roots will be in the LHP. Moreover, if there are differences in sign along the first column, the number of sign changes is equal to the number of roots in the RHP.

Consider the following simple example (refer to Fig. 15.1 with $L(s) = 0$, $H(s) = 1$, $G_F(s) = 1$, $G(s) = G_cG_p(s)$):

$$G_c(s)=\frac{4}{s},\quad G_p(s)=\frac{3s+50}{s^2+9s-2}\Rightarrow G(s)=\frac{4(3s+50)}{s(s^2+9s-2)}$$

Then, the closed-loop system transfer function $G_{cl}(s)$ is given by

$$G_{cl}(s)=\frac{Y(s)}{R(s)}=\frac{G_cG_pG_F}{1+G_cG_pH}=\frac{\left(\frac{4}{s}\right)\left(\frac{3s+50}{s^2+9s-2}\right)(1)}{1+\left(\frac{4}{s}\right)\left(\frac{3s+50}{s^2+9s-2}\right)(1)}=\frac{4(3s+50)}{s^3+9s^2+10s+200}$$

The characteristic polynomial, $s^3 + 9s^2 + 10s + 200$, may be arranged in a Routh array as follows:

$$\begin{array}{c|cc} s^3 & 1 & 10 \\ s^2 & 9 & 200 \\ s^1 & b_1 & b_2 \\ s^0 & c_1 & \end{array}\qquad b_1=\frac{-1}{9}\begin{vmatrix}1 & 10\\ 9 & 200\end{vmatrix}=\frac{-110}{9},\qquad b_2=\frac{-1}{9}\begin{vmatrix}1 & 0\\ 9 & 0\end{vmatrix}=0$$

$$c_1=\frac{-1}{b_1}\begin{vmatrix}9 & 200\\ b_1 & b_2\end{vmatrix}=\frac{-1}{\frac{-110}{9}}\begin{vmatrix}9 & 200\\ \frac{-110}{9} & 0\end{vmatrix}=200$$

Examining the first column of the Routh array, we find the sequence of coefficients 1, 9, $\frac{-110}{9}$, and 200. Since there is a sign change in going from 9 to $\frac{-110}{9}$, and a sign change going from $\frac{-110}{9}$, to 200, we have two sign changes. This implies that there are two roots in the RHP. The remaining root is in the LHP. If we instead have the controller $G_c(s)=\frac{K}{s}$, the closed-loop characteristic polynomial is given by $s^3 + 9s^2 + (3K - 2)s + 50K$. Computing the Routh array, we have

$$\begin{array}{c|cc} s^3 & 1 & 3K-2 \\ s^2 & 9 & 50K \\ s^1 & -\frac{23}{9}K-2_1 & 0 \\ s^0 & 50K & \end{array}\qquad b_1=\frac{-1}{9}\begin{vmatrix}1 & 3K-2\\ 9 & 50K\end{vmatrix}=-\frac{23}{9}K-2$$

$$c_1=\frac{-1}{-\frac{23}{9}K-2}\begin{vmatrix}9 & 50K\\ -\frac{23}{9}K-2 & 0\end{vmatrix}=50K$$

In order for this polynomial to be stable we must have all the coefficients be positive. This means we must have $-\frac{23}{9}K-2>0$ or $K<-\frac{18}{23}$, and $50K > 0$ or $K>0$. Since we cannot have $K>0$ and $K<-\frac{18}{23}$, then we cannot have any value of K such that this polynomial is stable. In this case, we would want to use a different controller for this system.

Standardized Second-Order Systems

Although actual systems are usually of higher order than second-order, the standardized (prototype) response of this kind of system to either a step input or a sinusoidal input is customarily used. The system is given by the transfer function

$$\frac{Y(s)}{R(s)} = \frac{\omega_n^2}{s^2 + 2\zeta\omega_n s + \omega_n^2}$$

where ζ is the *damping ratio*

ω_n is the *(undamped) natural frequency*

This is the simplest system with complex poles, which occur when $0 < \zeta < 1$. Important quantites for this system are given by

$$\omega_r = \omega_{\text{resonant}} = \omega_n\sqrt{1-2\zeta^2} \text{ for } 0<\zeta<\frac{1}{\sqrt{2}}, \text{ the resonant frequency} \quad \textbf{(15.3a)}$$

$$\omega_o = \omega_n\sqrt{1-\zeta^2}, \text{ the oscillatory (ringing) frequency} \quad \textbf{(15.3b)}$$

$$t_p = \frac{\pi}{\omega_n\sqrt{1-\zeta^2}}, \text{ the peak time (time at which the output is at its maximum)} \quad \textbf{(15.3c)}$$

$$M_p = e^{-\pi\zeta/\sqrt{1-\zeta^2}}, \text{ the overshoot} \quad \textbf{(15.3d)}$$

The quantities that describe this response are usually used to describe and approximate higher order ones. A simplification of Fig. 15.1, where $H = 1$, $G_C = 1$, $G_F = 1$, $L(s) = 0$, and the plant $G_p(s) = \frac{K}{s(s+a)}$, results in Fig. 15.2. Note that in Fig. 15.2, $\omega_n^2 = K$ and $\zeta = \frac{a}{2K}$ for the standard second order system.

The *damping ratio* ζ (zeta) is related to whether the system is underdamped ($\zeta < 1$), critically damped ($\zeta = 1$), or overdamped ($\zeta > 1$). Furthermore, by defining the undamped natural frequency as ω_n (the oscillatory frequency if $\zeta = 0$), one may normalize the time axis with this value and generate the standardized response curves for the ideal second-order system. For this simple system and its system transfer function (see Fig. 15.2b), the solutions for step responses are as shown in Fig. 15.3 with normalized notation. This notation normally becomes part of the system specifications, or figures of merit.

The curves for these figures of merit are given for the time solution, thus eliminating the need for computing inverse Laplace transforms. As zeta approaches zero, the undamped step response plot becomes sinusoidal and the time-to-first-peak is π on the normalized time scale. Clearly, for damped sinusoids, the peak will always be a number somewhat larger than 3.14. If one remembers this relationship, it will frequently give a check for an approximate answer on the examination.

As a short example, assume for Fig. 15.2 that $G_p(s) = \frac{25}{s(s+2)}$. Then the closed-loop transfer function is

$$G_{cl}(s) = \frac{25}{s^2 + 2s + 25} = \frac{\omega_n^2}{s^2 + 2\zeta\omega_n + \omega_n^2}$$

Here $\omega_n = 5$, $\zeta = 0.2$, and from the normalized curves, one immediately determines that the percent overshoot is approximately 52% and the peak value occurs at about 3.2 on the normalized time scale (i.e., $\omega_n t_p = 3.2$). Therefore $t_p = \frac{2.3}{\omega_n} = \frac{2.3}{5}$ = 0.64 seconds.

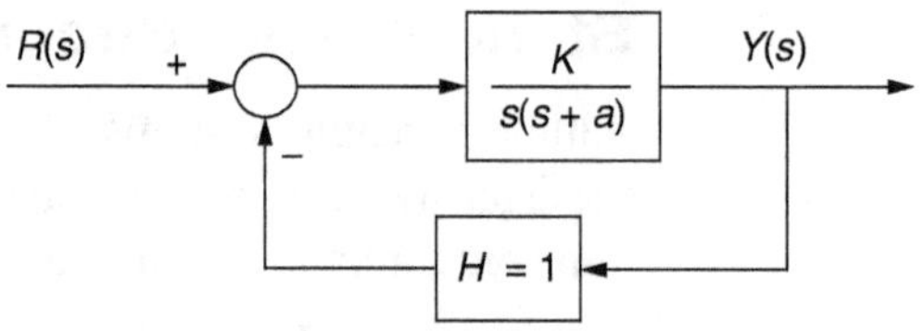

Figure 15.2 An ideal second-order system in feedback form

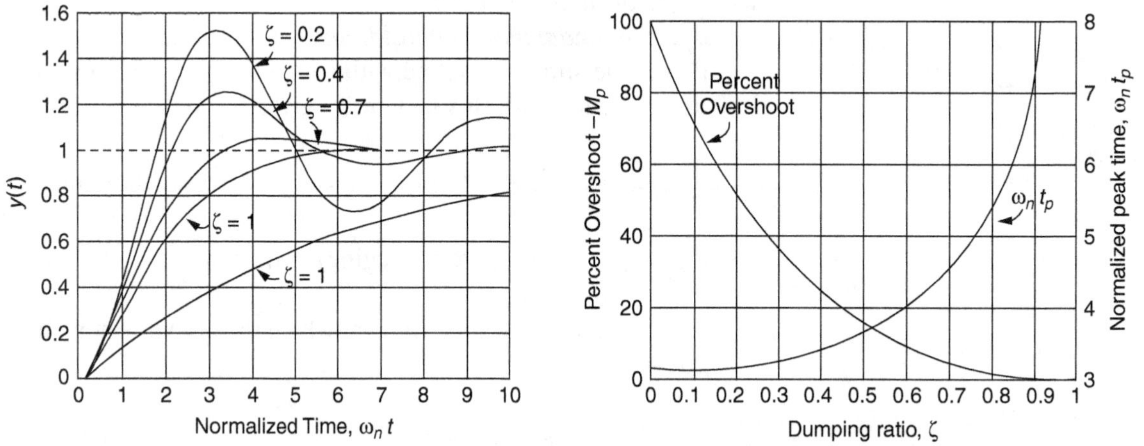

(a) Step Response (b) Percent Overshoot and Peak Time

Figure 15.3 Standardized second-order response curves

Steady-State Gain and System Error

The steady-state gain (or dc gain) and the steady-state error of a system can be found using the final value theorem (FVT) of the Laplace transform. Using the FVT requires that all poles of the system be located in the LHP (i.e., negative real parts). The error is defined to be the difference between the reference input and the output (i.e., $e(t) = r(t) - y(t)$). We usually consider the plant $G_p(s)$, which is applied in the closed-loop setting of Fig. 15.1 (assuming that $L(s) = 0$). By the FVT, $e_{ss} = \lim_{t\to\infty} e(t) = \lim_{s\to 0} sE(s)$, and from Equation 15.1, $E(s) = R(s) - \dfrac{G_cG_pG_F}{1+G_cG_pH}R(s) = \dfrac{1+G_cG_p\left(G_F-H\right)}{1+G_cG_pH}R(s)$. The most common reference input used for testing is a unit step input, which has $R(s) = \frac{1}{s}$. This is essentially a constant (dc) signal. The dc gain K_p for the (open-loop) system is given by Equation (15.4a) and for steady-state error e_{ss}, by Equation 15.4b, where a unit step input is assumed.

$$\text{dc Gain Constant, } K_p = \lim_{s\to 0} G(s) \tag{15.4a}$$

$$K_p = \lim_{s\to 0} G(s) = \lim_{s\to 0} G_F(s)G_c(s)G_p(s) \text{ (open-loop dc gain)}$$

$$\text{System Error } (R-C) = \lim_{s\to 0} s\left(\frac{R(s)}{1+G(s)}\right) \tag{15.4b}$$

$$e_{ss} = \lim_{t\to\infty} e(t) = \lim_{s\to 0} sE(s) = \lim_{s\to 0} s\frac{1+G_cG_p(G_F-H)}{1+G_cG_pH}R(s) = \lim_{s\to 0}\frac{1+G_cG_p(G_F-H)}{1+G_cG_pH}$$

Bode Plots

Characterization of electronic systems in the frequency domain is directly related to time-domain system response. The response of a linear time-invariant system, $x_o(t)$, to an arbitrary input, $x_i(t)$, can be characterized in the time-domain by its impulse response, h(t):

$$x_o(t) = \int_0^t h(t-\tau)x_i(\tau)\,d\tau \tag{15.5}$$

While the convolution integral of Equation 15.5 has great utility in many situations[1], a frequency-domain characterization of the system is more typical. The frequency-domain response of a system can be obtained by taking the Fourier Transform of the output quantity, $x_o(t)$:

$$x_o(\omega) = F\{x_o(t)\} = \int_{-\infty}^{\infty} x_o(t)e^{-j\omega t}\,dt \tag{15.6}$$

which reduces to

$$x_o(\omega) = H(\omega)\,x_i(\omega). \tag{15.7}$$

The spectrum of the output quantity, $x_o(\omega)$, is the product of the input quantity spectrum, $x_i(\omega)$, and the transfer function of the system, $H(\omega)$. The impulse response and the transfer function of a system are related by the Fourier Transform:

$$H(\omega) = F\{h(t)\}. \tag{15.8}$$

This frequency-domain transfer function is characterized by its two parts:

- $|H(\omega)|$ — the magnitude response, and
- $\angle H(\omega)$ — the phase response.

One of the most useful representations of these two quantities is a pair of plots. The typical format for these plots is the magnitude (on either a linear or a decibel scale) or the phase (in either degrees or radians) as the ordinate and frequency (on a logarithmic scale) as the abscissa. While many computer simulation programs exist for the efficient creation of such plots, much insight into the functioning of a filter (or any electronic circuit), and the dependence of the responses to circuit parameter variation, can be gained by the manual creation of simple straight-line approximations to these magnitude and phase plots. Plots of the magnitude of the transfer function, in decibels, and the phase of the transfer function are called *Bode plots.*[2] The two plots together form a *Bode diagram.*

Mathematical Derivations

The response of a linear system to sinusoidal inputs can be described as the ratio of two polynomials in frequency, ω:

$$H(\omega) = K_o \frac{Z_m(\omega)}{P_n(\omega)}. \tag{15.9}$$

---

1 Time-domain characteristics of electronic circuits and the relationship of these characteristics to the frequency-domain characteristics are discussed in Chapters 10 through 13.

2 Named for H. W. Bode. One early reference is his book *Network Analysis and Feedback Design*, Van Nostrand, New York, 1945.

Where $Z_m(\omega)$ is a mth order polynomial whose roots identify the m zeroes of the response. The roots of $P_n(\omega)$ identify the n poles. For all real electronic systems, the response must not increase as frequency becomes infinite; thus the number of poles must be equal to or larger than the number of zeroes, $n \geq m$. Equation 15.9 can be expanded to be of the form:

$$\mathrm{H}(\omega) = K_o \frac{1 + (j\omega)a_1 + (j\omega)^2 a_2 + \ldots + (j\omega)^m a_m}{1 + (j\omega)b_1 + (j\omega)^2 b_2 + \ldots + (j\omega)^n b_n} \qquad \textbf{(15.10)}$$

Each of the two polynomials, $P_n(\omega)$ and $Z_m(\omega)$, can be written as a factored product of multiples of four types of simple function, hereafter identified as *factors*, $\{\mathrm{F}(\omega)\}$:

1. K_o — a constant
2. $j\omega$ — a root at the origin
3. $1 + \dfrac{j\omega}{\omega_o}$ — a simple root at $\omega = \omega_o$
4. $1 + 2\zeta\dfrac{j\omega}{\omega_o} + \left(\dfrac{j\omega}{\omega_o}\right)^2$ — a complex conjugate root pair

Each of these four simple functions has a straight-line approximate Bode representation. The use of decibels (a logarithmic function) as a vertical scale for the magnitude plot and a linear scale for phase converts the product of the factors into the *sum* of the factor magnitudes (in dB) and the *sum* of the factor phases. Therefore, the total system response plot becomes the sum of the plots of the individual simple factors.

Bode Plots of the Factors:

The Bode straight-line approximate representation of each of the four simple factors is unique. The representations for a constant and a root at zero frequency are exact: the other two representations are less accurate. A discussion of each Bode representation follows, and a summary can be found in Figure 15.4.

A constant The most simple of the factors is a constant.

$$\mathrm{F}(\omega) = K_o \qquad \textbf{(15.11)}$$

Here the magnitude is constant at $20 \log |K_o|$. The phase plot is also constant at $\theta = 0°$ or $\theta = 180°$ depending on the mathematical sign of K_o.

A pole or zero at zero frequency A pole or zero at the origin also has a simple Bode representation. The factor is of the form:

$$\mathrm{F}(\omega) = j\omega \qquad \textbf{(15.12)}$$

The magnitude plot is a straight line on a logarithmic frequency scale:

$$|\mathrm{F}(\omega)|\mathrm{dB} = 20 \log |j\omega| = 20 \log(\omega) \qquad \textbf{(15.13)}$$

If the factor is in the numerator (indicating a zero), this straight line has a slope of +20 dB/decade:[3] denominator factors (poles) have a slope of –20 dB/decade. In each case, the line passes through the point {0 dB, 1 rad/s}.

The factor phase is constant at $\theta = 90°$ (or π radians). Consequently the phase plot for zeroes will be at +90° and at –90° for poles.

A simple pole or zero Single poles and zeroes not at the origin have more complex plots. The factor form for a simple pole is:

$$F(\omega) = 1 + \frac{j\omega}{\omega_o}, \tag{15.14}$$

where ω_o is the pole (zero) frequency. The magnitude of the factor is given by:

$$|F(\omega)|_{dB} = 20 \log \sqrt{1 + \left(\frac{\omega}{\omega_o}\right)^2} = 10 \log\left|1 + \left(\frac{\omega}{\omega_o}\right)^2\right|. \tag{15.15}$$

The phase is given by:

$$\angle F(\omega) = \tan^{-1}\left(\frac{\omega}{\omega_o}\right) \tag{15.16}$$

These two components of the simple factor are shown in Figure 15.4 as if the factor were in the denominator (representing a pole). Also shown in the figure are the Bode straight-line approximate plots.

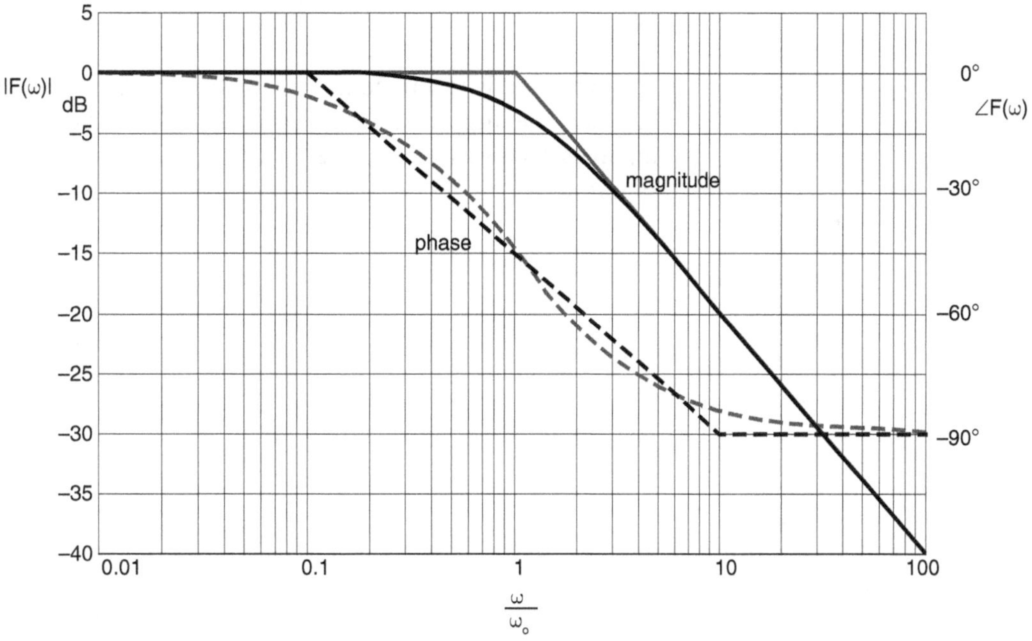

Figure 15.4 A Simple Pole Bode Diagram

3 A decade is a change in frequency by a factor of ten (10). A slope of 20 dB/decade is also identified in some sources as 6 dB/octave, where an octave is a frequency change by a factor of two (2).

The Bode plot of the magnitude is an asymptotic approximation. If $\omega \langle\langle \omega_o$, $F(\omega) \approx 1$ and the magnitude plot is constant at 0 dB. If $\omega \rangle\rangle \omega_o$,

$$|F(\omega)|_{dB} \approx 20\log\sqrt{\left(\frac{\omega}{\omega_o}\right)^2} = 20\log(\omega) - 20\log(\omega_o) \qquad \textbf{(15.17)}$$

This approximation is a straight line with slope of 20 dB/decade that intersects the 0 dB line at $\omega = \omega_o$. The approximation has its greatest error (~3 dB) at $\omega = \omega_o$.

As can be seen in Figure 15.4, the factor phase never exceeds 90° and essentially all phase change takes place within ± one decade of ω_o. Beyond one decade the phase is approximated by a constant:

$$\omega < 0.1\,\omega_o \quad \text{--}\ \angle F(\omega) = 0^\circ$$
$$\omega > 10\,\omega_o \quad \text{--}\ \angle F(\omega) = 90^\circ$$

Within ± decade of ω_o, the phase can be approximated by a straight line of slope 45°/ decade:

$$0.1\,\omega_o < \omega < 10\,\omega_o \quad \text{--}\ \angle F(\omega) = 45^\circ\{\log(10\omega/\omega_o)\}$$

This straight-line Bode approximation has a maximum error of ~5.7°.

Complex conjugate pole or zero pairs A complex conjugate root pair presents a more complex relationship. The appropriate form of the factor is given by:

$$F(\omega) = 1 + 2\zeta\frac{j\omega}{\omega_o} + \left(\frac{j\omega}{\omega_o}\right)^2 \qquad \textbf{(15.18)}$$

Where ω_o is identified as the resonant frequency and ζ is the damping factor.[4] A plot of the magnitude and phase response for a complex pair of poles with the damping factor as a parameter ($0.2 \leq \zeta \leq 0.9$ in increments of 0.1) is shown in Figure 15.4.

4 The damping factor lies in the range, $0 \leq \zeta < 1$, for complex conjugate root pairs.

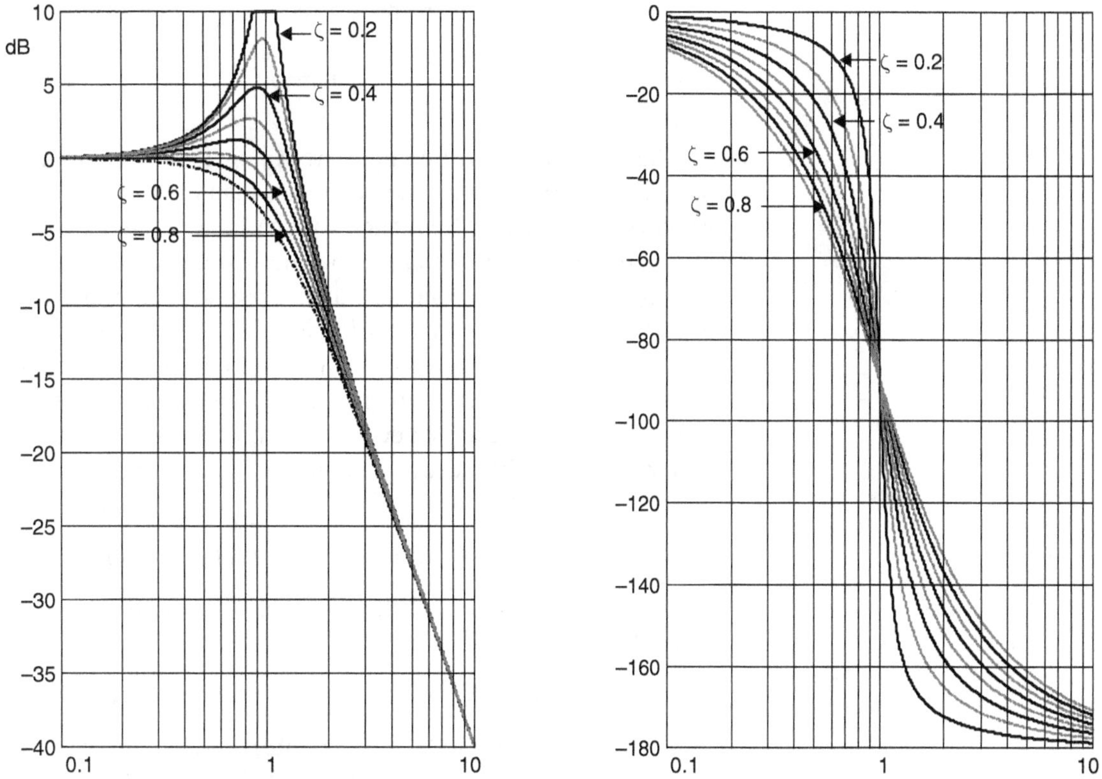

(a) (b)

Figure 15.5 Complex Conjugate Pair Pole Frequency Response
(a) Magnitude, (b) Phase

The variation of the plot with damping coefficient makes straight-line approximations near the resonant frequency questionable. Still, at about a third of a decade or larger from the resonant frequency, reasonable approximations of the magnitude plot can be made. Once again, if $\omega \langle\langle \omega_o$, $F(\omega) \approx 1$ and the approximate magnitude plot is constant at 0 dB. If $\omega \rangle\rangle \omega_o$,

$$\left|F(\omega)\right|_{dB} \approx 20\log\left|\left(\frac{j\omega}{\omega_0}\right)^2\right| = 40\log\omega - 40\log\omega_o \qquad \textbf{(15.19)}$$

In this region the magnitude has a slope of 40 dB/decade with an intercept of the 0 dB axis at $\omega = \omega_o$. Near the resonant frequency, there can be a large difference between the approximate Bode magnitude plot and the true magnitude plot. Depending on the application, corrections to the curve may be necessary. These corrections can usually be accomplished with the addition of only a few data points and judicial interpolation. While calculation of a variety of points is possible, two significant data points are the peak magnitude of the "bump" in the curve (if one exists) and the magnitude at the resonant frequency. For damping coefficients less than $1\sqrt{2}$, a peak in the magnitude response occurs at

$$\omega_{peak} = \omega_o\sqrt{1-2\zeta^2}, \qquad \textbf{(15.20)}$$

that has value (on a linear scale),

$$\left|F(\omega_{peak})\right| = \frac{1}{2\zeta\sqrt{1-\zeta^2}}. \qquad \textbf{(15.21)}$$

The magnitude at the resonant frequency is given by:

$$|F(\omega_o)| = \frac{1}{2\zeta}. \tag{15.22}$$

The phase plot for a complex root pair is also complicated by the damping coefficient. At frequencies much smaller than the resonant frequency, the phase is near-constant at 0°. At frequencies much larger than ω_0, the phase is about 180°. Near ω_0 the Bode approximate curve must be a straight line. There are two reasonable approximations: a ζ-independent approximation and an approximation that depends on ζ. Either approximation is valid in most applications.[5]

The most simple Bode approximation to the phase plot ignores the variation of the true phase plots with the damping coefficient, ζ. In this ζ-independent approximation, the Bode phase plot consists of three straight lines. More than one decade from the resonant frequency, the approximate phase is constant:

$$\omega < 0.1\,\omega_0 \quad \text{--}\ \angle F(\omega) = 0°$$
$$\omega > 10\,\omega_0 \quad \text{--}\ \angle F(\omega) = 180°$$

Within ± decade of ω_0, the phase can be approximated by a straight line of slope 90°/ decade:

$$0.1\,\omega_0 < \omega < 10\,\omega_0 \quad \text{--}\ \angle F(\omega) = 90°\{log(10\omega/\omega_0)\}$$

The ζ-dependent Bode phase approximation follows the variation in phase with damping coefficient and keeps the three straight lines approach changing the frequency ranges and the slope near the resonant frequency. The constant phase regions are a function of ζ and are described as:

$$\omega < \omega_0/10\zeta \quad \text{--}\ \angle F(\omega) = 0°$$
$$\omega > 10\zeta\,\omega_0 \quad \text{--}\ \angle F(\omega) = 180°$$

The phase between the two constant phase regions is approximated by a straight line of slope (90/ζ)°/decade passing through the point ω_0, 90°:

$$\omega_0/10\zeta < \omega < 10\zeta\,\omega_0 \text{ -- } \angle F(\omega) = \frac{90°}{\zeta}\left(\log\left(\frac{\omega}{\omega_o}\right)\right) + 90°$$

Figure 15.5 shows the ζ-dependent Bode phase approximation for two values of ζ along with the actual phase plots and the ζ-independent Bode phase approximation.

5 The authors prefer the ζ-**dependent** approximation since it has less phase error and reduces to the more simple case for ζ = 1. The ζ-independent approximation has wide usage due to its more easily constructed format.

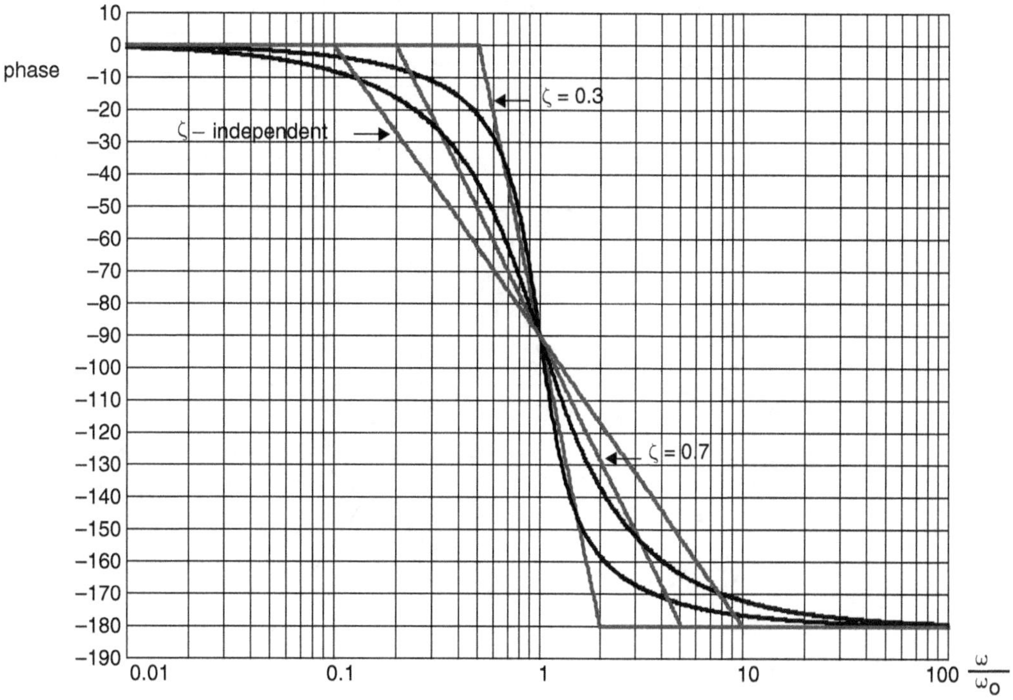

Figure 15.6 The ζ-Dependent Bode Phase Approximation

The Bode approximate plots for each of the four factors are summarized in Table 15.1 as if the factors are in the denominator. Factors in the numerator will have *positive* slopes and mathematical signs but otherwise be similar in shape. Total Bode plots are the sum of the plots of the factors.

Table 15.1 Bode Factor Magnitude and Phase Plots (factors in denominator)

Factor	Bode Magnitude Plot	Bode Phase Plot
K_o	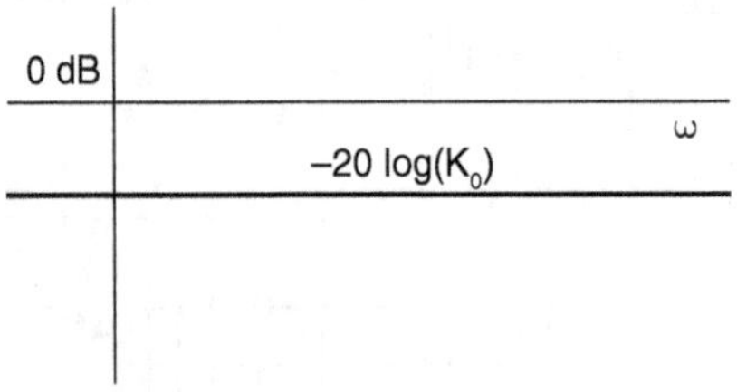	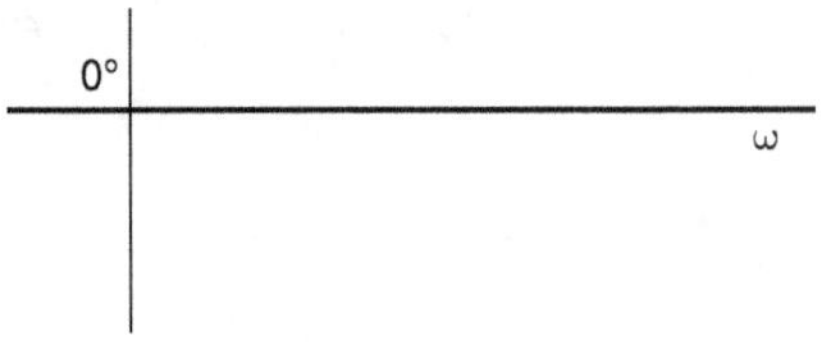
$j\omega$	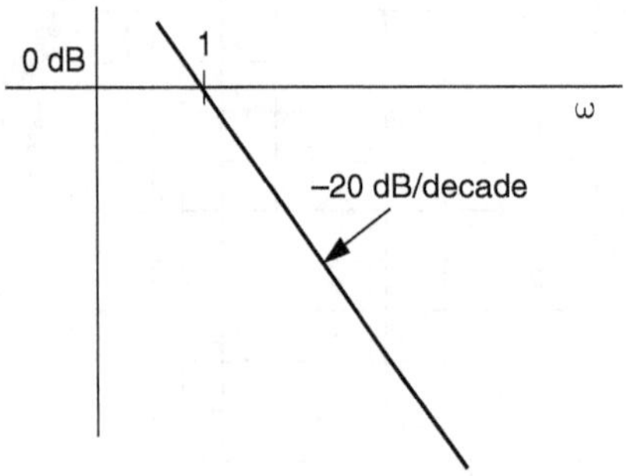	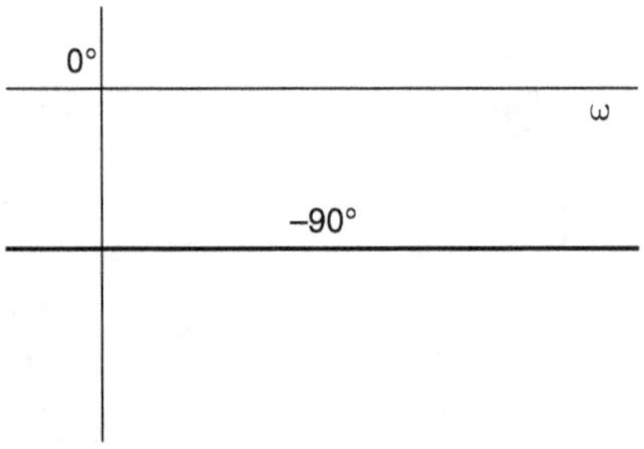
$1+\dfrac{j\omega}{\omega_o}$	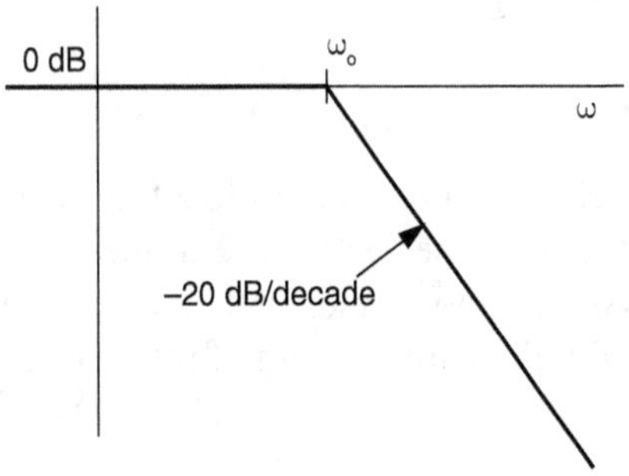	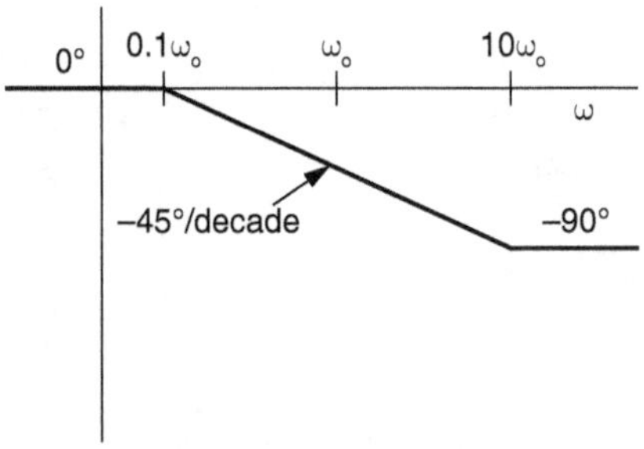
$1+2\zeta\dfrac{j\omega}{\omega_o}+\left(\dfrac{j\omega}{\omega_o}\right)^2$	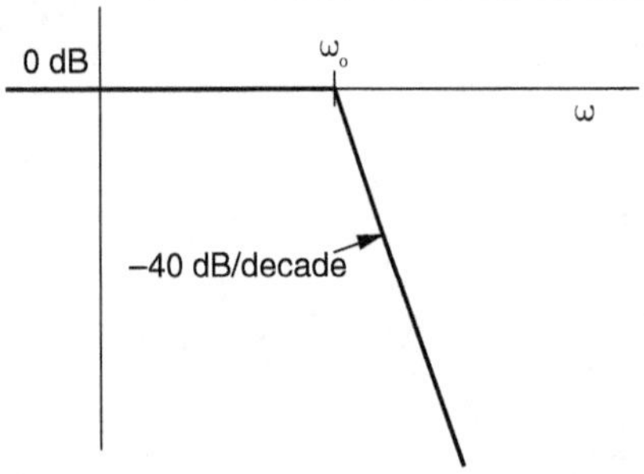	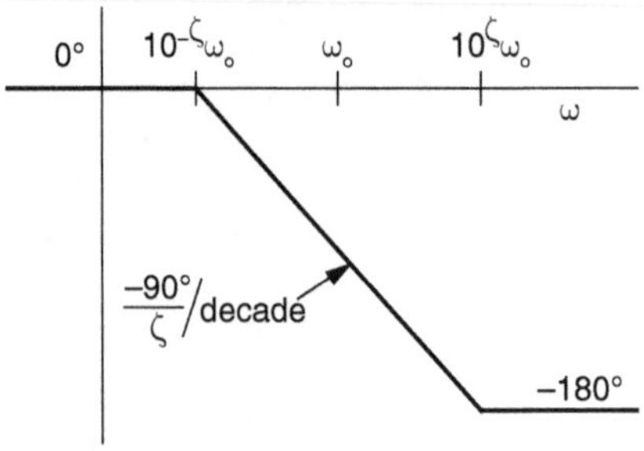

System Compensation

A basic, properly designed system should meet its design specifications (figures of merit) and the basic requirement of stability. A typical approach to control system design is to begin working with the simplest types of controllers and moving to more complex controllers if the simple ones do not suffice. In the design process, the root locus technique is typically used, though it is not usually tested on in the FE exam. Instead, general questions about various types of controllers may be asked, each relating to the relative merits of each type.

Of the several methods possible for questioning, the two most common are PID compensation and lead or lag networks. A simple closed loop control system consisting of a controller and a process (or plant) is shown in Figure 15.7.

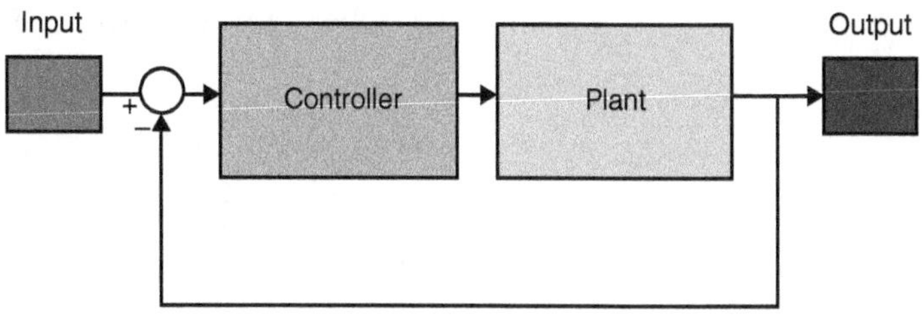

Figure 15.7

The input to the system is the "setpoint" (i.e., the desired output). The input to the controller is the error where

error = present output – setpoint.

The two steps in the design of a control system are the following:

1. Mathematically model the plant to be controlled.
2. Design the controller.

The block diagram of a PID controller in the time domain is shown in Figure 15.8.

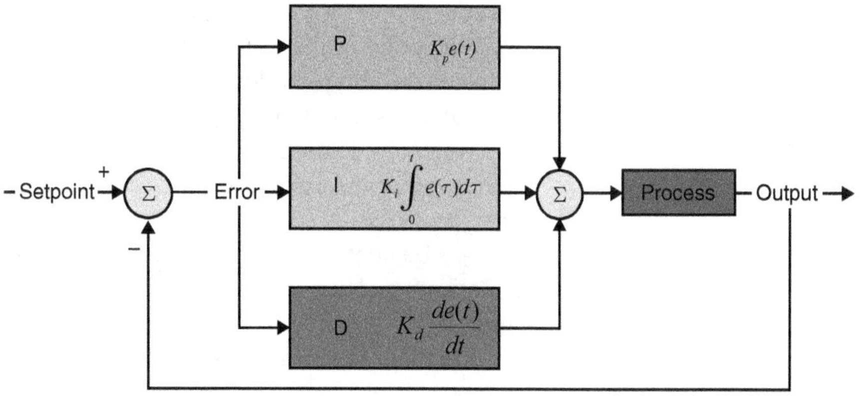

Figure 15.8

Taking the Laplace transform of the terms for Proportional (P), Integral (I), and Derivative (D) gains are:

Proportional Gain: $G_p = K_p$

Integral Gain: $G_i = K_p(\frac{1}{\tau_i s}) = K_i$

Derivative Gain: $G_d = K_p(\tau_d s) = K_d$

and the Controller Gain term in the frequency domain is

$$G_c = G_p + G_i + G_d = K_p\left[1+\left(\frac{1}{\tau_i s}\right)+\tau_d s\right]$$

For a PID Compensator/Controller, the PID gain is:

$$G_c = K_p\left(1+\frac{1}{\tau_i s}+\tau_d s\right) \quad \textbf{(15.23a)}$$

The controller gain terms for lead and lag compensation are

$$G_c = \left(\frac{1+sT_1}{1+sT_2}\right), \text{ with } T_1 > T_2 \text{ for lead, and } T_1 < T_2 \text{ for lag}$$

$$G_c(s) = \frac{1+\tau_1 s}{1+\tau_2 s}, \text{ with } \tau_1 > \tau_2 \text{ for lead, and } \tau_1 < \tau_2 \text{ for lag} \quad \textbf{(15.23b)}$$

These controllers (sometimes called *compensators*) place poles and zeros at strategic locations. If one were to use just the PD controller ($\tau_i \to \infty$), it would place a zero at $s = \frac{-1}{\tau_d}$, whereas a PI controller ($\tau_d = 0$) would place a pole at $s = 0$ and a zero at $s = \frac{-1}{\tau_i}$. In general, a properly designed PD controller tends to cut down on system overshoot and shorten the time-to-first-peak. On the other hand, a simple PI controller reduces the steady-state error. The difficulty with adding the pole at $s = 0$ is that stabilizing the system is more difficult. Using all three terms, the PID can effectively control a wide range of systems and is thus the most commonly used controller type.

The lead/lag controller is not as difficult to design as the PID. This controller adds a pole and a zero. The lead controller places the zero closer to the origin than the pole (in the LHP). The effect of this is to reduce overshoot and t_p and to enhance stability. The lead controller tends to decrease system error but may give greater overshoot and t_p. Questions on the examination relating to these controllers (often implemented by simple networks) would probably be limited to general trends rather than actual calculations because of the time-intensive nature of the design process.

A PID controller consists of a Proportional element, an Integral element, and a Derivative element, all three connected in parallel. All of them take the error as input. K_p, K_i, K_d are the gains of P, I, and D elements, respectively.

Let the transfer function of the plant be

$$\frac{1}{s^2 + 20s + 30}$$

The step response of a system is the output of the system when the input to the system is a unit step. The open loop step response of the above plant is:

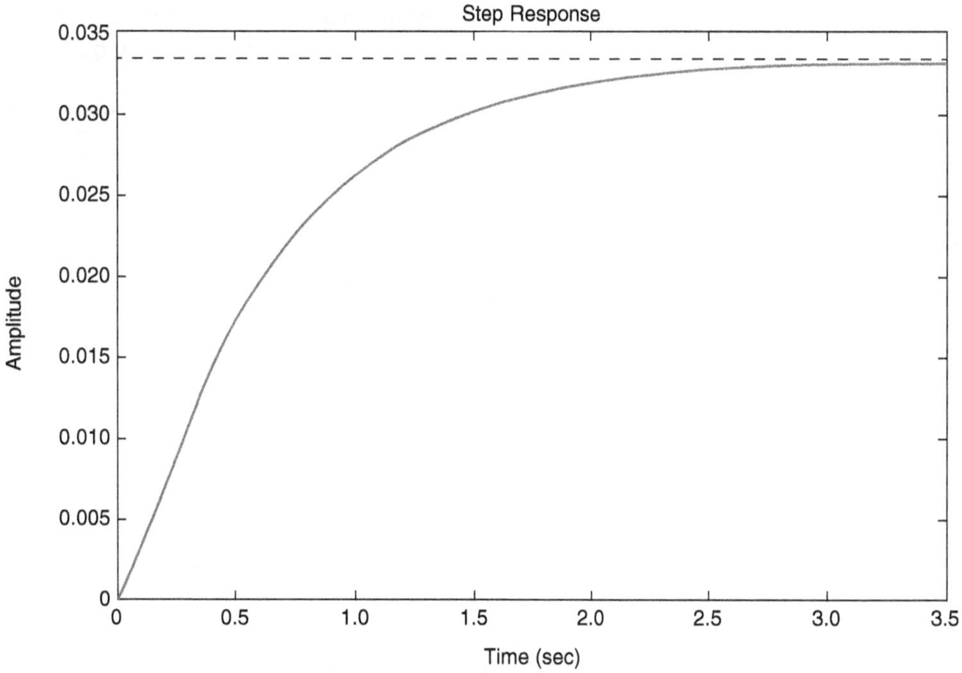

Figure 15.9

The step response output settles close to 0.035. The steady state error is therefore equal to

$$1.0 - 0.035 = 0.965.$$

This error is high. The settling time is around three seconds.

Applying the gain proportional element on the system output, $K_p = 10$, $K_i = 0$, $K_d = 0$, the step response of the system is:

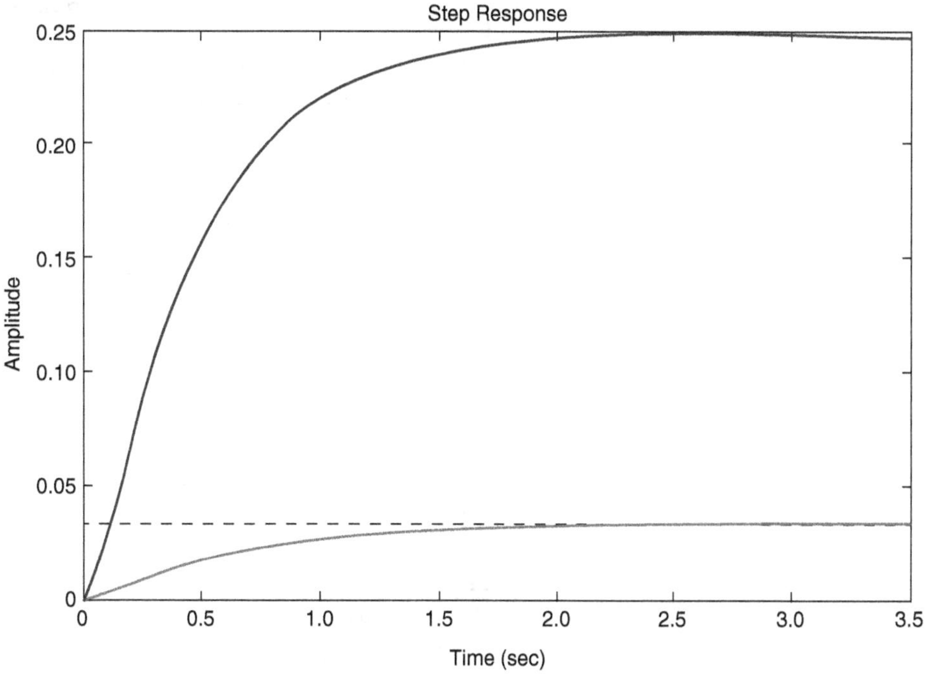

Figure 15.10

The output is now 0.25 yielding a better response than the open loop response.

Increasing the proportional gain to $K_p = 100$, $K_i = 0$, $K_d = 0$, the step response of the system is yields a response shown by Figure 15.11.

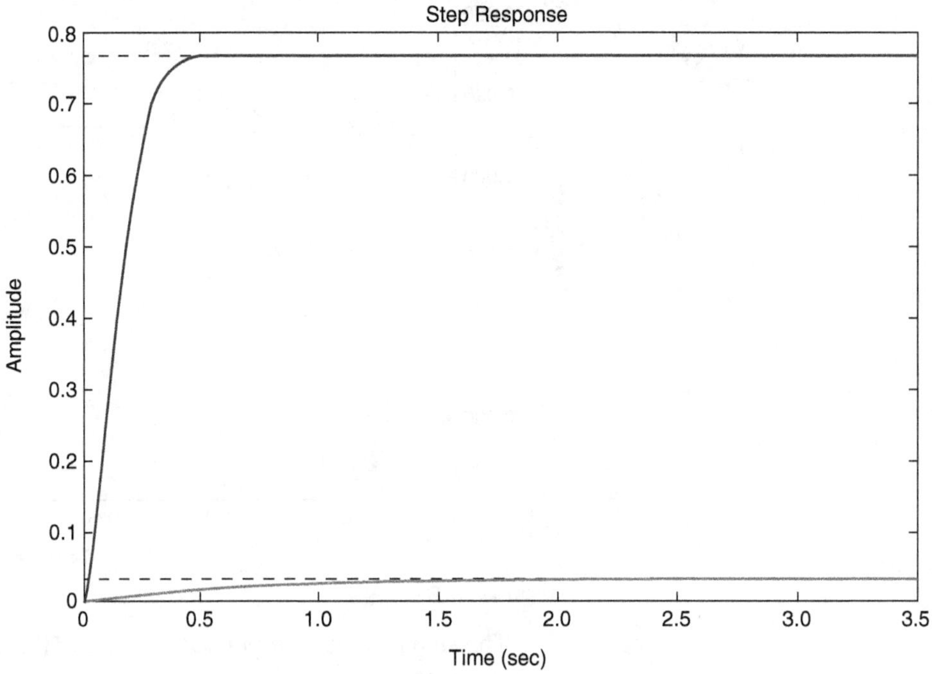

Figure 15.11

The steady state output is now 0.77. It is clear that increasing K_p will reduce the steady state error.

Increasing K_p further to $K_p = 200$, $K_i = 0$, $K_d = 0$, the step response of the system is

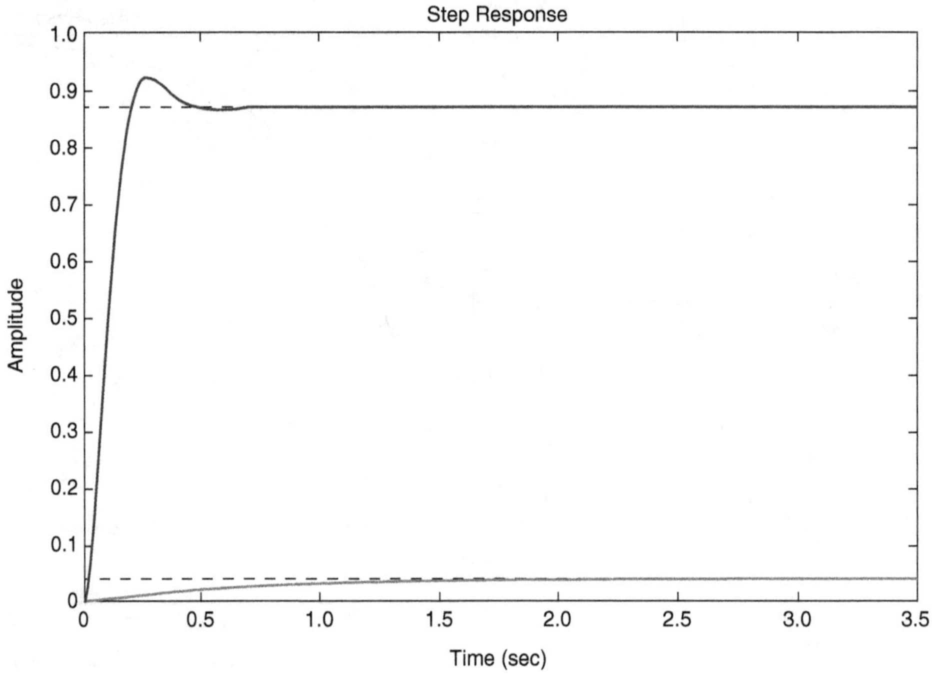

Figure 15.12

The steady state output is 0.87. At this gain, ripple is exhibited in the output. If K_p is increased further, it will only lead to an increase in ripple or overshoot. The rise time also has decreased. Also observe that there is a small steady state error $(1 - 0.87 = 0.13)$.

The conclusion is that increasing K_p will reduce the steady state error. However, continually increasing K_p will increase overshoot. Also K_p reduces rise time.

Keeping the last proportional gain, increase the integral gain term to $K_p = 200$, $K_i = 10$, $K_d = 0$. The resulting step response of the system is shown in Figure 15.13.

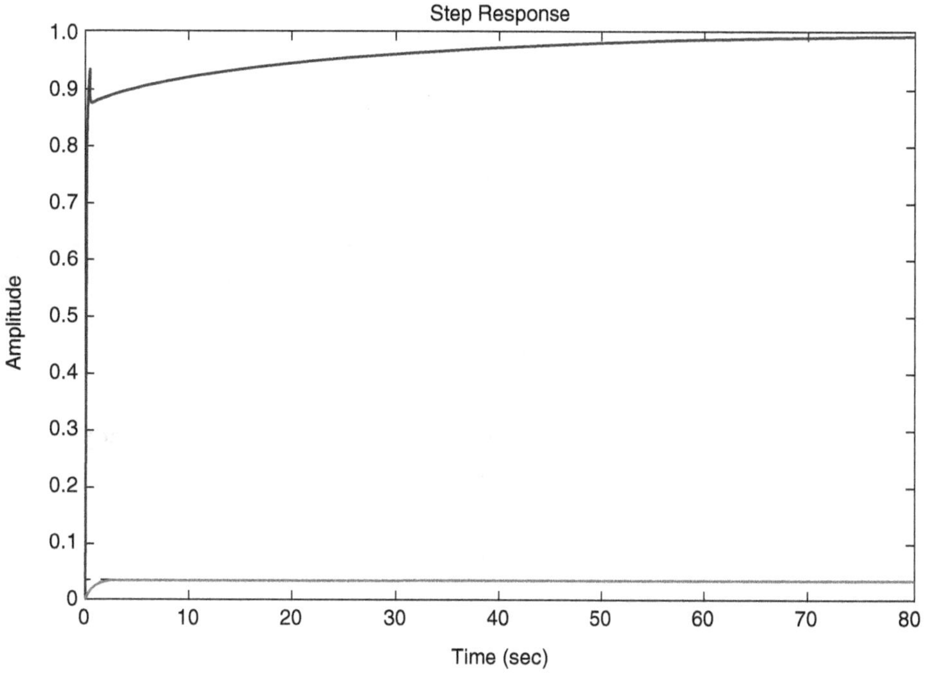

Figure 15.13

The steady state output is now close to 0.99. That's very close to the setpoint. However, the settling time has increased.

Increasing the integral gain term, so that $K_p = 200$, $K_i = 200$, $K_d = 0$, the step response of the system shows that the rise time is reduced, and the steady state error is minimized as shown in Figure 15.14.

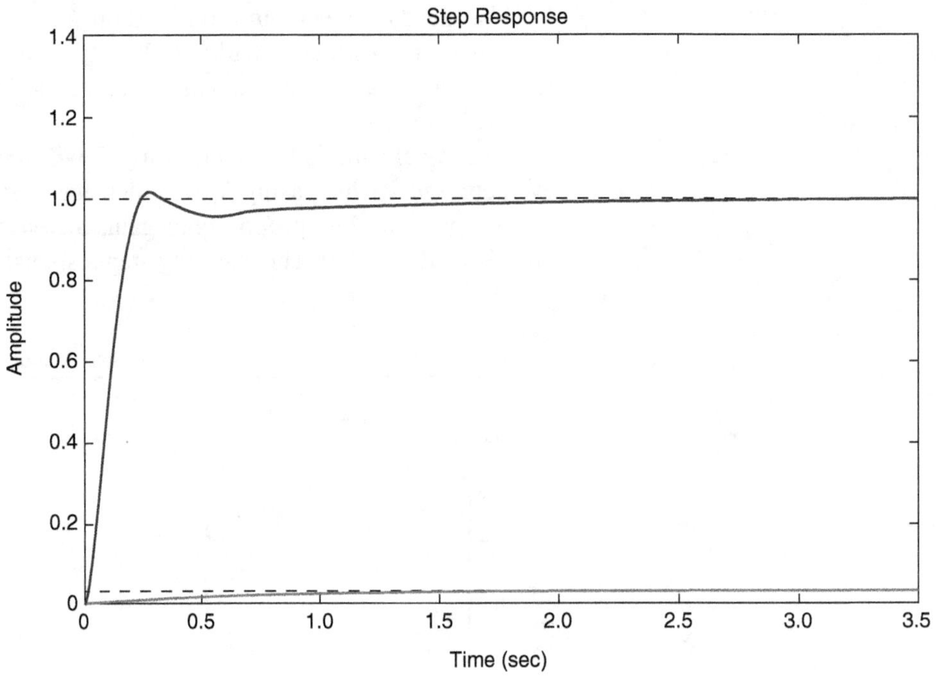

Figure 15.14

Increasing the integral gain further, $K_p = 200$, $K_i = 300$, $K_d = 0$, the step response of the system exhibits a steady state error of nearly zero as shown in Figure 15.15.

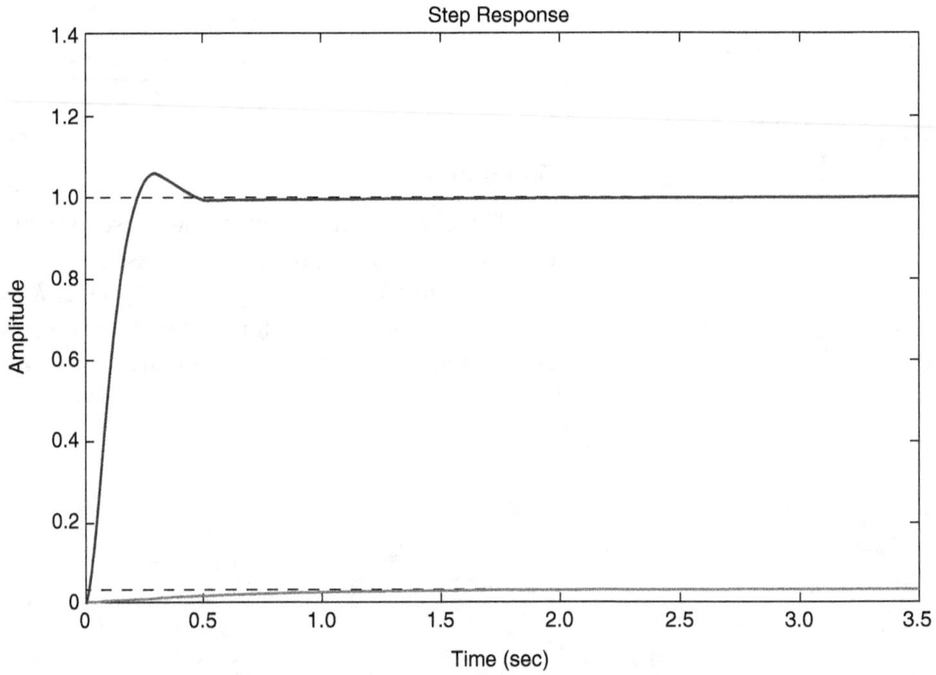

Figure 15.15

However, increasing K_i has resulted in overshoot. Further increasing K_i will result in increased overshoot.

Therefore, K_i eliminates the steady state error. However, continually increasing K_i results in increased overshoot. K_i reduces rise time.

Varying the derivative gain term so that $K_p = 200$, $K_i = 300$, $K_d = 10$ results in the response shown in Figure 15.16.

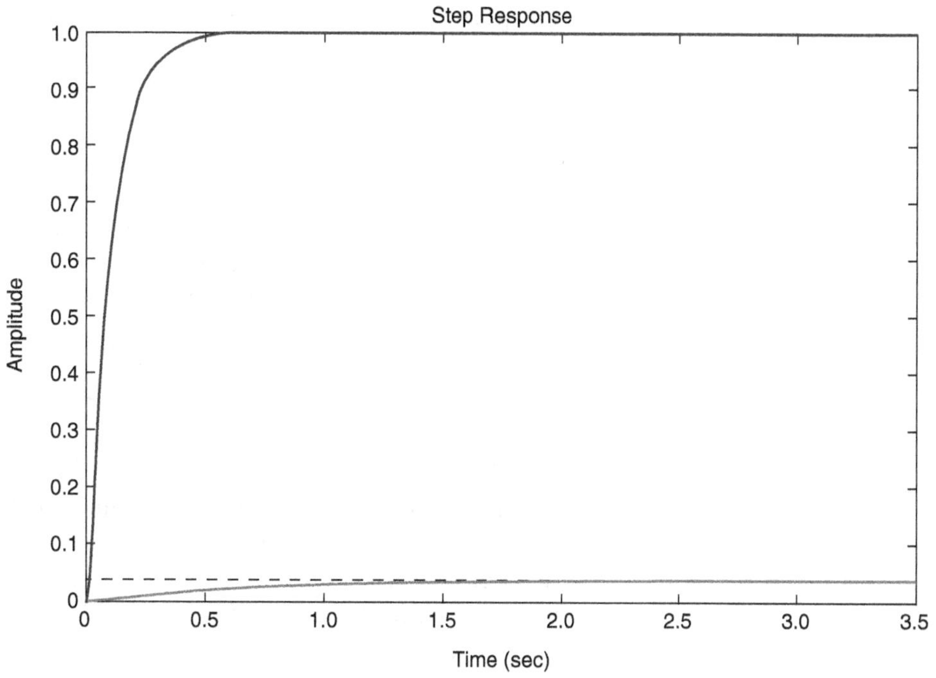

Figure 15.16

The overshoot has been eliminated. The settling time is also decreased. It is shown that K_d decreases the overshoot and reduces settling time.

So the resulting PID values for our plant are $K_p = 200$, $K_i = 300$, and $K_d = 10$. The previous process is known as manual tuning of PID.

STATE VARIABLES

A state-variable (or state-space) description of a system is a description in which the state of the system at any time is succinctly captured in a set of variables. This is an important way to represent a system because many systems naturally yield state-space descriptions. For example, in RLC networks, the natural state variables are inductor currents and capacitor voltages. In mechanical systems, the natural state variables are positions and velocities.

The state variable description for a linear, time-invariant system is generally of the form

$$\dot{x}(t) = Ax(t) + Bu(t), \text{ (state equation)} \qquad \textbf{(15.24a)}$$

$$y(t) = Cx(t) + Du(t), \text{ (output equation)} \qquad \textbf{(15.24b)}$$

where

$x(t)$ is the state of the system at time t and is an $n \times 1$ vector
$u(t)$ is the input (forcing, or control) vector of dimension $m \times 1$
$y(t)$ is the output of the system and is of dimension $p \times 1$

This is a first-order matrix differential equation and may have a nonzero initial condition $x(0)$. When $p = m = 1$, the system is called a *single-input, single-output (SISO) system.* Otherwise it is called a *multi-input, multi-output (MIMO) system.* The general solution to this matrix differential equation is given by

$$x(t) = e^{At}x(0) + \int_0^t e^{A(t-\tau)}Bu(\tau)d\tau$$

$$y(t) = Ce^{At}x(0) + \int_0^t Ce^{A(t-\tau)}Bu(\tau)d\tau + Du(t)$$

It is possible to convert from one representation to another, from a state-space form to a transfer-function form. For example, if you are given the transfer function that follows, you may wish to work with a state-model.

$$G_p(s) = \frac{b_{n-1}s^{n-1} + \cdots + b_1 s + b_0}{s^n + a_{n-1}s^{n-1} + \cdots + a_1 s + a_0}$$

Since the transfer function describes only the input and output behavior of the system, whereas the state model actually details an interior set of coordinates, there are actually an infinite number of state model coordinates for a given transfer function. Thus, a number of *canonical* (standard) forms have been derived. One of the most common is called the *controllable* (or *phase-variable*) *canonical form.* In this form, we have the matrices

$$A = \begin{bmatrix} 0 & 1 & 0 & \cdots & 0 \\ 0 & 0 & 1 & \ddots & \vdots \\ \vdots & \vdots & \ddots & \ddots & 0 \\ 0 & 0 & \cdots & 0 & 1 \\ -a_0 & -a_1 & \cdots & -a_{n-2} & -a_{n-1} \end{bmatrix}, \qquad B = \begin{bmatrix} 0 \\ 0 \\ \vdots \\ 0 \\ 1 \end{bmatrix}$$

$$C = \begin{bmatrix} b_0 & b_1 & \cdots & b_{n-2} & b_{n-1} \end{bmatrix}, \qquad D = 0$$

For any given state model of a system, we may obtain the transfer function for the system by taking the Laplace transform of both the state equation and the output equation and eliminating the state variable. This gives

$$Y(s) = C(sI - A)^{-1}x(0) + (C(sI - A)^{-1}B + D)U(s)$$

When we have zero initial condition ($x(0) = 0$), then we see that the transfer function for this system is defined as $C(sI - A)^{-1}B + D$. This is not particularly easy to compute because it requires a symbolic matrix inverse.

Although the probability of in-depth questions on state variables may be minimal (one or two questions), it is recommended that one should at least review how to convert to the state variable format and then how to solve it, by either time domain or Laplace techniques.

PROBLEMS

15.1 For a typical SISO system (refer to Fig. 15.1) assume that the transfer function, $G_c(s)$, has a dc gain greater than unity, that $G_F(s) = G_p(s) = 1$, and that there is a load disturbance, $L(s)$. Which has the greater effect on the output ($Y(s)$), the input $R(s)$ or the input $L(s)$ at dc?

15.2 The Routh array for a fourth order polynomial is made and all the entries in the first column are positive except the third, which is negative. How many roots lie in the right half of the s-plane?

15.3 For a second-order system with $\zeta < 1$, will the natural oscillatory frequency (i.e., ringing frequency) to a step input be the same as the resonant frequency?

15.4 For an ideal SISO, simple, second-order system, what will be the dimensions of the system matrix A?

15.5 A typical simple second-order system may be described by the following linear differential equation:

$$\ddot{\theta}(t) + 2\dot{\theta}(t) + 25\theta(t) = 25u(t)$$

Find the system matrix A, the input distribution matrix B, and the output matrices C and D for the system. [*Hint:* Define $x_1(t) = \theta(t)$ and $x_2(t) = \dot{\theta}(t)$] Also, find the percentage of the maximum displacement of θ for a unit step input to the system.

SOLUTIONS

15.1 If we define

$$G_1 = \frac{G_C G_p}{1 + G_C G_p H}, \qquad G_2 = \frac{G_p}{1 + G_C G_p H}$$

then the output $Y(s) = G_1 R + G_2 L$. Note that $G_1 = G_1 G_2$. At dc, $G_c > 1$, and thus the magnitude of G_1 is greater than that of G_2. Thus R has the greater impact.

15.2 Since two sign changes appear (one from the second to third term, and another from the third to fourth term), it is clear that two roots appear in the RHP.

15.3 Referring to Equations (15.3a, b), obviously the term under the radical sign will be smaller for the resonant frequency. Therefore $\omega_r < \omega_o$. Note, however, that ω_r is really only defined when $0 < \zeta < \frac{1}{\sqrt{2}}$.

15.4 Since the order of the characteristic polynomial of the system is 2, then A will be a 2×2 matrix.

15.5 Following the hint, we define $x_1(t) = \theta(t)$ and $x_2(t) = \dot{\theta}(t)$. We thus see that $\dot{x}_1(t) = \dot{\theta}(t) = x_2(t)$ and that

$$\begin{aligned} \dot{x}_2(t) &= \ddot{\theta}(t) = -2\dot{\theta}(t) - 25\theta(t) + 25u(t) \\ &= -2x_2(t) - 25x_1(t) + 25u(t) \end{aligned}$$

We also have the output equation $y(t) = \theta(t) = x_1(t)$. Putting these equations into an overall state equation, we have

$$\dot{x}(t) = \begin{bmatrix} \dot{x}_1(t) \\ \dot{x}_2(t) \end{bmatrix} = \begin{bmatrix} 0 & 1 \\ -25 & -2 \end{bmatrix} \begin{bmatrix} x_1(t) \\ x_2(t) \end{bmatrix} + \begin{bmatrix} 0 \\ 25 \end{bmatrix} u(t) = Ax(t) + Bu(t)$$

and the output equation

$$y(t) = [1 \quad 0] \begin{bmatrix} x_1(t) \\ x_2(t) \end{bmatrix} = Cx(t)$$

Computing the transfer function for this system, we have

$$G(s) = \frac{Y(s)}{U(s)} = C(sI - A)^{-1} B = [1 \quad 0] \begin{bmatrix} s & -1 \\ 25 & s+2 \end{bmatrix}^{-1} \begin{bmatrix} 0 \\ 25 \end{bmatrix}$$

$$= \frac{[1 \quad 0]}{s^2 + 2s + 25} \begin{bmatrix} s+2 & 1 \\ -25 & s \end{bmatrix} \begin{bmatrix} 0 \\ 25 \end{bmatrix} = \frac{25}{s^2 + 2s + 25}$$

Since this is a second-order system we have

$$\omega_n^2 = 25\,(\omega_n = 5), \text{ and } 2\zeta\omega_n = 2, \text{ or } \zeta = \frac{1}{5} < 1.$$

From the standardized second-order curves (see Fig. 15.3), the percent maximum overshoot is found to be approximately 52%.

CHAPTER 16

Communications

OUTLINE

NEED FOR MODULATION

In a carrier communication system, the baseband signal of a low-frequency spectrum is translated to a high-frequency spectrum. This is achieved through modulation. The aim of this topic is to explore the reasons for using modulation. Modulation is defined as a process by virtue of which some characteristic of a high-frequency sinusoidal wave is varied in accordance with the instantaneous amplitude of the baseband signal.

Two signals are involved in the modulation process: the baseband signal and the carrier signal. The baseband signal is to be transmitted to the receiver. The frequency of this signal is generally low. In the modulation process, this baseband signal is called the *modulating signal.* The waveform of this signal is unpredictable. For example, the waveform of a speech signal is random in nature and cannot be predicted. In this case, the speech signal is the modulating signal.

The other signal involved with the modulation is a high-frequency sinusoidal wave. This signal is called the *carrier signal* or *carrier.* The frequency of the carrier signal is always much higher than that of the baseband signal. After modulation, the baseband signal of low frequency is transferred to the high-frequency carrier, which carries the information in the form of some variations. After the completion of the modulation process, some characteristic of the carrier is varied such that the resultant variations carry the information.

The carrier signal is represented by the equation:

$$e_c = E_c \sin(\omega_c t + \phi) \qquad \textbf{(16.1)}$$

In Eqn. (16.1), c is an indicator that this equation represents the carrier signal. The components of this equation are as follows:

- e_c: Instantaneous amplitude of the carrier
- E_c: Amplitude of the carrier
- Angular frequency of the carrier, such that $\omega_c = 2\pi fc$, where fc is the frequency carrier, also called the central frequency
- ϕ: Initial phase of the carrier signal

Eqn. (16.1) has three parameters namely, amplitudes (E_c), frequency (ω_c), and phase (ϕ). In principle, these parameters have constant values for a particular sinusoidal wave. According to the definition of modulation, some characteristic of the carrier signal is varied in accordance with the modulating signal. After modulation, any one of the three parameters of the carrier signal, namely, frequency or phase, is varied keeping the remaining two constant. The baseband signal is then carried by these variations. The type of the modulation is decided by the parameter chosen to vary.

For example, if amplitude of the carrier is chosen to vary in accordance with the instantaneous amplitude of the baseband signal, keeping frequency and phase constant, the resulting modulation is called amplitude modulation. Frequency modulation and phase modulation are also obtained in a similar way.

Low-frequency baseband signals are thus translated to a high-frequency carrier such that the information is coded in the variations in one of the parameters of the carrier. At the receiver side, these variations are detected through the demodulation process to recover the original baseband signal.

The following can be summarized with reference to modulation.

- The baseband signal is known as the modulating signal.
- The baseband signal is a low-frequency signal.
- The carrier signal is always a high-frequency sinusoidal wave.
- During the modulation process, the modulating signal varies the frequency, y, amplitude, or phase of the carrier in accordance with its instantaneous amplitude.
- After modulation, the carrier is said to be modulated by the modulating signal.
- The output of the modulator is called the modulated signal.

The process of modulation in a communication system increases its cost and complexity. This may be considered as a disadvantage. However, modulation is extensively used in most communication systems. There is a definite need for using modulation. There can be problems if modulation is not used. Scrutinizing these problems can explain why modulation is required.

The baseband signal will be transmitted as it is. However, if modulation is not employed, the system designer could confront the following problems:

- Antenna height
- Narrow banding
- Poor radiation and penetration
- Diffraction angle
- Multiplexing

AMPLITUDE MODULATION (AM)

Introduction to Modulation

Modulation is the process of translating a baseband (low-frequency) signal to a higher frequency one. There are two main reasons to do the modulation:

- To allow simultaneous transmission of two or more signals by translation to different frequencies
- To utilize the propagation properties of signals at different wavelengths (frequency)

Carrier Modulation

The modulation process changes some characteristics of a high-frequency sinusoidal carrier described by the equation

$$s(t) = E \times \cos(\omega t + \varphi)$$

where E is the peak amplitude of the carrier, ω is the angular frequency of the carrier in radians per second, t is time, and φ is the initial phase of the carrier at time zero.

In the previous equation, there are two properties that can be changed: the amplitude (E) and the angular position (φ). If the amplitude is changed, it is amplitude modulation (AM); if the phase is changed (φ of the cosine function), it is angular modulation. Angular modulation can be characterized as frequency modulation (FM) or phase modulation (PM). There is no essential difference between the two types of angular modulation.

Sidebands and Modulation Degree

In amplitude modulation the amplitude of a carrier is changed proportional to the amplitude of the modulating signal. Figure 16.1 shows a time domain display of an amplitude modulated carrier.

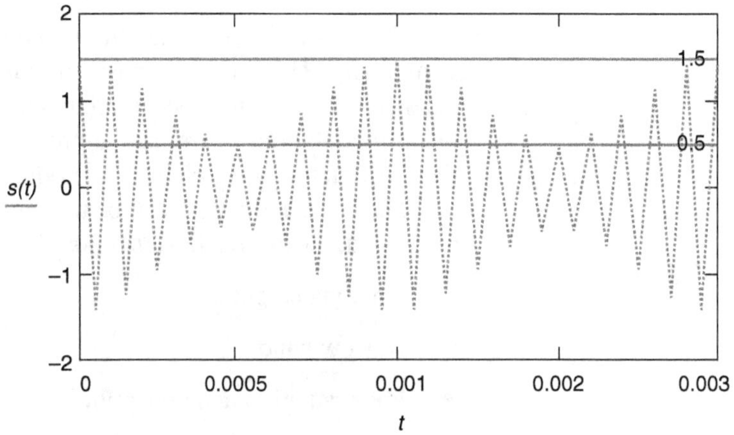

Figure 16.1 Amplitude Modulated Carrier in the Time Domain

Modulation degree is 0.5, or 50% (explained in detail later in this section). The wave shown in Figure 16.1 is the sum of three sinusoids of different frequencies. One of these sinusoids is the carrier, and the other two are sum and difference of the carrier and the modulating signal. The sum and difference frequencies are called upper and lower sideband (USB and LSB, respectively). Figure 16.2 shows the frequency domain view of the amplitude modulated carrier where f_c is the carrier frequency, and f_m is the baseband or modulating frequency.

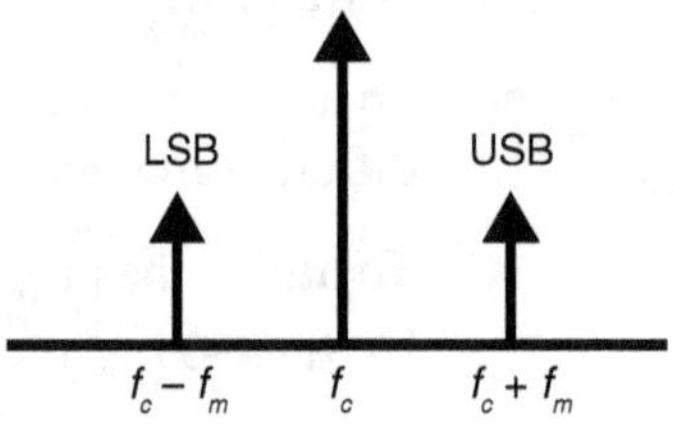

Figure 16.2 Amplitude Modulated Carrier in the Frequency Domain

The degree of modulation m is often expressed in percent and calculated as shown in Figure 16.3 and the following equations.

Figure 16.3 Amplitude Modulation Calculation

$$m = \frac{E_{max} - E_c}{E_c}$$

Since the modulation is symmetrical,

$$E_{max} - E_c = E_c - E_{min} \leftrightarrow \frac{E_{max} - E_{min}}{2}$$

the equation for m can be rewritten to

$$m = \frac{E_{max} - E_{min}}{E_{max} + E_{min}}$$

When the carrier component and the sideband components are in phase, they add together and form the maximum signal amplitude E_{max},

$$E_{max} = E_c + E_{usb} - E_{lsb}$$

where E_c is the carrier frequency amplitude, E_{usb} is the upper side band amplitude, and E_{lsb} is the lower side band amplitude.

The modulation degree m can now be expressed as

$$m = \frac{E_{max} - E_c}{E_{max} + E_c} = \frac{E_{usb} + E_{lsb}}{E_c}$$

Since $E_{usb} = E_{lsb} = E_{sb}$, then

$$m = 2\frac{E_{sb}}{E_c}$$

For 100% modulation ($m = 1$), the amplitude of the sideband is one-half of the carrier and, thus, one-fourth the power in the carrier. The power in the two sidebands are then 50% of the power in the carrier.

The relationship between the carrier frequency and the frequency of the sidebands is given by (using trigonometric identities):

$$s(t) = A\left(1 + m \cdot f(t)\right)\cos\left(\omega_c t\right)$$

$$f(t) = \cos\left(\omega_m t\right)$$

$$s(t) = A\left(1 + m \cdot \cos\left(\omega_m t\right)\right)\cos\left(\omega_c t\right)$$

$$s(t) = A\cos\left(\omega_c t\right) + \frac{m \cdot A}{2}\cos\left(\omega_c + \omega_m\right)t + \frac{m \cdot A}{2}\cos\left(\omega_c - \omega_m\right)t$$

where A is the amplitude of the modulated signal and $f(t)$ is the baseband signal, which in this case is a cosine signal $\cos(\omega_m t)$.

The resultant signal $s(t)$ is the carrier with the two sidebands. The frequency of the sidebands is the sum and difference of the carrier frequency and the modulating frequency as shown in Figure 16.2.

The curve in Figure 16.4 shows a carrier $f_c = 10$ kHz modulated with $f_m = 1$ kHz. The modulation degree is 80% (0.8). The equation used to generate the curve is: (Amplitude A is assumed to be unity)

$$s(t) = [1 + m \bullet \cos(\omega_m t)] \bullet \cos(\omega_c t)$$

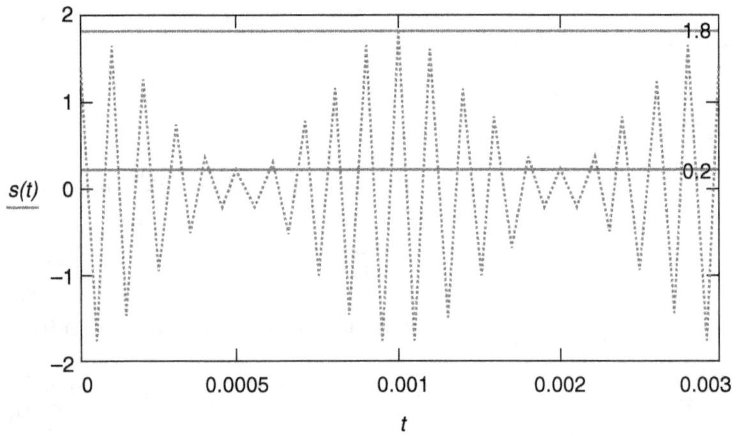

Figure 16.4 Amplitude Modulation

The maximum amplitude is 1.8, and the minimum is 0.2. This gives the modulation degree m of 0.8 (equation for $_m$ expressed as function of E_{max} and E_{min}), equal to the value used for the generation of the curve.

Amplitude modulation is linear modulation. The frequency of the sideband components is shifted linearly from the carrier with the modulation signal.

Overmodulation occurs when more than the required amount of modulating signal is impressed on a carrier than is required to achieve modulation. Overmodulation is also known as *flattopping*. Overmodulation causes distortion and produces splatter (spurious emissions) on adjacent frequencies. To avoid disturbance of nearby services in the spectrum, it is important to prevent overmodulation.

Single Sideband (SSB)

All of the information in the amplitude modulated signal is found in one of the sidebands. Transmitting the carrier and both sidebands is waste of power. In a single sideband (SSB) with a suppressed carrier, only one of the sidebands is transmitted and a greater efficiency at the transmitter is obtained because the redundant information is eliminated. To demodulate the SSB signal, it is necessary to reinsert the carrier in the receiver. SSB generation can be carried out in two methods: the filter method and the phasing method.

Filter Method

The carrier and the modulating signal is applied to a balanced modulator in which the resulting signal output contains sidebands but suppresses the carrier frequency signal. The signal from the modulator goes through a narrow bandpass filter with a bandwidth of the desired part (for voice communication about 3000 Hz). Figure 16.5 shows the SSB filter method.

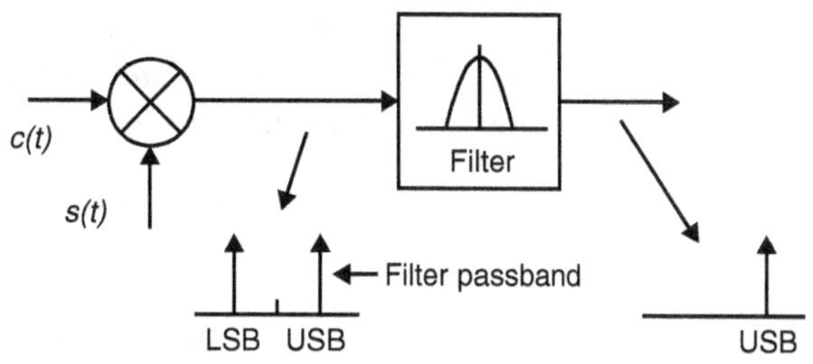

Figure 16.5 SSB filter method

The carrier signal $c(t)$ is balanced out in the balanced modulator, and the output is the lower and upper sidebands (LSB and USB). LSB is not in the filter passband and, after the filter, only USB is remaining. The filter helps to suppress the remaining carrier component that is not balanced out in the modulator.

The filter cannot have infinitely steep skirts, thus, the response of the filter must begin to roll off about 300 Hz from the carrier frequency. This effect limits SSB ability to transmit low baseband frequencies (bass). SSB is mainly used for voice communication and is popular in the HF-band, 3 - 30 MHz.

Phasing Method

In the phasing method, the carrier and the modulating signals are split into equal components with 90° phase difference (quadrature signals). These signals are applied to balanced modulators and, when the outputs are summed, one sideband is reinforced while the other is cancelled.

A single sideband may be generated using two balanced modulators, each driven with identical amplitude carrier and modulating signals. The two voltages applied to one modulator are in quadrature (out of phase by 90°) from those applied to the other one.

Figure 16.6 shows the balanced modulators with in and out signals. Signals with index I are in phase components, and signals with index Q are quadrature components.

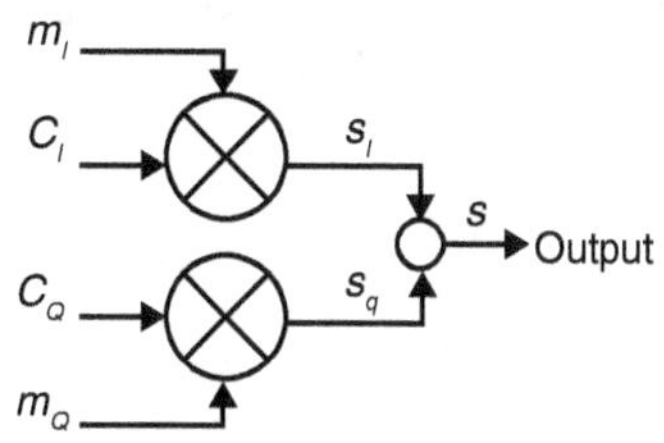

Figure 16.6 Balanced Modulator

Signal out from the inphase balanced modulator s_i is

$$s_i = V_c V_m \cdot \sin \omega_c t \cdot \sin \omega_m t$$

and the signal out from the quadrature balanced modulator s_q is

$$s_q = V_c V_m \cdot \cos \omega_c t \cdot \cos \omega_m t$$

The sine and cosine parts from the carrier and the modulating signal are spaced 90°. To express the sin and cosine products in signals s_i and s_q, the following trigonometric identities will be used:

$$\sin A\ \sin B = \frac{1}{2}\cdot\left(\cos\left(A-B\right)-\cos\left(A+B\right)\right)$$

$$\cos A\ \cos B = \frac{1}{2}\cdot\left(\cos\left(A+B\right)+\cos\left(A-B\right)\right)$$

The s_i and s_q signals expanded to sum and difference of the carrier and modulating signal are

$$s_i = \frac{1}{2}\cdot V_c\cdot V_m\cdot\left(\cos\left(\omega_c-\omega_m\right)t-\cos\left(\omega_c+\omega_m\right)t\right)$$

$$s_q = \frac{1}{2}\cdot V_c\cdot V_m\cdot\left(\cos\left(\omega_c+\omega_m\right)t+\cos\left(\omega_c-\omega_m\right)t\right)$$

When s_i and s_q are added, the sum signals cancel and result is

$$s = s_i + s_q = \frac{1}{2}\cdot\left(V_{Ci}V_{Ci}+V_{Cq}V_{Cq}\right)\cdot\left(\cos\left(\omega_c-\omega_m\right)t\right)$$

$$+\frac{1}{2}\cdot\left(V_{Ci}V_{Ci}-V_{Cq}V_{Cq}\right)\cdot\cos\left(\omega_c-\omega_m\right)t)$$

Only the difference signal, lower sideband, remains in signal s after inphase and quadrature signals are summed. In the case where there is a phasing error where the phase relationship between the in-phase and quadrature signals are not 90 degrees, or if the amplitudes of the in-phase and quadrature carrier signal, and the modulating signal are unequal, then the upper sideband is not completely eliminated. The amount of carrier in the output signal depends on the balance (carrier suppression) in the modulators.

ANGLE MODULATION (FREQUENCY MODULATION AND PHASE MODULATION)

Definitions

In angular modulation, the phase of the carrier is changed. The carrier is described as:

$$s(t) = A\times\cos(\omega t+\varphi)$$

and φ is changed with the modulation signal.

In frequency modulation, the instantaneous frequency deviation of the modulated carrier to the frequency of the unmodulated carrier is proportional to the instantaneous amplitude of the modulating signal. In phase modulation, the instantaneous phase deviation of the modulated carrier to the phase of the unmodulated carrier is proportional to the instantaneous amplitude of the modulating signal.

For angular modulation, the definition modulation index m is used. m is expressed as:

$$m = \frac{\Delta f_p}{f_m} = \Delta\Phi_p$$

where m is modulation index, Δf_p is peak frequency deviation, f_m is frequency of the modulation signal, and $\Delta\Phi_p$ is peak phase deviation in radians.

The equation shows that the modulation index m is really an indication of peak phase deviation, both in FM and PM. Note that the equation for m does not include the frequency of the modulating signal. The frequency or phase deviates in proportion to the instantaneous amplitude of the modulating signal independent of the rate of the amplitude changes.

Bandwidth of FM and PM Signals

Mathematical analysis shows that angular modulation of a cosine-wave carrier with cosine-wave modulating signals generates an infinite number of sidebands spaced by the modulating frequency. The relation between the power in the carrier and the sidebands is Bessel function of the modulation index m. Figure 16.7 shows curves [Bessel functions $Jn(x,y)$] for the carrier and the first and second order sidebands as a function of m.

Note that for a modulation index of 2.4 the amplitude, of the carrier is zero.

When m increases, more of the power will be in the higher order sidebands. Table 16.1 shows the amplitude of the carrier and the five first order sidebands.

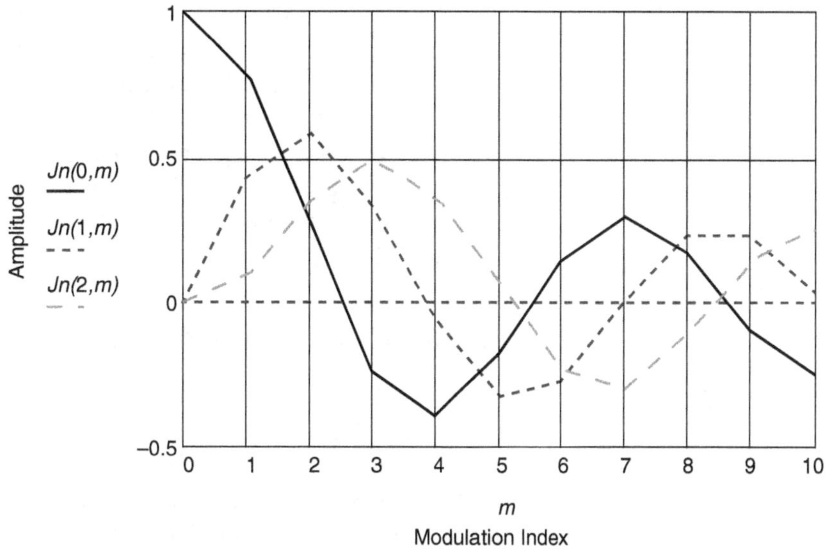

Figure 16.7 Carrier and Sideband Amplitude Versus Modulation Index. $J_n(0,m)$ is carrier, $J_n(1,m)$ is first order sideband, and $J_n(2,m)$ is second order sideband.

Table 16.1 Carrier/sideband Amplitude Versus Modulation Index

Carrier/sideband Modulation Index	0	1	2	3	4	5
$m = 1$	0.7652	0.4401	0.1149	0.01956	0.002477	0.00025
$m = 2$	0.2239	0.5767	0.3528	0.1289	0.034	0.00704
$m = 3$	−0.2601	0.3391	0.4861	0.3091	0.132	0.04303
$m = 4$	−0.3971	−0.06604	0.3641	0.4302	0.2811	0.1321
$m = 5$	−0.1776	−0.3276	0.04657	0.3648	0.3912	0.2611

When the modulation index $m = 1$, most of the power is in the carrier and the first order sideband. The power in the sideband increases with higher values of modulation.

Narrow Band FM Versus Wideband FM

Narrowband FM is used in voice communication systems where some amount of distortion is acceptable. In FM broadcasting where music is to be transmitted, high quality (low distortion) is required and wideband FM is used. (The distortion depends on the number of sidebands transmitted.)

The definition of narrowband FM is when the modulation index is less than $\pi/2$ (≈ 1.57). High-quality wideband FM sidebands with amplitude down to 1/100 (–40dB) are transmitted, while narrow band FM sidebands with amplitude down to 1/10 (–20dB) are transmitted. An approximation of the required bandwidth of narrow band FM is given by

$$B = 2\Delta f_{\text{peak}} + 2 f_m$$

where B is bandwidth, Δf_{peak} is peak frequency deviation from unmodulated carrier frequency, and f_m is the frequency of the modulating signal.

An FM broadcast station (wideband) has a maximum frequency deviation of $\Delta f_{\text{peak}} = 75$ kHz. The highest modulation frequency f_m is 15 kHz. This gives a modulation index of $m = 5$, and the resulting signal has eight significant sideband pairs. The required bandwidth can be calculated as $2 \times 8 \times 15$ kHz $= 240$ kHz. For modulation frequencies below 15 kHz, m increases but the spacing between sideband components decreases, and analysis shows that the bandwidth with 15 kHz modulating frequency will not be exceeded. Thus the required bandwidth calculation can be done using the highest modulation frequency and the maximum frequency deviation.

FM is a Nonlinear Process

FM and PM are nonlinear processes. It has no linear relationship between the modulating signal and the sidebands. The sidebands and the carrier changes amplitude when the modulation index is varied. The sum power of all these components is equal to the power in the unmodulated carrier. Thus, FM and PM can be amplified in nonlinear class-C amplifiers with high efficiency. This makes FM suitable for portable communication equipment.

Phase Modulation

In the case of phase modulation, the signal is expressed as

$$s(t) := \cos\left(\omega_c \cdot t + K_1 \cdot \Phi(t)\right)$$

where

$\Phi(t) = \cos(\omega_m t)$ is the modulating signal
K_1 is a constant of the system.

Figure 16.8 shows curves of $s(t)$ and $\Phi(t)$ in the time domain, that is the phase variation (frequency variation) of the carrier versus the modulating signal.

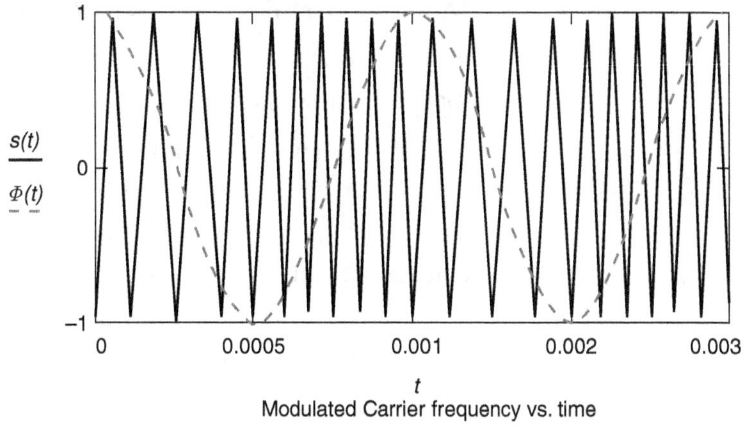

Figure 16.8 Phase Modulated Signal, Frequency Versus Time

The phase of the unmodulated carrier varies linearly with the modulation signal.

Narrow Band Frequency Modulation

FM is defined as narrowband for modulation indexes less than π/2. This section shows some mathematics of narrowband FM. The frequency modulated carrier is expressed as

$$s(t) = \cos(\omega_c t + m \cdot \sin(\omega_m t)$$

where

$$m = \frac{\Delta\omega_{peak}}{\omega_m} = \frac{\Delta f_{peak}}{f_m}$$

To simplify further analysis of FM, the case where

$$m << \pi/2$$

(usually $m < 0.2$) is considered. The frequency modulated signal $s(t)$ is written as using trigonometric identities

$$s(t) = [\cos\omega_c t \cdot \cos(m \cdot \sin\omega_m t) - \sin\omega_c t \cdot \sin(m \cdot \sin\omega_m t)]$$

With the requirement to m << π/2

$$\cos(m \cdot \sin\omega_m t) = 1 \quad \text{and} \quad \sin(m \cdot \sin\omega_m t) = m \cdot \sin\omega_m t$$

thus

$$s(t) - \cos(\omega_c t - m \cdot \sin\omega_m t \cdot \sin\omega_c t) = \cos(\omega_c t) + \frac{m}{2}\cos(\omega_c + \omega_m)t - \frac{m}{2}\cos(\omega_c - \omega_m)$$

This resembles the equation for the AM case except that the lower sideband is reversed. The resultant sideband vector sum is always in phase quadrature with the carrier. In narrow band FM with very small m ($m < 0.2$), the bandwidth usage is equal to AM. Narrow band FM is used in applications where requirement to distortion is not severe as in voice communication systems for taxis, amateur radio VHF/UHF, police, and so forth.

Wideband Frequency Modulation

The carrier signal s(t) is expanded using trigonometric identities as done in the math of narrowband FM.

$$s(t) = \cos(\omega_c t + m \cdot \sin(\omega_m t)$$
$$s(t) = [\cos\omega_c t \cdot \cos(m \cdot \sin\omega_m t) - \sin\omega_c t \cdot \sin(m \cdot \sin\omega_m t)]$$

Modulation index m in the equation is not small, and the terms $\cos(m \times \sin\omega_m t)$ and $\sin(m \times \sin\omega_m t)$ are expanded using Bessel function of the first kind.

$$\cos(m \cdot \sin\omega_m t) = J_0(m) + 2J_2(m) \cdot \cos 2\omega_m t + 2J_4(m) \cdot \cos 4\omega_m t + \ldots$$
$$\sin(m \cdot \sin\omega_m t) = 2J_1(m) \cdot \sin\omega_m t + 2J_3(m) \cdot \sin 3\omega_m t + \ldots$$

$$\begin{aligned} s(t) &= J_0(m) \\ &- J_1(m) \cdot [\cos(\omega_c - \omega_m)t - \cos(\omega_c + \omega_m)t] \\ &+ J_2(m) \cdot [\cos(\omega_c - 2\omega_m)t + \cos(\omega_c + 2\omega_m)t] \\ &- J_3(m) \cdot [\cos(\omega_c - 3\omega_m)t - \cos(\omega_c + 3\omega_m)t] \\ &+ J_4(m) \cdot [\cos(\omega_c - 4\omega_m)t + \cos(\omega_c + 4\omega_m)t] \end{aligned}$$

The wideband FM modulated carrier consists of a carrier and an infinite number of sidebands with amplitude proportional to $J_n(m)$. The equations show that even-order sideband pairs are collinear with the carrier component, while the odd-order pairs are in quadrature to the carrier component.

Frequency Modulation Versus Phase Modulation

FM cannot be applied to an amplifier stage, but PM can. PM is, therefore, readily adaptable to transmitters employing oscillators of high stability, such as crystal-controlled ones. PM of an amplifier stage with good linearity yields a maximum practicable modulation index of about 0.5.

To increase the deviation, multiplication is used, typically by eight or more. The modulation is applied to an amplifier stage at low frequency prior to the multiplication stages.

PM has inherent pre-emphasis, and PM received on an FM receiver sounds "tinny." PM can generally be converted into FM by choosing the frequency response of the modulator so that its output voltage is proportional to $1/f_m$, that is, integration of the modulating signal. The reverse is also true. FM can be converted to PM if the modulator output voltage is made proportional to f_m, that is, differentiation of the modulating signal.

Digital Modulation

The RF spectrum is limited and has to be divided among an increasing number of services and users. With digital modulation schemes and their effects on overall system efficiency, it is possible to obtain greater capacity and convey more information than with analogue ones in the same bandwidth.

Developers of radio communication systems face the following constraints:

- Available bandwidth
- Permissible power
- Noise level of the system

Different types of digital modulation exists, each with its pros and cons. Examples are:

- ASK (Amplitude Shift Keying)
- FSK (Frequency Shift Keying)
- PSK (Phase Shift Keying)
- QPSK (Quadrature Phase Shift Keying)
- MSK (Minimum Shift Keying)
- QAM (Quadrature Amplitude Modulation)
- $\pi/4$ DQPSK (Differential Quadrature Phase Shift Keying)

Initially in digital transmission, the information to be transmitted is in the form of a sequence $a(n)$ comprising of elements from a set a, $a \in \{0,1\}$. The modulator converts the sequence of logical ones and zeros into a sequence of analogue signals suitable for transmission in the RF channel. The conversion of the digital signals into baseband signals is referred to as baseband modulation, while the conversion into RF signals is referred to as RF carrier modulation.

This section gives an introduction to the main types of the digital modulation methods.

Noise in the Communication Channel

In a communication channel, it will be noise and other distortions that degrade the capacity.

Fundamental Data Capacity

Shannon showed in his famous paper of the fundamentals of data communication that the capacity of the Gaussian white noise limited communication channel is:

$$C = B \log_2 \left(1 + \frac{S}{N}\right)$$

where C is channel capacity in bit/second, B is the bandwidth of the channel in Hz, S is the signal power in Watts, and N is the noise power in Watts.

Shannon's formula is a theoretical limit, and practical implementations are worse than the capacity bound given by the formula.

Signal to Noise Ratio, E_b/N_0

The noise most commonly used in comparing different digital modulation methods is the *Additive White Gaussian Noise* (AWGN). The white noise is the noise you hear in an FM broadcast receiver (without muting) when tuned off stations, and it is called white due to it containing frequency components from low frequency into the microwave region. In a receiver, the noise spectrum will be limited with the transfer function of the receiver, but the noise energy that passes will add to the data signal and decrease the distance between signaling states.

In digital systems, a common terminology for describing the signal-to-noise ratio is the E_b/N_0, the energy of a single data bit to the noise power density. E_b/N_0

is a dimensionless quantity and is the signal-to-noise ratio per bit. It is often expressed in dB.

The amplitude of the noise voltage is random. As an example, at one moment the amplitude is 0.2 Volt, and in the next one it is 1.0 Volt. In calculation of the Bit Error Rate (BER), the Gaussian distribution is used for noise voltage amplitude. The use of Gaussian distribution closely models what happens in the real world. To calculate the BER, one question has to be answered: How often does the noise voltage exceed a certain signal amplitude of the opposite polarity? This is not easy to answer, but a mathematical function, *the complementary error function erfc()*, has been defined to answer the question.

Signaling, Antipodal, Orthogonal, and Nonorthogonal

Digital transmission formats in general fall into three types:

Antipodal	The signaling states are exact opposites of one another. *Antipodal* means that the signaling states (phase states) are as far apart in the phase plane as possible.
Orthogonal	The signaling states have a phase difference of 90° and do not affect each other.
Nonorthogonal	The signaling states affect each other to some degree, usually negatively.

Antipodal Signaling

Two level PSK (2PSK) is antipodal signaling. A phase shift of 180° is used for the two signaling states, ("1") and ("0"). Figure 16.9 shows the phase shift on a carrier and how it is viewed in the phase plane.

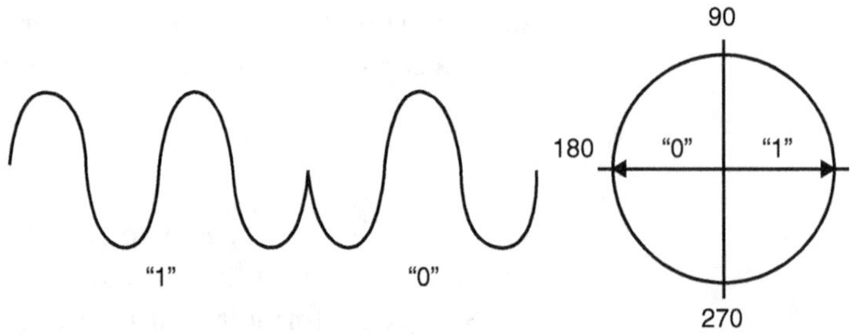

Figure 16.9 Phase States of Antipodal Signaling

As shown in Figure 16.9, the phase shifts 180° when signal to be transmitted shifts from "1" to "0".

In the PSK, demodulator to detectors can be used: one for the inphase signal with the carrier and one for the out-of-phase signal with the carrier. The two detectors have output of opposite polarity, and when the phase shifts, the polarity of the outputs of the detectors changes. The two different phase detectors are always both participating in the decision about what value the output data is going to be.

Each state affects both channels, and this is called antipodal signaling.

Orthogonal Signaling

The definition of orthogonality can be shown mathematically and visualized with multiplication of two waveforms. S_i and S_q are the signals, which are cosine and sine ones.

$$S_i(t) = \cos(\omega t) \quad \text{and} \quad S_q(t) = \sin(\omega t)$$

A frequency of one megahertz is used in the example. The following equation shows the result of the two signals, S_i and S_q, multiplied and integrated over a time period of one microsecond, the cycle time of the signals.

$$\int_0^{(1\cdot 10)^{-6}} s_i(t)\cdot s_q(t)dt = 0$$

The two signals, S_i and S_q, are orthogonal over time interval T when the previous equation is zero, as is the case. Thus, cosine and sine waves are orthogonal. This property of the cosine and sine waves are used in IQ modulation, which are popular in many applications of digital transmitters.

Bit Error Rate (BER) Calculations for PSK and FSK

The following equations and curves in Figure 16.10 shows BER calculations for PSK and FSK with coherent and noncoherent demodulation. (Coherent and noncoherent demodulation is not within the scope of the FE exam).

Table 16.2

$erfc(x) = 1 - erf(x)$	The *complementary error function erfc(x).*
$f(x) = 20\log(\sqrt{2})$	x here the power ratio, E_b/N_0, per bit. Voltage ratio is the square root.
$cPSK(x) = \frac{1}{2} erfc\left(\sqrt{x}\right)$	This formula gives the BER for 2PSK, antipodal signaling. 2PSK is normally used as a reference for other digital modulation methods.
$cFSK(x) = \frac{1}{2} erfc\left(\sqrt{\frac{x}{2}}\right)$	This formula gives the BER for 2FSK signaling coherently demodulation.
$NoncFSK(x) = \frac{1}{2} e^{-\frac{x}{2}}$	This formula gives the BER for 2FSK, signaling noncoherently demodulation.

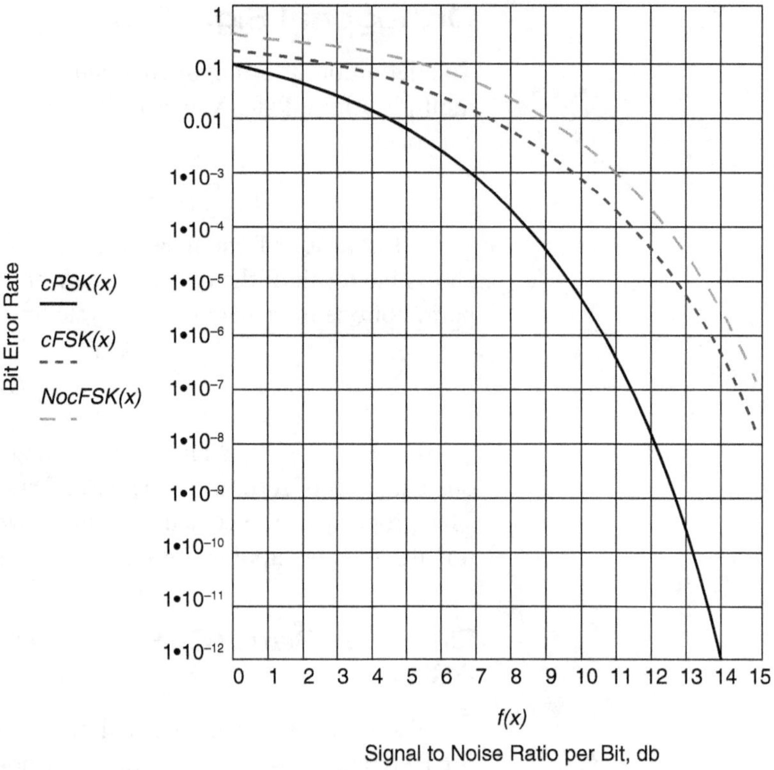

Figure 16.10 Digital Modulation Performance Versus Signal to Noise Ratio

As can be seen from the curves of Figure 16.10, a 10 dB of E_b/N_0 gives a BER of about 2×10^{-5} for PSK and about 10^{-3} for FSK, both coherently demodulated. From the curves, it is found that to obtain a given BER, FSK needs an additional 3 dB in the signal-to-noise ratio compared to PSK.

This is due to the fact that in PSK, information from both the signaling states, 0° and 180°, are used to determine the symbol received. In FSK, only information from one signal is used; it is not the opposite frequency of the one used for a symbol transmission. The signal information output from the detector is then twice for PSK compared to FSK, which gives the 3 dB improvement.

Noncoherent demodulated FSK has higher requirement to signal-to-noise ratio than coherent demodulated FSK. As can be seen from the curves, the penalty paid with using noncoherent demodulation is small, and it is used in many applications due to its lower implementation complexity.

IQ-Modulation

The GSM specification for maximum frequency and angle error during a transmission burst are so tight that modulating a VCO would be incapable to meet the requirements. An IQ modulator provides better results and is popular in many applications. This section briefly reviews IQ modulation.

IQ Formats

The modulation can be expressed in terms of *I*, the in phase component, and *Q*, the quadrature component, of the signal. The *I*- and *Q*-components map amplitude and phase in the IQ plane, and the points in the plane are called constellation points. Figure 16.11 shows the IQ plane with three signals at different constellation points.

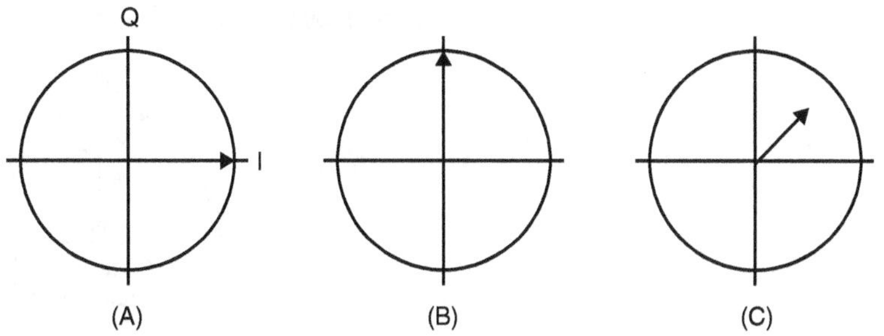

Figure 16.11 IQ plane

In (A), the I-component is unity and the Q-component is zero. The amplitude is unity and phase is zero.

In (B), the I-component is zero and Q-component is unity. Amplitude is unity, but the phase of the signal is +90°.

In (C), the I- and Q-components are 0.5. Amplitude is now 0.707 and phase is +45°.

Amplitude and phase modulation is accomplished by changing the I- and Q-components.

In the following example, some mathematics of IQ modulation are shown. The signals $s_i(t)$ and $s_q(t)$ are the I- and the Q-components, which are multiplied with a modulation signal with amplitude A.

Amplitude values used are: $A_1 = 1$, $A_2 = 0$, $A_3 = 0$, $A_4 = 1$, $A_5 = \sqrt{2}/2$ and $A_6 = \sqrt{2}/2$.

The following equations, $m_1(t)$, $m_2(t)$, $m_3(t)$, show how the modulation is applied. Figure 16.12 shows the curves of the signals $m_1(t)$, $m_2(t)$, $m_3(t)$.

$$m_1(t) = A_1 s_i(t) + A_2 s_q(t)$$
$$m_2(t) = A_3 s_i(t) + A_4 s_q(t)$$
$$m_3(t) = A_5 s_i(t) + A_6 s_q(t)$$

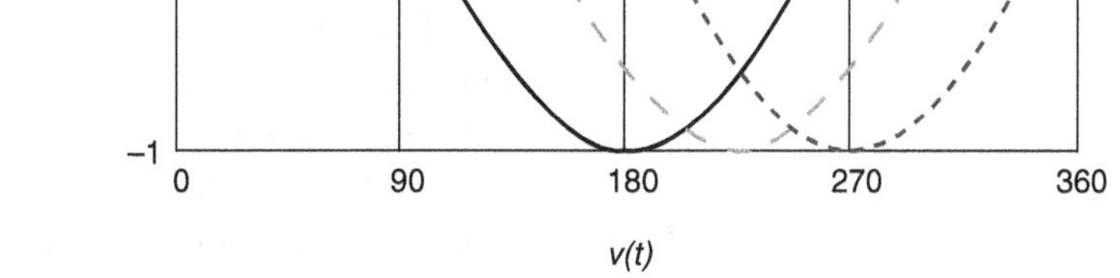

Figure 16.12 I/Q modulation

In $m_1(t)$, the I-signal is unity and Q-signal is zero. In $m_2(t)$, the I-signal is zero and the Q-signal is unity.

The curves in Figure 16.12 show $m_2(t)$ 90° in advance of $m_1(t)$ as expected. In $m_3(t)$ both the I- and Q-signals are square root of two half. The phase difference is now 45° compared to $m_1(t)$.

Figure 16.13 shows the IQ modulator implementation.

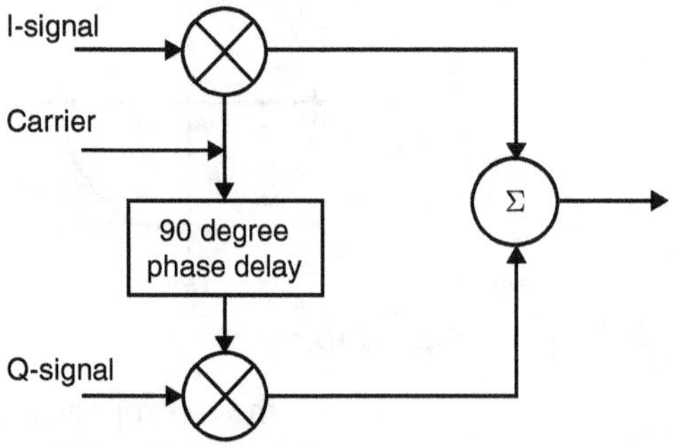

Figure 16.13 IQ Modulator Implementation

With the IQ-modulator, precise control of the amplitude and phase of the carrier is obtained.

Digital Modulation Formats

This section explains the main digital modulation formats, their spectral efficiency, and properties for practical systems.

Modulation Types

The baseband digital data signal is to be modulated onto a carrier for transmission, and the modulation can be carried out in different ways with different properties. Important characteristics of the modulated signal are:

- emitted signal bandwidth,
- error performance, and
- implementation complexity.

Three distinct properties of the carrier can be changed: amplitude, frequency, and phase. In analogue modulation, it is known as AM (Amplitude Modulation), FM (Frequency Modulation), and PM (Phase Modulation). Their digital representations are ASK (Amplitude Shift Keying), FSK (Frequency Shift Keying), and PSK (Phase Shift Keying).

Amplitude Shift Keying (ASK)

In amplitude shift keying, the amplitude of the carrier is varied following the binary source (digital baseband signal). In the simplest form, the carrier is turned on and off to represent the ones and zeroes.

This is known as on-off keying (OOK). An example is Morse code transmission where the alphabet is a combination of short and long pulses of the carrier. Figure 16.14 shows an example of the amplitude modulated carrier using OOK.

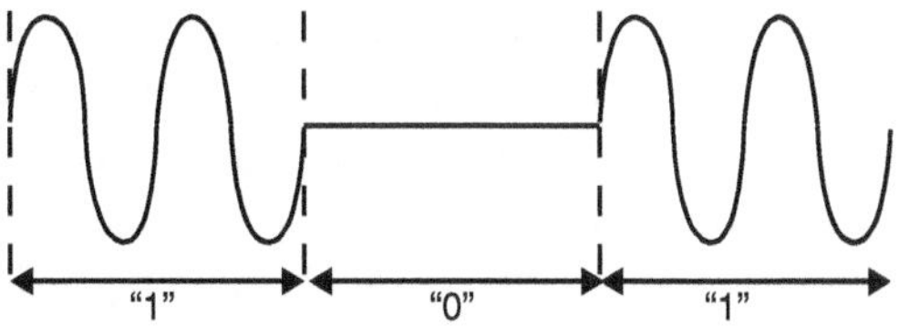

Figure 16.14 Amplitude Shift Keying

One problem with the OOK is the interference and noise in the receiver in time intervals of no transmission.

A carrier with no modulation needs an infinite small bandwidth to be received. Keying the carrier on and off produces sidebands (upper and lower) corresponding to the period of the keying. A keying frequency of 50 Hz will have sidebands of multiples of 50 Hz above and below the carrier. The distribution of power in the sidebands depends on the rise and fall time of the pulsed carrier. Using a receiver with narrow bandwidth, the noise power will be small. The narrowband modulation, in the case of Morse code, is possible to detect in channels with high level of noise and interference as often found in the HF-band (3 MHz to 30 MHz).

ASK is not used in many applications. Amateur Morse code transmission is one example of current usage.

Frequency Shift Keying (FSK)

FSK is a simple form of modulation and has been used for many years due to its low implementation complexity. FSK is constant envelope modulation, that is, the amplitude of the RF-signal is constant.

This simplifies transmitter amplifier, which can be nonlinear, class C, with high efficiency. Examples of modern applications using FSK are paging systems and cordless telephone systems including DECT (Digital Enhanced Cordless Telephone).

In FSK, one frequency is used to represent the logical "1," and another frequency the logical "0". This modulation is called 2FSK. Two level FSK can be viewed as a special form of amplitude modulation with two different carriers switched on and off as shown in Figure 16.15.

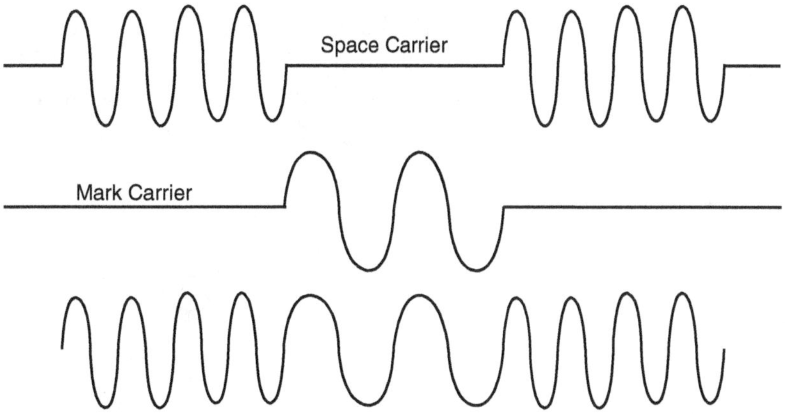

Figure 16.15 FSK Viewed as a Sum of Two Amplitude Modulated Carriers

Random digital data has a $\sin(x)/x$ roll-off. To obtain optimal demodulation, the carriers shall be spaced so that spectral nulls from current carrier is at the other carrier frequency. Figure 16.16 shows a system with ±1/2T deviation.

The FSK spectrum is a superposition of two spectra. As shown in Figure 16.16, when one carrier is at maximum, the other one is at zero. The signaling states are orthogonal when it is no cross-talk between them as with the ±1/2T deviation. The real part of the orthogonality is zero when the carriers are spaced 1/2T apart, which is equal to ±1/4T deviation. This is known as Minimum Shift Keying.

FSK modulation can be done in different ways. In case of a transmitter with a VCO (Voltage Controlled Oscillator) as a carrier source, it can be modulated with shifting the frequency with the signaling state to be transmitted. One problem arises when the baseband signal has a spectrum from DC. The VCO controlling loop will try to compensate for frequency changes that fall within the loop passband, as will be the case with the low frequency content of the baseband modulating signal. One solution to this problem is to modulate the reference oscillator with the low frequency content and the VCO with the high frequency content. Another method to do the modulation is to use IQ-modulation.

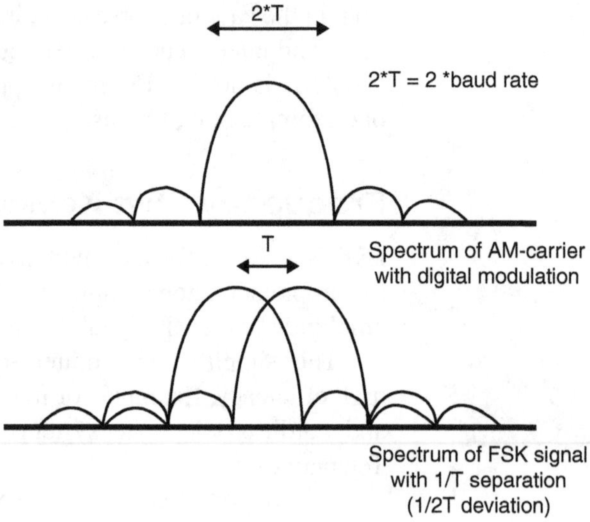

Figure 16.16 FSK Modulation with ±1/2T Deviation

Phase Shift Keying (PSK)

In PSK the phase, the carrier is varied according to the source baseband data signal. For binary phase shift keying (BPSK), the phase shift is 180°. BPSK is like FSK: a simple form of digital modulation. BPSK can be generated using a balanced mixer, and the two signaling states are 180° apart as shown in Figure 16.17.

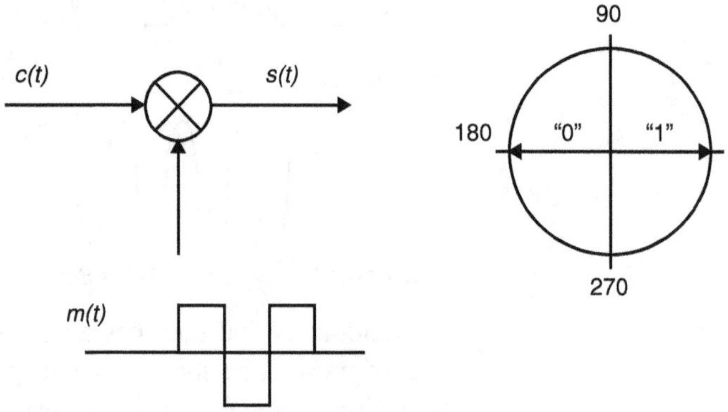

Figure 16.17 PSK Modulation and Signaling States

The carrier signal $c(t)$ is applied to the mixer. The modulating signal $m(t)$ is bipolar square wave data and output signal $s(t)$ is the PSK modulated carrier. The "1" and the "0" are the two signaling states spaced 180° apart. Figure 16.18 shows the PSK waveform.

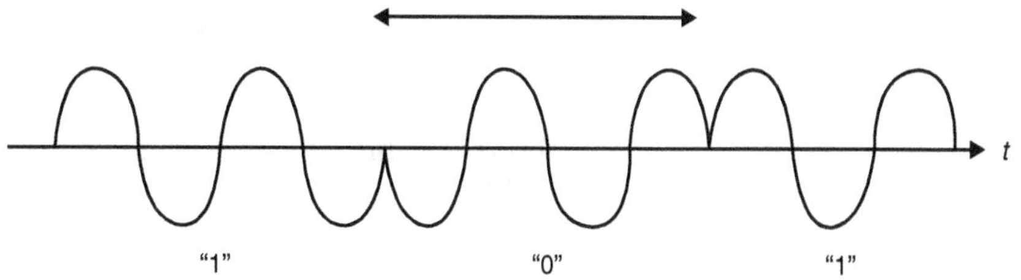

Figure 16.18 Phase Shift Keying Waveform

Abrupt phase changes from 0° to 180°, when the data shifts from "1" to "0", gives a wide spectrum. To narrow the spectrum, the baseband digital signal is low-pass filtered. In many applications, the cosine roll-off filter is used. The filtering slows the phase change and narrows the spectrum.

In BPSK the amplitude goes through the origin (shown in Figure 16.17) when the phase shifts between 0° to 180°. This means that for some time, the amplitude is zero. To follow the amplitude fluctuation, a linear amplifier is required in the transmitter. If a nonlinear amplifier is used, the amplitude fluctuation will be distorted and the spectrum will grow wider again; the effect of the filtering is removed. PSK is a linear type of modulation.

Another popular form of PSK uses four phase states that are spaced 90° apart. Two bits in the data stream can then be coded in the four states, and twice the data will be transmitted in a given bandwidth. With half the bandwidth, the same amount of data can be transmitted as with BPSK. The four-state PSK is called Quadrature Phase Shift Keying, QPSK, and is more efficient measured in spectrum usage than BPSK.

It is possible to decrease the phase spacing from 90° as in QPSK. This is called mPSK where *m* is the number of bits per baud. For example, a phase state spaced 45° apart gives eight possible constellation points in the IQ plane. Three data bits can be transmitted per phase state. The noise margin in the receiver demodulator will suffer due to the closer phase state spacing. As *m* increases, the noise margin decreases. For wireless applications, *m* greater than eight is rarely found.

After transmission through a channel that only adds white noise to the wanted signal, referred to as the additive white Gaussian noise (AWGN) channel, BPSK is optimal with respect to the bit energy to noise power density ratio E_b/N_0. BPSK is used as reference for other types of digital modulation. The bandwidth efficiency is inadequate for terrestrial applications while it is used in deep space satellite communication where extremely weak signals are to be detected.

Quadrature Amplitude Modulation (QAM)

In wireless digital systems where more than three bits per symbol shall be transmitted, QAM is often used. In QAM, both the amplitude and phase of the carrier is varied according to the baseband data signal. The constellation diagram of 16QAM, in which four bits per baud can be sent, is shown in Figure 16.19.

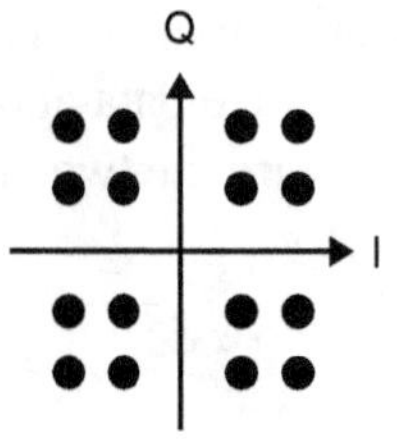

Figure 16.19 16QAM Constellation Diagram

This modulation format produces a more spectrally efficient transmission than BPSK, QPSK, and 8PSK. Note that QPSK is equal to 4QAM.

Offset Quadrature Phase Shift Keying (OQPSK)

Bandlimited PSK needs linear amplifiers, which is not power efficient. Other forms of PSK with less amplitude fluctuations for class C amplification are developed.

The first variation is OQPSK. In QPSK, the I and Q bitstreams are switched simultaneously. In OQPSK, the I and Q bitstreams are offset with one bit period (one half of the symbol period). This is shown in Figure 16.20.

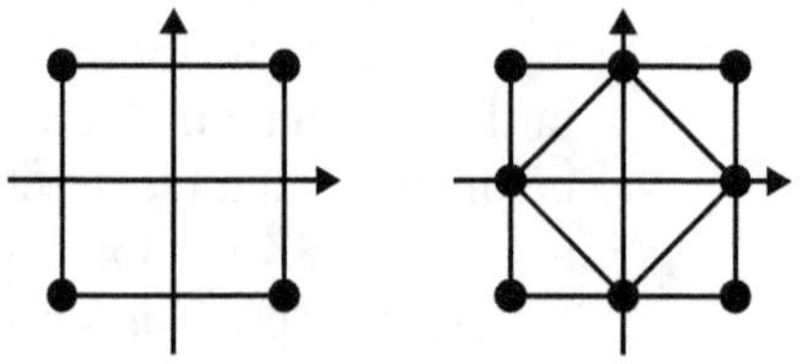

Figure 16.20 Constellation Diagram QPSK and OQPSK

Since the transitions of I and Q are offset at any given time, only one of the two bitstreams changes state. This creates a different constellation. The signal trajectories are modified by the offset of the I and Q bitstreams so that the carrier amplitude does not go through or near the origin (the center of the constellation). The reduced amplitude variation, about 3 dB for OQPSK versus 30 to 40 dB for QPSK, allows less linear and more efficient power amplifiers to be used.

Optimum Filters

When a RF carrier is modulated with a square wave data signal, a wide spectrum is produced. Filtering allows the transmitted bandwidth to be significantly reduced without losing the content of the data. A key question that arises is how to determine the optimum frequency response of a system. There are different types of filters. The most common types are

- Gaussian filters,
- raised cosine, and
- square root raised cosine.

Any fast transition in a signal requires a wide bandwidth. Filters do the function of slowing down the transition and then reduce the bandwidth. Some types of filters cause the trajectory of the signal between states to overshoot, which requires more power to transmit. The carrier power cannot be limited (clipped) without causing the spectrum to spread out again.

Filtering can also create InterSymbol Interference (ISI). Filtering in the frequency domain causes the energy to spread out in the time domain. Figure 16.21 shows a simple example of a first order low pass filter fed with a square wave signal.

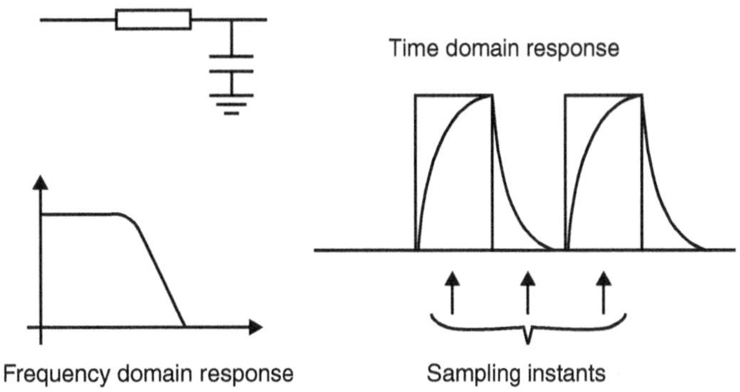

Figure 16.21 Simple Filtering in Frequency and Time Domain

Consider the sequence one-zero. Energy from one bit "leaks" into the next bit due to intersymbol interference. This effect makes the margins for bit decoding in the receiver less.

The place where it is easiest to control the frequency response is at baseband. This is because the filter function to the channel response is most obvious; in fact, it is the same function. Filtering at the RF carrier is theoretically possible, but in practice, difficult to control precisely. (At higher carrier frequencies, VHF and UHF, it is impossible.)

Gaussian Filters

Gaussian filters will have small blurring from the previous signaling state, and a trade-off has to be done between bandwidth efficiency and the inter symbol interference due to the blurring that can be tolerated.

The Gaussian filter has a Gaussian shape in both the frequency domain and the time domain. The name Gaussian relates to the equality between the filter response and the shape of the Gaussian normal distribution curve.

Gaussian filters are used in GSM, which uses constant envelope GMSK modulation, due to the advantages in carrier power and bandwidth efficiency.

Raised Cosine Filters

One family of filters used in many applications using linear modulation methods like PSK, QPSK and QAM is the raised cosine one. The filter roll-off is determined with factor a, which varies from zero to one. An a of zero means a perfect brick-wall filter (i.e., a filter that passes frequencies below the corner frequency unattenuated), and attenuates frequencies above corner frequency 100%. The brick-wall filter is impossible to implement and in practice for RF transmission a between 0.2 and 0.5 is used. In Figure 16.22, roll-off of the raised cosine filter for $\alpha = 0.3$ (f_0), $\alpha = 0.5$ (f_1), and $\alpha = 1.0$ (f_2) with data baud rate 8k baud is shown.

Note that the responses pass through one-half at half the baud rate. This is an important property of the raised cosine filter. The occupied bandwidth of a system is calculated as

$$\text{occupied bandwidth} = \text{symbol rate} \times (1 + a)$$

As noted earlier in this chapter, filtering in the frequency domain causes signal energy to be spread out in the time domain; the filter rings in the time domain. The raised cosine filter has the important property that the ringing passes through zero at the symbol rate. Figure 16.23 shows the impulse response of the raised cosine filter in the time domain.

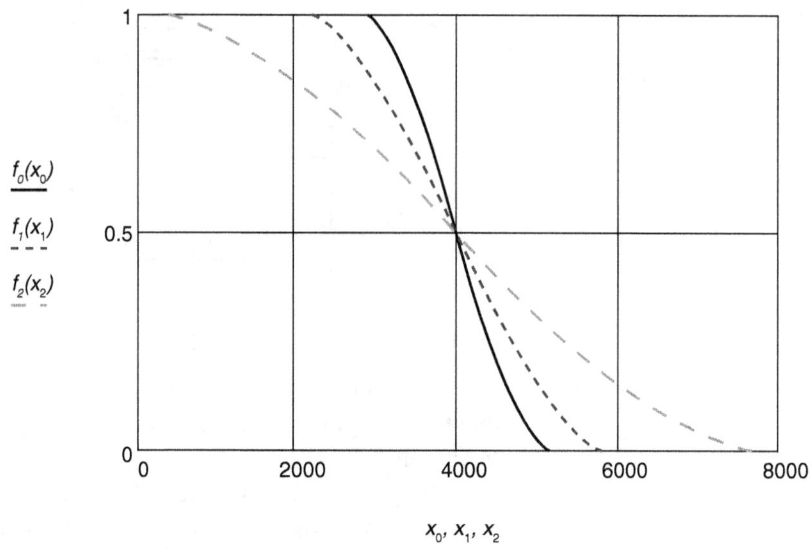

Figure 16.22 Raised Cosine Filter Roll-off

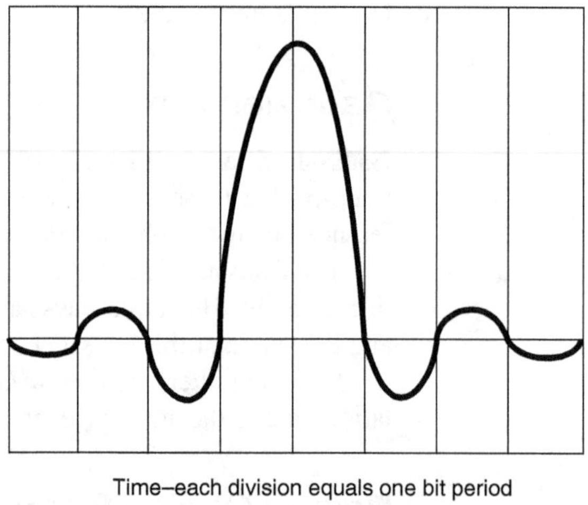

Figure 16.23 Raised Cosine Filter Time Domain Response

The ringing from previous data bits adds energy to the current one, but when the sampling instant is chosen at a time when the ringing passes through zero, it has no impact on the decoding. Filtering causes the amplitude to change and for some time instants to overshoot. The overshoot requires more power to be transmitted, and the transmitter power amplifier must be capable of transmitting the effect at the overshoots without distortion. This effect is not wanted from a cost and efficiency point of view. Figure 16.24 shows examples of signal trajectories between the signaling points for different α.

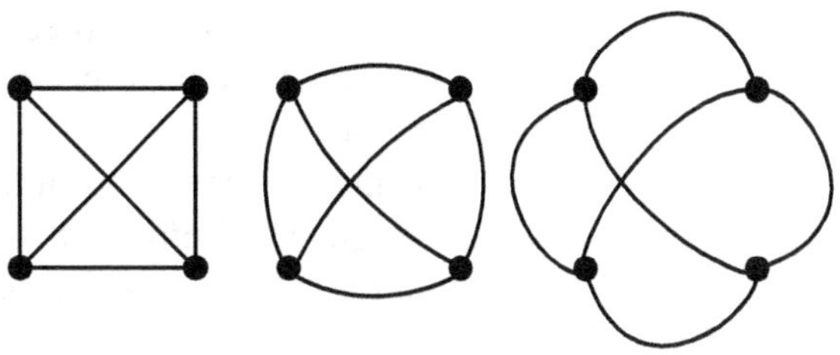

Figure 16.24 Effect of Different Filter Bandwidth

No filtering means an a of infinity, which requires infinite bandwidth. The maximum peak power is equal to the power in the symbol states, and no extra power is required due to the filtering. With $\alpha = 0.375$, the power in the trajectories between the symbol states exceeds that in the symbol state itself. It is a trade-off between bandwidth and power efficiency.

It has been shown that the optimum response in a digital transmission system is obtained when equal filters are used in the transmitter and receiver. The total response is the two responses multiplied with each other, and then using the square root of the response in the transmitter and receiver gives the total response as desired. The filter to be used in the transmitter is then the square root raised cosine.

MULTIPLEXING

Multiplexing is a form of data transmission in which one communication channel carries several transmissions at the same time. The telephone lines that carry our daily conversations can carry thousands, or even more, conversations at a time using multiplexing concept. The exact number of simultaneous transmission depends on the type of communication channel and the data transmission rate.

Economics of scale play an important role in the telephone system. It costs essentially the same amount of money to install and maintain a high-bandwidth trunk as low-bandwidth trunk between two switching officers. Consequently, telephone companies have developed elaborate schemes for multiplexing many conversations over a single physical trunk.

Accordingly, the communication channel is shared in such a way as to maximize the utilization of the channel capacity. Thus, the method of dividing a single channel into many channels so that a number of independent signals may be transmitted on it is known as multiplexing.

Multiplexing schemes can be divided into two basic categories:

- Frequency-division multiplexing (FDM)
- Time-division multiplexing (TDM)

Frequency-division multiplexing (FDM) is the technique used to divide the bandwidth available in a physical medium into a number of smaller independent logical channels with each channel having a small bandwidth. The method of using a number of carrier frequencies, each of which is modulated by an independent speech signal, is, in fact, frequency-division multiplexing.

When many channels are multiplexed together, 400Hz is allocated to each channel to keep them well separated. First the voice channels are raised in frequency, each by a different amount. They can then be combined because no two channels occupy the same portion of the spectrum. Notice that even though there are gaps (guard bands) between the channels, there is some overlap between adja-

cent channels because the filters do not have sharp edges. This overlap means that a strong spike at the edge of one channel will be felt in the adjacent one as non-thermal noise.

Frequency-division multiplexing works best with low-speed devices. The FDM schemes used around the world are to some degree standardized. A wide-spread standard is 12 400-Hz each voice channels (300Hz for user, plus two guard bands of 500Hz each) multiplexed into the 60 to 108 KHz band. Many carriers offer a 48 to 56 kbps leased line service to customers, based on the group. Other standards up to 230000 voice channels also exist.

Example 16.1

The allocated spectrum is about 1 MHz, or roughly 500 to 1500 kHz. Each channel is operating in a portion of the spectrum, with the interchannel separation great enough to prevent interference. This system is an example of frequency-division multiplexing.

Advantages of FDM

1. User can be added to the system by simply adding another pair of transmitter modulator and receiver demodulators.
2. FDM system support full duplex information flow, which is required by most of application.
3. Noise problem for analog communication has lesser effect.

Disadvantages of FDM

1. The initial cost is high. This may include the cable between the two ends and the associated connectors for the cable.
2. A problem for one user can sometimes affect others.
3. Each user requires a precise carrier frequency.

Time-division multiplexing (TDM) is another popular method of utilizing the capacity of a physical channel effectively. Each user of the channel is allotted a small time interval during which they may transmit a message. Thus, the total time available in the channel is divided, and each user is allocated a time slice. In TDM, users send message sequentially one after another. Each user can, however, use the full channel bandwidth during the period he has control over the channel. The channel capacity is fully utilized in TDM by interleaving a number of messages belonging to different users into one long message. This message sent through the physical channel must be separated at the receiving end. Individual chunks of message sent by each user should be reassembled into a full message.

Unfortunately, TDM can only be used for digital data multiplexing. Since local loops produce analog signals, a conversion is needed from analog to digital in the end office where all the individual local loops come together to be combined onto outgoing trucks.

Example 16.2

In some countries, the individual stations have two logical subchannels: music and advertising. These two alternate in time on the same frequency: first a burst of music, then a burst of advertising, then more music, and so on. This situation is time-division multiplexing.

Advantages of TDM

1. Uses single links.
2. Does not require a precise carrier matching at both end of the links.
3. Use of capacity is high.
4. Each to expand the number of users on a system at a low cost.
5. No need to include identification of the traffic stream on each packet.

Disadvantages of TDM

1. The sensitivity to other user problems is high.
2. Initial cost is high.
3. Technical complexity is more.
4. The noise problem for analog communication has greater effect.

Multiplexing is the set of techniques that allows the simultaneous transmission of multiple signals across a single data link. Whenever the transmission capacity of a medium linking two devices is greater than the transmission needs of the devices, the link can be shared in order to maximize the utilization of the link, such as one cable can carry several hundred channels of television.

Types of Multiplexing

There are two basic techniques:

1. Frequency-division multiplexing (FDM)
2. Time-division multiplexing (TDM)
   - Synchronous TDM
   - Asynchronous TDM

These types of multiplexing are shown in Figure 16.25.

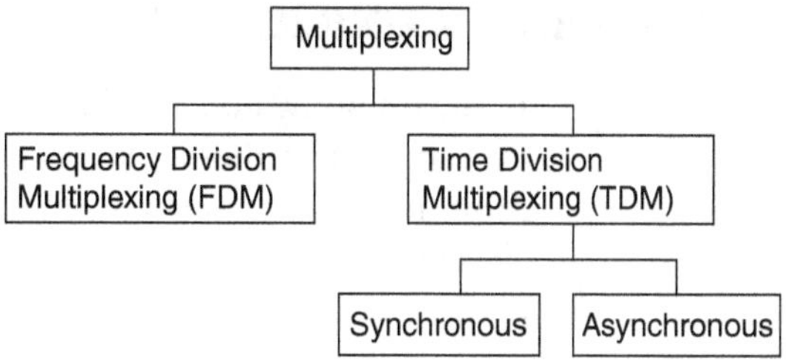

Figure 16.25

FREQUENCY-DIVISION MULTIPLEXING (FDM)

In FDM, signals generated by each sending device modulate different carrier frequencies. These modulated signals are then combined into a single composite signal that can be transported by the link. The carrier frequencies have to be different enough to accommodate the modulation and demodulation signals. Figure 16.26 illustrates the FDM process. The multiplexing process starts by applying amplitude modulation into each signal by using different carrier frequencies. Both signals are then combined

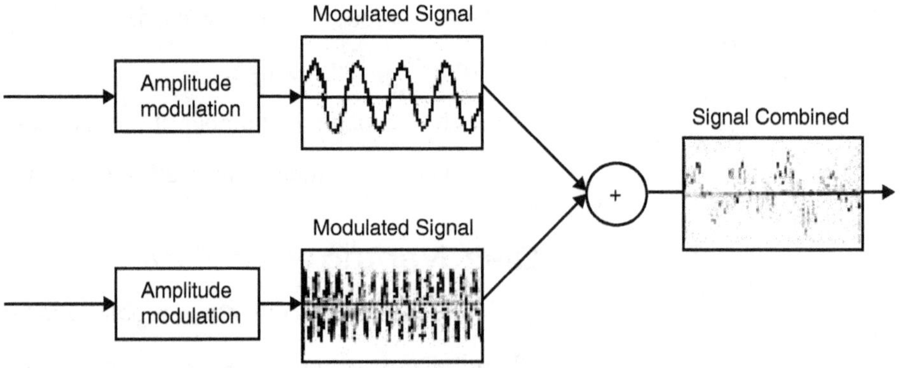

Figure 16.26 Multiplexing - FDM

In demultiplexing process, we use filters to decompose the multiplexed signal into its constituent component signals. Then, each signal is passed to an amplitude demodulation process to separate the carrier signal from the message signal. Finally, the message signal is sent to the waiting receiver. The process of demultiplexing is shown in Figure 16.27.

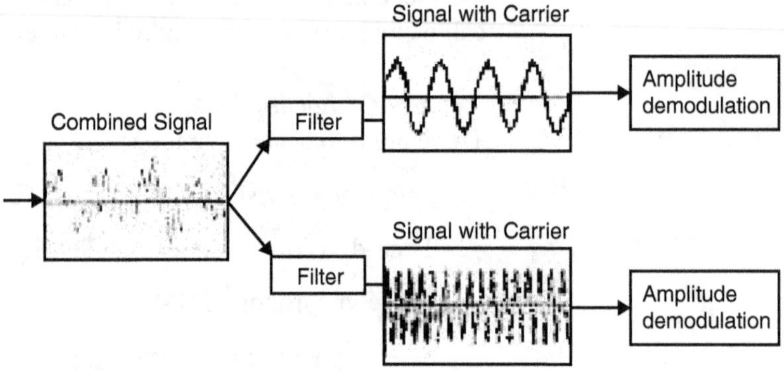

Figure 16.27 Demultiplexing - FDM

TIME-DIVISION MULTIPLEXING (TDM)

In the time-division multiplexing, multiple transmissions can occupy a single link by subdividing them and interleaving the portions. We say that TDM is a round robin use of a frequency. TDM can be implemented in two ways: synchronous TDM and asynchronous TDM.

Synchronous TDM

The multiplexer allocates exactly the same time slot to each device at all times, whether or not a device has anything to transmit. Time slot 1, for example, is

assigned to device 1 alone and cannot be used by any other device as shown in Figure 16.28.

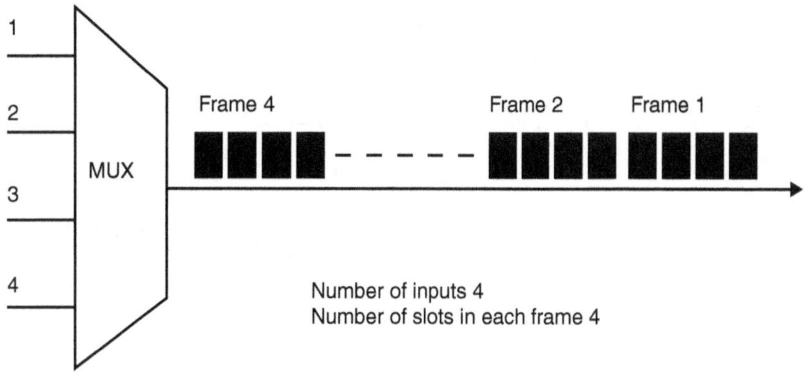

Figure 16.28

Frames

In synchronous TDM, a frame consists of one complete cycle of time slots. Thus the number of slots in frame is equal to the number of inputs.

Figures A and B in Figure 16.29 are an example of how the synchronous TDM works.

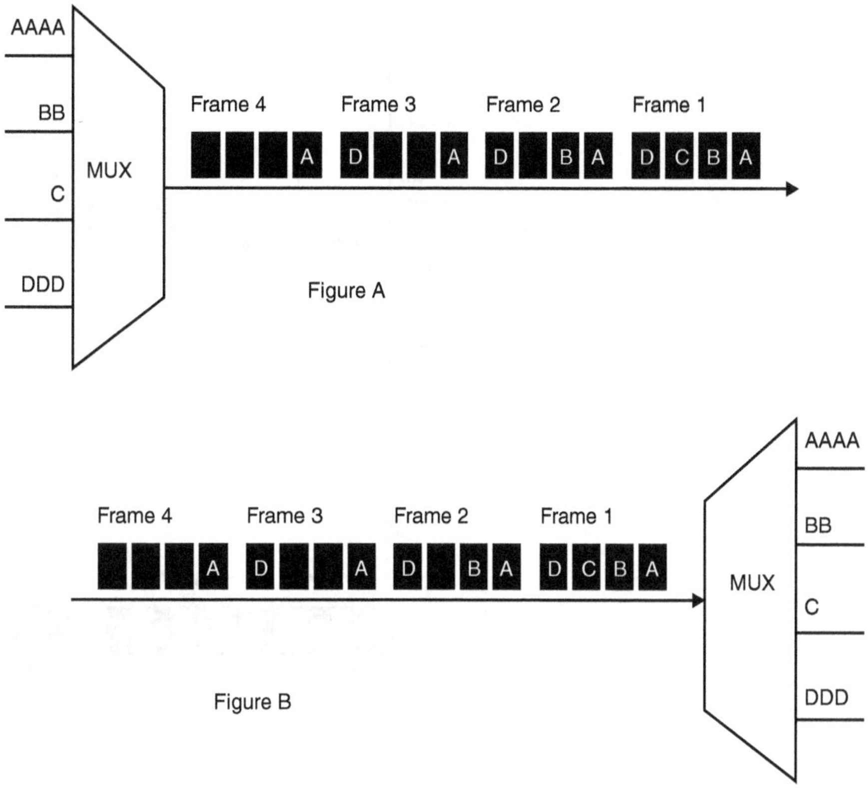

Figure 16.29

Asynchronous TDM

In asynchronous TDM, each slot in a frame is not dedicated to the fix device. Each slot contains an index of the device to be sent to an *a* message. Thus, it is not neces-

sary for the number of slots in a frame to be equal to the number of input devices. More than one slot in a frame can be allocated for an input device. Asynchronous TDM allows for maximization of the link. It allows a number of lower-speed input lines to be multiplexed to a single higher speed line, as shown in Figure 16.30.

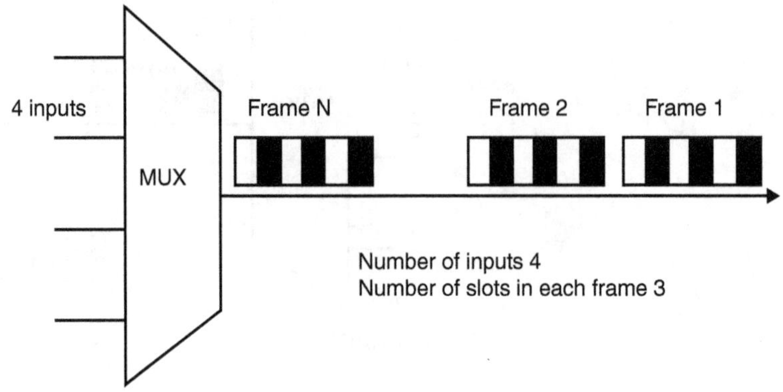

Figure 16.30

Frames

In asynchronous TDM, a frame contains a fixed number of time slots. Each slot has an index of which device to receive.

Figures A and B in Figure 16.31 are examples of how asynchronous TDM works.

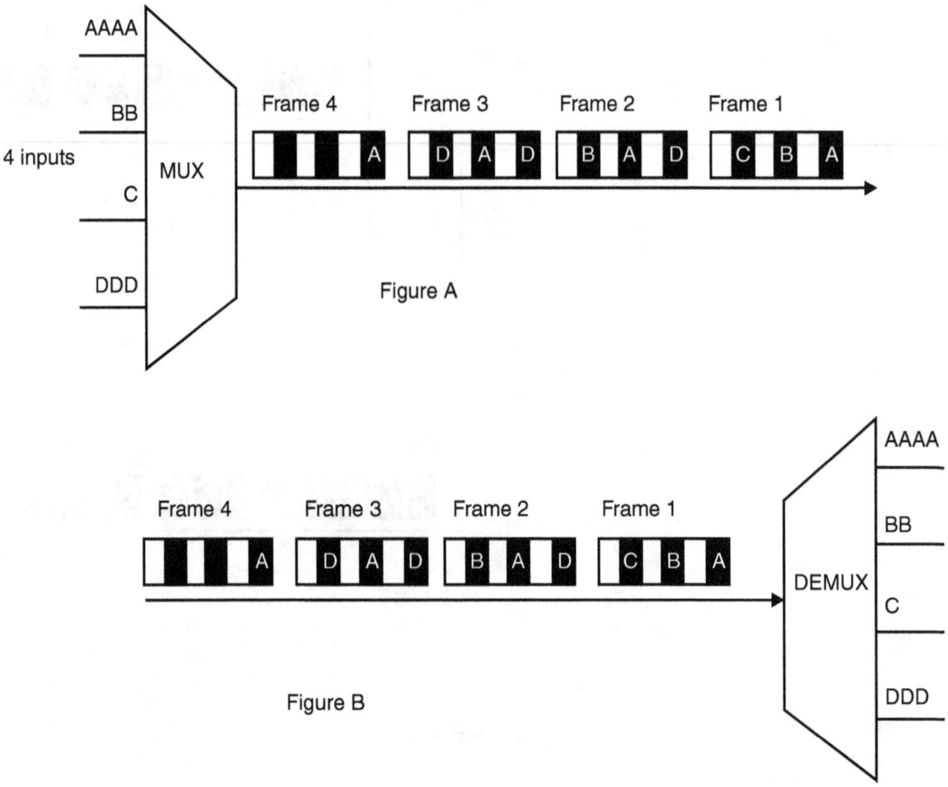

Figure 16.31

REFERENCES

Tom McDermott. *Wireless Digital Communications: Design and Theory*. Tucson Amateur Packet Radio Corporation, 1996.

Smith, David R. *Digital Transmission Systems: Third Edition*. New York: Springer, 2003.

Hewlett Packard. *Digital Modulation in Communication Systems – An Introduction: Application Note 1298*, 1997.

Hewlett Packard. *Spectrum Analysis Amplitude & Frequency Modulation: Application Note 150-1*, 1996.

American Radio Relay League. *The ARRL Handbook for Radio Amateurs*. American Radio Relay League, 1999.

Wes Hayward and Doug DeMaw. *Solid State Design for the Radio Amateur*. American Radio Relay League, 1994.

PROBLEMS

16.1 Consider the periodic square wave shown in Exhibit 16.1. Determine the rms amplitude of the 7th harmonic of the Fourier series.

16.2 For the periodic wave shown in Exhibit 16.1, determine the A_0 term of the Fourier series if it is known that $V_{max} = V_m = 10$ V.

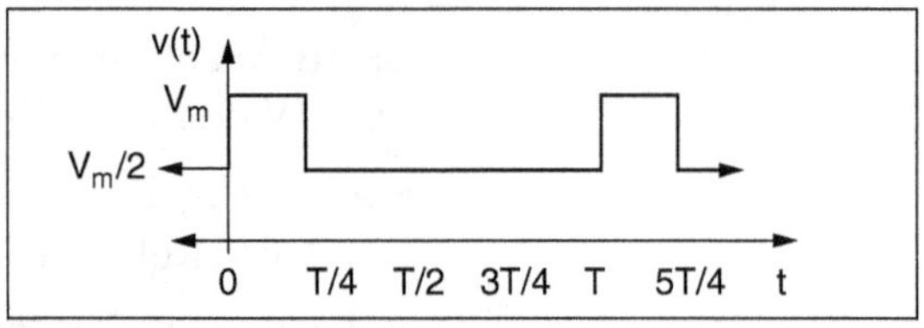

Exhibit 16.1 A periodic wave form

16.3 Assume that two signals (a carrier signal f_c and a modulating sinusoid with frequency f_s, where $f_c >> f_s$) are product-modulated (DSB-SC). Determine the product signal $v(t)$. Assume that the peak amplitude of the carrier is unity.

16.4 Assume that the following two signals are passed through a product modulator

$$x_m(t) = A_{m1} \cos \omega_m t + A_{m2} \cos 3\omega_m t$$
$$x_c(t) = A_c \cos \omega_c t$$

Further assume that $\omega_c >> \omega_m$ and $A_{m2} = \frac{A_m}{10}$. Determine the approximate output signal of the lower sideband.

16.5 Refer to Problem 16.4. Assume the output of the product signal passes through a sharp mid-band filter to eliminate the higher sideband completely and to eliminate most of the lowest frequency component (so that only the translated frequency component of the higher component modulating frequency passes). This filter output frequency again passes through another product modulator that has a carrier frequency that is five times higher than the original (that is, $\omega_{c\,new} = 5\omega_c$). What is the highest frequency component of the output signal of this last modulator? Let $\omega_c = 50$ krad/s and $\omega_m = 1$ krad/s.

SOLUTIONS

16.1 Since all A_n coefficients are zero and only *odd* values of B_n are considered, then for B_7, the f_7 sinusoidal component of the Fourier series is given as $f_7 = \left(\frac{10}{\pi}\right)\left(\frac{1}{7}\right)\sin(7\omega_o t)$. The rms value of this sinusoid is the maximum value divided by the square root of 2, or $f_{7\,\text{rms}} = \left(\frac{10}{\pi}\right)\left(\frac{1}{7}\right)\left(\frac{1}{\sqrt{2}}\right)$ $= 0.321$ units.

16.2 The A_0 term is normally found by taking the average of the integral of $f(t)$ over a full period. However, one recognizes this term as nothing more than the dc average over the period, which, of course, is the average area of the two rectangles

$$\text{Area}_1 = V_m\left(\frac{T}{4}\right), \qquad \text{Area}_2 = \left(\frac{V_m}{2}\right)\left(\frac{3T}{4}\right)$$

and thus

$$A_0 = \frac{1}{T}(\text{Area}_1 + \text{Area}_2) = \frac{1}{T}\left(\frac{V_m T}{4}\right)\left(1+\frac{3}{2}\right) = \frac{5}{8}(10) = 6.25\ \text{V}.$$

16.3 The solution is:

$$v(t) = \frac{V_{m-\max}}{2}[\cos(2\pi(f_c - f_s)) + \cos(2\pi(f_c + f_s))]$$

16.4 Since $\omega_c >> \omega_m$, the product expression is given as

$$x_m(t)\times x_c(t) = (A_{m1}\cos\omega_m t + A_{m2}\cos 3\omega_m t)A_c\cos\omega_c t$$
$$= A_c A_{m1}\left(\cos\omega_m t\cos\omega_c t + \frac{1}{10}\cos 3\omega_m t\cos\omega_c t\right)$$

Since the amplitude of the higher frequency component of $x_m(t)$ is small compared to the fundamental amplitude, then

$$x_m(t)\times x_c(t) \approx A_c A_{m1}\cos\omega_m t\cos\omega_c t$$
$$= \frac{A_c A_{m1}}{2}(\cos((\omega_c - \omega_m)t) + \cos((\omega_c + \omega_m)t))$$

The lower sideband frequency expression, $[x_m(t) \times x_c(t)]_{LSB}$, may be given as

$$[x_m(t)\times x_c(t)]_{LSB} = \frac{A_c A_{m1}}{2}\cos((\omega_c - \omega_m)t) = \frac{A_c A_{m1}}{2}\cos(2\pi(f_c - f_m)t)$$

where $\omega = 2\pi f$.

16.5 The modulating signal to this last modulator is $\omega_{m\,\text{new}} = (\omega_c - 3\omega_m)$, therefore the output of the last modulator involves the new lower and upper sideband frequencies and the upper sideband is the one of interest

$$\omega_{\text{upper}} = \omega_{c\ \text{new}} + \omega_{m\ \text{new}} = 5\omega_c + 3\omega_m$$
$$= (5)(50\times 10^3) + (3)(10^3) = 253\times 10^3\ \text{rad/sec}$$

CHAPTER 17

Computer Networks

OUTLINE

When computers are connected in a network, the functions and tools that each computer provides can be shared with other computers. Networks exist for one major reason: to share information and resources.

Networks can be very simple, such as a small group of computers that share information, or they can be complex, spanning large geographical areas.

TYPES OF NETWORKS

LANs (Local Area Networks)

A network is any collection of independent computers that communicate with one another over a shared network medium. *LANs are networks usually confined to a geographic area,* such as a single building or a college campus. LANs can be

small, linking as few as three computers, but often link hundreds of computers used by thousands of people. The development of standard networking protocols and media has resulted in worldwide proliferation of LANs throughout business and educational organizations.

WANs (Wide Area Networks)

Wide area networking combines multiple LANs that are geographically separate. This is accomplished by connecting the different LANs using services such as dedicated leased phone lines, dial-up phone lines (both synchronous and asynchronous), satellite links, and data packet carrier services. Wide area networking can be as simple as a modem and remote access server for employees to dial into, or it can be as complex as hundreds of branch offices globally linked using special routing protocols and filters to minimize the expense of sending data sent over vast distances.

A WAN is any network that crosses metropolitan, regional, or national boundaries. Most networking professionals define a WAN as any network that uses routers and public network links. The Internet fits both definitions.

WANs differ from LANs in the following ways:

- WANs cover greater distances.
- WAN speeds are slower.
- WANs can be connected on demand or permanently connected; LANs have permanent connections between stations.
- WANs can use public or private network transports; LANs primarily use private network transports.
- WANs can use either full- (simultaneous bidirectional) or half-duplex (omnidirectional for each transmit-receive operation) communications. LANs have typically used half-duplex communications, although many local area networks today use full-duplex communications.

The Internet is actually a specific type of WAN. The Internet is a collection of networks that are interconnected and, therefore, is technically an *internetwork* (Internet is short for the word internetwork).

A WAN can be centralized or distributed. A centralized WAN consists of a central computer (at a central site) to which other computers and dumb terminals connect. The Internet, on the other hand, consists of many interconnected computers in many locations. Thus, it is a distributed WAN.

Internet

The Internet is a system of linked networks that are worldwide in scope and facilitate data communication services such as remote login, file transfer, electronic mail, the World Wide Web, and newsgroups.

With the meteoric rise in demand for connectivity, the Internet has become a communications highway for millions of users. The Internet was initially restricted to military and academic institutions, but now it is a full-fledged conduit for any and all forms of information and commerce. Internet websites now provide personal, educational, political and economic resources to every corner of the planet.

Intranet

With the advancements made in browser-based software for the Internet, many private organizations are implementing intranets. *An intranet is a private network utilizing Internet-type tools* but available only within that organization. For large organizations, an intranet provides an easy access mode to corporate information for employees.

MANs (Metropolitan Area Networks)

This refers to a network of computers within a city.

VPN (Virtual Private Network)

VPN uses a technique known as tunneling to transfer data securely on the Internet to a remote access server on the workplace network. Using a VPN helps save money by using the public Internet instead of making long-distance phone calls to connect securely with the private network. There are two ways to create a VPN connection: by dialing an Internet service provider (ISP) or connecting directly to Internet.

Network can be divided into two main categories

- Peer-to-peer
- Server-based

In peer-to-peer networking, there are no dedicated servers or hierarchy among the computers. All of the computers are equal and, therefore, known as peers. Normally each computer serves as client/server, and there is no one assigned to be an administrator responsible for the entire network.

Peer-to-peer networks are good choices for needs of small organizations where the users are allocated in the same general area, security is not an issue, and the organization and the network will have limited growth within the foreseeable future.

The term *client/server* refers to the concept of sharing the work involved in processing data between the client computer and the most powerful server computer.

The client/server network is the most efficient way to provide:

- databases and management of applications such as spreadsheets, accounting, communications, and document management;
- network management; and
- centralized file storage.

The client/server model is basically an implementation of distributed or cooperative processing. At the heart of the model is the concept of splitting application functions between a client and a server processor. The division of labor between the different processors enables the application designer to place an application function on the processor that is most appropriate for that function. This lets the software designer optimize the use of processors, thus providing the greatest possible return on investment for the hardware.

Client/server application design also lets the application provider mask the actual location of application function. The user often does not know where a specific operation is executing. The entire function may execute in either the PC or server, or the function may be split between them. This masking of application function locations enables system implementers to upgrade portions of a system over time with minimum disruption of application operations, while protecting the investment in existing hardware and software.

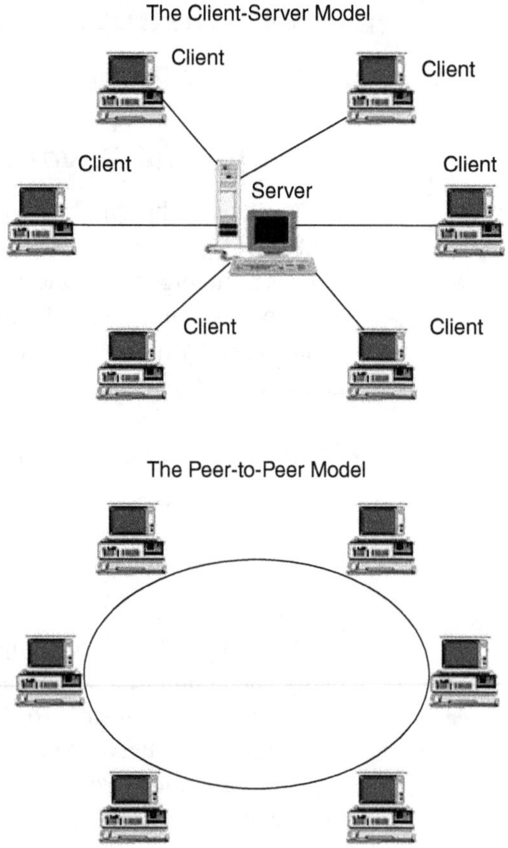

Figure 17.1

Host, Workstation, and Server

Networks are made up of lots of different components, but the three most common network entities are the host, workstation, and server. Each one of these items can be found on most networks.

Hosts

The term *host* covers pretty much every other networking device, but it can also refer to a workstation and server and is most commonly used when discussing TCP/IP-related services and functions.

Workstations

In the classic sense, a *workstation* is a powerful computer used for drafting or other math-intensive applications. The term is also applied to a computer that has multiple central processing units (CPUs) available to users. In the network environment, normally the term refers to any computer that is connected to the network and used by an individual to do work.

It is important to distinguish between workstations and clients. A *client* is any network entity that can request resources from the network; a workstation is a computer that can request resources. Workstations can be clients, but not all clients are workstations. For example, a printer can request resources from the network, but it is a client, not a workstation.

Servers

In the truest sense, a *server* does exactly what the name implies: it provides resources to the clients on the network ("serves" them, in other words). Servers are typically powerful computers that run the software that controls and maintains the network. This software is known as the *network operating system.*

TCP stands for Transmission Control Protocol and IP stands for Internet Protocol. The term TCP/IP is not limited just to these two protocols, however. Frequently, the term TCP/IP is used to refer to a group of protocols related to the TCP and IP protocols such as the User Datagram Protocol (UDP), File Transfer Protocol (FTP), terminal emulation protocol (TELNET), and so on.

Network protocols are standards that allow computers to communicate. A protocol defines how computers identify one another on a network, the form that the data should take in transit, and how this information is processed once it reaches its final destination. Protocols also define procedures for handling lost or damaged transmissions or "packets." TCP/IP (for UNIX, Windows, and other platforms) and AppleTalk (for Macintosh computers) are two of the types of network protocols used.

Although each network protocol is different, they all share the same physical cabling. This common method of accessing the physical network allows multiple protocols to peacefully coexist over the network media and allows the builder of a network to use common hardware for a variety of protocols. This concept is known as "protocol independence."

Table 17.1 Important Protocols and Their Job

Protocol	Acronym	Its Job
Point-to-Point	TCP/IP	The backbone protocol of the Internet. Popular also for intranets using the Internet.
Transmission Control Protocol/ Internet Protocol	TCP/IP	The backbone protocol of the Internet. Popular also for intranets using the Internet.
Internetwork Package Exchange/ Sequenced Packet Exchange	IPX/SPX	This is a standard protocol for the Novell Network Operating System.
NetBIOS Extended User Interface	NetBEUI	This is a Microsoft® protocol that doesn't support routing to other networks.
File Transfer Protocol	FTP	Used to send and receive files from a remote host.
Hyper Text Transfer Protocol	HTTP	Used for the Web to send documents that are encoded in HTML.
Network File Services	NFS	Allows network nodes or workstations to access files and drives as if they were their own.
Simple Mail Transfer Protocol	SMTP	Used to send e-mail over a network.
TELNET		Used to connect to a host and emulate a terminal that the remote server can recognize.

In the United States in the late 1960s, DARPA (the Defense Advanced Research Project Agency) noticed that there was a rapid proliferation of computers in military communications. Because they can be easily programmed, computers provide flexibility in achieving network functions that is not available with other types of communications equipment. The computers then used in military communications were manufactured by different vendors and were designed to interoperate with computers from that vendor only. Vendors used proprietary protocols in their communications equipment. The military had a multivendor network but no common protocol to support the heterogeneous equipment from different vendors.

In TCP/IP terms, a host is any network device that has an IP address. Workstations, servers, and any other network device (as long as it has one or more IP addresses) can all be considered hosts. In conversation, the word *host* is used to describe any minicomputer or server. The term *host* comes from the era when the only intelligent devices on the network were mainframes, which were commonly referred to as hosts regardless of TCP/IP functionality.

Standards Organizations

A wide variety of organizations contribute to internetworking standards by providing forums for discussion, turning informal discussion into formal specifications, and proliferating specifications after they are standardized.

Most standards organizations create formal standards by using specific processes: organizing ideas, discussing the approach, developing draft standards, voting on all or certain aspects of the standards, and then formally releasing the completed standard to the public.

Some of the best-known standards organizations that contribute to internetworking standards include the following:

- **International Organization for Standardization (ISO)**—ISO is an international standards organization responsible for a wide range of standards, including many that are relevant to networking. Its best-known contribution is the development of the OSI reference model and the OSI protocol suite.
- **American National Standards Institute (ANSI)**—ANSI, which is also a member of the ISO, is the coordinating body for voluntary standards groups within the United States. ANSI developed the Fiber Distributed Data Interface (FDDI) and other communications standards.
- **Electronic Industries Association (EIA)**—EIA specifies electrical transmission standards, including those used in networking. The EIA developed the widely used EIA/TIA-232 standard (formerly known as RS-232).
- **Institute of Electrical and Electronic Engineers (IEEE)**—IEEE is a professional organization that defines networking and other standards. The IEEE developed the widely used LAN standards IEEE 802.3 and IEEE 802.5.
- **International Telecommunication Union Telecommunication Standardization Sector (ITU-T)**—Formerly called the Committee for International Telegraph and Telephone (CCITT), ITU-T is now an international organization that develops communication standards. The ITU-T developed X.25 and other communications standards.

- **Internet Activities Board (IAB)**—IAB is a group of internetwork researchers who discuss issues pertinent to the Internet and set Internet policies through decisions and taskforces. The IAB designates some Request For Comments (RFC) documents as Internet standards, including Transmission Control Protocol/Internet Protocol (TCP/IP) and the Simple Network Management Protocol (SNMP).

The *Open System Interconnection (OSI) reference model* describes how information from a software application in one computer moves through a network medium to a software application in another computer. The OSI reference model is a conceptual model composed of seven layers, each specifying particular network functions. The model was developed by the International Organization for Standardization (ISO) in 1984, and it is now considered the primary architectural model for intercomputer communications. The OSI model divides the tasks involved with moving information between networked computers into seven smaller, more manageable task groups. A task or group of tasks is then assigned to each of the seven OSI layers. Each layer is reasonably self-contained so that the tasks assigned to each layer can be implemented independently. This enables the solutions offered by one layer to be updated without adversely affecting the other layers. The following list details the seven layers of the Open System Interconnection (OSI) reference model:

- Layer 7—Application
- Layer 6—Presentation
- Layer 5—Session
- Layer 4—Transport
- Layer 3—Network
- Layer 2—Data link
- Layer 1—Physical

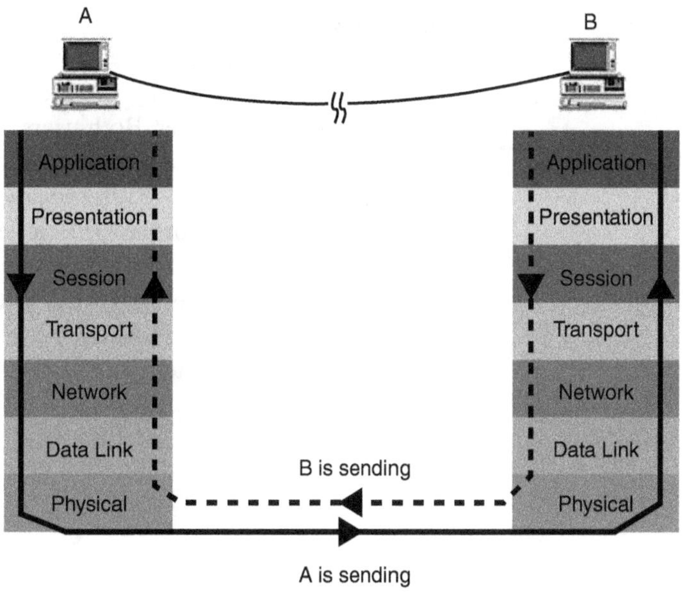

Figure 17.2

Note: A handy way to remember the seven layers is the sentence, "All people seem to need data processing." The beginning letter of each word corresponds to a layer.

- All—Application layer
- People—Presentation layer
- Seem—Session layer
- To—Transport layer
- Need—Network layer
- Data—Data link layer
- Processing—Physical layer

Table 17.2 OSI Reference Model

Seven Independent Layers
Application
Presentation
Session
Transport
Network
Data link
Physical

Characteristics of the OSI Layers

The seven layers of the OSI reference model can be divided into two categories: upper layers and lower layers.

The *upper layers* of the OSI model deal with application issues and generally are implemented only in software. The highest layer, the application layer, is closest to the end user. Both users and application layer processes interact with software applications that contain a communications component. The term upper layer is sometimes used to refer to any layer above another layer in the OSI model.

The *lower layers* of the OSI model handle data transport issues. The physical layer and the data link layer are implemented in hardware and software. The lowest layer, the physical layer, is closest to the physical network medium (e.g., the network cabling) and is responsible for actually placing information on the medium.

Table 17.3 illustrates the division between the upper and lower OSI layers.

Table 17.3 OSI Reference Model

Two Sets of Layers Make Up the OSI Layers	
Application	Application
	Presentation
	Session
Data Transport	Transport
	Network
	Data link
	Physical

The OSI model provides a conceptual framework for communication between computers, but the model itself is not a method of communication. Actual communication is made possible by using communication protocols. In the context of data networking, a *protocol* is a formal set of rules and conventions that governs how computers exchange information over a network medium. A protocol implements the functions of one or more of the OSI layers.

A wide variety of communication protocols exist. Some of these protocols include LAN protocols, WAN protocols, network protocols, and routing protocols. *LAN protocols* operate at the physical and data link layers of the OSI model and define communication over the various LAN media. *WAN protocols* operate at the lowest three layers of the OSI model and define communication over the various wide-area media. *Routing protocols* are network layer protocols that are responsible for exchanging information between routers so that the routers can select the proper path for network traffic. Finally, *network protocols* are the various upper-layer protocols that exist in a given protocol suite. Many protocols rely on others for operation. For example, many routing protocols use network protocols to exchange information between routers. This concept of building upon the layers already in existence is the foundation of the OSI model.

OSI Model and Communication Between Systems

Information being transferred from a software application in one computer system to a software application in another must pass through the OSI layers. For example, if a software application in System A has information to transmit to a software application in System B, the application program in System A will pass its information to the application layer (Layer 7) of System A. The application layer then passes the information to the presentation layer (Layer 6), which relays the data to the session layer (Layer 5), and so on down to the physical layer (Layer 1). At the physical layer, the information is placed on the physical network medium and is sent across the medium to System B. The physical layer of System B removes the information from the physical medium, and then its physical layer passes the information up to the data link layer (Layer 2), which passes it to the network layer (Layer 3), and so on, until it reaches the application layer (Layer 7) of System B. Finally, the application layer of System B passes the information to the recipient application program to complete the communication process.

A given layer in the OSI model generally communicates with three other OSI layers: the layer directly above it, the layer directly below it, and its peer layer in other networked computer systems. The data link layer in System A, for example, communicates with the network layer of System A, the physical layer of System A, and the data link layer in System B shown in Figure 17.3.

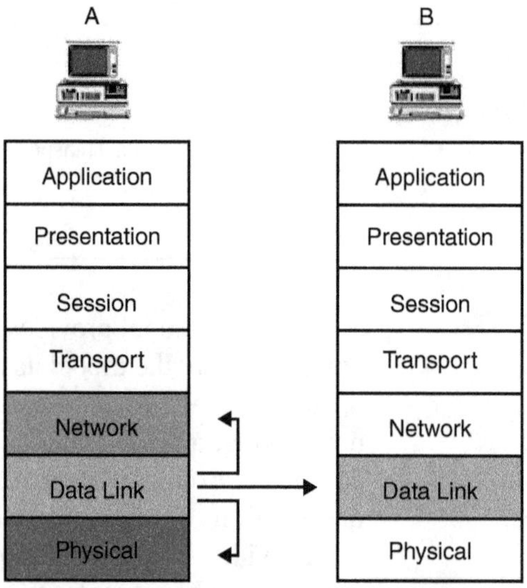

Figure 17.3 OSI Model Layers Communicate with Other Layers

Nearly all other devices were known as dumb terminals. As TCP/IP came into the picture, only the mainframes, or hosts, received IP addresses. This is the same era that produced the term *gateway* to refer to any Layer 3 intermediate device, such as a router. Just as the term *gateway* remains in common use today, such as in the very common term *default gateway*, the term *host* is still used. However, its use is much broader now that nearly every end and intermediate device is intelligent and has at least one IP address, which makes them hosts.

OSI Model Physical Layer

The physical layer defines the electrical, mechanical, procedural, and functional specifications for activating, maintaining, and deactivating the physical link between communicating network systems. Physical layer specifications define characteristics such as voltage levels, timing of voltage changes, physical data rates, maximum transmission distances, and physical connectors. Physical layer implementations can be categorized as either LAN or WAN specifications.

OSI Model Data Link Layer

The data link layer provides reliable transit of data across a physical network link. Different data link layer specifications define different network and protocol characteristics, including physical addressing, network topology, error notification, sequencing of frames, and flow control. Physical addressing (as opposed to network addressing) defines how devices are addressed at the data link layer. Network topology consists of the data link layer specifications that often define how devices are to be physically connected, such as in a bus or a ring topology. Error notification alerts upper-layer protocols that a transmission error has occurred, and the sequencing of data frames reorders frames that are transmitted out of sequence.

Finally, flow control moderates the transmission of data so that the receiving device is not overwhelmed with more traffic than it can handle at one time.

The Institute of Electrical and Electronics Engineers (IEEE) has subdivided the data link layer into two sublayers: Logical Link Control (LLC) and Media Access Control (MAC).

The *Logical Link Control (LLC)* sublayer of the data link layer manages communications between devices over a single link of a network. LLC is defined in the IEEE 802.2 specification and supports both connectionless and connection-oriented services used by higher-layer protocols. IEEE 802.2 defines a number of fields in data link layer frames that enable multiple higher-layer protocols to share a single physical data link. The *Media Access Control (MAC)* sublayer of the data link layer manages protocol access to the physical network medium. The IEEE MAC specification defines MAC addresses, which enable multiple devices to uniquely identify one another at the data link layer.

OSI Model Network Layer

The network layer defines the network address, which differs from the MAC address. Some network layer implementations, such as IP, define network addresses in a way that route selection can be determined systematically by comparing the source network address with the destination network address and applying the subnet mask. Because this layer defines the logical network layout, routers can use this layer to determine how to forward packets. As a result, much of the design and configuration work for internetworks happens at Layer 3, the network layer.

OSI Model Transport Layer

The transport layer accepts data from the session layer and segments the data for transport across the network. Generally, the transport layer is responsible for making sure the data is delivered error-free and in the proper sequence. Flow control generally occurs at the transport layer.

Flow control manages data transmission between devices so that the transmitting device does not send more data than the receiving device can process. Multiplexing enables data from several applications to be transmitted onto a single physical link. Virtual circuits are established, maintained, and terminated by the transport layer. Error checking involves creating various mechanisms for detecting transmission errors, while error recovery involves acting, such as requesting that data be retransmitted, to resolve any errors that occur.

The transport protocols used on the Internet are TCP and UDP.

OSI Model Session Layer

The session layer establishes, manages, and terminates communication sessions. Communication sessions consist of service requests and service responses that occur between applications located in different network devices. These requests and responses are coordinated by protocols implemented at the session layer. Some examples of session-layer implementations include Zone Information Protocol (ZIP), the AppleTalk protocol that coordinates the name binding process; and Session Control Protocol (SCP), the DECnet Phase IV session layer protocol.

OSI Model Presentation Layer

The presentation layer provides a variety of coding and conversion functions that are applied to application layer data. These functions ensure that information sent from the application layer of one system would be readable by the application layer of another system. Some examples of presentation layer coding and conversion schemes include common data representation formats, conversion of character representation formats, common data compression schemes, and common data encryption schemes.

Common data representation formats—or the use of standard image, sound, and video formats—enable the interchange of application data between different types of computer systems. Conversion schemes are used to exchange information with systems by using different text and data representations, such as EBCDIC and ASCII. Standard data compression schemes enable data that is compressed at the source device to be properly decompressed at the destination. Standard data encryption schemes enable data encrypted at the source device to be properly deciphered at the destination.

Presentation layer implementations are not typically associated with a particular protocol stack. Some well-known standards for video include QuickTime and Motion Picture Experts Group (MPEG). QuickTime is an Apple computer specification for video and audio, and MPEG is a standard for video compression and coding.

Among the well-known graphic image formats are Graphics Interchange Format (GIF), Joint Photographic Experts Group (JPEG), and Tagged Image File Format (TIFF). GIF is a standard for compressing and coding graphic images. JPEG is another compression and coding standard for graphic images, and TIFF is a standard coding format for graphic images.

OSI Model Application Layer

The application layer is the OSI layer closest to the end user, which means that both the OSI application layer and the user interact directly with the software application.

This layer interacts with software applications that implement a communicating component. Such application programs fall outside the scope of the OSI model. Application layer functions typically include identifying communication partners, determining resource availability, and synchronizing communication.

When identifying communication partners, the application layer determines the identity and availability of communication partners for an application with data to transmit. When determining resource availability, the application layer must decide whether sufficient network resources for the requested communication exist. In synchronizing communication, all communication between applications requires cooperation that is managed by the application layer.

Some examples of application layer implementations include Telnet, File Transfer Protocol (FTP), and Simple Mail Transfer Protocol (SMTP).

Information Formats

The data and control information that is transmitted through internetworks takes a variety of forms. The terms used to refer to these information formats are not used consistently in the internetworking industry but are sometimes used interchange-

ably. Common information formats include frames, packets, datagrams, segments, messages, cells, and data units.

A frame is an information unit whose source and destination are data link layer entities. A frame is composed of the data link layer header (and possibly a trailer) and upper-layer data. The header and trailer contain control information intended for the data link layer entity in the destination system. Data from upper-layer entities is encapsulated in the data link layer header and trailer. In Table 17.4, the basic components of a data link layer frame are shown.

Table 17.4 Data from Upper-Layer Entities Makes Up the Data Link Layer Frame

Frame		
Data link layer header	Upper layer data	Data link layer trailer

A *packet* is an information unit whose source and destination are network layer entities. A packet is composed of the network layer header (and possibly a trailer) and upper-layer data. The header and trailer contain control information intended for the network layer entity in the destination system. Data from upper-layer entities is encapsulated in the network layer header and trailer. Table 17.5 shows the basic components of a network layer packet.

Table 17.5 Three Basic Components Make Up a Network Layer Packet

Packet		
Network layer header	Upper layer data	Network layer trailer

The term *datagram* usually refers to an information unit whose source and destination are network layer entities that use connectionless network service.

The term *segment* usually refers to an information unit whose source and destination are transport layer entities.

A *message* is an information unit whose source and destination entities exist above the network layer (often at the application layer).

A *cell* is an information unit of a fixed size whose source and destination are data link layer entities. Cells are used in switched environments, such as Asynchronous Transfer Mode (ATM) and Switched Multimegabit Data Service (SMDS) networks. A cell is composed of the header and payload. The header contains control information intended for the destination data link layer entity and is typically 5 bytes long. The payload contains upper-layer data that is encapsulated in the cell header and is typically 48 bytes long.

The length of the header and the payload fields always are the same for each cell. Table 17.6 depicts the components of a typical cell.

Table 17.6 Two Components Make Up a Typical Cell

Cell

Network layer header	Upper layer data

53 bytes

Data unit is a generic term that refers to a variety of information units. Some common data units are service data units (SDUs), protocol data units, and bridge protocol data units (BPDUs). SDUs are information units from upper-layer protocols that define a service request to a lower-layer protocol. Protocol data unit (PDU) is OSI terminology for a packet.

Connection-Oriented and Connectionless Network Services

In general, transport protocols can be characterized as being either connection-oriented or connectionless. Connection-oriented services must first establish a connection with the desired service before passing any data. A connectionless service can send the data without any need to establish a connection first. In general, connection-oriented services provide some level of delivery guarantee, whereas connectionless services do not.

Connection-oriented service involves three phases: connection establishment, data transfer, and connection termination.

During connection establishment, the end nodes may reserve resources for the connection. The end nodes also may negotiate and establish certain criteria for the transfer, such as a window size used in TCP connections. This resource reservation is one of the things exploited in some denial of service (DOS) attacks. An attacking system will send many requests for establishing a connection but then will never complete the connection. The attacked computer is then left with resources allocated for many never-completed connections. Then, when an end node tries to complete an actual connection, there are not enough resources for the valid connection.

The data transfer phase occurs when the actual data is transmitted over the connection. During data transfer, most connection-oriented services will monitor for lost packets and handle resending them. The protocol is generally also responsible for putting the packets in the right sequence before passing the data up the protocol stack.

When the transfer of data is complete, the end nodes terminate the connection and release resources reserved for the connection.

Connection-oriented network services have more overhead than connectionless ones. Connection-oriented services must negotiate a connection, transfer data, and tear down the connection, whereas a connectionless transfer can simply send the data without the added overhead of creating and tearing down a connection. Each has its place in internetworks.

Internetwork Addressing

Internetwork addresses identify devices separately or as members of a group. Addressing schemes vary depending on the protocol family and the OSI layer. Three types of internetwork addresses are commonly used: data link layer addresses, Media Access Control (MAC) addresses, and network layer addresses.

Data Link Layer Addresses

A *data link layer address* uniquely identifies each physical network connection of a network device. Data link addresses sometimes are referred to as *physical* or *hardware addresses*. Data link addresses usually exist within a flat address space and have a pre-established and typically fixed relationship to a specific device.

End systems generally have only one physical network connection and, thus, have only one data link address. Routers and other internetworking devices typically have multiple physical network connections and, therefore, have multiple data link addresses. Figure 17.4 illustrates how each interface on a device is uniquely identified by a data link address.

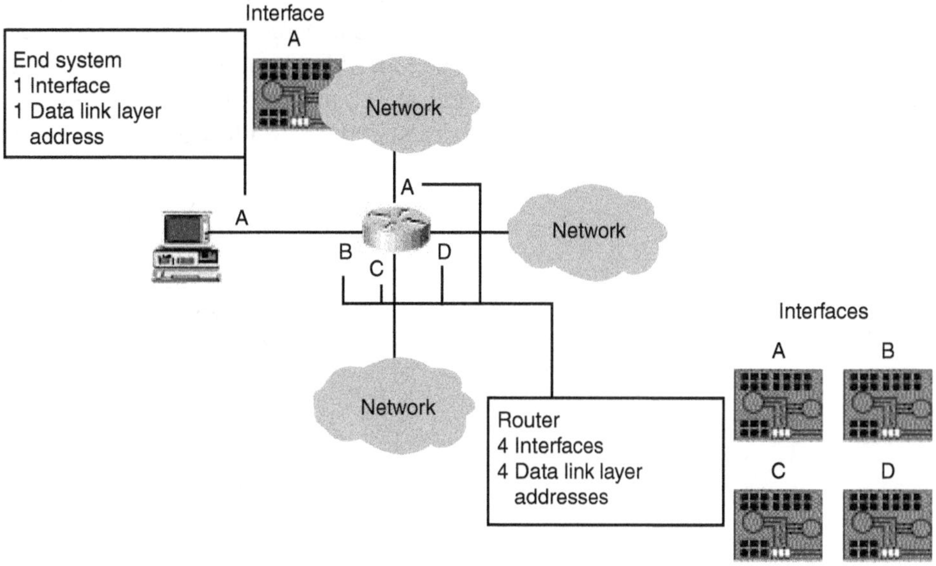

Figure 17.4 Each Interface on a Device is Uniquely Identified by a Data Link Address

MAC Addresses

Media Access Control (MAC) addresses consist of a subset of data link layer addresses. MAC addresses identify network entities in LANs that implement the IEEE MAC addresses of the data link layer. As with most data link addresses, MAC addresses are unique for each LAN interface. Table 17.7 illustrates the relationship between MAC addresses, data link addresses, and the IEEE sublayers of the data link layer.

Table 17.7 MAC Addresses, Data Link Addresses, and the IEEE Sublayers of the Data Link Layer are all Related

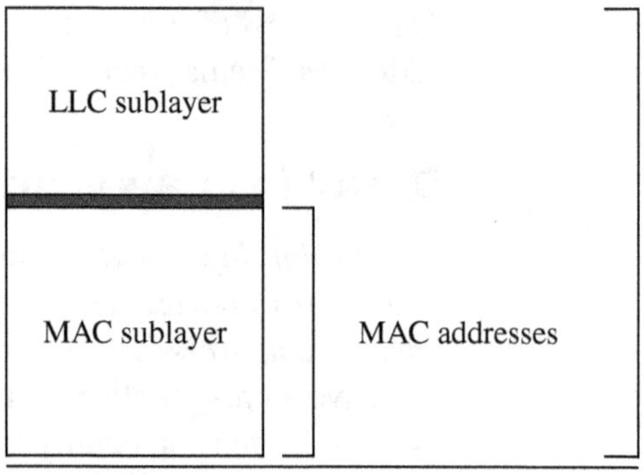

MAC addresses are 48 bits in length and are expressed as 12 hexadecimal digits. The first six hexadecimal digits, which are administered by the IEEE, identify the manufacturer or vendor and thus comprise the Organizationally Unique Identifier (OUI). The last six hexadecimal digits comprise the interface serial number or another value administered by the specific vendor. MAC addresses sometimes are called *burned-in addresses (BIAs)* because they are burned into read-only memory (ROM) and are copied into random-access memory (RAM) when the interface card initializes. Table 17.8 illustrates the MAC address format.

Table 17.8 MAC Address Contains a Unique Format of Hexadecimal Digits

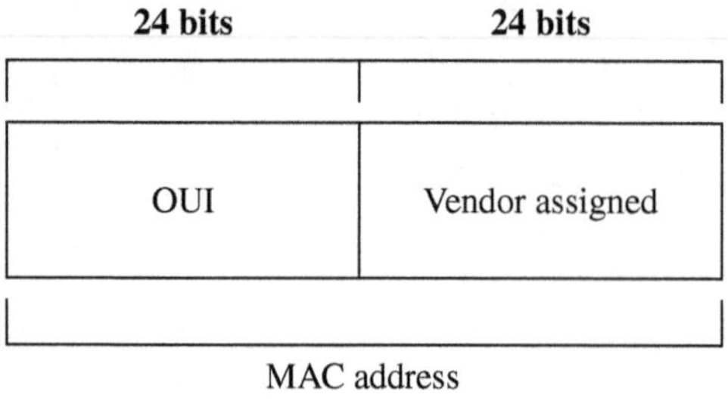

Mapping Addresses

Because internetworks generally use network addresses to route traffic around the network, there is a need to map network addresses to MAC addresses. When the network layer has determined the destination station's network address, it must forward the information over a physical network using a MAC address. Different protocol suites use different methods to perform this mapping, but the most popular is Address Resolution Protocol (ARP).

Different protocol suites use different methods for determining the MAC address of a device. The following three methods are used most often. Address Resolution Protocol (ARP) maps network addresses to MAC addresses. The Hello protocol enables network devices to learn the MAC addresses of other network

devices. MAC addresses are either embedded in the network layer address or are generated by an algorithm.

Address Resolution Protocol (ARP) is the method used in the TCP/IP suite. When a network device needs to send data to another device on the same network, it knows the source and destination network addresses for the data transfer. It must somehow map the destination address to a MAC address before forwarding the data. First, the sending station will check its ARP table to see if it has already discovered this destination station's MAC address. If it has not, it will send a broadcast on the network with the destination station's IP address contained in the broadcast. Every station on the network receives the broadcast and compares the embedded IP address to its own. Only the station with the matching IP address replies to the sending station with a packet containing the MAC address for the station. The first station then adds this information to its ARP table for future reference and proceeds to transfer the data.

When the destination device lies on a remote network, one beyond a router, the process is the same except that the sending station sends the ARP request for the MAC address of its default gateway. It then forwards the information to that device. The default gateway will then forward the information over whatever networks necessary to deliver the packet to the network on which the destination device resides. The router on the destination device's network then uses ARP to obtain the MAC of the actual destination device and delivers the packet.

The Hello protocol is a network layer protocol that enables network devices to identify one another and indicate that they are still functional. When a new end system powers up, for example, it broadcasts hello messages onto the network. Devices on the network then return hello replies, and hello messages are also sent at specific intervals to indicate that they are still functional. Network devices can learn the MAC addresses of other devices by examining Hello protocol packets.

Three protocols use predictable MAC addresses. In these protocol suites, MAC addresses are predictable because the network layer either embeds the MAC address in the network layer address or uses an algorithm to determine the MAC address. The three protocols are Xerox Network Systems (XNS), Novell Internetwork Packet Exchange (IPX), and DECnet Phase IV.

Network Layer Addresses

A *network layer address* identifies an entity at the network layer of the OSI layers. Network addresses usually exist within a hierarchical address space and sometimes are called *virtual* or *logical addresses*.

The relationship between a network address and a device is logical and unfixed; it typically is based either on physical network characteristics (the device is on a particular network segment) or on groupings that have no physical basis (the device is part of an AppleTalk zone). End systems require one network layer address for each network layer protocol they support. (This assumes that the device has only one physical network connection.) Routers and other internetworking devices require one network layer address per physical network connection for each network layer protocol supported. For example, a router with three interfaces each running AppleTalk, TCP/IP, and OSI must have three network layer addresses for each interface. The router, therefore, has nine network layer addresses. Figure 17.5 illustrates how each network interface must be assigned a network address for each protocol supported.

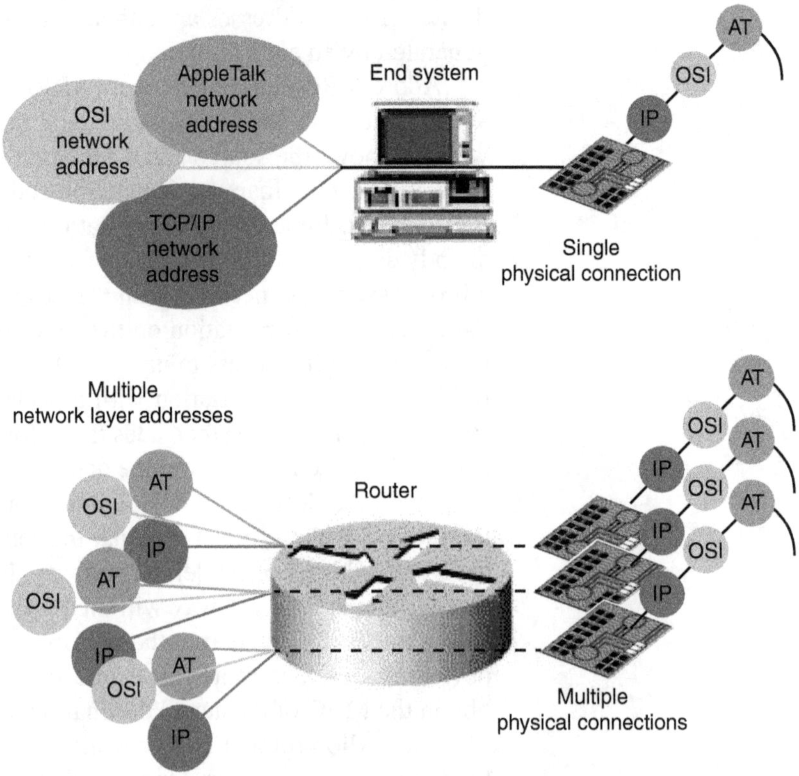

Figure 17.5 Each Network Interface Must be Assigned a Network Address for Each Protocol Supported

Hierarchical Versus Flat Address Space

Internetwork address space typically takes one of two forms: hierarchical address space or flat address space. A *hierarchical address space* is organized into numerous subgroups, each successively narrowing an address until it points to a single device (in a manner similar to street addresses). A *flat address space* is organized into a single group (in a manner similar to U.S. Social Security numbers).

Hierarchical addressing offers certain advantages over flat-addressing schemes. Address sorting and recall is simplified using comparison operations. For example, "Ireland" in a street address eliminates any other country as a possible location. The difference between hierarchical and flat address spaces is illustrated in Figure 17.6.

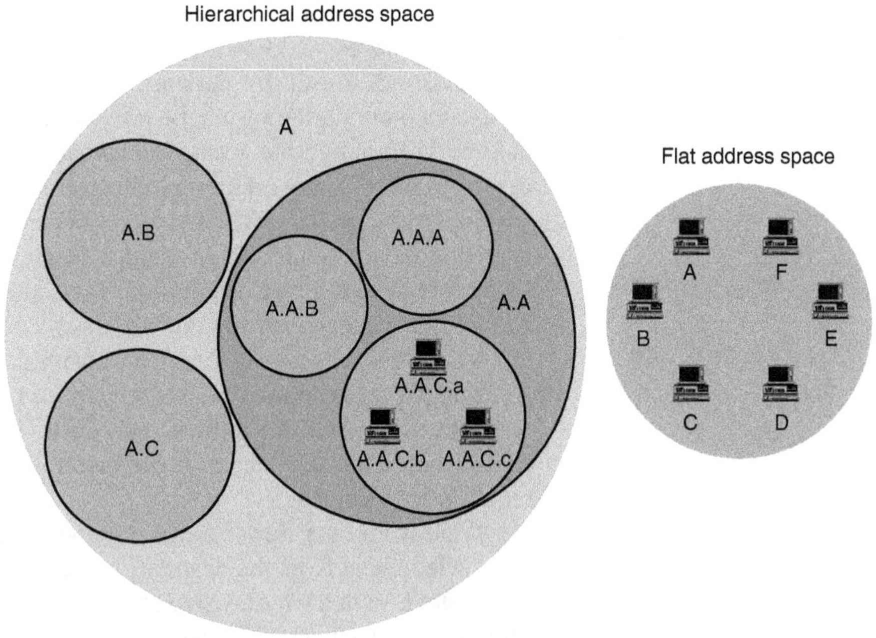

Figure 17.6 Hierarchical and Flat Address Spaces Differ in Comparison Operations

Address Assignments

Addresses are assigned to devices as one of two types: static and dynamic. *Static addresses* are assigned by a network administrator according to a preconceived internetwork addressing plan. A static address does not change until the network administrator manually changes it. *Dynamic addresses* are obtained by devices when they attach to a network by means of some protocol-specific process. A device using a dynamic address often has a different address each time that it connects to the network. Some networks use a server to assign addresses. Server-assigned addresses are recycled for reuse as devices disconnect.

Therefore, a device is likely to have a different address each time it connects to the network.

Addresses Versus Names

Internetwork devices usually have both a name and an address associated with them. Internetwork names typically are location-independent and remain associated with a device wherever that device moves (e.g., from one building to another). Internetwork addresses usually are location-dependent and change when a device is moved (although MAC addresses are an exception to this rule). As with network addresses being mapped to MAC addresses, names are usually mapped to network addresses through some protocol. The Internet uses Domain Name System (DNS) to map the name of a device to its IP address.

Flow Control Basics

Flow control is a function that prevents network congestion by ensuring that transmitting devices do not overwhelm receiving devices with data. A high-speed computer, for example, may generate traffic faster than the network can transfer it or faster than the destination device can receive and process it. The three commonly

used methods for handling network congestion are buffering, transmitting source-quench messages, and windowing.

Buffering is used by network devices to temporarily store bursts of excess data in memory until they can be processed. Occasional data bursts are easily handled by buffering. Excess data bursts can exhaust memory, however, forcing the device to discard any additional datagrams that arrive. Source-quench messages are used by receiving devices to help prevent their buffers from overflowing. The receiving device sends source-quench messages to request that the source reduce its current rate of data transmission. First, the receiving device begins discarding received data due to overflowing buffers. Second, the receiving device begins sending source-quench messages to the transmitting device at the rate of one message for each packet dropped. The source device receives the source-quench messages and lowers the data rate until it stops receiving the messages. Finally, the source device then gradually increases the data rate as long as no further source-quench requests are received.

Windowing is a flow-control scheme in which the source device requires an acknowledgment from the destination after a certain number of packets have been transmitted. With a window size of 3, the source requires an acknowledgment after sending three packets, as follows. First, the source device sends three packets to the destination device. Then, after receiving the three packets, the destination device sends an acknowledgment to the source. The source receives the acknowledgment and sends three more packets. If the destination does not receive one or more of the packets for some reason, such as overflowing buffers, it does not receive enough packets to send an acknowledgment. The source then retransmits the packets at a reduced transmission rate.

Error-Checking Basics

Error-checking schemes determine whether transmitted data has become corrupt or otherwise damaged while traveling from the source to the destination. Error checking is implemented at several of the OSI layers.

One common error-checking scheme is the cyclic redundancy check (CRC), which detects and discards corrupted data. Error-correction functions (such as data retransmission) are left to higher-layer protocols. A CRC value is generated by a calculation that is performed at the source device. The destination device compares this value to its own calculation to determine whether errors occurred during transmission. First, the source device performs a predetermined set of calculations over the contents of the packet to be sent. Then, the source places the calculated value in the packet and sends the packet to the destination. The destination performs the same predetermined set of calculations over the contents of the packet and then compares its computed value with that contained in the packet. If the values are equal, the packet is considered valid. If the values are unequal, the packet contains errors and is discarded.

Multiplexing Basics

Multiplexing is a process in which multiple data channels are combined into a single data or physical channel at the source. Multiplexing can be implemented at any of the OSI layers. Conversely, *demultiplexing* is the process of separating multiplexed data channels at the destination. One example of multiplexing is when

data from multiple applications is multiplexed into a single lower-layer data packet as shown in Figure 17.7.

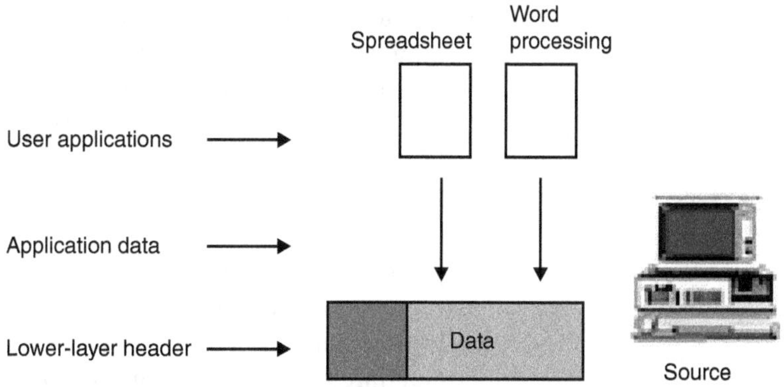

Figure 17.7 Multiple Applications can be Multiplexed into a Single Lower-Layer Data Packet

Another example of multiplexing is when data from multiple devices is combined into a single physical channel (using a device called a multiplexer), shown in Figure 17.8.

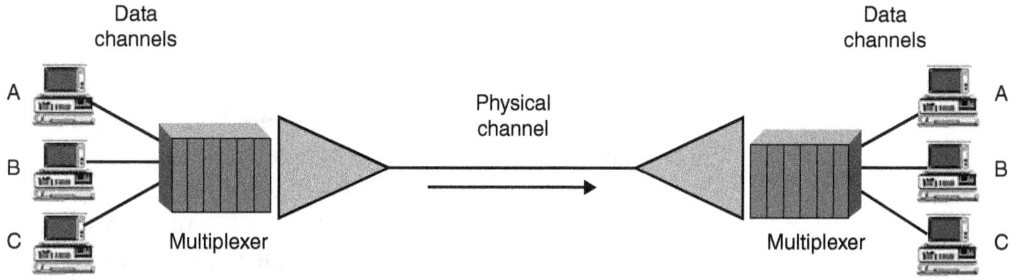

Figure 17.8 Multiple Devices can be Multiplexed into a Single Physical Channel

A *multiplexer* is a physical layer device that combines multiple data streams into one or more output channels at the source. Multiplexers demultiplex the channels into multiple data streams at the remote end and, thus, maximize the use of the bandwidth of the physical medium by enabling it to be shared by multiple traffic sources.

Some methods used for multiplexing data are time-division multiplexing (TDM), asynchronous time-division multiplexing (ATDM), frequency-division multiplexing (FDM), and statistical multiplexing.

In TDM, information from each data channel is allocated bandwidth based on preassigned time slots, regardless of whether there is data to transmit. In ATDM, information from data channels is allocated bandwidth as needed by using dynamically assigned time slots. In FDM, information from each data channel is allocated bandwidth based on the signal frequency of the traffic. In statistical multiplexing, bandwidth is dynamically allocated to any data channels that have information to transmit.

TYPES OF SERVERS

A *device server* is defined as a specialized, network-based hardware device designed to perform a single or specialized set of server functions. It is characterized by a minimal operating architecture that requires no per seat network operat-

ing system license and client access that is independent of any operating system or proprietary protocol. In addition the device server is a "closed box," delivering extreme ease of installation, minimal maintenance, and can be managed by the client remotely via a Web browser.

Print servers, terminal servers, remote access servers, and network time servers are examples of device servers that are specialized for particular functions. Each of these types of servers has unique configuration attributes in hardware or software that help them to perform best in their particular arena.

Print servers allow printers to be shared by other users on the network. Supporting either parallel and/or serial interfaces, a print server accepts print jobs from any person on the network using supported protocols and manages those jobs on each appropriate printer.

Print servers generally do not contain a large amount of memory; printers simply store information in a queue. When the desired printer becomes available, they allow the host to transmit the data to the appropriate printer port on the server. The print server can then simply queue and print each job in the order in which print requests are received, regardless of protocol used or the size of the job.

Multiport Device Servers Devices that are attached to a network through a multiport device server can be shared between terminals and hosts at both the local site and throughout the network. A single terminal may be connected to several hosts at the same time (in multiple concurrent sessions) and can switch between them. Multiport device servers are also used to network devices that have only serial outputs. A connection between serial ports on different servers is opened, allowing data to move between the two devices.

Given its natural translation ability, a multiprotocol, multiport device server can perform conversions between the protocols it knows, like LAT and TCP/IP. While server bandwidth is not adequate for large file transfers, it can easily handle host-to-host inquiry/response applications, electronic mailbox checking, and so forth. It is far more economical than the alternatives of acquiring expensive host software and special-purpose converters. Multiport device and print servers give their users greater flexibility in configuring and managing their networks.

Whether it is moving printers and other peripherals from one network to another, expanding the dimensions of interoperability, or preparing for growth, multiport device servers can fulfill specified needs, all without major rewiring.

Access Servers Access Servers listen for inbound requests to connect to the network from the outside. Remote access servers provide remote users (working at home or on the road) with a connection to the network, either via modems or an IP connection. While Ethernet is limited to a geographic area, remote users such as traveling sales people need access to network-based resources. Remote LAN access, or remote access, is a popular way to provide this connectivity. Access servers use telephone services to link a user or office with an office network. Dial-up remote access solutions such as ISDN or asynchronous dial introduce more flexibility. Dial-up remote access offers both the remote office and the remote user the economy and flexibility of "pay as you go" telephone services. ISDN is a special telephone service that offers three channels, two 64 Kbps "B" channels for user data and a "D" channel for setting up the connection. With ISDN, the B channels can be combined for double bandwidth or separated for different applications or users. With asynchronous remote access, regular telephone lines are combined with modems and remote access servers to allow users and networks to dial

anywhere in the world and have data access. Remote access servers provide connection points for both dial-in and dial-out applications on the network to which they are attached. These hybrid devices route and filter protocols and offer other services such as modem pooling and terminal/printer services. For the remote PC user, one can connect from any available telephone jack (RJ45), including those in hotel rooms or on most airplanes.

Network Time Servers A network time server is a server specialized in the handling of timing information from sources such as satellites or radio broadcasts and is capable of providing this timing data to its attached network. Specialized protocols such as NTP or udp/time allow a time server to communicate to other network nodes ensuring that activities that must be coordinated according to their time of execution are synchronized correctly. GPS satellites are one source of information that can allow global installations to achieve constant timing.

Application Server Hosts a network application.

Web Server Holds and delivers Web pages and other Web content using the Hypertext Transfer Protocol (HTTP).

Mail Server Hosts and delivers e-mail. It's the electronic equivalent of a post office.

Fax Server Sends and receives faxes (via a special fax board) for the entire network without the need for paper.

Telephony Server Functions as a "smart" answering machine for the network. It can also perform call center and call-routing functions.

Physical Topologies

A topology is basically a map of a network. The physical topology of a network describes the layout of the cables and workstations and the location of all network components. Often, physical topologies are compared to logical topologies, which define how the information or data flows within the network. The topologies are usually similar. It is important to note, however, that a network can have one type of physical topology and a completely different logical topology.

The cables or connections in a physical topology are often referred to as network media (or *physical media*). Choosing how computers will be connected in a company's network is critical. A wrong decision in the physical topology makes the media difficult to correct because it is costly and disruptive to change an entire installation once it is in place. The typical organization changes the physical layout and physical media of a network only once about every 10 years, so it is important to choose a configuration that allows for network growth.

The four most common topologies are as follows:

- Bus
- Star
- Ring
- Mesh

Bus Topology

In a *bus topology,* all computers are attached to a single continuous cable that is terminated at both ends, which is the simplest way to create a physical network. Originally, computers were attached to the cable with wire taps. This did not prove practical, so drop cables were used to attach computers to the main cable. In 10Base-2 Ethernet, no drop cables are used, but instead, a "T" is inserted in the main cable wherever a station needs to connect.

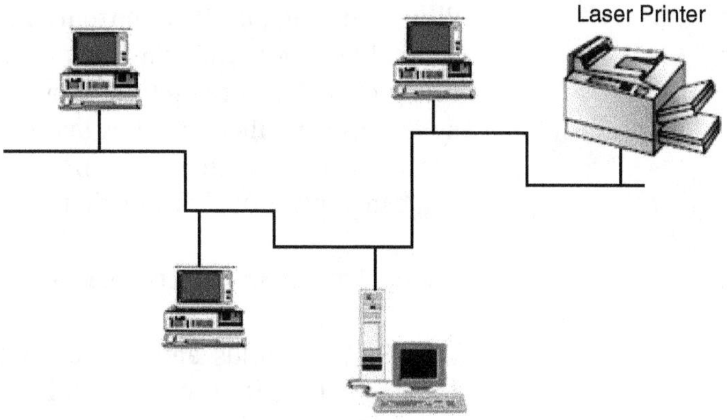

Figure 17.9 Example for Physical Bus Topology

When communicating on a network that uses a bus topology, all computers see the data on the wire. This does not create chaos, though, because the only computer that actually accepts the data is the one to which it is addressed. One can think of a bus network as a small party. David is already there, along with 10 other people. David would like to tell Joe something. David yells out, "Joe! Will you grab me a cup of coffee, please?" Everyone in the party can hear David, but only Joe will respond. A star network with a hub also operates in this manner.

As with most things, there are pros and cons to a bus topology. On the pro side, a bus topology has the following characteristics:

- Simple to install
- Relatively inexpensive
- Uses less cable than other topologies

The following characteristics describe the con side of a bus topology:

- Difficult to move and change
- Little fault tolerance (a single fault can bring down the entire network)
- Difficult to troubleshoot

Star Topology

Unlike those in a bus topology, each computer in a *star topology* is connected to a central point by a separate cable or wireless connection. The central point is a device known by such names as *hub, MAU, concentrator, switch,* and *access point,* depending on the underlying technology.

Although this setup uses more cable than a bus, a star topology is much more fault tolerant than a bus topology. This means that if a failure occurs along one of the cables connecting to the hub, only that portion of the network is affected, not the entire network. Depending on the type of device at the other end of that cable,

this may affect only a single device. It also means that new stations can be added just by running a single new cable.

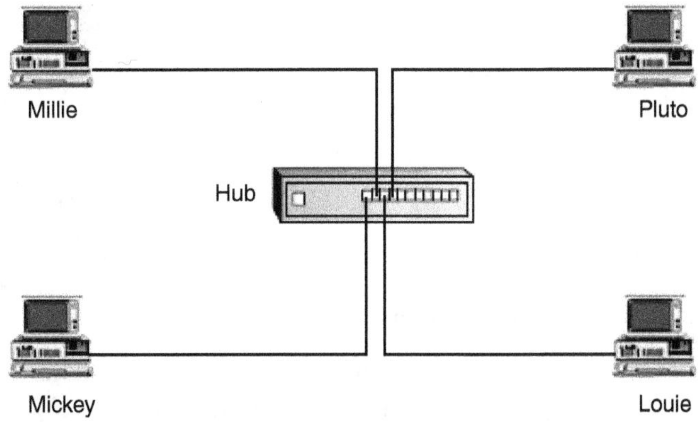

Figure 17.10 Star Topology with a Hub

The design of a star topology resembles an old wagon wheel with the wooden spokes extending from the center point. The center point of the wagon wheel would be considered the hub. Like the wagon wheel, the network's most vulnerable point is the hub. If it fails, the whole system collapses. Fortunately, hub failures are extremely rare.

As with the bus topology, the star topology has advantages and disadvantages. The increasing popularity of the star topology is mainly due to the large number of advantages, which include the following:

- New stations can be added easily and quickly.
- A single cable failure won't bring down the entire network.
- It is relatively easy to troubleshoot.

The disadvantages of a star topology include the following:

- Total installation cost can be higher because of the larger number of cables, but prices are constantly becoming more and more competitive.
- It has a single point of failure (the hub, or other central device).

There are two subtle special cases for the star topology, the point-to-point link and the wireless access point. It takes a firm understanding of what the devices making up the wireless network are capable of to be able to categorize the wireless topology. Wireless access points are nothing more than wireless hubs or switches, depending on capability, that are able to act as wireless bridges by establishing a wireless point-to-point connection to another wireless access point. Either use is reminiscent of the wired star/point-to-point topologies they emulate.

Ring Topology

In the *ring topology*, each computer is connected directly to two other computers in the network. Data moves down a one-way path from one computer to another. The good news about laying out cable in a ring is that the cable design is simple. The bad news is that, as with bus topology, any break, such as adding or removing a computer, disrupts the entire network. Also, because there must be a "break" in the ring in order to add another station, it is very difficult to reconfigure without

bringing down the whole network. For this reason, the physical ring topology is seldom used.

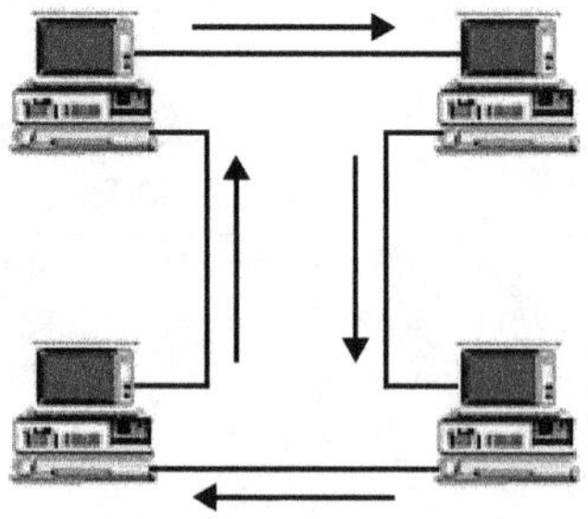

Figure 17.11 Ring Topology

A few pros and many cons are associated with a ring topology. On the pro side, the ring topology is relatively easy to troubleshoot. A station will know when a cable fault has occurred because it will stop receiving data from its upstream neighbor.

On the con side, a ring topology has the following characteristics:

- Expensive because multiple cables are needed for each workstation
- Difficult to reconfigure
- Not fault tolerant; a single cable fault can bring down the entire network

Mesh Topology

In a *mesh topology*, a path exists from each station to every other station in the network, resulting in the most physical connections per node of any topology. While not usually seen in LANs, a variation on this type of topology—the hybrid mesh—is used on the Internet and other WANs in a limited fashion. Hybrid mesh topology networks can have multiple connections between some locations, but this is done only for redundancy. In addition, it's called a hybrid because other types of topologies might be mixed in as well. Also, it is not a full mesh because there is not a connection between each and every node, just a few for backup purposes.

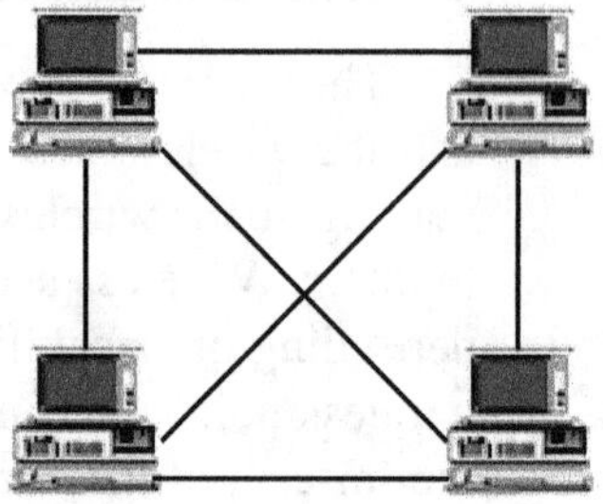

Figure 17.12

A mesh topology can become quite complex as wiring and connections increase exponentially. For every n stations, there will be $n(n - 1)/2$ connections. For example, in a network of 4 computers, there are $4(4 - 1)/2$ connections, or six connections.

If the network grows to only 10 computers, there will be 45 connections to manage. Given this impossible overhead, only small systems can be connected this way. The payoff for all this work is a more fail-safe, or fault-tolerant, network, at least as far as cabling is concerned.

Today, the mesh topology is rarely used, and then only in a WAN environment and only because the mesh topology is fault tolerant. Computers or network devices can switch between these multiple, redundant connections if the need arises. On the con side, the mesh topology is expensive and quickly becomes too complex. Using what is known as a partial mesh is a workable compromise between the need for fault tolerance and the cost of a full mesh topology. With a partial mesh, the same technology can be used between all devices, but not all devices are interconnected. Strategy becomes the name of the game when deciding which devices to interconnect.

Backbones and Segments

With complex networks, there must be a way of intelligently identifying which part of the network is being discussed. For this reason, it is common to break networks into backbones and segments.

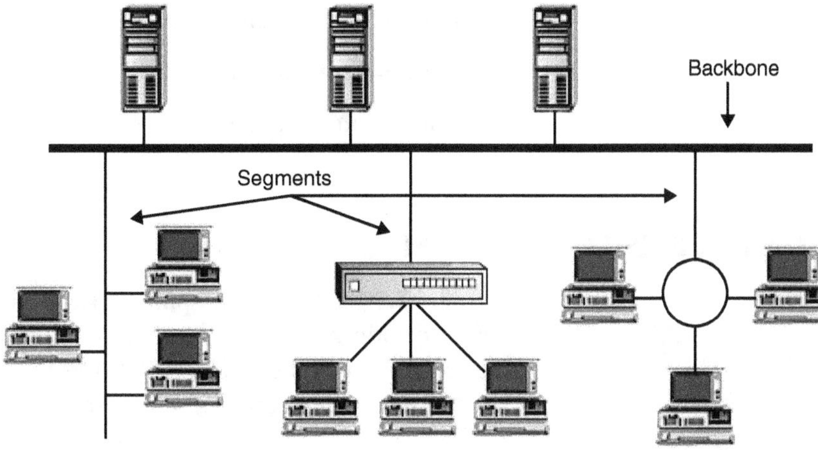

Figure 17.13

Backbone

A *backbone* is the part of the network to which all segments and servers connect. A backbone provides the structure for a network and is considered the main part of any network. It usually uses a high-speed communications technology of some kind, such as Fiber Distributed Data Interface (FDDI) or 1 or 10 Gigabit Ethernet. All servers and all network segments typically connect directly to the backbone so that any segment is only one segment away from any server on that backbone. Because all segments are close to the servers, the network is more efficient.

Segments

Segment is a general term for any short section of the network that is not part of the backbone. Just as servers connect to the backbone, workstations connect to segments. Segments are connected to the backbone to allow the workstations on them access to the rest of the network.

Selecting the Right Topology

Each topology has its advantages and drawbacks. The process of selecting a topology can be much like buying a pair of shoes. It's a matter of finding something that fits, feels right, and is within the design budget.

Creating a simple network for a handful of computers in a single room is usually done most efficiently by using a wireless access point and wireless network cards because they are simple and easy to install and don't require the running of cables. Larger environments are usually wired in a star because moves, adds, and changes to the network are performed more efficiently with a physical star than with any of the other topologies.

If uptime is required to the definition of fault resistant (that is, 99.9% uptime or less than 8 hours total downtime per year), serious consideration should be given to a partial mesh layout while keeping in mind *maintenance* requirements in the design. There will be $n(n - 1)/2$ connections to maintain in a full mesh configuration and a subset of that for a partial mesh, which may quickly exceed maintenance budgets.

Generally speaking, the following considerations are balanced when choosing a physical topology for the network:

- Cost
- Ease of installation
- Ease of maintenance
- Cable fault tolerance

ROUTER VERSUS SWITCH

A full understanding of computer networking and the function of its many components, including switches and routers, requires a knowledge of OSI (Open Systems Interconnection) model. The OSI model has seven layers ranging from the physical layer to the topmost application layer.

Router Versus Switch: Definition

A router is a computer networking device used to connect together multiple computer networks. These devices carry out intelligent exchange of data packets within these networks. Every router is charged with the responsibility of directing data packets to their right destinations, from point to point. Modern routers are mini computers with hardware and software designed to serve this purpose. Their prime function is to forward data and regulate internetwork data traffic.

A switch, or more precisely, a "network switch," is an electronic device that is used to integrate together small segments of a single network and is used to switch information between network devices or terminals. Also known as *network bridges*, these are integral linking elements of any Ethernet local area network.

Router Versus Switch: OSI Level Function

A router operates at Level 3 of the OSI model, which is also known as the "network layer." A router normally connects together multiple logical subnets that do not possess a common address on a network. They are Layer 3 switches carrying out data transfers at that level.

A network switch operates at the Layer 2 of the OSI model, also known as data link layer. Some switches that operate at data link layer, as well as the upper layers, are known as multilayer switches. When comparing routers and switches, the former reads and directs information by reading IP addresses of data packets, while

the latter uses Media Access Control (MAC) addresses. A router has a sophisticated algorithm-based software to determine optimum path for data transfer. However, network switches don't have that kind of sophisticated software.

A wireless router versus switch comparison would not be any different from the previous descriptions. The only difference is that wireless routers operate through a radio communication medium for data transfer instead of wired medium used by other routers. Network switches are always wired devices and never wireless. Routers play a bigger role in the integration of smaller networks into bigger ones than switches that function as links within a single network.

PROBLEMS

17.1 What are the layers of the OSI model?

17.2 Which layer determines path selection in an internetwork?

17.3 What types of things are defined at the physical layer?

17.4 What is one method of mapping network addresses to MAC addresses?

17.5 Which includes more overhead: connection-oriented or connectionless services?

SOLUTIONS

17.1 Application, presentation, session, transport, network, data link, and physical. Remember the sentence: "All people seem to need data processing."

17.2 Layer 3 is the network layer.

17.3 Voltage levels, time of voltage changes, physical data rates, maximum transmission distances, physical connectors, and type of media.

17.4 ARP, Hello, or predictable

17.5 Connection-oriented

CHAPTER 18

Digital Systems

OUTLINE

NUMBER SYSTEMS

By studying other number systems such as binary (base 2), octal (base 8), and hexadecimal (base 16), engineers will be able to represent digital system and computer system addresses and data. When discussing how a computer stores information, the binary number system becomes very important because this is the system that computers use. It is important that students understand that computers store and transmit data using electrical pulses, and these pulses can take two forms: "on" (1) or "off" (0).

The following topics treat the manipulation of numbers represented in different bases as well as the binary representation of negative integers and floating-point numbers.

Different Bases

The following are a series of examples that should help students understand how numbers are represented using different bases.

DECIMAL (base 10, 10^n)

possible digits: 0, 1, 2, 3, 4, 5, 6, 7, 8, 9

$$874\ 693\ 125 = 8 \times 100{,}000{,}000 + 7 \times 10{,}000{,}000 + 4 \times 1{,}000{,}000 + 6 \times 100{,}000 + 9 \times 10{,}000 + 3 \times 1000 + 1 \times 100 + 2 \times 10 + 5 \times 1$$
$$= 8 \times 10^8 + 7 \times 10^7 + 4 \times 10^6 + 6 \times 10^5 + 9 \times 10^4 + 3 \times 10^3 + 1 \times 10^2 + 2 \times 10^1 + 5 \times 10^0$$

BINARY (base 2, 2n)

possible digits: 0, 1

$$110\ 010\ 101 = 1 \times 256 + 1 \times 128 + 0 \times 64 + 0 \times 32 + 1 \times 16 + 0 \times 8 + 1 \times 4 + 0 \times 2 + 1 \times 1$$
$$= 1 \times 2^8 + 1 \times 2^7 + 0 \times 2^6 + 0 \times 2^5 + 1 \times 2^4 + 0 \times 2^3 + 1 \times 2^2 + 0 \times 2^1 + 1 \times 2^0$$

Some terminology used include *bits* and *bytes*. A bit is a single place for a data "0" or data "1." A byte is a group of 8 bits (e.g., 1010 1100).

Ob is sometimes used to indicate that it is a binary number (e.g., Ob10111111).

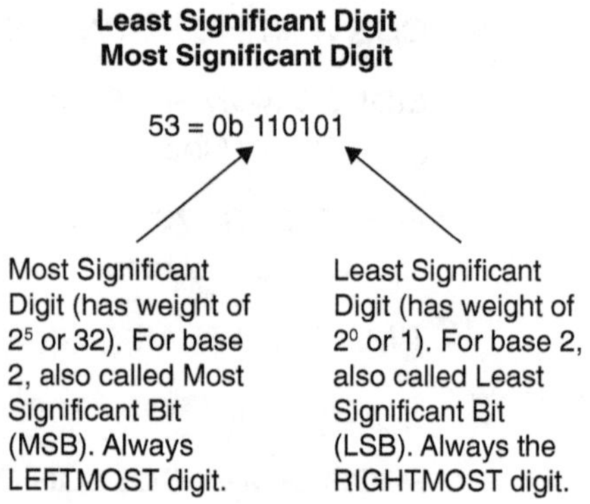

Figure 18.1

OCTAL (base 8, 8n)

possible digits: 0, 1, 2, 3, 4, 5, 6, 7

$$7\ 426\ 351 = 7 \times 262\ 144 + 4 \times 32\ 768 + 2 \times 4096 + 6 \times 512 + 3 \times 64 + 5 \times 8 + 1 \times 1$$
$$= 7 \times 8^6 + 4 \times 8^5 + 2 \times 8^4 + 6 \times 8^3 + 3 \times 8^2 + 5 \times 8^1 + 1 \times 8^0$$

HEXADECIMAL (base 16)

possible digits: 0, 1, 2, 3, 4, 5, 6, 7, 8, 9, A, B, C, D, E, F
(Note: In base 10, A = 10, B = 11, C = 12, D = 13, E = 14, F = 15)

$$3B2C4 = 3 \times 65\ 536 + B \times 4096 + 2 \times 256 + C \times 16 + 4 \times 1$$
$$= 3 \times 16^4 + B \times 16^3 + 2 \times 16^2 + C \times 16^1 + 4 \times 16^0$$

Ox is sometimes used to indicate that it is a binary number (e.g., OxA1F5).

CONVERTING BETWEEN BASES

When converting numbers from one base to another, there are four different types of conversions that the students will need to remember:

1. Any base → Decimal
2. Decimal → Any base

3. Octal/hexadecimal → Binary
4. Binary → Octal/hexadecimal

All of the conversions can be made using some of the NCEES-approved calculators. However, the NCEES-approved calculators limit their conversions to 16 bit binary numbers.

Fractional numbers can also be converted as follows:

Binary to Decimal

$$\begin{aligned} 0b1011.11 &= 1*2^3 + 0*2^2 + 1*2^1 + 1*2^0 + 1*2^{-1} + 1*2^{-2} \\ &= 8 \quad + 0 \quad + 2 \quad + \quad 1 \quad + 0.5 + 0.25 \\ &= 11.75 \end{aligned}$$

While the binary number system is very important because of its connection with computers, it is not the only other number system of importance. Two other number systems that are frequently seen are octal numbers and hexadecimal numbers. The octal number system is a base-8 number system and uses the digits 0 – 7 to represent numbers. The hexadecimal number system is a base-16 number system and uses the digits 0–9 along with the letters A–F to represent numbers. Table 18.1 shows a comparison of the first 16 numbers in the binary, octal, decimal, hexadecimal, BCD, and Gray code number systems.

Table 18.1

Binary Base-2	Decimal Base-10	Hexadecimal Base-16	Octal Base-8	BCD Code	Gray Code
0000	0	0	0	0	0000
0001	1	1	1	1	0001
0010	2	2	2	2	0011
0011	3	3	3	3	0010
0100	4	4	4	4	0110
0101	5	5	5	5	0111
0110	6	6	6	6	0101
0111	7	7	7	7	0100
1000	8	8	10	8	1100
1001	9	9	11	9	1101
1010	10	A	12	---	1111
1011	11	B	13	---	11110
1100	12	C	14	---	1010
1101	13	D	15	---	1011
1110	14	E	16	---	1001
1111	15	F	17	---	1000

Source: NCEES, *FE Reference Handbook: 9.0 Version for Computer-Based Testing*, (Clemson, SC, 2013) 213.

Recall the formula we learned from binary to decimal conversion:

$$DIGIT * BASE^{POSITION\ \#}$$

Now consider the octal number 1473.2_8. Each column of this number represents a power of eight.

512s	64s	Eights	Ones	Eighths
8^3	8^2	8^1	8^0	8^{-1}
1	**4**	**7**	**3**	**. 2**

Using the information from this table, the decimal value for 1473.2_8 can be found.

$$\begin{aligned} 1*8^3 &= 1*512 &&= 512.00 \\ 4*8^2 &= 4*64 &&= 256.00 \\ 7*8^1 &= 7*8 &&= 56.00 \\ 3*8^0 &= 3*1 &&= 3.00 \\ 2*8^{-1} &= 2*0.125 &&= +\ \underline{0.25} \\ & && \quad 827.25 \end{aligned}$$

From this analysis, 1473.2_8 is equivalent to 827.25_{10} in decimal.

For a hexadecimal number: $33B.4_{16}$, the columns of our table are now powers of 16.

256s	Sixteens	Ones	Sixteenths
16^2	16^1	16^0	16^{-1}
3	**3**	**B**	**. 4**

As before, the decimal value of $33B.4_{16}$ can be found. Notice that a substitution of 11_{10} has been made for the hexadecimal digit B in this conversion.

$$\begin{aligned} 3*16^2 &= 3*256 &&= 768.00 \\ 3*16^1 &= 3*16 &&= 48.00 \\ B*16^0 &= 11*1 &&= 11.00 \\ 4*16^{-1} &= 4*.0625 &&= +\ \underline{0.25} \\ & && \quad 827.25 \end{aligned}$$

The decimal number 827.25_{10} is 1473.2_8 in octal and $33B.4_{16}$ in hexadecimal.

Observing that groups of 4 bits in binary have assigned a hexadecimal equivalent, binary to hexadecimal and hexadecimal to binary conversions are easily accomplished.

0xA2F = 0b 1010 0010 1111
0x345 = 0b 0011 0100 0101

Binary to Hex is just the opposite. Create groups of 4 bits starting with the least significant bits. If last group does not have 4 bits, then pad with zeroes for unsigned numbers.

0b 1010001 = 0b 0101 0001 = 0x51
↑
Padded with a zero

This method is particularly useful when converting a binary number with more than 16 bits (the limit for binary conversion using NCEES-approved calculators).

SIGNED NUMBERS

Only positive numbers have been considered. To represent negative numbers, add an extra digit to the front of a binary number to indicate whether the number is positive or negative. In computer terminology, this digit is called a *sign* bit. Remember that a "bit" is simply another name for a binary digit. When the number is positive, the sign bit zero; when the number is negative, the sign bit is one. This approach is called the *Signed Magnitude Representation*. Notice that this is very similar to adding a minus sign in decimal.

In addition, there is a need to specify how many bits are in the numbers so that the sign bit van be identified. For example, when converting the decimal numbers -5_{10} and -1_{10} to binary using Signed Magnitude Representation, four bits will be enough to represent both.

1. First, convert 5 and 1 to binary.	**101 (5)** **1 (1)**
2. Add a sign bit to each one. Notice that "1" is padded with zeros so it will have four bits.	**0101 (5)** **0001 (1)**
3. To make the binary numbers negative, simply change the sign bit (most significant bit, which is a padded bit assigned "0") from "0" to "1."	**1101 (–5)** **1001 (–1)**

Be sure that there is no mistaking the number 1101_2 for 13_{10}. Since a 4-bit signed magnitude representation is being used, it is known that the first bit is the sign and the remaining three bits are the actual number.

While representing negative numbers with signed magnitude is simple, performing arithmetic with signed magnitude is difficult. Suppose signed numbers can be represented in such a way that all computations could be completed using only addition. This would allow computers to perform all arithmetic operations with only addition circuitry. Multiplication is really repeated addition, so this is not a problem. This leaves division and subtraction, but division is just repeated subtraction. How can subtraction problems be converted to addition?

Consider the subtraction problem $30_{10} - 6_{10}$. This problem can be converted to an equivalent addition problem by changing 6_{10} to -6_{10}. The problem is now restated as $30_{10} + (-6_{10}) = 24_{10}$. A similar process to this in binary is achieved by representing negative numbers as complements. Two ways of representing signed numbers using complements are shown: 1's complement and 2's complement.

Representing a signed number with 1's complement is done by changing all the bits that are 1 to 0 and all the bits that are 0 to 1. Reversing the digits in this way is also called complementing a number. For example, in 4-bit arithmetic, when representing the number -5_{10} in 1's complement:

1. First, write the positive value of the number in binary.	**0101 (+5)**
2. Next, reverse each bit of the number so 1s become 0s and 0s become 1s.	**1010 (–5)**

Table 18.2 is a table of 4-bit binary numbers in 1's complement notation. Notice that all of the negative values begin with a 1. Whenever 1's complement notation is used, the most significant bit indicates the sign of the number. The only exception to this rule is –0. In 1s complement, there are two ways of representing the number zero. Notice also that the values +0 to +7 are the same as the normal binary representation. Only the negative values must be complemented.

Table 18.2

Binary	Decimal
0111	+7
0110	+6
0101	+5
0100	+4
0011	+3
0010	+2
0001	+1
0000	+0
1111	0
1110	–1
1101	–2
1100	–3
1011	–4
1010	–5
1001	–6
1000	–7

Here is a quick summary of how to find the 1's complement representation of any decimal number x.

1. If x is positive, simply convert x to binary.
2. If x is negative, write the positive value of x in binary.
3. Reverse each bit.

Binary Coded

Another way to represent decimals in binary form is binary coded decimals (BCDs). BCDs are binary numbers that code each decimal digit separately as a four-digit binary number. For example:

$$95 = 1001.\,0101 = 10010101 \text{ (BCD)}$$
$$217 = 0010\ 0001\ 0111 = 1000010111 \text{ (BCD)}$$

The advantage to using BCDs is the size of the number is unlimited with perfect accuracy.

However, BCDs have several disadvantages. They use more memory since each decimal digit requires four binary digits, and arithmetic operations are difficult to program and significantly slower.

FLIP-FLOPS

Flip-flops (*f–f*) are among the most important elements in digital systems. This device has the ability to store information. Before discussing the various kinds of f–f, it is important to understand the operation of an *S–R latch* (which consists of two NOR gates cross coupled) as shown in Fig. 18.2.

The reader is encouraged to analyze this kind of circuit for practice. You should be able to verify that, regardless of what the previous output signal on Q was, a pulse 1 applied to S (called the set) results in a 1 signal at Q even after the pulse is removed. Also if a pulse 1 is applied to R (called reset), the top Q goes to zero and $\bar{Q}$ goes to 1. If no other signals are applied to either S or R, then the Qs remain at whatever value was obtained by applying the previous pulse. (This assumes that pulses will not be applied to both inputs at the same time; trying to both set and reset simultaneously is not allowed in this circuit.)

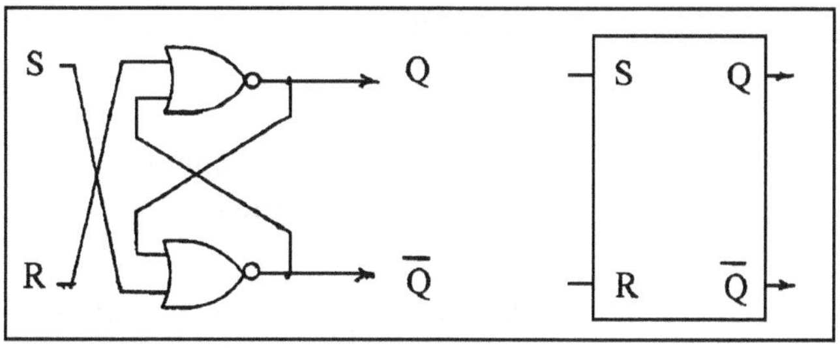

Figure 18.2 A basic S–R latch

Table 18.3 Flip-flop Symbols and Operation

FLIP-FLOP SYMBOLS: S-R f-f	J-K f-f	D f-f
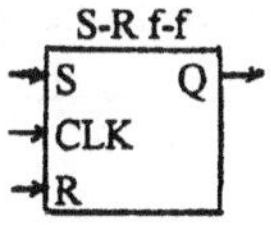	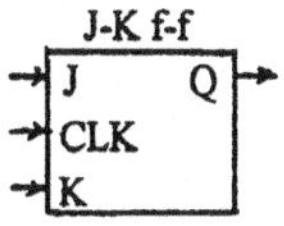	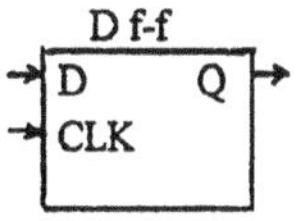

OPERATION:

S	R	Q_{n+1}
0	0	Q_n (no change)
0	1	0
1	0	1
1	1	x (unknown)

J	K	Q_{n+1}
0	0	Q_n (no change)
0	1	0
1	0	1
1	1	$\bar{Q}_n$ (toggle)

D	Q_{n+1}
0	0
1	1

By using additional kinds of gate circuits, one may create other kinds of f–f, including ones that only operate when another signal (or short pulse, a *clock pulse*) is applied. There are several kinds of f–f commercially available. It is expected that only the *S–R*, the *J–K*, and the *D* types (see the following) are likely to appear on the examination and that they will have clocked inputs. Also, although the bottom $\bar{Q}$ s may not be shown, they will be assumed. The notation to be used is such that Q_n implies the output on Q before the clock pulse arrives, and Q_{n+1} implies the signal on Q after a clock pulse arrives.

Table 18.3 indicates the various block diagrams and summarizes the operation of these kinds of f–f.

Notice that the S–R f–f is the same as the J–K except for one important condition. Whereas the inputs for the S–R f–f should never to be allowed to have both 1s input because the output is not determinable in that case, the J–K can have both 1s and the result on Q will merely be the complement of the value of Q just before the

clock pulse arrived (this action is called *toggling*). Of course there are many other conditions that may contribute to the operation of the flip-flops (such as another input called the *preset condition*, a clock input that only operates on the trailing edge of a clock pulse, etc.). However, the examination probably will be limited to the kinds listed in Table 18.3.

When working problems with flip-flops one should assume the following:

- The clock pulses are very narrow
- If the output Q of one f–f drives the input of another and if the two are driven from the same clock pulse source (synchronous operation), then the first Q output (before the clock pulse arrives) is the condition that drives the input to the second f–f

On the examination, also be aware that, to denote a complemented variable, many writers use a prime following the variable rather than a bar over it. The primed notation was used to facilitate typing the equations.

$$\overline{A} = A', \; \overline{\overline{A}} = A'' = A$$

Both methods are used in the following problems so that you will be accustomed to seeing either version on the exam.

State Machine Theory

A state machine is a machine that makes predictable transitions through a sequence of states based on external inputs and the current state of the machine. In digital electronics, the timing of the transition of the machine from one state to another is controlled by a register and a system clock, while the next state of the machine is determined by a combination of logic gates and embedded memory. A schematic representation of a state machine is shown in Figure 18.3.

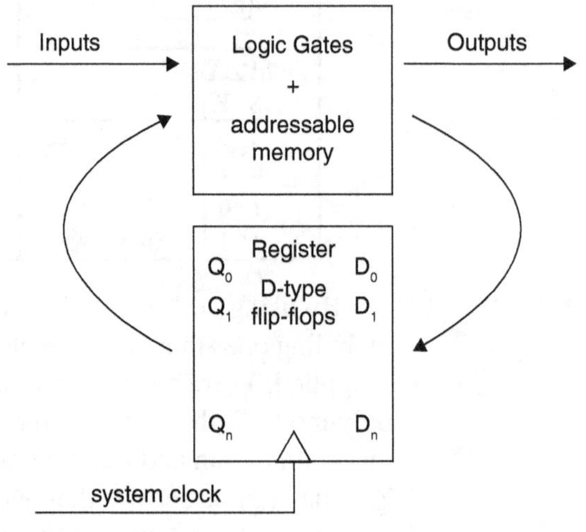

Figure 18.3

Figure 18.3 is a block diagram representation of a digital electronics state machine. A counter is one of the most basic state machines one can make. It simply makes a transition from one binary number (i.e., a state) to the next on each clock cycle. A two-bit counter would make this sequence of transitions (each number is a particular state):

$$00 \rightarrow 01 \rightarrow 10 \rightarrow 11 \rightarrow 00$$

State machines are the essential components that make a computer possible. Most computers are controlled by one counter (called the program counter) that steps through a simple numerical sequence. It becomes a computer when each number in that sequence is assigned an action. Any device that has this function is called *sequencer*.

External Input

Some state machines simply plod through from one state to the next. Others make transitions that are conditional upon some external input. In a synchronous counter, the "count enable" input produces this type of more sophisticated state machine. At each clock pulse, it either advanced to a new state or stayed at the same state depending on the condition of the other bit. This is an example of a state machine that changes state under the influence of an external control line. Note that the *next state* depends on *both* the external control and on the internal present state. This is what makes it sophisticated.

With this counter, the essence of all computers is revealed. The system steps through a sequence that depends on its current state and on external input. This is fundamentally no different than a personal computer displaying a view on the monitor and knowing to update the view periodically but also knowing to respond to any movements of the mouse.

Various types of state machines using D-type registers and logic gates are implemented. If the number of states is small, then the logic gate circuitry can be determined using Karnaugh maps.

Example **18.1**

T-type flip-flop

Consider a T-type flip-flop as a state machine. A T-type flip-flop has two states, 0 and 1, so only one D-type flip-flop is required. The block diagram for the state machine is shown in Exhibit 1.

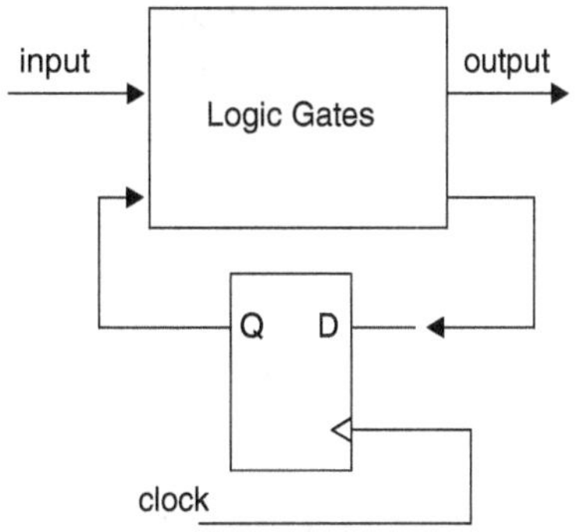

Exhibit 1 Block Diagram for the State Machine Representation of T-Flip-Flop.

In order to determine what circuitry to put into the "logic gates" block, construct the logic table for the state machine sequence, which is shown in Table 18.4.

Table 18.4

Input	Q_u	Q_{n+1} & D
1	1	0
1	0	1
0	1	1
0	0	0

From the logic table, we infer the associated Karnaugh map shown below in Exhibit 2.

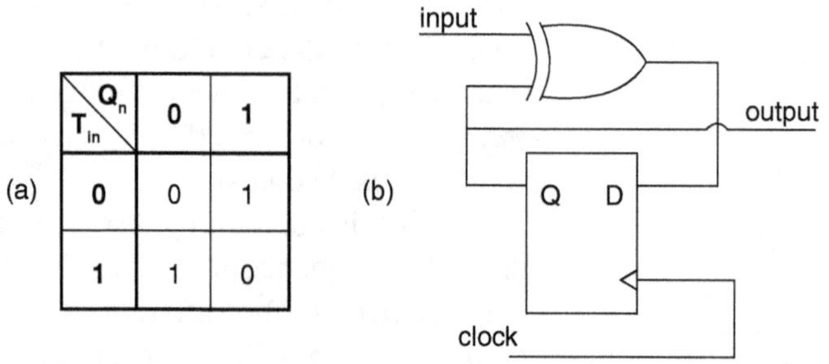

Exhibit 2 (a) The Karnaugh map for the T-type flip-flop state machine; (b) Circuit diagram for a T-type flip-flop.

The Karnaugh map is relatively straightforward and is equivalent to a XOR gate.

Consequently, the circuit for a T-type flip-flop consists of a D-type flip-flop and a single XOR gate as shown in Exhibit 2.

Sequencers

For a simple state machine that just steps from one state to the next, the design can be based on one or more counters with some external logic. The output logic for this device will decode the counter value and put a combination of output lines into operation. This circuit is called a *sequencer* because it steps through a simple sequence of operations.

A real world example of such a sequencer is the control unit of a dishwasher. The desired sequence might be the following:

1. Turn on the faucet for 5 minutes.
2. Turn on the washer heads for 10 minutes.
3. Pump out the water for 5 minutes.
4. Turn on the faucet for 5 minute.
5. Turn on the washer heads for 5 minutes.
6. Pump out the water for 5 minutes.
7. Turn on the heater for 15 minutes.

This sequence should start with the push of a button, run once, and stop. There are two common ways to implement such a sequence.

- A single master-counter that counts over the entire 50 minutes and uses logic on the outputs to decode which device should be on at any given count;

- A series of seven counters with predetermined timing (i.e., number of counts) and logic to insure that the counters start and stop counting in the proper order.

The optimal method depends on the details and complexity of the sequence to be generated. In the single counter method, a clock with a five-minute period might be selected.

The functional table for the sequencer may resemble the following:

Table 18.5 Counter Value Output Asserted

10	Faucet
9	Washer heads
8	Washer heads
7	Pump
6	Faucet
5	Washer heads
4	Pump
3	Heater
2	Heater
1	Heater
0	Nothing!

With a small number of steps, one can just use simple logic based on the counter's bits to determine how to turn on which output line.

Table 18.6 Counter Value Output Asserted

10 & 6	Faucet
9 & 8 & 5	Washer heads
7 & 4	Pump
3 & 2 & 1	Heater

From a table like this, one can then take the output bits from the counter and design an array of logic gates that will ensure the control lines are asserted on the correct count values.

Since decoding a sequence is so common, there are chips, such as the 74LS138, which perform these sorts of operations. They will take, say, a 3-bit binary number and turn on one of eight output lines based on the binary number encoded in the inputs.

TIMING DIAGRAMS

Timing diagrams are the main key in understanding digital systems. Timing diagrams explain digital circuitry functioning during time flow. Timing diagrams help to understand how digital circuits or sub circuits should work or fit into a larger circuit system. So learning how to read timing diagrams may increase your work

with digital systems and integrate them. Below is a list of the most commonly used timing diagram fragments:

- Low level to supply voltage:

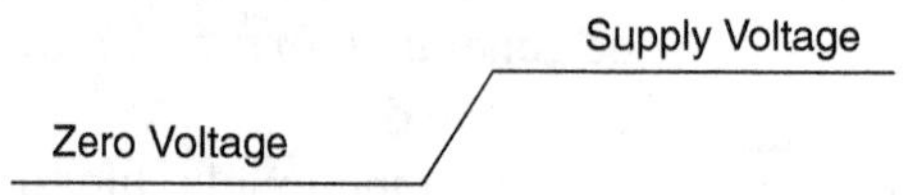

- Transition to low or high level:

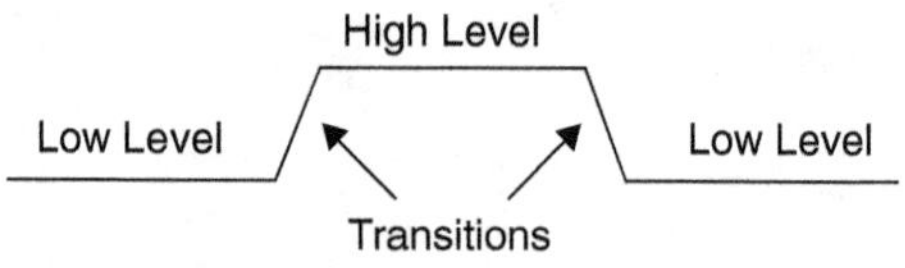

- Bus signals: parallel signals transitioning from one level to other:

- High impedance state:

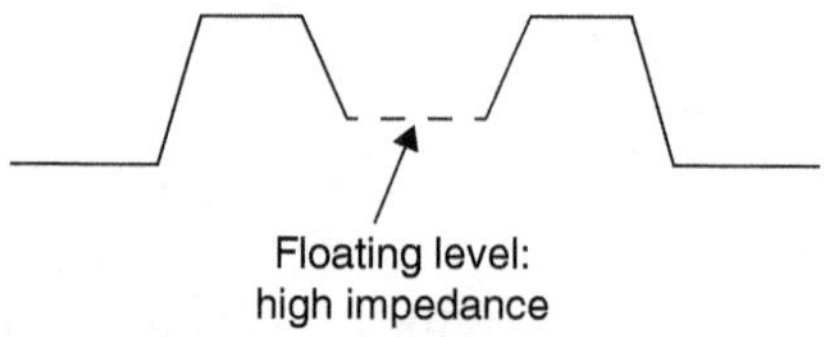

- Bus signal with floating impedance:

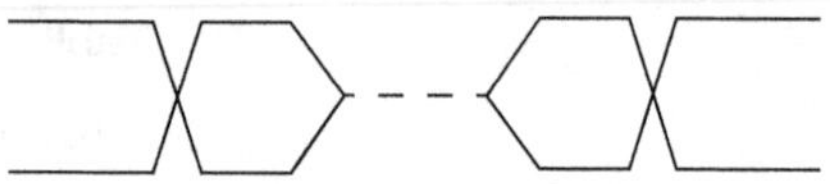

- Conditional change of one signal depending on another signal transition:

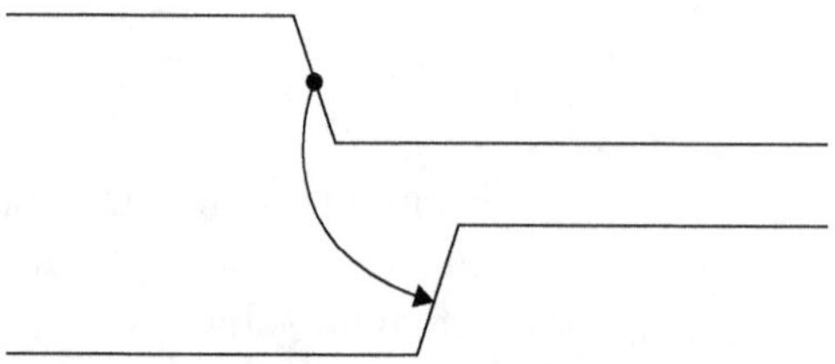

- Transition on a signal causes state changes in a BUS:

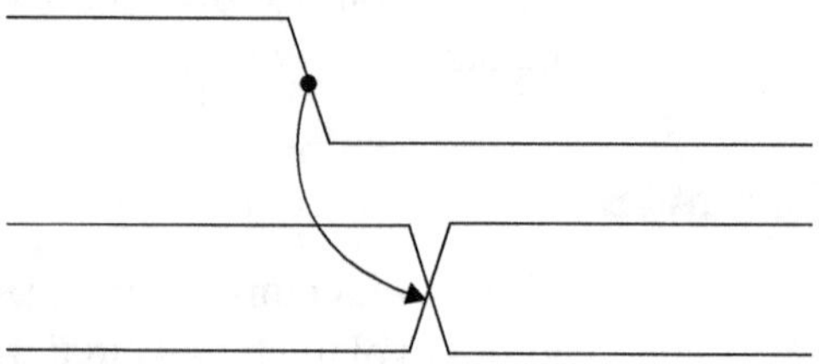

- More than one transition causes changes in a BUS:

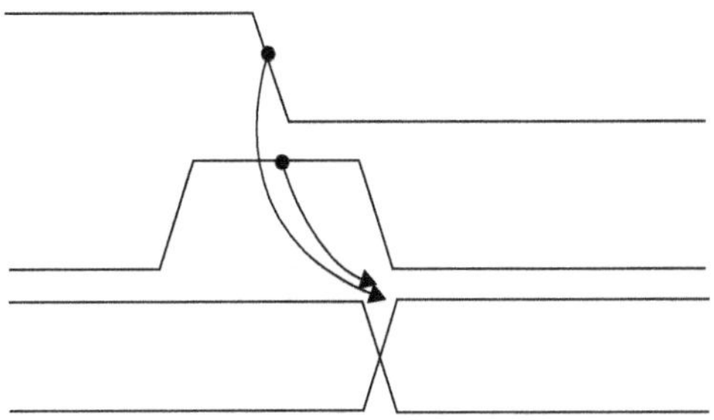

- Sequential transition: one signal transition causes another signal transition and second signal transition causes third signal transition.

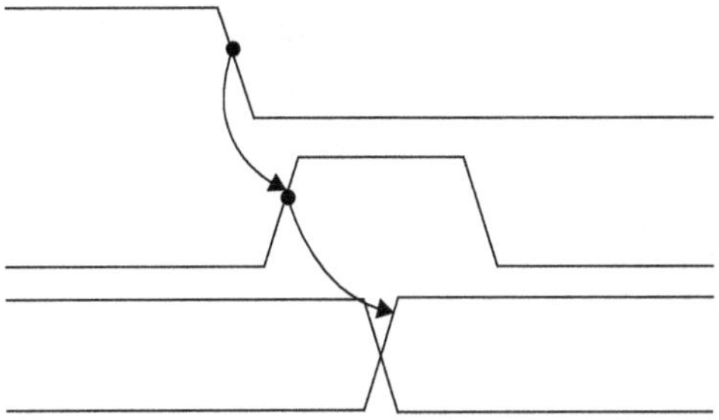

Timing diagrams together with a digital circuit can completely describe the circuit sequential operational characteristics. To understand the timing diagrams, follow all symbols and transitions in timing diagrams.

Example 18.2

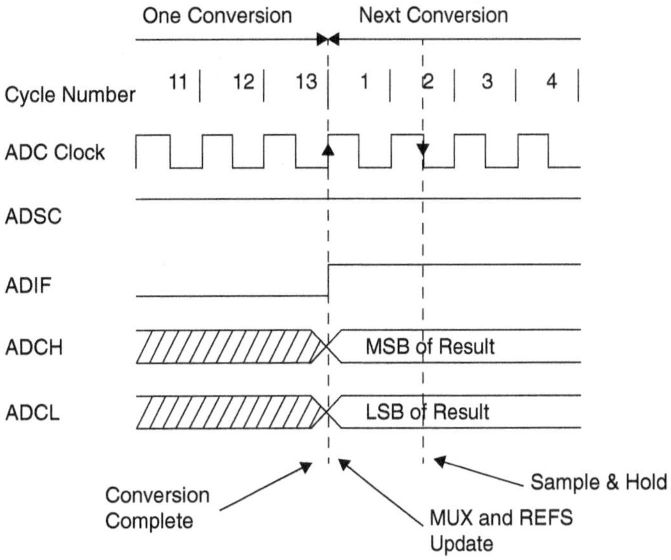

Exhibit 3

The cross hatched regions are "don't care" regions where the state can either be a logical "1" or "0".

The upwards arrow indicates a logical transition (or state change) on the rising edge of a clock, whereas the downwards arrow indicates a logical transition on the falling edge of a clock.

Realistic timing diagrams show delays using typical or maximum values as shown in Exhibit 4.

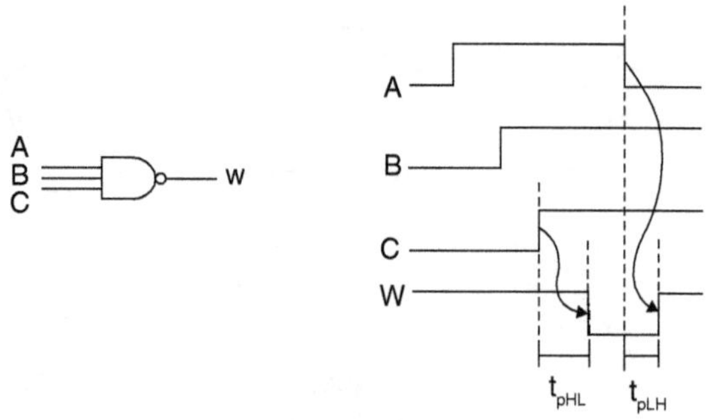

Exhibit 4

The delay between an input transition and the resultant output transition is called ***propagation delay.*** Propagation delay is measured between the centers of the transition time period.

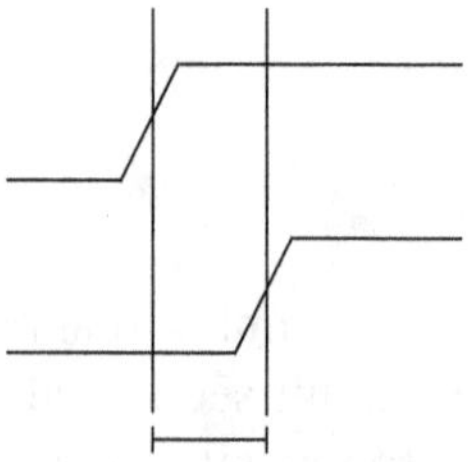

Exhibit 5

Propagation delay for an output transition from high to low is t_{pHL}. Propagation delay for an output transition from low to high is t_{pLH}. Notice that these two times are ***not*** necessarily the same for the same device.

Also of importance is transition time (i.e., the time it takes to fully transition between logical "1" and "0" or vise versa) as shown in Exhibit 6. Note that t_r is the rise time, t_f is the fall time, V_{IHmin} is the minimum input voltage for a logical "1," and V_{ILmax} is the maximum input voltage to a logical "0."

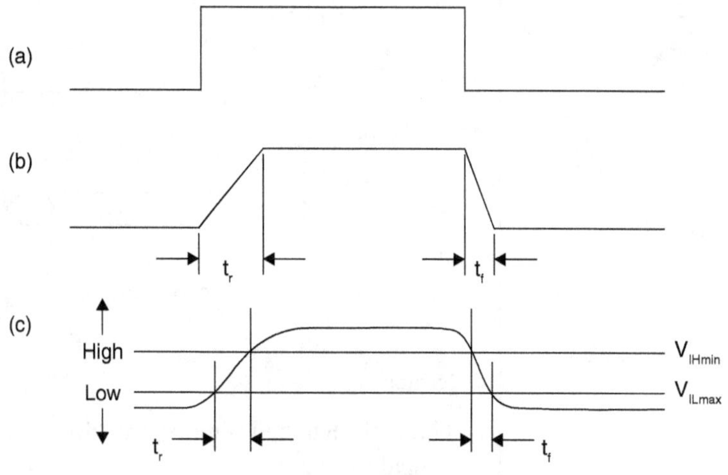

Exhibit 6

Timing diagrams can also show uncertainties in the propagation delay from logical high to low, t_{pHL}, due to variations in component specifications.

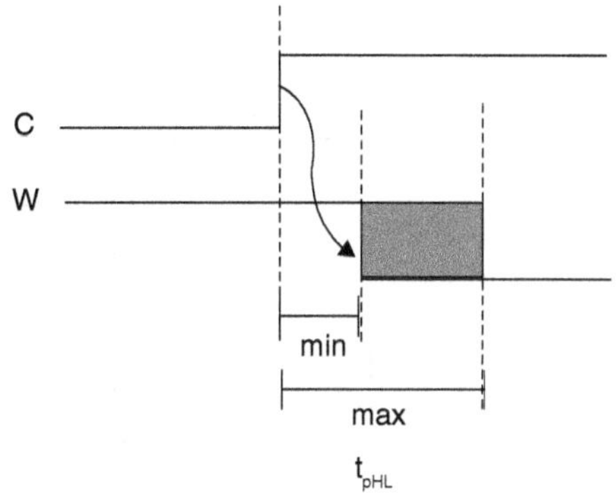

Exhibit 7

TIMING HAZARDS

Transient output behavior may not agree with predicted output due to delay differences. For example, a ***glitch*** is the presence of extra signal transitions, which are not predicted from the logic equations.

A ***static hazard*** is the ***possibility*** of a glitch when the output should not change. A ***static-1 hazard*** is present if changing a single input variable may produce output transitions but the output logic function is high (1) independent of this change.

Example 18.3

Static-1 Hazard

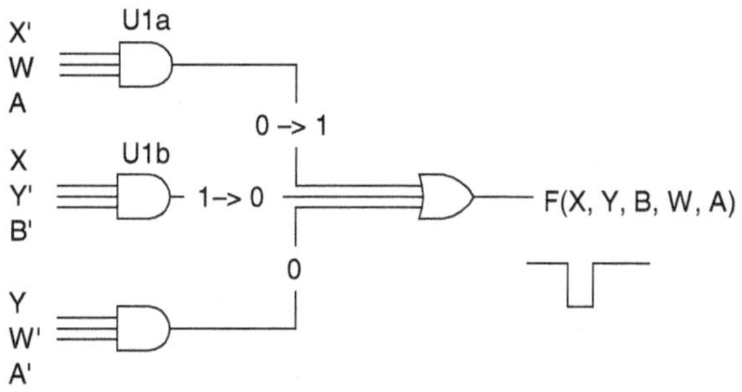

Exhibit 8

Consider an input change from (X = 1, Y = 0, B = 0, W = 1, A = 1) to (X = 0, Y = 0, B = 0, W = 1, A = 1). What happens? If the propagation delay from along the path of gate U1a is longer than along the path of gate U1b, then F could go low during that extra delay.

A properly designed OR-AND circuit will never have static-1 hazards. An AND-OR circuit may have static-1 hazards. These can be detected from a K-map by checking for adjacent minterms not covered by the same product term (AND gate) in the actual realization.

	X = 0					X = 1			
WA\YB	00	01	11	10	WA\YB	00	01	11	10
00			1	1	00	1		1	1
01					01	1			
11	1	1	1	1	11	1			
10					10	1			

The static-1 hazard can be detected by noticing that there are two adjacent minterms (3) and (19), which are not covered by a common product term. It can be eliminated by including an additional product term in the realization.

Exhibit 9

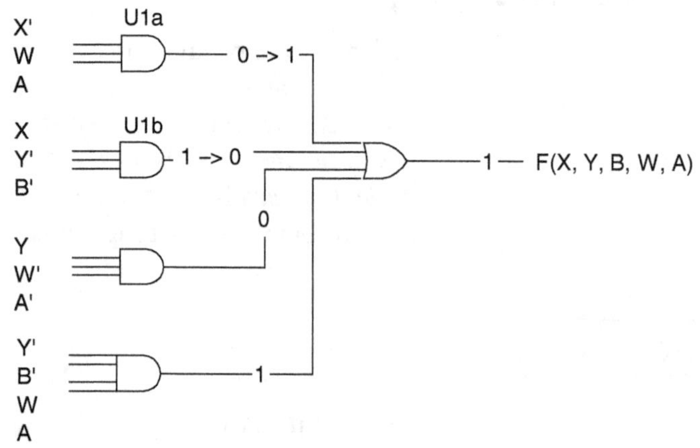

Exhibit 10 Hazard-Free Circuit

A ***static-0 hazard*** is present if changing a single input variable may produce output transitions but the output logic function is low (0) independent of this change. While hazards produce unexpected transitions and may be intermittent, proper design of synchronous sequential circuits should tolerate hazards.

A properly designed AND-OR circuit will never have static-0 hazards. An OR-AND circuit may have static-0 hazards. Check K-map for adjacent maxterms not covered by the same sum term (OR gate) in the actual realization.

A ***dynamic hazard*** is the possibility of a glitch when the output changes from low to high or high to low. Since the output is supposed to change, the presence of a glitch means the output makes more than one transition.

- low → high → low → high
- high → low → high → low

Dynamic hazards do not occur in properly designed two-level circuits. What is "properly" designed? No first-level gate has both true and complement forms of the same signal as inputs.

PROGRAMMABLE LOGIC DEVICES (PLDS)

Programmable Logic Arrays can be used to implement any combinational logic function and realized as a sum of products. The idea is to build a large AND-OR array with lots of inputs and product terms and programmable connections.

- *n* inputs
  - AND gates have 2*n* inputs—true and complement of each variable.
- *m* outputs, driven by large OR gates
  - Each AND gate is programmably connected to each output's OR gate.
- *p* AND gates ($p \ll 2^n$)

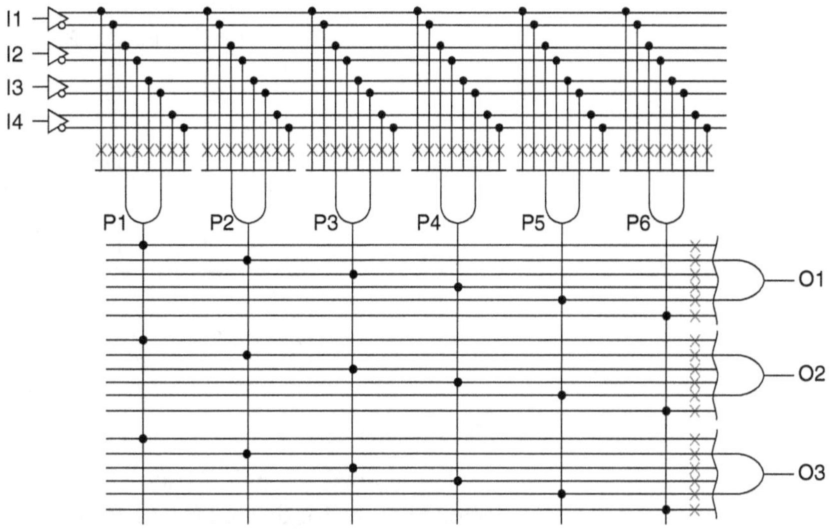

Figure 18.4 4x3 PLA, 6 product terms

A compact representation of the 4×3 PLA is shown in Figure 18.5:

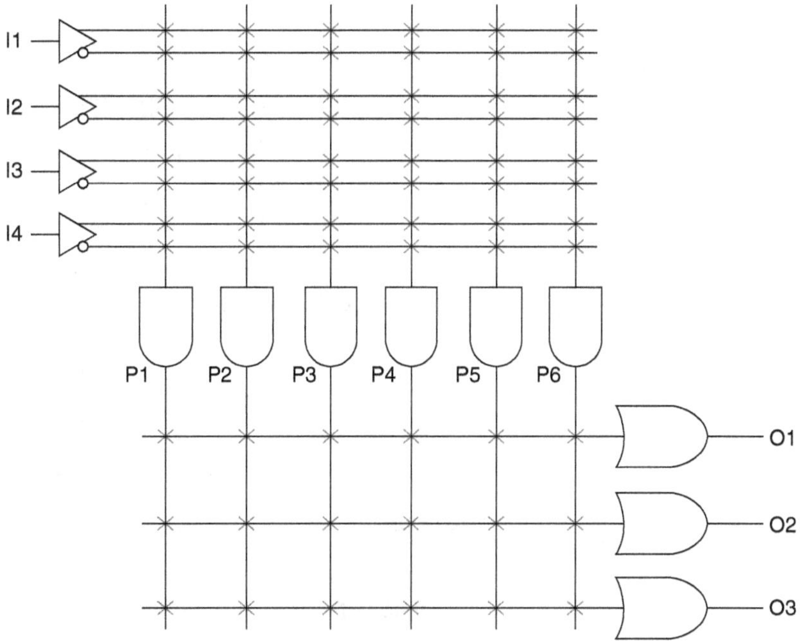

Figure 18.5

The product terms are shown in Figure 18.6:

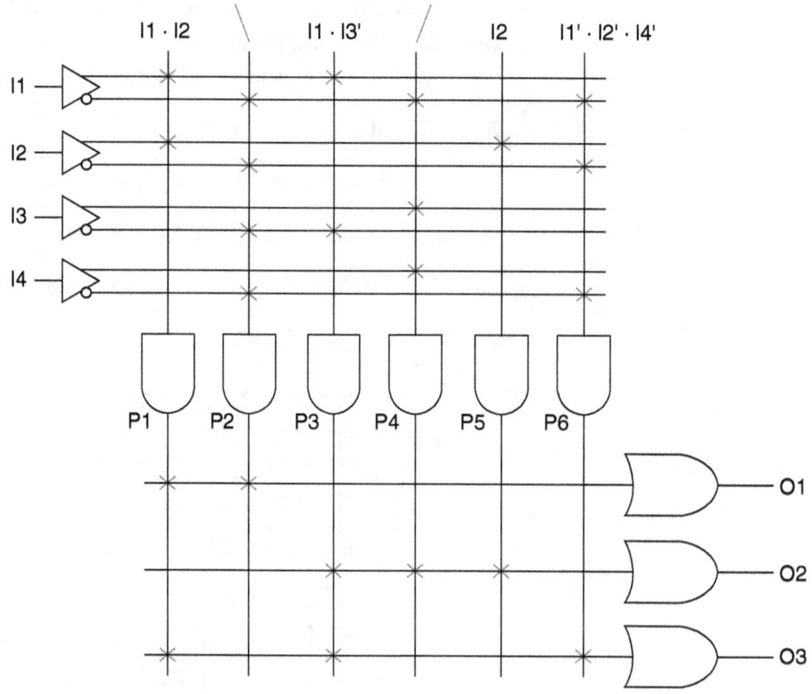

O1 = I1 · I2 + I1' · I2' · I3' · I4'
O2 = I1 · I3' + I1' · I3 · I4 · I2
O3 = I1 · I2 + I1 · I3' + I1' · I2' · I4'

Figure 18.6

Programmable Logic Arrays (PLAs) have "fused connections" that are connected to allow for desired functionality.

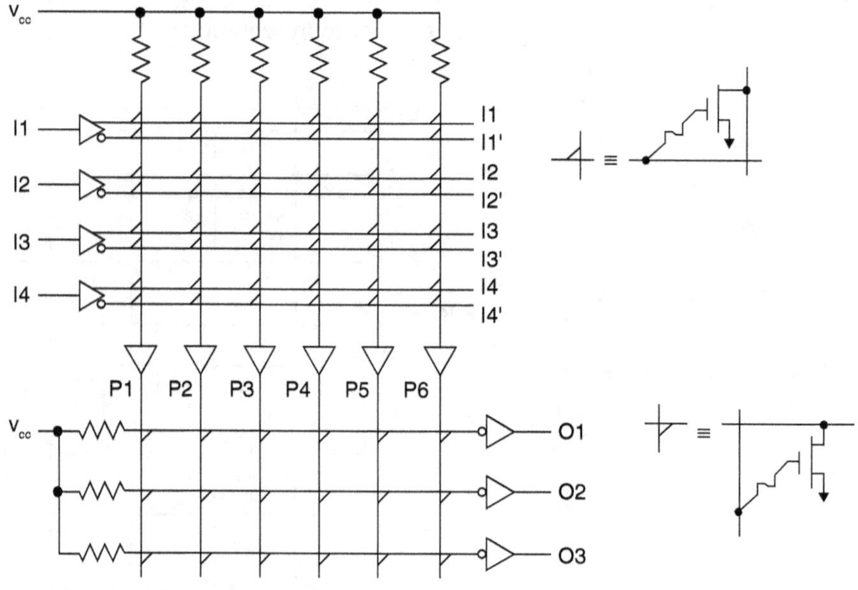

Figure 18.7 PLA Sample Diagram

Programmable Array Logic (PAL) are composed of fixed OR gate arrays. Each AND gate is permanently connected to a certain OR gate as shown in Figure 18.8.

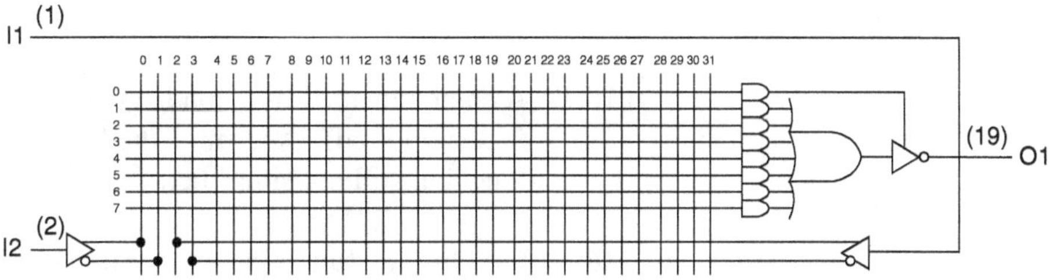

Figure 18.8

When designing with PALs, compare number of inputs and outputs of the problem with available resources in the PAL. Write equations for each output using ABEL (software tool).

Compile the ABEL program, and determine whether minimimized equations fit in the available AND terms. If there is a failure to fit the available AND terms, try modifying equations or providing "helper" terms.

PROBLEMS

18.1 A complemented function is given as $\overline{f}(A,B,C) = \overline{A}B + (A + \overline{C}) + \overline{A}BC$ (not simplified). Determine the function itself (i.e., the uncomplemented function, still not simplified).

18.2 Simplify the following expression:

$$f(A,B,C) = AB' + AC + AB'C'$$

18.3 We have two flip-flops, the first being a clock-triggered S–R type, the other being a clock-triggered J–K one. Both are fed from the same clock source. There is a "1" sitting on the S terminal of the first f–f (and a "0" on the R terminal); the Q output of the first f–f is connected to both the J and K terminals of the second f–f. Assume both f–f initially have "0" on the Q outputs. What is the Q output of the J–K f–f after two clock pulses?

18.4 Two signals, $f_A(t)$ and $f_B(t)$, are fed into an AND gate, the output of which is then fed into a NOR gate. At the same time, the signal $f_B(t)$ is fed into the same NOR gate (see Exhibit 18.4a). Assuming the signals are positive high, determine the output of the NOR gate as a function of time. (You may neglect the delay time.)

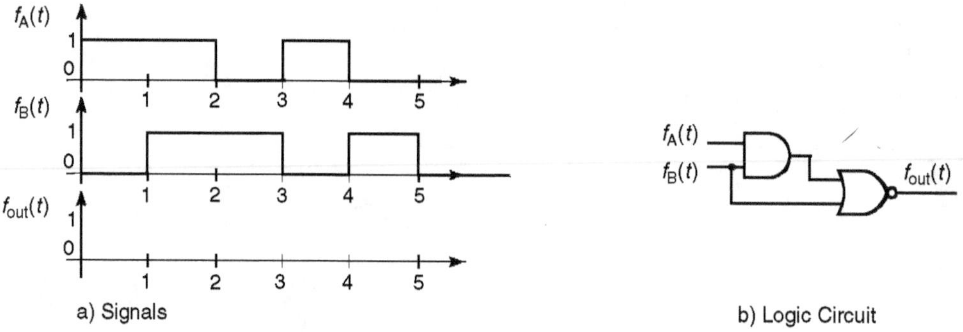

Exhibit 18.4a The output for two signals fed into a digital logic circuit

18.5 A type T (toggle) flip-flop may be made by adding two AND gates to an S–R type as shown in Exhibit 8.5a. If the signal $f_B(t)$ from Problem 18.4 (preceding) is fed into T, what is the signal $Q(t)$ shortly after t = 4? Assume $Q(t)$ is initially zero.

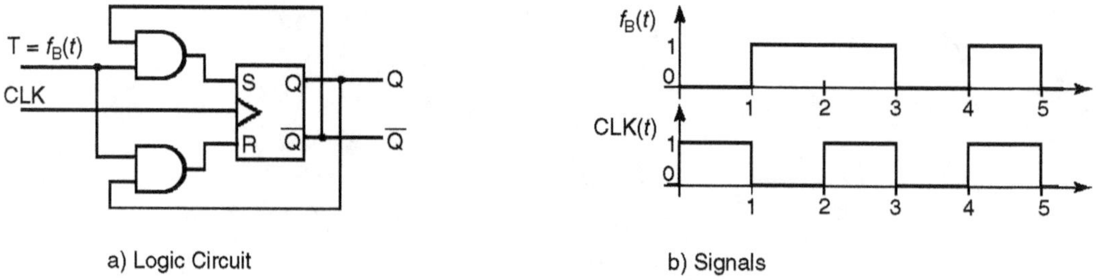

Exhibit 18.5a A T type flip-flop made from an S–R type

SOLUTIONS

18.1 Here some of the terms may be changed to ORed values by means of DeMorgan's theorem.

$$\overline{\overline{f}} = f = \overline{\overline{A}B + (A+\overline{C}) + \overline{A}BC} = (\overline{\overline{A}B})(\overline{A+\overline{C}})(\overline{\overline{A}BC})$$

$$= (\overline{\overline{A}} + \overline{B})(\overline{A}\,\overline{\overline{C}})(\overline{\overline{A}} + \overline{B} + \overline{C}) = (A+\overline{B})(\overline{A}C)(A+\overline{B}+\overline{C})$$

Answer: $f = (A+\overline{B})(\overline{A}C)(A+\overline{B}+\overline{C})$

18.2 One may use either a Karnaugh map or simple Boolean algebra techniques to simplify:

$$f = A(B' + C + B'C') = A(B'(1+C') + C) = A(B' + C)$$

Answer: $f = A(B' + C)$.

18.3 After the first clock pulse the S–R f–f will go to a 1 on Q At the same time J–K f–f that started with both inputs being a 0 will not change the Q output which was a 0 (i.e., will not toggle). However, the second clock pulse (since both J and K have 1 from the S–R Q output) will toggle from a 0 to a 1.

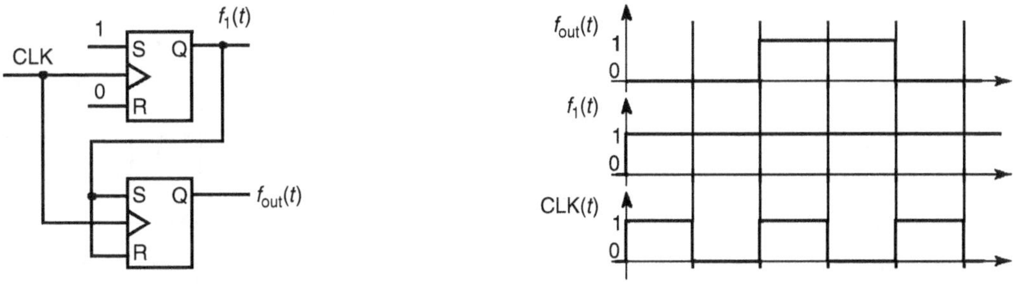

a) Logc Circuit b) Signals

Exhibit 18.3 Logic circuit connection and timing diagram

Answer: End of second clock pulse, Q (of the second f–f) will go to a 1.

18.4 From the truth table for an AND and a NOR gate one first finds the output of the AND gate, f_{AND}, as shown, then the signals $f_B(t)$ along with f_{AND} and passed through the NOR gate to give the desired $f_{out}(t)$ signal (see Exhibit 18.4b).

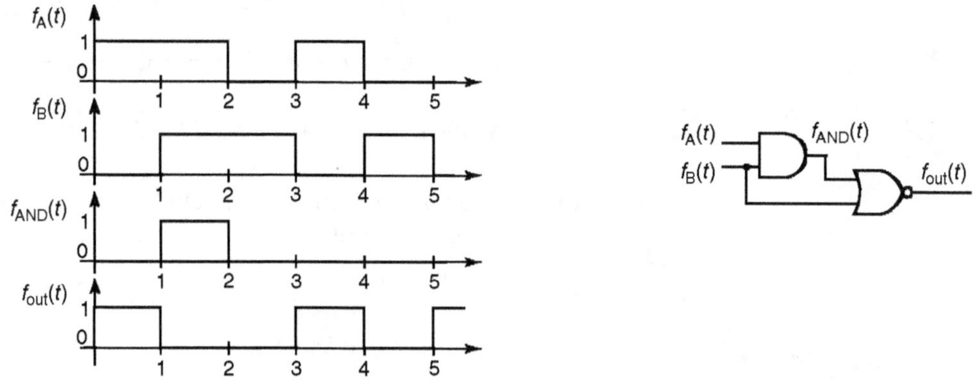

a) Signals

b) Logic Circuit

Exhibit 18.4b The output for two signals fed into a digital logic circuit

18.5 The solution is easily obtained by following through the Q signals for the various inputs as follows (see Exhibit 18.5b):

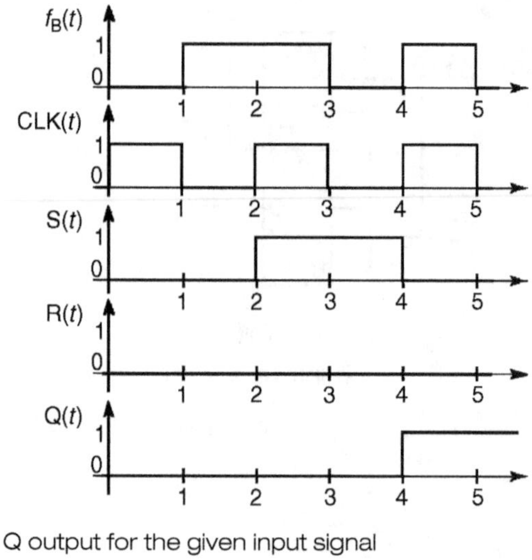

Exhibit 18.5b The Q output for the given input signal

CHAPTER 19

Computer Systems

OUTLINE

What is a microprocessor?

- A programmable device that reads binary instructions from memory, handles binary data as input and processes data according to instructions, and provides results as output.

What are the main components of a microprocessor?

- Central Processing Unit (CPU)
- Memory
- Input and Output (I/O)

Constitutes both hardware (h/w) and software (s/w)

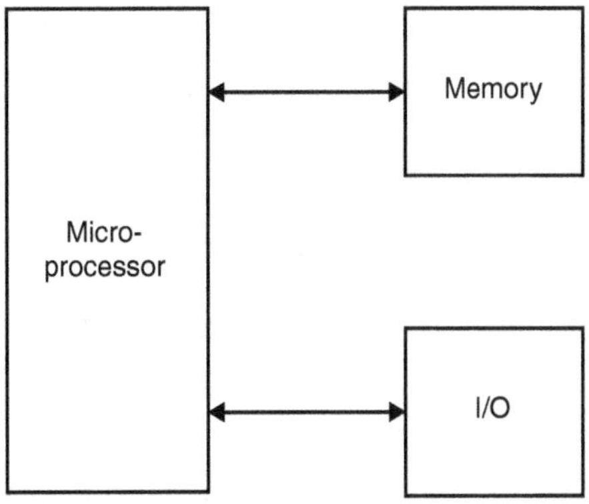

Figure 19.1 Simple Microcomputer Diagram

Microprocessors are controlled by programs, which translate to a set of instructions that the processor understands (e.g., air traffic control systems, PC, ATM systems, etc.).

Some applications of processors include embedded systems (e.g., ATC systems), reprogrammable computers (e.g., PC, workstations, etc.), and micro-controllers (e.g., all components included in ATM machines).

The components of a microprocessor include the following:

- Arithmetic/Logic Unit (ALU) and Control Unit (CU).
- The CPU contains registers to store data, the ALU to perform arithmetic operations, instruction decoders, counters, and control lines.
- ALU performs operations on data (e.g., addition, subtraction, logic operations, AND, OR, and EOR). The result is stored in register or memory.
- Register array as temporary store during execution of programs.
- Control Unit provides timing and control signals to all operations in the system ⇒ it controls the flow of data between the microprocessor and peripherals (e.g., memory, I/O devices, decoder, Network Interface Controller (NIC), etc.).
- System bus (made up of other buses) is a communications path between the microprocessor and the peripherals ⇒ wires that carry bits. All peripherals connect to system bus; however, microprocessor communicates with one at a time.

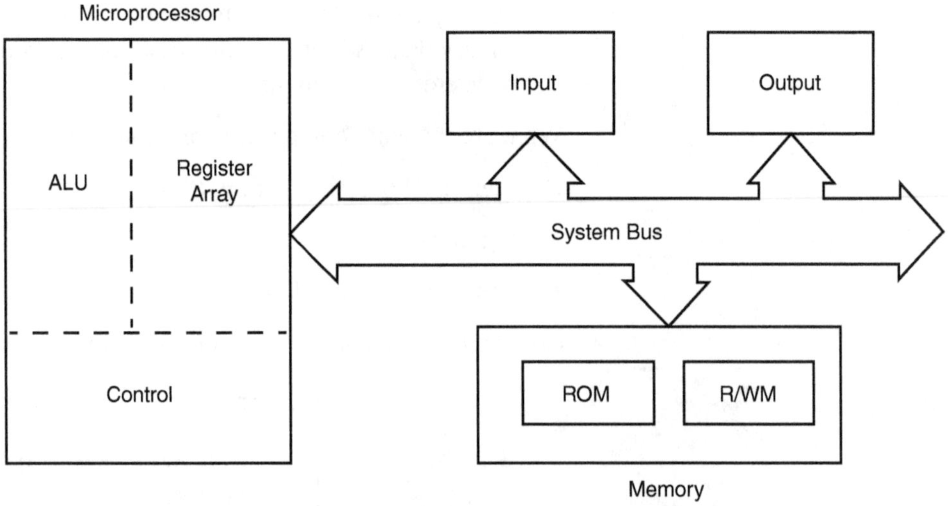

Figure 19.2 Microprocessor-Based System With Bus Architecture

- Operate in binary digits
  - The digits 0 and 1 are synonymous with low and high, classfied according to their word length (4, 8, 16, 32, 64 bits).
- Programmable device
  - Designed to execute binary instructions, which are stored in memory

- What is memory?
  - 8-bit registers store eight binary bits; several of these registers are arranged in a sequence of memory blocks. For example, a group of registers 1024 (2^{10}) 8-bit on a semiconductor chip is known as 1K bytes of memory. The user writes instructions and data into memory through an input device, and the microprocessor performs a given task (e.g., finds an answer).
  - Read Only Memory (ROM) and Random Access Memory (RAM)
- The relationship between the program instructions, ALU, CU, and register array follows:
  - Add operation includes micro-programs (made up of microcode), registers, logic gates, and clock; the clock initiates the add operation, the bit pattern of the add instruction initiates a sequence of clock signals, activates appropriate logic in ALU, and performs the add operation. This "add algorithm" is called microprogram, which is done at the design stage of the uP. The bit pattern that drives these canned micro-programs are made available to the programmer in the form of the "microprocessor instruction set."
  - Programmer designs programs (pseudo code, flow diagram) to implement an algorithm.
  - Codes the instruction (from the set) to do the job.
  - Enters each instruction sequentially through an input device.
  - CPU reads the bit pattern (instructions) one at a time, decodes them, initiates the appropriate micro-programs through the control unit, and performs the specific instruction.

A microprocessor works by storing programs in ROM, storing data in RAM and uses the system bus to fetch binary instructions from ROM, stores them in registers and decodes them, and executes the decoded instruction in the ALU. The result of the executed instruction could be to output a result to memory or LEDs, for example.

Generalized microprocessor units (MPU) can process data according to program-initiated operations; an MPU must be able to react to external events such as interrupts from a peripheral device. To perform these operations, the MPU requires logic signals to transfer information, control signals for timing, and clock circuitry. Not all μP have the necessary circuitry on one chip; some are on a set of chips. MPU defines a group of devices that can perform the operations similar to the CPU.

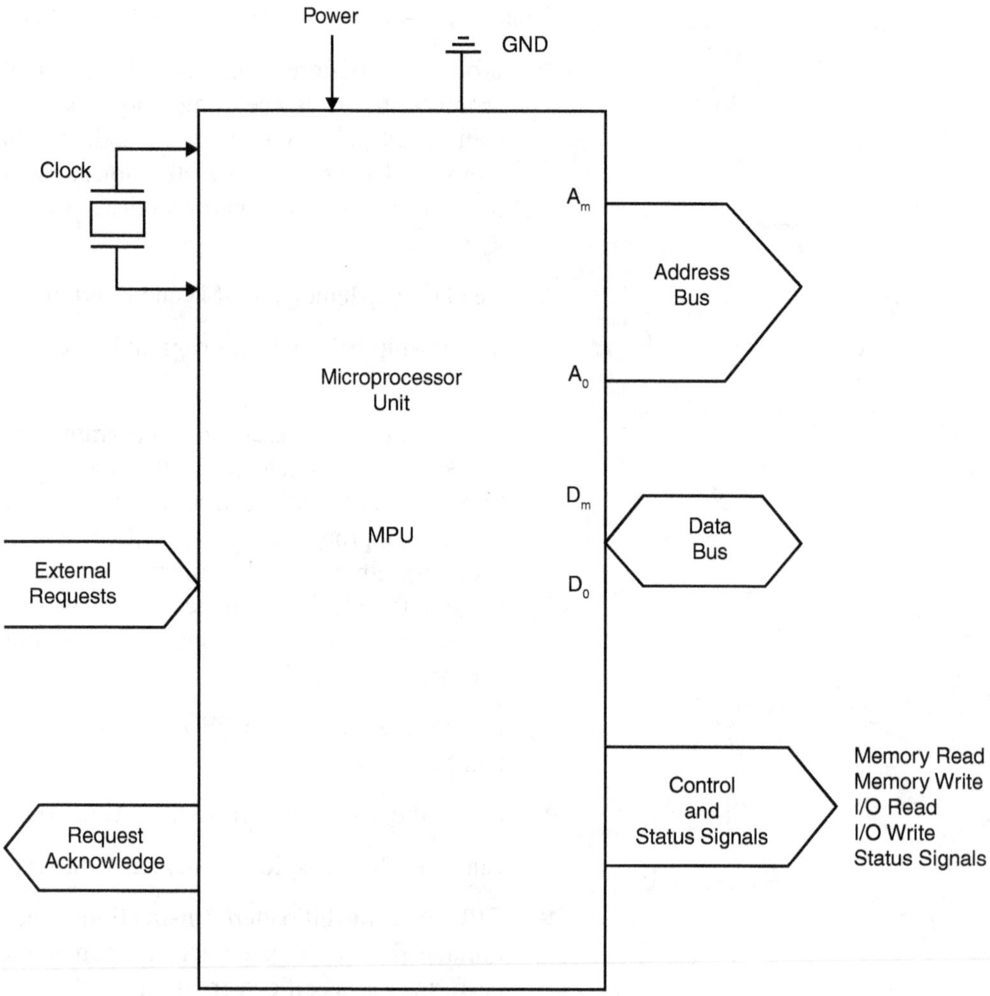

Figure 19.3 Generalized Microprocessor Unit

Program-initiated operations and buses read and write operations identify each memory and I/O register using an address (e.g., a small microprocessor can have a 16 bit address and can address up to 2^{15} registers). The data transfer is achieved with an I/O device by addressing, control signaling and timing, and data transfer.

The number of sets of communications lines required in an MPU are determined by the following:

- Address bus
  - Unidirectional bus that can address the memory map (e.g., 64K for 16 bit address bus)
- Data bus
  - Bidirectional bus—data flow in each direction. $D_0 - D_n$ in MPU. The size of the data bus determines the max size binary number that can be transferred and processed in a single instance—and, thus, influences the performance of the μP architecture considerably.

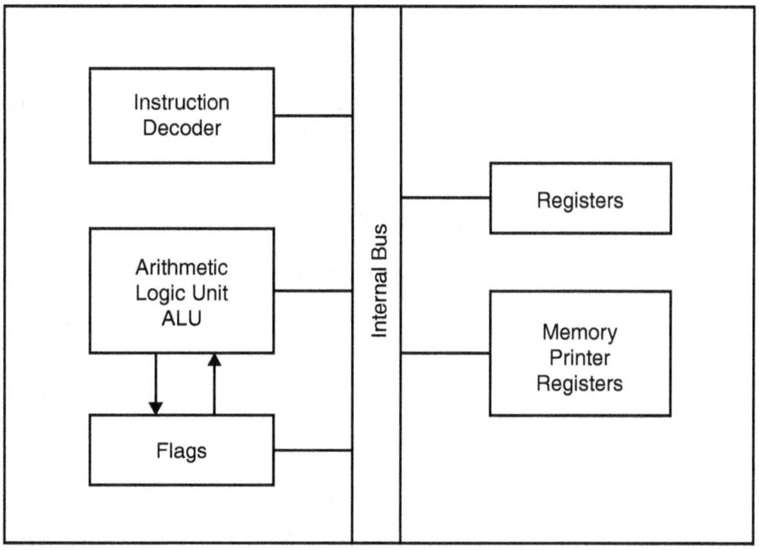

Figure 19.4 Internal Structure of an MPU

MPU-initiated control signals are individual signal lines generated by the MPU to indicate its operation. The MPU generates signals for

1. memory read,
2. memory write,
3. I/O read, and
4. I/O write.

These are timing signals that are used to enable and activate peripherals (e.g., to fetch an instruction from a memory read to enable the memory chip prior to transfer).

Externally initiated operations include:

- Reset
    - Start again, power-down reset, fault recovery?
- Interrupt
    - Interrupt the currently active program to process a critical event such as "packet arrived from the network" and then return to that program.
        - When would this not happen? (Clue: multitasking environment)
- Wait
    - When a peripheral response time is slow relative to the MPU (e.g., memory is generally an order of magnitude slow than clock speed). This signal can be used to delay the MPU operation until the device is ready.
- Bus request
    - When the MPU operations are too slow compared to the speed of the peripheral, the peripheral can request the use of the buses (e.g., DMA). Controllers can transfer data much faster than through the MPU.

- Clock signal
  - The bits of a binary instruction are associated with microcode inside the chip. When the MPU executes an instruction, it releases a series of micro-programs at precise intervals; therefore, MPU needs clock signals.

Review μP operations:

- Fetch an instruction
  - Signal, place a memory address on the address bus, read 8 bits from ROM, store the instruction, and increment a instruction pointer to the next address for the next instruction "fetch cycle."
- Decode an instruction
  - Is it a complete instruction? If not, how many more bytes need to be fetched before we have the complete instruction?
  - What type of operation is required on what data?
    - To perform these functions, the μP needs an instruction decoder that can interpret the fetched binary information.
- Storing data
  - μP gets data from memory, I/O, or as part of the instruction. It, therefore, needs a set of registers to store data/addresses temporarily before it can process the data.
- Executing instructions
  - Operations can be data copy, arithmetic operations, and decision making. The result of an operation (positive, zero, negative) needs to be indicated, and actions may be taken on the result.

Memory

What is memory?

- It is a circuit that can store bits, generally high and low voltage levels representing 1 and 0. A flip-flop or a latch is a basic element of memory.

What types of memory are there?

- Main memory (e.g., RAM, ROM) and storage (e.g., tape and disk). RAM is made up of registers. Each register has a group of flip-flops or field effect transistors that store bits of information. ROM stores information permanently in the form of diodes; the group of diodes can be viewed as a register.

Memory cell

- A latch that can store one binary bit; registers are made up of multiple memory cells.
- A simple latch with an input and enable bit (Figure 19.5a); stored bit is always available at output.
- Using tri-state buffer to the output of the latch (Figure 19.5b); stored bit can be read only when buffer is enabled.

- Using a tri-state buffer on the input to (Figure 19.5c) write into it by enabling the input buffer and read from it by enabling the output buffer.

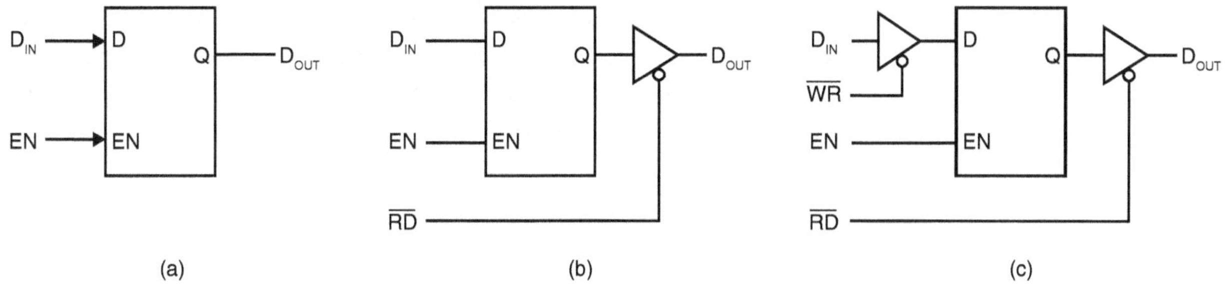

Figure 19.5 Latches as Storage Elements

There are a variety of memory word sizes that are used by microprocessors.

- 4×1 bit register
- 4×8 bit register (Figure 19.6a)—32 bits memory word size
    - To write into or read from any one of the registers, a specific register should be identified/enabled. This is a simple decoding function; 2-to-4 decoder can perform that function.
    - In this case, two more input lines A_1 and A_0, called address lines, are required by the decoder.
    - Each combination (00, 01, 10, 11) can identify or enable one of the registers (R0–R3).
- Two 4×8 bit register (Figure 19.6b)
    - If we have only 4-bit memory chips, we can combine two chips in parallel to make an 8-bit memory word.

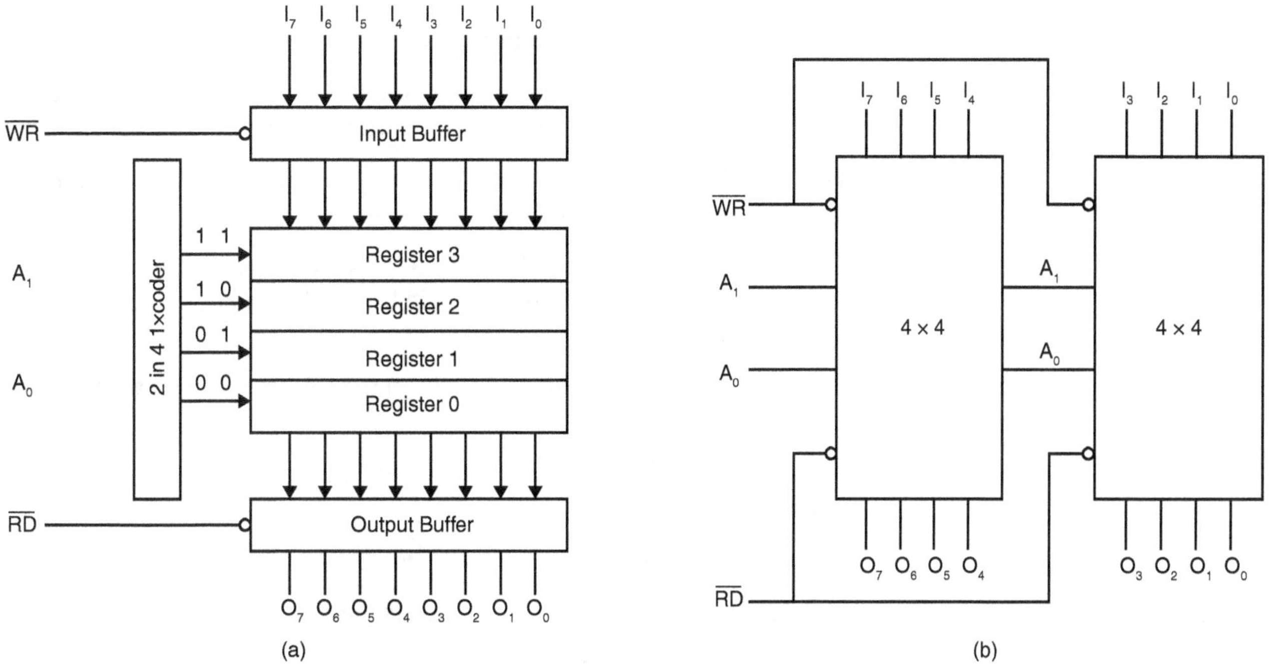

Figure 19.6 (a) 4×8 Bit Register (b) Two 4×4 Bit Registers

If we have two chips with 4 registers each, one address line (A_2) is used as a chip select, and the other two address lines (A_1 and A_0) are connected to both chips.

Figure 19.7b shows that chip select signal CS is active low, so that when A_2 is 0 (low) chip M_1 is selected, and when A_2 is 1 (high), chip M_2 is selected. The address on A_1 and A_0 will determine the registers to be selected. By combining the logic on A_2, A_1, and A_0, the memory addresses range from 000 to 111.

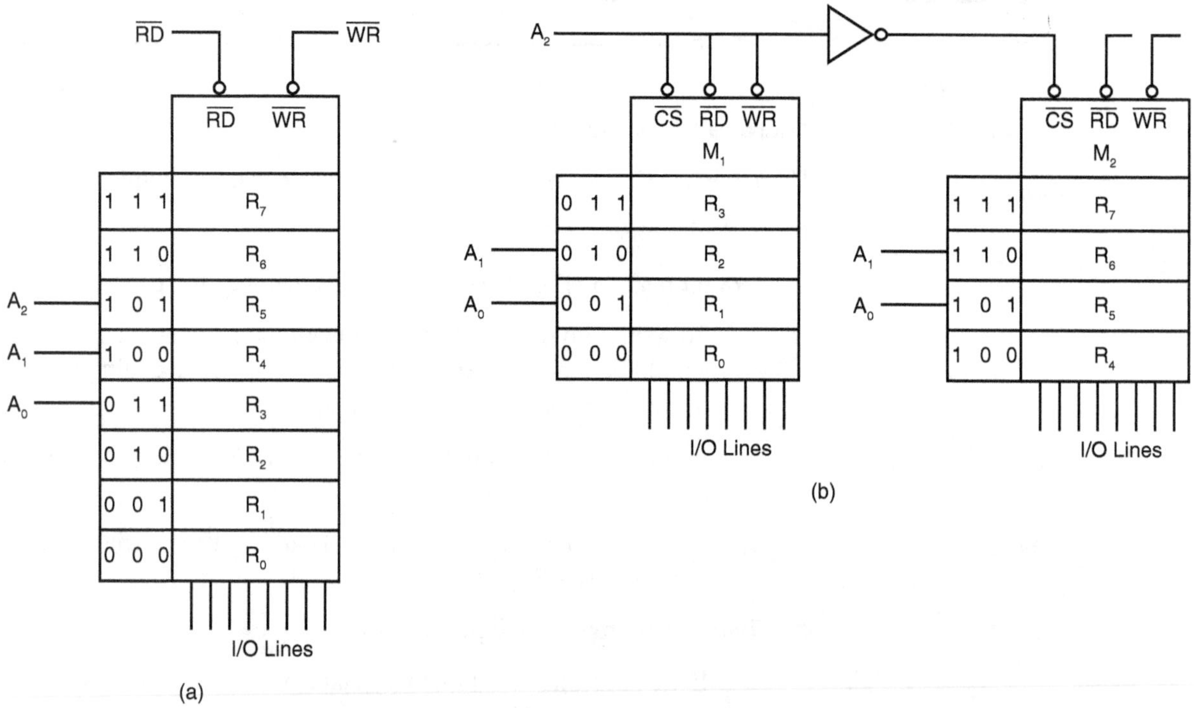

Figure 19.7 (a) Memory Chip with Eight Registers, (b) Two Memory Chips with Four Registers Each

Summary memory chip requirements:

- Address lines to identify memory register, CS signal to enable chip, and control signals to read from and write into memory
- Number of address lines is related to number of registers (2^n = number of registers, n is the number of address lines)
- If additional lines are available, they are used for CS. The memory address of a register is determined by the logic levels of all addresses (including lines used for CS).
- RD enables the output buffer. Data from the selected register are made available on the output lines.
- WR enables the input buffer. Data on the input lines are written into memory cells.

For memory mapped I/O devices:

- Assume memory chip with 256 registers, only 8 address lines ($2^8 = 256$).
  - How do we assign 16-bit address lines to 256 registers?

- Solution:
  - A_7-A_0 used to identify memory registers, remaining 8 lines (A_{15}-A_8) are connected to the CS line through inverters and the NAND gate. The memory chip is enabled when CS goes low. No other logic levels can select the chip.
  - The chip select addresses are determined by the hardware (inverters and NAND gate). Therefore, the memory map of the chip can be changed by modify the hardware.

For peripheral mapped I/O with 8 bit addressing:

- With 8 bits the MPU can identify 256 devices for I/O using control signals for read and write.
- This is sometimes called the I/O map (00-0xFFH).
- Individual addresses are called I/O device addresses or I/O ports.
- Cannot connect I/O device directly to bus; all connections must be made through tri-state interfacing devices. Memory is okay because internal address decoding, chip select logic.
- Steps in interfacing with I/O device
  - Place 8-bit address on the address bus, which is decoded by the external decode logic.
  - Send control signals (I/O read, write) to enable I/O device.
  - Data is transferred on data bus.

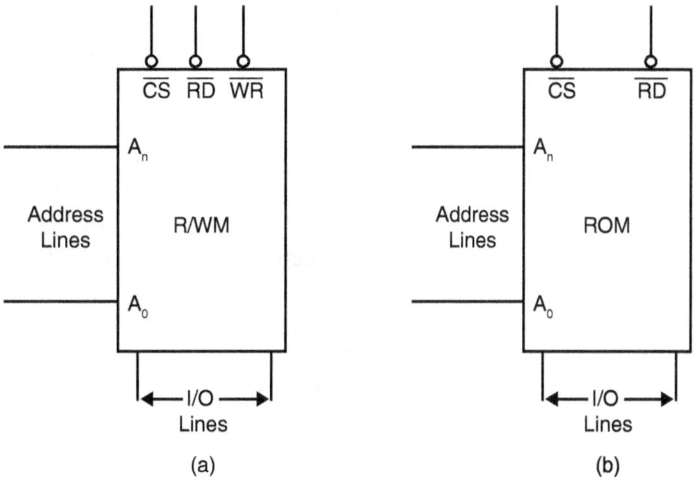

Figure 19.8 (a) R/W Memory Model, (b) ROM Model

For a memory-mapped I/O MPU system with 16 bit addresses, the MPU uses the same control signals and instructions as those for memory and follows the same steps as when it is accessing memory registers.

COMPUTER ARCHITECTURE

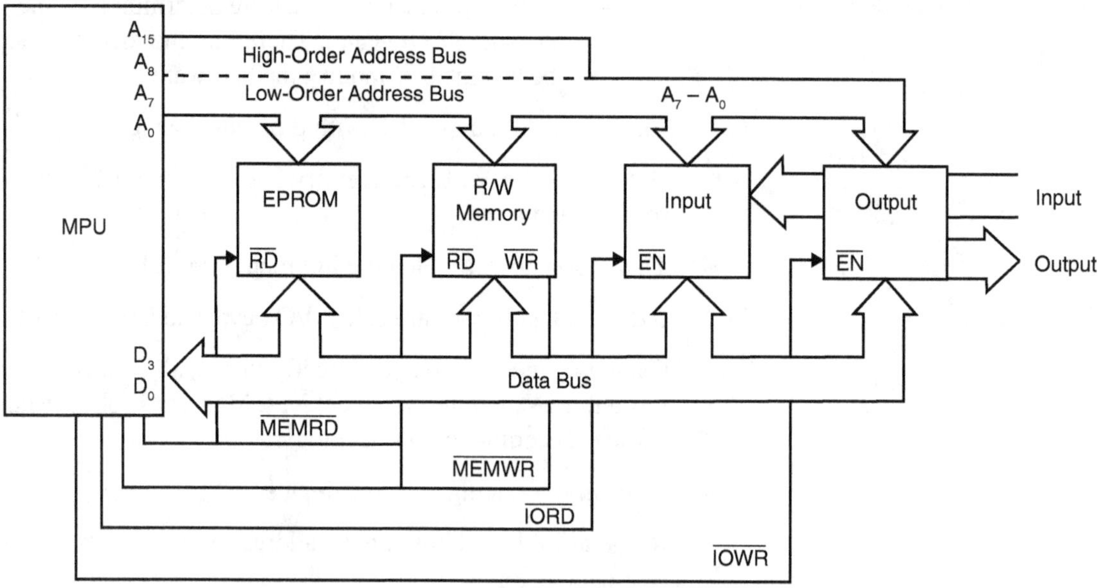

Figure 9.9 Example of a Microprocessor Based System

Pipelining

Pipelining is an implementation technique where multiple instructions are overlapped in execution. The computer pipeline is divided in **stages**. Each stage completes a part of an instruction in parallel. The stages are connected one to the next to form a pipe: instructions enter at one end, progress through the stages, and exit at the other end.

Pipelining does not decrease the time for individual instruction execution. Instead, it increases instruction throughput. The **throughput** of the instruction pipeline is determined by how often an instruction exits the pipeline.

Because the pipe stages are hooked together, all the stages must be ready to proceed at the same time. The time required to move an instruction one step further in the pipeline is called a **machine cycle**. The **length** of the machine cycle is determined by the time required for the slowest pipe stage.

The pipeline designer's *goal is to balance the length of each pipeline stage*. If the stages are perfectly balanced, the time per instruction on the pipelined machine is equal to

$$\frac{\text{time per instruction on nonpipelined machine}}{\text{number of pipe stages}}$$

Under these conditions, the speedup from pipelining equals the number of pipe stages. Usually, however, the stages will not be perfectly balanced. Besides, the pipelining itself involves some overhead.

Cache Memory

Cache is a small high-speed memory. It stores data from some frequently used addresses (of main memory).

Cache sits between the CPU and main memory. It is invisible to the CPU and only useful if recently used items are used again. Fortunately, this happens a lot. This property is called the *locality of reference*.

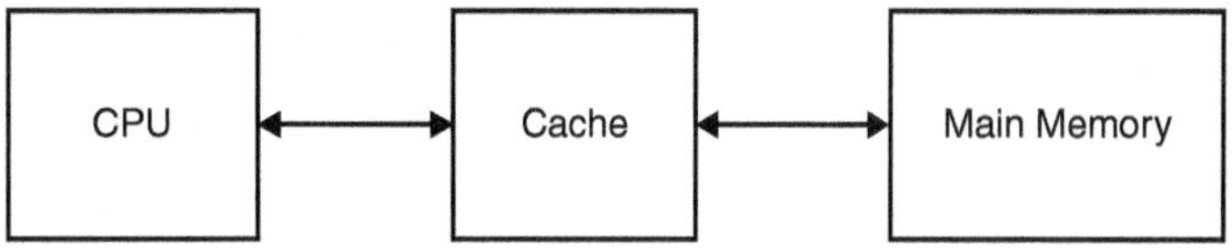

Figure 19.10

Cache memory exploits locality by:

- Temporal
  - When an item is accessed from memory, it is brought into the cache.
  - If it is accessed again soon, it comes from the cache and not main memory.
- Spatial
  - When we access a memory word, we also fetch the next few words of memory into the cache.
  - The number of words fetched is the *cache line size*, or the *cache block size* for the machine.
- Cache write policies
  - As long as it is only performing read operations, the cache is an exact copy of a small part of the main memory.
  - Write through cache—write to both cache and main memory. Cache and memory are always consistent.
  - Write back cache—write only to cache and set a "dirty bit." When the block gets replaced from the cache, write it out to memory.
- Typical modern cache architecture consists of:
  - L0 cache
    - On chip
    - Split 16 KB data/16 KB instructions
  - L1 cache
    - On chip
    - 64 KB unified
  - L2 cache
    - Off chip
    - 128 KB to 16+ MB

- Cache memory performance can be measured and calculated as follows:
  - No cache: Often about 10 cycles per memory access
  - Simple cache:
    - $t_{ave} = h_C + (1 - h)M$
    - C is often 1 clock cycle
    - Assume M is 17 cycles (to load an entire cache line)
    - Assume h is about 90%
    - $t_{ave} = 0.9\,(1) + (0.1)17 = 2.6$ cycles/access
  - $t_{ave} = h_1C_1 + (1 - h_1)h_2C_2 + (1 - h_1)\,(1 - h_2)M$
    - h_1 = hit rate in primary cache
    - h_2 = hit rate in secondary cache
    - C_1 = time to access primary cache
    - C_2 = time to access secondary cache
    - M = miss penalty (time to load an entire cache line from main memory)

A typical cache organization is shown in Figure 19.11.

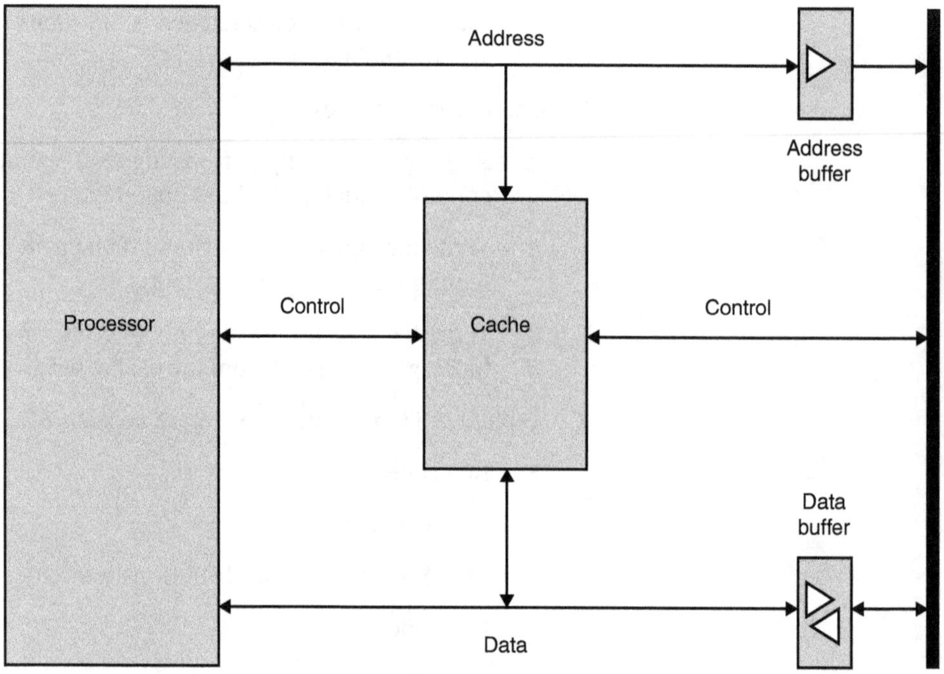

Figure 19.11

PROBLEMS

19.1 If we have 8 registers on one chip, how many address lines do we need? If we have two chips with 4 registers each, how do we do addressing?

19.2 How does the uP work?

19.3 What are main components of a uP?

19.4 What does an ALU do?

19.5 What is an instruction cycle?

19.6 What is an interrupt?

19.7 What is Direct Memory Access (DMA)?

19.8 Given a 30% duty-cycle clock, with a high-pulse width of 20 μs, what is the clock frequency in KHz?

19.9 All microprocessors have something that is called a program counter. What is this?

SOLUTIONS

19.1 One address line (A_2) is used as a chip select, and the other two address lines (A_1 and A_0) are connected to both chips.

19.2

- Programs stored in ROM.
- Data in RAM.
- uP uses the system bus to fetch binary instructions from ROM, stores them in registers and decodes them, and executes the decoded instruction in the ALU. The result of the executed instruction could be to output a result to memory or LEDs, for example.

19.3 Central Processing Unit (CPU), Memory, Input and Output (I/O)

19.4 ALU performs operations on data, (e.g., addition, subtraction, logic operations, AND, OR and EOR => result stored in register or memory).

19.5 Instruction cycle is the time taken to complete the execution of an instruction.
⇒1-6 machine/operation cycles; machine cycle is defined as the time required to complete one operation of accessing memory, accessing IO, and so forth.

19.6 When the peripheral is ready to transfer data, it sends an interrupt signal to the microprocessor (e.g., packet arrives from network).

19.7 DMA is an I/O technique for high-speed data transfer (e.g., transfer packets to memory).

19.8 0.3 * period = 20 us; so period = 20 us/0.3 = 66 us. Freq = 1/66 us = 15 KHz

19.9

- Counts the number of bytes in a program.
- Always holds one of the operands for an ALU operation.
- Specifies the upper 4 bits of a 12-bit data memory address.
- Holds the current instruction that is being executed.
- Specifies the address of the next instruction.
- Contains the flags that are affected by the current instruction.

CHAPTER 20

Software Development

OUTLINE

INTRODUCTION

Current information for the FE exam indicates that approximately 7% of the *morning session* of the exam will contain questions related to computers, regardless of exam discipline. This means that there will be approximately eight or nine questions related to computers in the morning session for all FE examinees. There may be additional questions related to *computer systems* in the afternoon for examinees taking the *electrical* FE exam. All examinees should have basic familiarity with the following computer topics:

- Terminology (e.g., memory types, CPU, baud rates, Internet)
- Spreadsheets (e.g., addresses, interpretation, what if, copying formulas)
- Structured programming (e.g., assignment statements, loops and branches, function calls)

These three broad areas are specifically identified as topic areas addressed on the FE exam by NCEES. These and similar topics will be covered in this review chapter. More advanced computer topics, such as computer architecture, interfacing, microprocessors, and software design, which could be covered in the *afternoon section* of the *electrical* exam, should be reviewed using materials appropriate to that exam.

TERMINOLOGY

Types of Computers and Networks

There are many types of computers. The predecessors of all modern day computers were **mainframe** computers. Mainframe computers are large computers that typically fill an entire room, require air conditioning, and support many hundreds of users. Large and especially fast computers are known as **supercomputers**. Supercomputers are used to model very complex phenomena such as the operation of the human brain, air currents resulting from a fire, or nuclear explosions. Supercomputers are sometimes referred to as **Cray** computers because Cray Research, Inc. (founded by Seymour Cray) is a noted manufacturer of supercomputers. Mainframe and supercomputers tend to be expensive to buy and maintain.

Slightly smaller computers, which might still fill a room but support only 10 to 100 users, are known as **minicomputers**. Minicomputers are not in much use today, having been displaced by networks of smaller computers.

Smaller and moderately less powerful computers used for engineering and scientific calculations are often referred to as **workstations**. Workstations typically are designed for one user but can support multiple users. Computers that are less powerful than workstations and that are used in the home or office are typically known as **PCs** (personal computers). PCs derive their name from the IBM-PC, but other similarly used computers, such as Apple's Mac family of computers, also are typically referred to as PCs. Both workstations and PCs are **microcomputers**. Over time, the prefix "micro" has tended to be dropped from the term, and most people simply refer to microcomputers as computers. Similarly, in recent years, the distinction between workstations and PCs has blurred, and low-end workstations may also be referred to simply as PCs.

The computer chips that go into consumer devices, such as microwave ovens, washing machines, and cellular telephones, are known as **microprocessors**. If the chip has advanced systems on it such as analog-to-digital converters, timer systems, and significant memory, then it is known as a **microcontroller**.

To obtain large computing power at small cost, computers are sometimes networked together such that individual computers can process different parts of one problem. This is sometimes referred to as **cluster computing** or **grid computing**. Cluster computing typically takes place on computers located in close proximity to one another. A common cluster computing arrangement is a **Beowulf Cluster**. Grid computing typically uses computers more widely dispersed over the **Internet**, a worldwide network of computers for the purpose of sharing information. An arrangement in which computing services, such as network support, hardware and software upgrades, and data storage, take place over the Internet is known as **cloud computing** or **computing in the cloud**.

A lot of information available on the Internet can be viewed using an **Internet browser**, a computer program written to easily access information provided on the Internet using **http (hypertext transfer protocol)**, a standard method for publishing information on the Internet. A key feature of http is the use of a **URL**, or **universal resource locator**. A URL provides a standard format for providing a computer address of where information resides on the Internet. **Search engines**, such as Google, Yahoo, and Bing, can provide URLs for sought-after information.

Computer Communication

Computer communication has always been important. Typically a monitor and keyboard were used to access mainframe computers. The monitor and keyboard were known as a **terminal**. Today, a PC is often used as a terminal for large computers. If the terminal has very low processing power, it is known as a **thin client**. If the terminal has significant processing power, it is known as a **fat client** or **thick client**.

Computers communicate by sending **bits** of data. A bit is the simplest piece of information that can be stored in a computer. It is represented by a one or a zero. Representing information in only one of two possible states is known as **binary** representation.

Early computers communicated to terminals and other equipment at slow rates typically measured in hundreds or thousands of **baud**. The baud rate is the greatest number of state transitions per second in a communication system. In older technology, this is equivalent to the **bit rate**, the maximum number of bits that can be transmitted per second. However, modern communication systems may send more than one bit of information per state transition, so baud and bit rate should not be used interchangeably. The speed of **RS-232** communication, a common serial communication standard, has typically been expressed in baud. Its maximum data rate is about 20,000 baud.

Serial communication is a method of communication in which only one bit of information is sent at a time. Sometimes the bit that is sent is not received correctly. To prevent this type of error, serial communication systems often send a **parity bit**. A parity bit is an extra bit sent with a group of other bits (usually numbering seven or eight) such that the number of 1s or 0s sent is always even or odd. If the receiver detects that it has received the wrong number of even or odd bits, it can request retransmission of the data. Serial communication tends to be much slower than **parallel** communication in which many bits are sent simultaneously over separate physical lines.

RS-232 serial ports have been common on many PCs for many years; however, communication on PCs now typically takes place over **Ethernet, firewire**, or **USB**. Ethernet is a communication standard primarily used for **local area networks** (LANs), physically connected computers sharing a small geographic region. Ethernet now supports data speeds up to 100 billion bits per second. Firewire and USB standards support speeds up to about 5 billion bits per second and are primarily used to connect computers to other noncomputer devices, such as digital video cameras, external hard drives, and other personal electronic devices. **Wide area networks** (WANs) are used to link LANs and other computer networks together over far-reaching geographical areas.

Example 20.1

Which of the following communication protocols would be most suitable for a new data communication center's local area network (LAN)?

(i) RS-232 (ii) Ethernet (iii) firewire (iv) USB

Solution

The correct choice is (ii) Ethernet. All other options are considerably slower than Ethernet and more likely to be used to connect computers to other noncomputer devices rather than to other computers. As more information is being sent over networks, a new data communication center needs the fastest communication standard.

Computer Memory

Computer memory and communication speeds are typically expressed in bits (b) or **bytes** (B) and bits per second (bps) or bytes per second (B/s). A byte consists of eight bits.

As computer memory has increased in size, prefixes have been used to indicate larger units of computer memory. This has led to some confusion in specifying computer memory. Because computer memory is utilized in sizes consisting of powers of two, a **kilobyte (KB)** is not 1000 bytes, but is actually 1024 (2^{10}) bytes. The confusion exists because the prefix kilo means 1000 in SI units. The confusion is even more pronounced because in computer information storage (such as in hard drives, tape drives, and removable disks) and in other computer-related usage (such as in clock speeds, operations per second, or data transfer rates), the standard SI meaning of the prefix is *typically* used. Consequently, a **megabyte (MB)** is 1,048,576 (2^{20}) bytes if referring to computer memory and is 1,000,000 bytes if referring to the storage capacity of a removable disk. A **gigabyte (GB)** indicates 2^{30} bytes of computer memory or 10^9 bytes of disk storage capacity. Likewise, a **terabyte (TB)** consists of 2^{40} bytes if referring to computer memory or 10^{12} bytes if referring to the total amount of data to be transferred to a computer over the Internet.

If the base 2 usage of the prefix is meant, especially when using it in reference to something other than computer memory, then the prefixes should be altered to kibi (2^{10}), mebi (2^{20}), gibi (2^{30}), and tebi (2^{40}) to reduce confusion. The **kibibyte**, **mebibyte**, **gibibyte**, and **tebibyte** are then abbreviated **KiB**, **MiB**, **GiB**, and **TiB**, respectively. Thus, a 200 GiB hard drive has $200 \times 2^{30} = 214{,}748{,}364{,}800$ bytes of storage capacity, whereas a 200 GB hard drive has $200 \times 10^9 = 200{,}000{,}000{,}000$ bytes of storage capacity.

Example 20.2

A supercomputer has 200 TB of computer memory. How many bits does this represent?

Solution

Because the reference is to computer memory, the TB abbreviation indicates the nonstandard use of the prefix *tera* to mean 2^{40}. Additionally, the number of bits must be found from the number of bytes (8 bits = 1 byte).

$$200\text{ TB} \times \frac{2^{40}\text{ B}}{1\text{ TB}} \times \frac{8\text{ bits}}{1\text{ B}} = 1{,}759{,}218{,}604{,}441{,}600\text{ bits}$$

Computer memory is typically referred to as belonging to **RAM** or **ROM**. For historical reasons, the name RAM was created to indicate *random access memory*, and ROM indicated *read-only memory*. However, the term *RAM* now indicates memory that is **volatile**, and *ROM* indicates memory that is **nonvolatile**. Volatile memory is memory in which the data is lost if power is removed, whereas nonvolatile memory retains its data even if power is removed. RAM is used to temporarily store data and program code while a computer is in operation. ROM is used to permanently store programs and other information that doesn't change (or at least doesn't change very often).

Although there are other types of RAM, the two most common types are **static RAM (SRAM)** and **dynamic RAM (DRAM)**. SRAM is faster than DRAM but is more expensive, takes up more space, and consumes more energy. It is typically used for a computer's **cache**. A cache is a separate memory structure that is used to rapidly access frequently used data or program code. Because of the disadvantages of SRAM, cache memory is typically much smaller than main memory. DRAM is typically used for main memory. DRAM is so named because the information is stored as a charge on a capacitor that gradually loses its charge. To keep from losing the data, the memory system must provide a periodic refresh charge. RAM chips are built on silicon wafers using complementary metal oxide semiconductor **(CMOS)** circuits. CMOS circuits are an especially energy-efficient means of storing data in RAM, especially if the transitions between the binary states occur infrequently.

Read-only memory (ROM) was initially just as the name states—memory that could only be read. The data or program code was placed into the memory chip during manufacture. This memory evolved into programmable ROM **(PROM)** memory, which was memory that could be programmed after manufacture but only programmed once. After a PROM was programmed, it could only be read and not written to again. This was followed by **EPROM** memory. EPROM stands for erasable programmable ROM. This memory type could be written to many times but only after erasing it via exposure to ultraviolet light through a quartz crystal window manufactured into the chip housing. **EEPROM** followed EPROM. EEPROM stands for electrically erasable PROM. Instead of needing ultraviolet light to erase the memory, this memory could be erased and reprogrammed by applying appropriate voltages to the chip.

Flash memory is a type of EEPROM and is commonly accessed via a USB port. This arrangement is referred to as a **pen drive**, **thumb drive**, **flash drive**, or **jump drive**. Sometimes hard drives and **CD** (compact disc) or **DVD** (digital video

disc or digital versatile disc) drives are considered to be ROM, especially if the CD or DVD disc can only be written to once.

Data transmission is slower in ROM as compared to RAM. Data transmission to or from a hard drive, CD drive, or DVD drive is extremely slow as compared to accessing other memory types. Although considerably slower, these drives have substantially more memory capacity than internal RAM or ROM. Storage capacity for hard drives is now commonly measured in hundreds of GB or tens of TB.

Example **20.3**

Which of the following memory types would most likely be used for a computer's cache memory?

(i) SRAM (ii) DRAM (iii) EPROM (iv) FLASH

Solution

The correct answer is (i) SRAM because it is the fastest type of RAM. ROM types of memory would never be used for a cache.

Example **20.4**

To what do the first two letters in the name of the memory type known as EEPROM refer?

(i) Enhanced Emitter (ii) Energy Efficient (iii) Exception Event

(iv) Electrically Erasable

Solution

The correct answer is (iv) Electrically Erasable. EEPROM is a type of read only memory (ROM) that can be erased and reprogrammed by applying appropriate voltages to the memory chip.

Program Execution

Execution of computer programs to process data takes place in the **central processing unit (CPU)**. This is a specialized circuit that once consisted of vacuum tubes or mechanical relays but is now built on silicon as an **integrated circuit (IC)**. An IC is a complex electrical circuit consisting of many transistors to implement one or more functions on a single silicon wafer. CPUs have many substructures, such as **arithmetic and logic units (ALUs)**, registers (also commonly known as **accumulators**), **buses**, and **control units**.

- **ALUs** are responsible for implementing data manipulation via arithmetic instructions such as add, subtract, and multiply. They also implement logic instructions such as logical AND, OR, and XOR (exclusive or).
- **Registers** or **accumulators** are special memory locations within the CPU used for holding data and intermediate results that are currently being accessed and manipulated by the ALU. They are also used for keeping track of which instruction in memory is to be executed next and for keeping track of the CPU's current operational state.

- **Buses** are the electrically conductive paths on which code, data, control information, and memory locations (addresses) are sent and received.
- The **control unit** is the circuit that makes all the subsystems work together appropriately. The control unit ensures data is written to or read from the appropriate registers at the appropriate times. The control unit may also assist with getting the next instruction from memory and other similar tasks.

The four main functions of the CPU are to *fetch*, *decode*, *execute*, and *write back* program code and data. The speed at which a CPU can accomplish these functions is often measured in **MIPS**, **million instructions per second**, also sometimes referred to as **MOPS**, **million operations per second**.

A single integrated circuit having more than one CPU is referred to as a **multicore processor**. Multicore processors can increase processing speed by sharing operations between two or more CPUs. Splitting processing tasks so that they can be shared between processors is known as **parallel programming**. An arrangement in which a CPU accesses both program code and data from a single memory structure is known as the **von Neumann architecture**. The **Harvard architecture** is an arrangement in which the CPU accesses program code from a memory structure that is separate and distinct from another memory structure used for holding data.

Number Systems and Data Types

CPUs are designed to work with code and data as binary numbers (0s and 1s). A computer program represented in binary is often referred to as **machine code**. As the digits of a binary number are examined from right to left, each digit represents a higher consecutive integer power of two. For example, the binary number 1101 represents the decimal number 13 because $1 \times 2^3 + 1 \times 2^2 + 0 \times 2^1 + 1 \times 2^0 = 8 + 4 + 0 + 1 = 13$.

Example 20.5

The binary number 110 corresponds to what decimal (base 10) number?

Solution

$$1 \times 2^2 + 1 \times 2^1 + 0 \times 2^0 = 4 + 2 = 6$$

The conversion of a decimal number to a binary number can be achieved by the method of remainders as follows. A decimal integer is divided by 2, giving an integer quotient and a remainder. This process is repeated until the quotient becomes 0. The remainders (in the reverse order) form the binary number. The following example illustrates this process.

Example 20.6

Convert decimal number 43 to a binary number.

Solution

	Quotient		Remainder
$43 \div 2 =$	21	+	1
$21 \div 2 =$	10	+	1
$10 \div 2 =$	5	+	0
$5 \div 2 =$	2	+	1
$2 \div 2 =$	1	+	0
$1 \div 2 =$	0	+	1

Answer: $(43)_{10} = (101011)_2$

Although the conversion from decimal to binary is straightforward, binary numbers are typically difficult for humans to read and understand, especially as the number of digits increase. A small improvement in readability was made by introducing **hexadecimal** (or **hex**) numbers. Hex numbers are formed by taking four binary digits at a time and using them to represent a base 16 number. This is accomplished by using the letters A, B, C, D, E, and F to represent decimal numbers 10, 11, 12, 13, 14, and 15, respectively. Thus, the binary number 1101, hexadecimal number D, and decimal number 13 are all equivalent. The equivalent decimal number can be found for a hexadecimal number in a manner similar to that for a binary number.

Example 20.7

Find the equivalent decimal value for the hexadecimal number 25E6.

Solution

$$2 \times 16^3 + 5 \times 16^2 + 14 \times 16^1 + 6 \times 16^0 = 8192 + 1280 + 224 + 6 = 9702$$

Fractional binary values can be represented by including digits to the right of a radix point (commonly understood as the decimal point for decimal numbers). For instance, the binary number 1101.101 is equivalent to the decimal number 13.625 because $1101.101 = 1 \times 2^3 + 1 \times 2^2 + 0 \times 2^1 + 1 \times 2^0 + 1 \times 2^{-1} + 0 \times 2^{-2} + 1 \times 2^{-3}$, which is equivalent to $8 + 4 + 0 + 1 + 0.5 + 0 + 0.125 = 13.625$.

A similar procedure can be followed for hex numbers. To find equivalent binary or hex numbers from a decimal number, repeatedly divide the decimal number and all remainders by integer powers of 2 or 16, respectively. For instance, the decimal number 2672 is A70 in hex because 16^2 divides into 2672 ten times and 16^1 divides into the remainder seven times and 16^0 divides into the final remainder zero times.

Alternatively, conversion from decimal to hexadecimal may be carried out in a manner similar to that for decimal to binary conversion, with the divisor 2 (or multiplier in the case of fractions) replaced by 16.

Example 20.8

Convert the base 10 integer 458.75 to base 16 equivalent value.

	Quotient		Remainder	Hexadecimal
458 ÷ 16	28	+	10	A
28 ÷ 16	1	+	12	C
1 ÷ 16	0	+	1	1
	Integer		**Remainder**	**Hexadecimal**
.75 × 16	12		0	C
458.75 = 1CA.C				

If fractional values of a number are never needed, all of the available bits can be used to represent an **integer** data type. Because there must always be a finite number of bits used to represent a number, fractional numbers will often suffer from **round off**, or **rounding error**. For instance, if a binary number only had four digits available to represent a fractional value, any fraction that couldn't be exactly represented as an integer multiple of $1/2^4$ would be represented as the nearest integer multiple of $1/2^4$. This creates a rounding error of as much as $1/2^5$ = 0.03125. A limited number of digits for the fractional portion creates a limit to the precision of a binary number.

Similarly, a limited number of digits for the integer portion creates a limit to the range of a binary number. To help alleviate these limitations, the **floating point** data type was created. Floating point data permits the radix point to move (float) among the binary digits depending on whether greater range of the number is needed or whether increased precision is needed. It can be thought of as a type of scientific notation representation of numbers for computers. Common floating point number standards consist of **single precision**, **double precision**, and **quadruple precision**. These standards are able to accurately represent about 7, 16, and 34 significant figures, respectively. If a computation is attempted that cannot be represented by the computer, a **NaN** (Not a Number) data type might result. Examples of these types of computation might be trying to divide by zero or taking the square root of a negative number.

Character data types are often used to represent letters of the alphabet or the character representation of the numerals zero through nine or punctuation. Some other special symbols and control characters may also be represented by the character data type. Some of these include the symbol for a new line, carriage return, and bell sound. Common codes for representing character data include **ASCII (American Standard Code for Information Interchange), EBCDIC (Extended Binary Coded Decimal Information Code), and Unicode**. ASCII and EBCDIC are used for the English language alphabet and symbols. Unicode is an evolving standard used to represent alphabets and writing symbols of many different languages of the world. When character data is put together, as in forming a name, it is often referred to as a **string**.

Example 20.9

Which of the following would most likely be an example of a character string?

(i) 241.38
(ii) 2.4138e2
(iii) 241
(iv) Two hundred forty-one and thirty-eight hundredths

Solution

The correct answer is (iv) Two hundred forty-one and thirty-eight hundredths. Although all of the answers could be strings if the character representation of each of the digits were being displayed, only (iv) is the *most likely* example of a character string. This is because answers (i) and (ii) could also be examples of floating point data types, and answer (iii) could be an example of an integer data type. Only answer (iv) uses a significant number of alphabetic letters and dashes to guarantee it to be a character string.

Placing a number of data values in a continuous section of memory with one data value sequentially following the next is often referred to as a **data array**. This arrangement often makes processing of the data faster because the data can be easily loaded into the computer's cache memory for ready access. Data arrays may be one-dimensional arrays (as in a single column or row) or two-dimensional arrays in which there are multiple columns and rows of data (as in a matrix). Higher dimensional arrays are possible but not as common. A data array often uses a **pointer**, a variable that "points" to the location of the array, to provide access to the data within the array.

Computer Languages

To process data, computer programs are necessary. Originally, programs were written by physical switches or circuits that were opened or closed to represent the 0s or 1s of machine code. However, this was very difficult for humans to do without making mistakes, so **assembly languages** (or **assembler languages**) were developed. Assembly languages use short **mnemonics** to correspond to a specific instruction available to the CPU. For example, the instruction LDAA might stand for Load Accumulator A. Once the program is written in assembly language, a separate program known as an **assembler** converts the assembly code into machine code. The resulting file created is known as an **executable** because it can be directly loaded and executed on the computer.

Even though assembly languages were a vast improvement over writing programs in machine code, they were still difficult to use, especially as data processing tasks became more complicated. For this reason, **high-level languages** were created to make programming easier. Examples of high-level languages include Fortran, Basic, C, Java, Matlab, and Python. Similar to assemblers, **compilers** convert high-level languages into machine code so that executables are available to work directly on the computer. As long as a compiler is available for any given computer, high-level languages can usually be compiled to work on the computer with little or no modification to the original programming code. **Compiler errors** occur when the program is compiled if there are errors in the code that the compiler cannot process. A syntax error is a common error made by programmers. A **syntax error** occurs when the rules for how the language is to

be used are not followed. An example of a syntax error is trying to use a variable before the variable is **declared** in a statement that names the variable and describes its data type.

Interpreted languages are also considered high-level languages. Interpreted languages do not need to be compiled and an executable is not generated. Interpreted languages are "interpreted" into machine code at runtime. This has some advantages in that variables and arrays can be created and altered "on the fly," but also has disadvantages in that the code executes more slowly, and an **interpreter** must exist on the machine in order for the interpreted language to run. Fortran and C are usually compiled into executables; whereas Matlab and Python are usually interpreted.

High-level languages use **functions** (which may also be known as **subroutines**, **procedures**, or **methods**) to break code into smaller reusable sections. Functions often need **parameters** (the datum or data) passed to them to execute properly. Parameters may be passed using **call-by-value** or **call-by-reference**. Call-by-value sends the data values directly to the function, whereas call-by-reference sends the function the memory location of where the data is stored. Functions may or may not return values to the program that originally called it.

Structured programs use three main structures to process data. These are **sequence**, **looping** (or **repetition**), and **decision** (or **choice**). Sequence is the process by which code executes only one instruction at a time, and each instruction executed follows in sequential order as determined by the programmer. Looping involves execution of an instruction or a sequential list of instructions repeatedly until some condition is satisfied. The determination for looping can be made prior to the loop beginning (pre-test) or after the loop has started execution (post-test). In structured programming, loops should only have one entry point and exit point. A decision is used to determine whether a given condition is true or false or what condition exists so that a program **branch** (a change in the flow of program execution) can take place.

As programs have become larger, **object oriented programming (OOP)** has become a major programming paradigm. Object oriented programming organizes programs around the data as objects rather than organizing around the tasks that must be performed on the data. Many believe OOP makes maintenance of programs easier, especially as the programming code becomes very large.

Operating Systems

A PC needs programs in order to interface with its own input and output devices, control those devices, and manage resources. These programs are known as **operating systems**. Some common operating systems include Unix, Linux, Mac OS, and Microsoft Windows. Operating system functions are generally accessed through an **API** (an **application program interface**). An API ensures that the operating system is in control of resources and that computer hardware is not *directly* controlled by the user or other programs. Operating systems permit other work productivity programs (**application programs**) to also run on the computer. Common application programs include programs for word processing, e-mail, spreadsheets, database management, presentation graphics, Internet browsers, and accounting programs. In addition to these, engineers often use application programs for **CAD (computer aided design)** and **CAM (computer aided manufacturing)**. Many application programs work with the user using a **GUI (graphical user interface)**. A GUI makes interacting with an application program (or operating

system) easier by visually displaying options available and making those options easily selectable by a mouse or other input device.

Computer Security

Many operating systems and networking application programs implement security features to protect computer data and prevent unauthorized use of computers. A **password** is a sequence of letters, numbers, and other characters that must be provided before the operating system or networking program will permit access to computer data and programs. Typically, passwords should be changed often and consist of an unobvious sequence of character data involving both upper and lowercase letters, numbers, and other symbols. In some cases, passwords may be necessary to access computer data.

Encryption is also used to protect passwords and sensitive data. Encryption scrambles and encodes the data or password such that it is not readily seen or understandable without a key. A common method of providing encryption over the Internet is by using **SSL, secure socket layer**. The URL for Web sites using SSL begin with https rather than http.

Damage to data can occur due to a **computer virus**, **malware**, **spyware**, or other deliberate destruction by an unauthorized user. A computer virus is software written to cause damage to another computer's files or operation and to replicate itself so that it can be spread to other computers. **Antivirus software** is software that attempts to recognize computer viruses and inactivate them before they can infect a computer or replicate. Malware is any software written by unscrupulous people to cause damage to a computer's data, whether or not it is self-replicating. Spyware is software written to record or search for sensitive information on a computer to send to the spyware's programmer in order to steal information such as credit card numbers or computer passwords. People who write such programs are known as **crackers**, and sometimes **hackers**, although the term *hacker* is sometimes used to denote skilled programmers who don't necessarily have any malicious intent for the code they write.

Often a **firewall** is used to prevent unauthorized access to a computer over the Internet. A firewall carefully checks transmitted information over a network to make sure only authorized information is being conveyed. Some computers require **biometric data** to gain access to the computer. Biometric data is information about an individual that is uneasy to copy and is often used to provide a higher level of security for gaining computer access. Examples of biometric data would include a fingerprint or iris scan.

Some unauthorized people will try to gain access to computers by **spoofing**. This is an attempt to gain access by convincing the computer's security features that the unauthorized person is someone else or another computer that does have authorized access. Another commonly used method to try to gain unauthorized access to a computer is by **phishing**. Phishing is an attempt, usually via e-mail, to convince a user that the person sending the e-mail is someone who can be trusted and that the user should send confidential information such as passwords or banking information.

STRUCTURED PROGRAMMING

To solve a problem by using a computer program, an algorithm is usually developed. An **algorithm** is an ordered sequence of steps to take to arrive at a solution.

In the early days of computers and computer programs, there were no clear and concise rules to follow in implementing an algorithm in a computer program. Two of the earliest computer languages, assembly and BASIC, permitted the use of the *jump* and *goto* instructions, respectively. Although a computer could implement these instructions without any problems, human programmers overused them to their own detriment. Because no structured rules existed, programmers were left to implement the algorithm in whatever way they could to arrive at a solution. The resulting code solutions often were difficult to read and understand by people other than the original programmer. Such code also was prone to error because the programmer had not considered all the possible circumstances in which program execution could be altered by a goto statement. If the code ever needed to be upgraded, it was often difficult to follow the logical sequence and know what parts of the code should be changed and what should remain the same. Thus, program maintenance was difficult to achieve. Large blocks of code were often written to implement the algorithm all at once. This too made it difficult for others to keep track of all the variables that were being used, what the variables' current values were, and when program execution left the current sequence or jumped back in. As programming tasks became more complicated and larger code needed to be written, a real need for code that was easy to read and understand became apparent.

Structured programming is a concept generally credited to Edsger Dijkstra. He advocated much less dependence on the *goto* statement, even that it should be eliminated. Dijkstra articulated simple rules to make programming easier to read, understand, and maintain. To eliminate the rat's nest of code generated by overuse of the *goto* statement, structured programming specifies that there should be only one entry point and exit point within a loop, function call, or sequence of instructions. The entry or exit point should be determined by a decision statement that clearly indicates the condition or conditions under which the program execution could change (that is, under what conditions the program could *branch* to execute other instructions). Similarly, structured programming specifies that code should be modular. This means that large problems should be broken into smaller problems that can be solved first; the smaller solutions are then pieced together to solve the large problem. This top-down design approach means that function calls should be used to solve smaller portions of the problem. This keeps the code modular so that it is easy to see what small problem is being solved, the logical steps taken to solve it, and how it relates to solving the big problem without the confusion of solving too much at one time. Once the function is developed and well tested, it can be reused in other code, making new code development times shorter and facilitating code upgrades and maintenance. Indenting distinct chunks of code improves its readability and is another important contribution of structured programming. For example, the programmer might indent a section of instructions all pertaining to the same loop function.

In structured programming, only three main control structures are needed:

1. Statements for sequential execution of instructions, such as assignment statements
2. Decision statements, such as an *if-then-else*, for causing program branching
3. Repetition statements, such as the *while-do* or *for* looping commands

To also help develop algorithms and make programs easier to read and understand, programmers use flowcharts and pseudocode to illustrate the algorithm.

Example **20.10**

Which of the following is considered to be good structured programming technique?

(i) Frequent use of the *goto* instruction

(ii) Frequent use of the *jump* instruction

(iii) An absence of function calls

(iv) Code that is broken into small sections

Solution

The correct answer is (iv) Code that is broken into small sections. This is the idea of modularity that makes the code easily readable and understandable as subsections that solve a small part of the larger problem rather than trying to solve the entire problem in one large block of code.

Flowcharts

An algorithmic flowchart is a pictorial representation of the step-by-step solution of a problem using standard symbols. Some of the commonly used shapes are shown in Figure 20.1. Consider the simple problem in Example 20.11.

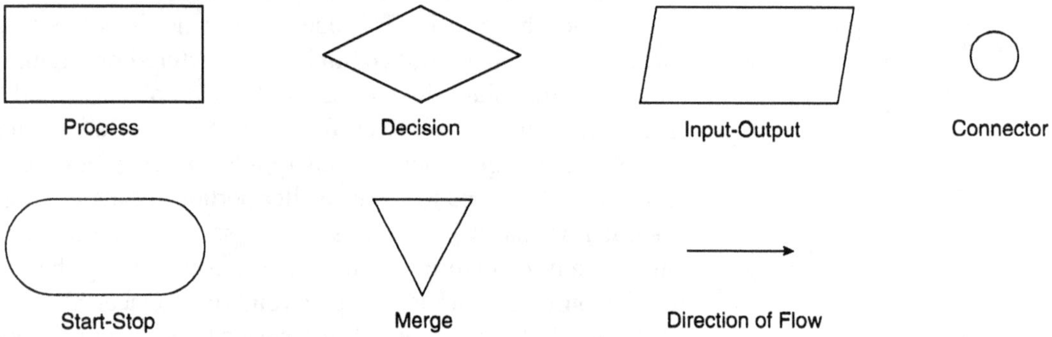

Figure 20.1 Flowchart Symbols

Example 20.11

A present sum of money (P) at an annual interest rate (I), if kept in a bank for N years, would amount to a future sum (F) at the end of that time according to the equation $F = P(1 + I)^N$. Prepare a flowchart for $P = \$100$, $I = 0.07$, and $N = 5$ years. Then compute and output the values of F for all values of N from 1 to 5.

Solution

Exhibit 1 shows a flowchart for this situation.

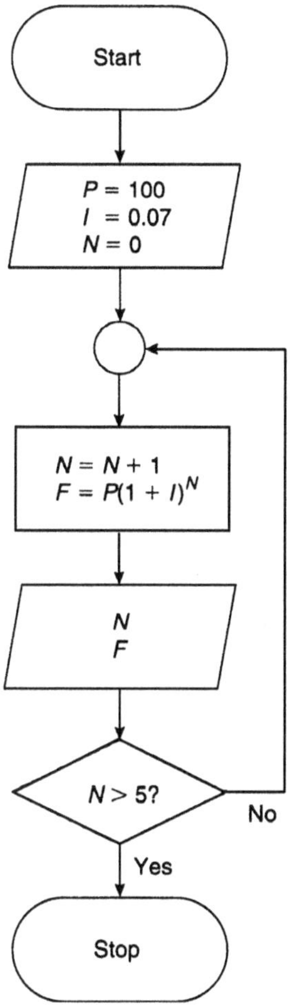

Exhibit 1
Algorithmic Flowchart

Example 20.12

Consider the flowchart in Exhibit 2.
The computation does which of the following?

(i) Inputs hours worked and hourly pay and outputs the weekly paycheck for 40 hours or less.

(ii) Inputs hours worked and hourly pay and outputs the weekly paycheck for hours worked including over 40 hours at premium pay.

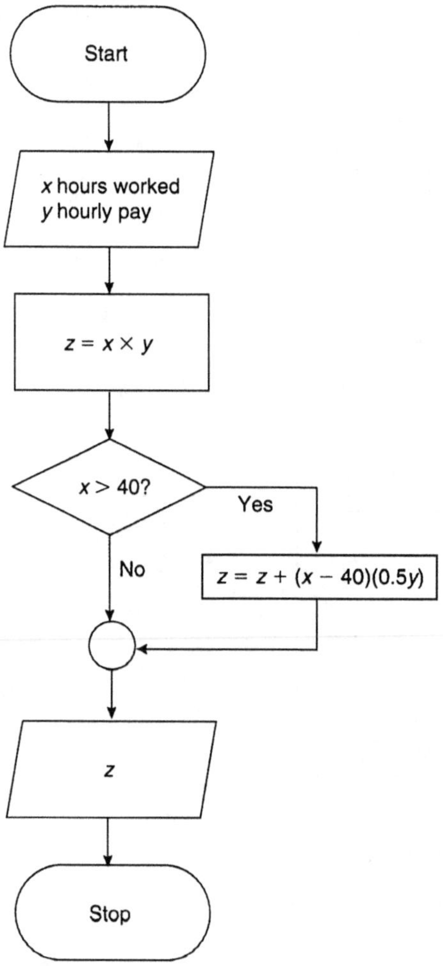

Exhibit 2

Solution

The answer is (ii).

Pseudocode

Pseudocode is an English-like language representation of computer programming. It is carefully organized to be more precise than a simple statement, but may lack the detailed precision of a flowchart or of the computer program itself.

Example 20.13

Prepare pseudocode for the computer problem described in Example 20.11.

Solution

```
INPUT P, I, and N = 0
DOWHILE N < 5
COMPUTE N = N + 1
   F = P (1 + I)^N
OUTPUT N, F
IF N > 5 THEN ENDDO
```

SPREADSHEETS

For today's engineers the ability to create and use spreadsheets is essential. Although several spreadsheet application programs exist, the most popular is Microsoft's Excel. The following explanations and examples are applicable to any spreadsheet package.

As noted in Figure 20.2, three types of information may be entered into a spreadsheet: text, values, and formulas. Text includes labels, headings, and explanatory text (columns A and B of Figure 20.2). Values are numbers, times, or dates (columns C, D, and E of Figure 20.2). Formulas combine operators and values in an algebraic expression (column F of Figure 20.2).

Figure 20.2 Example Spreadsheet

	A	B	C	D	E	F
1	**Last Name**	**First Name**	**Date**	**Age**	**Answers Correct**	**Percentage Correct**
2	Dempsey	Lou	4/17/2010	22	138	76.7
3	Johnson	Nathan	10/30/2010	26	105	58.3
4	Smith	Julie	10/30/2010	21	162	90.0

A **cell** is the intercept of a column and a row. Its location is based upon its column-row location; for example, B3 is the intercept of column B and row 3. Columns are labeled with letters across the top of the spreadsheet, and rows are labeled with numbers on the side. To change a cell entry, the cell must be highlighted using either an address or a pointer.

A group of cells may be called out by using a **range**. Cells A1, A2, A3, A4 could be called out using the range reference A1:A4 (or A1..A4). Similarly, the range A2, B2, C2, D2 could use the range reference A2:D2 (or A2..D2).

In order to call out a block of cells, a range callout might be A2:C4 (or A2..C4) and would reference the following cells:

A2 B2 C2
A3 B3 C3
A4 B4 C4

Formulas may include cell references, operators (such as + ,–,*,/), and functions (such as SUM, AVERAGE). The formula SUM(A2:A6) or SUM(A2..A6) would be evaluated as equal to A2 + A3 + A4 + A5 + A6. Built-in formulas such as

SUM or AVERAGE must be preceded by the @ symbol or an equals sign (=) in order to be recognized as a formula as opposed to text.

Relational References

Most spreadsheet references are relative to the cell's position. For example, if the content of cell A5 contains B4, then the value of A5 is the value of the cell up one and over one. The relational reference is most frequently used in tabulations, as in the following example for an inventory where cost times quantity equals value and the sum of the values yields the total inventory cost.

Inventory	Valuation		
	A	B	C
1 Item	Cost	Quantity	Value
2 box	5.2	2	10.4
3 tie	3.4	3	10.2
4 shoe	2.4	2	4.8
5 hat	1.0	1	1.0
6 Sum			26.4

In C2, the formula is A2*B2, in C3 A3*B3, and so forth. For the summation the function SUM is used; for example, SUM(C2:C5) in C6.

Instead of typing in each cell's formula, the formula can be copied from the first cell to all of the subsequent cells by first highlighting cell C2 then dragging the mouse to include cell C5. The first active cell, C2, would be displayed in the edit window. Typing the formula for C2 as = A2*B2 and holding the control key down and pressing the enter key will copy the relational formula to each of the highlighted cells. Since the call is relational, the formula in cell C3 is evaluated as A3*B3. In C4 the cell is evaluated A4*B4. Similarly, edit operations to include copy or fill operations simplify the duplication of relational formulas from previously filled-in cells.

Arithmetic Order of Operation

Operations in equations use the following sequence for precedence: exponentiation, multiplication, or division, followed by addition or subtraction. Parentheses in formulas supercede normal operator order.

Absolute References

Sometimes one must use a reference to a cell that should not be changed, such as a data variable. An absolute reference can be specified by inserting a dollar sign ($) before the column-row reference. If B2 is the data entry cell, then by using B2 as its reference in another cell, the call will always be evaluated to cell B2, regardless of which cell a formula might be copied to. Mixed reference can be made by using the dollar sign for only one of the elements of the reference. For example, the reference B$2 is a mixed reference in that the row does not change but the column remains a relational reference. Thus, a formula copied using this mixed reference would be relative to column B but unchanging in its reference to row 2.

The power of spreadsheets makes repetitive calculations very easy. Changing a value in one cell automatically updates every other cell that references it. Furthermore, program-like commands can be used in spreadsheets by executing a macro. Macros permit the execution of a large number of spreadsheet commands that have been previously recorded or programmed by the user.

All spreadsheet programs allow for changes in the appearance of the spreadsheet. Headings, borders, or type fonts are usual customizing tools. Spreadsheets also permit presentation of data as line graphs, bar graphs, pie charts, and other figures. This makes spreadsheets especially valuable for report generation and presentation.

Example **20.14**

Which of the following tasks is possible within a spreadsheet?

(i) Creating a graph
(ii) Creating reports
(iii) Analyzing data
(iv) All of these are possible.

Solution

The correct answer is (iv). All of these are possible within a spreadsheet. All of these tasks are easily done in a spreadsheet. There are very few things that can't be done, especially if the user knows how to use macros.

Example **20.15**

A spreadsheet has the values 5, 10, and 15 in cells A1, A2, and A3, respectively; and the formula A1 + A2 in cell B2. What value will display in cell B3 if the formula from cell B2 is copied to cell B3?

(i) 15
(ii) 20
(iii) 25
(iv) 30

Solution

The correct answer is (ii) 20. The $ symbol represents absolute addressing within spreadsheets, and its absence indicates relative addressing. Thus, when the formula is copied from cell B2 to B3, the values added are the value 5 in cell A1 and the value 15 in cell A3. Thus, the formula in cell B3 will be A1 + A3, and the value displayed will be 20.

Example **20.16**

Which of the following would likely be most difficult to incorporate into a spreadsheet cell?

(i) A jpeg image
(ii) Text representing a name
(iii) Value representing currency
(iv) Cell shading and/or borders

Solution

The correct answer is (i) a jpeg image. Although it is quite easy to insert an image into a spreadsheet, inserting one into an individual cell is not possible. There are ways to make it seem as if an image is inserted into a cell, but this is not easily done. The other answer choices are all easily inserted or performed within a spreadsheet cell.

Example **20.17**

A spreadsheet has the values 2, 4, and 6 in cells A1, A2, and A3, respectively. It also has values 3, 5, and 7 in cells B1, B2, and B3, respectively. What is displayed in cell D8 if it contains the formula @SUM(A1:B3)?

(i) 12
(ii) 15
(iii) 27
(iv) An error would result.

Solution

The correct answer is (iii) 27. Referencing cells in this manner provides the sum of all the values in the block. Where the formula is located (in this case, cell D8) is irrelevant unless the formula is copied to another cell. The format of the formula is correct in that it must start with the @ or = symbol, and the argument for the formula must either be specified with a colon (A1:B3) or two periods (A1..B3).

GLOSSARY OF COMPUTER TERMS

Accumulators	Registers that hold data, addresses, or instructions for further manipulations in the ALU
Address bus	Two-way parallel path that connects processors and memory containing addresses
AI	Artificial intelligence
Algorithm	A sequence of steps applied to a given data set that solves the intended problem
Alphanumeric data	Data containing the characters a, b, c, …, z, 0, 1, 2, …, 9
ALU	Arithmetic and logic unit
ASCII	American Standard Code for Information Interchange, 7 bit/character (Pronounced AS-key)
Asynchronous	Form of communications in which message data transfer is not synchronous, with the basic transfer rate requiring start/stop protocol
Baud rate	Number of state transitions that can be realized per second. Often equivalent to bits per second
BIOS	Basic input/output system
Bit	0 or 1
Buffer	Temporary storage device
Byte	8 bits
Cache memory	Fast look-ahead memory connecting processors with memory, offering faster access to often-used data
Channel	Logic path for signals or data
CISC	Complex instruction-set computing
Clock rate	Cycles per second
Control bus	Separate physical path for control and status information
Control unit	Ensures all subsystems within CPU work together appropriately
CPU	Central Processing Unit, the primary processor

Data buffer	Temporary storage of data
Data bus	Separate physical path dedicated for data
Digital	Discrete level or valued quantification, as opposed to analog or continuous valued
Duplex communication	Communications mode where data is transmitted in both directions at the same time
Dynamic memory	Storage that must be continually hardware-refreshed to retain valid information
EBCDIC	Extended Binary Coded Decimal Interchange Code—8 bits/character (pronounced EB-see-dick)
EPROM	Erasable programmable read-only memory
Expert systems	Programs with AI, which imitate the knowledge of a human expert
Floppy disk	Removable disk media in various sizes, $5^1/_4$", $3^1/_2$"
Flowchart	Graphical depiction of logic using shapes and lines
Gbyte (GB)	Gigabytes: 1,073,741,824 or 2^{30} bytes; a measurement of computer memory
Half-duplex communication	Two-way communications path in which only one direction operates at a time (transmit or receive)
Handshaking	Communications protocol to start/stop data transfer
Hard drive	Disk that has nonremovable media
Hardware	Physical elements of a system
Hexadecimal	Numbering system (base 16) that uses 0–9, A, B, …, F
Hierarchical database	Database organization containing hierarchy of indexes/keys to records
I/O	Input/output devices such as terminal, keyboard, mouse, printer
IR	Instruction register
Kbytes (KB)	Kilobytes: 1024 or 2^{10} bytes; a measurement of computer memory
LAN	Local area network
LIFO	Last in–first out
LSI	Large scale integration
Main memory	That memory seen by the CPU
Mbytes (MB)	Megabytes: 1,048, 576 or 2^{20} bytes; a measurement of computer memory
Memory	Generic term for random access storage
Microprocessor	Computer architecture with Central Processing Unit in one LSI chip
MODEM	Modulator-demodulator
MOS	Metal oxide semiconductor
Multiplexer	Device that switches several input sources, one at a time, to an output
Nibble	Four bits
Nonvolatile memory	As opposed to volatile memory, does not need power to retain its present state
OCR	Optical character recognition
OS	Operating system
OS memory	Memory dedicated to the OS, not usable for other functions
Parallel interface	A character (8-bit) or word (16-bit) interface with as many wires as bits in interface plus data clock wire.
Parity	Method for detecting errors in data: one extra bit carried with data, to make the sum of one bit in a data stream even or odd
PC	Program counter or personal computer
Peripheral devices	Input/output devices not contained in main processing hardware
Program	A sequence of computer instructions
PROM	Programmable read-only memory
Protocols	Established set of handshaking rules enabling communications
Pseudocode	An English-like way of representing programming control structures
RAM	Random access memory
Real time/Batch	Method of program execution: real-time implies immediate execution; batch mode is postponed until run on a group of related activities
RISC	Reduced instruction set computing
ROM	Read-only memory
Sequential storage	Memory (usually tape) accessed only in sequential order (n, $n + 1$, …)
Serial interface	Single data stream that encodes data by individual bit per clock period

Simplex communication	One-way communication
Static memory	Memory that does not require intermediate refresh cycles to retain state
Structured programming	Use of programming constructs, such as Do-While or If-Then-Else, to produce code that is logical and easy to follow
Synchronous	Communications mode in which data and clock are at same rate
Transmission speed	Rate at which data is moved, in baud (bits per second, bps)
Virtual memory	Addressable memory outside physical address bus limits through use of memory mapped pages
Volatile memory	Memory whose contents are lost when power is removed
Words	8, 16, or 32 bits
WYSIWYG	What you see is what you get
16-bit	Basic organization of data with 2 bytes per word
32-bit	Basic organization of data with 4 bytes per word
64-bit	Basic organization of data with 8 bytes per word

PROBLEMS

20.1 In spreadsheets, what is the easier way to write B1 + B2 + B3 + B4 + B5?

a. Sum (B1:B5)
b. (B1..B5) Sum
c. @B1..B5SUM
d. @SUMB2..B5

20.2 The address of the cell located at row 23 and column C is:

a. 23C
b. C23
c. C.23
d. 23.C

20.3 Which of the following is *FALSE*?

a. Flowcharts use symbols to represent input/output, decision branches, process statements, and other operations.
b. Pseudocode is an English-like description of a program.
c. Pseudocode uses symbols to represent steps in a program.
d. Structured programming breaks a program into logical steps or calls to subprograms.

20.4 In pseudocode using DOWHILE, which of the following is *TRUE*?

a. DOWHILE is normally used for decision branching.
b. The DOWHILE test condition must be false to continue the loop.
c. The DOWHILE test condition tests at the beginning of the loop.
d. The DOWHILE test condition tests at the end of the loop.

20.5 A spreadsheet contains the following formulas in the cells:

	A	B	C
1		A1 +1	B1 +1
2	A1 ^2	B1^2	C1^2
3	Sum (A1:A2)	Sum (B1:B2)	Sum (C1:C2)

If 2 is placed in cell A1, what is the value in cell C3?

a. 12
b. 20
c. 8
d. 28

20.6 A spreadsheet contains the following:

	A	B	C	D
1		3	4	5
2	2	A$2		
3	4			
4	6			

If you copy the formula from B2 into D4, what is the equivalent formula in D4?

a. A$2
b. C4
c. C4
d. C$2

20.7 The hexadecimal number 2DB.A is most nearly equivalent to which decimal number?

a. 731.625
b. 731.10
c. 453.625
d. 341.10

20.8 The decimal number 1938.25 is most nearly equivalent to which hexadecimal number?

a. $(792.25)_{16}$
b. $(792.4)_{16}$
c. $(279.4)_{16}$
d. $(279.04)_{16}$

20.9 The type of office computer that would most likely be found at an engineer's desk is a:

a. mainframe
b. minicomputer
c. workstation
d. microcontroller

20.10 Which of the following is *NOT* considered an Internet search engine?

a. Bing
b. Google
c. Unix
d. Yahoo

20.11 Which term describes a worldwide network of computers for sharing information?

a. Beowulf cluster
b. Cloud computing
c. Internet
d. LAN

20.12 The baud rate of an old serial communication system is the same as the bit rate. If the baud rate is 9600, transmitting a 500 KB file would take:

a. 1 minute
b. 7 minutes
c. 2 minutes
d. 18 minutes

20.13 If the data rate for USB 3.0 is 4.8 billion bps, the file size that can be sent in 30 seconds is:

a. 1800 KB
b. 18 MB
c. 1.8 GB
d. 18 GB

20.14 Which of the following types of memory is considered to be nonvolatile?

a. Cache
b. DRAM
c. Flash
d. SRAM

20.15 Which of the following drives typically uses EEPROM memory?

a. CD
b. DVD
c. Hard drive
d. Thumb drive

20.16 Which of the following is *NOT* likely to be found as a subunit of a CPU?

a. ALU
b. Control unit
c. Registers
d. Transformer

20.17 Which of the following data types would give the *BEST* precision?

a. Floating point
b. Integer
c. Long integer
d. Unsigned integer

20.18 Which of the following is *NOT* a standard for encoding character data types?
a. ALPHA c. EBCDIC
b. ASCII d. Unicode

20.19 Which of the following programming language types would be the hardest for a human to code, read, and understand?
a. Assembly c. Interpreted
b. High-level d. Machine

20.20 Each of the following is another term for "function" *EXCEPT*:
a. declarative c. procedure
b. method d. subroutine

20.21 An application program is *MOST* likely to use which of the following to interact with the computer's operating system?
a. API c. GUI
b. CAM d. URL

20.22 Which of the following is *NOT* used as a safeguard for preventing unauthorized computer access?
a. Antivirus software c. Firewall
b. Biometrics d. Spoofing

20.23 A spreadsheet has the values 15, 18, and 32 in cells A1, A2, and A3, respectively. If cell B1 has the formula A1 + A2 in it, and cell B2 has the formula B1 + A3 in it, what will be displayed in cell B2?
a. 32 c. 65
b. 55 d. 98

20.24 If the formulas in cells B1 and B2 from Problem 4.23 are now copied to cells C1 and C2, respectively, what value will be displayed in cell C2?
a. 55 c. 98
b. 65 d. 130

20.25 If the conditions described in problems 4.23 and 4.24 exist, and if the value in cell A1 is changed from 15 to 10, which cells would show a change in values displayed?
a. All cell values would change.
b. Only cell A1would change.
c. Only cells A2 and A3 do not change.
d. Only row 1 would change.

20.26 The operation used within a spreadsheet to execute many previously recorded commands in a manner similar to running a program is a:
a. functional c. system tool
b. macro d. vector tool

20.27 In structured programming, how many possible exit points should there be for a loop structure?
a. One c. None
b. Two d. As many as desired

20.28 A change in the order of program execution is known as:

a. branching
b. inclusion
c. slippage
d. yielding

20.29 Giving a variable an initial value or modifying its value is known as:

a. an assignment
b. a disclosure
c. a fixture
d. a method

20.30 In a flowchart, an oval-shaped symbol represents:

a. a decision
b. initialization
c. input or output
d. program start or stop

20.31 Pseudocode is useful for developing an algorithm because:

a. it can be directly compiled into machine language
b. it has a very easy-to-read, English-like structure
c. it is highly structured, making mistakes unlikely
d. it requires the programmer to think about all parts of a problem simultaneously

SOLUTIONS

20.1 **a.** Sum (B1:B5) or @Sum (B1..B5)

20.2 **b.**

20.3 **c.** Pseudocode does not use symbols but uses English-like statements such as IF-THEN and DOWHILE.

20.4 **c.** IF-THEN is normally used for branching. The DOWHILE test condition must be true to continue branching, and the test is done at the beginning of the loop. The DOUNTIL test is done at the end of the loop.

20.5 **b.** Plugging 2 into cell A1 of the spreadsheet produces the following spreadsheet display:

	A	B	C
1	2	3	4
2	4	9	16
3	6	12	20

The value of C3 is 20.

20.6 **d.** The formula contains mixed references. The $ implies absolute row reference, whereas the column is relative. The result of any copy would eliminate any answer except for the absolute row 2 entry. The relative column reference A gets replaced by C. The cell contains C$2.

20.7 **a.**

$$(2DB)_{16} = 2 \times 16^2 + 13 \times 16^1 + 11 \times 16^0 = 512 + 208 + 11 = 731$$
$$(.A)_{16} = 10 \times 16^{-1} = .625$$
$$(2DB.A)_{16} = 731.625$$

20.8 **b.**

		Quotient		Remainder	Hexadecimal Digit
1938 ÷ 16	=	121	+	2	2
121 ÷ 16	=	7	+	9	9
7 ÷ 16	=	0	+	7	7

$$(1938)_{10} = (792)_{16}$$

		Integer		Fraction	Hexadecimal Digit
0.25 × 16	=	4	+	0.00	4

$$(.25)_{10} = (.4)_{16}$$
$$(1938.25)_{10} = (792.4)_{16}$$

20.9 **c.** The key terms are *office* and *desk* and *most likely*. Only a workstation or PC (microcomputer) would be most likely to be at an engineer's desk. A microcontroller could conceivably be at an engineer's desk, but it is only likely if the engineer works with embedded systems.

20.10 **c.** Unix is an operating system, not an Internet search engine.

20.11 **c.** The key term is *worldwide*. Only the Internet fits this description.

20.12 **b.** In this case, the problem explicitly states that the baud rate and the bit rate are the same. This means that the communication system can transmit 9600 *bits* per second. To find the total number of seconds needed to send the file, multiply the file size by 8 bits per byte and divide this result by the baud rate. Finally, convert the number of seconds to minutes by dividing by 60 seconds per minute.

$$\text{Total time} = \frac{\left(500\times 10^3\ \text{B}\right)\left(\frac{8\ \text{bits}}{1\ \text{B}}\right)}{\frac{9600\ \text{bits}}{\text{s}}} \times \frac{1\ \text{minute}}{60\ \text{s}} = 6.94\ \text{minutes}$$

Note that had the file been 500 KiB, the transmission would still have been about 7 minutes.

20.13 **d.** To find the file size (in bits), multiply the data transmission rate by the total time. Then, convert the answer to bytes by multiplying 1 B/8 bits. Finally, use the standard SI definitions for KB, MB, or GB to determine the file size as provided in the answer choices.

$$\text{File size} = \frac{4.8\times 10^9\ \text{b}}{\text{s}} \times 30\ \text{s} \times \frac{1\ \text{B}}{8\ \text{b}} \times \frac{1\ \text{GB}}{1\times 10^9\ \text{B}} = 18\ \text{GB}$$

20.14 **c.** All of the memory types are RAM except for Flash memory. Flash memory is a type of EEPROM, which is nonvolatile memory.

20.15 **d.** A thumb drive uses Flash memory, which is a type of EEPROM.

20.16 **d.** Transformers are used to increase or decrease alternating currents and voltages. They are not found in CPUs.

20.17 **a.** Answers b, c, and d are all forms of integer data types; they cannot represent fractional values. The floating point data type permits the radix point to "float," or move, so that all or most of the significant figures can be used to represent a fractional value. For instance, the integer data types have poor precision in representing π because they can only represent π as the integer 3. The single precision floating point data type can represent π as 3.141593.

20.18 **a.** ASCII, EBCDIC, and Unicode are all standards for encoding character data.

20.19 **d.** Machine language consists of 1s and 0s. It would be the hardest for a human to read and understand.

20.20 **a.** Methods, procedures, and subroutines are all synonymous terms for function.

20.21 **a.** An application program is most likely to use an API, an application program interface, to interact with the operating system.

20.22 **d.** Spoofing refers to a method of attempting to gain unauthorized computer access. It is not a preventative safeguard.

20.23 **c.** With values 15, 18, and 32 in cells A1, A2, and A3, respectively, and with the formulas A1 + A2 in cell B1 and B1 + A3 in cell B2, cell B1 will have 15 + 18 = 33 in it, and cell B2 will have 33 + 32 = 65. In this case, the absolute addressing is irrelevant to the final calculation. In other words, the answer would have been the same if cell B2 had contained the formula B1 + A3.

20.24 **d.** In this problem, the relative or absolute addressing scheme is important to the copying procedure. After copying, cell C1 will have the relative addressing formula B1 + B2. Cell C2 will have a mixture of relative addressing and absolute addressing. Cell C2 will contain C1 + A3. With these formulas, C1 will have the value 33 + 65 = 98, and C2 will have 98 + 32 = 130.

20.25 **c.** Given that the conditions in problems 4.23 and 4.24 exist, changing the value of A1 will change every cell that directly or indirectly references A1. Changing the value of A1 from 15 to 10 would give the following results: A1 = 10, A2 = 18, A3 = 32, B1 = 10 + 18 = 28, B2 = 28 + 32 = 60, C1 = 28 + 60 = 88, and C2 = 88 + 32 = 120. Thus, all cells change except for cells A2 and A3.

20.26 **b.** A macro is a sequence of spreadsheet commands that can be recorded and executed, as is done in traditional computer programming.

20.27 **a.** In structured programming, there should be only one exit point for each loop structure. Having more than one exit point makes debugging and maintaining code very difficult.

20.28 **a.** The term branch or branching indicates a change in the order of program execution.

20.29 **a.** An assignment statement assigns or changes a value within a variable.

20.30 **d.** An oval shape denotes program initiation (start) or termination (stop). Decisions are represented by diamonds. Inputs and outputs are represented by rhomboids. Processing steps (which might include an initialization procedure) are presented by rectangles.

20.31 **b.** Pseudocode is useful for developing an algorithm because of its natural, easy-to-read, English-like structure. It permits the programmer to capture the basic ideas and sequences of the algorithm on paper without having to worry about programming syntax and other rules.